Future-oriented stud

C000038187

In this series:

New technologies and development
Biotechnologies in perspective
Culture des îles et développement/Islands' culture and development
From anticipation to action. A handbook of strategic prospective
Biotechnologies in developing countries: present and future. Vol. 1: Regional and national survey

Albert Sasson

Biotechnologies in developing countries: present and future

Volume 2:
International co-operation

UNESCO Publishing

The designations employed and the presentation of the material
in this publication do not imply the expression of any opinion whatsoever
on the part of the UNESCO Secretariat concerning the legal status of
any country or territory, or of its authorities, or concerning the delimitation
of the frontiers of any country or territory.

Published in 1998 by the United Nations
Educational, Scientific and Cultural Organization
7, Place de Fontenoy, 75352 Paris 07 SP
Composed by Eric Frogé, Paris
Printed by Imprimerie des PUF, 41100 Vendôme, France

ISBN 92-3-103460-X

© UNESCO, 1998
Printed in France

The author

Albert Sasson is Agrégé of the University (1958) and Doctor of Natural Sciences (Microbiology) of the University of Paris (1967). His research work in microbiology has dealt with the microflora of arid lands, and with free and symbiotic nitrogen-fixing micro-organisms. After a career at the Faculty of Science in Rabat (Morocco) from 1954 to 1973 (Dean of the Faculty from 1963 to 1969), Dr. Sasson joined UNESCO in 1974.

As a member of the Division of Ecological Sciences, he participated in the activities of the Programme on Man and the Biosphere (MAB), notably those concerning arid and semi-arid zones, and prepared major state-of-knowledge reports on tropical forest and grazing land ecosystems of the world (*Tropical Forest Ecosystems*, 1978; *Tropical Grazing Land Ecosystems*, 1979; *Écosystèmes forestiers tropicaux d'Afrique*, 1983).

From 1979 to 1985, he participated, within the Bureau of Studies and Programmning of the General Directorate of UNESCO, in the elaboration of the biennial programmes and the Medium-Term Plan of the Organization in science and technology. From 1985 to 1987, he was the Director of the Central Evaluation Unit of the General Directorate of UNESCO. In 1988, he was appointed Director of the Bureau of Programme Planning and, in November 1990, Director of the Bureau of Studies, Programming and Evaluation (including the Division of Statistics). On 1 September 1993, he has been promoted to the rank of Assistant Director-General. Retired on 1 April 1996, he was appointed as Special Adviser to the Director-General. A. Sasson is associate member of the Club of Rome.

In addition to 150 publications concerning his research and popularization activities in soil microbiology, algology and agrobiology (*Le rôle des micro-organismes dans la biosphère et l'avenir de la microbiologie appliquée*, 1970), Albert Sasson has published books and contributed to publications on biology teaching (*Teacher's Study Guide on the Biology of Human Populations*, 1974-75; *New Trends in Biology Education*, 1977; *Environmental Education: Teaching and Learning Principles*, 1987); on environment and development issues (*Développement et environnement – faits et perspectives dans les pays industrialisés et en voie de développement*, 1974; *Ingeniería y ambiente, formación ambiental para ingenieros*, 1982; *New Technologies and Development*, 1986); on food and nutrition (*Feeding Tomorrow's World*, 1990); and on biotechnologies (*Biotechnologies: Challenges and Promises*, 1984; *Biotechnologies and Development*, 1988; *Plant Biotechnologies for Developing Countries*, 1990; *Biotechnologies in Perspective*, 1991; *Biotechnology: Economic and Social Aspects. Issues for Developing Countries*, 1992; *Biotechnology and Natural Products. Prospects for Commercial Production*, 1992; *Biotechnologies in Developing Countries: Present and Future*. Vol. 1: *Regional and National Survey*, 1993).

Foreword

A previous volume of this series 'Future-oriented studies', entitled *Biotechnology in Perspective: Socio-Economic Implications for Developing Countries* (1991) aimed to disseminate reflection on the economic, social and cultural implications of biotechnological innovations for developing countries.

The subsequent volume in the same series, entitled *Biotechnologies in Developing Countries: Present and Future. Volume 1: Regional and National Survey* aimed to present a comprehensive overview of the status of biotechnology research and development in the developing world through a regional and national survey. It also included forecasts for the end of the century.

This second volume is devoted to international co-operation. Both volumes throw light on the implications of biotechnologies such as:

– the improvement in crop productivity and overall food production through the direct use of plant biotechnologies, as a complement to conventional breeding techniques;

– the improvement in the quality of agricultural and agro-industrial production, and the up-grading of food fermentations;

– the better integration of food production with bio-energy production and consumption at household and village levels;

– the increase and improvement in livestock production and health of domestic animals;

– the accurate diagnosis and prevention of human diseases;

– the possible extension of cash crops at the expense of food crops;

– the possible decrease in genetic diversity as a consequence of widespread distribution of new cultivars;

– the changes in income sources and employment;
– the role of the United Nations system and international co-operation in fostering the development of biotechnologies, particularly in developing countries;
– the contribution of the International Agricultural Research Centers and their network to the application of biotechnologies to agricultural and aquacultural production and development;
– the specific input of several major intergovernmental organizations to research-and-development activities and co-operation in biotechnologies in the developing world.
Co-operation at the international level which the United Nations agencies and related organizations are encouraging, helps to foster research, train specialists and technicians and promote collaboration among them, disseminate, and share of, specialized knowledge and know-how, and adpat biotechnologies to different social and econmic settings. By so-doing, international co-operation aims to reduce disparities and spread present and foreseen benefits of biotechnologies throughout the developing world.

Contents

Contents

Part I
United Nations system

Food and Agriculture Organization of the United Nations[1] (see p. 67)

The 1989 Food and Agriculture Organization of the United Nations (FAO) Conference gave priority to biotechnologies as a tool for improving crop productivity. Following the recommendations of this Conference and those of the FAO/CTA (Technical Centre for Agricultural and Rural Co-operation) Symposium on Plant Biotechnologies for Developing Countries (Luxembourg, June 1989), the Plant Production and Protection Division of the Agriculture Department (AGP) initiated the process of formulating a comprehensive policy on plant biotechnologies. This policy was included in the FAO's overall strategy for biotechnologies, stated in a 1993 publication.

The Plant Production and Protection Division had supported projects in genetic resources, crop production and protection, seed and planting material production and exchange. Some of these projects included the use of biotechnologies, e.g. mainly tissue culture for plant micropropagation, virus-free plant production, indexing and *in-vitro* conservation of plant germplasm. The activities carried out dealt with:

– assistance to national laboratories under the FAO Technical Co-operation Programme;

   – organization of training courses in plant biotechnologies;
   – provision of equipment to laboratories;
   – funding of publications on plant biotechnologies;
   – establishment of regional networks; and
   – support for international conferences and seminars.

Some of the countries benefiting from projects including components in biotechnologies were: Argentina, Bangladesh, Côte d'Ivoire, Cuba, Egypt, Ethiopia, Gabon, India, Mexico, Mozambique, Morocco, Nepal, Nigeria, Pakistan, Uganda, Uruguay, Viet Nam and Yemen.

1. Policy and strategies

In line with its mandate and the three major programme areas relating to information, provision of a forum for international debate on issues related to food and agriculture, and the contribution of technical assistance to Member States, the FAO sought to realize the positive impacts of biotechnologies while minimizing, if not completely eliminating, the negative effects. Thus, the FAO's strategy would concentrate on activities such as the collection and dissemination of information, monitoring and advice, facilitation of access to new technologies, provision of a forum for reviewing trends, development of appropriate guidelines and codes promoting the environmentally sound and equitable application of advanced biotechnologies, assistance to developing countries in identifying biotechnology needs and priorities, strengthening of their capabilities and assessment of socio-economic impacts.

With respect to monitoring and appraisal, the FAO would assess the potentials of advanced biotechnologies, as well as their limitations for agriculture, forestry and fisheries productions, with special reference to developing countries. Objectives would include increased yields, stabilized production, improved ecological sustainability, better food quality and reduced losses. The FAO would monitor and develop early warning systems to detect adverse effects of biotechnologies. Longer-term activities would include assessment of the propensity for widespread use of biotechnologies to modify established patterns of comparative advantages in food, agriculture, forestry and fisheries production and trade and to displace traditional commodities, and the implications thereof. The FAO would also monitor legal, socio-economic and other policy aspects of biotechnologies and alert Member States to the implications.

Regarding information, the FAO's informative systems AGRIS and CARIS were available to Member States, who would be assisted and encouraged to participate in information gathering and exchange. Under these systems, the FAO was setting up an electronic mail/bulletin board service, so as to enhance the speed at which critical information was delivered and provide an electronic conferencing capability for scientists in the various networks. Distributed products included printed bibliographies, specialized data-bases and diskettes or CD-ROM (Compact Disk Read Only Memory) for use with personal computers, *Animal Biotechnology*, a quarterly bulletin, distributing information extracted from AGRIS (initiatives were taken to extend in-depth coverage to other fields and in additional forms).

To increase access to new technologies and products, the FAO would serve as an intermediary between technology developers and users by defending the interests of developing countries and/or acquiring for them the beneficial results stemming from biotechnology research and its application. Thus, the FAO would act as an 'honest broker', matching the needs of developing countries and mobilizing funding support from donors and development banks for the implementation of clients' proposals.

Biotechnologies could assist in crop breeding and in producing industrial compounds from plants (Duvick, 1996):

1. Molecular biology-assisted crop breeding

Type of research	Current state in research and development	Current constraints	Prospects
New herbicide-tolerant varieties	Successful releases of herbicide-resistant maize, soybeans, sunflower and oilseed rape	Acceptance by farmers depended on superior yield performance and other agronomically desirable traits; size and extent of market demand remained to be established	Farmer experience with herbicide-tolerant varieties was increasing
Insect-resistant varieties	Series of genes from *Bacillus thuringiensis* (*Bt*) were readily available	Acceptance depended on ability to develop insect-resistant varieties in a way that would prevent rapid development of new insect genotypes overcoming the novel resistance genes	One type of resistance was readily available by the mid-1990s (*Bt* toxins)

| Molecular markers to identify important quantitative trait loci (QTL) | Some QTL had been tentatively identified but most of them seemed to be associated with only one or a few parental strains | Technology currently available was expensive | Cost of using molecular markers was coming down; more powerful experiments to detect useful QTL were expected to be designed in the next decade |

2. Production of industrial compounds in crop species

Type of compound	Current state in research and development	Current constraints	Prospects
Proteins	Genetically-altered plants producing antibodies, and antigens acting as oral vaccines	Extracting special proteins might be difficult because of the number of secondary metabolites in plant tissues; Purification of the extracted proteins to meet medical standards might be difficult	Large-scale production of antibodies for an effective immuno-therapy. No commercial products available yet
Oils	Research focused on oilseed rape, sunflower and soybeans; identification and cloning of key genes involved in the production of oils and waxes with industrial use, which could be transferred to plants; proposed compounds were erucic, lauric, petroselinic, gamma-linolenic, epoxy fatty acids, and jojoba wax	Insufficient knowledge of biosynthetic pathways for oil production	In 1995, Calgene Inc. produced transgenic oilseed rape producing high volumes of lauric acid, after transfer of a gene from the seed of *Umbellularia californica*; E.I. Du Pont de Nemours & Co., Inc. was testing transgenic soybeans with increased oleic acid and reduced saturated fats content

Carbohydrates	U.S. research and production focused on maize starch; naturally occurring genes such as waxy, amylose-extender, dull and shrunken-1, could be used to modify native maize starch; genetic transformation could allow production of starch with novel desired properties	Maize starch was widely used for producing high-fructose corn syrups (HFCS), fuel ethanol, glucose and dextrose, but modified native maize starch was used very little on an industrial scale; no genetically-engineered starch products were available by mid-1990s	Considerable market for HFCS (about 35% of caloric sweetener market in USA); conversely, markets for modified native maize starch were small

The fractured nature of the market for plant-produced industrial products contrasted sharply with the traditional markets for farm seeds. For instance, the potential value of the U.S. market for hybrid seed maize could be as high as $2 billion, whereas markets for industrial products derived from transformed crop species were often quantified in terms of millions of dollars. Potential customers for plant-produced industrial compounds fell into broadly divergent categories including paper manufacturers, paint companies and pharmaceutical corporations. This diversity contrasted strikingly with the relatively homogeneous group which generally made up most or all of the seed company customer base, that of farmers. In most cases, potential industrial customers had no acquaintance with the seed companies and vice versa (Duvick, 1996).

Chemical companies often had well-developed biotechnology departments set up to serve other aspects of their business. They could support plant breeding with biotechnologies to a greater degree than was possible for most seed companies. However, they were usually inexperienced in plant breeding and seed sales, and lacked a built-in base of farmer customers who knew them and were willing to try their new varieties. To remedy this problem, industrial companies were buying seed firms or coming to a collaborative arrangement with independent seed firms. Small seed companies in particular could benefit from these arrangements because they could not usually afford to support biotechnology research to the degree necessary for developing new varieties able to synthesize industrial products (Duvick, 1996).

Seed firms, for their part, were making collaborative arrangements downstream to food companies and chemical companies, and upstream to farmers producing the new specialty crops. A kind of vertical integration was being developed by seed companies to smooth production and distribution of the new class of small-volume plant-produced industrial compounds with specific end uses. This new kind of integration was intended to convince breeders that years of endeavour in developing the novel crop varieties would be compensated for by profitable seed sales or by some other form of reward. It also would ensure that farmers growing a perhaps lower-yielding crop species and handling it separately would be rewarded by a higher price for the crop. Lastly, it would guarantee the business firms buying the crop a steady flow of tested feedstocks (Duvick, 1996).

In the FAO's view, an intellectual property rights (IPR) system needed to be flexible enough to match development goals, policies and socio-economic priorities of individual countries while, at the same time, promoting innovation and the application of new biotechnologies. If the national capability in genetic improvement and biotechnological research was negligible, a country would benefit little from setting up an IPR system like that generally prevailing in industrialized countries. On the other hand, where the national capability was fairly developed and a market-oriented economy was in place, a system of plant breeders' rights (PBR) stimulating private sector investment and promoting healthy competitition and linkages between the private and public sectors might prove appropriate. Developing countries, according to the FAO, would be wise to opt for a PBR system with provision for farmer plantback, especially where farmers could not afford to buy seeds every year or were overlooked by the seed distribution system. The FAO believed it the responsibility of Member States to ensure that any IPR system they set up restricted neither access to, nor use of, genetic resources, nor inhibited promotion of research and technology development, nor adversely affected their vital socio-economic fabric.

With respect to the strengthening of national capabilities, the FAO had assisted several relatively well-positioned developing countries in assessing requirements and preparing the way, through institutional and human resources development, for biotechnological research and development. In some instances, assistance focused on biotechnologies for crop improvement, in others, on those for the production of vaccines and use of diagnostics in livestock health and reproduction activities. Furthermore, both through its Regular and Field Programme, where appropriate, the FAO planned to support developing countries in setting up biotechnology laboratories and in related training activities.

The FAO was also reinforcing assistance to developing countries in analyzing necessary and adequate social and economic policies for the development, adaptation and implementation of appropriate biotechnologies consistent with their capabilities, needs, aspirations and opportunities.

The FAO would continue to strengthen its programme on setting up collaborating laboratories providing invaluable services, not only as a reference for quality testing but also for training. For instance, arrangements were made to test recombinant vaccines under the FAO aegis. The FAO had set up a Collaborating Centre for Biotechnology Transfer at the University of California. The counterpart Molecular Virology Unit for Biotechnology Transfer was organized at the Pan-African Vaccine Centre for Ethiopia.

The FAO was promoting international, inter-laboratory co-operative research through networking, e.g. the Asian Network for Biotechnology in Animal Production and Health, the Computer-Assisted Analysis of Nucleic Acids and Protein Sequences (CANAPS) in Latin America and the Caribbean, covering seven countries, to be linked to similar European networks. The Technical Co-operation Network on Plant Biotechnology in Latin America and the Caribbean (REDBIO) began operations in January 1991 and an Asian Network on Plant Biotechnology, with some emphasis on genetic resources, was established in 1991. In the same year, the FAO funded the Biotechnology Workshop and Training for African Biotechnologists, organized by the International Institute of Tropical Agriculture as a first step toward the creation of an African Biotechnology Network. A Latin American Network on Animal Biotechnology was also created. The FAO was also sponsoring regional networks on preparation and distribution of diagnostic probes/monoclonal antibodies for rapid diagnosis of livestock and poultry diseases. Certain laboratories in selected national agricultural research systems would be strengthened to take a leadership role in specific areas. Results and products from these centres would be shared freely among all network members.

The FAO, through its Seed Exchange and Information Unit, continued to procure and supply seeds and planting materials of economically important crop species to various countries and also to projects executed by the FAO. By the early 1990s, the Unit was dispatching about 20,000 seed samples of over 300 species to more than 85 member countries. Quarantine facilities and capabilities were being strengthened to allow the safe transfer and exchange of germplasm in an increasing number of countries.

Other projects included assistance in setting up a seed storage facility for genetic resources in Tanzania and *in-vitro* conservation of sugar-cane germplasm in Cuba. Germplasm utilization projects included: root and tuber multiplication in the Caribbean; a global project for seed production of pasture and fodder plants; a global tropical soybeans project; date-palm research in the Near East and North Africa; and the introduction of oil-palm germplasm in Africa.

The Forestry Department was keeping abreast of new developments in genetics and breeding, including biotechnologies with potential in forestry development. The field programme related to the conservation and sustainable use of forest genetic resources had expanded considerably, placing emphasis on the strengthening of national institutions, including national seed centres, and subregional or ecological networking, and the promotion of technical co-operation among developing countries for those with similar environmental conditions and socio-economic needs.

The FAO had played a leading role in the preparation and implementation of the Tropical Forestry Action Plan, one priority of which was the conservation of tropical forest ecosystems.

Hardly one-tenth of the huge, forested area lost annually was being replaced (see p. 446). While great reliance was placed on conventional forestry practices and extensive forest management systems, a sharply intensified, if moderate, reorientation comparable to introduction of the higher-yielding varieties which had ushered in agriculture's 'green revolution', remained a clear, if largely untouched, option in tropical forestry. Yet, there were a few striking examples of rapid growth achieved with vegetative propagation of proven provenances of *Eucalyptus* species in Brazil (75–100 m^3 per hectare per year), in Congo (35–50 m^3), and in Zimbabwe (30 m^3), showing that these technologies augured well for similar replicable and broader efforts elsewhere. Biotechnologies could assist in the rapid, massive propagation of superior genotypes selected for adaptability and in the yield of specified goods and services. The FAO supported the application of biotechnologies to forest tree improvement and reforestation schemes. Several research and higher-education institutions in developing countries had embarked upon biotechnological approaches and refined techniques with varied results, while the FAO awarded an André Mayer Research Fellowship in October 1991 to an Australian researcher, to enable him to undertake a review aimed at:

– gathering available literature;

– defining the packages necessary for development of a biotechnological programme, eventually leading to significant results that could be extended from national 'centres of excellence' to other countries, on a regional basis;

– coming up with sound proposals, after consultations with special, leading institutions in Africa, the Near East, Asia, Latin America, the Caribbean and South Pacific, for an appropriate international assistance programme in biotechnologies applied to forestry and reforestation.

Finally, as a contribution to the development of the poor farmers, the FAO would promote biotechnological research and development of commodities often referred to as 'orphan commodities', not generally researched by industrialized countries, but of vital importance to most developing countries. It would strengthen national capabilities for applying biotechnological solutions to increasing and sustaining agricultural production under erratic rainfall, in saline soils and under other adverse environmental conditions in areas characterized by low and unstable productivity and inhabited by poor farmers.

2. Global Programme on Plant Biotechnology

The FAO's Global Programme on Plant Biotechnology aimed to strengthen the biotechnological capabilities of developing countries by:
– ensuring co-operation between advanced laboratories and national programmes in developing countries by networking;
– fostering research and development;
– communication and information systems;
– training and improvement of infrastructures.

In March 1993, the FAO hosted a panel of experts on plant biotechnologies, in Rome. The panel of experts agreed on the major areas for action of the Programme:
– information, dissemination and operation;
– establishing and providing advisory services;
– building institutional capacity.

The Programme was expected to act as a 'broker' for the exchange of information on: research and field testing; available technologies for specific crops; sources of diagnostics; characterization of plant germplasm; public and private plant biotechnology laboratories; and guidelines on procedures for plant material exchange.

The Programme was also providing Member States with advisory services on policy and technical issues relating to crop propagation, breeding, germplasm conservation and exchange, legal and biosafety issues; this could include both *ad hoc* advice and the setting up of a scientific and technical advisory committee to guide the implementation of plant biotechnology programmes.

With respect to capacity-building, the Programme was promoting the establishment of *in-vitro* culture laboratories in the least developed countries, strengthening existing institutional and crop networks, fostering private-public relationships; and providing research grants for equipment and maintenance costs. In addition, the Programme played an important role in the transfer of applied technology to end users and 'upstream' investigations into ways of strengthening national agricultural research (Commandeur, 1994*b*).

A major strategy was to create a flow of information and knowledge between laboratories, either in developed or developing countries, which were at the frontier of biotechnology research. This information flow together with plant germplasm formed a two-way system for stimulating strong links between supply and demand.

In this context, it was considered pertinent to compile and document available information on theses published on plant biotechnologies by Latin American scientists from 1980 to 1995. The principal objective of this initiative was to gather information on tissue culture, molecular biology and genetic engineering of plant species, in order to facilitate and promote the use of publications available in Latin America. The main expected benefits were:

– to allow access to published information;
– to promote communication among colleagues with similar interests (techniques, crops, climatic conditions, etc.);
– to avoid repetition of work and efforts;
– to provide the Technical Co-operation Network on Plant Biotechnology in Latin America and the Caribbean (REDBIO) activities with more themes;
– to promote the work of recent graduates and give acknowledgement to tutors and institutions (*REDBIO Circular Letter*, 9 October 1994, p. 6).

The Programme on Plant Biotechnology was being carried out in close collaboration with other United Nations agencies, funding institutions, centers belonging to the Consultative Group on International Agricultural Research (CGIAR, see p. 293) and other relevant organizations involving private industry and non-governmental organizations. The Joint FAO/IAEA Division Laboratory was involved in the Programme's training and research activities (see p. 252).

In collaboration with the International Plant Genetic Resources Institute, the Programme aimed to support research on medium-term (*in vitro*) and long-term (cryopreservation) conservation methods for vegetatively-propagated and recalcitrant seed-producing species. The Programme also intended to promote the application of molecular biology to the assessment of genetic diversity and to increasing genetic variability in breeding schemes (Commandeur, 1994*b*).

At regional level, the Programme was supporting networks in Latin America (REDBIO) and Africa (African Plant Biotechnology Network, APBNet). Similar networks were envisaged for North Africa, Asia and Eastern Europe.

On 4 July 1995, in the town of Varna on Bulgaria's Black Sea coast, a group of 20 or so Balkan plant scientists and biotechnologists agreed to set up a Balkan Plant Biotechnology Network (BPBN) to promote co-operation in agricultural and plant biotechnologies in the region. Sponsored by the FAO and UNESCO, the meeting followed up to a study commissioned by the FAO's Plant Production and Protection Division of the agricultural resources and needs of Eastern Europe, as well as of existing research and collaboration mechanisms. This approach was based on the REDBIO model. In the case of Eastern Europe, however, the region was too diverse - climatically, agronomically and politically - and too vast, to be encompassed by a single network. Therefore, three networks were envisaged one for Russia, a second for the northern and central Eastern European States (the Baltic States, Poland, Hungary, Czech Republic, Slovak Republic, Ukraine and Belarus), and the third for the Balkan countries (Hodgson, 1995).

The initial participants in the Balkan network were Albania, Bulgaria, Greece, Macedonia, Romania, Turkey and Yugoslavia, all of which were represented at the Varna meeting. An invitation to join the network was extended to Croatia and Slovenia, whose delegates were unable to attend. The stated overall objective of the BPBN was 'to establish free communication between plant scientists, in order to focus their expertise on the development and use of new technologies for agriculture, so as to improve the economies of the Balkan countries'. The network's co-ordinator for the first two-year period was the head of the Institute of Genetic Engineering (IGE) in Kostinbrod, Bulgaria (Hodgson, 1995).

The Institute of Genetic Engineering (IGE), Kostinbrod, near Sofia, Bulgaria, was established in 1985 as part of the Bulgarian Agricultural Academy. The IGE was considered the national scientific centre and co-ordinating unit for applying plant genetic engineering to agriculture to accelerate and improve crop breeding. More specifically, research focused on: the development and application of genetic engineering to create new crop varieties resistant to disease, herbicides and environmental stress; the large-scale commercial propagation of these new varieties; the application of DNA- and immunoenzymologically-based markers to the diagnosis of plant diseases and crop breeding.

Research projects addressed concrete agricultural issues and were implemented only once they had been discussed with breeders. They thus forged a tangible link between basic research, crop breeding and production. In defining areas for joint research with 25 cell and tissue-culture laboratories in Bulgaria and more than 50 groups world-wide, the IGE was guided by a 16-member International Consultative Council comprising scientists from Belgium, France, Germany, Hungary, Israel, Japan, the Netherlands, Ukraine, United Kingdom and USA, which met every two years.

The Institute had a staff of about 60. On average, the Bulgarian Agricultural Academy contributed approximately two-thirds of the budget, the rest coming from research contracts and international grants. In addition to having representatives in all Bulgarian specialized breeding centres, the Institute comprised the following departments and laboratories:

– Department of Cell Genetics (Laboratories of Somatic Embryogenesis, Cell Selection and Somaclonal Variation, Genetic Transformation and Somatic Hybridization, Phytopathology and Immunochemistry, Cytogenetics);

– Department of Molecular Genetics;

– Department of Biochemistry (Laboratories of Plant Physiology and Biochemistry, Enzymology and Immunochemistry).

The Institute was trying to compensate the shortfalls in government support by working closely with the UNIDO, International Atomic Energy Agency, European Union TEMPUS programme, FAO and UNESCO, or through bilateral agreements with research funding bodies in Belgium, the United Kingdom, the Netherlands and Japan. The IGE was also carrying out research for major corporations like Sandoz AG (Basel, Switzerland), Rhône-Poulenc (France), Zeneca Seeds plc (United Kingdom), Bayer AG (Leverkusen, Germany) and Bulgartabac (Sofia). The IGE was also part of a four-centre project, the Norman Borlaug Institute for Plant Science Research (see p. 677), which was forging links with laboratories at De Montfort University (Leicester, United Kingdom), the Czech Republic (Olomouc and Prague) and China (Beijing/Shanghai). In the wake of economic and political reforms in Bulgaria, the Institute had multiplied joint ventures with national commercial partners in order to commercialize its scientific achievements and assist Bulgarian breeding centres.

Up to 1996, achievements had been recorded in five research areas: disease and pest resistance, gene transfer and regeneration of transgenic plants, DNA polymorphism, stress resistance and cytoplasmic male sterility.

Thus, tobacco plants resistant to both tomato spotted wilt virus (TSWV) and wildfire (caused by *Pseudomonas syringae* pv. *tabaci*) had been obtained using the coat protein gene (for TSWV) and the *ttr* gene isolated by Meiji Seika Co. (and given by the Japanese company for basic and applied research) respectively. Second generations of these transgenic tobacco plants were being studied, but the full tolerance observed in some cultivars indicated that this method was suitable for accelerating breeding and solving problems of great economic importance. The selection of disease-resistant tobacco plants also relied on a method involving stem explants of haploid plants, exposure to cultural filtrates of *Phytophthora parasitica* var. *nicotianae* (black shank) and direct organogenesis.

The genes encoding the nucleocapsids of tomato spotted wilt virus (clone L-3) and plum pox virus (PPV) causing the 'sharka' disease had been isolated, sequenced and cloned. Although similar work had been done by Dutch and German researchers, these genes were the first of Bulgarian origin and ownership. The transfer of these genes (to tobacco and tomato for TSWV, and to plum, peach, apricot and cherry plants for PPV) would allow the development of tolerance to these viruses.

Research of this kind could be extended to sunflower and, once funding became available, researchers could turn a hand to developing resistance to insect pests, nematodes and weeds.

Gene transfer and regeneration were being optimized in alfalfa, tobacco, sunflower and plum, and it was envisaged to extend these techniques to grapes and carnations, after the satisfactory outcome of similar research on apple, sugar-beet and tomato. A new formula for obtaining genetically uniform alfalfa plants had been developed; it consisted of directly inducing an unlimited number of somatic embryos in a liquid nutrient medium. In this way, the genetic deviations occurring in callus-induced somatic embryos could be avoided. This method was suitable for large-scale somatic embryo production in airlift bioreactors. Drought-tolerant alfalfa plants were obtained through cell selection and gene transfer; these plants had a higher amino-acid content and lower saponin concentration (<0.2% compared to the normal 1.5% to 2%).

New forage- and brewery-type barley plants were selected via somaclonal variation after four years of research and field trials. They superseded the original cultivar 'Ruen' in early maturation (three to six days), lower stem (five to ten centimetres), lower protein content (0.2% to 1.2%) and higher yields (10%-15%). In addition, it was discovered that a pre-treatment of mature barley embryos by a medium containing 8 mg/litre of 2,4-D led to a significant increase in regeneration efficiency. This effect had been observed in several economically important barley cultivars.

Somatic hybridization allowed the transfer of tomato spotted wilt virus-resistance to *Nicotiana tabacum* from its wild relatives *N. alata* and *N. sylvestis*. Inter-species sexual hybridization and tissue culture methods had led to new carrot, celery and radish cultivars: the 'Morrion' carrot cultivar, a hybrid of *Daucus carota* var. *Boissieri* and *D. carota* var. *hollandicus*, which produced a red or purple pigment and could be used for natural colouring in food industry; the 'Despyna' celery cultivar, a hybrid of *Apium graveolens* and *Petroselinum hortense*; and the 'Fantasy' raddish cultivar, a hybrid between cabbage and raddish with interesting traits, e.g. lengthened shape, edible leaves, increased vitamin C content and a rootstock that ripened seven to ten days earlier without becoming hollow.

Accelerated *in-vitro* propagation had been achieved for carnations and pharmaceutical plants (peppermint, lavender, summer snowflake).

The development of DNA fingerprinting techniques was another of the Institute's achievements. These were used for identifying varieties of key Bulgarian crop species (barley, wheat, sunflower, alfalfa, grapes and carnation) and varieties derived from somaclonal variation (rice, barley, wheat, sunflower); diagnosing pathogens like *Phytophthora parasitica* and *Pseudomonas syringae* of tobacco and new pathogens; mapping genes encoding economically important traits and resistance to stress and diseases (e.g. resistance to powdery mildew in inter-specific wheat x *Aegilops variabilis* substitution lines and to *Cercospora oryzae* in rice); studying position effects on the expression of genes encoding key agronomic traits in the reconstructed karyotypes of barley; and mapping the genomes of sunflower and grapes (once funding became available).

A polyclonal antibody against the nucleocapsid encoding gene of tomato spotted wilt virus had been produced, the advantage of such an antibody over antibodies against the whole virus being the possibility of identifying not only the strain from which the gene had been isolated, but all other virus strains. Polyclonal antibodies had also been produced against the following viruses: arabis mosaic, artichoke Italian latent, bean yellow mosaic, beet necrotic yellow vein, carnation mottle, carnation ringspot, grapevine Bulgarian latent, grapevine fanleaf, hembane mosaic, potato viruses M, Y, X, S, tobacco mosaic, tobacco necrosis, tobacco ringspot, tomato aspermyi, tomato bushy stunt.

Polyclonal antibodies against zeatin, zeatin-riboside, iso-pentenyl-adenine, iso-pentenyl-adenosine and indolyl-3-acetic acid allowed the study of the role of phytohormones in differentiation and dedifferentiation processes.

Drought-tolerant lines of alfalfa isolated *in vitro* were being analyzed to check whether there was any correlation between drought tolerance and overproduction of proline. Model systems (e.g. *Arabidopsis thaliana* and *Nicotiana tabacum*) were used in selection experiments to investigate the molecular bases of drought tolerance.

Cytoplasmic male sterility applications in sunflower were expected to be tested in maize, tobacco, tomato, sugar-beet and pepper as soon as funding became available.

The Balkan Plant Biotechnology Network (BPBN) had set itself the goals of identifying problems of mutual interest, making an inventory of resources and establishing effective communication between research laboratories and the applied sector, including research-and-development companies. One of its strengths was that many of the individuals involved had either worked in Western Europe or North America - and might therefore be able to attract external funding. For instance, as the only member of the European Union in the BPBN, Greece could be a particularly important link to the biotechnology research-and-development funding programmes administered by the European Commission. In Greece, the National Agricultural Research Foundation (NAGREF), set up in February 1995, aimed to attract international funding. It could help the BPBN reach the relevant funding sources (Hodgson, 1995).

The Network immediate goals were fairly modest, i.e. compilation of an inventory of research projects in the region including their level of development and workshops involving larger groups of scientists, to define co-operation strategies. In the longer-term, one major concern was the intellectual property policy for plants, particularly the role that multinational seed companies might play in stimulating or hampering the efforts of the Balkan nations. In 1995, few of the Balkan countries were signatories of the Union for the Protection of New Varieties of Plants (UPOV) convention, leaving the majority of them free to develop varieties botanically different from existing ones. At the same time, they were effectively prevented from registering their new varieties in the potentially lucrative markets of the parties of the UPOV. But all this was set to change: Bulgaria was expected to enact a law in 1996 permitting it to accede to the UPOV convention. Other Balkan countries would follow suit. Indeed, one specific aim of the Network was to link product-oriented research to protection of intellectual property rights (Hodgson, 1995).

In a move to co-ordinate its own training schemes under the Global Programme on Plant Biotechnology with those of other international organizations, particularly at regional level, the FAO had signed a number of agreements, such as that with the UNESCO Biotechnology Action Council-BAC-fellowship scheme in support of REDBIO applications for scholarships and that with the Inter-American Institute for Co-operation on Agriculture (IICA) to jointly strengthen and support plant biotechnology and biosafety activities (research and advanced training).

The FAO programme entitled Farmer-Centred Agricultural Resource Management (FARM) contained a subprogramme on biotechnology and biological diversity involving China, India, Indonesia, Nepal, Sri Lanka, Thailand, The Philippines and Viet Nam. Initiated in 1993, the subprogramme was entrusted with the task of setting up an information-sharing network baptised Asian Bioinformatics; assessing the potential of new biotechnologies to contribute to integrated pest management, biological nitrogen fixation and micropropagation for reforestation schemes; and evaluating the role of biotechnologies to support the conservation of biological diversity by farming communities (Commandeur, 1994*b*).

3. Plant genetic resources and biological diversity

Biological diversity or biodiversity refers to the variety of the world's organisms, and the assemblages they form. 'Genetic diversity' covers all inheritable biological diversity (including interspecific and intraspecific variation, and a large part of ecosystem diversity). 'Genetic resources' refers more specifically to that part of genetic diversity of actual or potential value. The FAO concentrated on those genetic resources currently known to be of use to humankind, especially in food and agriculture, including crop and forestry species, livestock and fish. Biological diversity was therefore of direct concern to the FAO because it formed the basis of agriculture, forestry and fisheries. Although all genetic diversity is of potential value in the long term, the FAO emphasized those aspects of biological diversity of immediate importance for ensuring equitable and sustainable development.

Since 1946, the FAO had been involved in the conservation and use of genetic resources for agriculture. The 1961 Technical Meeting on Plant Exploration and Introduction, organized and hosted by the FAO in Rome, could be considered the first official acknowledgement of the importance of *ex-situ* conservation for agricultural purposes on an international scale. Wider political recognition of the issue would come a few years later when the 'green revolution' was in full swing. The 1967 FAO/IBP Technical Conference on the Exploration, Utilization and Conservation of Plant Genetic Resources was organized by the United Kingdom-based International Biological Programme (IBP) and the

FAO; it laid the foundations for the scientific rationale behind *ex-situ* conservation on an international scale (Pistorius, 1995).

With the establishment in 1974 of the International Board for Plant Genetic Resources (IBPGR) within the Consultative Group on International Agricultural Research (CGIAR), conservation of plant genetic resources became defined in terms of the requirements of International Agricultural Research Centers supporting the 'green revolution'; the result was the current *ex-situ* CGIAR gene bank network. A division of labour between the FAO and CGIAR was a logical next step. While the latter remained in charge of collections, the FAO as an intergovernmental agency developed legal guidelines on the conservation of plant genetic resources and access to them. In particular, the free exchange of plant germplasm was a major and controversial subject of debate during the FAO Conferences in 1979, 1981 and 1983.

In addition to its programmes dealing with the conservation of forest genetic resources, the FAO was involved in wildlife and protected area programmes. Since 1985, the FAO had been working with the United Nations Environment Programme (UNEP) on developing activities for the improved management and conservation of animal genetic resources at national and regional levels. The Animal Genetic Resources Data Bank, established in co-operation with the FAO, was potentially a global information centre for the improved conservation and use of indigenous breeds in the developing regions.

The 1983 FAO Conference adopted the International Undertaking, despite the reservations expressed by eight member countries (Canada, France, Germany, Japan, New Zealand, Switzerland, United Kingdom and USA). The first ever comprehensive international agreement on plant genetic resources, the Undertaking sought to 'ensure that plant genetic resources of economic and/or social interest, particularly for agriculture, will be explored, preserved, evaluated and made available for plant breeding and scientific purposes'. The Undertaking was based on 'the universally accepted principle that plant genetic resources are a heritage of mankind and, consequently, should be available without restriction'. 'Plant genetic resources' included both new biotechnological products (commercial varieties and breeding lines) and farmers' varieties and wild materials. Unrestricted access was also defined: free of charge, on the basis of mutual exchange or on mutually agreed terms. See Wiegele (1991).

In order to overcome some countries' reservations, the Undertaking was further qualified and interpreted by a number of complementary resolutions negotiated through the Commission on Plant Genetic

Resources and adopted unanimously by the FAO Conference before being annexed to the Undertaking. The first such resolution (4/1989) provided a consensus interpretation of the Undertaking which recognized that the latter's definition of Plant Breeders' Rights was not inconsistent with that adopted by the Union of the Protection of New Varieties of Plants (UPOV) Convention of 1978. A second resolution (5/1989) recognized 'Farmers' Rights' and a third (3/1991) reaffirmed that the concept of heritage of mankind was subject to the sovereign rights of nations over their genetic resources[2] (see p. 67) and agreed that farmers' rights would be implemented through an international fund on plant genetic resources. In this third resolution, it was also agreed 'that breeders' lines and farmers' breeding material should only be available at the discretion of their developers during the period of development'.

The agreements embodied in these resolutions had led to new qualifications of the principle of 'unrestricted access', i.e.:

– firstly, by re-asserting that the concept of heritage of humankind was subject to sovereign rights of countries over their plant genetic resources;

– secondly, by clarifying that free access did not necessarily mean free of charge, by, on the one hand, recognizing that Plant Breeders' Rights were not incompatible with the Undertaking and, on the other hand, by recognizing Farmers' Rights, both of which allowed for some kind of compensation;

– thirdly, by limiting the benefits of the Undertaking, including access to genetic resources, to those adhering to the Undertaking; and

– fourthly, by limiting the scope of the free access provision to exclude breeders' lines and farmers' breeding material.

While the rights of breeders, already adopted in many industrial countries, were being reinforced through revisions of the UPOV Convention, as well as through national and international agreements on intellectual property rights, including patents, farmers' rights were yet to be implemented and an international fund established.

During the 1980s, when the FAO functioned as the main forum for plant genetic resources issues, the United Nations Environment Programme (UNEP) increasingly focused on these same issues and on biological diversity. The Convention on Biological Diversity was prepared by UNEP and signed by 150 countries in June 1992 at the United Nations Conference on Environment and Development (Earth Summit) in Rio de Janeiro; by early 1996, it had been ratified by more than 130 countries.

Countries which were parties to a convention might also have the choice of becoming parties to legally-binding instruments, known as protocols, that might be subsequently renegotiated to give effect to the aims and objectives of the Convention. The need for protocols and the terms of reference for their renegotiation were determined at meetings held under the auspices of Conferences of the Parties (CoPs or regular meetings of the 167 signatories of the Convention), where attendance was not, as the name implied, limited to parties to the Convention but included observers from countries which had not ratified the Convention, United Nations agencies and intergovernmental organizations (such as the Organization for Economic Co-operation and Development) as well as non-governmental organizations (NGOs) lobbying on behalf of interest groups such as the environmental movement and industry. However, participation in official decision-making was restricted to parties to the Convention (Meek, 1996).

Both the Undertaking and the Convention on Biological Diversity provided for access on mutually agreed terms and left open the question of whether the terms should be agreed on a multilateral or bilateral basis; but the Undertaking was considered more geared to a multilateral solution and the Convention to bilateral solutions. One of the main differences was that the International Undertaking was limited to plant genetic resources of interest to food and agriculture. Also, relevant was the fact that the Convention was a legally-binding agreement, while the Undertaking remained voluntary, and that the Convention on Biological Diversity did not deal with the conditions of access to existing *ex-situ* genetic resources outside the country of origin.

At the 27th FAO Conference (November 1993), it was agreed that the revision of the International Undertaking would be carried out through a process of intergovernmental negotiations, i.e.:

– in early 1996, extraordinary meetings of the Commission on Plant Genetic Resources were to agree on a complete second draft of the revised Undertaking and consider options for its future legal and institutional status;

– by mid-1996, the Fourth International Technical Conference on Plant Genetic Resources and high-level meetings was to agree on the text of the revised Undertaking.

The definition of the conditions of access to plant genetic resources for food and agriculture together with the realization of farmers' rights as part of a multilateral agreement on mutually agreed terms, would make the Global System for the Conservation and Utilization of Plant Genetic Resources fully operative. The Global System would include:

– the World Information and Early Warning System on plant genetic resources;

– an international network of *ex-situ* collections, *in-situ* and on-farm conservation areas with complementary basic agreements on gene banks;

– a voluntary International Code of Conduct for Plant Germplasm Collecting and Transfer; and

– the Global Plan of Action on Plant Genetic Resources, comprising a Report on the State of the World's Plant Genetic Resources for Food and Agriculture (see p. 38) and the International Fund, which was supposed to contribute to making farmers' rights a reality.

A primary function of the Code of Conduct was to serve as a point of reference until such time as individual countries established their own codes, or regulations, for germplasm collection, conservation exchange and use. It drew upon the example of the FAO Code of Conduct on the Distribution and Use of Pesticides, published in 1986, which served as a model for regulations in more than 20 countries.

Adopted by the FAO Conference in 1993, this Code of Conduct provided a framework of bilateral agreements, the conditions of which were to be determined by the countries concerned, including those which might not yet have ratified the Convention of Biological Diversity and/or adhered to the Undertaking. The Code provided guidelines for collectors applying for permits and for their issuance by state authorities, and set out minimum responsibilities for collectors, sponsors, curators and users of collected germplasm. It covered both the collecting and transfer of germplasm. It was agreed that the Code could be updated, amended or modified when appropriate, through the Commission, to ensure it adapted to changing needs and circumstances.

The Code of Conduct aimed to:

– promote the collection, long-term conservation and use of plant genetic resources, in ways respectful of the environment;

– achieve a better balance in economic benefits between the users and donors of germplasm, and the caretakers of wild plant resources;

– ensure the safe exchange of plant genetic resources, and associated technologies and scientific information;

– reduce environmental degradation and the loss of genetic diversity; and

– foster the direct participation of farming communities, as well as of scientists and organizations in countries where germplasm was collected, in plans and actions for the conservation and use of plant genetic resources.

Regarding the international network of germplasm collections, 31 countries indicated their willingness to make the collections part of it, during the fifth session of the Commission on Plant Genetic Resources (1993).

On 26 October 1994, in Washington, D.C., the Consultative Group on International Agricultural Research (CGIAR) and the FAO signed an agreement placing under the auspices of the FAO the international plant genetic resources collections housed in the International Agricultural Research Centers' gene banks. The CGIAR collections contained at that date more than 500,000 accessions, which included up to 40% of all unique samples of major food crop species held by gene banks world-wide. The agreement came as a welcome conclusion to a long negotiating process initiated in 1987 when the FAO asked the CGIAR Centers to bring their gene banks officially under its auspices.

The IARCs' germplasm now fell under the auspices of the FAO's Global System for the Conservation and Sustainable Use of Plant Genetic Resources, itself under the one-member-one vote 110 country jurisdiction of the International Undertaking on Plant Genetic Resources. The International Plant Genetic Resources Institute (IPGRI) was expected to oversee a CGIAR system-wide integrated genetic resources programme to guide policy and management of all the genetic resources units of the individual IARCs (see p. 441). The latter were holding the germplasm in trust for the benefit of the international community, under stipulated standards, but they were not supposed to claim ownership nor seek any intellectual property rights over it. The IARCs also committed themselves to preventing others from patenting the material (in *Seedling*, the Quarterly Newsletter of Genetic Resources Action International-GRAIN, vol. 11, no. 4, December 1994, p. 21).

In December 1990, it was recommended that the FAO convene a Fourth International Technical Conference on Plant Genetic Resources in 1996, to follow up the three previous conferences held in 1967, 1973 and 1981. This Fourth Conference was convened by the FAO in Leipzig from 17 to 23 June 1996. In November 1995, during the 28th session of the FAO Commission on Plant Genetic Resources, the following main goals of the FAO Global Plan of Action on Plant Genetic Resources had been announced:

– explore and collect important and/or threatened plant genetic resources, and monitor genetic diversity and erosion;

– identify and overcome the obstacles for the utilization of conserved resources in order to promote their use;

– develop and promote methods for on-farm and community-level conservation and use of plant genetic resources as part of an integrated conservation and utilization strategy;

– promote *in-situ* conservation of wild plants as part of an integrated conservation strategy, and identify sites for *in-situ* conservation;

– strengthen plant breeding and pre-breeding capabilities, utilize greater diversity in plant breeding and promote approaches that maintain diversity;

– facilitate access to plant genetic resources, information and technologies;

– promote the development of legal and other mechanisms to protect the rights of germplasm providers;

– develop methods for the economic evaluation of plant genetic resources;

– promote national and regional planning for conservation and sustainable use of plant genetic resources and integration with sustainable agriculture.

In 1996, the FAO published the first (draft) Report on the State of the World's Plant Genetic Resources for Food and Agriculture. Based on 154 country reports, 11 subregional meetings and the FAO's World Information and Early Warning System (WIEWS) data-base, the Report represented an unprecedented attempt to review and assess the state of plant genetic resources in agriculture. It revealed that the number of seed-keeping facilities world-wide had jumped from 54 in the late 1970s (of which 24 had a long-term storage capacity) to a total of 1,308 national, regional and international germplasm collections in the mid-1990s. Of these, 397 were maintained under long- or medium-term storage conditions, most of the rest being active working collections for use by researchers and plant breeders. For the purpose of conservation, the base collections, held under long- or medium-term storage conditions, were the biggest, as they supposedly contained unique material for use in the future. According to the FAO Report, there were about 6.1 million accessions under *ex-situ* conditions by the mid-1990s: 600,000 in the CGIAR (Consultative Group on International Agricultural Research) system and 5.5 million in national collections and regional gene banks. Some 50% to 65% of the accessions (3–4 million) were in base collections; about 90% were kept under cold storage, while 80% were kept in field banks and less than 1% *in vitro*. More than 80% of the accessions were held in national banks and 45% in just twelve countries (Brazil, Canada, China, France, Germany, India, Japan, Republic of Korea, Russia, Ukraine, United Kingdom and USA) [*Seedling*, the Quarterly Newsletter of Genetic Resources Action International-GRAIN, vol. 13, no. 2, June 1996, pp. 5–13].

During the run-up to the Fourth International Technical Conference on Plant Genetic Resources (Leipzig, June 1996), it was reported that some 75 countries had seed-storage facilities suitable for medium or long-term storage, but that only 35 countries had secure long-term seed-storage facilities, if measured according to internationally-accepted criteria. To these secure national collections, one would have to add nine of the CGIAR gene banks and four regional gene banks which were in a decent state. The FAO Report pointed out with concern that one of the major gene banks in the world – the Vavilov Institute (VIR) in Russia, which held the world's third-biggest wheat collection, as well as important collections of other crop species (e.g. barley, maize, rice, lentil, sugar-beet and cotton), did not meet these criteria. The VIR had only medium-term storage facilities (*Seedling*, vol. 13, no. 2, June 1996, pp. 5–13).

In their reports, countries noted gene-bank problems such as:

– inadequate equipment, particularly in cooling units (reported by a number of African countries, Romania and Viet Nam), lack of seed-cleaning and humidity-control equipment;

– irregularities in electricity supply (reported by a number of African countries, Bangladesh, Cuba, Iraq and Turkey);

– difficulties in seed drying, especially in the humid tropics.

In addition, the FAO Report stressed that, in many of even the few secure facilities, 'full safety duplication was lacking and there was often a large backlog of accessions for regeneration'. When all was said and done, the impressive number of 1,308 collections of 6.1 million samples boiled down to perhaps a dozen of truly secure, safe and up-to-date conservation facilities (*Seedling*, vol. 13, no. 2, June 1996, pp. 5–13).

One of the main problems gene banks around the world were facing was regeneration. In order to stay alive, seeds stored in gene banks needed to be grown, harvested and regenerated once in a while. As the FAO Report stated, if a gene bank had to regenerate its entire collection once every ten years, one could expect routine regeneration needs to be 10% annually. But the FAO Report gave a different view of reality: some 95% of countries reported a far higher level of need. Of the 95 countries providing information about regeneration activities, at least 71 (together holding nearly 3 million accessions) 'experienced some difficulties in regenerating their collections'. The FAO concluded that almost half (48%) of all stored seeds world-wide were in dire need of regeneration. But the Report also warned that some of these seeds 'may already have lost their viability or genetic integrity, or they may be from populations where re-collecting may prove more cost-effective then regeneration'. However, for many of the accessions, re-collecting might prove impossible, because they had become extinct in their natural environment (*Seedling*, vol. 13, no. 2, June 1996, pp. 5–13).

Although countries in the South were most affected by this regeneration backlog, both the CGIAR gene banks and some countries in the North (such as the USA and Japan) were also affected. Part of the problem stemmed from the fact that, at the time the gene-bank system was set up, nobody had anticipated the needs and costs of the long-term maintenance of accessions. One notorious example was the spread of expensive gene banks in some Asian countries, built with Japanese aid, several of which were now virtually being empty or not functioning. The global picture, according to the FAO Global Plan of Action to conserve and use genetic resources, was 'a steady deterioration of many facilities and their ability to perform even basic conservation functions' (*Seedling*, vol. 13, no. 2, June 1996, pp. 5–13).

The FAO Report noted that there was a lot of unco-ordinated and unknown duplication among the world's stored seeds. Overduplication was a waste of time and money and should be minimized. On the other hand, duplication of unique accessions and their storage in other gene banks was crucial to ensure their security in the face of unexpected losses (because of fire, earthquakes, war, etc.). The FAO Report stated that of the 50% of countries which provided information, only 11 countries indicated that their collections (430,000 accessions) were fully duplicated somewhere, 51 countries reported partial duplication and 10 countries reported no duplication at all (*Seedling*, vol. 13, no. 2, June 1996, pp. 5–13).

Genetic erosion in the banks might be widespread. For instance, the FAO reported that a review of the U.S. gene banks (based on tests conducted between 1979 and 1989) showed that 29% of the U.S. collections had seed-germination rates that were either unknown (21%) or less than 65% (8%). Furthermore, 45% of the accessions had less than 550 seeds. This meant that an important part of the U.S. collections was either dead or dying, or might have too few seeds to guarantee survival of genetic diversity. Another example was provided by the Latin American Maize Programme (LAMP). In 1991, only half of the accessions could be evaluated due to lack of viable seed (*Seedling*, vol. 13, no. 2, June 1996, pp. 5–13).

As for the representation of crops in *ex-situ* collections, the high proportion of cereals (48%) reflected not only their key role in global food security, but also in Northern agriculture and international commodity trade. By contrast, tuber and root crop species, like sweet potato, cassava and potato, accounted for only 4% of global accessions. Bananas and plantains were represented by a mere 10,500 accessions. Many locally valuable crop species had only just started to be collected and regional base collections were being kept by national gene banks. The FAO admitted that there were very few accessions of medicinal plants. Information on the type of accession (whether wild relatives, local varieties or breeding lines) was only available for one-third of global accessions. Globally, 48% of accessions were advanced cultivars or breeding lines, 36% were old cultivars or farmers' varieties and only

15% were wild or weedy plants or crop relatives (*Seedling*, vol. 13, no. 2, June 1996, pp. 5–13).

It was crucial to store adequate information on the accessions held *ex situ*. The FAO Report indicated that, although 37% of national collections and nearly all the CGIAR gene banks had passport data (i.e. basic data such as the sampling date and site), in most collections this data referred only to the country of origin. Plant breeders often developed their own collections because of the lack of information on collections in the gene banks. The rates of characterization and evaluation were also very low; as a result, the accessions of national collections were not fully utilized even by current gene bank clients: the breeders. Exceptions to poor characterization were the countries of Western Europe, East Asia, North America, Ethiopia, India and The Philippines. While some gene banks had their collections fully documented, computerized and even put on the Internet (as was the case for the Vavilov Institute and the U.S. base collections), others had not documented any of their accessions (*Seedling*, vol. 13, no. 2, June 1996, pp. 5–13).

Nevertheless, a great number of accessions were exchanged world-wide. For instance, over the three-year period 1992–1994, the CGIAR Centers had distributed an annual average of over 120,000 accessions to national programmes world-wide. The CGIAR mostly exchanged seeds with itself, or with the host countries of the individual International Agricultural Research Centers (IARCs): between 1992 and 1994, 55% of the accessions sent out went to sister institutes, 34% to developing countries, 9% to developed countries and 2% to the private sector. During the same three-year period, the USA distributed 116,897 samples to 126 countries (*Seedling*, vol. 13, no. 2, June 1996, pp. 5–13).

The FAO Report stressed the need to improve the current gene bank system through rationalization, regional and international collaboration and the filling of existing gaps, both in the number of plants covered and in the information on them. The unavoidable erosion of genetic diversity in the gene banks in the long term, even under the best long-term storage conditions, pointed to the need for greater efforts toward *in-situ* conservation, particularly in the agro-ecosystems, in close co-operation with farming communities (*Seedling*, vol. 13, no. 2, June 1996, pp. 5–13).

A draft of the Global Plan of Action on Plant Genetic Resources was discussed during the Leipzig Conference. Another aim of the latter was to formulate the Leipzig Declaration on Conservation and Sustainable Utilization of Plant Genetic Resources for Food and Agriculture. This Declaration formulated general rules and principles regarding access, conservation and use of plant genetic resources, and was of a less technical nature than the Global Plan of Action. Minimal consensus was reached on the Declaration due to such issues as national sovereignty, technology transfer and finance.

The Global Plan of Action on Plant Genetic Resources (GPA) contained about 346 recommendations derived from data assembled in the Report on the State of the World's Plant Genetic Resources for Food and Agriculture, the main backround document for the GPA. In Leipzig, agreement was reached on about 95% of the items constituting the recommendations of the GPA. The most significant elements were the following:

   – The most preferable conservation strategy was a combination of *in-situ* and *ex-situ* storage. Local and indigenous knowledge should be recognized as important components of surveying and inventorying activities. Participatory, on-farm management of plant genetic resources was recommended, although no consensus was reached on the issue as to whether this should be supported by financial revenues from farmers' rights. Regarding *in-situ* conservation, the GPA explicitly demanded more attention for wild relatives which could be used for the improvement of food crop species. Many of the world's nature parks, it stated, contained wild relatives, but received little concern.

Regarding *ex-situ* conservation, the GPA intended to give high priority to safeguarding as much diversity as possible in *ex-situ* collections while countries had national sovereignty over, and responsibility for, their *own* plant genetic resources. More funds were requested to support *ex-situ* 'core' collections containing a selected and characterized amount of entries already available in *ex-situ* collections.

   – With respect to the use of plant genetic resources, the GPA supported a sustainable agriculture through diversification of crop production and a broader diversity in crops. Various strategies were opted for, starting with a further support for seed production and distribution in the public sector. A relatively new strategy to increase the demand for diverse plant genetic resources was to develop new (niche) markets for local varieties and 'diversity-rich' products. The issue of the use of plant genetic resources subject to property rights 'in accordance with applicable international agreements and national legislation' was not resolved. Neither was the exchange of plant genetic resources for technology. Furthermore, the final section of the GPA on 'Ensuring a fair and equitable sharing of benefits' which demanded on effective implementation of farmers' rights was not agreed upon (Pistorius, 1996).

Besides the intergovernmental actions and negotiations concerning the conservation and use of plant genetic resources, other related initiatives had been taken. A consultation was organized by the Swedish Agency for Research Co-operation with Developing Countries, involving government experts from Asia, Africa, Europe and the Americas, as well as representatives of international bodies. At these meetings, the concept of Farmers' Rights and an international fund to enforce them was supported. The Keystone Center, an American non-profit making organization, initiated an International Dialogue on Plant Genetic Resources in 1988, which brought together more than 90 participants from 30 countries. The consensus reached was quite significant in that participants were representative of governments, industry, non-governmental and inter-governmental organizations, even if they were attending in a personal capacity. The Keystone Center's third and final plenary session was held in Oslo, in June 1991. Here, it was agreed that preventing 'genetic erosion' was an urgent task requiring international commitment. A proposed Global Plant Genetic Resources Initiative would require $300 million annually to strengthen existing programmes and institutions. For the 1993–2000 period, an estimated $1.5 billion would be required.[3] (see p. 67) In the Final Consensus Report, suggestions were provided as to how the fund supporting the Initiative could be managed so as to ensure national sovereignity and commitment, as well as equity between suppliers of plant genetic resources, technology and information at global, regional, national and community level.

The Oslo meeting also dealt with intellectual property protection and agreed that it could stimulate innovation in certain market conditions. When applied to plant genetic resources, however, it could have a negative impact on farmers and/or breeders actively maintaining important genetic diversity as part of their activities. Developing countries choosing to implement a plant breeders' rights system would be advised to retain provisions allowing farmers plantback of protected varieties. This was especially important for farmers unable to afford to buy seeds every year or who were not consistently within reach of a seed distribution infrastructure, thereby reduced to relying on seeds saved from the previous season. The Keystone Center report tried to reconcile the positions of industrialized and developing countries, particularly between private industry and community activities.

The conservation, accessibility and use of plant genetic resources were not only the main goals of the FAO Global Plan of Action on Plant Genetic Resources, but also the core subjects of the Conferences of Parties (CoP) which followed the establishment in 1992 of the Convention on Biological Diversity.

The first Conference of the Parties (CoP-1) took place in Nassau, The Bahamas, from 28 November to 9 December 1994. It was attended by 722 registered participants from 277 delegations; these included 94 of the 106 nations that had ratified the Convention on Biological Diversity, 37 observer nations, 13 United Nations agencies/ programmes, 25 other intergovernmental organizations and 108 non-governmental organizations. Major issues and decisions related to:

– the financial mechanism to operate the Convention; the Global Environment Facility (GEF) had been operating as the interim financial mechanism before being restructured in 1994; developing countries were concerned as to how the new mechanism would operate and which modalities would need to be developed to enable the CoP to make inputs into project-funding decisions;

– the United Nations Environment Programme (UNEP), which had housed the interim Secretariat, was selected as the organization to house the Secretariat;

– the interim Secretariat had been based in Geneva, but a permanent location for the Secretariat was required; offers from Kenya (Nairobi), Spain (Sevilla) and Switzerland (Geneva) had been received and CoP-1 decided which criteria to be used in making a choice between the three proposed locations;

– a budget for the Permanent Secretariat of $5.7 million for 1995 was presented, but contributions by the ratifying countries to this budget would be voluntary;

– how to set up the Clearing House Mechanism and its scope required by the Convention had already been the subject of considerable discussion, CoP-1 agreed to mandate the Secretariat 'to prepare a comprehensive study containing concrete recommendations' which would also 'need to draw on all relevant existing institutional structures'; a pilot phase of operation was planned for 1996–1997;

– the medium-term work programme was discussed at length, with property rights, compensation and biosafety to the fore; existing legislation on property rights was to be compiled, and it was decided 'to establish an *ad hoc* group of experts with balanced regional representation' to prepare a review of risk assessment and existing guidelines and legislation.

The second Conference of the Parties (CoP-2) took place in Jakarta in November 1995, just half a year before the Fourth International Technical Conference. The FAO Conference Resolution 7/93 called for the adaptation of the FAO Undertaking in harmony with the Convention on Biological Diversity. However, how the Convention would be integrated into the Global System was a pending issue for future Conferences of Parties. Simultaneously, the Commission on Plant Genetic Resources attempted to maintain the Global System as a fixed item on the agenda during the two first Conferences of Parties. One could be forgiven for wondering whether a single programme would not be the best solution (Pistorius, 1995).

The difference between UNEP Convention on Biological Diversity and FAO Undertaking and Global Plan of Action was that the latter offered a more detailed and specific agreement on plant genetic resources for food and agriculture (often land races), these being a distinct subset of biological diversity. Unlike wild biological diversity as dealt with in the Convention, these resources were developed, enhanced and maintained by farmers, and often needed continual human intervention, because they could not survive in the wild; they addressed a number of human needs including food, medicines and fibre; they constituted a limited number of species; they were generally more dependent on intra-species genetic diversity than inter-species diversity; and they were unequally distributed, thus creating inter-dependency among countries for their conservation and sustainable use (Pistorius, 1995).

An important step toward the implementation of the FAO Global Plan of Action was the CGIAR move to place its twelve gene banks under the auspices of the FAO in December 1994. Both the Convention on Biological Diversity and the Global Plan of Action focused on *in-situ* conservation and both supported the sustainable use of plant genetic resources *in situ*. However, some non-governmental organizations feared that if either one of the organizations became dominant, this would be detrimental to the other (Pistorius, 1995).

Another difference between the Convention and the Global Plan of Action was that the latter focused on farmers' rights as a primary mechanism for protecting 'the rights of the providers of genetic resources', while the Convention involved a much wider range of beneficiaries. The Convention stressed national sovereignty over genetic resources as being part of biological diversity in the broadest sense. In addition, the role of indigenous communities (and not specifically farmers) in the implementation of national conservation policies had been a key issue of the first two Conferences of Parties. Although the preparatory documents of the Fourth International Technical Conference referred to indigenous communities, farmers' rights appeared to be an important, but still unresolved, issue. The FAO Commission on Plant Genetic Resources referred to *Agenda 21* and the Keystone meeting in Madras (1990), both calling for recognition of farmers' rights, to emphasize the importance of this concept. However, it was not clear how farmers' rights related to the national sovereign rights of States and what role the Commission on Plant Genetic

Resources would play in setting up a benefit-sharing mechanism between farmers and governments wishing to exercise their rights. The Fourth International Technical Conference offered an opportunity for a better understanding of the relations between the Convention on Biological Diversity follow-up and the FAO Global Plan of Action. A number of experts were of the opinion that, although plant genetic resources for food and agriculture were acknowledged as key elements of biological diversity by both fora (FAO Commission on Plant Genetic Resources and the Conferences of Parties), a unified mechanism would save a lot of time and resources (Pistorius, 1995).

On the agenda of the third Conference of Parties to the Convention on Biological Diversity (CoP-3), held in November 1996 in Buenos Aires, were agricultural biological diversity, the outcome of the FAO Fourth International Technical Conference on Plant Genetic Resources and a progress report on the renegotiation of the International Undertaking on Plant Genetic Resources. Another item for discussion was the implementation of Article 8j of the Convention, which dealt with the knowledge of indigenous and local communities. According to non-governmental organizations such as Genetic Resources Action International (GRAIN, Barcelona), the logical place for a final agreement on agricultural biological diversity was a special legally-binding protocol under the Convention. This notion was increasingly being accepted in the policy arena, including by the FAO. It was also important that Article 8j be further elaborated in such a way as to effectively enable communities to regain control over their knowledge and living resources.

GRAIN recalled some basic principles:

– any legal instrument and action plan must clearly spell out how local farming communities managing genetic resources would be supported and empowered; rather than more 'compensation' for their contribution, local farming communities needed control over their resources;

– this logically meant that the centre of gravity of any concerted effort must move from *ex-situ* conservation to the *on-farm* management of genetic resources;

– on the legal front farming communities must be granted unequivocal rights over their germplasm and knowledge; this should not only include the right to benefit from, to share and to further develop crop germplasm, but also the right to say no to any intended appropriation or commercialization of their resources and knowledge; this logically meant that any agreement on prior informed consent procedures should include full participation and consent of those working with agricultural biological diversity at the local levels;

– full participation of local farming communities in the setting of priorities and implementation of agricultural research must be guaranteed; this would have important implications for the current research systems, at both national and international levels.

In many developing countries, the contribution of the informal sector to plant breeding, seed supply and conservation was more important than that of the public sector. For instance, in several countries of southern Africa, the use by farmers of certified sorghum seeds from research institutions constituted less than 5% of the total area sown to this crop species, while the use of certified bean, rice and groundnut seeds was virtually non-existent in that region. Most farmers relied on their own varieties. Similarly, a survey made in Costa Rica, Honduras and Nicaragua revealed that farmers relied on their own varieties for 44% of seeds in the case of maize and for 37% in the case of beans (Montecinos, 1994).

That was why the Community Biodiversity Development and Conservation Programme (CBDC) was set up in January 1993, with financial support from some major 'Northern' donors, in order to bridge the gap between the informal and formal sectors in the vast area of plant breeding in relation to the preservation and rational utilization of biological diversity.

The CBDC was an important outcome of the 1991 Keystone Dialogue session. The objectives of the CBDC Programme were to investigate and assess community innovation systems in conservation and use of plant genetic resources; support these systems; and suggest ways of improving formal institutional support for community innovation systems. The members of the Programme were: the Centre for Genetic Resources (CGR), a division of the Centre for Plant Breeding and Reproduction Research (CPRO-DLO), a public research centre in the Netherlands; the Community Technology Development Association (COMMUTEC), a non-governmental organization from Zimbabwe; the Ethiopian Biodiversity Institute, a public gene bank; Genetic Resources Action International (GRAIN), a non-governmental organization (NGO) from Spain; the Latin American Consortium for Agroecology and Development (CLADES), an NGO with a regional network based in Chile; the Norwegian Centre for International Agricultural Development (NORAGIC), a public research centre from Norway; Rural Advancement Foundation International (RAFI), an NGO from Canada; the South-East Asian Regional Institute for Community Education (SEARICE), an NGO regional network based in The Philippines (Manicad, 1996).

The CBDC Programme was funded by the Directorate General for International Cooperation (DGIS) of the Dutch Ministry of Foreign

Affairs, the International Development Research Centre (IDRC, Ottawa) and the Swedish International Development Agency (SIDA); the budget amounted to $5.5 million for a four-year period. Although the Programme was initiated in 1995, the first activities were limited to an inventory of biodiversity in the regions due to delayed funding remittances from the donors (Manicad, 1996).

All the organizations involved in the Programme had at least ten years of experience in plant genetic resource (PGR) conservation or policy studies and advocacy.

The South-East Asian Project of the CBDC Programme involved the Mekong Delta in Viet nam, Nam Province in Thailand, Sabah in Malaysia and Bohol in The Philippines. In Viet Nam, the SEARICE network, in co-operation with Can Tho University, was in charge of assessing the performance of local landraces and modern varieties of rice in irrigated, rainfed and flooded systems under different socio-cultural conditions. The researchers were conducting comparative laboratory analyses of landraces and modern varieties in terms of seed quality. The research work also aimed to make policy recommendations concerning PGR conservation and development in the Province. In Bohol, the SEARICE network, together with local farmers' organizations, were investigating the genetic diversity of planting materials, with particular emphasis on root crop species such as sweet potato, taro and yam. In The Philippines, these tubers were called the 'poor people's crops'; they were commercially unprofitable for private seed companies, but essential for the food security of marginalized farmers (Manicad, 1996).

The Latin American Project involved NGOs in Brazil, Colombia, Peru and Chile, all members of the CLADES network. Activities involved the reappraisal and reactivation of local plant genetic resources and their broader utilization; reappraisal of farmers' knowledge and skills; and enhancing formal institutions' awareness of farmers' practices and their contribution to PGR conservation. The particularity of the Project was that farmers participated in the whole process of conservation and utilization of PGR. In Colombia, for instance, farmers were trained in the appraisal and planning of farming systems and involved in community actions to achieve wider crop diversity. Farmers also participated in the identification of species and varieties for research. In Chile, participating communities had initially identified the existing diversity of native forest and medicinal plants, and useful cultivated and protected plants; they had also enumerated uses of native and exotic plants (Manicad, 1996).

The African Project initially comprised two public agricultural research centres in Ethiopia and Sierra Leone, and an NGO in

Zimbabwe. In Ethiopia, planned activities included strengthening the capacity for improving landraces of the Ethiopian Biodiversity Institute, farm communities and formal institutions; community-managed on-farm landrace selection; an evaluation and enhancement programme for major food crop species; the establishment of linkages between the formal and informal crop improvement technologies; and the promotion of a community-based crop improvement network (Manicad, 1996).

The International Technical Programme (ITP) was based at the NORAGIC and CGN; its main activities included devising research methods for assessing plant genetic resources, farmers' breeding techniques and local seed supply systems. The CPRO-DLO, which housed the CGN, provided laboratory facilities for genetic analysis, seed analysis and data-processing equipment. The International Policy Programme (IPP) had a decentralized structure and comprised RAFI and GRAIN, and regional representatives. It focused on advocating policies, setting up institutions and legal mechanisms in support of community-based biodiversity activities. The IPP also assessed and proposed mechanisms to deal with the ethical and policy implications of the Programme (Manicad, 1996).

Since the Keystone Dialogue in 1991, it had taken the CBDC Programme three years to reach agreement on joint action between most of the NGOs, which were very critical of the 'green revolution'; and the formal organizations, many of which promoted the 'green revolution' and supported it. The parties had come to a mutual understanding that both formal and non-formal institutions had their limitations and potential, and could therefore benefit each other. Both parties also needed to agree on resolving conflicts arising from issues of representation, accountability, methods of work, and interpretation of concepts like 'participation' and 'integrity'. The protocol contained details on the responsibility and accountability of formal institutions, but was vague on the NGOs' accountability. This was obvious from the CBDC publication entitled *Cultivating knowledge: genetic diversity, farmer experimentation and crop research*. The NGOs could not give a clearcut guarantee that they represented their communities and debates and literature questioning the presumed comparative advantage of NGOs were piling up, most of the criticism coming from within the NGOs themselves. There were also the issues of research focus and objectives. Formal institutions tended to concentrate only on understanding genetic variation, the process of genetic selection and recombination within communities. The NGOs were concerned about translating these studies into an analysis of how to empower farming communities. However, formal institutions did appreciate that working with NGOs meant putting the development perspective before research (Manicad, 1996).

Despite the problems, all parties agreed that the main strength of the CBDC Programme lay in the diversity of organizations and working approaches. Being a global Programme, it offered numerous opportunities to test hypotheses in diverse environments and under various socio-economic conditions. The working experience gained by the formal and non-formal institutions, despite the conflicts, offered the chance to formulate research policies that favoured farming communities in marginalized situations. The CBDC Programme was not simply a scientific study, it also embodied a strong political component of policy-making that backed farmers' conservation systems and the development of countries in the South. In addition, the Programme approach was gaining recognition in international agricultural research circles. For instance, the CGN was involved in designing a research programme concerning *in-situ* conservation for the International Plant Genetic Resources Institute; the CGN was also discussing farmers' participatory breeding methods with plant breeders of the Consultative Group on International Agricultural Research; this was considered a breakthrough because scientists had long shied away from involving farmers in crop breeding (Manicad, 1996).

Until the Convention on Biological Diversity came into force in 1992, the world's genetic resources were considered to be the common heritage of humankind, i.e. open to access without restrictions. Article 3 of the Convention affirmed that States had the sovereign right to exploit their own resources pursuant to their own environmental policies. Article 15 of the Convention addressed access issues. It stated that the authority to determine access to genetic resources rested with each national government and was subject to national legislation. Article 15 was worded as follows:

– 'States shall facilitate access to genetic resources for environmentally sound use;

– the access shall be subject to prior informed consent and based on mutually agreed terms;

– the Convention provides for the sharing of benefits derived from genetic resources with the country of origin, or the country providing such resources if acquired in accordance with the Convention.'

The wording of articles 16 and 19 of the Convention on Biological Diversity, which dealt with access to biological diversity, the sharing of benefits and technology transfer left national governments considerable leeway as to the extent and manner in which they regulated access to biological diversity and involvement in product development and marketing. The Convention offered little guidance as to the nature and mixture of appropriate benefits, or what constituted a fair and equitable share, or even who qualified as beneficiaries. A number of stakeholders, namely providers, collectors and users, were involved in the discovery and development of products derived from biological diversity (Ten Kate, 1995).

Providers were generally departments of federal, State and local governments, managers of protected areas, local and indigenous communities and private landowners. For certain countries, bioprospecting might be one of several sustainable uses of biological diversity that would be appropriate as part of a national strategy. Governments were expected to ensure that biological diversity policies were well integrated in other relevant areas of policy, such as tenure of land and genetic resources, science and technology, health, trade and industry. In order to assess the country's potential as a source of biological diversity and services in prospecting, governments were encouraged to work with provider institutions, whether private or public, to raise awareness about possible markets and the kinds of products and services needed in each sector, and to learn about the safety, efficacy and quality regulations for marketing the products, and, most importantly, the quality standards demanded by consumers in each proposed market. The pharmaceutical market was likely to be the largest global market for prospecting: while some \$200 billion represented global annual sales of pharmaceuticals, an estimated \$40 billion was the result of bioprospecting (Ten Kate, 1995).

The seed market was much smaller, as was the contribution made to it by wild biological diversity. A joint survey by Cambridge University and the World Conservation Monitoring Centre of 20 plant breeding and seed corporations to determine the source of their germplasm for various crop groups revealed that the companies surveyed obtained 81.5% of all their germplasm from commercial cultivars, the rest originating from wild species maintained *in situ* and *ex situ*, from *in-situ* landraces and from landraces stored in gene banks. Companies' interest in investing in bioprospecting was therefore limited but, when they were interested, they looked for specific features. According to the then Business Council for Sustainable Development, the following factors influenced companies' choice of countries in which to prospect: macro-economic and political stability, reliable legal and property systems, an educated work force and an adequate physical infrastructure (roads, power, communications) [Ten Kate, 1995].

Collectors and users often complained of the complexity of the regulations and procedures governing access to genetic resources.

Within a single country, it might be necessary to seek permits from more than half a dozen different government departments at federal, State and local levels. Once permission was granted, collectors could find on arrival at the site that the rules had changed. This caused confusion, delay, expense and uncertainty for the collector. Governments could address these problems by designating a national focal point for biological diversity issues to streamline access applications and facilitate partnerships with foreign and national stakeholders (Ten Kate, 1995).

While the prior, informed consent of contracting parties at national level was a requirement for access to biological diversity, a close reading of the Convention suggested that, at the local level, prior, informed consent and benefit sharing were encouraged but not required. Sharing benefits at the local level and dedicating part of the profits to specific conservation measures were thus the key to successful long-lasting bioprospecting partnerships. Governments would be wise to invite and facilitate participation by business, non-governmental organizations and local communities in the formulation of the national biological diversity strategy and in specific bioprospecting projects. For instance, in Costa Rica, the National Institute for Biodiversity (INBIO) had been involved in the development of policy and legislation related to bioprospecting. It had shared benefits by working with the local university and employing over 70 local people, including 46 lay Costa Ricans as 'parataxonomists' to collect and prepare specimens for its inventory. Another 28 staff, of whom 12 were professionals and technicians, worked in the prospecting department and four laboratory technicians and the six ecochemists on the International Cooperative Biodiversity Groups (ICBG) project (Ten Kate, 1995). See also p. 205.

It was up to local and indigenous communities and non-governmental organizations to lobby government for national laws, policy and procedures. One issue gaining recognition in international debate was that of how the benefits from biological resources might be shared with indigenous and local communities. This was especially important when one realized that these groups had played an important role over the centuries in the selection and propagation of current genetic resources. These were no established institutions that safeguarded the rights of indigenous and local communities. In addition, national legal regimes pertaining to biological diversity and intellectual property protection were silent on the rights of indigenous and local communities (Mugabe and Ouko, 1994).

In October 1993, the Andean Pact countries – Bolivia, Colombia, Ecuador, Peru and Venezuela- approved a common plant breeders' rights statute. The responsibility for preparing a draft directive for access to genetic resources was assigned to the Junta del Acuerdo de Cartagena (JUNAC), the administrative body of the Andean Pact. The JUNAC contracted the World Conservation Union (IUCN) and the Peruvian Center for Environmental Law -a private consultant- for this drafting work. In July 1994, a meeting was held in Colombia to discuss the draft; it was attended by representatives of environmental non-governmental organizations, indigenous people organizations and government experts. At a second meeting hosted by the Ministry of Environment of Venezuela in August 1994, a common Colombian-Venezuelan proposal was discussed, then presented to a meeting of government representatives (Jaffé and Rojas, 1994*b*).

It was observed that both the IUCN and Colombian draft proposals emphasized the equitable distribution of profits to indigenous people from resources they traditionally used. Although they did not ignore the rights of indigenous people, many participants considered other problems as being more concrete and urgent, such as management of *ex-situ* collections and control of scientific investigations, (Jaffé and Rojas, 1994*b*).

The discussions also revealed strong nationalistic positions regarding genetic resources management and deep suspicion about motives and the urgency to facilitate access. There was, however, consensus on the assignment of a strong role to the state in the control of access, an aspect perceived as inadequately covered in the draft prepared by the IUCN. Many strongly opposed intellectual property protection, as they equated protection with appropriation of resources (Jaffé and Rojas, 1994*b*).

The representatives of indigenous communities consulted by the IUCN were unfamiliar with the issues discussed. They subscribed to the importance of genetic resources for themselves but saw no urgency to establish an access regime quickly. Persons working directly with genetic resources (such as plant breeders, *ex-situ* collection managers), on the other hand, saw it as important to settle the rapid question of access to genetic resources as quickly as possible. They expressed frustration about the political and philosophical tone of the debate, which they would have wished more technical (Jaffé and Rojas, 1994*b*).

On 18 May 1995, a Philippine Presidential Executive Order decreed that, thereafter, prospectors would be bound to negotiate all research agreements with the government, and to seek prior, informed consent from local communities and indigenous peoples, with whom they were to share the benefits: 'prospecting of biological and genetic resources shall be allowed within the ancestral lands and domains of indigenous cultural communities only with the prior, informed consent of such communities, obtained in accordance with the customary laws of the

concerned community'. In addition, there were a number of minimum set terms for commercial and academic research agreements:
- a limit on the samples to be collected and exported;
- a complete set of all specimens to be deposited with the Philippine National Museum;
- all Philippine citizens to be entitled to access to collected specimens and relevant data deposited abroad;
- the collector to inform the Philippine Government and affected local and indigenous communities if a commercial product were derived from its activites;
- provisions for the payment of negotiated royalties or other forms of compensation to the National Government, local or indigenous cultural communities and individual person or designated beneficiary where there was commercial use;
- involvement of Philippine scientists in the research and collection process at the cost of the collector;
- transfer of equipment to a Philippine institute where appropriate;
- payment of a fixed fee to the Department of Environment and Natural Resources;
- in the case of endemic species, the technology to be made available to a designated Philippine institution for use locally and commercially without paying a royalty to the collector (although other agreements could be negotiated) [Barber and La Viña, 1995].

In 1988, the Proyecto de Estudio para el Manejo de Areas Silvestres de Kuna Yala (PEMASKY, Study Project for the Management of Forest Areas of Kuna Yala) and the Asociación de Empleados Kunas (AEK, Association of Kuna Employees) of Panama had produced a manual to regulate scientific research in their area. Researchers were required to: develop a proposal outlining the timing, extent and potential environmental and cultural impact of a research programme, for endorsement by the Scientific Committee of PEMASKY; secure approval for the collection of species from the Scientific Committee of PEMASKY (collections might not include any endangered species, might not be used for commercial purposes and must be constituted in a non-destructive manner); undergo an orientation into the culture of the Kuna Yala respecting the norms of the communities in which they worked; include Kuna collaborators, assistants, guides and informants in their research programme and provide them with training in relevant scientific techniques; leave samples with the PEMASKY Scientific Committee of all specimens (for the collections at the University of Panama) and copies of photographs or slides taken during the research programme; introduce no exotic plant or animal species. Additionally, research was restricted to certain areas of the reserve, prohibited in some sites such as ceremonial or sacred spots and controlled in other specific sites such as some forest areas under community management (Posey and Dutfield, 1995).

In April 1993, the New York Botanical Garden and the Awa Federation, a legal institution which administered the land held under communal title by the Awa of Cachi in Ecuador, signed a two-year agreement for academic scientific research. The agreement included the following terms:

– all scientists were bound to ask for written permission to carry out studies, setting out a description of objectives, size and composition of the research party, length of research programme, species or object of study and the manner in which the research would benefit the Awa community;

– the request for permission was to be given with a minimum of two months notice, since dispersed communities only met four times a year for four days;

– research groups were limited to five people;

– local guides and informants were to accompany all scientists;

– the removal of any object from Awa territory not approved by the Federation was prohibited;

– payments to the Awa Federation members for their services were to be in accordance with a fee scale established by the Federation;

– the Awa Federation was to be acknowledged in all publications (Posey and Dutfield, 1995).

The initiative to revise the Access to Genetic Resources Bill was taken by Senator Marina Silva, representative of the Labour Party in the State of Acre, Amazon Region. Together with the Brazilian focal point of the Convention on Biological Diversity (CBD), the General Coordinating Office on Biological Diversity (COBIO) of the Ministry of the Environment, Water Resources and the Legal Amazon, the National Research Centre for Genetic Resources and Biotechnology (CENARGEN), and a few environmental NGOs, the Senator organized a workshop in August 1996 and was planning a series of four public hearings in major cities around the country in an attempt to gather support for an improved version of the Bill (Alencar and Van der Ree, 1996).

The proposed Bill sought to implement parts of the CBD and was inspired by the Colombian Proposal on the Regulation of the Protection, Conservation and Use of Biological Diversity and Genetic Resources. The proposed Bill had been criticized because it dealt only with access to genetic resources from the provider country's point of view, which might be suitable in the Colombian case, but not from the Brazilian perspective considering the country's great dependence on exotic genetic resources for its own agriculture. Secondly, the issues of technology transfer and national capacity-building (technical, scientific, institutional and managerial) in the conservation and utilization of biological resources were barely mentioned. Thirdly, 'collective intellectual property rights', which referred to the recognition of indigenous and local knowledge about biological resources were a crucial element of the proposed Bill, yet it gave no provision for regulating these rights. Lastly, the issue of benefit-sharing still needed more fine-tuning, as this was crucial for full implementation of the CBD (Alencar and Van der Ree, 1996).

Collectors generally came from botanical gardens, university departments, research institutes, private contractors or local and indigenous communities. They were expected to comply with host countries' laws and procedures governing access to biological diversity and apply for relevant permits. In the absence of elaborated policies, collectors were to abide in any event by a voluntary code of conduct. The users were the pharmaceutical, seed, agrochemical and biotechnology corporations that would develop or market the products resulting from bioprospecting. If the immediate suppliers had themselves entered into supply agreements entailing benefit-sharing with those along the supply chain, companies were morally bound to ensure that benefits were shared ultimately with those owning and protecting the resources. Through collaborative research, development agreements and joint ventures with the suppliers of genetic resources, a company could help its suppliers build on their capacity to add value to raw genetic resources, improve quality control and share with them the fruits of their own biotechnology research and development. Where possible, companies were encouraged to purchase products further up the value chain than raw materials, for instance extracted or processed materials, and pay for value added through the supply of information related to the activity or the materials themselves, or the results of research and development. This would often be easier for a company with a long-term relationship with a supplier, which was confident of the quality of the service and which had an incentive to transfer technology and training to the supplier (Ten Kate, 1995).

In reality, national biological diversity strategies were needed which would thoroughly address the sustainable use of biological diversity and ensure that *ad-hoc* bioprospecting activities maximized potential benefits for participating countries and stakeholders. Since the terms of most agreements remained confidential, it would be difficult to review their contribution to sustainable development. It was also difficult to predict the future demand by users for access to biological diversity for prospecting activities. It was generally thought that bioprospecting had a modest future. However, if suppliers, collectors and users adhered to the guidelines laid out in the Convention and in some national policies, it should enable them to make the most of the opportunities that did exist (Ten Kate, 1995).

During the negotiations leading up to the Convention, most developing countries argued that access to genetic resources by (firms from) industrialized countries would facilitate the South's access not only to products arising from genetic resources, but also to technologies pertaining to the conservation and use of these resources. The Convention did indeed recognize the link between access to genetic resources and technology transfer (Juma and Mugabe, 1994; Juma, Mugabe and Ojwang, 1994).

Partnerships between institutions in the countries supplying genetic resources and corporations from the recipient countries could be a useful mechanism for facilitating access to these resources, transferring technology and technological capacity-building in developing countries. However, these partnerships were not as numerous as they should be and the owners of biological resources seemed to put more emphasis on the acquisition of sophisticated equipment than on manpower and institutional development. The value of genetic raw materials could be enhanced if the material was put through a process of indentification, collection and screening by the owners of the biological resources before they presented it to a potential recipient. Developing countries could play their part, by establishing a reputation as a reliable partner in the screening process (Mugabe and Ouko, 1994).

There was a need to review and revise patent laws in developing countries, which overlooded the rights of those supplying genetic material. A protocol covering the cultural property rights of indigenous people would strengthen the provision on indigenous knowledge within the Convention (Mugabe and Ouko, 1994).

The Convention on Biological Diversity could be strengthened by:
– considering the negotiation of a protocol on the basis of principles already developed in instruments such as the FAO Code of Conduct for Plant Germplasm Collecting and Transfer;
– formulating a model law which could be used by various countries to adopt domestic laws, protect genetic resources and regulate conditions for technology transfer;
– dealing with the issue of regulating access to genetic resources

through material transfer agreements, which generally fell in the domain of trade secret law;

– strengthening farmers' rights to ensure they received compensation, stimulate conservation and enhance local innovation;

– States recognizing individual and communal rights, so as to empower communities and help establish the legal basis for ensuring that collection of genetic resources or local knowledge returned some benefit directly to the local communities (Mugabe and Ouko, 1994). See also Khalil, Reid and Juma (1992).

In January 1993, the African Centre for Technology Studies (ACTS) and the Stockholm Environment Institute organized the International Conference on the Convention of Biological Diversity in Nairobi to discuss how to implement the Convention. The contributions by the participants were to form the basis of a book edited by Sanchez and Juma (1994). It was they who coined the word 'biodiplomacy' to designate 'international negotiations to reach agreements on matters related to biological resources and the essential ecological services rendered by the Earth's ecosystem'. The term 'international' asserted national sovereignty over resources and the book offered a first guideline for countries wishing to be involved in international negotiations of this kind. Access to genetic resources, the issue of national sovereignty, the North-South transfer of technology and finances were all treated in detail, the authors assessing the options open to the various States confronted with the task of implementing the Convention.

The first Conference of Parties to the Convention on Biological Diversity (CoP-1) established an Ad-Hoc Group of Experts which met in Madrid in July 1995 and received advice from a panel of experts who had met two months earlier in Cairo. The task of the group was to consider the need for, and scope of, a Biosafety Protocol and report to CoP-2 in Jakarta in November 1995. CoP-2 recognized the potential importance of the International Technical Guidelines on Safety in Biotechnology being developed in a parallel process by the United Nations Environment Programme (UNEP), noting that these could be used as an interim regulatory mechanism while the protocol was being developed and subsequently as a complementary means of developing national capabilities in regulation. Negotiations on the Biosafety Protocol would not be limited to parties to the Convention. The first meeting of the open-ended international working group set up by CoP-2 took place in Denmark in July 1996. This working group reported to CoP-3 in Buenos Aires in November 1996 on progress in the negotiations, which were expected to be concluded by 1998 (Meek, 1996).

4. Animal genetic resources

The FAO had released information on the genetic erosion of animal diversity with respect to breeds used world-wide for food and farming: one-third of the 4,000 or so breeds of farm animals were threatened with extinction (GRAIN, 1994*a*).

In the early 1990s, cattle, pigs and poultry formed a world population of some 13 billion head, most of these chickens, i.e. more than double the human population. According to the FAO, animals accounted for 19% of the world's food basket directly, but also provided draught power, manure and dung as fertilizer for crops, especially in the developing countries, bringing their overall contribution to global agriculture up to 25%. From the viewpoint of species diversity, whereas evolution had produced more than 40,000 species of vertebrates, less than 20 were making a significant contribution to the world's food supply. The bulk of meat production came from pigs, cattle and poultry, whereas milk was almost entirely supplied by cows: in the early 1990s, according to FAO estimates, 40% of world meat was produced by pigs, 29% by cattle, 29% by poultry and 8% by other domestic animals; 88% of milk was produced by cows, 8% by buffaloes, 2% by sheep and 2% by goats. This data omitted such species as the camel, deer and rabbit, as well as fish and game, which could be vital at local level; it also masked regional differences: for instance, in India, buffaloes contributed more milk than did cattle, whereas in China, 80% of the meat produced was pork (GRAIN, 1994*a*).

Whereas some 70% of all cattle and 60% of all pigs and poultry lived in developing countries, only 30% of all milk and 40% of all meat was produced by these countries. This could be related to feed consumption: whereas, in India and sub-Saharan Africa, only 2% of all grain consumed was fed to animals, in the USA this figure could be as high as 70%; every hectare of agricultural land in the Netherlands was backed up by 8 hectares of land somewhere in the developing countries – be it planted with cassava or soybeans – to grow the feed crop species for its intensive livestock husbandry (GRAIN, 1994*a*).

Farming aside, domestic livestock was a vital form of capital, especially for the poor: many peoples raised animals as an essential source of cash for when times were bad or heavy investment was called for; animals were used as collateral to obtain loans or for dowries and could always be quickly converted into currency. Women often took care to fatten pigs or raise small animals for bartering or trading for household needs. In addition, for many communities, animals also played an important role in rituals and religious traditions (GRAIN, 1994*a*).

Hunted or trapped wild animals provided food, hides, furs and bone. They were also a live source of income from tourism (hunting and natural reserves or parks) and could be sold. Most of the aquatic animals on which people relied as food in the developing countries (e.g. fish, shrimps and prawns, crabs, molluscs, frogs) were wild or semi-wild, whether caught or farmed (GRAIN, 1994a).

Domestication of animals had started some 11,000 years ago, shortly after the domestication of plants, when settled farming had become a new option for supplying food. Goats and sheep were the first animals to be tamed, followed by cattle and pigs in the Near East. As was the case for plants, the vast majority of domesticated animals had their origin in developing countries: besides those from the Near East, chickens came from South-East Asia, turkeys from Latin America and buffaloes from India; not to mention 'minor' species like guinea pigs, yaks, musk oxen and miscellaneous fowl and small ruminants (GRAIN, 1994a).

Over time, domesticated animals spread massively with people and settled into new environmental niches. Natural selection was not only governed by extreme temperatures, humidity, feed supply, parasites, disease, etc., but also by mating strategies used by rural people to combine desirable features in offspring through selection and breeding. This had resulted in a range of indigenous breeds. For instance, the Criollo cattle in South America had evolved from initial cattle introduced from Spain or Portugal in the 1500s; over the past 500 years, the cattle had developed traits allowing them to live on poor nutritional-value feeds and withstand environmental stress. Several traditional African cattle herds, among them the small N'Dama or Lagunes breeds, had developed tolerance to trypanosomiasis – a debilitating and often fatal disease affecting 30% of sub-Saharan Africa's cattle. The Chinese had bred the rare Taihu pig, which assimilated a very high proportion of forage in its diet, reached sexual maturity in 64 days and produced an average litter of 16 piglets. Asians indeed could boast of having developed more than 140 different breeds of pig, compared to only 19 for the North Americans (GRAIN, 1994a).

Only in the past 150–200 years had farmers and herders in temperate climates (the future industrialized countries) begun intensive, controlled breeding practices to develop animal types, duly recorded in herdbooks. It was the strict control of their pedigree that enabled them to be identified as distinct breeds. This approach was seldom followed in developing countries. Thus, a genetically-diverse population of many millions of cattle in northern India went by the encompassing name of Haryana, whereas the difference between Holstein and Red Holstein cows in northern Europe was no greater than one single recessive gene. Therefore, by the diversity of European livestock, we mean the number of visually different breeds developed and not necessarily the extent of genetic diversity they embody (GRAIN, 1994*a*).

As with crop species, economic pressures had led farmers to concentrate on the most productive breeds. This trend had impoverished animal genetic diversity. Thus, according to FAO estimates, half of the breeds existing at the beginning of the twentieth century in Europe had become extinct. One-third of the remaining 770 breeds were in danger of disappearing between 1995 and 2015. The Friesian herd constituted 60% of the dairy cattle community in the European Union, having gradually replaced other breeds over past decades (GRAIN, 1994*a*).

Nowadays, livestock husbandry in the industrialized countries was geared toward higher yields in intensive feeding lots, as a result of combining genetic selection and management policies. The average dairy cow in the USA produced twice as much milk as in the 1960s. Fat thickness in Danish pigs had halved. Broiler chickens matured in six weeks instead of three months and turkeys had been bred with such a wide breast that they could no longer mate naturally. The development of artificial insemination techniques and the use of frozen embryos enabled one bull to fertilize hundreds of cows. Superovulation, followed by *in-vitro* fertilization and embryo transfer to surrogate females, made it possible to produce up to one hundred offspring from a single female; this technique could be used to save endangered species by transferring their embryos to surrogate females of a relative breed or species (GRAIN, 1994*a*).

Developing countries were importing exotic temperate breeds at an increasing rate. Imported breeds were either raised in intensive feedlots or crossed with indigenous breeds. In the first case, the objective was to constitute dairy herds around the main cities, or to produce meat for local consumers or even for export. Frozen sperm and embryos were also being flown from Europe and the USA to developing countries to improve livestock. For instance, the U.S. company University Genetics had signed a $9 million contract with the Indonesian Government to buy Holstein cow embryos, a similar contract having been signed with China (GRAIN, 1994*a*).

Genetic erosion in the case of wild animals had received a lot of publicity. Habitat destruction, change of land-use patterns and environment degradation were the main culprits. Whereas natural parks and ecotourism were on the rise, little attention had been paid to the importance of wild animal resources to the livelihood of local communities and their role in conservation. Even less publicity had been accorded to aquatic resources important for food and agriculture. Fish cultivation was based on a few species, including two major ones, tilapia and carp. Yet the genetic base of the Nile tilapia farmed in Asia was reported as being too narrow; consequently, a determined endeavour to diversify was necessary, so as to avoid a few 'superbreeds' enhancing genetic uniformity and the dependence of local people (GRAIN, 1994*a*).

In contrast to crop genetic resources, national programmes for animal conservation were few and far between. In 1992, the FAO launched a five-year Global Animal Genetic Resources Programme aimed at rescuing local animal breeds, such as the Shiwal cow of Pakistan, the Taihu pig of China, the N'Dama cattle of West Africa and the South American Criollo cattle. The FAO hoped to include this $15 million programme in the World Bank's Global Environment Facility created after the United Nations Conference on Environment and Development held in Rio de Janeiro in June 1992. Already in the 1980s, the FAO Animal Genetic Resources Group had recommended the creation of regional animal gene banks for cryogenic storage of semen, embryos, DNA and, if feasible, ovocytes, as the most appropriate means of preserving endangered species. During 1988, regional gene banks had been set up in Ethiopia and Senegal, China and India, Argentina, Brazil and Mexico; these were located in national facilities with necessary equipment and supplies from the FAO. There was more than one centre in each region so that split samples could be stored to reduce risks of loss. Countries wishing to store germplasm of their endangered breeds were responsible for the collection of samples and their shipment to the gene bank. Legally, ownership of the germplasm remained with the country of origin; provisions were made for access by third parties presenting valid claims for use; users were expected to replenish the gene bank when possible with semen or embryos from regenerated animals. The FAO's animal gene bank system was supported by a global animal genetic data-base of the European Association for Animal Production based in Hanover. Originally set up for Europe, this data-base had been extended to cover all countries of the world.

The Addis Ababa-based International Livestock Centre for Africa (ILCA) had decided to carry out an inventory of Africa's indigenous breeds. In addition, non-governmental organizations (NGOs), such as the American Minor Breeds Conservancy in the USA, the Rare Breeds

Survival Trust in the United Kingdom and the Pro Specie Rara in Switzerland, were running programmes for livestock preservation in the industrialized countries. The NGOs tended to champion the *in-situ* conservation of animal genetic diversity, i.e. in the form of live populations, rather than the *ex-situ* approach (i.e. stored genetic material). In fact, according to FAO estimates, 85% of all foetal populations of livestock breeds stored under *ex-situ* conditions were housed in, or controlled by, the industrialized countries. The NGOs claimed that conservation would only have a future if linked to sustainable utilization; hence the need for decentralized and farmer-implemented conservation (GRAIN, 1994*a*).

At a meeting on conservation and use of animal genetic resources organized in Latin America by the Tropical Agriculture Research and Training Centre (CATIE) in 1992, one non-governmental organization-sponsored initiative reviewed concerned the preservation of Criollo cattle. The so-called RAREN project carried out in Nicaragua between the Italian NGO Crocevia and the National Agrarian University of Managua was focusing on the Reyna cow, a Criollo breed native to Nicaragua and well-adapted to local conditions. In this project, on-farm conservation and breeding were carried out by small farmers directly. It was expected that a Latin American network of NGOs would be set up to work on on-farm conservation and breeding and improvement of Criollo cattle (GRAIN, 1994*a*).

The lessons drawn from decade-long debates on the preservation and use of plant genetic resources should be borne in mind, so as to avoid useless conflictual debates and competition between agencies, secure an effective global system for preserving and using animal genetic diversity by all those concerned, and in particular meet the needs of small farmers. The Convention on Biological Diversity was a prime mechanism for undertaking animal genetic conservation programmes, addressing livestock, wildlife and aquatics, although little discussion or thought had been devoted to farm animals. It would be wise to involve the FAO and the Consultative Group on International Agricultural Research (CGIAR) in this area; this was already the case for the International Livestock Research Institute (ILRI), born of the merger between the ILCA and ILRAD, respectively in Addis Ababa and Nairobi, which was expected to start operations in 1995.

Of the CGIAR animal-oriented institutes or centres, only the International Centre for Living Aquatic Resources Management (ICLARM) was thinking in wider terms of individuals' participation and control over resources, and the combination of *ex-situ* and *in-situ* conservation strategies (GRAIN, 1994*a*).

5. Examples of technical co-operation and assistance

In Cuba, among the projects funded by the United Nations Development Programme (UNDP) and executed by the Food and Agriculture Organization of the United Nations (FAO) over the 1976–1992 period, those related to biotechnologies included: technical assistance to the Research Centre of the National Aquaculture Enterprise in fostering fish production in inland waters; selection of drought-resistant sugar-cane varieties; assistance to increasing fodder production; technical support to the National Plan for Shrimp Cultivation (Plan Nacional de Cultivo del Camarón); national network of embryo transfer centres,[4] (see p. 68) and training of Cuban technicians in the appropriate methods; production of improved seeds.

As of July 1993, a number of projects were being implemented under the Programme for technical Co-operation with the FAO: cultivation of micro-algae as feed for larvae of marine fishes grown at the Experimental Laboratory of Mariculture, Tunas de Zaza; *in-vitro* conservation of sugar-cane germplasm; cultivation and genetic improvement of *Tilapia* sp.; use of micro-algae in pollution control and use of the algal biomass as feed; production of soybean seeds. During the 1976–1989 period, several projects were implemented under the same Programme for Technical Co-operation with the FAO: biological control of sugar-cane pests; production of improved tomato seeds; artificial insemination; aquaculture; control of the 'blue fungus', a parasite of tobacco; improvement of citrus selection and cultivation; seed certification; study of shrimp migrations to define the periods and amounts of capture, as well as appropriate locations and timing for developing the crustacean; cultivation of oysters; apiculture; production of biogas; embryo cryopreservation; production of potato 'seed', with a view to reducing or even eliminating annual imports of potato 'seed' amounting to about $10 million; detection of mycotoxins in foodstuffs; production of inoculants for fodder legume species; regulation of the flowering period of the mango tree; improvement of the local sheep breed Pelibuey (using embryo tranfer); cultivation of prawns; commercial production of agar-producing algae; conservation and breeding of marine tortoises.

In 1994, the FAO approved a project on *in-vitro* conservation of vegetable, root and tuber germplasm, which was to be implemented by the Instituto Nacional de Investigaciones Fundamentales y Agricultura Tropical (INIFAT, National Institute for Basic Research and Tropical Agriculture). For more than 80 years, this Institute had been collecting, conserving and studying genetic resources of vegetables, cereals, oilseeds and other species. It also housed the National Germplasm Bank for these species, its activities being devoted to short- and medium-term conservation, as well as to the maintenance of collections in the field. New installations for the germplasm bank were under construction. The project's objective was to introduce *in-vitro* conservation and cryopreservation techniques for long-term storage of germplasm. Therefore, activities were oriented toward applying existing methodologies for the different species and management of the *in-vitro* germplasm bank; training local specialists and technicians in the *in-vitro* conservation of germplasm of vegetables, tubers and other related species; and defining minimum requirements for the facilities to permit *in-vitro* storage. The services provided by the FAO included an international consultant, specialists in *in-vitro* techniques, including germplasm conservation, technical support from FAO headquarters in Rome, the purchase of supplies and equipment. The project was expected to contribute to the conservation of germplasm for prolonged periods of time, thus reducing the risk of genetic diversity loss (*REDBIO Circular Letter*, 8, June 1994, p. 7).

From May 1986 to 1994, the FAO provided assistance to the National Agricultural Research Institute (NARI) of Guyana for developing the Plant Tissue Culture Laboratory. The Laboratory was mainly a research facility, with an average annual production of 8,000 specimens of clean planting material for farmers. It was part of the National Seed Programme. If operated primarily as a commercial venture with a staff complement of six technicians, the facility would produce approximately 45,000 plantlets annually. By the mid-1990s, it was focusing on plant micropropagation and germplasm storage of local varieties such as plantain, banana, pineapple, cassava, sweet potato and yam. The Laboratory was also working on crop improvement.

The weaning of cassava plantlets cultured in liquid media was being investigated for the development of an efficient hardening system. For yam, a study of the type of media and photoperiod requirements for the induction of microtubers in *Dioscorea trifida* was being carried out.

In 1993 and 1994, crop improvement research on rice and plantain varieties was implemented, with a view to selecting salt-tolerant rice varieties and producing, through irradiation, mutant plantain cultivars with resistance or tolerance to Moko disease. Callus cultures of *Oryza sativa* cv Rustic had been tested with various concentrations of salt and the regeneration of plants from calli had been tried.

Proposed research topics for the period from 1995 to 2000 included continuation of the propagation scheme with the incorporation of a new crop species, *Citrus sinensis* (sweet orange), used locally and affected by the tristeza virus; the development of improved plantain cultivars tolerant or resistant to Moko disease; the cleansing of yam material for planting and verification of the disease-free status. The NARI Plant Tissue Culture Laboratory was also planning the commercialization of technological packages and the implementation of new research projects on a contractual basis.

A technical co-operation project sponsored by the FAO in Uruguay focused on producing disease-free 'seed' in potato, boniato, garlic and strawberry. Among other aspects, it had established the basis for an asexual 'seed' production system and perfected modern laboratory techniques in *in-vitro* culture, diagnostic services and for detecting virosis. Simultaneously, an intensive training programme was executed for technical staff, while another disseminated knowledge among farmers. The project's recommendations referred to developing a 'seed nursery' system, adapting laboratory techniques to large-scale production and promoting methodologies for genetic improvement and disease diagnosis. Emphasis was laid on on-going virus detection studies in all species encompassed by the project and on possible alternative hosts until self-sufficiency in antisera production could be attained.

The 'Las Brujas' Experimental Station of the INIA (National Institute of Agricultural and Livestock Research) served as the base for operations over the project's 18-month, three-phase execution period. Participating in the project were researchers from Argentina, Mexico and Cuba. It launched the large-scale production of plants obtained by multiplying meristems of potato, boniato, garlic and strawberry. By the project's end, the potential capacity for routine laboratory production would be equivalent to the national demand for these crops of around 500,000 microplants per year. In the sixth year of implementation, the project was expected to spawn 'seed nurseries' of 20 hectares of garlic, 50 hectares of boniato, 70 hectares of strawberries and 600 hectares of potatoes, to meet domestic demand. It was thought feasible to implement a system for routine micropropagation and a programme for maintaining and conserving *in-vitro* germplasm to offer the latest technology to farmers for massive propagation of highly productive varieties. The availability of this planting material would save around $25 million annually for Uruguay (*REDBIO Circular Letter*, 7, November 1993, p. 7).

Notes

1. 175 Member States at the end of 1995 and a regular budget of $650 million for 1996–1997.

2. For instance, on 13 April 1993, Australia changed its national legislation to ensure that the government detained all intellectual property rights over the continent's fauna and flora. This move was intended to prevent any individual, corporation or foreign country for gaining monopoly rights over the genetic treasures of Australia. Currently, a number of foreign companies were investigating the properties of various native Australian plants and animals for their medical use. For instance, indigenous frogs might produce substances which could be used in the treatment of human stomach ulcers; various marine and land animals, whose metabolism controlled the impact of sunlight on their bodies, could provide clues to fighting skin cancer. One Japanese entity had patented a compound derived from the Queensland Moreton Bay chestnut which had an impact on the AIDS virus. The new law allowed the federal government to demand royalties on the sale of any commercial product derived from local resources (*The Australian*, 14 April 1993).

3. The resources could be raised from the Global Environment Facility (GEF) in view of the high priority accorded by the GEF to the protection of biodiversity. The GEF was a co-operative venture of the United Nations Development Programme (UNDP), the United Nations Environment Programme (UNEP) and the World Bank. Under the chairmanship of the World Bank's Environment Department Director, the GEF was providing grants and low-interest loans to developing countries. Contributions to the GEF came from 32, mostly industrialized, countries, but also from China, India, Indonesia, Mexico and Pakistan. On the Implementation Committee, the World Bank, UNDP and UNEP (each with two representatives) decided on the type of projects to be funded, the World Bank identifying, appraising and supervising investment projects. The UNEP was expected to provide support for institution-building and training activities and foster needs assessment by developing countries in areas suitable for GEF funding. The UNEP was to set up and guide the Scientific and Technical Advisory Panel (STAP) of 'eminent environmental experts, providing policy and technical advice to GEF management'. In accordance with its mandate, the UNDP had a similar 'supporting role', its major function being to review projects on a country level and ensure co-ordination with recipient governments (Pistorius, 1992*a*).

   While the GEF proponents agreed that it aimed to respond to the developing countries' need for new and additional projects for the protection of biodiversity, the opponents, mainly members of the non-governmental organizations (NGOs) and representatives of several developing countries emphasized that contributions to the GEF fell short of satisfying developing countries' requests. Another general criticism concerned the World Bank's dominance in the tripartite venture. It was considered that the GEF did not properly ensure the link between development and environmental protection, as conceived in *Agenda 21* adopted by the United Nations Conference on Environment and Development (UNCED) [Pistorius, 1992*a*].

   The GEF's total initial budget of $1.4 billion was divided into three parts: a core fund ($845 million), a co-financed fund ($324 million) and money already reserved for the Ozone Layer Protection Fund established by the signatories of the Montreal Protocol ($200 million). The GEF reserved $240 million for the preservation of biological diversity, the remainder of the total GEF budget going to projects aimed at protecting the ozone layer (according to the Montreal Protocol), limiting emissions of greenhouse gases and protecting international waterways (Pistorius, 1992*a*).

   Most donations to the core fund ($845 million) came from European countries, i.e. France (20%), Germany (19%), Italy (11%), the United Kingdom (9%) and several others (12%). The USA and Japan also contributed to the GEF, but directed their donations to the co-financed fund. In contrast to the core fund, contributions to the co-financed fund were not tied to any pre-defined project. The USA and Japan contributed 44% and 40% to the fund respectively, but both countries participated in negotiations on the allocation of the total GEF budget (Pistorius, 1992*a*).

Most of the decisions about the GEF funding were taken on a consensus basis and meetings were attended by a comparable number of developing and industrialized countries. The donors were happy with a system of weighed voting on the basis of countries' financial contribution to the GEF, while the developing countries advocated changing to a majority voting system. Contributions by industrialized countries in 1993 were about 94% of the total and a system of weighed voting would deprive the developing countries of any kind of control over the GEF. At the April 1992 meeting, it was decided to maintain decision-making on a consensus basis (Pistorius, 1992*a*).

4. In biotechnologies applied to animal health, the Centre of Genetic Engineering and Biotechnology (CIGB) had developed hyperimmune sera against eight mycoplasma species affecting tissue cultures, as well as six olignonucleotide probes for nucleic acid diagnosis of six mycoplasma species. Diagnostic kits were evaluated and standardized (ELISA-SUMA) for poultry diseases (e.g. encephalomyelitis, reovirus, Newcastle disease and influenza A). Molecular biology techniques were used for the diagnosis of Aujeszky disease, IBR, BVD and foot-and-mouth disease. The CIGB had delivered agglutinating antisera of *Escherichia coli* K88 and K99, F41, 987P to the Centre for Epizootics and Diagnosis of the Institute of Veterinary Medicine for 48,000 identification tests, as well as sufficient monoclonal antibodies for 6,000 identification tests of porcine dysentry.

About thirty vaccines had been developed, predominantly against poultry diseases, to meet the national demand for vaccines against poultry bronchitis and encephalomyelitis. Recombinant vaccines against *Escherichia coli* fimbriae K88 and K99, and against *Boophilus microplus* had been evaluated and 14,000 doses produced of the vaccine against trichophytosis in rabbits. Field trials used 70,000 doses of the live vaccine against *Eimeria tenella*, the agent of poultry coccidiosis. See p. 186.

United Nations Educational, Scientific and Cultural Organization[1] (see p. 124)

1. Microbial Resources Centres Network

In 1974, a project on the Development of an integrated programme defining the use and preservation of microbial strains for deployment in environmental management was formulated by the United Nations Educational, Scientific and Cultural Organization (UNESCO), in consultation with the Microbiology Panel of the International Cell Research Organization (ICRO), and approved for implementation by the United Nations Environment Programme (UNEP). Within the framework of the project, it was decided to create a network of Microbial Resources Centres (MIRCENs) responding to the needs of developing countries and with the aim of contributing to the collection, preservation, identification and distribution of microbial germplasm. The centres were also to engage in the dissemination of information relevant to microbial strains and their uses, and in regional and inter-regional research and training activities (DaSilva and Taguchi, 1987). Within the framework of UNESCO-UNEP collaboration over the 1975–1985 period, six pilot MIRCENs were set up in Brazil, Egypt, Guatemala, Kenya, Senegal and Thailand. Since 1985, within UNESCO's Regular and Participation programmes and in collaboration with the United Nations Development Programme, the MIRCEN network had expanded to include 31 centres in 23 countries in 1997 (Table 1).

Table 1. The MIRCEN network

Nitrogen fixation	Department of Soil Science, University of Nairobi	Nairobi, Kenya
Nitrogen fixation	Laboratoire de Microbiologie, Institut sénégalais de recherches agricoles (ISRA)/Institut français de recherche scientifique pour le développement en coopération (ORSTOM)	Dakar, Senegal
Industrial microbiology and biotechnologies	University of the Orange Free State, Faculty of Science, Department of University of the Orange Free State, Faculty of Science, Department of Microbiology and Biochemistry	Bloemfontein, South Africa
Nitrogen fixation and biotechnologies	Faculty of Agriculture, Ain Shams University	Hadayck-Shoubra, Cairo, Egypt
Microbial biotechnologies	Institute of Microbiology, Chinese Academy of Sciences	Zhongguancun, Haidian, Beijing, China
Bioconversion technologies	Department of Applied Biology, The Chinese University of Hong Kong	Shatin, New Territories, Hong Kong
Aquaculture	Central Institute of Freshwater Aquaculture	Kausalyaganga, Bhubaneswar, Orissa, India
Marine biotechnologies	Department of Microbiology, College of Fisheries, University of Agricultural Sciences	Mangalore, India
Biotechnologies	Division of Biotechnology, Iranian Research Organization for Science and Technology	Tehran, Iran
Fermentation technology	IC Biotech, Faculty of Engineering, University of Osaka	Osaka, Japan
World Data Centre	Centre for Information Biology, National Institute of Genetics	Shizuoka, Japan

Fermentation, food-processing and waste recycling	Thailand Institute of Scientific and Technological Research (TISTR)	Chatuchak, Bangkok, Thailand
Biotechnologies and biochemical engineering	Department of Microbiology, University of Queensland	St Lucia, Brisbane, Australia
Biotechnologies	Planta Piloto de Procesos Industriales Microbiológicos (PROIMI)	San Miguel de Tucumán, Argentina
Nitrogen fixation	Institute for Agricultural Research (FEPAGRO, formerly IPAGRO)/ Faculdade de Agronomia	Porto Alegre, Rio Grande do Sul, Brazil
Biotechnologies and waste recycling	Applied Research Division, Central American Research Institute	Guatemala City, Guatemala
Microbial biotechnologies	Department of Plant Science, The University of the West Indies	St. Augustine, Trinidad and Tobago
Culture collections and patents	Belgian Co-ordinated Collections of Micro-organisms, Université catholique de Louvain	Louvain-la-Neuve, Belgium
Biotechnologies	Centre de transfert de microbiologie-biotechnologies, Institut national des sciences appliquées (UPS-INSA)	Toulouse, France
Culture collections and patents	German Collection of Micro-organisms and Cell Cultures	Braunschweig, Germany
Culture collections and patents	Department of Microbiology, University of Horticulture and Food Industry	Budapest, Hungary
Biotechnological Information Exchange System (BITES)	UNESCO International Centre for Chemical Studies	Ljubljana, Slovenia
Bio-informatics	Department of Bacteriology, Karolinska Institute	Stockholm, Sweden
Biotechnologies	The International Institute of Biotechnology	Canterbury, Kent, United Kingdom

Mycology	Commonwealth Agricultural Bureaux (CAB) International Mycological Institute (IMI)	Egham, Surrey, United Kingdom
Culture collections and patents	National Collection of Type Cultures, Central Public Health Laboratory	London, United Kingdom
Biochemical engineering and biotechnologies	Department of Chemical Engineering, University of Waterloo	Waterloo, Ontario, Canada
Nitrogen fixation	Cell Culture and Nitrogen Fixation Laboratory, U.S. Department of Agriculture, BARC-West	Beltsville, Maryland, USA
Marine biotechnologies	Maryland Biotechnology Institute, University of Maryland	College Park, Maryland, USA
Culture collections and patents	American Type Culture Collection (ATCC)	Rockville, Maryland, USA
Nitrogen fixation	Nitrogen Fixation by Tropical Agricultural Legumes (NifTAL) Project, College of Tropical Agriculture and Human Resources	University of Hawaii, Paia, USA

The MIRCENs were associated with academic or governmental institutions. These associations encouraged and developed, in co-operation with other national, regional or international organizations, novel approaches to technological development and national resource management (Pramer, 1992).

Each MIRCEN was maintaining a collection of reference cultures of micro-organisms. Some of these cultures originated from sources such as the American Type Culture Collection. Others were microbial strains isolated by scientists working at the MIRCEN or in association with it. The centres were both depositories and sources of microbes. Upon request, they distributed cultures of specific microbes important in the production of food, environmental management and commercial biotechnologies to interested academic, governmental and industrial laboratories (Pramer, 1992).

The MIRCENs in regions with agrarian-based economies focused on agriculture, in particular symbiotic nitrogen fixation and other microbial processes for increasing food production. Much attention was given at these MIRCENs to *Rhizobium* research and relevant training activities. This was the case in Brazil, Kenya, Senegal and the USA.

Some MIRCENs focused on biotechnologies, e.g. bioconversions (microbial transformation of wastes into protein in animal feed or into methane used as a fuel in furnaces or ovens), pollution abatement and bioremediation using microbes.

The MIRCENs were increasingly using recombinant DNA techniques and other genetic tools in research and training projects.

2. Nitrogen Fixation by Tropical Agricultural Legumes (NifTAL) Project

The NifTAL Project received MIRCEN status in 1982. It was initiated in 1975, when the United States Agency for International Development (U.S. AID) contracted with the University of Hawaii to help farmers in developing countries step up agricultural production. This initial contract (1975–1982) drew on the expertise of the College of Tropical Agriculture and Human Resources (CTAHR), Department of Agronomy, University of Hawaii, Honolulu, for the setting up of an interdisciplinary unit called NifTAL (Nitrogen Fixation by Tropical Agricultural Legumes). The NifTAL's overall goal was to enhance tropical agriculture efficiency through biological nitrogen fixation by the legume-rhizobium symbiosis, so as to enable developing country farmers to reduce dependence on chemical nitrogen fertilizers (Somasegaran and Ben Bohlool, 1991).

SYMBIOTIC AND NON-SYMBIOTIC NITROGEN-FIXING MICRO-ORGANISMS

World production of grain legumes continued to increase linearly with population. As legume production (200 million tonnes in 1995) was about 10% of cereal production, it was not surprising that legume consumption was also about 10% that of cereals, with a high of 12.5% recorded in countries dependent on low protein root crops and a low of 7.5% in countries with high animal protein diets. However, even in societies with a high consumption of animal protein, forage and grain legumes were still the most important sources of livestock feed.

Legumes were also complementary to cereals in an agronomic sense: they had been used in crop rotation for 3,000 years in China and there were written records of legume/cereal rotations that dated back to Roman times. Improved performance of cereals grown after legumes was certainly well documented, but its cause might be attributable to an increased nitrogen content from legume symbiotic fixation, improved soil conditions or the breaking of disease or pest cycles.

On a world scale, 90% of food crops were consumed in the country where they were grown, Canada being one of the few exporters of food commodities. During the 1980s, Canada's production of grain legumes had increased rapidly. By 1994, it exported more than 1.5 million tonnes of legumes, which generated more than $500 million.

Table 2 recapitulates the estimated amounts of nitrogen fixed by various legume crop species under field conditions. In addition to symbiotic bacteria (*Rhizobium* and *Bradyrhizobium* genera) associated with legume root nodules, reports of significant promotion of plant growth following seed inoculation with rhizobacteria stimulated interest in these micro-organisms. Plant growth-promoting rhizobacteria (PGPR) were a specialized group of rhizobacteria, isolated from the rhizosphere, that colonized and persisted in and on the roots of plants. They were reported to improve growth of cereals, oil-seed crop species, vegetables, and annual and perennial legumes. The phrase *nodulation-promoting rhizobacteria* (NPR) was suggested following studies showing an increase in nodule number and mass for soybeans co-inoculated with PGPR and bradyrhizobia. Further effects of NPR-rhizobia co-inoculation included enhanced root and shoot weight, plant vigour, nitrogen fixation and yield. These effects were observed on legume species such as bean, soybeans, alfalfa, clover, lentil and pea (*Biological Nitrogen Fixation – BNF – Bulletin*, 1993, vol. XII, no. 1, p. 4).

Table 2. Estimated amounts of nitrogen fixed by various legume crop species under field conditions (from FAO, 1984, in Somasegaran and Ben Bohlool, 1991)

Plant species		(Nitrogen fixed) (kg N/hectare/year)
Food legumes		
Calapo	*Calopogonium mucunoides*	370–450
Horse bean	*Vicia faba*	45–552
Pigeon pea	*Cajanus cajan*	168–280
Cowpea	*Vigna unguiculata*	73–354
Mungbean	*Vigna mungo*	63–342
Guar	*Cyamopsis tetragonoloba*	41–220
Soybeans	*Glycine max*	60–168
Chickpea	*Cicer arietinum*	103
Lentil	*Lens esculenta*	88–114
Groundnut	*Arachis hypogaea*	72–124
Pea	*Pisum sativum*	52–77
Bean	*Phaseolus vulgaris*	40–70

Forage legumes

Tick clover	*Desmodium intortum*	897
Sesbania	*Sesbania cannabina*	542
Leucaena	*Leucaena leucocephala*	74–584
Centro	*Centrosema pubescens*	126–398
Alfalfa	*Medicago sativa*	229–290
Subclover	*Trifolium subterraneum*	207
Ladino clover	*Trifolium repens* var. *gigantea*	165–189
White clover	*Trifolium repens*	128
Stylo	*Stylosanthes* spp.	34–220
Vetch	*Vicia villosa*	110
Puero	*Pueraria phaseoloides*	99

Compounds, such as siderophores, which facilitated the uptake of nutrients (e.g. iron), or the NPR-mediated production of phytohormones, had direct effects on plant growth. The mechanisms by which the NPR maintained a competitive advantage for survival in the rhizosphere might indirectly promote plant growth. For instance, a reduction in the population of deleterious rhizosphere micro-organisms, particularly the fungal plant pathogens, could be due to the excretion of antibiotics by the NPR, the end result being that the NPR provided a root environment more conducive to the symbiotic association of rhizobia with their host plants. Increased root and shoot growth could also be linked to the production of phytohormones by the NPR that were detected *in vitro*; their production in the rhizosphere needed to be examined further (*Biological Nitrogen Fixation – BNF – Bulletin*, 1993, vol. XII, no. 1, p. 4).

Preliminary studies on the involvement of the NPR with the plant defence indicated that pathogenic micro-organisms elicited a hypersensitive reaction (HR) in incompatible tissue and induced the accumulation of fungitoxic compounds called phytoalexins. Symbiotic *Rhizobium* spp. were reported to induce low accumulation of phytoalexins in root nodules of soybeans and faba beans. Rhizospheric bacteria, or their products, had the capacity to activate plant defence genes. Treatment with NPR induced the production of HR and phytoalexins in white bean cotyledons and hypocotyls. The population size of NPR required to induce phytoalexin production was similar to that detected on white bean in natural systems. This ability of rhizobacteria to colonize the cotyledon in sufficient numbers to induce phytoalexin production had potential applications for disease control involving plant defence mechanisms (*Biological Nitrogen Fixation – BNF – Bulletin*, 1993, vol. XII, no. 1, p. 4).

Among the most common isolates of nitrogen-fixing bacterial

species associated with cereal crops and other grasses to have been described, one could cite *Azospirillum, Azotobacter, Bacillus, Beijerinckia* and *Enterobacteriaceae*. Representatives of other genera included *Acetobacter, Alcaligenes, Azoarcus, Campylobacter, Herbaspirillum* and *Pseudomonas*-like bacteria. In general, nitrogen-fixing root-associated diazotrophs were soil bacteria able to colonize the root surface, although some, including *Azospirillum*, could invade the superficial layers of the cortex. It also appeared that nitrogen-fixing strains of *Acetobacter* and *Herbospirillum* were obligate endophytes found in the vascular system of the plant (Elmerich, 1995).

The *Azospirillum* genus belongs to the alpha subgroup of proteobacteria and is therefore closely related to various other soil bacteria, including *Rhizobium* and photosynthetic bacteria such as *Rhodospirillum*. Five species had been described on the basis of phenotypic properties and DNA relatedness: *A. brasilense, A. lipoferum, A. amazonense, A. halopraeferens*, and *A. irakense*. These bacteria were Gram-negative chemoorganotrophs of vibrioid shape, with a polar flagellum; lateral flagella were present when the bacteria were grown on a solid surface. They had a respiratory metabolism under both aerobic and anaerobic conditions, where nitrate could be used as a terminal electron acceptor. Cells contained granules of poly-beta-hydroxybutyric acid, which accumulated under nitrogen-limiting conditions. Old cultures contained non-motile forms resembling cyst-like structures. Ecological distribution of *Azospirillum* was extremely wide: strains had been found in association with monocotyledons, including maize, rice, sugar-cane, sorghum, forage grasses, and dicotyledons (Elmerich, 1995).

Azospirillum cells contained plasmids of medium- and high-molecular weight (in the range of 300 megadaltons or more). A 90MDa plasmid of *A. brasilense* strain Sp7 had been studied in particular detail and it was found that this plasmid encoded functions related to motility and synthesis of polar and lateral flagella. In addition, some genes located on the symbiotic plasmid of *R. meliloti* (*nod PQ, exo B* and *exo M*) and an *exo C* homologue were also located on the 90 MDa plasmid; thus, the latter had been designated pRhico (rhizocoenic) on account of its role in plant association (Elmerich, 1995).

Azospirillum induced an enhanced proliferation of the lateral roots and of root hairs; deformation and branching of root hairs had been also observed; a large proportion of bacteria were anchored to the root surface by fibrillar material. Bacteria were also found in the intercellular spaces of the superficial layers of the cortex. Root inoculation resulted in improved mineral and water uptake, consistent with a plant growth-promoting effect. *Azospirillum* was also known to produce siderophores and bacteriocins, which might serve as biocontrol agents in the struggle for survival with other members of the soil microflora. Motility and a chemostatic response toward root exudates was generally recognized as the first step in the colonization process before attachment and proliferation on the root surface (Elmerich, 1995).

Attachment appeared to be a two-step process: a rapid and reversible adsorption onto the root system, followed by irreversible anchoring of the bacteria; this first step might be mediated by a bacterial adhesin which had been identified as the polar flagellum; anchoring was due to the synthesis of fibrillar material consisting of bacterial polysaccharides and glycoproteins, probably similar to the fibrillar material produced during flocculation in cultures grown on fructose. These polysaccharides could bind plant lectins and might therefore contribute to adhesion to root surfaces (Elmerich, 1995).

The plant growth-promoting effect was currently attributed to production of indolyl-3-acetic acid (IAA) and other phytohormones. It was suggested that *Azospirillum* possessed several pathways for IAA synthesis, because no mutant totally deficient in IAA production could be isolated (Elmerich, 1995).

A survey of field inoculation world-wide over 20 years concluded that significant increases in yields of from 5% to 30% could be achieved by inoculation with *Azospirillum*, in particular when the use of fertilizer was low. Experiments using the ^{15}N isotope dilution technique confirmed that, in some cases, biological nitrogen fixation could account for several per cent of the total nitrogen in the plant. This supported the assumption that nitrogen-fixation genes should be expressed to some extent during association with the host plant (Elmerich, 1995).

Azospirillum fixed nitrogen under micro-aerobic conditions in the absence of ammonia. Nitrogenase activity was subject to reversible inactivation *in vivo* by ammonia, a mechanism similar to that found in photosynthetic bacteria. Nitrogen-fixation genes homologous to the *Rhizobium* ABC genes had been found in *Azospirillum*, but the regulation of their transcription was different, as was that of the structural gene, *gln A*, for glutamine synthetase (GS); this enzyme, coupled with glutamate synthase (COGAT), ensured synthesis of glutamine and glutamate, precursors of all cellular nitrogenous compounds (Elmerich, 1995).

In Brazil, Döbereiner and her collaborators at the EMBRAPA (Brazilian Agricultural and Livestock Research Enterprise)/CNPAB in the State of Rio de Janeiro had been working on diazotrophs associated with sugar-cane in an attempt to explain the substantial contribution of biological nitrogen fixation to some Brazilian sugar-cane genotypes. Using sugar-cane juice as the substrate of a semi-solid culture medium, they had isolated a new species, *Acetobacter diazotrophicus*, which seemed to be well adapted to the conditions prevailing in sugar-cane stems and roots. These bacteria grew best with 10% sucrose and a low pH, conditions which enabled about half of the nitrogen fixed by the bacteria to be excreted; not only did the stems and roots show any nitrate-reductase activity, but ammonium assimilation was reduced by 65% with high sucrose concentrations (Döbereiner and Baldani, 1995).

A. *diazotrophicus* was found in large numbers (up to 10^7 per gram of fresh weight) in roots, stems and leaves of sugar-cane collected in all major sugar cane-growing areas of Brazil, and also in specimens from Australia, Cuba, Mexico and Uruguay. In addition, it could be isolated from *Pennisetum purpureum*, a sugar-rich grass propagated vegetatively, as well as from roots, stems and tubers of sweet potatoes. Attempts to isolate this diazotroph from cereals, other forage grasses and weeds collected within sugar-cane fields had all failed, thereby confirming the restriction of this micro-organism to sugar-rich plants propagated vegetatively (Döbereiner and Baldani, 1995).

Herbaspirillum seropedicae was originally isolated from cereal roots, but was also found in stems and leaves of rice and maize, and especially sugar-cane. This was considered a true diazotroph with nitrogen-fixation efficiencies comparable to *Azospirillum* spp. Inoculation of *H. seropedicae*, which was only successful with the aid of vesicular-arbuscular mycorrhizae or in monoxenically grown plants, occurred almost exclusively in plants of the Gramineae family. Another somewhat slower-growing diazotrophic bacterium, isolated from roots and stems of various cereals, tuber plant species and palm trees, had been included in the genus *Burkholderia* using molecular biology methods (Döbereiner and Baldani, 1995).

According to Döbereiner and Baldani (1995), the discovery of endophytic diazotrophs could go some way toward explaining the substantial contributions of biological nitrogen fixation to sugar-cane, forage grasses and rice. These bacteria, which colonized xylem and other plant tissues in large numbers, had many advantages when compared with rhizospheric bacteria, which had to compete with other soil micro-organisms for root exudates and decomposed before their fixed nitrogen became available to the plant. The lack of nitrate-reductase activity, and especially the excretion of almost half of all the nitrogen fixed by *Acetobacter diazotrohicus* so necessary to the plant, made such associations more similar to the legume symbioses.

The nitrogen-fixing diazotroph *Alcaligenes faecalis*, isolated from rice roots in 1977, was found to synthesize nitrogenase in high ammonium culture medium (30mM). The two component proteins of the enzyme were isolated and purified to homogeneity; nitrogenase activity was absent, but when the ammonium in the culture medium was exhausted, nitrogenase activity was derepressed. Non-nodular endorhizospheric nitrogen fixation was found: *Alcaligenes faecalis* not only accumulated on the rice root surface, but also entered the root cells. By using a variety of methods, including immunofluorescence and scanning electron microscopy, *A. faecalis* was observed growing within rice root cells and living symbiotically with callus induced from the cells. *A. faecalis* also grew and fixed nitrogen in inter- and intracellular spaces in the rice plant. The bacterium was incorporated into rice protoplasts and found to multiply in the leaves and roots of plants regenerated from the protoplasts. The bacteria fixed nitrogen in these regenerated plants, as revealed by ^{15}N analysis. Trans-conjugants containing multiple copies of *nif*A or *ntr*C-*nif* A genes were constructed; these strains carried pCK3 and pCK5 plasmids containing *nif* A fragments, and pCA1841 containing *ntr*C-*nif* A genes. With the aid of transposon Tn5, the *nif* A (or *ntr*C-*nif* A) was randomly inserted and integrated into the chromosomal genome of *A. faecalis*. These mutants could fix nitrogen in high-ammonium media, thereby increasing rice yields by 6% to 9%. The transconjugants were released for field use in China in 1989. More than 200,000 hectares of wetland rice were inoculated with the transconjugants in both 1991 and 1992 (*Biological Nitrogen Fixation – BNF – Bulletin*, 1993, vol. XII, no. 1, p. 5).

In 1991, British, Australian, Chinese and Mexican scientists formed the International Rice Nodulation Group with backing from the Rockefeller Foundation and the United Kingdom's Overseas Development Administration. The task before the Group was to make rice behave like legumes by fixing its own nitrogen. To that end, they began by looking at all the strains of rhizobia world-wide. The strain that caught their attention was the rhizobium associated with the tropical shrub legume, *Sesbania*. These plants had nitrogen-fixing nodules not only on their stems, but on their roots as well. The rhizobia entered *Sesbania* plants by what was termed 'crack entry': when lateral roots emerged, the rhizobia gained access through the crack in the root skin and, being invasive and tolerant of oxygen, they could penetrate further into the root and become established; the root then thickened and turned into a nodule.

Research by Cocking at the Department of Life Science, Nottingham University, showed that these rhizobia used 'crack entry' to invade the roots of rice, wheat, maize and oilseed rape and, once inside, formed a symbiotic association. Laboratory tests indicated that the rhizobia fixed as much atmospheric nitrogen in rice and wheat roots as they did in *Sesbania*.

During a visit to the NifTAL in August 1992, Cocking reported on their progress in inducing nodular structures on cereal roots. They had earlier induced nodular structures on rapeseed and rice by first treating the roots with cellulase and pectolyase enzymes followed by inoculation with rhizobia. The enzymes apparently degraded root components which normally prevented rhizobial infection. Altered root development was observed in rice, rapeseed, wheat and maize in response to rhizobia, even without enzyme pre-treatment.

Field trials with wheat were carried out in Egypt at the beginning of 1995, followed by trials with rice in India and maize in Mexico. The bonus of that research was that it involved no genetic engineering or new technology. All that was required was for cereal seed to be put with, or inoculated with, the appropriate rhizobia. It also seemed likely that this simple procedure would be easily tranferable to resource-poor farmers.

RESEARCH SUPPORT AND TECHNICAL ASSISTANCE

The NifTAL had built a resource capacity in Hawaii to provide national legume programmes in developing countries with research support, information, technical assistance services and multi-tiered training in biological nitrogen fixation (BNF). In 1987, the NifTAL began its second decade under a service agreement known as Improved BNF through Biotechnology. The five programmes under this new agreement were:

– development of genetic technologies for improving *Rhizobium*-legume symbiosis in crop and tree species;

– development of methods for monitoring micro-organisms in the environment;

– generation of environmental data-bases for predicting symbiotic and saprophytic performance of rhizobia;

– establishment of regional biological nitrogen fixation centres;

– technical assistance to commercial inoculant producers;

– computer communication networks, production and publication of communication materials (quarterly release of a computerized bibliography to biological nitrogen fixation researchers world-wide).

For most of its existence, the NifTAL/MIRCEN had operated in a networking and collaborative mode for attaining goals and objectives in training, education, publication, and research and development. In 1979, a planning workshop was held to design the protocol for a world-wide network of field trials. Collectively known as the International Network of Legume Inoculation Trials (INLIT), these field trials were organized as an international collaborative effort to determine whether, under defined conditions, a yield increase could be obtained through legume inoculation. The INLIT trials ran from 1980 to 1981 and focused primarily on major tropical crop legume species. Results from the 224 completed trials run by 99 researchers in 28 countries indicated that a significant inoculation response could be obtained with soybeans 80% of the time and with chickpeas and lentils about 50% of the time, particularly during the first planting of any of these crop species (Somasegaran and Ben Bohlool, 1991).

Growing out of the INLIT concept and experience, a more complex and ambitious network known as the Worldwide Rhizobial Ecology Network (WREN) was introduced in 1987 with funding in part through a grant from the National Science Foundation (NSF). Twenty-two participants from 18 countries, mostly in the tropics, collaborated on developing a model to predict legumes' response to inoculation, which varied with legume species and site-specific environmental conditions. Another significant step was taken in 1988 in launching a training programme for private volunteer organizations (PVOs) and Peace Corps (PC) workers to impart basic knowledge necessary for transferring BNF technology to developing country farmers. In the Biological Nitrogen Fixation and Legume Management (BNF/LM) Outreach Project, the consortium formed by the PVOs, PC and the NifTAL Project/MIRCEN was implementing BNF assessment, training and inoculant production in developing countries. During its first year, the project focused efforts on Haiti, Indonesia, Nepal, Senegal and Uganda. The project activities ranged from extension materials to applied research setting up collaboration between organizations (Somasegaran and Ben Bohlool, 1991).

TRAINING ACTIVITIES

Since 1976, NifTAL had been training qualified personnel in biological nitrogen fixation. By the autumn of 1992, it had trained over 500 scientists, technicians and extension personnel from 67 countries (49% in Asia, 26.5% in Africa, 16.5% in Latin America and 8% elsewhere). The training activities included: post-graduate training (MSc. and PhD. candidates from the University of Hawaii or collaborating universities were awarded research assistantships); interns' and visiting scientists' participation in collaborative research projects with NifTAL staff (while conducting their projects, the visitors received individually designed instruction on such topics as rhizobial microbiology, inoculant production and legume agronomy; the participants were generally supported by their governments or by international funding agencies); training courses (the basic six-week course in legume/rhizobium technology was first offered in 1976, covering all aspects of the topic through hands-on laboratory, field and greenhouse work supported by lectures and demonstrations, so that participants could conduct their own biological nitrogen fixation-related research. Experience gained in conducting the basic course in legume/rhizobium symbiosis had led to the production of a laboratory manual; the revised and updated second edition of this widely cited manual was published in 1992.

Furthermore, the NifTAL specialized in a 'training of trainers' programme for extension personnel from government, business and private voluntary organizations. After gaining a comprehensive understanding of the applied aspects of biological nitrogen fixation, the participants received training materials to help them transfer this knowledge to other extension agents and farmers.

The following units were being offered as specialized separate courses or in any combination: general rhizobial microbiology; strain identification; genetic technology of rhizobia; inoculant production; inoculant quality control; inoculant enterprise development; and extension training. The NifTAL was also exploring opportunities to present biological nitrogen fixation technology training as an integral component of broader programmes. For instance, legume-based biological nitrogen fixation could effectively complement efforts in sustainable agricultural systems, ecosystem restoration and conservation, erosion control and soil nutrient management.

LEGUME INOCULANT PRODUCTION AND MARKETING

The NifTAL had a new focus on promoting private sector investment into legume inoculant production and marketing. The main target beneficiaries, however, were not commercial procedures but farmers who would benefit from high-quality and readily available inoculants appropriate to their needs. Assistance to the private sector was the means to an end: to renew farmer confidence in biological nitrogen fixation by delivering a quality product. The first approach was assistance to private entrepreneurs and established companies, some of them already engaged in agricultural input manufacturing or distribution, in the setting up of inoculant production facilities, marketing, product development and internal quality control. The second approach was to encourage government and/or university research facilities to play a role more in keeping with their technical capabilities, including external quality control, certification and applied research activities related to commercial farming. The third approach concerned extension and market development, including both public and private sector field extensionists with a special emphasis on training and promotion.

The NifTAL had developed a computer programme to evaluate the potential profitability of inoculant production enterprises: the Financial Analysis for Inoculant Manufacturing Enterprise (FAIME) was designed to assess the feasibility of starting a legume inoculant production facility or evaluate an existing enterprise. The programme was based on production data collected from private and government inoculant producers in several countries. It allowed the user to build a financial model of the business and 'play' with its components prior to taking any actual risk. Different strategies allocating resources for start-up operations might be analyzed and different modes and scales of production and pricing might be modeled. One of the most powerful features of this interactive programme was the Sensitivity Analysis, with which the user could make changes in the values assigned to various financial and technical options. The FAIME would then project the effect of these choices on the financial health of the business.

The NifTAL had designed several different models of bioreactors for *Rhizobium* culture; they were inexpensive, low maintenance investments for small-to-medium-scale inoculant production facilities. The size of the production facility and the demand for inoculant determined which model was appropriate for a particular site. For instance, 4-litre glass bioreactors were being used in Haiti, while a 20-litre bioreactor had been set up in Ethiopia (in *NifTAL BNF Bulletin*, vol. XI, no. 1, 1992, p. 2). A 141-litre bioreactor faithful to the principles and design of the NifTAL Project/MIRCEN prototype was built in Thailand in collaboration with the Thailand Department of Agriculture and NifTAL Project/MIRCEN's Biological Nitrogen Fixation Resource Center (BNFRC). The development of this inexpensive and easy-to-use bioreactor was a significant contribution to inoculant production technology. Several of these bioreactor units were being used in Indonesia, Kenya, Morocco, Nigeria, Thailand, Uganda and Zambia (Somasegaran and Ben Bohlool, 1991). With UNESCO assistance, these bioreactors had been made available to MIRCEN laboratories in Kenya, Mali and Senegal.

In 1982, the NifTAL Project/MIRCEN first published its findings that liquid cultures of rhizobia could be diluted with sterile water prior to aseptic injection into gamma-irradiated peat. The resulting peat inoculants set quality standards when prepared this way.[2] [(see p. 124)] This result, which eliminated the requirement for large bioreactors, formed the basis for production by some small-scale producers of peat inoculants in Finland, Haiti, Morocco, Thailand and the USA. The 'dilution' procedure was used to initiate inoculant production for approximately 8,800 hectares of soybeans in Zambia as part of the Zamare Project (Somasegaran and Ben Bohlool, 1991). See also Somasegaran and Hoben (1994).

The NifTAL Project/MIRCEN's mandate for research was neither a commodity nor regionally orientated. The goal of the research programme was to address the technical constraints on a fuller utilization of BNF technology, so that small farms in developing countries could reap the maximum benefit possible from BNF. The effects of soil stresses such as low phosphorus fertility, salinity, drought and acidity, could directly affect inoculants or rhizobia in the soil or at infection sites on plant roots. These same stresses might also affect root growth, susceptibility of infection sites and plant photosynthetic capacity, which limited energy sources for the reduction of nitrogen in root nodules. Environmental stress might also come from other micro-organisms competing for resources on the root surface and for infection sites, at the expense of the selected, highly efficient strains. Even soil nitrogen availability might be considered a stress upon symbiosis since the assimilation of inorganic nitrogen substitutes directly for fixed nitrogen and legume cultivation could therefore deplete soils of nitrogen under certain circumstances. Developing models which quantitatively described the impact of various environmental and management factors on the performance of legumes was one way to make data more useful across many environments (Somasegaran and Ben Bohlool, 1991).

Although the specifics of host-strain interaction – which ultimately determined the potential of the symbiosis – were not well understood, this area of research held the promise that farmers would be able to enhance BNF in their fields and thereby increase crop production. That is why the NifTAL scientists were studying these relationships using field trials, laboratory and greenhouse experiments and, most recently, biotechnological and genetic approaches. Some other useful techniques were hydroponics and split-root systems to better control the experimental variables (Somasegaran and Ben Bohlool, 1991).

The NifTAL was also engaged in the isolation of gene segments that could be used as specific DNA hybridization probes to identify elite tropical rhizobial strains. DNA restriction fragment length polymorphism (RFLP or DNA fingerprinting) could detect genetic heterogeneity within serogroups. To realize this potentially more detailed genetic analysis required careful hybridization probe selection. Also, it would be highly desirable to arrive at a strain identification probe capable of identifying other *Rhizobium* spp. and detecting genetic rearrangements or mutations of a rhizobial strain. One class of genetic elements with the potential to fulfill these probe selection criteria were mobile elements such as transposons and insertion sequences.

In 1988 and 1991, insertion sequence (IS) elements from *Rhizobium meliloti*, were used as hybridization probes to identify primarily *R. meliloti* strains by 'IS fingerprinting'. A given IS element isolated from one *R. meliloti* strain would also be found in 10% to 100% of other *R. meliloti* strains, producing a unique IS fingerprint for each strain containing the IS element.

IS elements were relatively small sequences of 'mobile DNA' with the ability to copy themselves and insert themselves into another location of DNA with resulting copy numbers from 1 up to 40. They were 'jumping genes' like transposons which carried selectable antibiotic resistance genes, but differed from them because IS elements only carried the genes necessary for their mobility. Consequently, IS*Rm1* (from *R. meliloti* strain 1021), the first IS element isolated from rhizobia, was discovered as the causative agent of frequent spontaneous *nif* (insertion) mutations in strain 1021. Positive selection, broad-host-range bacterial vectors, such as pUCD 800, were IS elements, pUCD 800 entrapped an IS element by insertional inactivation of the *sac B* gene. The wild type *sac B* gene product, levansucrase, caused bacterial lysis or inhibition of growth, when 5% sucrose was included in the growth medium.

CO-OPERATIVE PROJECTS

The NifTAL Project/MIRCEN, the Indian Agricultural Research Institute and the G.K.V.K. University of Agricultural Sciences in Bangalore, India, collaborated in solving problems limiting the legume-rhizobium symbiosis under the Indo/U.S. Science and Technology Initiative. The effect of crop history and environment on rhizobial populations was studied in Karnataka State. In 1991, agreements were concluded between the NifTAL Project and the Director of India's Fertilizer Development Centre, also in charge of the Development and Demonstration of Biofertilizers Project for India, sponsored by the FAO and UNDP. The agreements concerned training and inoculant technology transfer. Pulses being a major dietary protein source in India, the use of rhizobia for crop improvement was a top priority of the Fertilizer Project. Other micro-organisms receiving attention included *Azotobacter, Azospirillum* and phosphate-solubilizing bacteria. The project had four major components: assembly of a germplasm collection; inoculant production; training and extension services; quality control of inoculants. The project was expected to have a significant impact on measures taken to meet India's growing need for low-cost inputs to increase legume production (in *NifTAL BNF Bulletin*, vol. XI, no. 1, 1992, p. 5).

Collaborative efforts between the NifTAL Project/MIRCEN and Thailand's Department of Agriculture supported the development of practical ways to extend BNF: the BNF Resource Center (BNFRC) encouraged research on, and adaptation of, tropical BNF technology and increased food production in tropical Asia through services, training and resource support. The scientific staff of the NifTAL Project/MIRCEN initiated collaborative research projects with international agricultural research centres, universities and individual scientists, such as in The Philippines. In this country, the production and conservation of fixed nitrogen in crop systems and management strategies to enhance BNF was investigated, as well as the application of starter nitrogen to legumes to determine how these recommendations affected the performance of native rhizobia. In Malaysia, collaborative research focused on selecting and testing acid-tolerant *Leucaena* (a forage tree legume), and rhizobia for forage production in acid soils. In Ghana, research addressed soybean inoculation response with indigenous rhizobia in African soils (Somasegaran and Ben Bohlool, 1991).

Inoculant production technology was at the heart of the NifTAL's transfer programme and therefore a critical part of research endeavours toward developing the most cost-effective, reliable and efficient process possible. Appropriate low-cost and medium-scale production systems were developed and were being used in several countries, e.g. Myanmar (ex-Burma), Pakistan, Sri Lanka, Thailand and Zambia. In addition to providing appropriate equipment, the NifTAL focused research work on developing computer programmes to accurately estimate numbers of rhizobia in soil, or screening rhizobia by looking at the chlorophyll content of leaves, and identifying rhizobia by suitable serological and genetic methods (Somasegaran and Ben Bohlool, 1991).

The NifTAL and the International Institute of Tropical Agriculture (IITA) were collaborating on a study of the symbiosis between promiscuously nodulating soybean genotypes and their affiliated *Bradyrhizobium* spp. Studies included the nature of this group of rhizobia in relation to total indigenous bradyrhizobia, their presence in representative soils in Africa and their symbiotic effectiveness across several IITA lines. Results from this collaborative work might have important management implications for these varieties, once released.

Rice, the world's primary food staple, was grown on 145 million hectares by the early 1990s, 87% of which were in lowlands. Although nitrogen fertilizer was an essential input in modern lowland rice production, large amounts of soil nitrogen were lost from lowland rice soils during the transition between flooded and non-flooded conditions; if this loss of soil nitrogen could be prevented, its use efficiency would increase.

Once the waters submerging a flooded rice crop subsided, organic and ammonium forms of nitrogen dominated in the soil with negligible amounts of nitrate nitrogen. Subsequent soil drying favoured aerobic nitrogen transformations: while mineralization of organic nitrogen produced ammonium which was rapidly nitrified, nitrate accumulated in the aerobic soil during the dry season. The soil underwent transition from an aerobic to an anaerobic phase with the onset of rainfall and subsequent flooding for the wet season rice crop. Nitrate was lost through denitrification or leaching during this transition period typified by intermittent, then continuous, soil flooding. Plants, including legumes, could assimilate this form of nitrogen.

Reducing nitrogen fertilizer might be possible by minimizing the loss of nitrogen gained through biological nitrogen fixation and recycling nitrogen captured between crop seasons through plant residues. Managing native soil nitrogen and nitrogen derived from biological nitrogen fixation had great significance for the long-term sustainability of lowland rice-based cropping systems.

Since 1989, the NifTAL and the International Rice Research Institute (IRRI) had been collaborating to investigate the processes and extent of soil nitrate accumulation and loss, and to define the roles of grain and green manure legumes in capturing soil and atmospheric nitrogen. The collaboration agreement supported research and development on biological nitrogen fixation applications for rice-based cropping systems, the training of researchers and the maintenance of rhizobial germplasm.

RHIZOBIAL GERMPLASM REPOSITORY

The NifTAL Project/MIRCEN was maintaining nearly 2,000 strains of rhizobia isolated from the root nodules of various tropical grain, forage and tree legume species. A catalogue detailing the characteristics of the rhizobia had been compiled and distributed to more than 200 researchers in 67 countries. The entire collection was computerized for quick access and retrieval of strain identification. The NifTAL Project/MIRCEN served as a rhizobial germplasm repository because a significant proportion of the strains were donations from institutions world-wide. The rhizobial germplasm provided the inoculant rhizobia for testing in the INLIT experiments; the tested strains had become standard strains for inoculant production in many developing countries (Somasegaran and Ben Bohlool, 1991).

A catalogue listing available antisera had been published and made available to researchers. Antisera and matched strains were used to distinguish introduced rhizobial strains from all others. Antisera were distributed free of charge for researchers in developing countries. High-quality research inoculants for crop, forage and tree legumes were also supplied (Somasegaran and Ben Bohlool, 1991).

COMMUNICATION AND INFORMATION ACTIVITIES

The NifTAL Project/MIRCEN's communication section was responsible for meeting requests for general information about the project and information on specific research topics on biological nitrogen fixation. Beginning in 1979, the newsletter *BNF Bulletin* was distributed three times a year to more than 1,700 interested persons in 100 countries. The continuing bibliography mailed with the newsletter contained a listing of recent articles of interest to BNF researchers. The illustrated concept series were one-page teaching and reporting papers. In 1988, at UNESCO's request, the series became a joint publication with UNESCO's partial financial support. Up to 1992, five papers in this series had been produced and distributed free of charge, in addition to the following instruction manuals: *Methods in legume-Rhizobium technology, Legume inoculants and their use, Applied BNF technology: a practical guide for extension specialists* (Somasegaran and Ben Bohlool, 1991).

In 1991, the NifTAL converted to computerized data-bases of citations. The NifTAL Library also subscribed to AGRICOLA on compact laser disk; this data-base contained citations of articles added to the U.S. Department of Agriculture's National Agricultural Library since 1972 and was updated quarterly. The NifTAL was conducting literature searches in AGRICOLA for developing country biological nitrogen fixation researchers (in *NifTAL BNF Bulletin*, vol. XI, no. 1, 1992, p. 8).

ACHIEVEMENTS AND PROSPECTS

To sum up, the NifTAL Project/MIRCEN was geared to support international co-operation, especially in developing countries where BNF could significantly improve agriculture production. The NifTAL focused mainly on developing *Rhizobium* germplasm resources for tropical legumes and increasing technical capabilities of national institutions. There were significant constraints to delivering biological nitrogen fixation (BNF) technology to the field. The NifTAL's original director, Sheldon Whitney, had added a legume management programme. His successor, Jake Halliday, initiated extensive international network activities to field test germplasm and increase legume inoculation response. The NifTAL's research staff developed low-cost bioreactor systems and inoculant production training was emphasized to improve inoculant products. Research efforts at the NifTAL expanded under Ben Bohlool's leadership, especially in the area of molecular biology and rhizobial ecology. Ecological research led to the development of models for predicting rhizobia performance in the field, which were useful for planners and investors in BNF technology development.

The NifTAL joined Texas A&M, Hawaii, Cornell and North Carolina State Universities as a member of the Soil Management Collaborative Research Support Program (TropSoils CRSP), through which BNF technology could be integrated into the larger issues of soil and natural resource management. Another aspect of NifTAL's recent evolution included collaboration with the International Agricultural Research Centres; this linkage was expected to enhance the use of BNF in cropping systems.

Technology transfer could be accomplished between the NifTAL Project/MIRCEN and the sister MIRCENs, international agencies, institutions of higher learning, private volunteer organizations, national governments and other organizations. The Project successfully demonstrated the positive aspects of BNF in agriculture of developing countries through its research, networking, technology development, education and training, outreach and information services and rhizobial germplasm and antiserum services. A key component of BNF technology transfer involved the provision of highly effective rhizobia for the legumes (Somasegaran and Ben Bohlool, 1991).

The NifTAL's client-driven approach had helped to focus research, training, communications and enterprise development efforts. The NifTAL had embarked on a significant effort to facilitate commercial production and marketing of quality legume inoculant products, backstopped by research, and packaging and quality control methodologies. Training programmes were expanded to include business and marketing elements. Genetic resource development targeted forestry species, as well as the survival and performance of rhizobia in inoculants.

The Nitrogen Fixing Tree Association (NFTA) was a non-profit making organization that encouraged a better understanding and use of nitrogen-fixing trees to help satisfy the wood-product demands in developing countries. Since its inception in 1981, the NFTA had evolved into an international network of 1,400 individuals in over 112 countries with a shared interest in nitrogen-fixing trees. The association promoted judicious planting and management of nitrogen-fixing trees to conserve soil and water, develop sustainable land-use systems and safeguard against destruction of natural environments. Planting nitrogen-fixing trees appropriate to the climate and social conditions could improve rural landscapes and the quality of life of families dwelling in these areas.

In 1992, the NFTA moved to the island of Maui from its former headquarters at the University of Hawaii's Waimanalo Research Station, under the same roof as the NifTAL, thus reinforcing the linkage between the tree and rhizobial biological nitrogen fixation technologies.

3. Bangkok MIRCEN

In 1976, representatives of UNESCO, UNEP and International Atomic Energy Agency (IAEA), and of the Panel on Microbiology (UNEP/UNESCO/ICRO) had visited South-East Asia with the objective of setting up a microbial resources centre for the region. The Thailand Institute of Scientific and Technological Research in Bangkok was selected as the Centre's location. This MIRCEN specialized in food fermentation and waste recycling (e.g. conversion of crop wastes into food protein through mushroom cultivation). Six laboratories in the region were associated with the MIRCEN as co-operative laboratories: U.P.-NSRC culture collection, University of The Philippines; FMIPA-UI, University of Indonesia; Department of Botany, National University of Singapore; Department of Microbiology, National University of Malaysia; Department of Biology, the Chinese University of Hong Kong; Department of Microbiology, Kasetsart University, Bangkok, Thailand (Chang *et al.*, 1992).

By the mid-1990s, the Bangkok MIRCEN was maintaining over 1,800 strains of bacteria and fungi, preserved mainly in freeze-dried form, and made accessible to the relevant institutions in the region. Catalogues of its holdings were prepared and extensively distributed. Up to 1992, this MIRCEN had distributed over 1,000 cultures, free of charge, both within and outside the region. Furthermore, about 600 cultures had been obtained from several local and overseas institutions (Chang *et al.*, 1992).

In addition to co-operation among laboratories affiliated to the Bangkok MIRCEN, the Centre was also involved in activities implemented by the UNESCO Regional Network for Microbiology in South-East Asia. These activities contributed to enhancing the academic standard of microbiology, as well as to improving the quality of culture collections and their utilization.

4. China MIRCENs

Since being set up in 1988, the China MIRCEN at the Institute of Microbiology, Chinese Academy of Sciences, Beijing, had carried out the following activities:

– a survey of microbial resources of agricultural or environmental importance (e.g. edible and medicinal mushrooms, insecticidal bacteria and viruses, symbiotic nitrogen-fixing bacteria and actinomycetes);

– laboratory investigations on fermentation optimization, enzyme purification and immobilization of penicillin acylase, enzyme electrodes for glucose analysis, etc.;

– application of several microbial processes to waste-water treatment;

– a training course on microbial processes, jointly with the Brisbane MIRCEN;

– establishment of microbial strain data-base at the Institute of Microbiology, with information on more than 3,000 bacteria and yeast strains (1991) that could be connected to a national network including the data-bases of the seven culture collection centres in China (Song, 1991).

In 1991, following a request from the Chinese University of Hong Kong, a MIRCEN was established at the Department of Biology of this University in the area of bioconversion technology. Research on several aspects of food fermentation and mushroom production from agricultural wastes was carried out at this MIRCEN, while efforts were being made to strengthen activities on strain selection, food fermentations and waste recycling, with particular emphasis on safety and acceptability of genetically engineered strains (Chang *et al.*, 1992).

RESEARCH ON MUSHROOMS

In 1990, a survey concluded the existence of 625 edible mushroom species in China. About three-fourths of these edible mushrooms belonged to 52 different genera of two Ascomycete families and 20 Basidiomycete families, while the rest was distributed more or less sparsely in 75 'other' genera of six Ascomycete families and 13 Basidiomycete families. Seventy species of edible mushrooms belonging to 31 different genera could be cultivated on logs, sawdust bags and other natural or supplemented artificial substrates to their fruiting body stage. More than ten different species of edible mushrooms were produced on a commercial scale and available on the market concurrently or sequentially the year-round (Song, 1991).

At the Chinese MIRCEN, high-yielding strains of *Lentinus edodes* were bred, while genetic studies at the molecular level using the RFLP (restriction fragment length polymorphism) technique were being conducted on the various strains (wild and cultivated) of *L. edodes* and *Auricularia auricula*. In addition, investigations into cropping systems in mushroom cultivation aimed to set up low-cost year-round intensive production schemes suiting the present-day Chinese economic standards. These were: mushroom houses, open field under vegetable or forest tree shade, or discarded air-raid shelters (Song, 1991).

The use of mushrooms for various medicinal purposes was also a long-standing practice in China; a book published in 1987 recorded 272 species of medicinal fungi, most of them having been adopted by folk medicine as extracts of their fruit bodies. Recent surveys revealed that the total number of medicinal fungi in China amounted to 387 species belonging to 137 genera and 51 families. Besides the anti-tumour and immuno-modulating activity of their polysaccharide components on which most of the research work focused, medicinal mushrooms were used for preventing and curing infectious diseases, neurological disorders, haemorrhages, indigestion, arthritis, dizziness, neurosthenia and as an anti-pyretic, diuretic, laxative, general tonic or to regulate menstruation or blood circulation. However, the biologically active compounds had scarcely been scientifically investigated (Song, 1991).

SYMBIOTIC NITROGEN FIXATION

Regarding symbiotic nitrogen fixation, 500 strains of root nodule bacteria had been isolated from 800 nodule samples and successfully back inoculated to the surface-sterilized seeds of their respective host plants. Among the 120 species of legumes collected in the Xinjiang autonomous region, the nodulation of 50 species belonging to 21 genera were new records. Furthermore, strains of fast-growing soybean rhizobia were isolated only from soil and soybean nodules collected in China; these strains were considered, on the basis of several traits, members of a new genus, *Sinorhizobium* (Song, 1991).

Rhizobial strains were found on nodules of *Astragalus sinicus* only in China and Japan. *A. sinicus* was an important winter-growing green manure species in southern China. Inoculation of this species increased plant yield by 15% to 30% and the nitrogen content of the inoculated host plant by 2.0% to 2.5% in relation to the uninoculated plant. A new species of *Rhizobium*, *R. huokuii*, was proposed to accommodate the rhizobial strains isolated from *A. sinicus* (Song, 1991).

Many of the indigenous strains of symbiotic nitrogen-fixation bacteria from Xinjiang autonomous region were resistant to adverse environmental conditions and could therefore be of value in the development of biofertilizers in other arid areas (Song, 1991).

Symbiotic actinomycete-produced nodules were collected on non-leguminous plant species in the Xi-shuang-ban-na area of Yunnan Province. The study of pure cultures of *Frankia* isolated from these nodules showed that they were different from the genotypes isolated in the USA (Song, 1991).

BIOPESTICIDES

With respect to insect pest control, the total number of insect viruses recorded in China amounted to more than 300 by the mid-1990s, whereas the world record was 1,671 in 1986. These included nuclear polyhedrosis viruses, granular viruses, cytoplasmic polyhedrosis viruses, densoviruses, picornviridae, poxviridae and non-inclusion, as yet unidentified viruses. Nearly a dozen different insect viruses had been used for pest control in cotton and tobacco fields, vegetable farms, tea plantations, orchards, forests and pasture lands. A nuclear polyhedrosis virus (BSNPV) was a successful viral insecticide against *Buzura suppressaria*, a devastating pest in tea and citrus plantations in China, India, Japan and Myanmar (ex-Burma). The Chinese researchers had purified the virus and prepared the biopesticide formulation (Song, 1991).

Surveys of insecticidal bacteria were carried out during the period 1989–1991 from 55 different environments in the Yunnan and Guizhou Province. Of the 4,070 soil samples and dead insect specimens, 175 strains of *Bacillus thuringiensis* and 341 strains of *Bacillus sphaericus* were isolated. A number of strains of *B. thuringiensis* were found to be active against Diptera, Lepidoptera and Coleoptera pests, whereas one strain of *B. sphaericus* was potent against mosquito larvae, with particular success against *Culex pipiens fatigans* and *Culex pipiens pallens* (Song, 1991).

ENZYMOLOGY

An enzyme kit for blood sugar determination containing hexokinase and glucose-6-phosphate dehydrogenase, a uricase kit for determining uric acid and a malate dehydrogenase kit for assaying aminotransferase was officially tested for clinical use. The malate dehydrogenase from *Bacillus stearothermophilus* was an enzyme of excellent storage stability and thermostability, hence the advantage of using the kit containing this enzyme. Two other kits containing bilirubin oxidase and glycerol dehydrogenase and lipoprotein lipase were also considered satisfactory (Song, 1991).

Enzyme electrode and flow injection analysis for glucose, enzyme electrode for uric acid and differential model enzyme field effect transistor (FET) sensitive to penicillin had been developed. In the latter case, the sensor could be used for more than 1,000 assays and had a storage life of more than eight months (Song, 1991).

MICROBIAL WASTE-WATER TREATMENT

Microbial strains for treating waste-waters for industries containing such pollulants as chlorobutadiene, acetaldehyde, acrylonitrile, trinitrotoluene, cyclotrimethylene-trinitroamine, thiocyanate, azodyes and triphenylmethanes were screened. Microbial processes for bioremediation were being used on a commercial scale to treat 10,000 tonnes of waste-water daily (Song, 1991). A training course on microbial process development with participants from China, Singapore and Thailand had been organized by the MIRCENs of Beijing and Brisbane with the support of UNESCO and within the framework of an Australian Academy of Science/Chinese Academy of Science Exchange Programme (Song, 1991).

Microbial Resources Data-base of China

Co-sponsored by the China Scientific Data-base Committee and the Chinese Academy of Sciences, a Microbial Resources Data-base of China (MRDC) was introduced in 1987. Data included basic information on the collected strains (strain number, scientific name, place and date of isolation, habitat, growth medium and temperature, method of preservation, name of the depositor, strain characteristics). The MRDC possessed basic information on 3,068 strains of bacteria and yeasts. The Chinese Committee of Culture Collections of Micro-organisms had also started setting up its data-base network for all seven microbial culture collection centres in China, following the data structures and software developed at the MRDC (Song, 1991).

5. Brisbane MIRCEN and MIRCEN-Biotechnology Pacific Regional Network

A survey conducted by the Brisbane MIRCEN (Australia) revealed that no training courses in microbiology and biotechnology existed in 1991 throughout the whole Pacific region – a region consisting of 27 Island States of which Papua New Guinea and Fiji were prominent members, strongly supported economically by the South Pacific Commission, and with two major universities, the Papua New Guinea University in Port Moresby and the University of the Southern Pacific, with its main campus in Suva, Fiji. A smaller, National University was located in Apia, Western Samoa. However, the agricultural programmes in plant breeding and plant improvement via tissue culture and protoplast fusion were active in Papua New Guinea and Fiji, whereas Tahiti had developed an aquacultural centre.

With the assistance of the Australian National Commission for UNESCO, Massey University and the Cawthorn Institute in New Zealand, and government officials from many of the Pacific Island nations, the Brisbane MIRCEN (Queensland, Australia) had been able to establish 105 contacts in 21 of the 27 Pacific Island nations. The latter had expressed the wish to co-operate in a MIRCEN-Biotechnology Pacific Regional Network Development Programme. In 1989, a seminar held in Suva, Fiji, within the framework of the International Conference on Agricultural Development in the Pacific Islands in the 1990s, revealed that: there was an almost complete lack of trained microbiologists in the Pacific region; none of the three universities had a department of microbiology or degree course on this subject; fermentations and water-quality control, as well as waste-disposal control, were carried out mainly by 'biologists or engineers' equipped with only marginal knowledge of microbiology; rhizobia or algae could replace chemical nitrogen fertilizers and the latter could serve as fish feed in Western Samoa and other Island States; there was a need to produce mushrooms in Tonga and surrounding nations (Doelle, 1991).

The next step, after setting up the MIRCEN-Biotechnology Pacific Regional Network with executive members from Australia, New Zealand, Fiji, Tonga, Western Samoa and Papua New Guinea, was to develop joint ventures in microbial biotechnologies, with special emphasis on creating centres for teaching and research development. The first co-operative research programmes were dealing with microbial processes for waste treatment, mushroom production and the replacement of firewood with alternative energy sources (Doelle, 1991).

6. Nairobi MIRCEN

The MIRCEN at the University of Nairobi, in the Department of Soil Science, was co-ordinating activities implemented in East Africa. During the 1980s, regional co-operation fostered by the MIRCEN at Nairobi had been strengthened through five regional co-ordinating meetings between applied microbiologists from Kenya, Sudan, Zambia, Uganda, Tanzania and Rwanda.

Furthermore, together with the Agricultural Society of Kenya, the Nairobi MIRCEN had helped in translating the results of UNESCO-supported research on biofertilizers into rural market products with instructions in English and Swahili. The trade name of the legume inoculant produced by the Nairobi MIRCEN was Biofix. Its production and supply steadily increased during the 1980s, from 40 kg in 1981 to 1,500 kg in 1990. Between 1992 and 1993, average sales of inoculants were estimated at 1,350 kg per year. Sales had remained lower than expected, mainly because most farmers were experiencing a drop in income owing to poor harvests caused by droughts. Another contributing factor was the cutback in government spending as part of structural adjustment policies, with the resultant drop in financial support to agricultural extension programmes (Mugabe, 1994). However, potential production was estimated at 1,500 kg to 1,800 kg of rhizobial inoculant per annum.

Of the total inoculant produced, 40% was destined for common beans, 23% for alfalfa, 14% for soybeans and 9% for *Desmodium*.

Altogether, inoculants were produced for 19 legume species. A campaign mounted with prospective donors aimed to extend inoculant technology to farmers and government extension agents. In addition, it was planned to initiate advertising and marketing programmes. Ultimately, production needed to become commercialized for broad-scale availability of legume inoculants through farmer co-operatives and retail seed suppliers. The Nairobi MIRCEN planned to continue selecting and producing *Rhizobium* inoculants for economically important legumes via rural education programmes.

Another significant result of the Nairobi MIRCEN concerned the use of locally isolated micro-organisms in the biological control of crop pests and vectors of tropical diseases. Research was also being carried out on the effect of high temperatures (38°-40°C) on the survival, growth and efficiency of local strains of *Rhizobium phaseoli*; on the fixation of ^{15}N by 12 higher-yielding and bushy bean varieties (*Phaseolus vulgaris*); on the isolation of *Rhizobium phaseoli* strains tolerant of soil acidity; and on fodder legumes, their fixation properties and their contribution to the productivity of grazing lands in Kenya (Clark and Juma, 1991).

In June 1991, at a Nairobi MIRCEN workshop, 10 participants involved in inoculant manufacturing in Kenya, Uganda, Zambia and Zimbabwe reviewed the 'Improved use of rhizobial inoculants as a means of increasing biological nitrogen fixation throughout East and Southern Africa'. They shared information on the production and distribution of inoculants and identified common constraints on the adoption of biological nitrogen fixation technology and recommended the setting up of a regional research network to identify the effectiveness of indigenous rhizobia and to target areas where inoculation response was likely to occur (in *NifTAL BNF Bulletin*, vol. XI, no. 1, 1992, p. 7).

7. West Africa MIRCEN

In Senegal, research on biological nitrogen fixation had been initiated in 1975, firstly on annual grain legumes (soybeans, niebe – *Vigna unguiculata*, groundnut, voandzou – *Voandzeia subterranea*, green bean), then on perennial plants (e.g. *Casuarina equisetifolia*, *Acacia* sp. and *Prosopis* sp.).

The West Africa MIRCEN had been set up in February 1983 and was included in the research programmes of the Senegalese Institute for Agricultural Research (ISRA) in Bambey. In July 1991, the MIRCEN was transferred to the ISRA-ORSTOM (French Scientific Research

Institute for Development in Cooperation) research centre in Dakar-Bel Air. The objectives of the West Africa MIRCEN were to: build up a collection of *Rhizobium* strains and mycorrhiza for use in agriculture and forestry; develop inoculants; serve as a centre for disseminating information on biological nitrogen fixation throughout West Africa, and for training staff in this field; and prepare and distribute a newsletter.

With the assistance of the FAO and United Nations Environment Programme (UNEP), an important *Rhizobium* culture collection was established: more than 500 *Rhizobium* strains for soybeans, groundnut, niebe, voandzou, *Sesbania rostrata, Acacia albida* and *Acacia senegal* were maintained and distributed. A collection of green bean rhizobia was being set up, as well as an inoculum production unit. This production unit will allow extension work on biological nitrogen fixation in village nurseries for the propagation of saplings. This was considered the base for an FAO Technical Co-operation Project aimed at extending biological nitrogen fixation in West Africa.

Taxonomic studies were being carried out on the Rhizobiaceae as a prelude to extending co-operation between the ISRA-ORSTOM research centre and other MIRCENs for the exchange of strains, analysis of their diversity using molecular biology techniques, access to taxonomic information and greater interaction between researchers from developing countries and industrialized countries.

Biological nitrogen fixation was being studied in *Voandzeia subterranea, Phaseolus vulgaris* and *Acacia albida*, as a first step to screening the most effective *Rhizobium* strains and best performing associations plant/*Rhizobium*.

The West Africa MIRCEN had also initiated the production – at an experimental stage – of ectomycorrhizae (*Glomus* sp.) in forest nurseries, as well as endomycorrhizae (*Pisolithus* sp.) for inoculating *Eucalyptus* and Australian acacias saplings produced in village nurseries. Technical leaflets were published for the users of these inoculums.

A small-scale bioreactor developed by the NifTAL MIRCEN in Hawaii was supplied to the ISRA/ORSTOM research centre in Dakar.

At the Department of Plant Biology of the University C.A. Diop, Dakar, and in relation with the West Africa MIRCEN, a team of researchers had launched a project entitled 'Horizon 2000, Research and Development for Soil Fertility', the objectives of which were to promote: molecular biology techniques for the study of nitrogen-fixing plants and their symbiotic micro-organisms, and pathogens; the use of ^{15}N techniques for evaluating the amount of nitrogen fixed; the use of *Rhizobium* inoculants; training of technicians and young researchers in the manipulation of these techniques; and the dissemination of information on soil fertility among the project's research partners. The first stage of the project concerned the use of cowpea (*Vigna unguiculata*) and *Acacia raddiana* for improving soil fertility in the Centre-North region of Senegal.

At the same Department, research was being carried out on the influence of litter on nitrification. Once nitrifying strains from various provenances had been identified, their physiological behaviour was studied according to the pH, temperature and nature of the litter. It was found that the optimum pH was 7.8 for nitrate-producing strains and 8.2 for nitrite-producing ones, while the optimum temperature was 28 °C and 23 °C respectively. The following species had been selected to study the influence of the litter: pine needles (*Pinus maritima*), two grasses (*Agrostis setacea* and *Malinia coerulea*), *Polytrichum formosum*, gorse and a heather (*Erica ciliaris*). Pine and polytrichum litters were found to inhibit nitrification, while that of gorse activated it. These results were to be applied to litters of nitrogen-fixing trees in West Africa.

At the Laboratory of Microbiology of the ISRA-ORSTOM research centre, *in-vitro* culture of *Catharanthus roseus* was being carried out to study the production of indol alkaloids in the leaves (vincristine and vinblastine) and roots of this species (ajmalicine and serpentine, with anti-hypertension properties). Preliminary findings indicated that the production of alkaloids in both the leaves and roots was maximum after 90 days of culture, i.e. during the first flowering period; and that variations in alkaloid production were not marked when one was dealing with a clone derived from *in-vitro* culture or with two clones derived from the micropropagation of two distinct seedlings (less than 15%).

With respect to regional co-operation, in October 1995, the West Africa MIRCEN organized a regional workshop on streamlining the production and use of *Rhizobium* inoculants in the region. On this occasion, technical information was exchanged between representatives of laboratories from Côte d'Ivoire, Gabon, Guinée, Mali, Niger, Senegal, Sierra Leone and Togo. Furthermore, there was close interaction between these activities in West Africa and the MIRCEN of the Cell Culture and Nitrogen Fixation Laboratory of the U.S. Department of Agriculture, Beltsville, Maryland.

From 27 November to 1 December 1995, the third regional meeting of the West Africa MIRCEN was held in Dakar at the ISRA-ORSTOM research centre. The meeting objectives were to: present the various national culture collections of *Rhizobium* and mycorrhiza, as well as the research by laboratories participating in the network; design a regional project on the contribution of plant biotechnologies to the maintenance of soil fertility in West Africa.

This regional project aimed to study the biodiversity and ecology of micro-organisms associated with annual and perennial legumes, as well as the contribution of nitrogen fixation to the maintenance and/or restoration of soil fertility in different agro-ecosystems. The project consisted of selecting an annual or perennial legume species (or both) in each country of the West Africa MIRCEN network; determining the soil physico-chemical characteristics before and after experiments in the concerned agro-ecosystems; isolating and characterizing the native *Rhizobium* strains, in order to guarantee an effective inoculation of the chosen legumes; and identifying, for each chosen legume, the species, variety or provenance giving rise to a positive nitrogen balance in the local environmental conditions.

With respect to research in the various member countries of the West Africa MIRCEN, the meeting took stock of the following results and trends.

In Côte d'Ivoire, research on biological nitrogen fixation was attracting interest from the national scientific community. Some 15 researchers were working on food legumes (soybeans and cowpea), fodder legumes (*Stylosanthes* sp. and *Mucuna* sp.), creeping legumes used as cover plants in coconut, oil-palm and rubber plantations (i.e. *Pueraria* sp. and *Calopogonium* sp.). The tree legumes, *Acacia mangium* and *Acacia auriculiformis*, were the subject of intensive research on their association with coconut trees on the sea shore. Agricultural parameters were being defined, microbial studies undertaken and *Rhizobium* strains isolated from cowpea were maintained in a culture collection. The use of ^{15}N was envisaged in a national project covering economically important crops.

In Gabon, banana and plantain were being micropropagated at the FAO-CIAM Laboratory, near Libreville. Once the plantlets had been cleansed of all viruses through the cultivation of meristems, a new propagation method developed in the laboratory through microcuttings of the stems of young vitroplants could produce healthy, vigorous banana and plantain plantlets in five to six weeks. Owing to the fact that the stem of banana and plantain trees was not a real stem, but resulted from the assemblage of foliar sheets, the results obtained by the Gabonese researchers changed the perception of the *in-vitro* multiplication of monocotyledons. At the same time, by increasing the regeneration capacity of banana and plantain in the laboratory, the Gabonese researchers compensated the low yield of conventional propagation techniques using offshoots.

In the southern part of Mali, with an annual rainfall of 900 mm to 1,200 mm, the predominant crop was cotton and chemical fertilizers were used on soils, which proved, costly for farmers. The recent introduction of the legume species *Dolichos lablab*, in association with maize, aimed to improve soil fertility and supply feed to oxen used for tillage. The overall objective of better using the *Dolichos/Rhizobium* symbiosis was to understand the ecology of rhizobia associated with *Dolichos* in a fallow system, evaluate the response of *Dolichos* to inoculation and fertilizers, assess the quantity of nitrogen fixed and transferred to the soil and to produce the *Rhizobium* inoculant on a small scale. A bioreactor developed by the NifTAL MIRCEN in Hawaii had been supplied to the Soil Microbiology Laboratory at the Higher Institute for Training and Applied Research (ISFRA, Institut supérieur de formation et de recherche appliquée), Bamako.

In Niger, soils were very poor in nitrogen and phosphorus. The Niger's Institute for Agricultural Research, in close collaboration with the West Africa MIRCEN, was carrying out research on biological nitrogen fixation and mycorrhization of plant species. At a first stage, *Rhizobium* strains able to effectively inoculate the main legumes cultivated in Niger were being identified. At a second stage, it was intended to undertake the mycorrhization of plants, in order to enhance the absorption of phosphorus from rock phosphate extracted locally and used as a fertilizer.

At the International Institute of Tropical Agriculture (IITA), Ibadan, collection of rhizobia had started in the late 1970s. Several effective strains of cowpea and soybean cultivars tested in field inoculation trials enhanced growth and grain yield by 150% over the non-inoculated control plants. In 1995, there were 562 cowpea and 98 soybean rhizobial strains preserved in ampoules at the IITA Microbiology Laboratory.

Rhizobia had been isolated from shrub and tree legumes (*Leucaena leucocephala*, *Sesbania rostrata*, *S. grandiflora*, *S. punctata*, *Tephrosia vogelii* and *Acacia albida*) in the 1980s. Isolates from bush fallow, grassland and under *Leucaena* crop had been identified and screened for antibiotic resistance, effectiveness and cross inoculation. The two most promising strains to emerge from testing under field conditions, IRC 1045 and IRC 1050, enhanced *Leucaena* biomass production and persisted in the soil one year after the trial. These trials indicated that *Leucaena* required inoculation if it was to take hold and that subsequent inoculation by rhizobia of the same field was superfluous.

Since 1993, soils from Zaria, Mokwa, Zonkwa, Kaya, Zagon Kataf and Kano (moist savannah zone) had been used to isolate rhizobial strains for soybeans and cowpea. Rhizobial strains were also isolated from soils in Patigi, Ibadan, Bauchi, Kaduna and Zaria and for 15 herbaceous legumes (*Mucuna pruriens* var. *utilis*, *M. pruriens*, *Crotalaria verrucosa*, *Chaemacrista rotunfidolia*, *Centrosema pascuorum*, *C. brasilianum*, *Lablab purpureus*, *Stylosanthes hamata*, *S. scabra*, *Macroptilium atropurpureum*, *Clitoria termatea*, *Pseudovigna argentea*, *Aeschynomene histria*, *Psophocarpus palustris* and *Pueraria phaseoloides*). Further rhizobial strains were isolated from soils and *Mucuna* nodules on 32 farms in the Mono province of the Benin Republic, where *Mucuna* was needed for *Imperata* control and soil fertility maintenance.

In Sierra Leone, *Gliricidia sepium* was an important, fast-growing, multipurpose tree with a widely adapted provenance that produced high biomass and regenerated copiously after pruning. Compared with *Senna siamea* and *Gmelina arborea*, it was the most compatible with Sierra Leone's major food crops (rice, maize, cassava and cowpea) in alley farming. Poorly nodulated by indigenous soil rhizobia, *G. sepium* responded to inoculation, fixing an average of 276 Kg of nitrogen per hectare when pruning was done after six months of growth. Cowpea was grown either as a monocrop or in rotation with rice to restore soil fertility in the highlands. Some cultivars with high phosphorus-use efficiency had been identified: they fixed a relatively big amount of nitrogen and more than 50% of their roots were infected by vesicular-arbuscular mycorrhiza.

Since *Gliricidia sepium* could fix a relatively big amount of atmospheric nitrogen, responded to inoculation and was compatible with cowpea and other food crops in alley farming, it was recommended that *Rhizobium* inoculants and mycorrhiza be used systematically in order to achieve greater crop yields and maintain soil fertility in the poor highlands of Sierra Leone.

In Togo, under the Network for Alley Farming in Tropical Africa (phase I), trials had been carried out from 1990 to 1992 to screen multipurpose tree species, preferably legume trees, capable of growing on the poor ferralitic soils of Glidji and on the ferruginous soils of Amoutchou and Sarakawa. Eleven species had been studied with respect to their growth rate, wood production and leaf biomass, their capacity to develop tap roots, the amount of nitrogen in the leaves and their contribution to soil fertility and crop yields. It was found that *Leucaena leucocephala*, *Senna siamea*, *Gliricidia sepium* ILG55 and *Albizia lebbeck* were the best performing legume species in alley farming on the ferralitic soils of Glidji. These trees could produce an average 5 tonnes to 11 tonnes of foliage per hectare and 4 tonnes to 11.8 tonnes of wood per hectare; they also had a positive impact on soil fertility and maize yield.

Since 1994, the above-mentioned species, with the addition of *Enterolobium cyclocarpum*, had been introduced on 47 farms in the Vo region and Lakes district. This constituted the second phase of the Network for Alley Farming in Tropical Africa, namely testing the adoption of agroforestry systems by farmers.

As the MIRCEN in Porto Alegre (Brazil) had done with the Latin American Association of Rhizobiology (ALAR), the East and West Africa MIRCEN networks had pioneered the use of rhizobial fertilizers and institutionalization of the African Association for Biological Nitrogen Fixation (AABNF) which, in 1984 and 1988, held conferences on MIRCEN premises in Kenya and Senegal with the support of the UNEP, FAO and UNESCO. The conference themes were Biological Nitrogen Fixation in Africa and Maximizing Biological Nitrogen Fixation for Agricultural and Forest Production in Africa, respectively. The 1990, 1992 and 1994 meetings of the AABNF were held in Ibadan, Nigeria, Rabat, Morocco, and Harare, Zimbabwe, their themes being Biological Nitrogen Fixation and Sustainability of Tropical Agriculture, Acquisition and Promises of Research on Biological Nitrogen Fixation in Africa and Agronomic, Socio-economic and Environmental Benefits of Biological Nitrogen-Fixing Systems in Africa.

In 1994–1995, UNESCO implemented a project entitled Biotechnologies and human resources development for Africa, with a view to strengthening existing research institutions in sub-Saharan Africa already carrying out microbial and plant biotechnological research, and facilitating the transfer of research results to rural industries. Under this project, field trials involved the application of a soil conditioner (ECO-Agrogel) for tomato seedlings and medicinal plant species, *Phytolacca dodecandra*, in co-operation with the University of Swaziland; the gel was also tested as a medium for growing roses. The trials with tomato seedlings, conducted by the Faculty of Agriculture, confirmed the utility of this gel for the cultivation of vegetables in arid and semi-arid soils. This was also true for *P. dodecandra*, whose berries contained saponin-like compounds, that inhibited the growth of molluscs, vectors of schistosomes. The gel could also serve as a culture medium for the growth and transplant of rose seedlings, avoiding the detrimental effects of drought and root infection.

As a follow-up to earlier UNESCO-supported activities in Africa, a project on the bioconversion of waste into bio-energy was initiated at the University of Swaziland, at the Manziki Industrial Vocational Training Centre. Preliminary work dealt with the bioconversion of

600 kg of fruit and vegetable waste (from the Centre's kitchen) in an Indian-type digestor, thus allowing for the production of 12 m³ of biogas per day – enough to meet the energy needs of the Centre's kitchen for the preparation of pickled cucumbers, marmalades and jams.

Grants were made available for the following research projects:

– genetic improvement and production of papaya, carried out by the department of Plant Biology, Cheikh Anta Diop University in Dakar, and the Senegalese Institute for Agricultural Research;

– use of DNA markers in genome mapping of cowpea (*Vigna unguiculata*), within a collaboration between the West Africa MIRCEN in Dakar, Cheikh Anta Diop University and the National Centre for Agronomic Research;

– genetics, physiology and taxonomy of *Pleurotus tumefaciens*, grown on different lignocellulosic substrates, at the Department of Botany, University of Benin, Benin City, Nigeria, in collaboration with the Institut für Bodenbiologie, Braunschweig, Germany.

8. South Africa MIRCEN

In 1995, a MIRCEN was set up at the Department of Microbiology and Biochemistry of the University of the Orange Free State (UOFS), Bloemfontein, South Africa. This MIRCEN was expected to foster regional and international co-operation above all in Southern Africa.

The Departments of Microbiology and Biochemistry, founded in the early 1960s within the Faculty of Science of the UOFS, were amalgamated in 1988. Seven years later, the resulting Department included fifteen full-time staff, one associate staff member and two honoray professors lecturing to more than 700 undergraduate students in sixteen courses. In addition to BSc., MSc. and PhD. degrees in biochemistry and microbiology, the Department administered a multidisciplinary MSc. in biotechnology. About 30 students graduated with a BSc. degree with majors in biochemistry and microbiology each year.

The Department had developed a wide-ranging post-graduate research programme in molecular biology, forest biotechnology, mycology and yeast physiology, fermentation technology, lipid production and lipid enzymology, protein biochemistry and environmental microbiology. In 1995–1996, about 70 students were pursuing post-graduate training in the Department which was a major player in the Sasol (South African Coal, Oil and Gas Corporation)

Centre for Biotechnology at the University of the Orange Free State. Since 1990, the Department had been home to the Tree Pathology Co-operative Programme (TPCP), a venture between the major actors in the South African forestry industry and the University of the Orange Free State. The Programme was based on a membership concept where forestry organizations were members and contributed to a collaborative effort through the payment of annual fees. The University in turn provided the infrastructure necessary to conduct research on tree diseases.

The research carried out under the TPCP (which involved the Institute for Commercial Forestry Research and the companies of H.L. & H. Timber Products, Sappi, Mondi and SAFCOL) focused on those fungi which caused tree diseases, degraded timber or were potentially valuable for the pulping process. Notorious tree pathogens studied at the molecular level and from the ecological viewpoint were: *Cryphonectria cubensis*, causing a serious stem canker disease in *Eucalyptus*; *Sphaeropsis sapinea* that devastated pine plantations after hail; a species of *Ceratocystis*, causing wilt disease of wattle trees; species of *Ophiostoma* (a group that included the Dutch elm disease agent), which were important not only as tree pathogens but also because of their potential value in pulp production and monoterpene conversion; *Fusarium subglutinans*, the pitch canker agent in pines (this disease had only been recently recorded in South Africa and was a serious threat to the forestry industry; the status of this pathogen in relation to other groups within *Fusarium subglutinans* needed to be defined, in particular through sexual compatibility studies); and *Eucalyptus* rust, which was causing serious damage to young *Eucalyptus* plantings in Brazil (the fungus was not found in South Africa).

Monoterpenes are a group of 10-carbon compounds that play an important role in plant defence mechanisms. The research carried out in the Department focused on their toxicity to fungi, their biotransformations, their induction in *Pinus* species during fungal infection and their *de novo* synthesis by *Ceratocystis* species. Both yeasts isolated from monoterpene-rich environments and ophiostomatoid fungi were being studied for their potential bioconversion of monoterpenes.

The Department had always demonstrated a broad interest in researching yeasts and yeast-like fungi. Current research focused on taxonomic and ecological studies aimed at providing strains for biotransformations and expanding the range of the pharmacologically important, ascomycetous family of the Lipomycetaceae. This had given rise to collaboration with research groups in Germany, the Netherlands and Japan. Fungal population genetics using molecular taxonomy was another important subject of research[3] (see p. 124). It was being conducted in association with the tree pathology research group. Understanding the population diversity of a pathogen was considered an important contribution to controlling the disease and its proliferation. Genetic diversity of a fungal pathogen was not only determined by its genome, but also by extrachromosomal nucleic acid, the most common of which was ds RNA. In some fungi, this ds RNA was associated with hypovirulence. The presence of ds RNA was therefore being investigated in South Africa's more important tree pathogens, with a view to using ds RNA as a means of biological control.

Research on *Fusarium* taxonomy and mycotoxins was part of South Africa's Medical Research Council Programme on Mycotoxins and Experimental Carcinogenesis (PROMEC). In 1988, under this Programme, food-borne carcinogenic mycotoxins produced by *Fusarium moniliforme* in maize were isolated and chemically characterized. Given the name of fumonisins, they occurred naturally in maize world-wide, caused outbreaks of mycotoxicoses in farm animals and liver cancer in rats, and were a risk factor for oesophageal cancer in humans. Consequently, fumonisins were being intensively researched world-wide and were a major focus of PROMEC.

The Department had a strong research focus on the physiology and application of yeasts and other fungi for the production of various commodities. One line of research concerned the study of osmoregulation in yeast, *Saccharomyces cerevisiae*, and its adaptation to osmotic stress. It had been shown that many genes played a role in osmoregulation, some of them involved in the transduction of osmotic stress signals, in the synthesis and accumulation of intracellular glycerol, or in the control of the adaptation process. The fruit of these studies could find application in the food, beverage and chemical industries.

The production of ethanol, biomass and other commodities by yeasts from renewable resources and various industrial waste materials was being studied. Yeasts and other fungi had also been screened for the production of cellulolytic and xylanolytic enzymes. This applied research was accompanied by more basic work on membrane physiology and transport, ethanol tolerance as well as osmotolerance. Collaboration had been established with Spain's Institute of Biomedical Research in Madrid regarding the mechanisms of catabolite repression in yeasts.

Much work had been done on the: production of microbial biomass ('single-cell protein') from starchy substrates, pentose sugars (obtained from hemicellulose hydrolysate) and monocarboxylic acids; ethanol fermentation of starchy substrates and pentose sugars by yeasts, as well as the production of high-value metabolites, such as gibberellic acid and the orange pigment astaxanthin. This work involved the creation of hyperproducing strains by conventional mutagenesis. Current research focused on the production of high-value lipids by fungal cultures, xylanase production and amylase production, starch saccharification and ethanol production by genetically engineered yeasts. Special emphasis was placed on investigating the effects of culture conditions (batch, fed-batch and continuous bioreactors) on growth, product formation and microbial physiology, and the quantification of these effects in terms of growth kinetics. With the emergence of a modern fermentation industry in South Africa, research and training in fermentation technology were particularly relevant.

The isolation, biology and ecology of oleogenous fungi, including yeasts, were all justified by the fact that these micro-organisms not only produced high-value oils containing essential fatty acids, such as arachidonic acid and gamma-linolenic acid, but some of these fungi could also be used to produce pharmacologically potent lipid hormones (e.g. prostaglandins). Fungal isolation procedures tailor-made for certain lipid biotechnological processes were being followed, so as to ensure that the most suitable oleogenous fungus from indigenous fungal biodiversity was obtained and its production optimized. A lipid biotechnological process had been patented internationally by Sasol Industries, which concerned the production of fatty acids (gamma-linolenic, arachidonic and eicosapentaenoic acids) from industrial wastes. Research focused on the biotransformation of these fatty acids into oxidized lipid hormones, such as 3-HETE, a novel biologically active eicosanoid discovered in the Department. The same research team was involved in projects to bring large-scale consumption of toxic over-oxidized fryer oil by underprivileged communities in South Africa to an end.

The main research thrust of the Department's Lipase Group, as part of the SASOL Centre for Biotechnology, involved purification, physico-chemical and kinetic characterization of ester hydrolases, including their three-dimensional structure. The cloning and expression of lipase genes in foreign hosts was studied with a view to designing large-scale production processes for industry. The production of lipases from transgenic *Aspergillus* sp. was found to be slightly better than from yeast. The isolation and characterization of a relatively thermostable lipase from *Flavobacterium odoratum* and a psychrophilic lipase from *Pseudomonas maltophilia* were considered promising for industrial application.

Studies on the metabolism of nitrile compounds by *Candida fabianii* consisted of the induction, purification and kinetic characterization of nitrilase enzyme(s), in order to provide a means of synthesis of chiral carboxylic acids with application in the fine chemical or pharmaceutical industries.

The main research thrust in environmental bacteriology was the use of naturally selected and metabolically optimized bacterial strains, which were essential for water purification and pollution abatement. Special emphasis was placed on the use of selected propionibacterial strains and their role in the granulation phenomenon found in the biomethanization process. The study of this phenomenon would contribute to the optimization of the anaerobic digestion process. The taxonomy and ecology of the anaerobic bacteria belonging to the genus *Propionibacterium* were important due to the various industrial applications of these bacteria, e.g. in the manufacture of Swiss cheese. In addition, propionic acid and a variety of bacteriocins produced by strains of this genus were commercially used as food preservatives. However, although *Propionibacterium* was largely beneficial, many detrimental effects in the food industry could be ascribed to members of the genus; consequently, the correct identification of these strains was crucial. An identification system based on the use of molecular biology techniques had been developed to identify these bacteria accurately and rapidly.

In addition, a biodegradability assay was being developed to obtain a rapid indication of the potential suitability of industrial effluents for anaerobic digestion. As many types of effluent contained toxic compounds, this assay would give an indication of which specific trophic group would be affected and the degree of inhibition; the anaerobic digestion of potentially hazardous industrial streams and biodegradability. The assay would also contribute to the study of bacterial diversity in various natural ecosystems and industrial processes.

A multidisciplinary team was working on biopulping and biobleaching. Research included the production of microbial hemicellusases, the application of enzymes in the modification of wood pulp properties and determination of the structure of hemicellulose in wood and pulp. The study finding might lead to a new technology being applied in the pulp industry that would reduce chlorine use and alleviate pollution.

Among the main research achievements of the Department, which was a major player in the Sasol Centre for Biotechnology at the University of the Orange Free State, one could cite:

– the application of molecular biology techniques (polymerase chain reaction and restriction fragment length polymorphism) to the development of an extremely rapid technique for identifying certain groups of fungi;

– the development and functioning of various laboratory and pilot-scale anaerobic digesters;

– the isolation and characterization of various *Propionibacterium* species from anaerobic digesters and Leerdammer cheese;

– the development of a rapid identification system for the *Propionibacterium* genus based on molecular biological characteristics;

– the characterization of xylose transportation systems in commercially important yeasts and the technology of fermentation of D-xylose to ethanol;

– the development of an overproducing mutant yeast for the production of the orange pigment, astaxanthin;

– the first publication on the effect of light on pigment production by the yeast *Phaffia rhodozyma*;

– processing data and micro-organisms for the production of microbial biomass ('single-cell protein') from various carbon substrates;

– technology for pilot-plant scale production of microbial biomass ('single-cell protein') from monocarboxylic acids, in collaboration with the company Sastech;

– discovery and characterization of hypovirulence in a number of important tree pathogens;

– discovery of important fungal diseases of trees and design of appropriate and effective control strategies under the Tree Pathology Co-operative Programme;

– discovery of the production of biologically active lipid hormones from arachidonic acid by yeasts; isolation of a unique hormone, 3-hydroxy-eicosatetraenoic acid (3-HETE), produced by the yeast species *Dipodascopsis uninucleata*;

– granting of an American patent for the discovery of a process for the production of high-value lipids from industrial effluents;

– patenting of a biotechnological process to produce evening primrose oil and cocoa butter equivalents from industrial effluent, using fungi;

– elucidation of a homology-derived three-dimensional structure of the lipase from *Galactomyces geotrichum*;

– development of a procedure for the expression of a bacterial lipase and the lipase modulator protein in a foreign host.

9. Cairo MIRCEN

The Cairo MIRCEN was established to serve various aspects of applied and environmental microbiology in the Arab States and North Africa. A Unit of Biofertilizers was established in 1980 as part of the Cairo MIRCEN; its activities included: the isolation and collection of the most suitable and effective native micro-organisms for the production of biofertilizers; the study of interactions between these micro-organisms and their host plants; the supply of inoculants such as legume inoculants,[4] [(see p. 124)] cyanobacteria, associative nitrogen-fixers, *Frankia* and mycorrhizae. These activities' main objectives were to reduce the costs of agricultural production by decreasing the amount of nitrogen fertilizer conventionally used; to abate environmental pollution; and enhance plant growth and productivity.

In addition to its collaboration with Egyptian research institutions (such as the Ministry of Agriculture and Land Reclamation, the National Research Centre, the Desert Institute, Alexandria University and the Suez-Canal University at Ismailia), the Cairo MIRCEN maintained co-operation links with UNESCO, UNEP, FAO, the International Development Research Centre (IDRC, Ottawa), the ORSTOM (French Scientific Research Institute for Development in Cooperation). It organized international training courses (in 1985 on mycorrhizae, in 1986 on the production and application of legume inoculants, and in 1990 on biofertilizer technology).

10. Latin America MIRCENS

In 1979, a MIRCEN was created in the Applied Research Division of the Central American Research Institute for Industrial Technology (ICAITI, an intergovernmental entity involving El Salvador, Guatemala, Honduras, Nicaragua and Panama), Guatemala City, following an agreement concluded with UNESCO. This MIRCEN covered the Central American countries, Colombia, Mexico and the Caribbean. The MIRCEN's activities focused on biotechnologies and included:

– short courses organized only with MIRCEN resources (up to 1992, six courses had been organized, four of them at the ICAITI's headquarters in Guatemala City), whose subjects covered the utilization of agro-industrial wastes for feed and chemicals, biopesticides and culture collections;

– seminars, symposia and other meetings;
– attendance at special meetings and congresses, and distribution of their proceedings to the network's members (e.g. an international congress on the science of edible mushrooms, a meeting in solid-state fermentation);
– research projects which benefited researchers from Honduras, El Salvador, Nicaragua and Costa Rica (León, 1991).

The ICAITI's Applied Research Division was working on agro-industrial wastes and by-products, like coffee pulp, sugar-cane residues, essential oil plant wastes, for the production of ethanol for fuel, biofertilizers, microbial biomass for feed, edible mushrooms grown on lignocellulosic wastes, feed from solid-state fermentations, anaerobic digestion of waste. More recent research work focused on biopesticides, as well as extension services to help local industries comply with the new laws and regulations on environmental protection (León, 1991).

At the Argentine MIRCEN in San Miguel de Tucumán, research was being carried out on industrial and food microbiology, bacterial enzyme production for industrial use and automatization of microbial cultures. As part of collaboration with the National Universities of San Juan and Tucumán, researchers enjoyed access to the facilities of the PROIMI (Pilot Plant for Microbial Industrial Processes). Ferrero and Siñeriz (1994) were working on the extraction of alkaline protease from bacterial strains. Since the introduction of protease in the 1960s as a detergent additive, its commercial use had progressed rapidly. The most important of industrial enzymes, protease represented 60% of total sales, two-thirds of which were of microbial origin. The microbial protease commercialized the most was the alkaline proteases from *Bacillus licheniformis*, used in manufacturing detergents. The Argentinan researchers had isolated a strain of *B. licheniformis* (MIR 29) which could produce large quantities of alkaline protease in both batch and continuous culture. In certain conditions, the enzyme was almost totally excreted, favouring recovery of the enzyme using simple means of obtaining cultures and one-step purification methods. The researchers were trying to develop a culture medium that would increase productivity and reduce production costs for alkaline protease (in *Abstracts of Biolatina '94, Second Latin American Congress of Biotechnology and First Argentinian Congress of Biotechnology*, Buenos Aires, 6–8 June 1994, p. 32).

In collaboration with Spanish researchers, Ragout *et al.* (1994) were working on the microflora present in the traditionally-made Asturian cheese, Afuega'l Pitu, to select those strains presenting the best acidifying and protein-degrading properties, and test in milk their behaviour. These strains were selected on the basis of their capacity for producing 0.6%-0.9% of lactic acid in milk after 12 hours of incubation at 30°C. Of 40 isolated strains, eight belonging to the genera *Lactococcus* and *Leuconostoc* were selected (in *Abstracts of Biolatina '94, Second Latin American Congress of Biotechnology and First Argentinian Congress of Biotechnology*, Buenos Aires, 6–8 June 1994, p. 28).

Spencer *et al.* (1994) had isolated baker's yeast strains with ideal traits for industrial use. A comparative study was carried out on various strains of *Saccharomyces cerevisiae* isolated from commercial products or culture collections. Once the strains that performed best in the laboratory had been selected, a series of protoplast fusion tests was run with the aim of genetically improving or modifying industrial strains with regard to their assimilation of starch, speed of substrate consumption, specific rate of growth and raising capacity in ordinary dough (in *Abstracts of Biolatina '94, Second latin American Congress of Biotechnology and First Argentinian Congress of Biotechnology*, Buenos Aires, 6–8 June 1994, p. 35).

The same researchers achieved the fusion of protoplasts belonging to *Saccharomyces* and *Kluyveromyces*. By using this technique, they succeeded in transferring the ability to assimilate starch to strains of *Kluyveromyces lactis* that naturally possessed the trait of assimilating lactose, and also obtained hybrid strains of this yeast and *Saccharomyces cerevisiae* (in *Abstracts of Biolatina '94, Second Latin American Congress of Biotechnology and First Argentinian Congress of Biotechnology*, Buenos Aires, 6–8 June 1994, p. 34).

The same protoplast fusion technique was used to produce yeast strains that could ferment D-xylose into ethanol. With hybrid strains, the concentration of ethanol reached 7g per litre of culture medium. The objective of this research work was to produce yeast strains capable of fermenting hemicellulose, whose major component was a polymer of xylose (xylan) and which contributed 15% to 35% of dry biomass from agro-industrial and forestry wastes (Spencer *et al.*, in *Abstracts of Biolatina '94, Second Latin American Congress of Biotechnology and First Argentinian Congress of Biotechnology*, Buenos Aires, 6–8 June 1994, p. 40).

Ducrey Santopietro *et al.* (1994) were working on *Phaffia rhodozyma*, an imperfect yeast, whose main trait was the production of astaxanthin; optimum conditions for the production of the pigment were 22° C, a pH of 4.5 and low concentration of carbon source. Fed-batch cultures would be the commercially viable alternative. A computing programme was thus developed which, linked to an *in-situ* biomass measurement system, controlled the process by starting up the feed and regulating it to maintain the specific growth rate required (in *Abstracts of Biolatina '94, Second*

Latin American Congress of Biotechnology and First Argentinian Congress of Biotechnology, Buenos Aires, 6–8 June 1994, p. 29).

The Porto Alegre MIRCEN, Brazil, set up in 1978, had as its main objectives the training of scientists, dissemination of rhizobiology throughout Latin America and the preservation of genetic resources of *Rhizobium*.

Up to the end of 1994, eleven short-term courses (of two- to three week-duration) had been organized and more than 250 microbiologists and agronomists had been trained in *Rhizobium*-legume symbiosis. Half of these trainees were from 19 other countries of Latin America and the Caribbean, and the other half from Brazil.

In addition, the Soil Microbiology Group of the Federal University of Rio Grande del Sur (UFRGS) had proposed a post-graduate course on Agricultural and environmental microbiology since 1989. Some 35 microbiologists had obtained their MSc. degree in basic and applied microbiology and biotechnology from the UFRGS. The 30-month degree course comprised both theoretical and practical work and research in one of the following areas: soil microbiology and biological nitrogen fixation; biodegradation and biodeterioration – agricultural and industrial residues, fuels, biocorrosion, plastics; food microbiology; biological control of insects and plant diseases; plant pathology and genetic pathogen/host inter-relation; molecular biology; and fermentative processes.

In 1994–1995, five scientists were trained at the Porto Alegre MIRCEN through the fellowship scheme of the UNESCO Biotechnology Action Council.

Over 1,000 *Rhizobium* and *Bradyrhizobium* strains were being maintained in the Porto Alegre MIRCEN culture collection. All rhizobial cultures known to be efficient inoculants had been freeze-dried and the remainder were following suit. The collection held both strains native to Brazil and strains imported from other countries. The species were the following: *Rhizobium loti, R. meliloti, R. leguminosarum* bv. *phaseoli,* bv. *trifolii,* bv. *viceae, Bradyrhizobium japonicum* and *Bradyrhizobium* sp. (cowpea group and miscellaneous). The seventh edition of a computerized catalogue listing all the strains was published in 1995. A catalogue listing all the efficient strains held in Latin American laboratories was also available.

In 1993, the cumulative number of cultures dispatched since 1978 was 5,720, distributed among 15 Latin American countries and 23 countries in other parts of the world. In order to check the maintenance of their potential for nitrogen fixation, 26 growth-chamber experiments were carried out on the recommended strains in 1994. Furthermore, over 20,000 serological tests had been performed to identify strains in 6,000 nodules from field and greenhouse experiments and 300 identity checks on the strains.

A high number of efficient strains were released to industrial production of inoculants, principally for soybeans and temperate legumes. The activities of the FEPAGRO – Institute for Agricultural Research (formerly IPAGRO), the other partner of the MIRCEN, focused on the distribution of efficient rhizobia to inoculant manufacturers and research institutions, small-scale production of high-quality inoculants for small farmers, experimental stations and extension agencies, quality control of inoculants and production of anti-sera for strain identification. More than 2,200 packages of inoculants were produced in 1994.

Several of the joint projects on alternative carriers or additives for inoculants, cryoprotectants for cell lyophilization and new techniques for rhizobia identification were already operational. The MIRCEN/FEPAGRO was overseeing the official quality control of inoculants produced by manufacturers under an agreement with the Federal Ministry of Agriculture, as well as an informal control requested by farmers and manufacturers.

A research project on the development of liquid legume inoculants involved the Porto Alegre MIRCEN, the Laboratory of Microbiology of the University of Buenos Aires and the Laboratory of Soil Microbiology of the Uruguayan Ministry of Agriculture. Benefiting from UNESCO support, the project consisted of carrying out laboratory and greenhouse experiments on a liquid inoculant developed in the laboratory of Balatti at the University of Buenos Aires.

The First Meeting of the Legume Inoculant Manufacturers of the MERCOSUR (Common Market of the South, involving Argentina, Brazil, Paraguay and Uruguay) was held in November 1994 in Porto Alegre, under the aegis of the Federal Ministry of Agriculture of Brazil. It was attended by representatives of inoculant manufacturers, government officials and research institutions. The meeting proposed a number of regulations for a common market of legume inoculants, including requirements for the marketing, production and quality control of products. Another meeting was held in 1995.

The Porto Alegre MIRCEN was also an active partner in the Latin American Meeting on Rhizobiology, the XVIIth session of which was held in Havana in October 1994 and the XVIIIth session in Santa Cruz, Bolivia, in 1996.

Since 1987, the Soil Microbiology Group of the Department of Soils in the UFRGS had gained the collaboration of two microbiologists specialized in biodegradation and biodeterioration. Short courses could therefore be organized in these areas. Research focused on biodegradation of petroleum and paper industry residues, biocorrosion of metals, biodeterioration of hydrocarbon fuels and the impact of industry biocides on the environment. A data-bank and practical manual in biocorrosion and biofouling were being set up and prepared in collaboration with the University of La Plata, Argentina; INTEVEP, Venezuela; University of Campeche, Mexico; Higher Technology Institute, Lisbon; and the University of Madrid.

11. Other MIRCENs and MIRCEN-related activities

The University of Maryland Biotechnology Institute (UMBI) comprised four centers: the Center for Advanced Research in Biotechnology (CARB), the Center of Marine Biotechnology (COMB), the Medical Biotechnology Center (MBC) and the Center for Agricultural Biotechnology (CAB). Part of the UMBI's mission was to interact with industry and other vehicles of economic development for the State of Maryland. In addition, it had developed industrial partnerships within the State, across the USA and abroad.

Established in 1984, the COMB had expanded to encompass production of transgenic fish, molecular genetics of marine bacteria (inclusive of deep sea and hydrothermal vent isolates) and production of metabolites by marine organisms. The Maryland MIRCEN at the COMB provided a venue for training international students and visiting scientists in marine biotechnology (e.g. from Africa, Latin America, Malaysia, Taiwan and Thailand).

The MIRCENs in Japan and the United Kingdom, the latter coupled with the Commonwealth Agricultural Bureaux (CAB) International Mycological Institute (Kew, Surrey), operated highly sophisticated fermentation equipment and culture systems for the production of microbial, plant and animal cells. These MIRCENs also conducted instructional programmes designed specifically to give scientists from developing countries an understanding of bioengineering, as well as hands-on experience with the latest equipment and experimental procedures in biotechnologies (Pramer, 1992).

Granted permission by the Japanese Ministry of Education, Science and Culture, the International Centre of Co-operative Research in Biotechnology (IC Biotech) had participated in the promotion of research and training at the Osaka MIRCEN. The latter, at the Faculty of Engineering, Osaka University, was founded in April 1985 to promote international scientific co-operation and train young scientists from developing countries in biotechnologies. The MIRCEN also functioned as the Japanese national focal point for the UNESCO Regional Network for Microbiology in South-East Asia and conducted the international post-graduate university course in microbiology (set up in 1973), as part of UNESCO's activities in the basic sciences. This course (12-month duration) was being organized by the Japanese National Commission for UNESCO, Osaka University, Tohoku University, the University of Tokyo, Kyushu University and Kyoto University, with the support of the Japanese Government, UNESCO and ICRO (Chang *et al.*,1992).

In 1990, in collaboration with the United Nations Development Programme (UNDP), a MIRCEN with network activities in biotechnologies was established at The University of the West Indies, St. Augustine, Trinidad and Tobago, for the Caribbean region. This MIRCEN organized courses and regional conferences.

In 1992, a MIRCEN was established in Tehran at the Division of Biotechnology, Iranian Research Organization for Science and Technology, following collaboration with the UNDP. Research focused essentially on combatting malaria and insect vectors, using preparations of *Bacillus thuringiensis*.

Informatics MIRCENs were located in industrialized countries, although their facilities and know-how were used to train scientists from the MIRCENs in developing countries. The MIRCEN at the Centre for Information Biology, National Institute of Genetics, Shizuoka, Japan, housed the World Data Centre, which had catalogued microbes in 571 collections in 65 countries world-wide. This information had been computerized, automated and made available as a data-base to members of the MIRCEN network to save money and time in the search for particular microbial species (Pramer, 1992).

The main outcomes of the European project Microbial Biotechnology and Bioengineering-Biotechnological Applications were as follows:

– the building and application of the Biotechnological Information Exchange System (BITES);

– the strengthening of the existing national collections of microbial germplasm for technological use and the establishment of new ones, and the butressing of their international networking;

– biotechnological treatment of municipal and industrial wastes, production of biochemicals and optimization of biotechnological processes.

116

For the establishment and working of the BITES, 72 information specialists from 11 countries (Albania, Bulgaria, Croatia, Czechoslovakia, Hungary, the former Yugoslav Republic of Macedonia, Malta, Poland, Romania, Slovenia and Turkey) were equipped with the UNESCO CDS/ISIS software for building data-bases, and trained in one-week courses for its use (DaSilva, 1997).

The Biotechnological Information Exchange System (BITES) provided a mechanism for filling information gaps and developing information exchange services, with particular emphasis on agricultural foodstuff processing, production of specialty chemicals, aquaculture, waste-water management and new technologies. The focal point of BITES was the UNESCO International Centre for Chemical Studies in Ljubljana, Slovenia (Smits, 1991).

In 1990, BFN Net-MIRCEN was set up by the Stockholm MIRCEN for scientists engaged in biological nitrogen fixation research, with a view to exchanging scientific results and field experience, and fostering communication and co-operation among and between BNF MIRCENs and other organizations. In addition, the MIRCEN in Stockholm focused on introducing computer engineering to facilitate information exchange.

The development of information support systems for biotechnological applications was considered an important tool as reliance on bibliographic and specialized data-bases was growing. The information data-base was a network system that linked geographically scattered individuals together through the use of home or office computers to a remote computer. This facilitated interactions amongst monodisciplinary endeavours, and helped bridge the gap between microbiologists, chemists, computer scientists and engineers by providing them with a common computer language and methodology for deleting, modifying, and reassorting the genes and gene products (DaSilva, 1997).

Since 1980, *MIRCEN News* had been issued once a year to provide an overview of national, regional and international activities carried out by the individual MIRCENs. In 1985, the *MIRCEN Journal of Applied Microbiology and Biotechnology* came out for the first time and, in 1990, in a joint venture with the International Union of Microbiological Societies (IUMS), the journal expanded into the *World Journal of Microbiology and Biotechnology*, becoming the official journal of the MIRCEN network (Smits, 1991).

12. Co-operation and transfer of knowledge and technology

The MIRCENs established in technologically advanced countries functioned as bridges with those in the developing countries, thereby establishing the basis for possible twinning and joint ventures. For instance, the MIRCENs in Argentina and Guatemala, with the support of those from Canada[5] (see p. 125), Japan and the United Kingdom, had designed and tested bioreactors for optimizing production processes of fermentation products such as ethanol and yeast, as well as enzymes of commercial value or steroid hormones (Pramer, 1992). Similarly, the MIRCENs in Bangkok and Beijing benefited from co-operation with those of Australia and Japan. The Chinese and Australian Academies of Sciences were part of a joint venture supporting the exchange of research staff in each country. The MIRCENs in Australia, Japan and the United Kingdom also provided long-term training for young research students from developing countries (Smits, 1991).

Furthermore, the collaboration of the American Society for Microbiology (ASM), over a ten-year period, co-hosted with UNESCO scientifc sessions in its prestigious Annual Conferences, and was an advocate in obtaining U.S. federal funding for numerous MIRCEN projects based in the developing countries. This co-operation, monitored by an ASM MIRCEN Committee kept pace with changing concepts, issues, priorities, and emerging patterns and styles of co-operation that varied from face-to-face interaction to non-verbal electronic communication. The UNESCO/ASM Travel grant scheme developed in close collaboration with the American Academy of Microbiology was indicative of the progress achieved.

This progress was also borne out in the changing role of the MIRCENs, which, at one time, sent fellows abroad for training, were now receiving and training fellows in different fields of expertise. The increasing award of the UNESCO MIRCEN fellowships and professorships testified to the capability built up in the MIRCENs especially those located in the developing countries and those countries in the transition phase of reconstruction and development (DaSilva, 1997).

The MIRCEN network had been greatly strengthened by incorporation of the American Type Culture Collection (ATCC), National Collection of Type Cultures (NCTC), Hungarian Type Culture Collection and German Collection of Micro-organisms and Cell Cultures.

The UNESCO MIRCEN network was evaluated a number of times, from the Bull and Miles exercise of 1978 through the Halliday review of 1980 to the Pramer and Komagata evaluation of 1991–1992. Furthermore in 1990 while UNDP/Africa reviewed the MIRCEN collaboration with the African Biosciences Network, a similar exercise was undertaken by UNDP/Latin America within the framework of the joint UNESCO/UNIDO/UNDP Project in Biotechnology for Latin America and the Caribbean (DaSilva, 1997).

The MIRCENs could serve as regional centres for technology transfer, as well as convenient centres for the deposit and exchange of research materials such as unique DNA sequences, nucleic acid probes, hybridomas, and genetically engineered micro-organisms. They could also carry out contract research and their instructional programmes could be expanded to include training courses in biotechnologies and molecular biology (Pramer, 1992).

There was a growing hope that the MIRCENs constituted a novel mechanism in a constantly changing world to tackle issues of intellectual property and bio-informatics. It was also an example in which the interaction of research, education and development was increasingly being complemented by innovation, excellence and tradition (DaSilva, 1997).

A UNESCO Panel on Applied Microbiology and Biotechnology had convened and conducted a series of international meetings on the global impacts of applied microbiology (GIAM). These GIAM conferences were dedicated to the economic advancement of developing countries through applications of microbiology and biotechnologies. There were ten GIAM conferences up to 1995, most of these taking place in developing countries, such as Brazil, Ethiopia, India, Nigeria and Thailand; the 1993 GIAM Conference was held in Malta and the 1995 Conference in Denmark (Pramer, 1992).

13. Biotechnology Action Council

The Biotechnology Action Council (BAC), set up in 1990, was a group of scientists invited by UNESCO's Director-General in their personal capacity to assist, advise, organize and help implement activities in plant and aquatic biotechnologies. The BAC did not enjoy the status of a non-governmental organization. Technical services were provided free of charge, on a voluntary basis, by the individual members of the BAC. The BAC Secretariat, which received no financial assistance for overhead costs, was located temporarily at the institute where the BAC chairman worked.

The BAC short-term fellowship programme was designed to stimulate and facilitate research and training in plant and aquatic biotechnologies and related environmental biotechnologies. Through this scheme scientists (up to 40 years old), particularly from developing countries, were encouraged to carry out research at advanced centres (up to three months) and to learn techniques not normally available in their own countries.

Between 1 September 1991 and the end of 1995, a total of 224 short-term fellowships, from a pool of nearly 1,000 applicants, were awarded to young men (125) and women (99) scientists in microbial plant and aquatic biotechnologies. Of the fellows, 43 came from Africa, 65 from Asia, 19 from the Arab States, 60 from Europe, 52 from Latin America and the Caribbean; the awardees represented 78 countries and went to host laboratories in 32 countries; each fellowhip was worth approximately $4,000.

In addition, for the 1993–1995 period, thirteen UNESCO/BAC professorships were designed to allow the biotechnological community in developing countries (Brazil, China, Cuba, Egypt, Jamaica, Jordan, Malaysia, South Africa, Thailand, Turkey and Viet Nam) to invite internationally recognized biotechnologists to lecture and/or conduct laboratory experiments in a chosen biotechnology field at the host institution. The programme objectives were to: benefit from research advances in biotechnologies of special relevance to the agricultural, health, veterinary, environmental and industrial sectors; establish collaboration in research and training with colleagues from other regions of the world; enhance further local research; and update existing biotechnological curricula and laboratory protocols. In 1995, a professorship was awarded to a Hungarian microbiologist for a one-month period to lecture at the University of Natal and ten underprivileged universities in South Africa.

Within the framework of the BAC, two UNESCO chairs were created, one at the University of Beijing in plant biotechnology and one at Makerere University, Uganda, in post-harvest food technology. In 1992–1995, in co-operation with other international organizations, including the International Society of Plant Molecular Biology, twelve two- to three-week training courses and specialized seminars in plant and aquatic biotechnologies were organized or supported.

During the same 1992–1995 period, more than 400 complimentary copies of laboratory manuals were provided upon request to institutions and researchers in 73 developing countries, as a means of disseminating laboratory protocols for research in biotechnologies and overcoming young researchers' isolation from modern advances.

Under the BAC, in 1995–1996, five Biotechnology Education and Training Centres (BETCENs) were set up in national institutions:

Hungary, Godollo Agricultural Biotechnology Center, for Eastern Europe and the Mediterranean; Bethlehem University, Bethlehem, Palestine, for Arab States; Mexico, Irapuato, Centre for Research and Advanced Studies of the National Polytechnic Institute, for Latin America and the Caribbean; China, Qingdao, Ocean University of Qingdao, for Asia; and South Africa, Pretoria, Vegetable and Ornamental Plant Institute, for Africa. The BETCEN in China was devoted to aquatic biotechnologies, while the four others were for plant biotechnologies. The BETCENs were expected to provide opportunities for both short- and long-term training and research in biotechnologies, to promote regional collaborations and networking, and to serve as sites for international training courses and workshops. The host institutions contributed to the BETCENs by providing staff and facilities.

A project funded by the United Nations Development Programme (UNDP) in Iran, under the Iranian Research Organization for Science and Technology (IROST), aimed to produce bio-insecticides for the control of malaria. Considered one of the most successful UNDP-assisted projects in the review carried out by the UNDP in December 1994, it might have far-reaching implications for the struggle against malaria insect vectors, while at the same time liberating substantial foreign exchange for the import of insecticides. In addition, the project results could be extended to other developing countries faced with the resurgence of malaria and in need of environment-friendly bio-insecticides. The latter were based on a strain of *Bacillus thuringiensis* named Bt-14 isolated in Iran by Dr. Moazami, a renowned Iranian woman scientist; it had been applied in Qeshm Island and in other malaria-affected areas and had proven fully satisfactory in controlling the disease vector. About 1.5 tonnes of bio-insecticides had been produced and field-tested, thus meeting the project's immediate objective, i.e. to transfer know-how for the production and formulation of microbial insecticides at a pilot scale of 1 tonne per year. In addition, the bio-insecticide had been approved by the Biological Control Section of the World Health Organization (WHO) and the International Reference Centre of *Bacillus* affiliated to the FAO at the Pasteur Institute in Paris.

With the support of the Red Crescent Society, a multipurpose pilot plant with a 500-tonne per year capacity for the production of the bio-insecticide was planned; 300 tonnes were to be used locally and 200 tonnes exported. It was estimated that the functioning of this plant would save more than $400 million, currently spent on importing chemical insecticides for controlling the malaria insect vector alone. In addition to obtaining private sector involvement in this large-scale project, the IROST, Red Crescent Society and UNDP organized a meeting at the Ministry of Economics and Finance to review means of obtaining additional financial resources through other international organizations like the Islamic Development Bank or the Global Environment Facility.

Among the major lessons learnt from this project was that important achievements could be obtained with minimal input, if this were allocated in a timely and appropriate manner and the project was effectively backstopped (by the UNDP and UNESCO). In this case, a total of $222,000 from the UNDP had sufficed to make the pilot plant fully operational with outstanding results.

14. World Federation for Culture Collections

The World Federation for Culture Collections (WFCC) was a federation of the International Union of Microbiological Societies (IUMS) and a commission of the International Union of Biological Sciences (IUBS) with responsibility for promoting and developing culture collections of micro-organisms and cultured cells world-wide[6] (see p. 125). It fostered communication between collections, their users and the scientific and industrial community in general.

The WFCC operated through a series of committees. The WFCC Education Committee had published a series of books and prepared educational video tapes. The increasing demands on culture collections for authenticated, reliable biological material and associated information made it vital to conserve the microbial gene pool for future study and highlighted the shortage of centres of expertise in culture isolation, maintenance, documentation and taxonomy. To meet the needs of scientists, especially those working in developing countries, the WFCC Education Committee had begun publishing Technical Information Sheets (TIS) on various collection-related matters, with financial support from UNESCO. TIS provided guidelines for good practice in culture collections. It also offered advice to scientists in developing countries who were using micro-organisms and cell cultures in their investigations and who were often faced with the problems of availability, safe handling, cultivation, maintenance, conservation, identification, packing, shipping, deposition and ordering of cultures from collections.

In response to the increasing popularity and demand for TIS, UNESCO had provided financial support for the reproduction of all

TIS collectively in the form of a booklet entitled *Technical Information for Culture Collections Curators in Developing Countries*. The methods listed in this booklet had been developed to show how a high standard of results could be achieved in laboratories with modest resources and without sophisticated equipment.

15. Microbial Strain Data Network

The Microbial Strain Data Network (MSDN) was established in 1987, with the sponsorship of four committees of the International Council of Scientific Unions (IUMS, CODATA, WFCC and COBIOTECH), to run a world-wide service from its secretariat in Cambridge, United Kingdom. The MSDN had published a directory of laboratories, culture collections and data centres storing specific information on micro-organisms and cultured cells; in addition, it linked other relevant data-bases, such as the World Data Centre in Japan, the Tropical Data-base in Brazil, the MICIS and MINE data-bases in Europe and a number of important biotechnology information sources. The MSDN was accessible 24 hours a day world-wide; costs were kept low, with users including a number of MIRCENs.

Notes

1. 185 Member States as of December 1996, plus 3 Associate Members; the regular budget for 1996–1997 was $518.4 million and $ 544.4 million in 1998–1999.

2. While early inoculation methods had involved the transfer of soil from the roots of well-nodulated plants to the seed at planting time, the standard inoculant for the past few decades had consisted of a peat-based carrier inoculated with a large population of an effective strain of *Rhizobium* or *Bradyrhizobium* spp. Peat was an effective carrier because of its high water-holding capacity, good buffering capacity and high nutrient content. Significant advances in the formulation and delivery of *Rhizobium* inoculants included: the use of high-quality peats, some pre-sterilized and altered to promote growth and give the *Rhizobium* a better chance of survival; the application into the furrow of granulated peat inoculants to provide high populations of *Rhizobium*, particularly in soils difficult to colonize; and the availability of freeze-dried powders and liquid formulations. The use of seed augers, typical of Western Canada, made the application of liquid inoculants to seed very easy, while row-cropped legumes permitted in-furrow application of a liquid inoculant. Small-seed legumes, such as alfalfa, were pre-inoculated with *Rhizobium* in clay powders, a challenge that remained to be taken up for the medium- and large-seeded grain legumes (Nelson and Hynes, 1995).

   In addition to rhizobial inoculants, there was interest in developing co-inoculants containing other micro-organisms capable of improving legume growth. These included rhizobacteria, which promoted nodulation, nitrogen fixation, plant vigour and yield via mechanisms such as phytohormones, antibiotic or metal-binding compound production; bacteria or fungi, which protected against specific root pathogens, and others which boosted the nutrient supply via phosphate solubilization. These co-inoculants were expected to become increasingly important for a sustainable agriculture using fewer chemicals, but challenges remained with respect to microbial survival in the carrier or seed coating and as to ways of obtaining consistently beneficial effects under a variety of environmental conditions (Nelson and Hynes, 1995).

3. Morphological and physiological comparisons revealed two major groups of yeasts, ascomycetes and basidiomycetes. Resolution was based on phenotypic characters which were shown from comparisons of nuclear DNA (nDNA) complementarity to be strain-specific. Genetic resolution of species relationships was limited, however, as nDNA relatedness extended only to sibling species. With the advent of molecular sequencing, the examination of the relationship had been extended between species. Sequencing focused on ribosomal DNA (rDNA), because ribosomes were present in all cellular organisms and had a common evolutionary origin. Other conserved molecules, however, might be equally suitable and should be examined to verify rDNA-determined phylogeny. Phylogenetic analysis of rDNA sequences showed that the ascomycetous yeasts were a sister group to the euascomycetes, while basidiomycetes were broadly related to the smut fungi and clearly separate from the Agaricales. Sequence analysis confirmed species groupings in presently-accepted genera in some cases, but often showed previous taxonomic errors. Close relationships were found among certain other species by making molecular comparisons, thus changing the present restrictions of their genera (Kuntzman, National Center for Agricultural Utilization Research, Illinois, USA, in *Australasian Biotechnology*, vol.6, no. 3, 1996, p. 154).

4. Inoculant production in Egypt was initiated in 1950, using a carrier composed of Nile silt, gelatin, charcoal, sugar and phosphate. It supported approximately 10^6 rhizobia

per gram, but was easily saturated, resulting in anaerobic conditions; this mixture was used until 1978. From 1979 to 1982, 'Jiffy 7' expandable peat-pot disks were inoculated with 50ml broth culture and distributed in sterilized plastic cans. This technique enabled the incorporation of high numbers of rhizobia (10^9), but autoclaving was expensive and often did not prevent contamination, affected the water-holding capacity and produced toxins. Since 1982, imported fine-ground peat had been used, but importation costs constrained inoculant production. As Egypt had no peat deposits, a variety of other substrates were tested, including bagasse and berseem (*Trifolium alexandrinum*) straw. Thus far, 'stretching' the imported peat by adding equivalent weights of indigenous vermiculite clay had produced the most suitable carrier. Egypt saved an estimated $80 million per year by using rhizobial inoculants, according to the head of research, Soils and Water Research Institute (SWRI) in Giza, near Cairo. Approximately 95% of all soybeans planted in Egypt were inoculated. Each year, the SWRI Biofertilizer Production Unit produced 300,000 units of 200g-bags of rhizobial inoculant called OKADIN, Arabic name for nodule (*Biological Nitrogen Fixation – BNF – Bulletin*, 1993, vol.XII, no.1, p.4).

5. Production of grain legumes, particularly pea and lentil, had increased considerably in Western Canada. Prior to the 1970s, production of these grains was virtually non-existent; however, the total area planted in 1991 reached approximately 200,000 hectares and 250,000 hectares, respectively. This increase in acreage was due to:
    - lower prices for cereals;
    - higher demand for peas by European livestock producers;
    - desire to change crop rotation;
    - sequences for better disease control;
    - improved soil structure.

Both lentil and pea were nodulated by *Rhizobium leguminosarum*. It was estimated that 85% to 90% of the farmers used an inoculant, and that they were using the same inoculant for both crop species. Pea, which was less drought-tolerant than lentil, was usually cultivated in the wetter, more northerly regions of Western Canada, while lentil was more common in the southern part of the Prairies. Inoculation responses by lentil were spectacular due to the low indigenous populations of *R. leguminosarum* in drier areas. Researchers at the University of Saskatchewan were looking at environmental parameters which might enhance the survival of introduced rhizobia in wetter areas and if these newly introduced rhizobia could compete for nodulation with the indigenous rhizobia.

Avenues were being explored to replace part of the inorganic fertilizers with biologically fixed nitrogen through the use of a green-manure cover crop during the summer fallow year. In these systems, up to 20% of the nitrogen recovered by spring wheat was derived from the incorporated green manure. The recovery of applied nitrogen fertilizer was between 23% and 34% depending on whether a crop residue was incorporated or not, and on the residue type of a previous crop. Total nitrogen losses were consistently higher when fertilizer was used as a source of nitrogen compared to green manure nitrogen. However, nitrogen losses from green manure crops occurred and were largely due to ammonia volatilization after cutting and to denitrification after periods of heavy rainfall.

While in the 1970s, Nitragin (located in Milwaukee, Wisconsin) was the only major company that had inoculants available in Canada, in the early 1990s various new companies (Philom Bios, MicroBioRhizoGen) were producing and selling inoculants developed especially for growing conditions encountered in Western Canada. Even the ESSO company entered the inoculant business with a new branch known as ESSO-Ag. Biologicals.

6. Established in 1925, the American Type Culture Collection was an independent

non-profit making organization devoted to the acquisition, preservation and distribution of micro-organisms, viruses, fungi, yeasts, protozoa, plant tissue and cell cultures, and recombinant DNA materials. In 1995, the ATCC housed the most diverse collection of cultures in the world. Holdings numbered over 55,000 different strains of algae, animal viruses, bacteria, cell lines, human DNA probes, hybridomas, oncogenes, phages, plasmids, plant tissue cultures, plant viruses, yeasts and protozoa.

Microbial services offered at the ATCC included culture identification, cryopreservation, freeze-drying of micro-organisms and biological reagents, proprietary culture safekeeping, plasmid preparation, mycoplasma testing, karyotyping and virus purification. In addition, the ATCC was an international patent culture depository, that operated an international hybridoma data-bank and had established an on-line data-base of human DNA probes and chromosome-specific libraries to assist the Human Genome initiative.

The ATCC had been conducting conferences and multidisciplinary hands-on workshops since 1983. These educational activities were designed to meet the specific training and informational needs of the research and industrial scientist, biotechnologist, physician, technician, administrator or patent attorney. Training made up 50% to 75% of each workshop in the form of inter-active hands-on laboratory exercises and demonstrations intermingled with lectures. The courses were conducted by ATCC professional staff or by guest scientists who were recognized experts in their field.

United Nations Industrial Development Organization

1. International Centre for Genetic Engineering and Biotechnology

In 1982, the United Nations Industrial Development Organization (UNIDO, Vienna) organized a meeting in Belgrade to examine the possibility of creating an International Centre for Genetic Engineering and Biotechnology (ICGEB). It took over four years for the concept to become reality, through the combined efforts of a Preparatory Committee, consisting of representatives of the signatories of the Centre's statutes, and a Panel of 13 Scientific Advisers (PSA).

As of March 1995, 50 nations had signed the Statutes of the ICGEB, 35 of which had ratified them. The Centre became an autonomous intergovernmental organization in 1994. The UNIDO continued to be represented on the Centre's Board of Governors as a non-voting member. The Board superseded the Preparatory Committee as the policy-making body with a Council of Scientific Advisors rather than the PSA. On 20 June 1986, following the screening of candidates by the PSA, an ICGEB director was appointed by the Preparatory Committee for a period of three years. In 1989, Arturo Falaschi, a molecular biologist specializing in human molecular genetics, former Director of the Italian National Research Council's Istituto de Genetica, Biochimica Evoluzionistica in Pavia, was appointed ICGEB Director.

The ICGEB was composed of two components, one located in New Delhi and the other in Trieste, Italy. The head of the New Delhi component was K.K. Tewari, an Indian plant molecular biologist teaching at the University of California, in Irvine. F. Baralle, a molecular pathologist from Argentina, joined the Centre in 1990 as head of the Trieste component. The scientific and administrative management was the responsibility of the Director and the Heads of the Centre's two component laboratories in Trieste and New Delhi. The research staff at each laboratory consisted of senior scientists directing research groups composed of junior scientists, support staff and trainee fellows.

The activities of the ICGEB had been prepared and launched as a UNIDO (Industrial Technology Development Division) special project since 1986. The Preparatory Committee agreed upon a three-year interim programme initiated in 1987. This programme aimed in particular to acquire buildings and equipment, and attract scientists. In April 1989, the interim programme was rescheduled and, in order to guarantee continuity, a rolling five-year programme was approved by the Preparatory Committee (De Groot, 1990).

The budget for the 1992–1996 period amounted to $72 million. Funds were provided by the Governments of India and Italy, the AREA Science Park of Trieste – the authority administering the science park where the Trieste component was located –, and as voluntary contributions by the participating countries. The Centre's programme was also supported by grants from foundations, industry and other United Nations organizations. In addition, in March 1990, a first agreement was signed with a private company: the Bombay pharmaceutical firm Wockhardt Ltd was to contribute about $3 million to research at the ICGEB's New Delhi component on products including insulin and the hepatitis B vaccine (De Groot, 1990). The Statutes having come into force in February 1994, it was up to the Board of Governors to decide the nature and quantum of assessed contributions from member countries for financing the Centre, which would begin operations five years hence.

In 1995, the Centre employed more than 200 staff in Trieste (7,000 m^2) and New Delhi (1,800 m^2). New facilities of 10,000 m^2 in the New Delhi component were completed by the end of 1994 (Taylhardat and Zilinskas, 1992; Komen, 1993).

The ICGEB's activities aimed to strengthen research and development in member countries by:

– providing developing countries with a necessary 'critical mass' environment to pursue advanced research in biotechnologies (it hosted research facilities inaccessible to the great majority of developing countries);

– training schemes and collaborative research with affiliated centres (21 as of March 1995) to ensure that significant numbers of scientists from member countries were trained in areas of direct relevance to their specific problems;

– acting as the co-ordinating hub of a network of affiliated centres while serving as localized nodes for distribution of the ICGEB's information and resources.

Since mid-1987 and until the end of 1992, the ICGEB had provided training for more than 900 scientists from 35 developing countries (Komen, 1993). The five-year programme involved 12 senior scientists and 36 associate scientists supported by 16 post-doctoral fellows and 48 technicians. Over the five-year period, outputs would include a total of at least 40 work years for senior scientists, 99 work years for associate and assistant scientists, and 53 work years for research associates.

The ICGEB's research programme covered three major areas:

– plant biology, with emphasis on crop improvement;

– human health, with emphasis on infectious disease control and vaccine production;

– biomass conversion, with emphasis on lignocellulose degradation.

The Trieste component's research staff addressed the following research topics:

– molecular biology of human viruses (human papilloma viruses, hepatitis B and C, HIV and rotaviruses);

– mechanisms of DNA expression and replication in normal and cancerous tissue;

– infectious diseases and molecular biology of genetically based diseases (hyperlipidemia, hypertension, cystic fibrosis, granulocyte pathology, adducin gene polymorphisms, study of fibronectin and tenascin);

– characterization of antigenic determinants of tumours and virus-infected cells;

– molecular biology/enzymology of lignin degradation;

– structure-function relationships in cytokines and DNA-binding proteins.

In Trieste, interaction with the local scientific community was well established. Possible access to a very powerful X-ray source from a synchrotron and to a Neuroscience Centre, both located in the AREA Science Park, would further strengthen the ICGEB's research capability.

In New Delhi, research staff were working on:

– novel recombinant diagnostics, vaccines and drugs for treating malaria, hepatitis B, hepatitis E and HIV;

– crop improvement, using genetic engineering, to obtain transgenic plants and stress-resistant rice cultivars;

– production of drugs and multi-epitope antigens via genetic engineering.

Recent developments and future trends in recombinant and synthetic vaccines were discussed at the December 1992 International Symposium on Recombinant and Synthetic Vaccines, jointly organized by the ICGEB and India's National Institute of Immunology. Work in this field at the ICGEB had resulted in the production of a recombinant hepatitis B vaccine. Its large-scale production was in the hands of an Indian pharmaceutical company. The latter was also responsible for marketing another product obtained from the ICGEB's research on making genetically engineered micro-organisms produce proteins in satisfactory quantities; the collaborating company funded part of the virology group's research (Komen, 1993).

Research in the early 1990s focused on the poorly understood hepatitis E virus, endemic to Asia, Africa and Central America, with a view to cloning and sequencing the genome of the Indian isolate of hepatitis E virus, and developing recombinant diagnostics and vaccines. Furthermore, a synthetic peptide was developed at the ICGEB with potential use as a vaccine against hepatitis B. Limited human trials were carried out in 1993. The replicability of this approach to other viruses was examined, which resulted in the development of a diagnostic kit for the HIV-1 virus; the diagnostic kit was to be marketed by the Indian pharmaceutical company, Lupin Labs (Komen, 1993).

The collaborating companies had entered into special agreements with UNIDO: any new technology developed at the ICGEB, even if protected by an ICGEB-owned patent, was expected to be made available to the member countries and their scientists (Komen, 1993).

Insect-resistant transgenic plants were being evaluated at the New Delhi component. These plants needed better resistance to the yellow stem borer; they had been obtained by inserting the soybean trypsin inhibitor in rice tissue, through protoplast bombardment. It was expected that the soybean trypsin inhibitor would also be toxic to other important insect pests. A longer-term approach to obtain insect resistance in rice focused on the mapping of insect resistance genes in rice, through restriction fragment length polymorphism (RFLP) analysis. Encouraging results had been obtained in the localization of a gene present in the rice cultivar, *Phalguna*, that conferred resistance to gall midge. Therefore, this gene could be isolated and cloned in order to use it in transformation experiments. In this project, the ICGEB was collaborating with Cornell University, Ithaca, New York, and the Japanese Rice Genome Organization (Komen, 1993).

The ICGEB provided training both in-house and at affiliated

centres. Long-term post-doctoral schemes allowed young scientists from member countries to participate in current research. Fellowship duration varied from 12 to 24 months. In 1992, trainee fellowships ranged between $15,000 and $20,000 per year. A 36-month pre-doctoral fellowship scheme leading to doctoral degrees, was initiated in 1992, in co-operation with the International School of Advanced Studies (ISAS-SISSA), Trieste University. Short-term training, focused on specific subjects or techniques, was provided by the ICGEB, either in-house or at affiliated centres. In 1990, training for nationals from ICGEB member countries consisted of about 190 work years at the Centre, 108 work years at affiliated centres, 2,232 trainee weeks of short-term training at the Centre and 828 trainee weeks at affiliated centres. The number of short-term and long-term training courses was expected to gradually grow to 48 and 40 respectively in 1994–1995 (Taylhardat, 1989).

Regarding workshops and courses conducted at the ICGEB, the 1992–1996 programme provided for up to 24 weeks of workshops annually at each of the two components. There were also two- to three-week laboratory courses conducted by affiliated centre staff and invited lecturers; the ICGEB provided up to 80% of their cost. Up to five such courses were taking place annually. Lastly, annual research-oriented meetings were scheduled to take place under the ICGEB's five-year programme.

A Conference on Biotechnology Research-and-Development Trends: Science Policy for Development was held from 2 to 6 October 1992 at the ICGEB's Trieste component, with a view to: articulating linkage between technology trends in the life sciences, developing countries' needs and policies of international development agencies; helping donor institutions refine their biotechnology policies; and harmonizing international biotechnology initiatives. The Conference, open to participants from the ICGEB member countries, policy- and decision-makers from United Nations agencies, other international organizations and donor foundations with active biotechnology programmes, aimed to learn more about innovative research and the problems of developing countries, forming new research partnerships, defining criteria for technology choices, increasing the awareness of policy-makers to the problem-solving and income-generating potential of biotechnologies, and furthering public/private sector interaction, as well as promoting joint ventures. The subjects selected for discussion at the Conference were: vaccine development for major Third World diseases and diagnostic biotechnologies; biomass and industrial toxic wastes; agricultural biotechnologies (Third World commodity and 'orphan' crops, arid land plants, biotechnologies and crop breeding, biological diversity); technology transfer and policy issues; and bio-informatics. Round-table discussions focused for each subject on the implementation and impact of on-going international initiatives, scientific strategies, regulatory constraints and social and economic considerations.

Requests by member countries for affiliation had been appraised by the PSA and approved by the Preparatory Committee. A government proposing affiliation for a national centre was responsible for guaranteeing a high standard of research at its centre. Affiliated centres were likely to become the focal points of national efforts in biotechnologies and serve as models for other local research institutions. The affiliated centres formed a global research network, hosting many of the Centre's training activities and channelling ICGEB resources and services to local institutions. The Collaborative Research Programme was set up to stimulate research between the ICGEB and the network of affiliated centres, and to develop research activities of specific interest to participating countries. Under the five-year programme, the Centre's annual expenditure for collaborative research amounted to $1 million.

A Forum of Scientists from the ICGEB member countries and affiliated centres was held from 30 September to 1 October 1992 at the ICGEB's Trieste component, with a view to: strengthening biotechnology co-operation among member countries and affiliated centres; identifying priority research areas of regional interest; and defining the strategy of the ICGEB's Collaborative Research Programme.

The ICGEB helped developing countries to meet their needs by providing access to an advanced computer service laboratory located at the Trieste component. The laboratory provided remote access to a range of major U.S. and European public data-bases, in addition to those of the Centre and its software library.

The ICGEB acted as an information repository by:

– gathering and collating information on research activities in the member countries;

– hosting information on commercial products developed by member countries' institutes, such as restriction enzymes, diagnostic reagents and vaccines;

– monitoring matters related to patent laws, the release of genetically engineered micro-organisms into the environment and biosafety procedures or legislation.

Furthermore, the ICGEB was supplying commonly-used strains of micro-organisms, as well as synthetic polypeptides and oligonucleotides.

It provided technical advice to member countries on request, for the formulation of a national biotechnology policy, definition of research goals, development of national bio-industry and the setting up of national biotechnology laboratories.

The ICGEB was promoting the harmonization of biosafety procedures and regulations in its member countries, within the framework of the UNIDO/WHO/UNEP/FAO Informal Working Group on Biosafety. The UNIDO, as part of this Working Group and in association with some 50 experts including from the OECD, had developed an International Voluntary Code of Conduct for release of genetically-modified organisms (GMOs) into the environment. The Code attempted to harmonize existing guidelines, capturing the minimum commonly accepted principles, into an international framework in the form of a code of conduct for the release of GMOs. The guidelines expressed in the code were meant to be user friendly, serve the promotion of research-and-development and environmental applications of GMOs. They provided guidance to national authorities on taking quick decisions on proposals for introducing GMOs, on helping industry to commercialize GMO-based products, on avoiding trade barriers and facilitating consumer confidence and acceptance.

The ICGEB included in its programme yearly training courses on biosafety. In 1992, in collaboration with the United Nations Environment Programme (UNEP) and the Microbial Strain Data Network (MSDN), a meeting was organized to evolve a data-base concerning biotechnology and the release of genetically modified organisms.

The UNIDO had also initiated a Biotechnology Information Network and Advisory Service (BINAS) offering remote access to data-bases of national biotechnology legislation, regulatory authorities and experts. The BINAS would simplify the process of making informed decisions on the choice of available regulatory options and advise governments. It would assist the bio-industry in identifying competent authorities responsible for permits to conduct field trials and commercialize transgenic products, as well as the information requirements for this purpose.

Through the ICGEBnet, the ICGEB disseminated currently available computer technology to its research community. The principal mechanism for remote access for the ICGEBnet resources functioned via the X.25 Public Data Network (PDN). The ICGEBnet was connected to the ITAPAC X.25 PDN via a leased data communication line allowing for 16 simultaneous incoming connections. In addition, access to the ICGEBnet could be gained through the INTERNET. The

ICGEB's main objectives were to provide computational assistance to the ICGEB molecular biologists in planning experiments, as well as analyzing protein and nucleic acid sequences; provide on-line access to the major sequence data-bases, including the nucleic acid sequence data-base of the European Molecular Biology Laboratory (EMBL), which was updated daily; and promote the rapid sharing of information and collaboration among ICGEB member country scientists through an international computer link, electronic bulletin boards, electronic mail services and a host of freely available PC softwares. The ICGEBnet was part of the informatics network of the European Molecular Biology Laboratory (EMBnet).

Apart from UNIDO, the ICGEB maintained close contacts with the WHO, FAO, UNEP, UNESCO, IAEA (International Atomic Energy Agency), OECD, the European Commission and the European Molecular Biology Laboratory (EMBO); collaboration was well-developed both with the International Centre of Theoretical Physics (UNESCO/IAEA) and the International Centre of Science and High Technology, located in Trieste under UNIDO auspices.

Advocates of the ICGEB saw the centre as offering opportunities to research units and bioscience-based industries in the industrialized world for establishing co-operative agreements with their counterparts in developing countries. They also recognized that the process of setting up the Centre had been difficult, much more so than its UNIDO promoters had imagined in 1982, or the governments deciding on its creation could have foreseen. Both parties were nonetheless convinced that, with an increasing diversity of member countries, the Centre was set to become an institution of excellence in scientific research.

Most of the industrialized countries were yet to join the ICGEB. These countries might be under the mistaken impression of a heavy financial commitment that went with membership. Under the Statutes, consideration would be given to assessed contributions five years after the entry into force of the Statutes. In the intervening period of five years, participating countries were expected to make voluntary contributions in increasing amounts, so as to reach the level of their assessed contributions by the end of that period. The subject of a scale of assessment had been taken up by the ICGEB Preparatory Committee to facilitate the work of the Board of Governors later on. It was expected that the larger the number of countries participating, the smaller would be each one's contribution.

In spite of criticism of pre-ICGEB political power struggles, the setting up of the ICGEB seemed to have increased government awareness and stimulated not only the formulation of national biotechnology programmes, but also the creation of national centres for co-ordinating biotechnology research-and- development. Some governments had set up or upgraded national centres involved in biotechnology and genetic engineering research-and-development. The Centre's influence was potentially greater than its size and budget supposed, due to its network of affiliated centres and the connections established with scientists throughout the world (Taylhardat, 1989).

The ICGEB had published over 100 research articles in peer-reviewed journals. An agreement had been entered into with two companies to commercialize products developed at the Centre, which included a diagnostic kit for AIDS infection. A patent had been filed on the synthetic peptide with potential for being developed into a vaccine against hepatitis B.

2. Activities of the Biotechnology and Genetic Engineering Unit

The UNIDO's Biotechnology and Genetic Engineering Unit had undertaken the following activities:
  – identification of national and regional research-and-development priorities, monitoring of technological trends, sensitization of policy-makers, scientists and technologists, and development of data-bases and bio-informatics networks;
  – national biotechnology policy formulation (e.g. biotechnology programmes in several African countries and advisory services);
  – research co-operation between institutions of industrialized and developing countries (e.g. in vaccines, bioremediation of oil pollution and enhanced oil recovery, lactic acid fermentation);
  – transfer of technology through investment promotion and technological co-operation at the enterprise level (e.g. group meetings on commercialization of biotechnology-derived products, on the application of biotechnologies to food-processing in Africa);
  – monitoring of regulatory issues, such as patenting and biosafety; formulation of safety guidelines for biotechnology research and manufacture for developing countries (e.g. development of a voluntary international code of conduct on the release of genetically modified organisms into the environment);
  – national institution capability-building through strengthening of research-and-development and production infrastructures (e.g. institutional capability-building in Egypt and Sudan, increasing co-operation with ICGEB-national affiliated centres).

Thus, the UNIDO was striving to serve expanding biotechnological capabilities in developing countries and to harness biotechnologies for a sustainable development.

A UNIDO-sponsored research project to develop high-protein content lactic beverages from vegetables had been under way since January 1987 at the Korea University, Department of Food Technology, College of Agriculture, Seoul, and the Massachusetts Institute of Technology, Cambridge, USA. Lactic acid fermentation of plant materials was widely used in the processing of foodstuffs in many African and Asian countries. The acid produced in cooked cereals enhanced the keeping quality of many staple dishes in Asia and Africa, e.g. couscous in Senegal, ogi in Nigeria, idli in India, nasha in Sudan, kishk in Egypt and erera in Ethiopia. Lactic acid was a means of preserving perishable foodstuffs. Good examples were Korean kimchi and fermented fish products in Asia. However, few studies had been carried out on vegetable lactic acid fermentations, as compared to the vast range of research conducted on dairy products, such as cheese and yoghurt (Lee, 1992).

The UNIDO-sponsored project's main objectives in its first phase were to establish optimum pre-treatment conditions for cereal submitted to lactic acid fermentation and to select and improve microbial strains. The benefits of pre-fermentation and extrusion-cooking of rice prior to lactic fermentation were demonstrated. The pre-fermentation of rice by *Bacillus laevolacticus*, isolated from sikhae, a traditional Korean fermented fish product, and *Saccharomyces cerevisiae*, and a subsequent extrusion cooking, improved the solubilization of the rice-soymilk mixture during digestion. However, substantial amounts of protein were lost as residue after centrifugation of the fermented broth. The research project's original plan was to solve this problem by manipulating the enzyme activity of lactic acid bacteria. An alternative method entailed enzymatic hydrolysis of proteins to the point where they were soluble at their iso-electric points but did not produce a bitter flavour (Lee, 1992).

The Department of Biotechnology at the Technical University of Denmark (DTH) enjoyed expertise and extensive experience in flavour control during fermentation, especially with hydrolyzed protein products. During the project's second phase, collaborative work was therefore carried out with this DTH department. It was found that different types of proteolytic enzymes produced distinct degrees of bitterness in soymilk hydrolyzate, and some strains of lactic acid bacteria, e.g. *Leuconostoc mesenteroides*, could reduce the amount of bitter peptides in fermented broth. Extrusion-cooking of cereals improved the physical stability and sensory acceptability of lactic acid fermented cereal products. The Korea Food Research Institute's research team had developed a process of risogurt production, a curd-type yoghurt analog made from rice and soybean protein, and had applied for its Korean patent right. Pilot-plant scale production was completed and the product was showing good acceptability in consumer tests:

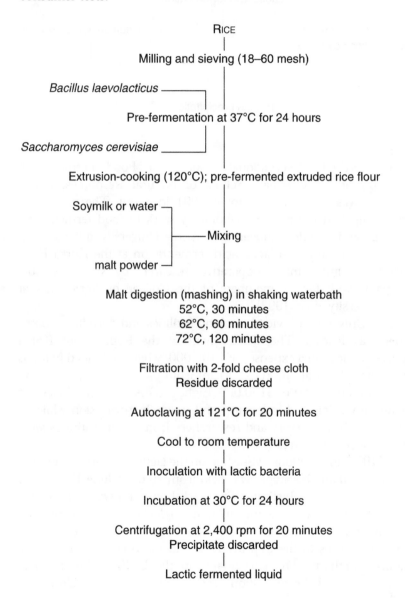

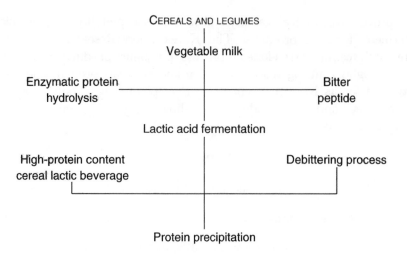

The UNIDO's International Course for Food Fermentation Technology at the Graduate School of Natural Resources, Korea University, was initiated in October 1991 in Seoul. The ten-month course comprised lectures and laboratory work in food fermentation technology and genetic engineering at Korea University, a two-month pilot plant trial on cereal lactic acid fermentation at the Korea Food Research Institute and co-operative research by the individual participants with faculty members of the College of Agriculture at Korea University (Lee, 1992).

Korea University provided teaching facilities and dormitory rooms for overseas fellows. The Government of the Republic of Korea supported educational expenses of $100,000, while the United Nations Development Programme (UNDP) in Seoul paid travel expenses and stipends for a total cost of $130,000. Eight professors of the College of Agriculture participated in lectures and research supervision while an additional eight professors and researchers from other institutes were invited as special lecturers (Lee, 1992).

A UNIDO international workshop on the lactic acid fermentation of non-dairy food and beverages was held from 26 to 28 June 1992 at the Korea Food Research Institute. The workshop's aim was to exchange ideas and collect available information on lactic acid fermentation, especially underutilized plant food materials, and to study the potential of biotechnologies in the improvement and industrialization of these traditional methods. The participants in the UNIDO International Course for Food Fermentation Technology at Korea University contributed to the workshop, as well as experts from Denmark,

Massachusetts Institute of Technology, Technical University of Berlin and Senegalese Food Research Institute (Lee, 1992).

As part of the Industrial Development Decade of Africa (IDDA), the UNIDO supported a project for developing small-scale, low-cost and energy-efficient technologies suited to rural areas for fermenting cassava into gari. Under a sub-contract agreement with the UNIDO, the Federal Institute of Industrial Research Organization (FIIRO) in Lagos, Nigeria, in collaboration with the African Regional Centre for Engineering Design and Manufacturing, set up a gari-processing plant and conducted workshops for transfer of the technology in the region.

In co-operation with the African Agency for Biotechnology and the African Regional Centre for Technology, and within the Industrial Development Decade of Africa, the UNIDO organized from 13–16 December 1993 an African Regional Symposium on Food Fermentation Technologies in Dakar, Senegal, with special reference to lactic acid and cassava fermentation, and mushroom cultivation technology. The objectives of the meeting were to: review and consolidate information in current research on upgrading traditional biotechnological processes, the genetic improvement of microbial starter cultures, lactic acid fermentations, mixed-culture fermentations and cassava fermentations; strengthen networks of African scientists and researchers working in these fields and establish sustainable networking arrangements; review the elements necessary to successfully transfer existing research-and-development results to the industrial sector; and establish contacts between African scientists working in biotechnologies, industrialists and funding sources in commercialization of research results.

Of the thousands of mushroom species regarded as edible world-wide, some twenty were cultivated on a commercial scale. Mushroom cultivation was an economically profitable biotechnology process for converting agricultural wastes. Global annual production had been assessed in excess of 4.3 million tonnes. In Uganda and Nigeria, the species *Pleurotus* was cultivated in rural environments using agricultural wastes with minimum technological input, providing employment and additional income for farmers, women in particular. In South Africa, mushroom production had developed into a $10 million industry since the late 1970s. The recommendations adopted by the meeting stressed that: the mushroom industry needed to be expanded throughout Africa; the UNIDO was expected to carry out an economic feasibility study to assess the potential of mushroom production in Africa; five regional mushroom culture collection centres comprising north, south, east, west and central Africa would be set up to characterize and distribute mushroom species to interested growers, provide information exchange and conduct training programmes on mushroom cultivation and production; spawn production would be promoted through entrepreneurs, with funds mobilized for training, equipment and distribution; an inventory of fungi and mushrooms would be made with a view to conserving and sustainably using these organisms (*UNIDO Mushnet Newsletter*, January 1994, no. 1, pp. 1–2).

The UNIDO convened an expert group meeting on the Commercialization of Biotechnology from 28 October to 1 November 1991 at its headquarters in Vienna, Austria. Attended by 34 experts from governments, academia and industry in some 20 countries from both the North and South, the meeting's overall objectives were to: review both general and product-oriented policies and progammes in industrialized and developing countries related to the commercialization of health-care and food-processing biotechnologies; identify the success factors and constraints on bringing products to market; and propose means of promoting biotechnology applications, in particular through international co-operation.

The meeting recommended that: a maximum of existing resources and programmes in specialized institutions be devoted to providing broader exposure and training in bio-engineering, scientific training and management (UNIDO being involved in such training activities); innovative mechanisms be implemented to enable collaboration with expatriate residents in industrialized countries, in order to foster biotechnology commercialization; countries develop appropriate incentive mechanisms to encourage active involvement by scientists in product commercialization, and allow scientists to gain rewards from the commercialization of biotechnologies developed by them in public institutions, while providing adequate support in securing patent rights; UNIDO promote the concept of 'development parks' by encouraging, in the first instance, the International Centre for Genetic Engineering and Biotechnology (ICGEB) to set up such an infrastructure near its centres; UNIDO's Trust Fund mechanisms be used by companies and institutions for commercialization of research results.

With respect to adequate financing, the meeting recommended that: in addition to the provision of seed capital in developing countries, the consortium approach be fostered as one means of providing capital, encouraging university-investor linkages and maximizing the utilization of existing infrastructure resources; research programmes have a product focus in order to be attractive to investors; UNIDO seek funds from international sources, as well as from industry, in order to assist enterprises in developing countries and assess projects or requests from individual enterprises so as to increase their funding.

Regarding government policies, it was recommended that: research-and-development priorities be focused on selected areas according to each country's competitive advantage; government departments play a more pro-active role in science-based enterprise development with appropriate incentive mechanisms to promote public-private interface technology transfer from abroad, university-industry links, tax policy and financial incentives; environmental costs no longer be considered external to projects or products; regulations be scientifically based, flexible and commensurate with risks; collaboration be encouraged at national level between academia, industry and government staff in the field of regulation; UNIDO take a more active role by promoting international co-operation for the adoption of common principles for safety guidelines related to biotechnology applications; UNIDO collect and disseminate appropriate information on regulations or guidelines applied in other countries.

The meeting also recommended that: developing countries devise appropriate strategies on intellectual property rights and patents, as this contributed to creating an environment for unrestrained development of science-intensive commercial enterprises; information services and exchange be promoted within and between developing countries with the assistance of UNIDO; all efforts be made, especially at the international assistance level, to strengthen biotechnology infrastructures; mechanisms be set up to encourage risk ventures, incorporating attractive financing options; and UNIDO integrate elements on consumer aspects of biotechnology commercialization into its information and seminar activities.

The important contribution biotechnologies could make to industrialization of the developing countries was the subject of a meeting in Vienna on 20 October 1993 between the UNIDO and the Senior Advisory Group on Biotechnology (SAGB) – a group set up by the European Union in Brussels to follow up and advise on bio-industrial issues. The meeting examined regional and global co-ordination of biotechnology policies, harmonization of regulatory oversight and means of enhancing the exchange of information among academia, governments and industry (*European Bio News*, no. 5, November 1993). Furthermore, in an expert group consultation convened at the UNIDO from 27 to 29 October 1993, current developments and trends in biological diversity prospecting, including policy and technology management, and intellectual property rights, were discussed in depth.

In October 1993, the UNIDO approved the allocation of funding to set up a Centre for International Services to Mushroom Biotechnology

(CISM-BIOTEC) on the campus of The Chinese University of Hong Kong (CUHK)[1] (see p. 147). The Centre was developing a Mushroom Biotechnology Data-Base and Information Network (MUSHNET) for collecting and disseminating information relating to mushroom production and biotechnology. A Mushroom Depository and Gene Bank for the conservation of mushroom genetic resources would also be created. The Centre was also promoting technology transfer and services to organizations in developing countries through training courses, workshops and consultancies; it was undertaking research on mushroom biology, genetics, bioconversion of agricultural wastes, cultivation technology, mushroom products, processing and marketing. The CISM-BIOTECH was providing the necessary technological back-up for the promotion of national and regional development of mushroom and mushroom-related industries.

The Chinese University of Hong Kong represented a good location for the Centre, its Department of Biology having a long-standing tradition in research and training in mushroom biology. Starting in 1977, there had been six workshops, training courses, conferences or international meetings dealing with microbiological or mushroom topics which had been held at this Department. In addition, the headquarters for the Mushroom Society for the Tropics and South-East Asian MIRCEN were in the same Department. Here also was carried out the pioneering research that developed the now widely-used method of composting cotton wastes from textile mills for the production of the straw mushroom, *Volvariella volvacea*. This Department became one of the world research centers for specialty mushrooms and mushroom products. Eight academic staff, visiting scientists and numerous graduate students were working on the following projects:

– development of mushroom nutraceuticals – a new class of compounds extractable from mushrooms which might be used in the prevention and treatment of various diseases and could serve as dietary supplements to improve human health;

– enzyme production by edible mushrooms and optimization of growth substrate utilization for increasing mushroom yields;

– somatic hybridization of mushrooms by protoplast fusion; protoplast and molecular studies on *Volvariella volvacea*;

– construction of a genomic library for *V. volvacea*;

– influence of metals on the growth and metabolism of mushrooms;

– electrophoretic karyotype analysis of *Coprinus cinereus*, *Pleurotus ostreatus*, *Schizophyllum commune* and *Lentinus edodes*;

– genomic library, linkage map and germplasm bank of *L. edodes*;

– hepatoprotective, anti-tumour and immunomodulatory activities of mushrooms;
– detoxification of rapeseed meal by edible fungi;
– identification and biological evaluation of glucosidase inhibitors from mushrooms;
– analysis of staphylococcal enterotoxin in canned mushrooms;
– development of mushroom-based processes for upgrading food-industry wastes.

A broader definition of mushrooms was taken by stating that a mushroom is a macrofungus with a distinctive fruiting body which can be either epigeous or hypogeous. A macrofungus has a fruiting body big enough to be seen by the naked eye and to be picked up by hand. This more inclusive definition of mushroom included both Ascomycetes and Basidiomycetes, hypogeous as well as epigeous species, fleshy and non-fleshy textured macrofungi, edible or non-edible or poisonous, or medicinal species. Out of approximately 69,000 described species of the estimated 1,500,000 species of fungi, there were about 10,000 known species of fleshy macrofungi. It was estimated that about 5,000 species were regarded as edible mushrooms. The estimated number of deadly poisonous species was about 100 (Chang, 1993).

The first mushroom to be cultivated around 600 AD was *Auricularia auricula*. The mushroom species, which was being produced nowadays in the greatest amount, *Agaricus bisporus*, was not cultivated until 1600. Of the leading mushrooms of today that were cultivated before 1900, *Agaricus* was the only one that was not first cultivated in China. *Pleurotus ostreatus* was first cultivated in the USA, and several other species were initially cultivated in India. By the mid-1990s, about 80 of 5,000 species regarded as edible mushrooms had been experimentally grown, 40 economically-cultivated, some 20 commercially-cultivated, and five to six had reached an industrial scale in many countries. In addition, using breeding techniques, cultivated strains could be developed that were uniform, of stable yield, specialized for quality, growing on a substrate of a particular composition and adapted to specific environments (Chang, 1993).

By the early 1990s, the world production of edible mushroom species under commercial cultivation was estimated at 4.3 million tonnes. Between 1986 and 1991, mushroom production increased by 96.4% at an annual rate of 19.3%. During that period, all cultivated mushroom species increased, ranging from 30.9% for *Agaricus* up to 442.6% for *Pleurotus*, through 290.8% for *Auricularia* (Chang, 1993).

Mushroom biotechnology concerned mushroom products and encompassed mushroom biology, fermentation technology and bioprocessing, and marketing and management. Mushroom biology in this context would include, as an additional feature, the identification of medicinals (e.g. anti-tumour, hypocholesterolaemic and immuno-potentiating agents) and other value-added compounds (e.g. flavourings and colourings for the food and beverage industries, additives for the cosmetics industry). Fermentation technology and processing embodied the development of large-scale systems for the production of value-added compounds and the conversion of mushroom into other retail products (myco-meat, mushroom-based health drinks, soups, etc.).

Mushroom popularity was due to three highly desirable characteristics as food: a remarkable taste and flavour; nutritive qualities (high contents of protein with significant amounts of lysine and methionine, fibres, minerals and vitamins, low calorie, fat, sodium and cholesterol); easy processing (dried, pickled and canned to allow maximum storage and transportation). In addition, many edible mushrooms had been traditionally used in China and Japan for their medicinal and tonic properties. In most cases, active components were beta-glucans. Furthermore, PSK, a protein-bound polysaccharide preparation and PSP, a peptide-bound polysaccharide preparation, had been extracted from *Coriolus versicolor*, one of the well-known medicinal mushrooms. In Japan, PSK was reported the top-selling anti-cancer drug and its annual sales in 1987 reached $387 million, and accounted for 25.2% of the total sales of anti-cancer drugs which were worth about $1,000 million per year. PSK was widely prescribed for cancers of digestive organs (stomach, oesophagus, colon and rectum). It was believed that there was a great economic potential not only for PSK and PSP, but also for other protein-bound polysaccharide preparations from other mushrooms (Chang, 1993).

According to Chang (1993), mushroom science (dealing with mushroom production) and mushroom biotechnology (dealing with mushroom products) were the two pillars of the mushroom industry. In the past, mushroom industry concentrated mainly on the production of fresh canned and dried mushrooms; it had only one pillar. Nowadays, in addition to the value of the world mushroom crop estimated at $8.5 billion by the early 1990s, $1.2 billion was generated from mushroom products (based on the sale value of the products extracted from *Coriolus, Ganoderma, Lentinus, Schizophyllum* and other mushrooms). Mushroom industry seemed therefore to have a bright future (Chang, 1993).

The Department of Biology at CUHK had attracted funding from various sources since 1991 to support its research programme on mushrooms; it played a major role in the training of young scientists, especially from developing countries.

Moreover, the expanding world-wide interest in mushroom biology and biotechnology was illustrated by the holding of the First International Conference on Mushroom Biology and Mushroom Products in Hong Kong from 23 to 26 August 1993. The Conference was organized jointly by the Department of Biology, The Chinese University of Hong Kong, and by the UNESCO Network of Microbial Resources Centres (MIRCENs). Sponsors of the Conference included the UNIDO, FAO, UNESCO Regional Network for Microbiology in South-East Asia, International Society for Mushroom Science, International Union of Microbiological Societies, Beijing-Hong Kong Academic Exchange Centre (Hong Kong), Carl-Duisberg Gesellschaft-South East Asia Programme Office (Bangkok) and several corporations from Hong Kong, Japan and the USA.

Over 300 delegates from 43 countries attended the Conference. Major topics covered during the Conference included: fundamental aspects of mushroom biology, bioconversions and biocomposting, genetics and breeding, medicinal applications, nutrition aspects, cultivation technology, post-harvest processing and quality control issues. In addition, the Conference featured an exhibition of new technical equipment used in mushroom biotechnology.

The Conference served as a forum for exploring possibilities for future co-operation and research. Two important meetings were held during the Conference: the UNIDO Steering Committee for the Creation of an International Network for Mushroom and Bioconversion Biotechnology, and the Executive Committee Meeting of the International Society for Mushroom Science (*UNIDO Mushnet Newsletter*, June 1994, no. 2, pp. 1–2).

In response to the strong interest expressed at this First International Conference on Mushroom Biology and Mushroom Products, the World Society for Mushroom Biology and Mushroom Products was created in January 1996. The subjects of study included Ascomycetes as well as Basidiomycetes, and both fleshy and non-fleshy textured fruit bodies that might be edible, non-edible, poisonous, or have tonic/medicinal properties. By encompassing a wide range of scientific interests and subjects, the Society aimed to provide a forum for the enhancement and application of knowledge relating to basic and applied aspects of mushroom biology. The Department of Biology at The Chinese University of Hong Kong (Chang and Buswell) served as the focal node of the new Society (*UNIDO Mushnet Newsletter*, January 1994, no. 1, p. 2).

In collaboration with the World Bank, the UNIDO organized an international workshop from 16 to 20 November 1993 in Bangkok to identify priorities for research-and-development in marine biotechnologies with commercial applications in developing countries.

The UNIDO had been publishing the *Genetic Engineering and Biotechnology Monitor* since 1982; this quarterly bulletin on developments in biotechnologies and genetic engineering included scientific as well as commercial achievements and trends. It was helping professionals increase their awareness without having to go through scores of journals and periodicals.

Agenda 21, which comprised the recommendations of the United Nations Conference on Environment and Development (UNCED, Rio de Janeiro, June 1992), included provisions for specific activities in biotechnologies. An Inter-Agency Committee for Sustainable Development, in charge of following up the implementation of *Agenda 21* assigned UNIDO as Task Manager in Biotechnology. The UNIDO was therefore co-ordinating the activities of all other United Nations agencies contributing to *Agenda 21* in biotechnologies; this included the provision of consolidated technical inputs to information exchange, inter-Agency contact, joint activities and programmes. Regarding common strategies for implementing *Agenda 21*, the Task Manager provided not only technical input, but also contributed to the report by the Secretary-General of the United Nations to the Organization's General Assembly.

At the invitation of the United Nations' Administrative Committee on Co-ordination (ACC) Task Force on Science and Technology for Development, UNIDO commissioned an article on biotechnologies' contribution to sustainable development within the framework of the United Nations system. Among recommendations contained in the paper was a proposal to organize a Consultative Group on Biotechnology to accelerate research-and-development, and commercialization, and stimulate both support for, and the spread of, environment-friendly biotechnologies world-wide. Another article on intellectual property rights in relation to commercializing bio-technologies had been prepared for the ACC.

Note

1. The Chinese University of Hong Kong was founded in October 1963 and had its origin in three post-secondary colleges. The University offered a wide range of undergraduate programmes within the faculties of arts, business administration, education, engineering, medicine, science and social science. Through its 33 graduate divisions, the Graduate School also offered Doctorate, Master's and Diploma programmes. The total enrollment of the University was about 11,000, comprising 9,000 undergraduates and 2,000 post-graduate students. The University had six research institutes: Chinese Studies, Asia-Pacific Institute of Business, Science and Technology, Hong Kong Institute of Asia-Pacific Studies, Hong Kong Institute of Biotechnology (incorporated as a self-supporting research and development entity) and the Research Institute for the Humanities. While the principal medium of instruction was Chinese, English was also widely used. The University was international in outlook and enjoyed close associations with many universities, foundations and organizations abroad.

World Health Organization

The World Health Organization (WHO) was created in 1946, with headquarters in Geneva, six regional offices and over 100 country offices. At the end of 1996, it counted 190 Member States. The WHO staff totalled 3,800 and the biennial 1996–1997 budget amounted to $842.6 million (regular budget) and some $994 million extra-budgetary resources. The WHO provided technical co-operation in particular to developing countries, but was not a funding agency. The technical programmes of the WHO generally fell within three overall areas: health systems development, health promotion and care, disease prevention and control (De Groot, 1991).

1. Special Programme for Research and Training in Tropical Diseases

About fifty of the World Health Organization's programmes had a significant research component, often including biotechnologies. Among them, the Special Programme for Research and Training in Tropical Diseases (TDR) was one of the largest. It focused on a selected number of diseases: malaria, schistosomiasis, lymphatic filariasis (or elephantiasis), river blindness, African trypanosomiasis, Chagas' disease, leishmaniasis and leprosy (see Table 3). Research was directed toward the development of treatment drugs, vaccines for prevention, improved methods for early detection and improved vector control techniques. In the short term, biotechnologies were expected to have an impact on diagnostics, with the increasing use of monoclonal antibodies and nucleic acid probe tests (De Groot, 1991).

Table 3. Main diseases in the developing countries (with the estimated number of deaths per year at the end of the 1980s)

acute respiratory infections	10,000,000
circulatory ailments	8,000,000
diarrhoea	4,000,000
measles	2,000,000
cancer	1,700,000
malaria	1,500,000
tuberculosis	900,000
hepatitis B	800,000
whooping cough	600,000
typhoid	600,000
meningitis	350,000
schistosomiasis	200,000
syphilis	200,000
amoebiasis	70,000
rheumatic fever and heart disease	52,000
hookworm	50,000
diphtheria	30,000
dengue fever	15,000
hepatitis A	14,000
yellow fever	9,000

TDR activities on leprosy or Hansen disease (caused by the slow-growing bacterium *Mycobacterium leprae*) included field trials on the use of new bactericidal drugs. For many years, dapsone was the only available drug against leprosy, but had several drawbacks: long courses of treatment were necessary, patients risked a relapse and dapsone-resistant strains of *M. leprae* were becoming widespread. Multidrug therapy (MDT) was encouraging and the number of registered cases had fallen by 31% between 1985 and 1990. In 1990, the number of officially registered cases, spread over 93 countries, was 3.7 million, the actual number being two or three times higher. A promising new drug was ofloxacin, which showed in tests a higher degree of bactericidal activity than any other currently known. The TDR activities therefore consisted of setting up a multicentre field trial on regimens containing ofloxacin. Although the latter was costly, treatment was short, so that the total cost per treatment was expected to be little more than that of current MDT (De Groot, 1991).

Another aim of the TDR activities was to develop an effective vaccine against leprosy. The 60-year old Bacille Calmette-Guérin (BCG) vaccine against tuberculosis had a limited, variable effect. Field trials with a vaccine prepared by culturing *M. leprae* in armadillos were in progress. However, more promising in the long term might be vaccine development as a result of gene transfer from *M. leprae* into the

The estimated number of cases per year for the following diseases was:

Chagas' disease	16–18 million people infected, causing thousands of deaths
rabies	35,000 cases (usually fatal)
AIDS	more than 14 million people infected in sub-Saharan Africa and 5 to 7 million in the Asia-Pacific region, with a global total of 30 million by mid-1997
ascariasis	1 billion cases, under 10,000 deaths
giardiasis	250 million cases, under 10,000 deaths
poliomyelitis	150 million cases, under 2,000 deaths
leprosy	10–12 million people infected, 1,000 deaths
leishmaniasis	12 million people infected, causing 20,000 deaths in India in 1977–1978
trichuriasis	500 million cases, with unknown numbers suffering from blindness or neurological disorders
elephantiasis	90 million people infected, under 1,000 deaths
river blindness (onchocerciasis)	18 million cases and 330,000 blinded by the disease
Guinea worm	1 million cases, under 1,000 deaths
trypanosomiasis	25,000 new cases reported each year

Source: Walgate (1990)

BCG. In addition, vaccinia virus recombinants expressing the genes for several *M. leprae* antigens had been produced as potential vaccines (De Groot, 1991).

New diagnostic techniques were also needed to better understand the epidemiology and dynamics of disease development. The polymerase chain reaction (PCR) used to amplify the quantity of DNA, as well as the availability of *M. leprae*-specific DNA probes, allowed the detection of very low numbers of *M. leprae* bacilli in experimental samples and biopsies from leprosy patients (De Groot, 1991).

Advances in the molecular genetics of mycobacteria also offered the possibility of modifying *M. leprae* to make it cultivable *in vitro*, so as to better understand the development of resistance and availability of unlimited quantities of micro-organisms for biochemical fractionation into immunologically defined components (De Groot, 1991).

The TDR activities on leprosy were being carried out in co-operation with the following institutions and companies:

– The Research Centre for Genetic Engineering and Biotechnology (CIIGB) of the National Autonomous University of Mexico (UNAM), at Cuernavaca, State of Morelos, where amino-acid sequences of *M. leprae* proteins were synthesized and their immunizing effects were tested in guinea pigs;

– Daiichi Pharmaceutical Co., Tokyo, where clinical trials of ofloxacin were being conducted for the treatment of leprosy;

– Wellcome Foundation Ltd, Beckenham, United Kingdom, where anti-leprosy vaccines were produced for field trials (De Groot, 1991).

With the exception of leprosy, all the diseases studied under the TDR were transmitted by vectors, like insects. Pesticide resistance of an increasing number of insect vectors was a major problem; hence the key role played by the research on *Bacillus thuringiensis* H-14, commonly used against the larvae of the black flies, the vector of river blindness (onchocerciasis). The genes for the protein toxins of *B. thuringiensis* and *B. sphaericus* were sequenced, some of them (or part of the sequences) being incorporated into other bacteria and protozoa, in order to broaden their spectrum of vector control and increase the toxic potential. The release of such genetically engineered micro-organisms required risk-benefit analyses before it became a widespread practice (De Groot, 1991).

The TDR involved co-operation with research institutes and companies throughout the world. An in-house product development unit was also set up to judge in each case the appropriate type of collaboration. Increasingly also, such collaboration was being established in the developing countries. By the mid-1990s, more than 60% of the TDR total project funding – both research and development and capability strengthening – directly supported projects in developing countries (De Groot, 1991).

In 1989, the Initiative for Biotechnology Implementation aimed to create a small number of self-sufficient quality production facilities in the developing world. It identified researchers, laboratories and companies to develop and manufacture products as a result of research work. The projects often included a partnership with a training component in an institute from an industrialized country. The Initiative focused on local diagnostics production. For instance, a research team at the Oswaldo Cruz Foundation (FIOCRUZ), in Rio de Janeiro, Brazil, was concentrating on developing diagnostic kits for Chagas' disease based on recombinant proteins derived from *Trypanosoma cruzi*, the protozoan causal agent of the disease. The team devised an enzyme-linked immunosorbent assay (ELISA) tested on over 2,000 serum samples from patients living in areas with endemic Chagas' disease and from blood banks. The test was found to be more sensitive and specific than conventional ELISA tests. The Foundation's research team therefore intended to make the test on a large scale and produce it as a diagnostic kit (De Groot, 1991).

The transfer of technologies to institutes in developing countries was one of the TDR four research capacity-building objectives. About 25% of the TDR total budget was directed toward capability-strengthening activities. Some 63% was devoted to research-and-development programmes. For approximately three-quarters of its funding, the TDR depended on voluntary contributions mainly from official development assistance agencies of industrial countries. Almost-one quarter was provided by the United Nations Development Programme (UNDP), the World Bank and the WHO (De Groot, 1991).

2. Other programmes

Biotechnologies were also used in the: Programme for Rapid Diagnosis of Infection and Preparation of Diagnostic Reagents (nucleic acid probes and monoclonal antibodies for the identification of pathogens); Programme for Vaccine Development (molecular biology and genetic engineering techniques), especially to meet the requirements of children's vaccinations in developing countries (one-dose or one-shot vaccines), with the ultimate goal of developing a product containing many immunizing vaccines, delivered in one single dose shortly after birth (De Groot, 1991).

Whereas biotechnologies might be useful in the production of relatively cheap diagnostics, most biotechnology-derived vaccines were expensive, at least initially. Vaccines currently used by the WHO usually cost a few U.S. cents, while a genetically-engineered anti-hepatitis vaccine cost around $10–15 a dose ($150 the three doses in Western Europe in 1997). A wider availability could only be realized if the price were decreased to at least $1 (De Groot, 1991).

In 1981, the WHO set up the Action Programme on Essential Drugs and Vaccines (DAP) with two main objectives: ensuring the regular supply of safe and effective drugs and vaccines of acceptable quality at the lowest possible cost; and promoting the national use of drugs. A model list was drawn up containing about 220 drugs and vaccines that could be considered essential in good medical practice and sufficient to meet most health needs. About 90% of these products were no longer protected by patents and could be manufactured without authorization at a reasonable cost. New products were put on the list only if they had a clear advantage over existing ones (De Groot, 1991).

3. Biotechnologies and human health: achievements, shortcomings and prospects

In the industrialized countries where health budgets amounted to several thousand U.S. dollars per capita per year, medical biotechnologies offered many opportunities. These included drugs produced by genetically-engineered micro-organisms or animal cells, faster blood tests using monoclonal antibodies or nucleic acid probes and new molecules produced through rational drug design. In the latter case, instead of screening thousands of compounds to see their effect on disease, with the greater understanding of pathogens and the human being's reaction to them, it would be possible to engage in rational drug design, whereby biochemists, immunologists and computer scientists would conceive the most effective molecules able to inhibit the pathogen invasion, multiplication or metabolism in the body. If cheap drugs could be designed to block these processes while leaving the human host unaffected, the parasites could be effectively controlled. Besides drugs, new and improved vaccines based on the immunogenic proteins of the pathogen could also play a major role in preventing the spread of diseases (Van Wijk and Komen, 1991).

Correa (1991*b*) concluded that biotechnologies were opening up new perspectives in pharmaceutical research thanks to the application of rational drug design; there were considerable delays in introducing expected biotechnology-derived drugs, the hottest competition occurring at the level of research-and-development laboratories rather than on the markets themselves; large pharmaceutical firms from developed countries had already set up a solid position in biopharmaceutical research-and- development and emerging markets, and major challenges for them could come from large firms from other sectors diversifying into pharmaceuticals, rather than from the specialized biotechnology companies (start-ups)[1] (see p. 242). Interdisciplinary teams made up of scientists from various disciplines and specialists in industrial techniques essential for scaling up production were needed, while the possible use of existing facilities in several production fields would result in substantial savings.

In the eighteen months up to April 1995, there were no less than 15 acquisitions among pharmaceutical groups, especially on the American market, the world's biggest. This trend had emerged in the early 1990s, when drastic cuts made in the health budget by many countries put an end to the steady rise in the price of medicines. Prices that had been rising by an annual 10% now had to be contained at the rate of inflation, i.e. about 3%. Pharmaceutical groups were aware of the potential drop in profit but confronted with two apparently contradictory requirements: enhancing their innovation capacity and, at the same time, increasing the delivery of generic products (i.e. medicines no longer protected by patents), which would be sold at a much lower price than new, protected products. It was true that, in this new environment, innovation was a top priority for any pharmaceutical group wishing to remain to the fore. It was imperative to focus research and development, while acknowledging that the cost of developing a new medicine amounted to about $200–300 million (including clinical assays), with only three chances out of ten of recovering the investment made (Gallois, 1995*a*).

Glaxo plc was a pharmaceutical multinational present in thirty countries in 1994. With an annual turnover of $9.7 billion, a profit of some $3 billion and 45,000 employees, it had been the leading British corporation in 1991 in terms of Stock Exchange capitalization. Its profit in 1995 (before tax) amounted to about $4 billion, showing a 30% increase over 1994. Glaxo plc's ambition was to become the leading pharmaceutical company in the world, with sales amounting to some $12 billion and an annual research budget close to $2.4 billion. Its Medical Research Centre near London, in Hertfordshire, cost the company more than $700 million. It housed the laboratories where new drugs were developed, in particular to replace those medicines expected to lose their patent protection or, in other words, become generic drugs. This was the case for Zantac, an anti-ulcer drug which had largely contributed to Glaxo's prosperity (Roche, 1995).

Zantac (ranitidine) was the world's biggest-selling drug: in 1994, with $4 billion sales, it represented 1.5% of the world market. In fact, according to the British research institute, IMS International, anti-ulcer drugs, with 5.3% of the world market (i.e. $12.4 billion in sales), trailed antibodies, which represented 10% of the world market (i.e. $23 billion in sales). Another anti-ulcer drug, Losec (omeprazole), produced by the Swedish company Astra AB, was a strong competitor for Zantac since coming onto the market in 1988; it had overtaken the first drug used in treating the gastric ulcer, Tagamet, produced by the British company SmithKline Beecham plc ($1.2 billion in sales in 1994), and which was in decline now that its patent protection had ended (Gallois, 1995*n*).

It was estimated that these three anti-ulcer drugs were the key to the success stories of three pharmaceutical groups between 1970 and 1990. The discovery of Tagamet had propulsed SmithKline Beecham plc among the ten leading pharmaceutical groups, until Glaxo's Zantac became a strong competitor during the early 1980s. Zantac represented almost half of Glaxo's annual turnover and enabled the British group, thanks to a sophisticated marketing network, to top the list of the ten major pharmaceutical corporations (Gallois, 1995*n*).

The discovery by Astra AB of Losec was a biochemical innovation: instead of acting, like Tagamet and Zantac, on the H2 receptors of the stomach and duodenum lining, Losec reduced the secretion of acid through the inhibition of the so-called proton pump of the lining cells.

This drug represented 40% of Astra AB's 1995 turnover and was the main reason for its rocketting expansion, from 40th to 15th place (in 1995) among the world's leading pharmaceutical groups. There was more good news: during the first quarter of 1996, sales of Losec in the USA increased by 57% compared to the same period in 1995. With a $415 million turnover in three months, the 1995 record ($1.3 billion) would certainly be topped; this would be due to the decision by the U.S. Food and Drug Administration to recommend Losec in the treatment of duodenum ulcers caused by *Helicobacter pylori* in some thirty countries, in combination with two antibiotics (Debove, 1996).

Losec represented more than one-third of the European market for anti-gastric ulcer drugs and more than 20% of the U.S. market. In 1996, it was the most widely sold drug in the USA. Astra AB's executives were confident that it would keep this dominant position till the end of the century, perhaps even world-wide, as patent protection of the drug was expected to come to an end in 2001 in the USA, 2002 in the United Kingdom, 2003 in Germany and 2004 in France. According to Astra AB's chairman, Losec (commercialized under the name of Mopral in France) had reached only 30% to 50% of its sales potential and would earn the company a turnover of between 30 billion and 50 billion Swedish Crowns in the medium term (Debove, 1996).

Competition was fierce between anti-ulcer drug producers. Rivalry was exacerbated by the fact that, once patent protection expired, manufacturers could copy the drug and sell it for less. SmithKline Beecham plc had suffered this fate and it would be the turn of Glaxo plc between 1997 and 2002, when its drugs would no longer be protected[2] (see p. 242). Astra AB was taking advantage of the validity of its patent on Losec till the beginning of the 21st century to broaden its marketing network through an agreement concluded with Merck & Co. Inc., the world's fourth-biggest pharmaceutical group (Gallois, 1995*n*).

In France, of a total annual turnover of $700 million (1994) concerning the medical treatment of gastric and intestinal diseases, anti-ulcer drugs represented $490 million. The share of proton-pump inhibitors (PPI) had overtaken that of anti-H2 drugs: $240 million compared to $200 million. The discovery of the role of the bacterium, *Helicobacter pylori*, in the aetiology of the gastric ulcer, was expected to reinforce the predominance of PPI drugs. The recommended treatment for the eradication of this bacterium included one PPI and two antibiotics (clarithromycine produced by the U.S. company Abbott and amoxicilline produced by SmithKline Beecham plc, the latter being no longer protected by a patent). It was forecast that patients would be treated in overwhelming numbers in coming years, which would markedly increase annual turnover for the manufacturers of these three drugs. Thereafter, annual sales would drop in correlation with the gradual eradication of the stomach ulcer. That explained why the pharmaceutical groups were reorienting their commercial strategies toward the treatment of oesophagus-lining inflammations by both the PPI and anti-H2 drugs (Gallois, 1995*n*).

The strategy of Glaxo plc was therefore to acquire a pharmaceutical company whose products were promising and profitable, so as to leave Glaxo plc enough time to conduct research for producing new drugs. This strategy included the purchase of Affymax, a company which had developed a technology for selecting new biologically effective molecules. Glaxo plc was also to finance research at Duke University, North Carolina, on preventing Alzheimer's disease. The University team had discovered a genetic link to common forms of the disease and hoped to develop a drug which might delay the onset of the brain disorder up to 20 years. Glaxo plc would have the right to sell the product, while licensing use of the patent Duke University would have filed on its genetic findings. This collaboration might earn both parties millions of dollars once the drug were discovered. In 1994, Alzheimer's disease affected some 4 million people in the USA yet there was only one drug on the market, Cognex, which was effective solely for mild-to-moderate forms of the disease.

Glaxo plc invested $14.7 billion in acquiring Wellcome. The latter was well known through its anti-herpes drug, Zovirax (which was to lose patent protection in 1997 in the USA), and AZT, used in the treatment of AIDS. These drugs would enable the new ensemble, Glaxo-Wellcome, to make a profit (Zantac and Zovirax represented about 40% of sales for each pharmaceutical group) while intensifying research to identify new medicines. In fact, some $2 billion was to be devoted by the new corporation to research on therapeutic compounds for the treatment of AIDS, hepatitis, cancer and migraine (Gallois, 1995*c*). In addition, in June 1996, Glaxo-Wellcome plc and SmithKline Beecham plc announced their collaboration on sequencing the genome of micro-organisms causing infectious diseases.

In taking over the number one place among pharmaceutical groups, Glaxo plc topped Merck & Co. Inc., the former biggest pharmaceutical company in the world. For the U.S. Whitehouse Station (New Jersey)-based company, strong demand for its anti-hypertension drugs helped increase sales 19% to $5.4 billion in the 1996 fourth quarter. Merck & Co. Inc. also had significant gains in sales from Fosamax, an anti-osteoporosis drug; Crixivan, the leading protease inhibitor of AIDS virus; and Zocor, a cholesterol-lowering agent. Net income in 1996 rose 21% to $1.04 billion in the quarter from $858 million a year earlier (*The Wall Street Journal Europe*, 29 January 1997, p. 3).

Glaxo plc's share in the world pharmaceutical market was expected to increase from the 1994 figure of 4.9% to 5.5%. It would have to ensure quick profits to make the investment worthwhile. In this respect, the closure of some sites was foreseen, as was the restructuration of the network. These measures concerned essentially the British installations. Of a total staff of 62,000, it was assumed that 15,000 posts would be abolished (Gallois, 1995*c*).

This acquisition by Glaxo plc was considered an important test for the pharmaceutical industry, which was going through a profound restructuration. The industry had come to a fork in the road: one path favoured an increase in size to secure a strong position on world markets, the other considered a strategy focused on successful niches the best guarantee. Glaxo plc had chosen the first approach (Gallois, 1995*c*).

In the fragmented pharmaceutical sector, where the world's ten leading groups[3] (see p. 242) held only 30% of the world market, estimated at $200 billion in 1994, the dominant trend was therefore toward mergers. Fusion also enabled new groups to acquire distribution networks, an important prerequisite to success. Thus, in July 1993, Wellcome and Glaxo plc had each signed an agreement with Warner-Lambert Co., the American distributor and specialist in self-medication and the sale of non-prescription, 'over the counter' drugs (Gallois, 1995*a*).

In 1994, American Home Products Corp. purchased American Cyanamid Co. for $9.7 billion. The earnings of the new company rose 29% in the fourth-quarter of 1996 to $503 million, from $390 million a year earlier. The company only posted sales growth of 5% to $3.48 billion in the quarter. Lower sales of painkillers Orudis KT and Advil hurt the company's sales comparisons (*The Wall Street Journal Europe*, 29 January 1997, p. 3).

Another example of concentration among pharmaceutical groups was the purchase by the German group, Hoechst AG, of Marion Merrell Dow Inc., the pharmaceutical subsidiary of the American chemical company Dow Chemical. This purchase took place in the second half of 1995. Hoechst AG needed to invest $7.1 billion (Gallois, 1995*e*).

In 1995, Hoechst AG came close to equalizing its 1989 record, when net profits reached $1.52 billion, a 65% increase over that of 1994, while the annual turnover increased by 5% to $35.42 billion[4] (see p. 242). That same year, Marion Laboratories had been purchased by Merrell Dow; the new company Marion Merrell Dow grouped 10,000 employees, with an annual turnover of $3.1 billion (1994) and 60% of its activity in North

America, compared to only 19% in Europe. Consequently, when, in August 1994, Dow Chemical announced the sale of its pharmaceutical subsidiary, Hoechst AG's reaction was immediate; it seized this chance to augment its 1% share in the American pharmaceutical market. Marion Merrell Dow could offer an effective distribution network, a great marketing competence, good, sustained relations with the American health authorities and a strong presence on the generic drug market. However, the American company no longer had either patented drugs in its portfolio, or promising molecules under active development through advanced research. It had nevertheless established ties with 14 biotechnology laboratories to develop new medicines (Gallois, 1995*e*).

To finance the acquisition, Hoechst AG had to transfer $2.5 billion to its American subsidiary, Hoechst Corporation; these funds would come from available resources and from the sale of non-priority subsidiaries (including cosmetic firms). The rest ($4.6 billion) would be constituted by bank loans. Hoechst AG's subsidiary, Roussel-Uclaf, would contribute $200 million by purchasing Dow Chemical's Latin American subsidiaries and, later on, affiliated European corporations. The major challenge was the development of new products between 2000 and 2005 (Gallois, 1995*e*).

The group's priority task, after acquiring Marion Merrell Dow, was to reorganize the pharmaceutical branch. This was a complex task due to the need to reconciliate the different business cultures of Hoechst, its French subsidiary Roussel-Uclaf and its new U.S. subsidiary. For instance, the latter, which had been completely absorbed by Hoechst, did not understand why Roussel-Uclaf, whose 40% of shares were still quoted on the Stock Exchange, had not received similar treatment. According to the U.S. partners, the complete integration of Roussel-Uclaf would facilitate the reorganization of the new group. This argument was not shared by the German mother company, for both financial and political reasons: French-German co-existence went back 27 years (Gallois, 1995*m*).

With a turnover amounting to 17 billion FF in 1996 (about $3.4 billion) and profits of 1.93 billion FF ($386 million), Roussel-Uclaf was redefining its research-and-development strategy to focus on two areas: anti-infectious disease drugs and medicines to treat bone diseases. In addition, a savings plan estimated at $42 million was to be implemented over three years and three structures were to group the current five subsidiaries, i.e. Roussel-Diamant, Hoechst-Houdé and Cassenne. All of these changes occurred during the group's move to new headquarters in Romainville, near Paris, where the company had been founded in 1920 by Gaston Roussel. The transfer was made on 1 May 1995 (Gallois, 1995*d*).

In 1968, Hoechst AG held an indirect minority stake in Roussel-Uclaf within the framework of research agreements. In 1974, two years after the death of Jean-Claude Roussel, Hoechst AG took the control of the group via the Société française Hoechst (SFH). In 1982, Roussel-Uclaf did not figure among the companies nationalized, although the French State held a 40% stake in it, thereby reducing SFH share to 54.5%. In 1990, the State transferred 35% of its stake to the nationalized Rhône-Poulenc. The remaining 5% was left with the State holding, Erap (Entreprise de recherches et d'activités pétrolières, Enterprise of Oil Research and Activities). Erap was a public establishment born of the merger in 1966 of the Régie autonome du pétrole (RAP) and the Bureau de recherche pétrolière (BRP). Erap was created to pool all the State's holdings in the Société nationale des pétroles d'Aquitaine, which was to become Elf Aquitaine in 1976. Over the years, Erap holding in Elf would shrink from 70% to 9.1%, subsequent to the latter being privatized in 1993. On 13 November 1996, the State sold its stake, thus recovering $2 billion. In addition, by selling its Erap stake in Roussel-Uclaf, the State recovered $356 million (Gallois, 1996*l*).

In 1993, Rhône-Poulenc sold its share on the Stock Exchange in France and elsewhere. In 1994, Hoechst AG, via the SFH, raised its share to 56.62% while adding to Roussel-Uclaf Hoechst laboratories in France and ARP in Germany. On 11 December 1996, still via the SFH, Hoechst AG announced its intention to acquire 43.4% of Roussel-Uclaf's capital through the purchase of shares on the Stock Exchange. In this way, Hoechst AG became the sole owner of the French company within the group Hoechst-Marion-Roussel. The purchase price was estimated at $3.62 billion and was considered one of the biggest operations on the Paris Stock Exchange in 1996. Despite the size of the amount, which was to be financed by borrowing, Hoechst's executives did not hesitate: the game was worth the candle (Gallois, 1996*l*).

On 10 December 1996, Hoechst AG announced the sale of its specialty chemical activities to Clariant, a Swiss company created in 1995 from Sandoz's former Division of Chemical Products. Hoechst AG would become a minor shareholder in Clariant which had an annual turnover of $5.4 billion. In making both decisions, the world leader in chemistry and fourth-biggest pharmaceutical group confirmed its focus on health under the leadership of its chairman since 1994. This strategy consisted of concentrating the group's activities on profitable sectors like health sciences (human and animal health, food and agrochemistry), at the expense of bulk chemistry (Gallois, 1996*l*).

The pillar of this new ensemble was Hoechst-Marion-Roussel (HMR), which looked attractive to investors: $10 billion invested in one and a half years, the equivalent of HMR annual turnover. This reshuffling provoked a redefinition of the contribution, in each of the three countries, to the group's research-and-development activities. In France, the focus was on anti-infectious disease drugs and on medicines to treat bone diseases; in Germany, on cardio-vascular, metabolic and rheumatic illnesses; and in the USA, on the central nervous system. With 3.6% of the world pharmaceutical market, HMR confirmed its fourth rank among the leading pharmaceutical groups, behind Glaxo-Wellcome plc, Novartis AG and Merck & Co. Inc. (Gallois, 1996*f*).

The absorption of Roussel-Uclaf by Hoechst AG raised the issue of the future of the anti-progesterone drug, RU 486 (mifépristone), developed by Roussel-Uclaf's biochemists in 1980. After publication of the first results on the contraceptive role of this molecule in 1983, RU 486 was authorized in France and China in 1987. Its first commercialization in 1988 was for a unique utilization: the medical alternative to a surgical interruption of pregnancy. In 1990, RU 486 was authorized in the United Kingdom and a year later in Sweden. The efficiency of RU 486, when associated with the administration of prostaglandins, was over 95%. The drug was available in the USA in 1997. It was estimated that several millions of women had interrupted their pregnancy through the administration of RU 486; one French woman out of four wishing to interupt their pregnancy had relied on this drug, following the advice of the medical team in charge of counselling women on the most appropriate solution to ending pregnancy.

For years, Hoechst's executives had been opposed to commercializing this drug; their attitude was based both on religious convictions and the fear of a boycott of Hoechst's products by anti-abortion organizations. In 1988, the German partners forced Roussel-Uclaf to discontinue the distribution of RU 486 in France but the French Government ordered that this commercialization be pursued (Gallois, 1996*f*). On 8 April 1997, Roussel-Uclaf and Hoechst AG announced their decision to stop producing RU 486 world-wide and to transfer without remuneration all their rights on this molecule to the former President of Roussel-Uclaf, Edouard Sakiz. The latter intended to create a company in charge of research and development on the contraceptive drug as well as of its production and commercialization.

After discussions with the French ministers of research, health and industry, Hoechst's executives committed their group to maintaining the research staff at Roussel-Uclaf, without excluding a reorientation of research. A foundation endowed with $44 million was set up to foster research programmes between HMR-France and universities. On the industrial side, all sites would be maintained, that in Compiègne, which was the main site of drug production in Europe for HMR, Romainville, near Paris, Neuville near Lyon and Vertolaye near Clermont-Ferrand, the two latter units being specialized in the production of raw materials for fine chemistry. On the social side, Roussel-Uclaf adopted the 35-hour working week without loss of salary and indicated that it would recruit 700 employees with open-ended contracts up to May 1999. Finally, the acquisition of Roussel-Uclaf was a good deal for its shareholders: since the beginning of 1996, the share had gained more than 70%, compared to 56% for other French groups such as Rhône-Poulenc, Sanofi and Synthélabo; the Roussel-Uclaf share had gained 150% of its value in July 1993 when Rhône-Poulenc sold its stake (35%) at a share price of 563FF (Gallois, 1996*f*).

The agricultural businesses of Hoechst AG and Schering AG had joined forces world-wide in 1994; they formed the joint venture AgrEvo AG. In North America, the company name was Hoechst-Nor-Am AgrEvo Company. The combined turnover of the new company was $2.3 billion and its research-and-development expenditure $200 million (i.e. 8%-10% of gross sales). As a result of the merger, AgrEvo AG had become the world's second-biggest manufacturer of crop protection products. The new company's global headquarters were in Frankfurt and the North American headquarters in Regina, Saskatchewan.

By mid-1996, AgrEvo AG acquired 95% of the Belgian biotechnology company, Plant Genetic Systems (PGS) N.V. This was the highest valuation ever placed on an agricultural biotechnology company. The combined research-and-development efforts of PGS and AgrEvo AG coupled with AgrEvo's strong market presence in the canola-growing regions of Canada, were expected to ensure market success for high-yielding hybrids, disease resistance, herbicide tolerance and other value-added traits in Canada's most important oilseed crop species.

PGS had rights to Basta-tolerance technology important to AgrEvo AG, which was using it in its herbicide-tolerance systems. Herbicide-tolerant canola was available in Canada and herbicide-tolerant maize was under joint development with Pioneer Hi-Bred International, Inc. and other maize-seed companies. PGS also gave AgrEvo AG access to hybridization technology (including hybrid oilseed rape already being commercialized).

In addition to purchasing PGS and acquiring 20.1% of the German biotechnology company, PlanTec AG, AgrEvo AG established co-operative agreements with Pioneer Hi-Bred International, Inc., Holden's Foundation Seeds, Cargill Inc., Limagrain (France), Hilleshög (Sweden) and KWS (Germany).

One could also cite the acquisition by the German chemical company BASF AG of the drug division of Boots, the leading British pharmaceutical distribution network. The four-month long negotiations concluded on 31 March 1995 on an agreed price of £840 million. This purchase placed the German corporation 30th among pharmaceutical groups in the world and broadened its range of prescribed drugs. In addition to being present in four areas (cardio-vascular, central nervous system, oncology and gastro-enterology drugs), BASF AG could now sell analgesic, anti-inflammatory, anti-depression drugs and a synthetic product to treat deficiencies of the thyroid gland (Gallois, 1995*f*).

The deal concerned not only prescription drugs, but also trademarks, research-and-development activities, production and distribution of the active substances. The annual turnover of BASF Pharma was expected to increase by 50%, from 2 to 3 billion Deutschemark (or about $2.1 billion) and 5,700 new employees were to join the group's 2,700 existing staff. The purchase would strengthen the position of BASF Pharma in the United Kingdom, USA, Spain and France. In the latter country, the German company was expected to hold 1% of the national pharmaceutical market, with annual sales of approximately $136 million (Gallois, 1995*f*).

Boots experienced difficulties in 1993 which forced it to withdraw a drug for treating heart disease from the market. After selling off its prescription drugs division, Boots focused activity on the distribution of body health-care products and comfort drugs (Gallois, 1995*f*).

In 1994, the French pharmaceutical group Sanofi[5] (see p. 243) was obliged to sell its biotechnological branch in order to purchase Sterling from Kodak and thus become a heavyweight among pharmaceutical groups with 1% of the world market. Consequently, in 1995, Sanofi had only two main branches: pharmacy (80% of annual turnover) and cosmetics (20%). In the latter sector, the company had come into the limelight at the beginning of by 1993 by purchasing Yves Saint Laurent. The group's president was determined to maintain the two branches to the point of excluding the hypothetical sacrifice of one to save the other. The 9 billion FF (about $1.8 billion) needed to purchase Sterling was a heavy burden for a group whose net profit amounted to some $300 million in 1994, but, in comparison to the amounts of money invested in similar mergers in the pharmaceutical sector, the funds needed to purchase Sterling were considered reasonable, due to the ties between Sanofi and Kodak. The two companies had indeed been linked since 1991, via the Alliance Sanofi Winthrop, so as to commercialize their prescription drugs throughout the world. The sale of Sanofi's biotechnology branch to the German firm VIAG and the abandonment of non-strategic activities had reduced the group's debt to 20% of its proper funds (Gallois and Gay, 1995).

With respect to the cosmetics branch, a number of non-strategic brands had been sold in 1994 and a long-term development strategy designed for the other brands. After a disappointing year for 1994, with an 8% drop in sales, and zero profits during the first half of 1996, Sanofi's President attributed this situation to the new trend toward multiplying quality products in mass distribution stores; consequently, only a few very well-known brands would remain profitable. Although Sanofi ranked among the top ten cosmetic groups in the world, it still had to struggle to make the profits expected of a group of its size (Galinier and Gallois, 1996).

The purchase of Sterling placed Sanofi on the U.S. market, as well as on the emerging Asian and Latin American markets. As the 24th group on the list of the leading pharmaceutical groups (in terms of annual turnover) in 1995–1996, but ranked tenth in terms of research funding ($600 million in 1995), Sanofi was member of the club of innovating companies producing new drugs. Indeed, after having invested between $3 billion and $4 billion in research over 15 years, Sanofi was coming close to its target in four drug areas: cardio-vascular thrombosis, central nervous system, osteoporosis and cancer (Gallois and Gay, 1995).

On 13 November 1996, Sanofi's executives announced the commercialization of a new preventive medicine called clopidogrel for certain common vascular diseases among high-risk groups. This statement was coincident with the publication on the same day in New Orleans of the results of an international study comparing the efficiency of clopidogrel with that of aspirin, generally used to prevent these diseases. These results were presented at the 1996 congress of the American Heart Association; they were the outcome of three years' work in 384 hospitals in 16 countries, involving 19,185 victims of a heart attack, cerebral vascular accident or an arteriopathy of inferior limbs. Often recurrent, these three diseases resulted from the presence in different places of the arterial system of obstructive lesions due to atheromas (i.e. deposits of lipids), which hindered blood circulation. The patients involved in the study received a daily dose of eitheir 325 mg of aspirin (i.e. the usual treatment to prevent recurrence of the disease) or 75 mg of clopidogrel (Nau, 1996*b*).

Both medicines had the property to prevent the aggregation of plaquettes which, in the presence of an atheroma, facilitated the formation of a blood clot or thrombus. The numerous studies conducted on aspirin demonstrated that this substance could reduce by about 27% the risk of heart or cerebro-vascular accidents. For obvious ethical reasons, Sanofi's new product could not be tested against a placebo, but the results presented in New Orleans showed it to be more efficient than aspirin: it could prevent about one-third of strokes and heart attacks, as well as arteriopathies of inferior limbs, whereas aspirin prevented only one-fourth of these affections, according to Sanofi's Director of Research and Development. In addition, the researchers in charge of the study, co-funded by Sanofi and the U.S. pharmaceutical group Bristol-Myers Squibb Co., stated that the efficiency of the new medicine was not altered by any side- effects relating to blood physiology. Only minor undesirable effects such as diarrhoea, skin eruptions and scratching, were observed (Nau, 1996*b*).

Sanofi requested authorization to commercialize the new drug in the USA and Europe at the beginning of 1997, in the hope that clopidogrel would be marketed in 1998. Although the cost of a treatment based on this new drug was not indicated, Sanofi mentioned that the research-and-development expenses amounted to between $260 million and $400 million, these being shared with Bristol-Myers Squibb Co. (Nau, 1996*b*).

While clinical studies on another new drug developed by Sanofi for treating osteoporosis were expected to be completed by the end of the first quarter of 1997, the French company had already obtained authorization to commercialize tiludronate for treating Paget's disease, which was due to bone proliferation. In addition, Sanofi had presented the files for registering a third new drug, this time against hypertension, irbesartan, with the European and U.S. relevant bodies at the end of September 1996. Sanofi's President stated that some 30 molecules of theirs were being submitted to human trials and that the company expected at least $1 billion from sales of clopidogrel, this figure being based on the sales of a similar product also used to prevent thrombosis. The U.S. market was the most promising one; hence the partnership with Bristol-Myers Squibb Co., as well as the purchase in the summer of 1996 of Bock, a U.S. laboratory, which doubled Sanofi's network of salespersons (Galinier and Gallois, 1996).

Sanofi's prospects for the year 2000 were bright. Its President stated that they had consolidated their presence on the international scene and whished to strengthen their position in each market without excluding alliances, whenever necessary, such as that with Bristol-Myers Squibb Co. Financially, the company possessed $4 billion in assets and a small debt. Sanofi, like other pharmaceutical groups, was hoping that its drugs would record large sales at world level, so as to enable it pursue expansion and fund research. That was why the company's President was not in favour of other acquisitions, nor of external growth. However, it would need money: firstly, in order to fund the development and marketing of new drugs; and secondly, in order to be present in other growth areas, e.g. through the purchase of competitor laboratories (Gallois and Gay, 1995). This strategy probably led Sanofi to sell its U.S. facilities for the production of injectable generic medicines (used in hospitals) to the U.S. pharmaceutical group Abbott in 1997 for $200 million. Sanofi's goal in the USA was to centre its activity on drugs sold in pharmacies following medical prescription.

On 20 October 1995, the French-American group Rhône-Poulenc Rorer (RPR)[6 (see p. 243)] held 67.2% of shares in the British pharmaceutical company, Fisons, after launching a public purchase offer in August 1995 of $2.86 billion. The aim of the purchase was to propulse RPR into fourth position among the world's leaders in the treatment of asthma and allergy. This costly external growth illustrated a change in the group's strategy: realizing that Rhône-Poulenc lacked the requisite billions of dollars to become one of the world's leading groups in chemistry and pharmacy, the President and his team had selected among the four fields of the group those activities where Rhône-Poulenc could become a leader. The acquisition of Fisons was to be followed by the lay off of 10% of employees (i.e. 2,900 persons) by the end of 1997 (1,600 in 1996) [Gallois, 1995*k*, 1996*a,b*].

On 9 May 1996, Rhône-Poulenc and the Danish Group Novo Nordisk announced their alliance for jointly commercializing substitution hormonal treatments, particularly those concerning the menopause. This commercialization concerned the whole world except Japan. In this pharmaceutical area, Novo Nordisk's annual turnover amounted to $148 million, thus placing it third in the world behind the U.S. group American Home Products Corp. and the Swiss Ciba-Geigy AG. Rhône-Poulenc, through this alliance, hoped to strengthen its capability for treating bone metabolism dysfunction (osteoporosis) and menopause.

In health care, concentration on specific drug-research areas preceded the acquisition of Rorer and these areas were to be stressed even more after the purchase of Fisons. RPR had invested £50 million for a period of seven years in the research carried out at Dagenham laboratories in the United Kingdom. The objective was to convert Dagenham site into a centre of excellence for research and development on asthma and inflammation. Also to pursue its search for new drugs, RPR concluded co-operative agreements with two well-known British research institutions: the University of Cambridge and The Imperial College, London. With an investment of £4 million over three years, this collaboration named TeknoMed aimed at developing techniques of combinatory chemistry and computer-assisted modelling (in *Biofutur*, no. 169, July-August 1997, pp. 41–42).

The Director-General of Rhône-Poulenc's pharmaceutical sector stated that 1995 had been a period of investment that should be followed by an acceleration in the sector's growth. Among the success stories, he mentioned the 20% average increase in sales of the top ten medicines sold by the company, the authorization by the European Union's health regulation bodies of taxotère (anti-cancer drug) and by the U.S. Food and Drug Administration of a medicine for the treatment of Charcot's disease (Gallois, 1996*a*).

In 1997, RPR's Australian subsidiary, Rhône-Poulenc Rorer (RPR) Australia, signed a research agreement with Amrad Discovery Technologies, Amrad's subsidiary, with a view to isolating potential drugs from natural substances to treat asthma and related diseases. Amrad agreed to use its data-base of natural product extracts, its screening know-how and its high technology for identifying potential drugs, while RPR was to contribute 15 million Australian dollars in exchange of having an exclusive access to purified plant extracts and some screening results. RPR also committed itself to supply more funds in case of discovery of interesting molecules and to transfer to Amrad royalties on future sales (in *Biofutur*, no. 169, July-August 1997, pp. 41–42).

Real success, indeed, would come with the discovery of new products and a better return rate. The latter was only 8% for Rhône-Poulenc Rorer, compared to more than 20% for the most efficient groups. That was why RPR was focusing on only a few areas: respiratory diseases, plasma proteins, oncology, infectious diseases and thrombosis (e.g. taxotère, anti-thrombotic lovenox and anti-infectious Synercide). In four years, the number of projects was halved and the time lapse for developing new products was shortened. These new products would generate about $2 billion in turnover over the 1995–2000 period; they would represent 30% of total sales in 2000, compared to 10% in 1995 (Gallois, 1996*g*).

On 19 December 1996, Rhône-Poulenc and Merck Agvet announced their intention to create a joint company on equal equity, which would combine the activities of each group relating to animal health and fowl genetics so as to become a world leader in this area. The new company, to be called Merial, would be operational by the second quarter of 1997; its initial annual turnover was estimatd at $1.7 billion.

An important aspect of Rhône-Poulenc's strategy was the decentralization process. For instance, to meet the new challenge concerning the group's position in Asia, all those interested in the region had been transferred from Courbevoie, near Paris, to Singapore. The objective was to double the annual turnover in Asia by the year 2000 to 15%-18% of RP's total turnover (Gallois, 1995*k*).

Efforts were being made to ensure a predominant position on the pesticides market for rice cultivation. Viet Nam, the world's third-biggest rice exporter behind the USA and Thailand, was among the first Asian countries to authorize the use of RP's Fipronil. The successful marketing of this pesticide would influence RP's position in Asia, where Hoechst AG (via AgrEvo AG), the British Zeneca plc and the Swiss Ciba-Geigy AG were already well established. In Viet Nam, RP was better known through its pharmaceutical products, with the presence of its subsidiary, Specia, dating back to 1935. Specia's plant near Ho Chi Minh City was being entirely renovated and an agreement had been concluded with the Vietnamese Government for the construction of a factory north of Hanoi for the production of nylon thread for tyres (Gallois, 1995*l*).

The French pharmaceutical company Synthélabo had signed a partnership agreement with the biotechnology company Genset, established in Paris in 1989 and specializing in human DNA sequencing. This entailed a $10 million subscription to Genset's capital, i.e. 4% of its total capital, and a contribution of $71 million to fund research on genes involved in prostatic cancer, with the objective of developing new drugs. The three-year agreement stipulated that, should a discovery be made, Genset would own the patents and Synthélabo would be the exclusive licensee. This was the second collaborative agreement to be signed by Synthélabo, which had been working with the U.S. company, Texas Biotechnology since 1994 on developing cardio-vascular medicines (Gallois, 1996*c*).

Genset whose objective was to systematically, rapidly and efficiently identify a great number of human genes and regulating regions associated with common diseases, was using an integrated approach based on four key gene technologies: high-resolution gene mapping, DNA sequencing and synthesis, and bio-informatics. In 1996, the company went public on the new market of Paris Stock Exchange and the U.S. Nasdaq (for about $103 million). During the first quarter of 1997, its turnover amounted to $3.02 million, a 84% increase over the turnover recorded one year earlier for the same period. Its research-and-development expenses also doubled in 1997, reaching $6.3 million, due to the opening of its mapping laboratory and the expansion of its high-sequencing unit. Consequently, the sequencing capacity of the company was expected to jump from 3 million bases a day to 10 million bases a day by the end of 1997 (in *Biofutur*, no. 169, July-August 1997, p. 39).

A world leader in synthetic DNA, Genset set up its data-base, SignalTag, and concluded a preliminary agreement with France's National Institute for Health and Medical Research (INSERM), with a view to creating a joint laboratory of physiology and molecular pathology. Genset was also expanding its world network for collecting human DNA samples to Israel and Argentina, in order to gather DNA samples from patients suffering from common diseases or mental disorders (in *Biofutur*, no. 169, July-August 1997, p. 39).

All these initiatives would enable Genset to have a dominant position on the genomic market by the beginning of the next century, a goal which implied new partnerships. In addition to its two industrial partners, Synthélabo (for the identification of the genes associated with prostatic cancer) and Johnson & Johnson-Ortho Pharmaceutical Corp. (for the identification of genes involved in schizophrenia), Genset was about to sign agreements with two other partners in 1997. The French company also wanted to patent not only its technologies and processes, but also the genes associated with common diseases (in *Biofutur*, no. 169, July-August 1997, p. 39).

This latter approach was not shared by its public competitor, the National Centre for DNA Sequencing, which started its operations by mid-1997. The Centre's Director was of the opinion that national centres should not apply for patents. This new centre was expected to fill a gap by entrusting the public sector with a research-and-development capacity in DNA sequencing and bio-informatics, which was hereto prevailing in the private sector (in *Biofutur*, no. 169, July-August 1997, p. 39).

The strategy of the American pharmaceutical group, Eli Lilly & Co., as presented by its president on 26 June 1995 in Paris, aimed to focus research on a limited number of diseases, enhance the group's presence throughout the world and strengthen partnerships and alliances. The group also planned to make some acquisitions so as to be present in all health areas. In 1994, Eli Lilly & Co., after reorientating its activities and reducing staff numbers, recorded its best results in 25 years: with the company moving up to 13th among the world's leading pharmaceutical groups, shares jumped by 60% and sales by 10%; turnover rose by 30% during the first quarter of 1995 (Gallois, 1995*i*).

Current research-and-development priorities concerned the central nervous system, endocrinian diseases, infectious diseases, cancer and cardio-vascular illnesses. In 1995, Eli Lilly & Co. was awaiting authorization to market in the USA a drug (Gemzar) against pancreas cancer. In the search for an effective treatment against Alzheimer's disease, Eli Lilly & Co.'s researchers had succeeded in genetically transforming mice displaying brain lesions characteristic of the disease; this research was being carried out in collaboration with some twenty biotechnology laboratories. Funding for this endeavour could come from the sales of Prozac, an anti-depressive drug, which represented about one-third of the company's total sales: $2 billion of a $7 billion total in 1994 (Gallois, 1995*i*).

The international development of Eli Lilly & Co. was being pursued with special emphasis on activities outside the USA, which represented 42.5% of total sales in 1994. The group's presence was becoming stronger in Eastern Europe and South America. France ranked third behind the USA and Japan, with an annual turnover of about $600 million and 1,300 employees in 1994; the American group owned, in Fegersheim, in Alsace, production facilities for manufacturing injectable products as cartridges and recombinant human insulin (Gallois, 1995*i*).

The group's international development was accompanied by the purchase in 1994 of the management firm, PCS Health Systems, for $4 billion; this acquisition gained Eli Lilly & Co. access to a data-base linking all physicians and chemists throughout the USA and enabled the group to monitor prescriptions delivered to about 60 million people. According to the president nominated in 1993, the convergence of health and information technologies would help the group anticipate needs and prevent certain diseases (Gallois, 1995*i*).

On 9 October 1995, the Swedish Federation of Shareholders, which mainly comprised small holders, approved the merger between the Swedish company Pharmacia AB and the U.S. corporation The Upjohn Co. of Kalamazoo (Michigan), thus giving birth to the world's ninth-biggest pharmaceutical group ($5.2 billion in annual turnover). Both the car-manufacturing corporation Volvo (holding 27.5% of Pharmacia AB's shares) and the Swedish State (14.1%) supported the merger. The new group, Pharmacia & Upjohn Inc., announced the closure of 40% of its industrial sites between 1996 and 2000, in order to make savings of about $400 million and reduce the research budget by 20%. On 6 January 1997, the new group sold its veterinary vaccine division to the German chemical and pharmaceutical company, Bayer AG. The transaction included the research-and-production facilities, manufacturing units, licensing rights and a diagnostic laboratory. By purchasing these, Bayer AG aimed to hold 10% of the U.S. animal health market in 2000, compared to 5% in early 1997.

However, despite the efforts made to cut costs and expand product breadth, investors were jarred by declining sales and earnings. On 23 April 1997, first-quarter earnings had dropped 16% due to unfavourable foreign exchange transactions, weak European markets and competition in the USA. Analysts reported that the company suffered from cultural clashes between the company's world-wide operations, including major research-and-development centres in Sweden, Italy and Michigan. This problems might have slowed the development of new drugs. In order to overcome these difficulties and to rebuild the investors' confidence, the former executive vice-president of American Home Products Corp. was appointed as President and chief executive of Pharmacia & Upjohn Inc. F. Hassan, the new President, had extensive international experience, including the development of American Home Products Corp.'s pan-European business strategy and building its presence in the Asia-Pacific region. He integrated American Cyanamid Co. into American Home Products Corp. in 1994 (*Bangkok Post*, 13 May 1997, p. 11). On 10 June 1997, the merger of Pharmacia & Upjohn Inc.'s subsidiary Pharmacia Biotech with its British counterpart, Amersham plc, to constitute Amersham Pharmacia Biotech, poised to become the world's second-biggest company specialized in biotechnological equipment and tools, was considered a good sign toward strengthening the U.S.-Swedish group.

On 6 November 1995, Johnson and Johnson-Ortho Pharmaceutical Corp. (no.7 among the world's leading pharmaceutical groups) signed a merger agreement with Cordis, a U.S. company manufacturing medical equipment and devices; the agreement, which valued Cordis at $1.8 billion, would put Johnson and Johnson in possession of a complete range of devices used in blood-vessel surgery (angioplasty).

The merger announced on 7 March 1996 of the Swiss pharmaceutical group Ciba-Ceigy AG (born in 1970 from the fusion of Ciba and J.R. Geigy) and its competitor Sandoz AG (the second-biggest Swiss pharmaceutical corporation) ushered in one of the greatest industrial merger of the century. It outshone the $25 billion purchase of the U.S. agro-food group RJR Nabisco by the raider Kohlberg Kravis Roberts (KKR) in 1989. It outstripped both the 1995 merger between Walt Disney and Capital Cities-ABC ($19 billion) and that of Glaxo and Wellcome ($15 billion). The biggest merger of the century was announced on 15 December 1996 between Boeing and McDonnell Douglas. The alliance between the two U.S. aeronautic companies gave birth to the world's biggest and most diversified aerospatial group and by far the greatest U.S. exporter. The figures spoke for themselves: about 200,000 employees for the new group, factories in 26 U.S. States, a turnover of $48 billion in 1997, a list of orders totalling $100 billion (by the end of 1996) and about three-fourths of the world market for civic aeroplanes.

The new group, Novartis AG, became the world's second-biggest pharmaceutical group, behind Glaxo plc, and streets ahead of the seventh-ranked Swiss pharmaceutical company, Roche AG. An annual turnover of $30 billion included $11.8 billion from pharmaceuticals (Leparmentier and Orange, 1996).

On 7 March 1996, at the Zurich Stock Exchange, the values of Ciba-Ceigy AG and Sandoz AG shares jumped by 28.4% and 19.6% respectively. The cumulative stock value of the two groups rose to 94 billion Swiss Francs, i.e. about $79 billion. Pharmaceuticals were expected to represent 59% of the annual turnover of Novartis AG, which would hold 4.4% of the world market. Phytosanitary and veterinary products would represent 27% of Novartis AG's sales, thus making it the world leader in this area, nutritional products constituting a further 14% of sales (Leparmentier and Orange, 1996).

Sandoz AG's shareholders would hold 55% of Novartis AG's shares, those of Ciba-Geigy AG holding the remainder. The merger was another striking example of the concentration the pharmaceutical industry had been undergoing since 1993. This was indeed true of most industrial sectors: size had become the obsession of managers and top executives, who had to cope with the so-called deregulation and globalization of business and trade. In pharmaceuticals, as in armaments, aeronautics or finance, all global markets, profits were amputated by harsh competition and the struggle to control a significant part of the world's market demanded huge investments. Concentration generated its own logic: companies or groups intent on remaining among the leaders were doomed to become giants. Thus the merger between Ciba-Geigy AG and Sandoz AG came in response to the acquisition of Wellcome by Glaxo plc in 1995 (Leser, 1996).

Since January 1995, European pharmaceutical groups had carried out eight major regrouping or merging operations for a value of more than $26 billion, in addition to a dozen operations of lesser magnitude, in order to broaden their drug portfolios. In every case, the same reasons were advanced: the need to pool resources in order to finance the soaring cost of research and development, each new pharmaceutical requiring an average investment of $200 million to $400 million. On the other hand, efforts by the world's governments to decrease health care expenses and the corresponding budget were pruning the profits of pharmaceutical groups, forcing them either to merge or drastically restructure their production services (Leparmentier and Orange, 1996).

Sandoz AG and Ciba-Geigy AG had been suffering from their average size over recent years; each had sold conventional products and boasted few innovative molecules; they had also faced competition from generic products, which copied successful and innovative drugs whose patent protection had come to an end. To remedy this, the new group, Novartis AG, was intending to invest more than 2 billion Swiss Francs in research and development and to launch 17 new products at least from 1996 to 1999. Furthermore, the merger was expected to lead to strong synergy in terms of research on new drugs, commercialization and presence on promising markets (Leparmentier and Orange, 1996).

In addition, on 15 October 1996, the leading European distributor of medicines, the German company Gehe, confirmed the sale of its subsidiaries manufacturing generic drugs. The subsidiary Azupharma, purchased by Sandoz AG for 1.2 billion Deutschemarks ($800 million) was to be included in Novartis AG, which would become the world leading manufacturer of generic drugs. The French subsidiary GNR Pharma had been purchased by the German group BASF AG.

The merger of Sandoz AG and Ciba-Geigy AG had an immediate impact on the redeployment of activities in areas where success was feasible. In 1995, Sandoz AG did away with its chemical branch by making it public under the name of Clariant; Ciba-Geigy AG was following the same path for its chemical activities, the new independent society having been introduced on the Zurich Stock Exchange and its shares distributed to Novartis AG shareholders. Sandoz AG had also decided either to sell its branch of chemical materials used in construction or to introduce it onto the Stock Exchange. All these measures focused on making Novartis AG a leader in the pharmaceutical sector (Leparmentier and Orange, 1996).

This objective was to be achieved thanks to previous agreements and partnerships concluded by Sandoz Pharmaceuticals (E. Hanover, New Jersey). The latter had commited to invest up to $100 million over ten years in oncology research at the Dana-Farber Cancer Institute (Boston); to provide Scripps Research Institute (La Jolla, California) with research funding of more than $300 million over ten years beginning in 1997, giving Sandoz first rights to Scripps Research Institute's medical discoveries. Sandoz and Scripps, with a research staff of over 650 Ph.Ds and M.Ds, had been undertaking joint research projects over the period 1993–1997 on immunology, central nervous system disorders, and cardio-vascular diseases. Sandoz also reviewed its collaboration with Cytel (San Diego, California) through an additional $5 million investment in Cytel, with a view to focusing on the development of therapies against chronic infectious diseases and cancers. Sandoz underscored its expansion in transplantation and gene therapy through its acquisition of 60% of SyStemix (Palo Alto, California) and its collaboration with Genetic Therapy Inc. (Gaithersburg, Maryland) and Bio-Transplant (Boston) [in *Bio/Technology*, vol. 11, no. 1, January 1993, p. 13].

The 1996 fourth-quarter results of Novartis AG confirmed that the group remained, with the London-based pharmaceutical and agrochemical group Zeneca plc, among Europe's fastest growing drug manufacturers. These results augured well for 1997.

Reporting full-year results as a single company for the first time, Novartis AG's 1996 revenue edged up 0.8% to 36.23 billion Swiss Francs ($25.34 billion). The 1996 net income, excluding non-recurring income and expenses, was roughly 4.2 billion Swiss Francs. Sales at Novartis AG drug division climbed nearly 16% during the fourth-quarter of 1996, although currency fluctuations accounted for about 10 percentage points of that increase. Several successful drugs inherited from Sandoz AG posted stellar double-digit growth. By contrast, sales of Ciba-Geigy AG's no. 1 drug, the anti-arthritic Voltaren, declined due to fierce competition from generic versions in the USA. Sales at Novartis AG remaining core life-science divisions rose 8% in 1996 to 27.6 billion Swiss Francs, with currency fluctuations accounting for two percentage points of the increase. During the fourth-quarter, sales from life-science divisions spurted nearly 15% – double the rate for 1996 first nine months – although the majority of the increase was currency-related, according to analysts (*The Wall Street Journal Europe*, 29 January 1997, p. 3).

Reaffirming earlier projections, Novartis AG reported that one-time merger-related expenses of 3.5 billion Swiss Francs, partially offset by 1.5 billion Swiss Francs in exceptional gains, were included in 1996 accounts to finance a three-year cost-cutting blitz expected to eliminate approximately 10,000 jobs and shave annual costs by 2 billion Swiss Francs by the end of 1998. Analysts expected about one-third of those cost-savings to materialize during 1997, giving a big boost to pretax profit growth. Judging from 1996 fourth-quarter figures, profitability would also be propelled by strong revenue expansion, analysts added (*The Wall Street Journal Europe*, 29 January 1997, p. 3).

Another example of the concentration wave was the purchase of the Austrian company, Immuno, by the U.S. firm Baxter on 29 August 1996. The cost of this purchase amounted to almost $700 million over three years and made the new group the world leader in products and services for blood transfusion, with an annual turnover estimated at $1.6 billion and a staff of 8,000 world-wide. Baxter-Immuno was therefore bigger than Centeon, the company formed in 1995 by Rhône-Poulenc Rorer and Hoechst AG, which held 24% of the world market with an annual turnover of $1 billion. The new group was expected to sell a wide range of products for transfusion therapies, including biotechnology-derived products, manufactured in its factories located in Europe and the USA and generated by research around the world. In September 1996, the U.S. group split into two companies: Baxter International specialized in the manufacture of medical products (including those of Immuno) and Allegiance, in charge of both distributing analytical products and surgical equipment, and the services responsible for managing medical costs (Gallois, 1996*d*).

The Swiss company, Roche Holding Ltd., the third-biggest among the Basel-based groups, had been focusing its activities on the pharmaceutical sector for the last decade, leaving aside electronics, for instance. When Roche Holding Ltd. acquired the U.S. company, Syntex, in 1994, for $5.3 billion, it overtook Ciba-Geigy AG in the pharmaceutical sector to rank among the world leaders (ranked seventh in 1996). Roche Holding Ltd. did not escape restructurations and the lay-off of 5,000 employees, the number of salaried workers dropping to 50,000 world-wide in 1997. With the development of new products, Roche Holding Ltd. was expecting to hold 4% of the world's pharmaceutical market, a threshold considered the critical proportion by specialists. In 1996, Roche Holding Ltd.'s annual turnover amounted to 16 billion Swiss Francs, i.e. some $12.8 billion, and its profits reached 3.9 billion Swiss Francs (Buhrer, 1996; Gallois, 1997*b*).

On 22 January 1997, Roche Holding Ltd.'s shares surged 7% on speculation that it could be poised to sell its underperforming Givaudan-Roure fragrances and flavourings division. The latter was the one unit that fit least into the company's strategy. The proceeds could be added to the company's $10 billion war chest for a major purchase, according to analysts. Roche Holding Ltd. could put together financing of $20 billion more if it wanted to acquire a company. For several years, British Zeneca plc, Warner-Lambert Co. in the USA and Sweden's Astra AB had jumped with the view that Roche Holding Ltd. could be looking at buying them.

On 26 May 1997, Roche Holding Ltd. announced the purchase of the German pharmaceutical company Boehringer Mannheim AG and the U.S. orthopedic firm DePuy Inc. for a total of $11 billion. Boehringer Mannheim AG was a family group founded in 1859, owned by Corange Ltd, a holding registered in Bermudas and with headquarters in Amsterdam; it was the fourth German pharmaceutical company and the 25th in the world, specialized in diagnostics (world's second-biggest group), employing 18,000 persons; its 1996 turnover was $3.4 billion. DePuy Inc., based in the State of Delaware, was the world's second-biggest company in orthopedic products; it was a 84.2% subsidiary of Corange Ltd, employing 2,900 persons; its 1996 turnover amounted to $700 million. This merging was expected to give birth to the world leading group specialized in diagnostics: the new group, Roche Boehringer Mannheim Diagnostics, was expected to have 13,500 employees and an annual turnover of about $3 billion. This conglomerate ranked seventh among the world leading pharmaceutical groups (Gallois, 1997*b*).

Roche Holding Ltd. was already well known for its diagnostic tests (it had a dominant position in the polymerase chain reaction -PCR-technology), whereas Boehringer Mannheim AG was Europe's leading group and the world's second-biggest one behind the U.S. company, Abbott, for reagents, automated devices and clinical biology equipment; it had been a pioneer in the self-monitoring of diabetes, which enabled a patient to monitor his/her glycemia and adapt the treatment. In addition to these activities which represented two-thirds of its annual turnover, Boehringer Mannheim AG was involved in the development of medicines against cardio-vascular diseases, cancer, bone and infectious diseases; there were some promising drugs such as Ibandronate for the prevention and treatment of osteoporosis. These products were considered complementary to those of Roche Holding Ltd. The objective of the merger was thus to offer the most appropriate combination of products to treat a disease in an integrated way. This new approach to disease management and patient care fit with the need to optimize health costs. The merger was expected to lead to strengthening the presence of Roche Holding Ltd. in Germany and Italy, as well as in Latin America (Gallois, 1997*b*).

The purchase by Roche Holding Ltd. of Boehringer Mannheim AG and DePuy Inc. was, in terms of funding, the third-biggest after the fusion of Ciba-Geigy AG and Sandoz AG in March 1996, and the purchase of Wellcome by Glaxo plc in January 1995. Analysts were of the opinion that the concentration wave in the pharmaceutical sector was not over, because after two years of mergers the first leading groups were holding each only 5% of the world pharmaceutical market (Gallois, 1997*b*).

Acquisitions and mergers were synonymous with major staff lay-offs. For instance, in January 1995, American Home Products Corp. (which ranked 5th among the world's pharmaceutical and health groups, with sales worth $6.5 billion in 1994), announced the suppression of 4,000 posts in the USA and around the world, following the purchase of American Cyanamid Co. (Gallois, 1995a). By the end of 1995, Roussel-Uclaf was negotiating a 10% reduction in staff (250–300 employees) at headquarters, the group Hoechst-Marion-Roussel aiming to shrink its staff from 45,000 to 37,000.

Ciba-Geigy AG had some 83,000 employees (including 15,000 in the USA) and Sandoz AG about 60,000. Novartis AG had announced the abolition of more than 10,000 of these posts. This was of major concern to political authorities of the Basel region, where chemical and pharmaceutical industries provided employment for many people; since 1990, several restructurations within these industries had led to the loss of 4,000 posts. It was not therefore surprising that the authorities had seen fit to remind Novartis AG of its full social responsibilities (Buhrer, 1996).

The same trend toward mergers or concentration, not to mention new partnerships, could be observed among chemical groups, which announced an improvement in their financial situation in 1994–1995 after four years of severe crisis. This was particularly true for the European groups, which were world leaders: more than half of the top 30 chemical companies were European and, of the ten world leaders, seven were European (three German, two French, one British and one Swiss) [Gallois, 1995g].

The concentration wave was affecting agrochemical groups, e.g. on 13 May 1997, Novartis AG purchased Merck & Co. Inc.'s division of phytosanitary products for $1.04 billion; on 14 May 1997, the U.S. company Dow Chemical acquired the 40% participation of Eli Lilly & Co. in the agrochemical firm Dow Elanco, spending $1.2 billion for this purpose and holding the whole capital of the firm. It also concerned the specialty chemicals market, estimated at about $80 billion in 1997, very fragmented and comprising some 40 companies. In December 1996, after the alliance between Hoechst AG and the Swiss company Clariant AG (ex Sandoz AG), which entailed a $3.7 billion transaction and the purchase by Hoechst AG of 45% of Clariant AG's capital, propelling the new group at the first world rank, the British ICI Ltd overtook it after buying, on 7 May 1997, Unilever N.V.'s activities relating to adhesives, aromas and fragrances, starches, etc., for about $9.2 billion. The objective for all these companies was to acquire a global size on very profitable markets which, in contrast to heavy chemistry, were not submitted to the vagaries of economic cycles. Specialty chemicals (e.g. adhesives, polymers, pigments) which were included in a wide range of products to improve their characteristics or optimize transformation processes, were manufactured in relatively small quantities and were very profitable (Gallois, 1997c).

Like in the health sector, mergers in chemistry occurred between groups of the same country or of close kinship. Thus, in specialty chemicals, the German company Veba AG became the first shareholder of the chemical group Degussa AG (36.4% of the whole capital) by investing $1.8 billion on 21 May 1997. Similarly, Hoechst AG brought its specialty chemicals activity to its Swiss neighbour, Ciba-Geigy AG. It should also be noted that an acquisition could be the only way to save a group which was designing a new industrial strategy. Thus, in 1993, ICI Ltd was the first chemical group which decided to split into two societies: Zeneca plc, centred on pharmacy, and ICI Ltd focused on chemistry. While the pharmaceutical branch was thriving, the chemical company was losing money due to its reliance on basic chemicals, submitted to economic cycles. ICI Ltd had therefore to change its strategy and strengthen its specialty chemicals branch (Gallois, 1997*c*). By mid-1997, ICI Ltd sold several subsidiaries of its Industrial Chemicals Division to the U.S. group DuPont de Nemours & Co., Inc. for £1.8 billion. This transaction was part of ICI Ltd strategy to focus on specialty chemicals, while withdrawing from low-profit chemicals, and to be able to finance the purchase of Unilever N.V.'s specialty chemicals subsidiaries.

Conversely, the participation of Veba AG in Degussa AG's capital was considered an operation among members of the same family. Veba AG acquired 36.4% of Degussa AG's capital which were in the hands of Henkel, Dresdner Bank and Munich Ré. This acquisition, financed by Veba AG's proper funds, was expected to enable the new group to hold an important position in the processing of precious metals and pharmacy (Gallois, 1997*c*).

Both Clariant AG and Ciba-Geigy Spécialités chimiques were doing well in 1997, with a strong growth in Asia, a good status in the USA and some hesitation in Europe. These results were justifying the strategy consisting of pursuing concentration and internationalization of the groups (Gallois, 1997*c*).

Contrary to the Swiss chemical groups, the German ones (Hoechst AG, Bayer AG and BASF AG) had been strongly hit by the recession of the early 1990s; furthermore, they were penalized by the valuation of the Deutschemark and confronted both with the need to integrate the chemical industry of former East Germany and with the lower wages paid by their foreign competitors. German groups were less competitive because of their high salaries, the cost of energy and the constraints imposed by strict legislation on environmental protection. This had led to massive staff layoffs and large-scale restructuration, measures that were to prove insufficient for climbing back to the prerecession profitability levels of the late 1980s (Gallois, 1995*g*). However, in 1996, Bayer AG's annual turnover rose 9% to 48.6 billion Deutschemarks and net profits reached 2.7 billion Deutschemarks (about $1.86 billion), a 13.5% increase over that of 1995.

BASF AG had been forced to reduce staff from 130,000 to 100,000 throughout the world, the most affected sites being the group's German factories. Furthermore, efforts had been made to transfer production to other countries, with the result that the turnover proportion in Germany was expected to decrease (Gallois, 1995*h*).

In order to improve the productivity and profitability of its factories, BASF AG was trying to concentrate several types of manufacturing on the same site, rather than multiplying the facilities. This strategy resulted in $700 million savings in its three European sites, Germany, Belgium and Spain. On 29 April 1997, BASF AG announced the breakdown of its production of inks and paints in Europe in three societies, so as to facilitate alliances or acquisitions. This restructuration was part of the optimization of BASF AG's non-cyclical activities initiated in the early 1990s and centred on five major areas: health and food, pigments, chemicals, plastics and fibres, and oil and gas. During that period, BASF AG had made more than 60 acquisitions, alliances or changes in investment, while at the same time concentrating its production on 'integrated industrial platforms'. For instance, on the Antwerpen site, in Belgium, 50 chemical facilities were located so that energy was used in an optimal way. Three integrated industrial platforms existed in Europe (Ludwigshafen, BASF AG headquarters; Antwerpen; and Tarragona in Spain), in addition to smaller production units (Gallois, 1997*a*).

This concept of integrated development was also prevailing in Asia. Over the five-year period 1997–2001, BASF AG was planning to invest 10 to 12 billion Deutschemarks with its local partners (including 8 billion from BASF AG itself) to build such integrated industrial platforms in Malaysia (Kuantan) and China (Nanjing). However, despite an 8% annual growth of the gross domestic product in South-East Asia, Europe, with an estimated market value of 600 billion Deutschemarks, remained the most important world market in chemicals, representing the double of that of South and East Asia (excluding Japan). BASF AG was therefore making 63% of its annual turnover in Europe, compared to 25% in North and South America and 12% in Asia (Gallois, 1997*a*).

In 1997, only activities relating to health-food and oil-gas had a two-digit growth rate of their sales, thus trebling or even quadrupling their results. These sectors altogether made up 30% of BASF AG's whole activity and 35% of its profits. In gas trade, BASF AG was a major actor in Germany and was prepared to the liberalization of the European Union market. In partnership with the Russian giant company, Gazprom, in the Wingas group, BASF AG was holding 10% of the market and was hoping to win 15%. The year 1997 was to be an exceptional year when the annual turnover of 50 billion Deutschemarks would be superseded, compared to 48.8 billion Deutschemarks in 1996 and a historical profit of 2.7 billion Deutschemarks (Gallois, 1997*a*).

The spreading of knowledge on genetic engineering and the availability of services and equipment facilitated the entry of developing countries' firms into the field of biotechnologies applied to the development of pharmaceuticals. The development of biotechnological capabilities was the result of adequately articulating human resources training, research-and-development, selecting products and building up productive facilities and marketing networks. Consequently, efforts to train scientists and technicians, as well as the design and implementation of research-and-development projects, would not pay off without the entrepreneurial ability to select products and market them at the right time at competitive rates (Correa, 1991*b*).

The selection of products for development and production was a critical issue. It had a strong impact on the amount of return, which depended on the type of product envisaged: products expected to replace similar bioproducts already on the market, but with advantages in terms of safety or availability (e.g. insulin, factor VIII, human growth hormone); products competing with chemically synthesized pharmaceuticals (e.g. atrial natriuretic factor); totally new products competing with other bioproducts (e.g. tissue plasminogen activator, streptokinase, urokinase); and totally new and exceptional products, such as interferons and interleukin-2 (Cometta, 1989).[7 (see p. 248)] Another important factor was whether the product was to be sold as bulk material (e.g. human serum albumin) in large quantities, or whether it was a high value-added compound with a smaller market, as in the case of interferons and factor VIII. The largest market was expected for anti-tumour agents, for which there were no alternative products, and for blood proteins (Correa, 1991*b*).

The short-term effect of medical biotechnologies lay in diagnostics. Biotechnology-derived diagnostic kits, based on monoclonal antibodies and molecular biology techniques, were replacing time-consuming and often relatively inaccurate conventional diagnostics.

For developing countries, the costs incurred in entering the biopharmaceutical market were particularly high if the original development of a biotechnology-derived product was sought. They might be more affordable if an imitative or licensing pathway was followed. The process was nevertheless facilitated by the wider dissemination of basic knowledge and access to biological materials (e.g. cloned genes, expression vectors, recombinant viruses) at a reasonable cost. Also, the price of some inputs, like restriction enzymes, synthetic nucleotides and nucleic acid probes, had fallen significantly. Cloning of genes upon request had become affordable for a small fee, as had DNA sequencing. When developing countries' firms had a highly qualified staff in contact with foreign research institutions and good access to published scientific information, satisfactory results could be obtained in the development of biotechnology-derived pharmaceuticals. As in the case of other advanced technological undertakings, the overall industrial infrastructure, including equipment maintenance, good technical staff, a reliable water and energy supply and cold transportation and storage facilities, were important to ensure successful and efficient production.

The involvement of developing countries in biotechnology-derived drug development and production should also take into account urgent public health needs, which were not necessarily tackled in the developed countries, e.g. bacteria-provoked dysenteries, cholera, typhoid fever and amoebic dysentry, together accounting for approximately 20 million deaths per year (Correa, 1991a,*b*).

4. Examples of medical biotechnology applications in developing countries

There are examples of sucessful achievements in biotechnologies applied to drug and vaccine production, and public health in developing countries.

In Argentina, in the late 1970s, the management of the Instituto Sidus, a national pharmaceutical enterprise founded in 1938, decided to delve into biotechnological research. In 1980, the Area of Biotechnology of the Instituto Sidus was created with the entrepreneurial support of Sidus and the contribution of an important group of scientists from the University of Buenos Aires. A special laboratory ($1 million invested in equipment) was then created, with cell culture, genetic engineering and protein purification facilities and equipment close to the pharmacological facilities for easy maintenance. In 1982, the company initiated production of leucocyte alpha-interferon, while benefiting from assistance from the Central Public Health Laboratory in Helsinki (which had developed a technique for producing interferon from leukocytes without any genetic engineering). The Argentine firm had succeeded in improving the purification process, reducing (ten-fold) the volume of processed substances and increasing overall productivity. The choice of interferon was a key factor in the laboratory's evolution, since it facilitated the exploration of novel manufacturing processes and the further development of molecular biology and genetic recombination techniques.

In 1983, successful technological and productive achievements led to the creation of BioSidus S.A. as an autonomous enterprise; the effective production of human leukocyte alpha-interferon was followed by highly purified leukocyte interferon for injectable use and by the attempts made to produce recombinant interferon. In 1987, the scientific and technical staff of BioSidus S.A. was awarded the Prize for innovations in biotechnology. In 1989, the company inaugurated its high-technology plant in Almagro, City of Buenos Aires; occupying 3,600 m^2 of covered surface area, it was equipped with the latest in instrumentation and strictly followed world-wide consensus regulations regarding biosafety. Using a genetically-engineered bacterium for the continuous production of interferon in a small bioreactor, production costs could be reduced markedly. Scaling up production was not difficult in this case, the difference between the pilot stage volume and production phase volume being insignificant (one and five litres respectively).

In Argentina, where five research groups had been working on erythropoietin and erythropoiesis since the 1950s, BioSidus S.A. began developing a recombinant human erythropoietin (Hemax) in 1990 within a joint venture with the U.S. company Elanex, only a year before effecting the country's first clinical trial. In August 1991, the company produced and commercialized Hemax, the first recombinant protein manufactured in Argentina. Later on, the recombinant human alpha-2 interferon was commercialized under the trademark Bioferon. Human leukocyte alpha-interferon, recombinant human alpha-2 interferon, bovine superoxide dismutase and recombinant human erythropoietin testified to the good results already obtained and to promising achievements. BioSidus S.A. could rely on the sales network of its parent company; although its experience and scope were limited to the domestic market, it was exploring export possibilities with some success (Correa, 1991*b*).

In addition, Bercovich *et al.* (1994) were able to clone and express the gene for human growth hormone in *Escherichia coli*; the hormone (a 191-amino-acid protein) was found in the periplasmic fraction of the transformed bacterial cells (in *Abstracts Biolatina 94, Second Latin*

American Congress of Biotechnology and First Argentinian Congress of Biotechnology, Buenos Aires, p. 74).

Similar results were obtained by Glikin *et al.* (1994) with respect to the expression in *E. coli* of a synthetic gene coding for the human epidermal growth factor (hEGF), which is a strong inhibitor of gastric secretion and which stimulates the proliferation of epithelial cells. It was used in the treatment of cornea ulcers, duodenum ulcers and skin diseases. The recombinant EGF was purified through affinity columns containing monoclonal antibodies against it. The purity of the product was confirmed by its amino-acid sequencing (in *Abstracts Biolatina 94, Second Latin American Congress of Biotechnology and First Argentinian Congress of Biotechnology*, Buenos Aires, p. 80).

Melo and Judewicz (1994) succeeded in cloning and expressing the gene for interleukin-4 in *E. coli*; the recombinant lymphokin represented up to 10%-15% of the total protein content of the bacterial cells. Produced by T-lymphocytes (CD4+), interleukin-4 was responsible for the production of immunoglobulins IgE and Igl in B-lymphocytes and acted as a growth factor in T-cells and mastocytes. Conversely, it inhibited the growth of macrophages and seemed to have an anti-tumour effect (in *Abstracts Biolatina 94, Second Latin American Congress of Biotechnology and First Argentinian Congress of Biotechnology*, Buenos Aires, p. 89).

Finally, Melo *et al.* (1994) could clone and express the gene for the human granulocyte colony stimulating factor (hG-CSF) in Chinese hamster ovary (CHO) cells. The concentration of the recombinant factor amounted to 10 mg per litre of culture. In addition, the factor was purified in affinity columns containing monoclonal antibodies against it and its biological activity was tested *in vitro* on a susceptible cell line. This factor was a peptide which activated the proliferation of precursors of neutrophiles and was very effective in treating neutropenia and cancer patients receiving cytostatic drugs (in *Abstracts Biolatina 94, Second Latin American Congress of Biotechnology and First Argentinian Congress of Biotechnology*, Buenos Aires, p. 88).

Cuba acknowledged a long tradition in the medical sciences, as illustrated by the work of its physicians, one of whom, Carlos J. Finlay, had discovered the vector of yellow fever at the end of the 19th century. However, it was not until 1960 that the first statement on a science policy related to the strategy and ethics of the new State was made. On 1 July 1965, the National Centre for Scientific Research (CENIC, Centro Nacional de Investigaciones Científicas) was created with the following objectives: to carry out research in biological sciences, biomedical sciences, technology and agriculture and livestock husbandry; to organize and promote scientific post-graduate studies; to follow-up the scientific activities both at national and international level. The CENIC provided technical services to many institutions throughout the country and had trained more than 8,000 professionals up to 1991 (Limonta, 1992). In addition to the CENIC, other institutions, such as the Cuban Institute of Animal Sciences (Instituto Cubano de Ciencia Animal, ICA), the Cuban Institute of Sugar-Cane Industry Derivatives (Instituto Cubano de Derivados de la Industria Azucarera, ICIDCA) and the Institutes of Medical Research, contributed to the development of research topics close to biotechnologies.

The end of the 1970s saw construction completed of the National Centre of Animal and Plant Health (CENSA, Centro Nacional de Sanidad Agropecuaria); the centre worked on animal health, genetic improvement and animal reproduction. Since 1981, it had played a key role both in the identification of exotic diseases affecting various crop species in Cuba and in the development of biotechnological components of crop protection and livestock husbandry.

The Government of Cuba's next move was to promote biotechnologies as one of the main industries for the nation's future development. Two events were crucial in this respect: the visit to Havana in 1980 by Randolph L. Clark of Anderson Hospital in Houston followed by the visit of two Cuban researchers to witness how interferon was administered at that hospital, and the stay, a few months later, of six Cuban scientists at the Central Public Health Laboratory in Helsinki, where they were trained under the direction of Kari Kantell in the production of human leukocyte interferon (Limonta, 1993*b*). In June 1981, a group of Cuban scientists capable of producing this interferon in a short period of time introduced its use in the treatment of epidemic viral diseases, such as type II dengue and acute haemorrhagic conjunctivitis.

In mid-1981, the Biological Front (Frente Biológico) was set up to accelerate progress in biotechnologies. The Front included research centres, teams and specialists in the life sciences, whose task was to evaluate the state of knowledge and set priority objectives, mobilize resources and the co-operative arrangements necessary for attaining these, identify new opportunities and design approaches for their realization. At the same time, multidisciplinary technical committees were set up to evaluate the research work, review specific problems and formulate suggestions for their solution. This overall strategy led to the creation in 1982 of the Centre of Biological Research (CIB, Centro de Investigaciones Biológicas), predecessor of the Centre of Genetic

Engineering and Biotechnology (CIGB, Centro de Ingenería Genética y Biotecnología) inaugurated on 1 July 1986; the Immuno-assay Centre (Centro de Immunoensayo, CIE), opened in 1987, produced the ultramicroanalytic system (SUMA, sistema ultramicroanalítico), a sophisticated and unique piece of equipment which read results through an ELISA system developed in Cuba. The ultramicroanalytic system used a tiny amount of reagent in comparison with standard systems utilized throughout the world (the SUMA was used for prenatal diagnosis of congenital malformations like neural tube defects and hypothyroidism); the National Centre for Laboratory Animal Production (CENPALAB, Centro Nacional para la Producción de Animales de Laboratorio), which provided animals for scientific research; the National Centre of Biopreparation (BIOCEN, Centro Nacional de Biopreparados), which produced vaccines and other biologicals; the transformation and renovation of the Pedro Kouri National Institute of Tropical Medicine (IPK, Instituto Nacional de Medicina Tropical Pedro Kouri), an epidemiological and biotechnological institute which provided clinical service, teaching and research on tropical diseases; and the New Finlay Institute.

At the CIB, researchers were able to produce human alpha- and gamma-interferons through the conventional and DNA recombinant process. Between 1982 and 1986, monoclonal antibodies and gene fragments were produced, new diagnosis methods were developed and CIB scientists were able to acquire advanced knowledge on genetic engineering, virology, tissue culture and fermentation processes. Furthermore, the training of many graduate students contributed to progress in research within the CIB.

Held in Havana from 4 to 6 August 1983, the First Cuban Seminar on Interferon was attended by 700 delegates from 34 countries. The seminar recommended the creation of the Sociedad Iberoamericana de Investigación sobre Interferón (Ibero-American Society for Research on Interferon), with the participation of Argentina, Bolivia, Colombia, Cuba, Dominican Republic, Mexico, Nicaragua, Peru, Spain and Venezuela. In 1984, the first issue of the periodical *Interferón y Biotecnología* (Interferon and Biotechnology) was published. From 20 to 22 February 1986, 900 researchers from 44 countries participated in the Second Cuban Seminar on Interferon and the First Cuban Seminar on Biotechnology. In April 1989, in addition to the Third Cuban Seminar on Interferon and the Second Seminar on Biotechnology, the First Ibero-American Congress of Biotechnology was held in Havana. In August 1990, Havana played host again, this time to the Second Latin American Congress of Biotechnology. Similar international events were scheduled for November 1994 (medical biotechnologies) and 1995 (agricultural and industrial biotechnologies).

The Centre of Genetic Engineering and Biotechnology (CIGB) covered an area of about 70,000 square metres in an eight-storey, air-conditioned building housing all centre divisions except the pilot plant. The installations in each division met international requirements for the manipulation of high-risk biological agents: cold chambers at +4_C and – 20_C, and P-4 containment laboratories. The main research divisions were:

– the Proteins and Hormones Division, dealing with the production, through genetic engineering, of proteins for use in human and veterinary medicine and including a laboratory for oligonucleotide and gene synthesis;

– the Vaccines and Diagnostics Division, involved in the production of vaccines against diseases by non-conventional techniques such as the cloning and expression of surface viral, bacterial or parasite antigens, as well as in the development and production of new diagnostics;

– the Hybridoma and Animal Modelling Division, concerned with the development and applications of murine and human monoclonal antibodies, as well as second-generation antibodies obtained by genetic engineering techniques; it also contributed to the development of transgenic animals, animal models for vaccines and toxicology tests, in addition to the evaluation of recombinant and non-recombinant products;

– the Energy and Biomass Division, working on industrial applications of biomass utilization, the development of technological processes (including the chemical and enzymatic transformation of substrates);

– the Plant and Fertilizer Division, involved in the improvement of crop species using genetic engineering and plant transformation, the development of varieties resistant to stress and pathogens, and the study of nitrogen-fixing organisms and associations;

– the Mammalian Cell Genetics, working on gene expression and cloning in mammalian cells, the use of tissue culture for the production of transgenic animals;

– the Restriction and Modification Enzymes Division, involved in the production of biological reagents required for the recombinant DNA techniques, like restriction enzymes, ligases, modification enzymes;

– the Analytical Unit, dealing with the analysis and purification of substances, using high-pressure liquid chromatography, mass spectrometry, protein crystallography, electron microscopy and immunomicroscopy, as well as the evaluation of biologival activity of peptides and proteins;

– the Quality Control Division, reporting directly to the CIGB's Director-General and composed of a selected group of scientists in charge of monitoring the purity, the structural integrity, the molecular composition, functions, clinical and pharmacodynamic properties, as well as the immune responses and side-effects of all CIGB products (Limonta, 1993*b*).

In addition to a pilot plant (6,300 square metres), the CIGB had space for raising animals in a controlled environment, five greenhouses, stables, a radioisotope laboratory with its own warehouse, power plant and a solvent-purification laboratory. The CIGB also had a four hundred-seat auditorium equipped with simultaneous translation facilities in four languages, five fifty-seat seminar rooms, a library, language laboratory, computer centre with access terminals and supporting facilities for workshops (Limonta, 1992).

The CIGB staff amounted to about 500; 80% of them were involved in research, the remainder being administrative and support staff. More than 230 held university degrees from Germany, Finland, France, Sweden, Switzerland, the United Kingdom and the USA (Limonta, 1993*b*).

The CIGB had made a considerable contribution to biotechnologies in Cuba, as had other research-and-development institutions (like the Immunoassay Centre, the Pedro Kouri National Institute of Tropical Medicine, the National Centre of Biopreparation) and in co-ordination with the CENIC, the CENSA, the Cuban Institute of Animal Sciences (ICA) and the Cuban Institute of Sugar-Cane Industry Derivatives (ICIDCA). These biotechnologies comprised:

– the production via genetic engineering of proteins and hormones for human and veterinary medicine;

– the production of vaccines and diagnostics for human and animal health;

– the transformation of biomass using chemical and enzymatic processes, as well as the production of industrial enzymes;

– the micropropagation and large-scale multiplication of plants;

– the improvement of crop species via plant transformation;

– the production of biofertilizers, biopesticides and diagnostic tools of pests and pathogens;

– the obtention of biological reagents needed for recombinant DNA techniques;

– the development and production of monoclonal antibodies via genetic engineering and their wide-ranging use.

Research activities in human and animal health needed efficient systems of reproduction and breeding of laboratory animals. In fact, high productivity had been achieved for reproducing eight different species and their peculiar strains: mice (eight strains), rats (five strains) and rabbits (three breeds). Innovative systems for producing balb-C mice with high hygienic and sanitary properties had been developed, in addition to strict monitoring of epizootics. The National System of Laboratory Animals (Sistema Nacional de Animales de Laboratorios) had been expanded to involve 53 institutions producing more than half a million animals, of which balb-C and OF1 mice raised in confined facilities represented more than 50%.

Progress had been made in the use of sugar-cane by-products, e.g. in the field of drugs: processes had been considerably improved for producing ferridextran, ß-glucans and dextran sulphate, and for co-ordinating the various scientific institutions involved. Co-operation with industry was well-established for the production of compost from sugar-cane wastes, biodessication of bagasse, production of edible mushrooms, yeast (both for animal and human consumption). Efforts were being made to sell Cuban technologies (e.g. related to the biotransformation of bagasse, edible mushroom production, livestock nutrition) to Latin American countries.

From the information contained in the Biosciences Directory in Cuba, it could be concluded that three-fourths of institutions oriented toward biotechnologies were research centres or universities and that their activities were distributed as follows:

Type of activity	Number of institutions (1993–1994)	Percentage
Production	38	40.4
Research and development	39	41.4
Services	15	16.0
Distribution	20	21.2

With respect to the areas of research and development, and production, the distribution was as follows:

Area	Number of institutions (1993–1994)	Percentage
Drugs	46	49.0
Plant biotechnologies	23	24.4
Agriculture	12	13.0
Livestock husbandry	4	4.2

Veterinary sciences	11	12.0
Energy	3	3.1
Chemical industry	8	8.5
Biometallurgy	2	2.1
Food industries	4	4.2

It could be concluded therefore that in 1993–1994 about half of the institutions related to biotechnologies in Cuba were in the area of drug research, development and production (49%), while only one-fourth were dedicating their work to plant biotechnologies.

The need to ensure a good and effective co-ordination between all institutions involved in biotechnologies, led to the creation of Scientific Poles (Polos Científicos). The first pole was that of the West of Havana, which regrouped 42 scientific, production and service institutions. In 1993–1994, ten poles existed throughout the country.

According to the estimates of the Cuban Academy of Sciences, approximately 8,000 people were working in biotechnology research and development in 200 institutes by the mid-1990s. Between 1988 and 1992, more than $300 million was invested in medical and pharmaceutical bio-industry (Elderhorst, 1994).

In biotechnologies applied to human health, research-and-development activities were being carried out on about 52 topics, among which the commercial production of recombinant alpha-2 and gamma-interferons, antihepatitis B vaccine and streptokinase deserve underlining. These wide-ranging efforts had resulted in 11 patent applications being filed in more than 30 countries, as well as both the recombinant alpha-2 interferon and anti-hepatitis B vaccine being registered in several countries throughout the world.

After having produced interferon in 1981 as a model for biotechnology development, the CIGB made this substance available to all health units in Cuba, where such diseases as hepatitis B, AIDS, solid tumours, laryngeal papillomatosis and haematopoietic tissue malignant neoplasia were treated. In 1988, after six years of clinical applications, the CIGB obtained official approval for recombinant interferon, the same year as Schering and Hoffmann-La Roche Inc. in the USA. In 1993, both alpha- and gamma-interferons were produced by the CIGB through conventional and genetic engineering techniques (Limonta, 1993a,b; 1995).

The epidermal growth factor (EGF), a 53-amino-acid peptide which stimulated epithelial cells in vitro and fibroblast proliferation, improved wound healing in treatment and had important applications in skin burns, diabetic ulcers, cornea ulcers and skin grafts, had been produced by companies with advanced biotechnological capability, like Chiron Corp. in the USA. The recombinant EGF was also produced in Cuba, which made possible its wide use in all burn treatment units, thus reducing hospitalization thanks to reduced patient recovery time. In 1989, the growth factors market value was estimated at $2.8–4.8 billion in the USA alone (Limonta, 1993*b*).

Another product that demonstrated Cuba's technological advance was the anti-hepatitis B vaccine, obtained by cloning and expressing the gene for the viral surface antigen (HBsAg) in yeast (*Pichia* sp.). This result permitted extensive vaccination in Cuba and the vaccine's commercialization outside the country. The production of this vaccine was part of the National Vaccine Programme, which included 12 projects involving 20 vaccines (one of these projects being devoted to the anti-hepatitis B vaccine). In addition to the CIGB protecting the Cuban population, the Centre's export capability made it one of the three major producers of recombinant anti-hepatitis B vaccine in the world (Limonta, 1993*b*)[8] (see p. 248).

The anti-meningitis B vaccine, Vamengoc-BC, active against infections by *Neisseria meningitidis*, group B, was developed and commercialized by the Finlay Institute, the Centre for Research and Production of Vaccines and Sera, a newly built vaccine production centre. This was the outcome of a policy directed toward guaranteeing the quality of the production process by balancing the increased use of the technology with good management. One important step in applying such a policy was the construction of the National Centre of Biopreparation (BIOCEN, Centro Nacional de Biopreparados), which represented a large-scale production facility for the products developed at the CIGB and other research institutions; the BIOCEN included flexible facilities to meet the variability of production and world market competitiveness (Limonta, 1993*b*).

Projects developing vaccines against cholera, leptospirosis and *Haemophilus influenzae* were at an advanced stage in 1994–1995. The project for developing a multiple vaccine against meningitis had induced research on the classification of meningococci strains both in Cuba and Latin America, using molecular biology techniques to study the genus *Neisseria*. The first plant for producing viral vaccines was built at the Finlay Institute in 1993, production priorities being vaccines against rabies (in tissue culture), measles and rubella, hepatitis A and C, flu, dengue and AIDS. Cuba was participating in the Regional Vaccine System (SIREVA) and the Pan-American Health Organization (PAHO) recognized Cuba's potential contribution to, among other regional projects, the production of vaccines against infant diseases.

In 1993, the CIGB was the only producer in the world of recombinant streptokinase. This enzyme, directed to the thrombolytics market, was considered the best stabilized, least antigenic preparation, with effects comparable to other similar naturally available products. The Cuban researchers had developed the recombinant streptokinase to be used mainly as a fibrinolytic substance in vascular obstructions in all intensive therapy ward units in Cuba. This achievement was also considered a milestone in the orientation of Cuban biotechnologies toward the external market (Limonta, 1993*b*; 1995).

The CIGB had developed broad expertise in large-scale fermentation (using 300, 500 and 1,500-litre bioreactors) and production of different recombinant proteins, with adequate downstream processing fulfilling the manufacturing and quality control requirements set up for these productions. The following proteins were synthesized through genetic engineering, some of them being produced on a large scale for commercial use (Limonta, 1992):

Protein	Host
Human alpha-interferon	*Escherichia coli*
Human gamma-interferon	Yeast, *E. coli*
Interleukin-2	*E. coli*
Epidermal growth factor (EGF)	Yeast
gap-41 of HIV-1	*E. coli*
gap-24 of HIV-1	*E. coli*
gap-36 of HIV-2	*E. coli*
Prochymosin of calf	*E. coli*, yeast
Human insulin	*E. coli*
Toxin of *Clostridrium haemolyticum*	*E. coli*
T-7 polymerase	*E. coli*
Thioredoxin	*E. coli*
Streptokinase	*E. coli*
Human gonadotrophic hormone	*E. coli*
HBsAg	Yeast, mammalian cells
Tissue plasminogen activator (tPA)	Mammalian cells
Human beta-interferon	Mammalian cells

More than 20 Cuban institutions were able to produce monoclonal antibodies, the number of which was steadily increasing. The IOR T3, the first monoclonal antibody developed in Cuba against the reject of transplants, was registered in Cuba as well as outside the country. In 1996, more than 40 types of monoclonal antibodies were being produced on a large scale, including for therapeutical purposes. Furthermore, diagnostic kits had been developed for the detection of HIV (human immunodeficiency virus strains 1 and 2), as well as of hepatitis C, using the ELISA and micro-ELISA systems; a diagnosis package concerning toxoplasmosis, rubella, cytomegalovirus and herpes (TORCH) had been developed through the ultramicroanalytic system. Two monoclonal antibodies had been evaluated for cancer detection, as well as antibodies IgG by golden/silver probes methods for HIV-1, HIV-2 and hepatitis C virus; ELISA diagnostic kits for the identification of the HTLV-1 (human tricholeukaemia virus) and hepatitis C had been developed; and the ELISA test for hepatitis A had been standardized for saliva samples, with a 96.8%-100% specificity and reduced diagnosis time from 48 hours to six hours. Diagnostics had been introduced into the national network system, so as to meet 81% of the demand in polyclinics and 47% of the demand in hospitals (Limonta, 1995).

The capacity for plasma recovery and for the production of haemoderivatives had been increased and new investigation areas opened. Immunoglobulin anti D (anti Rh) and human immunoglobulin enriched in IgM and IgA (IGEGAM), factor VIII ('Hemostac' F-8) and albumin were produced and registered.

With the participation of 26 institutions throughout the country, about 203 drug formulations had been produced, 115 of which had been approved by the State Centre for the Registration and Control of Drugs (Centro Estatal de Registro y Control de los Medicamentos). In 1993–1994, about 46 drugs were registered overseas and 140 submitted for registration in ten countries.

The supply of new drugs and diagnostic kits to national hospitals and polyclinics undoubtedly contributed to public health improvement in Cuba: an infant mortality rate of less than 11.9 per thousand and an average 74-year life expectancy at birth during the 1985–1990 period (Limonta, 1993*b*).

Cuba's researchers and executives responsible for developing biotechnologies applied to medicine and public health realized that in addition to industrial scaling-up, an appropriate marketing strategy was needed for advertising and selling the products. The need arose to create Heber Biotec S.A., a trading company born out of the laboratory for the purpose of marketing the CIGB's products. This creation was motivated by the fact that it was very difficult to introduce high-technology products onto the market without experienced business management, so as to grant an international credibility to the products. Heber Biotec S.A. was following a strategy based on the development of patentable products, the search for high-level collaborative work, and scientific and commercial exchange. Business relations with more than 80 countries across four continents, combined with the carefully controlled evaluation of products, following procedures used by the world's most prestigious institutions, were all signs that the Cuban company had found a niche in the trade, despite a number of limiting factors alien to the quality and efficiency of the products and their marketing possibilities. In addition, the accelerated training of managers was considered a key element, the goal being to design a flexible structure capable of generating strategies for an evolving market, i.e. a competitive structure (Limonta, 1993*a,b*). About 200 products were listed in the 1994 Heber Biotec S.A. catalogue.

Cuba was exporting biotechnology-derived medical products, mainly to Latin America and Caribbean countries. One of these products was the anti-meningitis B vaccine, commercialized as Vamengoc-BC. Administered in Cuba since 1986, it had boosted immunity in vaccinated children and adults. The vaccine had not only been registered in Bolivia, Brazil, Nicaragua, Paraguay and Uruguay, but also in Asian, European and African countries. In 1989, an important contract had been signed with Brazil for the export of 8 million doses of this vaccine worth $80 million. Later on, another 7.5 million doses had been sold to the same country. A potential meningitis epidemic in Colombia in 1990–1991 had been contained by the same vaccine. While Chile had initiated a one-year experiment with the vaccine in 1994, Argentina had registered the vaccine and imported it (Elderhorst, 1994).

Another export product was the anti-hepatitis B vaccine, Heberbiovac-HB, manufactured since 1987. Colombia imported the vaccine in early 1993 and it was later on registered in Venezuela. Other potential export products were PPG (ateromixol, a medicine to reduce the cholesterol concentration in the bloodstream), epidermal growth factor, streptokinase and interferons. According to Añé (1993), two enzymes (beta-galactosidase that aided the digestion of dairy products by those who were lactose-intolerant; and recombiant rennet for cheese making) showed great promise for co-operative production with enterprises in other Latin American countries. Production facilities for these enzymes already existed in Cuba and various investment options were being considered (Elderhorst, 1994).

In 1989, the BIOTEC data-base concerning institutions devoted to biotechnologies was set up by the Institute of Scientific and Technical Documentation and Information (IDICT, Instituto de Documentación e Información Científico-Técnica) of the Academy of Sciences of Cuba; its first printed version contained information on more than 5,500 institutions in 63 countries. The BIOTEC directory was later on published in 1990, 1991 and 1992 as printed material, and in 1992, for the first time in Cuba, a CD-ROM version of BIOTEC containing information on more than 6,800 institutions in 114 countries was marketed in Cuba. Furthermore, a Centre for Information and Consultancy in Biotechnology and Medical and Pharmaceutical Industry (Centro BIOTEC) was created, with a view to providing economic and commercial information services in addition to the conventional scientific information services. Market studies were carried out and promising possibilities identified. Communication infrastructures were being developed between institutions of the Scientific Pole West of Havana, with an eye to setting up a BIORED among them, i.e. a network of microcomputers with large possibilities of information exchange and access to data-bases (on magnetic tape or compact disks).

In 1995, the CIGB had been publishing the journal *Biotecnología Aplicada* for 11 years. The Journal was the communication vector of the Ibero-Latin American Society for Biotechnology Applied to Health (Sociedad IberoLatinoAmericana de Biotecnología Aplicada a la Salud), whose objectives were to: support the integration of the various Ibero-Latin American scientific institutions involved in biotechnologies applied to health by disseminating their results world-wide; establish co-operation among research teams in the region and those working elsewhere in the world on health biotechnologies. The Journal was supported by a grant from the Directorate-General of Cultural and Scientific Relations of the Spanish Ministry of Foreign Affairs, in response to a request for assistance by UNESCO in 1994. The Journal had the following characteristics:

– one-fourth of the articles published were signed by foreign authors, particularly those from developed countries;

– biomedical biotechnologies were the major focus, followed by molecular biology, plant biotechnology, bio-industry and automation of processes;

– an impact index of 0.168 was attributed to the Journal by a Spanish research team; although low, this index was higher than the Latin American average;

– the Journal was quoted in eight of the most important reference reviews (*Biosis, Current Biotechnology Abstracts, Derwent Biotechnology Abstracts, Cambridge Scientific Abstracts, Chemical Abstracts, Biological Abstracts, Index Medicus* and *Lila CS*).

Despite sucessful examples, most achievements in medical biotechnologies were still out of the reach of developing countries, where health budgets sometimes reached barely $4 per capita per year. Vaccine development costs were high and success not always assured. After identifying an effective immunizing agent in animals and preliminary human trials, it would cost $200–$300 million and ten to twelve years of development to arrive at a vaccine usable by paramedics in the field. Private companies were thus reluctant to be involved in such development, as it would be difficult to earn back the investments at prices the developing countries could afford. For instance, the California-based company, Genentech Inc., had agreed to produce a vaccine against the sporozoite stage of the malaria parasite; it backed out, however, upon realizing that the project would be unprofitable. Similarly, the British biotechnology agency, Rural Overseas Ltd, had considered developing vaccines against tropical diseases in The Philippines in collaboration with the National Institutes of Biotechnology and Applied Microbiology (BIOTECH) at the University of The Philippines, Los Baños. The project was abandoned because the market was too small (Van Wijk and Komen, 1991).

However, development in Colombia of a synthetic vaccine against the malarial agent by Patarroyo and his team was an exception worthy of note.

In 1997, according to the statistical data of the World Health Organization, malaria threatened one-third of the world population; each year, the mosquito-borne pathogen caused between 300 million and 500 million cases of malaria and killed between 1.5 million and 2.7 million people, mostly children under five years of age. Malaria was causing one death every 12 seconds in the world, and nine malaria patients out of ten were living in Africa, but malaria was again prevalent in India and other countries where it had been eradicated in the 1950s thanks to a campaign co-ordinated by the World Health Organization. In addition, malaria was debilitating and accounted for a substantial amount of productive days lost. In endemic areas, these effects were often cumulative, resulting in anaemia, particularly in children and pregnant women, and poor physical fitness.

In the mid-1990s, malaria was a more serious problem than in the 1970s and 1980s, due to the disruption of malaria control programmes in many countries, the development of insecticide resistance in vectors and of drug resistance by *Plasmodium falciparum*, the increased migration of people from non-endemic areas to areas where malaria was prevalent and changes in tropical environment following deforestation and urbanization. Furthermore, the greenhouse effect and the subsequent warming of the Earth would result in the re-appearance of the disease in countries located in regions that were currently protected.

The annual estimated direct and indirect cost of malaria in Africa was $1.8 billion in 1995, compared to $800 million in 1987.

The Ministerial Conference on Malaria, held in Amsterdam from 26 to 27 October 1992, emphasized that there was no single formula for the control of malaria and that sustainable cost-effective control must be based on local analysis. The conference promoted four actions: provision of early diagnosis and prompt treatment for all populations at risk; planning and implementation of selective preventive measures, including vector control; early detection, containment and prevention of epidemics; and strengthening of local capacities in basic and applied research to permit the regular assessment of a country's malaria situation. Most research on malaria was directed toward stopping the post-bite effect of the illness (Fernández Hermana, 1994).

In 1996, preliminary negotiations were initiated to create a new international major programme for controlling malaria in Africa: the African Malaria Initiative, which was to be established under the aegis of the World Bank, the World Health Organization and other international bodies such as the U.S. Agency for International Development and U.S. Centers for Disease Control, European Commission and Organization of African Unity. This would be a long-term programme, that would rely on the setting up of the needed infrastructures for controlling the disease and delivering health care throughout Africa. The head of the World Bank Department of Health, Nutrition and Population was convinced that the African Malaria Initiative would allow a better use of existing funds and attract new subsidies from the international community. The WHO devoted another $10 million in 1997 for the research on, and control of, malaria, which represented one-third of its annual current expenses in this area. In 1996, the Directors of the Institut Pasteur in Paris and U.S. National Institutes of Health organized discussions among researchers and with charity and development organizations in order to design an international strategy concerning research and collection of the needed funds. Their endeavours led to a meeting in Dakar in January 1997, which was attended for the first time by representatives of charity organizations, research institutes and funding institutions such as the World Bank. Another meeting was held in July 1997 in The Hague to follow up the results of the Dakar meeting.

In the early 1980s, Patarroyo, of the Department of Immunology, San Juan de Dios Hospital, Bogotá, Colombia, decided to devote research to chemically-synthesized vaccines and to focus on malaria. A number of elements were considered propicious for the team gathered by Patarroyo to develop a synthetic vaccine: malaria was endemic in Colombia and in the Amazonian forest lived the *Aotus* monkey, a nocturnal species which seemed like an ideal test subject before trying the vaccine on humans (Fernández Hermana, 1994).

In 1987, Patarroyo and his collaborators reported in *Nature* that a preparation made of peptides could protect monkeys against malaria. N-terminal amino-acid sequence analysis was performed for each of 12 proteins isolated from *in-vitro* cultures of *P. falciparum*. Following the solid-phase peptide synthesis methodology described by Merrifield in 1963, synthetic peptides were constructed - from the sequences - of the four antigens eliciting a protective or delayed response in later immunogenicity studies with *Aotus* monkeys. Each one of the 12 isolated and purified antigens was inoculated to *Aotus* monkeys, which were then challenged by intravenous inoculation of 5 million *P. falciparum* (FVO strain) infected red blood cells taken from naive donors. The results of this experiment showed that three of the antigens (155, 55 and 35 kilodalton proteins) presented a delay in the appearance of parasitaemias and one (83 kilodalton protein) induced sterilizing immunity (Patarroyo, 1995).

The next step in this series of experiments was to administer different combinations of the peptides using two or three different peptides in each mixture. Of the six monkeys immunized with a mixture of three peptides (83.1, 55.1 and 35.1), three developed low parasitaemias that peaked between days 10 and 15, significantly later than in the control groups, and went on to recover spontaneously. The remaining three animals never developed parasitaemia. At the 66th trial, a combination of these three peptides, the Synthetic *Plasmodium falciparum* 66 vaccine (SPf66), conferred good protection against the parasite. This experiment had been repeated several times with bigger groups of animals (1,400 monkeys) showing similar results (Patarroyo, 1995).

In 1988, phase-I trials of SPf66 on humans were initiated on 109 volunteer soldiers from the Colombian Military Forces, who were examined from the physical and mental health standpoints; 30 individuals were chosen for further testing. Results showed that the vaccine was well tolerated, with only minor local reactions being observed in a few cases. During phase-II trials, the efficacy of the protective immunity conferred by the vaccine was assessed through the experimental challenge of non-immune individuals originating from non-endemic areas. Thirteen of the individuals participating in phase-I trials were selected for testing of the vaccine. The volunteer soldiers were intravenously inoculated with 1 million wild-strain *P. falciparum*-infected erythrocytes, each of which could produce 16 merozoites to be released into the bloodstream. Twice a day, parasitaemia was monitored for each vaccinee and individuals with parasitaemia above 0.5% were treated. All the individuals were free to withdraw from the study whenever they chose to do so. Of the five individuals immunized with the SPf66 vaccine, three were protected, one withdrew in mid-trial and one required drug treatment. The calculated efficacy of the vaccine in this trial was 75% (Patarroyo, 1995). For the following trial (1992), 399 male volunteers aged 18 to 21, from the Colombian Military Forces, were chosen; 185 were vaccinated with SPf66 and 214 served as controls. Results showed that there were no statistically significant differences between the vaccinated and control groups, proving that the vaccine was completely safe for use in humans (Patarroyo, 1995).

The scientific community reacted negatively to these findings. Thus, in the USA, Miller, a malaria expert at the National Institute of Allergy and Infectious Diseases (Bethesda, Maryland), emphasized the highly dangerous amount of parasites found in the blood of non-vaccinated volunteers who were considered the controls of the vaccination trial. Others stated that Patarroyo had moved precipitously from animal trials to human trials, a hazardous practice for a vaccine not manufactured according to the most rigorous standards (Maurice, 1995).

Patarroyo riposted by testing the SPf66 in four clinical trials in Colombia on some 20,000 individuals. The results were striking: a demonstrated innocuity of the vaccine, high amounts of antibodies induced and protection against the parasite estimated at between 60% and 82%. These results were published in 1992 in two medical journals. However, Hayes of the London School of Hygiene and Tropical Medicine, complained that the clinical trials had not followed the international standards of a double-blind random trial; Greenwood, of the British Medical Research Council, stated that there were serious epidemiological shortcomings (Maurice, 1995).

Patarroyo pursued his clinical trials in Brazil, Ecuador and Venezuela. While the number of vaccinated persons was rising, pressure was being exerted on the countries' authorities to officially declare the SPf66 an anti-malaria vaccine. In 1990, the Ministers of Health of Bolivia, Colombia, Ecuador, Peru and Venezuela announced the launching of a massive vaccination programme in their countries. Fearing that the vaccine might be widely used before being validated, the World Health Organization (WHO) sent a group of experts to visit Patarroyo's facilities in Bogotá; they concluded that the effectiveness of the vaccine was not yet proven. In March 1991, the British Medical Research Council refused to support a clinical trial in Gambia in an area of high mortality due to malaria, because of doubts as to the quality and effectiveness of the SPf66 (Maurice, 1995).

However, a fragile balance was established between the supporters and the detractors of Patarroyo's findings. Another phase - III clinical trial (on the effectiveness of the vaccine) was conducted on Colombia's

Pacific Coast, at La Tola, on 1,548 adults. These first two big double-blind, placebo-controlled field trials of SPf66, yielding the highest efficacy rates (over 30%), were run with the help of Patarroyo's team in Colombia, where people faced a relatively low 'attack rate' by infected mosquitoes.

Spanish scientists working at the Superior Council for Scientific Research (CSIC) paid attention to the Colombian research team. Through them, Patarroyo registered his vaccine in Spain, the support of a European country putting him in a stronger position for effecting his trials. In September 1992, Patarroyo offered the results from his work for publication in the British weekly medical research journal, *The Lancet*. Only after strong pressure from those familiar with Patarroyo's work did *The Lancet* decide to publish the paper, six months later, on 20 March 1993 (Fernández Hermana, 1994).

Encouraged by the seriousness of the trials carried out at La Tola, researchers from European countries and from Africa conducted trials in Tanzania, with WHO assistance. The third big double-blind, placebo-controlled field trial, backed by the Swiss Tropical Institute of Basel, took place in Tanzania, where the 'attack rate' by mosquitoes was said to be among the highest in the world. The Ifakara Centre, Amani Centre and National Medical Research Institute – all of Tanzania – also collaborated in the trial. This study of 586 children in the village of Idete, led by Alonso of Spain's Barcelona-based Biomedical Research Foundation, reported an efficacy of 31%, but with wide error margins. The fourth trial led by Greenwood and D'Alessandro of the London School of Hygiene and Tropical Medicine, and supported by the United Kingdom's Medical Research Council, took place in Gambia, where the mosquito 'attack rate' was moderate. The vaccine had little effect and was associated with delaying or preventing malaria in only 8% of those treated.

Many public health experts considered the level of protection against the disease resulting from both the La Tola, Gambia and Tanzania trials insufficient and emphasized that current vaccines against a wide range of diseases offered vaccinated persons at least 80% to 95% protection. Patarroyo countered that, due to the prevalence of malaria, even 30% protection could save hundreds of thousands of lives, particularly those of children, and at least one hundred million fever accesses could be avoided. Other researchers, nevertheless, raised doubts about the statistical significance of the figures obtained: the latter referred to the number of fever accesses avoided during a determined period and not to the proportion of effectively protected persons (Maurice, 1995).

At the international symposium on the Etiology and pathogenesis of infectious diseases, held in Dakar from 10 to 13 April 1995, within the framework of the 'Year of Pasteur' (commemoration of the 100th anniversary of Pasteur's death), a series of higly critical comments were made on the results published by Patarroyo in *The Lancet*. The comments made publicly and privately at the Dakar symposium (in which Patarroyo did not participate) revealed the scepticism among specialists as to the reliability of the vaccine developed by the Colombian immunologist and his colleagues. In particular, according to Pierre Druilhe of the Pasteur Institute, who expressed the views of many chemists, the vaccine – the result of polymerization of several peptides – was very difficult to reproduce and its structure might change in the various preparations. Furthermore, the French specialist stated that there was no clearcut, indisputable evidence of the vaccine's efficiency or inefficiency (Nau, 1995*c*).

Published on 14 September 1996 in *The Lancet*, the results from the U.S. Army-sponsored trial of SPf66 among more than 1,200 children in Thailand from 1993 to 1995, showed no evidence of efficacy whatsoever. During the two-year, $1.5 million trial, said to be the most expensive and best-designed to date, roughly equal numbers of chilfren receiving the SPf66 vaccine (195) or a hepatitis B 'comparator' vaccine (184) experienced a first case of malaria. The authors, led by Ballou of the Walter Reed Army Institute of Research, concluded that, taken with other weak results, this data indicated that the SPf66 vaccine 'did not protect against clinical *falciparum* malaria'. Moreover, they wrote that the Thai data was so disappointing that 'further efficacy trials were not warranted'.

However, loathe to be accused of delaying large-scale use of a vaccine that might prove effective, the World Health Organization was willing to assist Colombia in its efforts to massively produce the vaccine and identify a cheap and reliable source of the amino-acids needed to manufacture it. The WHO also wanted to set up large-scale studies to shed light on the various issues posed by the effectiveness of the SPf66 (Maurice, 1995).

One aspect of all these developments worrying a number of experts and analysts was the publicity given by Patarroyo to an unsubstantiated vaccine. For instance, he had claimed in several press interviews that his vaccine was the *first* synthetic vaccine against malaria. In fact, it had been preceded by an imperfect prototype developed by Ruth Nussenzweig's team at New York University in the early 1980s. It would have been more exact to say that the SPf66 was the first synthetic vaccine to be widely tested in clinical trials. Patarroyo himself admitted the vaccine imperfections when donating the vaccine in May 1995 to the WHO on behalf of the Colombian people. The admission did not dissuade him from promoting his vaccine on a much-criticized lecture tour of South America. In response to the reproach that the tour had generated excessive publicity for a vaccine whose effectiveness remained unproven, Patarroyo cited the need to use his prestige to make himself heard in the political arena and to secure invaluable moral and financial support. As for the agreement signed by Patarroyo, under the sponsorhip of Colombia's vice-president, awarding the WHO the rights of exploitation of SPf66, this was considered by the WHO legal affairs section as no more than an agreement on 'legal principles'. If WHO officials were of the opinion that an agreement might be signed, important issues had first to be resolved, e.g. who would decide whether the vaccine was ready for manufacture and large-scale use and when would it be? And at what cost? (the price of less than 50 cents had been put forward) Who would manufacture the vaccine? (Maurice, 1995).

The fact remained that many researchers and public health officials still had doubts about the SPf66, e.g. What risks would be run by a country using the vaccine immediately? In young children, would the vaccine induce immunodepression making them vulnerable to attacks by the parasite, which could proliferate in their organism? If the vaccine prevented the usual manifestations of malaria (fever, pain, anaemia), would it augment the risk for patients later developing acute forms of the disease (pernicious access, which attacks the central nervous system)? If the vaccine proved ineffective on a large-scale, would it not make whole populations and donors reluctant to collaborate with trials on other vaccines? Not only that, but how many children inoculated with the ineffective vaccine would die because their mothers scorned treatment in the belief that their offspring were protected? (Maurice, 1995).

These questions were unlikely to prevent countries from requesting the Colombian vaccine. Nevertheless, it would be inappropriate to raise hopes about a vaccine still at the research stage, recalled Odile Mercereau-Puijalon, head of laboratory in the Unit of Experimental Parasitology at the Pasteur Institute in Paris and chairperson of the Committee of Malaria Immunology of WHO's Special Programme for Research and Training in Tropical Diseases (TDR). The same researcher, while recognizing that Patarroyo used scientific methods to test hundreds of peptides in monkeys and that his achievements were not the result of luck, considered that the SPf66 was not a miracle cure for malaria but a step in the right direction. For his part, Stephen Hoffman, who was running the malaria programme at the Naval

Medical Research Institute, Bethesda, Maryland, was of the opinion that Patarroyo's most significant achievement was the creation of a huge infrastructure in Colombia and the training of many young scientists. Godal, director of the WHO's TDR, considered that the Patarroyo's story showed that 'we could not still follow the normal, slow and careful course for vaccine development, while children were daily dying from malaria'. He was willing to obligate the $4.5 million needed to prove or disprove the effectiveness of the SPf66. The cost-effectiveness analysis made by the TDR researchers showed that, if the vaccine could be administered to children with other vaccines already distributed by the WHO's Extended Vaccination Programme, if it reduced infant mortality by 30% and if this effect lasted at least five years, the SPf66 could improve the health of the vaccinated population for at least ten times less than the cost of a preventive medicine (Maurice, 1995).

Further to the disappointing results published in 1996, Ballou thought it 'closed the door' on SPf66, because the vaccine no longer looked useful for immunization in high-attack areas like Africa and South-East Asia. But others remained optimistic. Alonso, for example, wrote: 'There is pretty strong evidence that SPf66 is worthwhile in Tanzania'; he suggested that genetic differences in the population, the local parasite, or even in the chemical composition of the vaccine might have produced varying results. He thought it was 'bizarre' to suggest that no further trials be undertaken. Patarroyo also thought that small chemical differences might have affected efficacy rates. Ballou dismissed this view, noting that studies showed that the versions of SPf66 used in Colombia and Thailand produced similar results in tests of immunogenicity.

As for the WHO, Engers, director of WHO's Malaria Research Steering Committee, stated that the Organization was somewhat disappointed, but the WHO planned to continue the Tanzanian trial of SPf66 in high-risk children and intended to evaluate these results before deciding on future trials. Engers also noted that the attention devoted to Patarroyo's vaccine had helped spur interest in malaria vaccine development. In 1997, there were at least three candidate vaccines waiting to be tested: a DNA vaccine designed by the U.S. Navy researchers; a new U.S. Army vaccine being developed in conjunction with SmithKline Beecham plc; and an Australian vaccine already in field trials in Papua New Guinea. Engers added: 'we see a bright future for second-generation malaria vaccines. The latest disappointment has only interrupted researchers' dream'.

5. Contribution of biotechnologies to the production of plant-derived drugs and phytochemicals

Approximately 119 pure chemical substances extracted from higher plants were used in medicine throughout the world. According to a 1988 report by the consultancy firm McAlpine, Thorpe and Warrier (United Kingdom), 'the market potential for herbal drugs in the 'Western' world could range from $4.9 billion in the next ten years to $47 billion by the year 2000 if the AIDS epidemic continued unchecked'. This expected growth was due to shifting consumer preferences away from chemicals and toward plant-derived drugs, and the fact that pharmaceutical companies were continuously seeking new compounds for medicines to improve their competitiveness (Komen, 1991e).

According to the World Health Organization (WHO), about 80% of people in developing countries still relied on traditional plant-derived drugs, the main reason being their low price. For modern pharmaceuticals, they depended heavily on imported drugs and technology. Thus, plant-derived drugs offered an interesting potential as resources for local industry and a substitute for costly pharmaceutical imports (Komen, 1991e).

Ethnobotanical evidence showed that many plants had proved useful to humankind as sources of medicines, insecticides, pigments, gums, flavours and other useful products; at least 24,000 different plants were thought to have been used world-wide in traditional medicine. The cultivation of some of these tropical and subtropical species was of some considerable industrial importance. Thus, plant sources of pharmaceuticals, such as *Cinchona* spp. (quinine), *Vinca rosea* or *Catharanthus roseus* (anti-cancer alkaloids) and *Dioscorea* spp. (contraceptive steroids) were amongst those contributing to a global trade currently valued at around $20 billion per annum.

Most of the world's medicinal plants were located in the tropics, which stored about 250,000 to 300,000 (two-thirds) of all plant species. Although at least 35,000 were estimated to be of medicinal value, up until now only 5,000 had been exhaustively studied for possible medical applications. A large proportion of these plants were found in rainforests. As deforestation accelerated, pharmaceutical companies expanded their screening programmes for natural products (Komen, 1991e).

Searching for new phytochemicals was largely a numbers' game in which companies screened many plant extracts and compounds through routine tests. One thousand plants subjected to 100 tests provided 100,000 chances of finding a useful effect. Random chance could be supplemented by knowledge in ethnobotany and chemotaxonomy to identify particularly promising targets for inclusion in searches. Traditional knowledge in societies and cultures with long histories of herbal use (e.g. China, India and Europe) had been invaluable in selecting species for scientific studies.

The development of highly specific bioassays to detect picogramme quantities of potentially useful compounds and automated screening technology made it possible to screen thousands of plant samples daily.

Once a screening 'hit' was made, the problems of molecular identification of the active principles, larger-scale development production and long-range commercial evaluations came into play. Of those 100,000 chances, only 0.1% might be valuable hits in testing; of those hits, only one material might give a successful commercial product.

These few successful systems would immediately serve as candidates for biotechnology-based improvements, because such improvements both offered proprietary technology and gave companies a competitive edge. Metabolic modification strategies would be designed to raise concentrations of target compounds in plants and suppress the formation of unwanted substances. New metabolic steps would be introduced. Gene transfer technology would be used to move synthesis pathways from scarce, hard-to-manage wild species to cultivated plants. Work by Yamada and his colleagues in the late 1980s showed how some metabolic pathways could be moved by breeding among plants engineered using each of the various steps. Equally promising technically was the engineering of plants to accumulate new polypeptides, ideally distinct from the plant's usual complex of substrates and recoverable as natural products in their own right.

Gene modifications in tomorrow's specialty plants would focus heavily on industrial value-added traits as opposed to agronomic performance traits. In the short term, most of these plants would be grown intensively in small acreages; their importance would grow if suitably improved types could be brought into use. Though their economic value would be high, most would never become big acreage crops. Some would require micropropagation as a production tool.

6. Screening operations for medicinal substances and phytochemicals

In 1980, the U.S. pharmaceutical industry did not set aside a red cent for the evaluation of plants. Fifteen years later, according to the Rural Advancement Foundation International (RAFI), more than 200 companies and research institutes around the world were assessing animal and plant compounds in the search for medicines (Reyes, 1996).

In 1989, the RAFI reported on the plant material collecting activities of Merck & Co. Inc. (New Jersey, USA) in Latin America, while The Upjohn Co. (Michigan, USA) was studying compounds from ancient Chinese herbal medicines, with a view to developing new drugs against cancer, cardiovascular diseases and neural disorders. In the USA, the largest tropical plant collecting effort was sponsored by the Federal Government's National Cancer Institute (NCI). In 1986, the NCI launched a five-year $2.8 million programme to screen thousands of exotic plants from tropical forests of Latin America, South-East Asia and Southern Africa. Drug development from plants would be left to private companies. In addition, the NCI intended to develop agreements that would benefit the countries of origin (Komen, 1991*e*).

Costa Rica had created a National Commission on Genetic Resources, through the Ministry of Agriculture and the Ministry of Science and Technology. In September 1991, Costa Rica's National Institute for Biodiversity (INBIO) concluded an arrangement with the North American pharmaceutical transnational, Merck & Co. Inc., through which the world's biggest (at that time; the fourth-biggest in 1996) drug company provided $1 million over two years to the INBIO to support the organization's 'chemical prospecting' – inventorying and collecting samples of plants, micro-organisms and animals – in Costa Rica's rainforests. INBIO scientists were carrying out screening of anti-bacterial and anti-fungal substances. In return, Merck & Co. Inc. enjoyed exclusive rights to screen, develop and, eventually, patent new products derived from those resources. Merck & Co. Inc. agreed to share 5% of any royalties arising from the sale of such products with the INBIO. From the Institute's point of view, this gave them absolute control over whoever was operating in Costa Rica's protected forests. From Merck & Co. Inc.'s point of view, the drug company had a secure and protected supply of new biological compounds to test and develop. The contract with Merck & Co. Inc. was one of many held by the INBIO, which also negotiated with a number of North-based companies, universities and conservation agencies (Kloppenburg and Rodriguez, 1992).

The INBIO was founded by the National Commission on Genetic Resources, set up by Executive Decree of the Costa Rican Government in October 1989 as a private, non-governmental, non-profit-making organization. Its purpose was to: survey the biological resources of Costa Rica; and protect that biological diversity by making it available for productive purposes and by establishing its utility, thereby generating a 'raison d'être' in economic terms to protect the natural resources. A \$4.9 million 'debt-for-nature swap' provided by a number of prominent North American foundations, as well as U.S. Government and Swedish Government development agencies, supplied the material means to initiate operations (Kloppenburg and Rodriguez, 1992). Debt titles were purchased at 15%-20% of their face value; the difference was invested, in local currency, into environmental protection, in order to compensate for the underfunding of national conservation programmes, due no doubt to the debt burden and structural economic adjustments.

In September 1990, a bill for the conservation of wildlife was introduced into the national Legislative Assembly by a Special Commission on the Environment. Articles 3 and 4 of the bill identified genetic resources as a national heritage, explicitly placed them in the public domain and reserved for the state the exclusive right to commercialize them. The bill would therefore reduce the INBIO's monopoly over the manner in which Costa Rica's genetic wealth was being marketed. The agreement concluded by the INBIO with Merck & Co. Inc. drew criticism from such organizations as the National Museum, the Federation of Associations for the Conservation of Nature and Environment and Biodiversity; they considered that the government had `abdicated its responsibility by allowing the INBIO to arrogate to itself the management of public property, while the INBIO was not a public organization (Kloppenburg and Rodriguez, 1992).

The Costa Rican event showed that, for the first time, scientists, a government and a transnational corporation were all voluntarily adhering to the principle that access to genetic resources merited compensation. The INBIO-Merck & Co. Inc. arrangement was the first instance of contractual conjunction of willingness to sell genetic resources and willingness to pay for them. The agreement therefore represented an important precedent for the future operations of companies, governments and scientific institutions in the exchange of biological resources. The key issue was no longer whether or not compensation was appropriate, but the conditions under which compensation would be paid and, most importantly, which social groups or institutions would have the right to determine those conditions (Kloppenburg and Rodriguez, 1992).

Although the income from genetic prospecting agreements was directed toward conservation activities, personnel training and the development of Costa Rican scientific capacity, rather than to personal or institutional benefit, the INBIO was not considered the appropriate decision-making body because a public resource was involved and only public institutions were accountable to broad social interests (Kloppenburg and Rodriguez, 1992).

As a result of public pressure, the INBIO agreed to pay a portion of the income derived from its genetic resources prospecting contracts to government agencies, such as the National Park Service and the Ministry of Natural Resources, Energy and Mines. It also planned to contract work to other universities and institutions in Costa Rica. In addition to a broader and more equitable distribution of the proceeds from such contracts, it was thought that an enhanced public oversight and a real public participation in the INBIO's planning and decision-making was crucial (Kloppenburg and Rodriguez, 1992).

In conclusion, the INBIO-Merck & Co. Inc. contract set a precedent for compensation for the appropriation of genetic resources by companies; it also enabled Costa Rica to generate financial income from its biological diversity and to direct it toward conservation and development, while providing a framework for training Costa Rican scientific staff. On the other hand, the controversy surrounding the contract demonstrated that, as the value of genetic resources (crop germplasm, wild medicinal plants) was recognized, there were struggles over the equity of the existing social arrangements to regulate access to, and ownership of, those materials. The INBIO precedent was considered inadequate by critics, because it conferred rights to the disposition of a public resource on a private entity, it did not permit sufficient public participation and failed to incorporate mechanisms for recognizing the potentially different rights of various social groups (Kloppenburg and Rodriguez, 1992).

The California-based Shaman Pharmaceuticals was set up in 1989 with an innovative strategy based on the premise that the use of indigenous knowledge greatly improved the odds of finding new active compounds. Shaman was carrying out laboratory analysis of plants used as medicinals in at least three geographically- distinct communities. The company worked with over 30 indigenous communities in Latin America, Africa and South-East Asia. Shaman was striving to find new technologies for drug discovery by integrating ethnobotanical, medical and plant chemical data (Reyes, 1996).

Shaman Pharmaceuticals had not marketed a single product up to 1996, but had made two patent applications in the USA for products derived from the sangre de drago, a plant of the *Croton* genus, widely used throughout the Amazonian basin due to its well-known medicinal properties: Provir, an oral medicine against a respiratory tract virus, and Virend, an anti-herpes medication. The plant species most commonly used was *Croton lechleri*, known for its wound healing, anti-inflammatory, anti-rheumatical, dermatological and anti-haemorrhoidal properties. An alkaloid with a healing capacity was found in the plant (Reyes, 1996).

In October 1992, Shaman sent a research expedition to eastern Ecuador to work with the Quichua indigenous community of Jatún Molino, in Pastaza province. The company planned to talk to the local healer and collect samples of medicinal plants used by the community. Since the company had not yet marketed any products, it was impossible to judge 'reciprocity' in relation to profits (Reyes, 1996).

In Peru, Shaman had signed a contract with the central office of COICA (Coordinadora de Pueblos Indígenas de la Cuenca Amazónica – Co-ordination of the Indigenous People of the Amazonian Basin). Shaman paid COICA a favourable price for the sangre de drago plant resources it needed for research, while the indigenous people co-ordinating the operation guaranteed quality control and sustainable resource management. Payment for collecting plants should not be confused with compensation for knowledge, when the former simply remunerated manual labour (Reyes, 1996).

The company talked about 'long-term reciprocity' once the profits started rolling in, which meant compensation for the communities even if they were no longer working with them. The Ecuadorian Quichuas had been promised compensation once Shaman's first product was marketed and benefit-sharing from any product developed in the future. Yet no mention had been made of what type of compensation would be granted, nor of who would be the beneficiaries. Although Shaman talked about sharing intellectual property rights with local communities, the two sangre de drago-derived products would be patented in the USA under the company's name (Reyes, 1996).

Since September 1993, the University of Arizona had been leading a medical bioprospecting project entitled 'Bioactive agents from dryland plants in Latin America'. This was one of the five projects of the International Cooperative Biodiversity Group (ICBG), sponsored by the U.S. National Institutes of Health (NIH) and the U.S. Agency for International Development. About 800 plant species were collected and classified during the first two and a half years of the project and several U.S. graduate students were conducting ethnobotanical field research in Latin America. A newsletter, *BIO-D Prospect*, informed about the Project development and could be downloaded from the Internet. The University of Arizona was collaborating with the Pontificia Universidad Católica de Chile in Santiago, the Instituto de Recursos Biológicos of the Instituto Nacional de Tecnología Agropecuaria (Institute of

Biological Resources of the National Institute for Agricultural and Livestock Technology, INTA) in Buenos Aires and other universities (Argentina and Mexico). The Project's corporate link was with Wyeth-Ayerst and American Cyanamid Co., The Medical and Agricultural Divisions of American Home Products Corp.

Project director of the College of Pharmacy of the University of Arizona stated that 'Intellectual property agreements were negotiated among all participating institutions before the project began. (...) If new drugs were developed and marketed, a percentage of royalties from the sales will go back to the communities that supplied the plant and to those individuals who provided information about the plant'. In this context, the INTA (Buenos Aires) and the University of California conducted a workshop to discuss, among other issues, Intellectual Property Rights and benefit sharing). Once having detected active compounds, one of the Project's concern (and understanding of benefit sharing) was the commercial production of these bioactive compounds by developing cash crop projects in the country of origin. The workshop, held in Buenos Aires from 28 to 29 March 1996, started to define the Project's own implementation of Farmers' Rights, claiming to be the 'first national and one of the first international workshops' doing so. It was concluded that half of the obtained benefits from license agreements would be used for the conservation of biological diversity and for agricultural projects agreed upon by the bioprospectors and representatives of local and indigenous communities. In the interest of the companies, these cash crop projects needed absolute confidentiality in the first stages. But even though the bioprospecting Project already collected 200 medicinal plant samples in Argentina, no representatives of local communities were ever consulted about it.

Since 1986, Biotics Ltd, a British corporation with headquarters in Guildford, Surrey, had been running a programme with European Commission support to promote the phytochemical screening of developing country flora by industrial and other specialized research organizations. In addition to the discovery and sustainable exploitation of new high-value plant products, the objectives of the Phytochemical Screening Programme were to enhance co-operation between Europe and developing countries, and to promote biotechnologies locally.

The Phytochemical Screening Programme ensured that participating developing countries received royalty payments or equivalent benefits linked to the commercialization of indigenous natural products. Inevitably, these benefits were realized downstream from the initial 'investment' of phytochemical resources. For that reason, Biotics Ltd was also promoting projects that could provide significant benefits in the short term, such as training and data-base development. This was the company's way of strengthening the skilled manpower base of developing countries for the exploitation of their phytochemical resources. At the same time, it sought to establish a standard protocol for reproducible extractions of indigenous flora, while providing opportunities for visiting specialists to pursue their own research.

The following categories of information were compulsory for a phytochemical computer data-base, considered an early priority: botanical aspects, chemotaxonomic aspects, ethnopharmacological features, chemical constituents, pharmacological and toxicological data (inclusive of clinical trials), agronomic data and propagation techniques, methods of processing and processed drug forms and formulations, methods of quality assessment, patented processes and holders of technology, market data (import and export statistics of raw plant drugs, including quantities, producer and importing countries).

Furthermore, specific collaboration had been discussed with the United Nations Industrial Development Organization (UNIDO) and a joint UNIDO/Biotics Ltd workshop was organized at the University of Sussex on The industrial utilization of medicinal plants. In addition to international collaboration, the workshop focused on two areas relative to the Phytochemical Screening Programme, namely training in phytochemistry and the development of national phytochemical data-bases.

A pilot project was launched early in 1989 involving the screening of Ghanaian flora by the British pharmaceutical group Glaxo plc. A second agreement was finalized months later between the British Technology Group and the Republic of Cameroon. Plant material collected by the Royal Botanic Gardens, Kew, was subsequently screened at Rothamsted Experimental Station (Agricultural and Food Research Council) for new insecticidal compounds, in a project funded by the British Technology Group.

Imperial Chemical Industries (ICI) Ltd was investigating the pharmacodynamic action of a collection of 200 extracts of Mauritian plants under an agreement with Mauritius, also arranged by Biotics Ltd. The British pharmaceutical company, SmithKline Beecham plc, drew most of the plant material for its natural product screening programme from Ghana and Malaysia, supplied through Biotics Ltd. In Thailand, systematic chemical evaluation of natural products had been discussed between Biotics Ltd and the chairman of the Department of Chemistry, Mahidol University. Chemical screening was facilitated by the 1987 compilation of Thai Medicinal Plants, specially prepared for the First Princess Chulabhorn Science Congress, an international congress on natural products, held in Bangkok. Of the 5,800 plant species indigenous to Thailand, 3,900 had not received any chemical, pharmacological or toxicological investigation prior to 1981.

In 1991, Biotics' programme involved the screening of more than 1,000 plant samples by bio-industrial organizations in the USA and United Kingdom. Biotics Ltd had set up a commercial laboratory facility, BioEx, for the preparation of plant extracts, which was also expected to train plant chemists from developing countries. It was hoped that BioEx would lead to the setting up in developing countries of a series of small-scale extraction laboratories operating in association with Biotics' screening programme (Komen, 1991*e*).

Its partnership with Bristol-Myers Squibb Co. (USA) would allow any interesting leads to be developed into products in a spirit of benefit-sharing. Bristol-Myers Squibb Co. would look for anti-infectious and dermatological medicinal compounds, and would screen for compounds with applications in cancer, cardio-vascular and central nervous system diseases. Similarly, as part of its benefit-sharing package with West African collaborators, Shaman Pharmaceuticals (USA) had provided laboratory materials and scholarships to a Nigerian research laboratory working on plant treatments for malaria and other diseases prevalent in the tropics of West Africa (Ten Kate, 1995).

There was also considerable potential for initiating collaborative screening of flora from Arab countries. These countries spanned a wide range of climatic and soil conditions, and had a broad plant genetic diversity; the Arabian Peninsula alone hosted 4,500–5,000 different plant species. This potential was highlighted in 1982 by a UNIDO Report (Medicinal and aromatic plants for industrial development) prepared at the request of the Arab Company for Drug Industries and Medical Appliances (ACDIMA). The Report underlined that phytochemicals and plant extracts were widely used as therapeutic agents in many Arab countries, about 20 phytochemicals and over 80 crude extracts being included in formulations regularly marketed. A detailed survey by leading companies in Egypt, Sudan, Syria and Iraq revealed that more than 25% of the trade items marketed by them contained one or more plant products.

Relevant programmes were already under way in natural product chemistry in several Arab countries, notably at the University of Jordan (Department of Chemistry), in Amman, where a new Natural Product Centre was planned, the ACDIMA and the Arab Pharmaceutical Manufacturing Company Ltd.

Biotics Ltd was considering the potential for extending the above strategy to include the in-depth phytochemical screening of economically important agricultural species. The aim was to identify new sources of marketable chemicals at considerably reduced costs. Using existing technologies, chemical inventories could be compiled of otherwise discarded agricultural residues, such as sugar-cane bagasse or, in the Arab region, date-palm residues; the same analytical procedure might equally be applied to marginal crops of importance to farmers in poorer rural areas.

In Canada, Botanical Alternatives Inc. had broad interests which included natural insecticides and replacements for synthetics. Efamol Inc. and Bioriginal Corp. were among the firms producing natural lipids with therapeutic properties. TPL Phytogen Inc. (formerly Towers Phytochemicals) and other therapeutics firms were involved in the taxol business. Canamino Inc. had progressed to large-scale production of selected natural products from oats. Fytokem Products Inc. was also searching for new commercial molecules. The herbal business in Canada and the USA was resurgent after nearly a century of eclipse.

The first link in the business chain in both Canada and the USA was the small grower or professional harvester of wild plants. The raw materials were then processed into powdered or pelleted forms, extracts or particular molecular products. These processors in turn passed the materials on to companies manufacturing brand-name products for retail sale to end-users.

The Japanese Marine Biotechnology Institute regularly collected samples of potentially valuable marine resources in the waters near Yap (Federated States of Micronesia) and other Pacific islands. They hoped to find bacteria which could be used to clean up oil spills, new agents to replace toxic barnacle-resistant paints, phytoplankton species that could turn atmospheric carbon dioxide into compost and pharmacologically active compounds. This could prove to be a highly lucrative business for the Institute, which was funded by private and public sources. It was estimated that as much as half of the next generation of pharmaceuticals would come from marine biotechnology research.

The Micronesian authorities were not yet benefiting much from the deal. In exchange for access to their waters, which contained about 60% of the world's coral species, the government received a copy of research reports, an analysis of the quality of sea-water and training for local scientists.

7. Production and processing of plant-derived medicines in developing countries

Some developing countries had started processing medicinal plants on a large scale. Research on traditional drugs in The Philippines had led to the identification of more than 300 medicinal plants. Researchers had interviewed over 1,000 village medicine men throughout the country. In 1989, a herbal medicine processing factory was set up in the Cotabato Province (Komen, 1991e).

The first of its kind in Asia when it opened in 1993, the Centre for Natural Product Research (CNPR) in Singapore studied plants and other natural products as potential cures for certain diseases, including cancer. It also studied traditional medicines, such as Chinese and Malay herbal remedies, to understand why these were effective. The Centre's primary objective being to operate and develop throughput screens in the search for bioactive molecules in natural products, the collecting of plant and soil samples was essential. Marine, microbial (equatorial fungi) and plant organism extracts were screened to isolate small molecules of therapeutic value. Members of the Centre's 30-strong professional staff planned to extend the collecting of samples in Singapore (an agreement had been signed with Singapore's Botanical Gardens for the supply of samples from local and regional plant species) to include other countries of the Asia-Pacific region. It had become common practice in the region for researchers to sign agreements with the countries from which they collected samples, so that the latter might share in any possible commercial profit if the product proved utilizable.

The Centre owed its existence to a joint venture between the British pharmaceutical group, Glaxo plc, Singapore's Economic Development Board (EDB) and the Institute for Molecular and Cell Biology (IMCB). Located at the IMCB at the National University of Singapore (NUS), the CNPR benefited from IMCB's experience in biology and biomedical sciences and from Glaxo's expertise. Prior to the Centre's opening, all scientific staff had been sent for training to Glaxo in the United Kingdom. Glaxo plc had a huge 'extract library' of plants already screened and was particularly helpful in providing the Singaporean team with new screens (bioassays) derived from its medical research. Part of the British pharmaceutical group's strength lay in the fact that it targeted screening efforts toward eight major therapeutic areas. Glaxo plc was not relying on random toxicity trials or conventional bioassays, but on such screens as specific cells, receptors and physiological signals, whose reaction to the extract indicated the potential for therapeutic utilization. Therefore, the results of screening depended as much on the biological activity of the samples as on the development of appropriate screens by sophisticated biomedical research, which was generally carried out by the big pharmaceutical corporations.

As far as funding was concerned, Glaxo plc had provided an initial S$20 million and EDB a total of S$10 million, the IMCB contributing the equivalent of S$10 million in research and infrastructural support; the IMCB was itself funded by Singapore's National Science and Technology Board. Over the first ten years, funding for the venture was guaranteed by the three co-founders, at an estimated total cost of more than S$60 million for the period up to 2003.

The CNPR approach and its partnership with Glaxo plc (comparable to the partnership between the INBIO in Costa Rica and Merck & Co. Inc.) showed clearly that a venture of this kind was not within the reach of all research institutions in a developing country. It was true that a number of developing countries wished to embark on screening their genetic resources to isolate new medicinal products; it was also true that building up an 'extract library' was not that difficult to achieve and that it could even be traded. Nevertheless, a screening venture could not be successful without strong research backstopping to provide the sophisticated screens (i.e. cells, enzymes, physiological signals, etc.) needed for identifying the biologically active compounds. At a later stage, once a compound was discovered, its development into a commercial product was another complex and costly venture.

Established by the National University of Singapore and the Economic Development Board (EDB) in 1994, the Bioscience Centre (BSC) was conducting and co-ordinating multidisciplinary research from its facilities in the University's Zoology Department. An initial grant of about S$6 million had been approved by the EDB for setting up the Centre. Enjoying core facilities and specialized equipment, the BSC promoted research by staff and students of the biological sciences departments of the NUS, on an individual department or collaborative basis. The Centre's main objectives were to:

– provide a multi-user central facility for research in biotechnologies relating to agrotechnology, aquaculture, horticulture, environmental management and marine living resources and pharmaceutical industries;

– conduct research on biologically active compounds from animals, plants and micro-organisms;

– serve as a vehicle for collaborating with industries and other institutions in Singapore or abroad in biotechnology-related programmes; provide a mechanism for establishing linkages and collaborations with overseas institutions and companies, as well as for initiating exchange programmes with institutions abroad;

– provide training for both undergraduate and post-graduate students through practical or project work undertaken at the Centre. The hands-on training and research experience would support the development of bio-industries in Singapore.

The following projects were being conducted or co-ordinated by the BSC:

– structure-function relationship of stonustoxin, a lethal toxin isolated from stonefish venom; this relationship was studied by modifying the molecule chemically, mapping the functional domains of the toxin by using monoclonal antibodies and locating a small fragment of the molecule for use as a pharmacological agent; stonustoxin exhibited potent hypotensive activity even in a tiny dose in the rat and human, giving it potential for being a candidate pharmacological agent in the treatment of hypertension;

– isolation and characterization of novel restriction enzymes from micro-organisms; the large battery of restriction enzymes available commercially were mainly Type II endonucleases, the majority recognizing 4–6 nucleotides; many of these endonucleases had been found with 7- and 8-base recognition sites; there were only about eight Type II restriction enzymes that recognized an octanucleotide sequence and most of these rare-cutters commanded a good price;

– screening for anti-malarial compounds from sponges and other marine organisms;

– isolation, purification and characterization of anti-microbial compounds in the blood cells of horseshoe crabs and study of the molecular basis of the anti-bacterial mechanisms; the gene for Factor C from the blood cells of horseshoe crabs had been cloned; it was being introduced into expression systems to obtain recombinant Factor C, which would be used to develop a test kit for Gram-negative bacteria;

– identification and characterization of new anti-coagulant and anti-platelet proteins from snake venoms; attempts to identify novel toxins from scorpion venoms were also under way, with a view to searching for specific ion channel blockers which affected neurotransmission; structure-function studies of these toxins could lead to novel pharmaceutical agents;

– isolation, purification and characterization of biologically active components from: sea anemones, jelly fishes, starfishes, micro-algae and corals; a non-enzymatic cytolysin, magnificalysin, had been isolated and characterized from a sea anemone and showed cytolytic and cardiotonic activities; research was under way to identify the specific sites determining these biological reactions and understand structure-function relationships of other sea anemone protein toxins, particularly phospholipases; the benthic Dinoflagellates and blue-green algae were rich sources of strain-specific biologically active compounds including ion-channel modulators and some of the most potent anti-fungal agents known; the BSC had collaborative links with Australian research institutions on compounds from benthic Dinoflagellates; work was being carried out on isolating and purifying the components of *Galaxea fascicularis* from the mucus of this coral species with cytotoxicity, haemolysis and procoagulation; as far as sessile marine animals were concerned, culture systems of the larvae of barnacles and other marine fouling organisms were being explored, in order to develop bioassays for anti-fouling compounds that would prevent the settling of fouling larvae on a surface;

– screening for insecticides and insect repellents from tropical plants might provide safe and non-toxic substances for use in the control of stored-product pests and other insects; as part of research on anti-coagulant and anti-platelet agents (which slowed the growth of various tumours and were important in preventing heart attacks), the BSC had set up primary screens for these agents from a variety of plants; anti-cancer and anti-HIV I protease compounds from plants and marine organisms were being extracted for screening.

In China, more than 40,000 different kinds of traditional plant drugs were produced. Some 60 factories were producing plant drugs, providing the country with a significant source of foreign exchange that was expected to grow (Komen, 1991*e*).

On 16 April 1994, the WHO made public the results of a study on treatment of acute forms of malaria. Carried out in Eastern Thailand over two years, the study was supervised by Dr.J. Karbwang of Mahidol University, Bangkok. It concerned 97 people affected by acute forms of malaria. The study showed that injections of artemether, an artemisinin derivative, were effective in treating these patients. Artemisinin or qinghaosu, extracted from *Artemisia annua*, had previously been identified as a possible anti-malaria drug, following a study made in China in 1972 on traditional medicine. The WHO's results demonstrated that, when treated with quinin, 18 patients out of 50 died while, when treated with artemether, only six out of 47 died. The WHO specialists concluded that, despite the restricted test group, the results were encouraging (Nau, 1994).

Other clinical trials with the same drug were being carried out in China, Viet Nam, Brazil and in several African countries where malaria was endemic. The artemether was produced by a Chinese laboratory and was being marketed at world level (e.g. in Côte d'Ivoire, Madagascar, Kenya and Nigeria) under the name of Paluther by the French chemical and pharmaceutical group Rhône-Poulenc-Rorer. The Government of Viet Nam decided to develop a cheap process of cultivating the plant locally as well as a simple extraction procedure of artemisinin from the leaves (Nau, 1994).

The main risk of the uncontrolled use of artemisinin and its derivatives was that the malaria parasites could become resistant to them. That is why the WHO recommended that the substances of this family be used in association with other drugs, such as mefloquin or doxycycline only in the areas where the parasites showed multiresistance to anti-malaria drugs. For its part, Rhône-Poulenc-Rorer stated that, for ethical reasons, this injectable drug was only recommended in the treatment of acute forms of malaria (Nau, 1994).

According to an announcement by the Swiss chemical and pharmaceutical company Ciba-Geigy AG[9] (see p. 248) in November 1994, an agreement had been signed with three Chinese partners [Institute of Microbiology and Epidemiology in Beijing, Kunming Pharmaceutical Factory in Kunming and CITIC (China International Trust Investments Corp.) Technology Inc. of Beijing] to develop a new anti-malaria drug. The latter would combine benflumetol, an anti-malaria substance developed at the Institute of Microbiology and Epidemiology, and artemether. The synergistic combination had proven effective against the disease and could be administered over a short period of time, according to Ciba-Geigy AG. There had already been clinical trials of the new drug in China and further trials were planned in Africa, East Asia and Europe in 1995–1996, so as to bring the drug onto the market as early as 1997. The finished product would be produced for export at Ciba-Geigy AG's facility in Changping, near Beijing, whereas the biologically active ingredients of the drug would be produced by the joint venture; the finished product for the domestic market would be produced at the Kunming Pharmaceutical Factory (*Asian Wall Street Journal*, Manila, 5 December 1994).

Research on medicinal plants in Madagascar had resulted in the discovery of valuable drugs. The most important medicinal plant in Madagascar was *Catharanthus roseus* (rosy periwinkle), which was used throughout the world to treat a variety of cancers and specifically for treating leukaemia in children. Two plant chemical compounds extracted from *C. roseus*, vinblastine and vincristine, possessed tumour-inhibiting properties. The plant's active content was, however, extremely low. Approximately two tonnes of crushed leaves yielded one gram of the two compounds, enough to treat a child for six weeks. Vincristine and vinblastine were discovered in the research laboratories of the American company, Eli Lilly & Co., which immediately recovered exclusive marketing rights through patent protection. In Madagascar, all medicinal plants for commercial use, with the exception of *C. roseus*, were collected from wild sources, resulting in the gradual disappearance of some species. For instance, due to indiscriminate collection and lack of cultivation, *Rauwolfia confertiflora* had almost disappeared. This plant species contained large quantities of reserpine, used in treating hypertension. *C. roseus* was widely grown on a commercial scale because of the increasing demand. Madagascar exported about 1,000 tonnes of *Catharantus roseus* annually; two companies, SOPRAEX and IMRA, were also actively working toward extracting plant materials on a commercial scale (Komen, 1991*e*).

8. Utilization of biotechnologies for the production of pharmaceuticals and phytochemicals

Plant tissue cultures could be used for the production of pharmaceuticals (alkaloids, steroids, terpenoids, flavonoids, enzymes), food additives (carotenoids, anthocyanins, betalains, vanilla), perfumes (rose, lavender, sandalwood oil, agarwood oil) and biopesticides. The utility of plant tissue cultures had been recognized in the early 1940s, but it was only in 1956 that the first patent on plant cell cultures was awarded to Routin and Nickel (U.S. patent 2,747,334). It would take another decade to demonstrate that plant cells in culture could produce metabolites in reasonable amounts. Kaul and Staba (1967) reported the production of visnagin by callus cultures of *Ammi visnaga*; Heble *et al.* (1968) reported the production of diosgenin by callus cultures of *Solanum xanthocarpum* (in Heble, 1993). The spurt in activity resulting from these demonstrations spawned the establishment of plant cell cultures with high amounts of metabolites:

Product	Plant species	Tissue culture (% dry biomass)	Plant (% dry biomass)
Ajmalicine	*Catharanthus roseus*	1.00	0.30
Anthraquinones	*Cassia tora*	0.33	0.21
	Morinda citrifolia	18.00	2.20
Diosgenin	*Dioscorea deltoidea*	2.00	2.00
Ginsenoside	*Panax ginseng*	(fresh biomass) 0.38	0.3–3.3

It had been observed that molecular, cellular and organ differentiation influenced product biosynthesis. For instance, Heble *et al.*, working with tissue cultures of *Plumbago zeylanica*, reported that plumbagin (2-methyl, 5-hydroxy, 1-4-naphthaquinone) synthesis occurred in the highly specialized pigmented cells; the cells could be selected from a heterogenous mass and cultured as a pure strain. Subsequently, similar observations had been made by Tabata *et al.* in tissue cultures of *Nicotiana tabacum*. Several methods had been used to select cell lines with high productivity, the simplest being visual selection on the basis of colour as in the case of *Plumbago* and *Lithospermum*. It was also possible to select clones by plating the cell suspensions and/or protoplasts. Working with *Coptis japonica*, Yamada *et al.* observed that selection of aggregates was more effective than single cells for the production of berberine (in Heble, 1993).

A large number of compounds are the products of organogenesis. In tissue cultures of *Atropa belladonna*, the synthesis of tropane alkaloids was associated with complete differentiation and development of plantlets. Similar observations were made with tissue cultures of *Tylophora indica* and *Artemisia annua*. Partially differentiated structures, such as multiple shoots and roots in culture, also produced substantial amounts of useful compounds: working with shoot cultures of *Rauwolfia serpentina*, Roja *et al.* observed that they produced more ajmaline than the roots of the parent plant and the cultures exhibited biochemical stability for long periods; shoot cultures of *Withania somnifera* produced significant amounts of withanolides; multiple shoot cultures of *Catharanthus roseus* produced vinblastine; root cultures of *Hyoscyamus muticus* synthesized high amounts of scopolamine (0.3%), a high-value drug. Organ cultures were generally stable, but it was difficult to cultivate them in big bioreactors (in Heble, 1993).

However, cultures could produce secondary metabolites even in the absence of organogenesis, e.g. those of *Catharanthus roseus*, *Dioscorea deltoidea* and *Rauwolfia serpentina*. Also, some of the important cultures belonging to this category were those of *Morinda citrifolia*, *Panax ginseng*, *Linum flavum* and *Glycyrrhiza glabra* (Heble, 1993).

The regulatory influence of auxins and cytokinins on the production of secondary metabolites by tissue culture had been reported in the 1970s in *Solanum khasianum* and *Nicotiana tabacum*. Working with *Catharanthus roseus*, Zenk *et al.* observed that growth hormones added to the medium strongly influenced the production of ajmalicine and serpentine. Similar observations had been made in *Dioscorea* cultures where diosgenin synthesis was influenced by the type of auxin added to the culture medium (in Heble, 1993).

Plant cells and organs had been successfully grown in 2-litre to 75,000-litre capacity bioreactors under precise nutritional and phytohormonal regimes. There were already industrial processes established for shikonin from *Lithospermum erythrorhizon*, ginsenosides from *Panax ginseng*, anhydrovinblastine from *Catharanthus roseus* and polysaccharides from *Echinacea pallida* (Heble, 1993).

The biggest bioreactor for plant cells had been developed in Germany (75,000-litre capacity) by the Diversa Company for the cultivation of *Echinacea* cells for the production of polysaccharides. A 20,000-litre bioreactor had been used by Nitto Electrical Industrial Co. Ltd for the production of *Panax ginseng* cells. Bioreactors of 200–800-litre capacity had been used for the growth of *Coleus blumei*, *Coptis japonica* and *Catharanthus roseus* cell cultures. There was considerable interest in developing bioreactors for organ cultures like multiple shoots and hairy roots, the latter of which had been grown in 500-litre bioreactors (Heble, 1993).

By using immobilized plant cells, the working volume for a given product formation could be effectively reduced; cell efficiency could be increased. Different types of bioreactors had been used with success for immobilized cells: Morris *et al.* (1983) cultured immobilized cells of *Catharanthus* in fluidized bed chemostat; Kabayashi *et al.* (1987) had developed a bioreactor for producing berberine by immobilized cells of *Thalictrum minus*. In these systems, products were leached out into the culture media and downstream processing would be even easier (in Heble, 1993).

Cell cultures had been used for the biotransformation of various exogenous substrates. These transformations included stereospecific reactions, such as hydroxylation, oxidation, reduction, glycosylation, esterification, epoxidation, hydrolysis, isomerization and dehydration. Alkaloids, such as codeinone, cathenamine, papaverine, tetrahydroberberine and anhydrovinblastine, had been used as substrates. Immobilized cells of *Digitalis lanata* performed efficient biotransformation of beta-methyldigitoxin to beta-methyldigoxin. A large number of monoterpenes had been transformed by plant cell cultures (Heble, 1993).

An industrially important transformation achieved was that of cardinolides of the digitoxin type. Working with cells of *Digitalis lanata*, Alfermann *et al.* (1983) demonstrated the scale-up from 1-litre flask cultures to a 200-litre bioreactor; the cells could transform beta-methyl-digitoxin to beta-methyl-digoxin from day 1 to day 18. Working with a selected cell line of *Digitalis lanata*, Heble observed that the biotransformation of beta-methyl-digitoxin occurred throughout the culture period in a 20-litre airlift bioreactor; the transformation was not affected by the growth cycle and at the end of day 30, 1 g per litre tranformation was observed; more than 95% of the substrate had been tranformed into a single product. Cell cultures therefore had the advantage of maximum substrate utilization together with stereospecificity in biotransformation (in Heble, 1993).

Certain enzymes involved in the biosynthesis of phytochemicals had been purified and the gene coding for them identified for transfer. For instance, the gene for a key enzyme in the indole alkaloid biosynthesis, strictosidine synthase, had been transferred to *Escherichia coli*; the gene for the sweet protein monellin had been transferred to plants. Gene cloning and transfer for viable production of phytochemicals was still in its infancy since the biosynthetic pathways for most of the chemicals were not clearly understood (Heble, 1993).

The transformation of roots by *Agrobacterium rhizogenes* into hairy roots and their subsequent cultivation in large-capacity bioreactors could be advantageous for the production of some useful compounds. Fast growth – from a single root tip, hairy root culture could grow from 2,500 to 5,000 times its size in three weeks – gave root cultures several other advantages, including a natural defence against infection. Japanese firms using this technique to scale up ginseng root cultures had applied for protection of their results (Komen, 1991*e*; Sasson, 1992*a,b*).

Analogous techniques for producing genetically-transformed shoots had been developed: 'shooty teratomas' were induced by infecting plant cells with certain strains of *Agrobacterium tumefaciens* and produced shoot-derived compounds *in vitro*. The molecular bases of shooty teratoma development were not as well understood as those of hairy root formation and the number of plant species successfully transformed to teratomas was much smaller than for hairy roots.

While hairy roots and shooty teratomas had been shown to produce high amounts of metabolites with good culture stability, the most challenging engineering problems were oxygen mass transfer and mixing. In submerged cultures, hairy roots tended to form dense, sponge-like clumps which were not easily penetrated by convective currents. At the Department of Biotechnology of the University of New South Wales, Sydney, experiments with *Atropa belladonna* hairy roots in a controlled flow apparatus and in airlift and stirred reactors had shown that intraclump dissolved oxygen concentrations were readily reduced to less than 20% air saturation depending on the clump size, root density and liquid flow velocity. In addition, the apparent critical oxygen tension for hairy roots in the absence of external mass transfer limitations was found to be relatively high at approximately 90% air saturation, most probably because of internal resistance associated with the root tissue itself. This meant that most large-scale root cultures without oxygen supplementation were very likely to be oxygen-limited.

If, in the whole plant, a precursor compound was synthesized in the roots then transported to the leaves for conversion into a more desirable or valuable product, separate shoot and root cultures would not be able to achieve complete synthesis *in vitro*. At the Department of Biotechnology of the University of New South Wales, a new mode of co-culturing roots and shoots in the same medium had been developed in order to synthesize, translocate and biotransform pharmaceutical alkaloids. So far, co-culture of roots and shoots had been very successful for producing the anticholinergic drug, scopolamine. The precursor metabolite, hyoscyamine, was synthesized in the roots, released into the medium, taken up by the shoots then converted enzymatically into scopolamine. The co-culture method had been applied to using the same plant species (*Atropa belladonna*) for the root and shoot components, and for cross-species co-culture where the roots and shoots were from different plants (*Atropa belladonna* and a *Duboisia leichhardtii* x *D. myoporoides* hybrid respectively) to expand the range of bioconversions that could take place. Of the steps involved in the co-culture process, the bioconversion was found to be rate-limiting. Factors such as the root/shoot fresh biomass weight inoculum ratio were also of critical importance to the success of the co-culture technique.

Modern pharmaceutical interest in taxol went back to the 1960s, but the medicinal properties of the yew tree had been known for centuries. In one of his seven books, collectively entitled On the Gallic Wars, published in 51 B.C., Julius Caesar recorded the death of the chieftain Catuvolcus, who committed suicide by drinking tea made from yew bark. In the northwestern USA, native American tribes such as the Quinault, Multnomah and Nez Percé utilized the Pacific yew bark as a disinfectant, an abortifacient and as a treatment for skin cancer (Nicolaou *et al.*, 1996).

In 1962, the botanist Arthur Barclay of the U.S. Department of Agriculture started the yew on a long and circuitous journey back to one of the most valuable trees in the Pacific Northwestern forests. The yew tree rehabilitation co-incided with a request by the National Cancer Institute (NCI) that researchers sample natural sources, such as plants, bacteria and marine organisms, in the hope of finding substances that might be useful as pharmaceuticals. Barclay chose to collect bark from Pacific yew trees in the Gifford Pinchot National Forest, located in Washington State (Nicolaou *et al.*, 1996).

222

Barclay's yew samples eventually ended up at the Research Triangle Institute in North Carolina. There, two chemists, Wani and Wall, discovered that a mixture containing the yew bark killed artificially-preserved leukaemia cells. By 1967, Wani and Wall had isolated the active ingredient from the mixture: a previously unknown chemical that they christened taxol because of its similarities to the family of chemicals known as taxanes and because the substance was found in plants of the genus *Taxus*. Although the name 'taxol' was still widely used generically, the pharmaceutical company Bristol-Myers Squibb Co. had registered Taxol as a trademark and encouraged the scientific community to use 'paclitaxel' instead. A 100-year-old Pacific yew tree (*Taxus brevifolia*) could provide only 1 gram of taxol, about half the amount needed for a single treatment (Nicolaou *et al.*, 1996).

The NCI did not consider the compound particularly promising. In early tests, other drugs worked just as well as, or better than, taxol for cancer treatment. But Wall, acting on a strong faith in its potential, continued to champion the substance to the NCI. In 1977, the agency agreed to investigate the matter further. But even after additional study, taxol still did not stand out from drugs already in the anti-cancer pipeline (Nicolaou *et al.*, 1996).

In 1978, Horwitz and one of her graduate students, Schiff, demonstrated that taxol killed cancer cells in a manner unlike that of any other drug known at the time. Over the next ten years, Horwitz's group probed the details of how taxol functioned in the human body. In particular, the team found that taxol bound to structures in the cell known as microtubules, which served as part of the cytoskeleton. When taxol attached itself to microtubules, these became extremely stable and static, making cell division impossible, thus killing the cells just as they began to divide[10] (see p. 248). Cancer cells divided more frequently than healthy cells, so the drug primarily attacked tumours in which runaway cell division occurred. But other rapidly dividing cells, such as white blood cells or hair cells, could also be affected; consequently, taxol was not without side effects when used to treat cancer. For instance, taxol could suppress a patient's immune system, deaden sensory nerves or cause nausea and hair loss (Nicolaou *et al.*, 1996).

By 1984, physicians at a number of hospitals, including the Dana-Farber Cancer Institute in Boston, Johns Hopkins Oncology Center in Baltimore, and Memorial Sloan-Kettering Cancer Center in New York City, began the first stage of human clinical trials to assess the safety of taxol. In one of these surveys, Rowinsky and his associates at Johns Hopkins reported unprecedented results: in more than 30% of patients whose tumours had previously defied conventional chemotherapy, taxol reduced the size of the growths; one patient was even cured. Other studies soon echoed these findings and taxol quickly slipped onto the pharmaceutical fast track (Nicolaou *et al.*, 1996).

Between 1984 and 1989, physicians could conduct only a limited number of extensive clinical trials. In 1989, the NCI and Bristol-Myers Squibb Co. signed a contract that arranged for the company to produce the compound for the NCI in exchange for gaining access to the results of the NCI's clinical trials. Soon after, Bristol-Myers Squibb Co. began large-scale harvesting of the Pacific yew, but predicted that supplies would last only five years (Nicolaou *et al.*, 1996).

Escagenetics Corp. (San Carlos, California) reported the successful production of taxol using the hairy root technique. Escagenetics' commercial production of tissue culture-derived vanillin had led the company into taxol tissue culture. Escagenetics Corp. was able to produce taxol at concentrations higher than those found in the bark and needles of the yew. The company's proprietary technique was also said to outyield the callus culture technique that Phyton Catalytic (New York, USA) was licensing from the U.S. Department of Agriculture to produce 'taxol or taxol-like compounds' on a pilot scale (Komen, 1991*e*).

Phytopharmaceuticals (India) had entered into an agreement (1994) with Sun Hill Glucose Co. Ltd of the Republic of Korea, a subsidiary of the Sam Young Group, for the production of taxol via plant tissue culture. The process had been tested in bioreactors with a capacity of up to 4,500 litres. Commercial production would be on scale of more than 30,000 litres, according to the Chairman of Escagenetics Corp., Phytopharmaceuticals' parent company. The resulting concentration of taxol on a dry biomass basis was said to be two orders of magnitude higher than that from the bark of the Pacific yew, which was not a source used in Phytopharmaceuticals' process.

Chemists exhibited a serious interest in taxol. Between 1983 and 1993, more than 30 research groups struggled to synthesize taxol or simpler, related compounds. But taxol, which contained 112 atoms, proved to be an exceedingly difficult molecule to construct; at times, it seemed unconquerable. Initially, many groups explored the technique known as semisynthesis in their attempts. In the early 1980s, Potier at the National Centre for Scientific Research of France (CNRS), along with Greene and his colleagues at the Joseph Fournier University in Grenoble, carried out the first successful semisynthesis of taxol. The investigators observed that taxol could be dissected into two parts: the complex centre of the molecule, known as the taxane core, and a simpler structure known as the side chain, connected to the core. While Potier and his group were screening the European yew (*Taxus baccata*) for taxol-like substances, they realized that the taxane core could be isolated from the needles of this plant species. They then figured out a straightforward way to attach the side chain. As the team obtained the taxane core from needles, which grew back after harvesting, the procedure offered hope that supplies of taxol might not always be limited (Nicolaou *et al.*, 1996).

During the summer of 1991, the U.S. Patent and Trademark Office granted a patent to Florida State University for a novel method of making a semi-synthetic version of the anti-cancer drug. The technique combined a substance called baccatin III with a synthetic chain to make a structure identical to natural taxol. Baccatin III was extracted from the needles of the common English yew, a relative of the Pacific yew (Komen, 1991*e*).

In 1993, Bristol-Myers Squibb Co. announced that it would no longer be harvesting Pacific yews. The company had adopted a process for the commercial production of taxol that was initially developed independently by Ojima of the State University of New York at Stony Brook and by Holton of Florida State University (Nicolaou *et al.*, 1996).

In 1994, the U.S. Food and Drug Administration (FDA) approved semisynthetic taxol, made in the laboratory and available in unlimited quantities, for the treatment of various cancers. Early that year, a team of physicians based at Emory University announced results from an extensive study of the drug. Instead of lamenting its scarcity, the researchers emphasized its unexpected potency. According to the findings, women suffering from advanced ovarian cancer who took taxol in combination with another anti-cancer medication lived an average of 14 months longer than patients who received other therapies. Taxol was therefore considered one of the most promising treatments for breast and ovarian cancers. Other studies demonstrated its effectiveness against lung cancer and melanoma (Nicolaou *et al.*, 1996).

As Potier, Greene and others focused their efforts on producing taxol by semisynthesis, researchers elsewhere, including Nicolaou and Guy at the Scripps Research Institute, continued to work on its total synthesis. In early 1994, two groups almost simultaneously reported total synthesis. Nicolaou, Guy and their colleagues first published the results of their work in *Nature*; Holton's group recounted its success in the *Journal of the American Chemical Society*. To further streamline the efficiency of their method, Nicolaou *et al.* assembled taxol using what is called convergent synthesis. Using this approach, one began with several small pieces and joined them together to obtain the desired product; in contrast, linear synthesis involved modifying a single starting compound sequentially. The final structure could be altered in a convergent synthesis fairly easily by introducing different building blocks at any stage of the process; in a linear synthesis, the choice of building blocks was much more restricted (Nicolaou *et al.*, 1996).

In 1991, Potier and his colleagues produced the first notable taxoid, which they named taxotère (N-dibenzoyl-N-tert-butoxycarbonyl-10-deacetyl taxol); it was prepared by semisynthesis from 10-deacetyl baccatin III, a non-cytotoxic precursor extracted from the needles of the European yew tree, *Taxus baccata*, which was then condensed by esterification with the side chain prepared by chemical synthesis.

Taxotère retained the unique mechanism of action of taxol and inhibited the depolymerization of microtubules to tubulin. At Rhône-Poulenc Rorer, Central Research and Clinical Research, it was found that, *in vitro*, taxotère was cytotoxic against murine and human tumour cells, *in vivo* against B16 melanoma. Nine out of the eleven murine tumours tested responded to taxotère. It was also found active with 80% complete regressions against advanced colon adenocarcinoma C38 and pancreatic ductal adenocarcinoma PO3. Toxicological studies had been performed on dogs and mice according to the U.S. National Cancer Institute's guidelines. Toxicological effects were observed mostly in tissues with high cell turnover (bone marrow, gastro-intestinal duct in mice and dogs) or in those where microtubules played an important role (peripheral nerves in mice only).

Physicians in Japan and Europe commonly used taxotère as a therapy for breast and ovarian cancers; in late 1995, the U.S. FDA approved taxotère for women with drug-resistant or metastatic breast cancer. Taxotère and taxol appeared to have subtle differences in their ability to treat certain cancers. Extensive use of both drugs in clinical trials would allow scientists to define any advantages that one might have over the other (Nicolaou *et al.*, 1996).

Nicolaou, Guy and their colleagues at the Scripps Research Institute had produced two important classes of taxol derivatives that might one day yield functional pharmaceuticals. First, they simplified the taxol structure and produced a taxoid that was somewhat easier to make than taxol but, in preliminary tests, could still kill certain types of cancer cells. Secondly, the group developed a class of taxoids that differed slightly at what seemed to be the region of taxol that attached to microtubules. Scientists were pursuing work to improve taxol potency by tinkering with this binding site and thus making taxol more efficient at connecting to microtubules and preventing cell division (Nicolaou *et al.*, 1996).

Due to its very low solubility in water, doctors currently administered taxol intravenously over a period of hours; the liquid medium used in this process, Cremophor El, had caused complications in some patients. A water-soluble compound would be much easier to handle. One new taxoid developed at the Scripps Research Institute dissolved in water and could possibly be administered with fewer side effects (Nicolaou *et al.*, 1996).

Because taxol was so resistant to solubility, investigators had analyzed its crystalline, or solid, structure. Unfortunately, the solid form of a molecule did not always accurately reflect the way the compound existed in the aqueous environment of the cell. By observing how dissolved taxoids attached to microtubules, scientists could learn which segments of the taxoid molecules were most likely to interact with cells. Obviously, if we wanted to modify taxol structure to better its effectiveness, we needed to know where and how this binding occurred, in order to enchance its ability to latch onto microtubules and thus kill the cells. After figuring out how to make big quantities of the originally scarce drug and finding new applications for its use in cancer therapy, scientists were now turning to another challenge, that of tinkering with the taxol structure until a less expensive, more effective medication was found (Nicolaou *et al.*, 1996).

On 29 December 1994, the French private pharmaceutical company Pierre Fabre announced that the U.S. Drug Administration approved its anti-cancer drug, navelbine, which could be commercialized in the USA. This was the first French-made anti-tumour compound authorized in the USA, as well as the first registered drug against lung cancer in the USA over the last 20 years. The drug was extracted from the leaves of *Catharanthus roseus*, then modified by semisynthesis. It had been developed through a genuine collaboration between the pharmaceutical company's researchers and those of the Institute of Chemistry of Natural Substances of the National Centre for Scientific Research (CNRS), at Gif-sur-Yvette, south of Paris, with the support of the National Agency for Valorization of Research (ANVAR).

Dabur Pharmaceuticals Ltd of India had launched an anti-cancer drug called intaxel used in the last stages of ovarian and breast cancer, when all other drugs had failed to cure the disease. It was one of two companies in the world making the drug. Intaxel was derived from the Asian yew tree found in the Himalayas. The process developed by Dabur extracted the drug from the tree's needles. The drug was found to be effective in 60% of cases during trials carried out by the company and, in a few cases, patients were completely cured.

Over the past three decades, several phytochemicals with biological activity had been identified from higher plants. Vincristine, vinblastine, artemisinin, taxol and podophyllotoxin were on the list of approved drugs. Some products, such as forskolin, castanospermine, ginkgolides and hypericin, were undergoing chemical trials. In 1992, the isothiocyanate sulforaphane, derived from broccoli, was shown by Talalay and colleagues at Johns Hopkins University to prevent some cancers; in 1994, the alkaloid michelamine-B, isolated from an obscure rain forest species, proved to have exceptionally powerful anti-HIV properties.

Most of these products were of very high value, ranging from $0.5 million to $9 million per kg; they were also excellent candidates for biotechnological production or of mixed biotechnological and chemical synthesis:

Product	Plant species	Price (DM/g)	Culture type	Yield
Ajmalicine	*Catharanthus roseus*	56.00	SC	0.2 g/l
Vinblastine	*C. roseus*	15,800.00	ShC	Trace
Vincristine	*C. roseus*	37,800.00	ShC	Trace
Ajmaline	*Rauwolfia*	15.50	SC	0.04 g/l
Vincamine	*Vinca minor*	29.50	SC	3.3 g/l
Ellipticine	*Ochrosia elliptica*	3,940.00	SC	0.005% dry biomass
Camptothecin	*Camptotheca acuminata*	720.00	SC	0.00025% dry biomass
Emetine	*Cephaelis ipecaccuanha*	39.50	RC	0.3–0.5% dry biomass
Berberine	*Coptis japonica*	16.50	SC	7 g/l
Sanguinarine	*Papaver*	72.00	SC	0.25 g/l
Colchicine	*Colchicum autumnale*	75.00	CC	1.5% dry biomass
Aconitine	*Aconitum*	1,120.00	Nil	
Diosgenin	*Dioscorea deltoidea*	100/kg	SC	2.0% dry biomass
Gingenosides	*Panax ginseng*	–	SC	0.4% dry biomass
Podophyllotoxin	*Podophyllum peltatum*	–	SC	0.2 mg/l

SC, suspension culture; ShC, shoot culture; CC, callus culture; RC, root culture.
Data collected from: Verpoorte and Heijden (1991), in Heble (1993).

Production of food additives, such as pigments, flavours and fragrances, was also the subject of active research in different laboratories world-wide for the synthesis of crocin, betaxanthines, bixin and anthocyanins. Among the flavours and fragrances, capsaicin and vanilla were commercially important candidates.

Vanillin was the first aromatic substance to be used world-wide. In 1994, the 2,000 tonnes produced from vanilla pods met only 20% of world demand and the final product was expensive: about $3,000 per kg of powder. The rest of the demand was met by chemically synthesized vanillin, the production of which amounted to several thousand tonnes for a per kg price of about $16 in 1994 (Galus, 1995).

In order for the natural vanilla production process to be profitable, it would need to be competitive with the chemical synthesis process. That is why the research work carried out in the European Union was supported through a $1.8 million contract concluded by the European Commission with two industrial companies, the French Agro-Industrie and the Danish Novo-Nordisk, the world leader in enzyme production, as well as with the British Institute of Food Research (Galus, 1995).

The consumer preference for natural vanilla made it a candidate for tissue culture; Escagenetics Corp., USA, had a patent for production of vanilla by plant cell cultures. The aromas of coffee and cocoa had also been produced by cell cultures (Heble, 1993).

At the Unit of Biotechnology of Filamentous Fungi of the French National Institute for Agricultural Research (INRA), in Marseille, it was found that a basidiomycete, *Pycnoporus cinnabarinus*, could produce vanillin. The substrate on which the fungus was grown was sugar-beet pulp, a cheap and abundant by-product; it was also rich in phenolic compounds necessary for the biosynthesis of vanillin. Ferulic acid, a precursor of vanillin, was introduced into the bioreactor, where the fungus growth and conversion of ferulic acid into vanillin was monitored by a computer. It was important to monitor the concentration of ferulic acid. If the acid accumulated to dangerous levels, it would kill the fungus; if it was degraded totally into carbon dioxide, there would be no bioconversion into vanillin. The French researchers had filed two patents, one in Europe in 1990 and another world-wide in 1994. Their medium-term objective was to produce several hundred milligrams of vanillin per litre of culture of the fungus. Subsequently, they would scale up production to industrial level (Galus, 1995).

The following table recapitulates a few food additives produced by plant cell and organ cultures:

Product	Plant species	Culture type	Yield (% dry biomass)
Betaxanthine	*Beta vulgaris*	SC	0.5
Bixin	*Bixa orellana*	CC	3–4
Anthocyanins	*Vitis vinifera*	SC	3–4
Crocin	*Gardinia jasmonoides*	CC	8 times less than *in vivo*
Vanillin	Vanilla	SC	100 mg/l
Mint terpenes	*Mentha*	ShC	–

SC, suspension culture; ShC, shoot culture; CC, callus culture.
Data collected from: Verpoorte and Heijden (1991), in Heble (1993).

With regard to perfumes, agar wood oil, a group of sesquiterpenes, was an important and expensive product; the oil was produced from the wood of the tree *Aquilaria agallocha*, when it was infected by fungi; the tree was highly localized in northeastern parts of India and Myanmar (ex-Burma). Other interesting candidates were patchouli, vetiver, geranium, mentha and sandalwood (Heble, 1993).

Therapeutic and digestive enzymes were also good candidates for biotechnological production. Thus, the production of papain, the major plant proteolytic enzyme, could be effectively increased by cloning elite papaya plants. Peroxidase was commercially produced by horseradish cells. Sweet proteins of commercial importance, monellin and thaumatin (3,000 times sweeter than cane sugar) were also good candidates (Heble, 1993).

Clonal propagation of identified source plants would give uniform plants which could be used in herbal formulations such as therapeutics, tonics and cosmetics. Potential candidates for cloning were *Withania somnifera, Rauwolfia serpentina, Centenella asiatica, Aloe, Phyllanthus embelica, Terminalia arjuna, T. belerica, T. chebula, Commiphora mukul, Azadirachta indica,* etc. (Heble, 1993).

The first commercial success with plant cell cultures had been for the production of shikonin, a pigment used in cosmetics, by Mitsui Petrochemical Co. Ltd, Japan. This was followed by several ventures, which were today in the spotlight:

Product	Plant species	Annual needs	Cost ($ per kg)	Biological activity
Vinblastine	*Catharanthus roseus*	5–10 kg	5 million	Anti–cancer
Vincristine	*C. roseus*	–	–	–
Ajmalicine	*C. roseus*	3–5 tonnes	1,500	Anti–hypertension
Podophyllotoxin	*P. hexandrum*	–	–	Anti–cancer
Codeine	*Papaver somniferum*	80–150 tonnes	650–900	Expectorant
Digoxin	*Digitalis lanata*	6 tonnes	3,000	Cardiotonic
Diosgenin	*Dioscorea deltoidea*	200 tonnes	20–40	Steroid hormones
Jasmine oil	*Jasminum*	100 kg	5,000	Fragrance
Mint oil	*Mentha*	3,000 tonnes	30	Fragrance
Vanillin (natural)	Vanilla	30 tonnes	2,500	Fragrance
Taxol	*Taxus brevifolia*	–	–	Anti–cancer

More than 50 major industries world-wide were working on plant tissue cultures, with a wide range of target molecules, like pharmaceuticals, food additives, aromas, biopesticides and enzymes. Japan was leading the race, with seven private corporations having created a common subsidiary in research and development on plant cell cultures: PCC Technology had been set up, with the support of the Japan Key Technology Centre, by Kyowa Hakko Kogyo Co., Mitsui Petrochemical Co. Ltd, Mitsui Toatsu Chemical Inc., Hitachi Ltd, Suntory Ltd, Toa Nenryo Kogyo Co. and Kirin Breweries Co. Ltd. Japan was followed by Germany and the USA (Heble, 1993).

Among the constraints and risk factors associated with plant cell and tissue cultures, one could cite:

– their slow growth as compared to micro-organisms, their doubling time ranging from between 20 and 60 hours; as a result, the cultures were vulnerable to microbial contamination and a great deal of expenditure went toward maintaining aseptic conditions;

– mutation frequency caused by the culture conditions, stress and phytohormones posed problems for the maintenance of stability of cultures;

– rare occurrence of highly productive cell lines, generally obtained through selection;

– difficulty in inducing the cells to produce the desired compound (the genes coding for plant chemical products were turned on only under special conditions);

– laborious excretion of secondary products by plant cells;

– high technology development costs, the gestation period being generally three to four years (Komen, 1991*e*; Sasson, 1992*a,b*).

The production of secondary metabolites (drugs, flavours, fragrances, dyes or insecticides) by means of plant cell cultures raised two issues: the technological and economical feasibility.

Regarding the effect of shear, recent studies showed that cultured plant cells resisted shear stress quite well. The successful culture of plant cells in the 60-cubic metre stirred tank type of bioreactors was clear evidence that the technology was feasible.

Regarding economic feasibility, the first biotechnology product, shikonin, had been produced at a cost of $4,500/kg in a 200-litre bioreactor. A study carried out in Japan showed that any substance of plant origin costing more than $80/kg could be produced by plant tissue culture techniques; this range would include a high number of phytochemicals. In case of micropropagated elite plants, the production cost would be around 50 cents to $1 per plant and the product yields could be effectively increased by two- to ten-fold. Techniques of cell immobilization, hairy roots and shooty teratomas could lower the final production cost. High-value candidates for plant tissue culture were:

Product	Plant species	Biological activity
Taxol	*Taxus brevifolia*	Anti-cancer (ovarian)
Camptothecin	*Camptotheca acuminata*	Anti-cancer
	Nothopodytes foetida	
Forskolin	*Coleus forskohlii*	Cardiotonic
Artemisinin	*Artemisia annua*	Anti-malaria drugs
Castanospermine	*Castanospermum australe*	Anti-AIDS
Hypericin	*Hypericum esculentum*	Anti-AIDS

Calculations made at the Division of Pharmacognosy, Leiden/Amsterdam Center for Drug Research, Leiden University, using ajmalicine production (0,3 g/l in a 14-day growth/production fedbatch type of process) in *Catharanthus roseus* cultured cells as a model, produced a price of $1,500 per kg for this compound. A hypothetical ten-fold increase in productivity brought the calculated price down to $430 per kg; expensive but still in the price range of a number of specialty chemicals. Yet, so far, only shikonin had found its way to the market. This was due to the fact that, for products of interest, production by cultured cells was low or non-existent. Examples of virtually no production at all were vinblastine and morphine.

Research therefore focused mainly on increasing productivity of plant cell cultures. Screening and selection of high-producing cell lines and optimization of growth and production media were more or less conventional approaches, well-known for improving the production of antibiotics by micro-organisms. In the case of plant cells, this had been quite successful for shikonin and berberine, leading to a productivity of respectively 3 g/l and 7g/l. In general, an about 10- to 20-fold increase had been achieved using these approaches for plant cell cultures with a basic level of production of the desired product but, for compounds not produced at all by plant cell cultures, these approaches were irrelevant.

Elicitation (e.g. by cell wall constituents of micro-organisms) resulted in the induction of certain plant species' secondary metabolite pathways leading to the production of phytoalexins. This approach was successful for improving the production of the alkaloid sanguinarine in poppy cell cultures. However, for products normally found in the leaves or roots of a plant, for instance, this approach did not work; for these pathways, the growth of differentiated cells was an alternative. Although several examples had been reported (e.g. tropane alkaloid production in root cultures and vinblastine in shoot cultures), from an economic viewpoint this approach was hardly promising. Consequently, more and more research endeavours were being made in metabolic engineering, which implied that one knew the secondary metabolite pathways, the enzymes and genes involved, as well as limitating steps.

Research at the Division of Pharmacognosy, Leiden/Amsterdam Center for Drug Research, focused on the production of terpenoid indole alkaloids in, *inter alia*, *Catharanthus roseus* cell cultures. Two genes had been cloned and their regulation was extensively being studied. The introduction of one of the genes encoding tryptophan decarboxylase (IDC), into *C. roseus* cells resulted in increased amounts of the enzymes and in greater tryptamine production. However, secologanin, the other intermediate necessary for biosynthesis, was apparently a major limiting factor as there was no evidence of an increase in alkaloid concentration. In tobacco, where both the *tdc*-gene and the gene encoding the enzyme responsible for the coupling of tryptamine and secologanin (strictosidine synthase) were introduced, strictosidine was formed after using secologanin as a substrate. These results showed that, in principle, it was possible to overcome a limiting step in a pathway, or even introduce new pathways in plants. It also became clear that, for every limiting step overcome, one would be faced with a new limiting step. Therefore, it would be of great usefulness to identify possible regulatory genes which might be targets for metabolic engineering to augment the production of secondary metabolites.

Strong research-and-development support was therefore a prerequisite for industrial production of secondary metabolites by plant cell and organ cultures. In fact, all commercial ventures were backed by the team leaders in medicinal plant biotechnologies (e.g. Staba in the USA, Zenk and Reinhard in Germany, Yamada, Furuya and Tabata in Japan) [Heble, 1993].

Molecular farming was defined by Moloney (1995) as the use of transgenic plants or animals to produce unusual and higher-value products, e.g. pharmaceutical proteins and polyhydroxybutyrate granules for manufacturing biodegradable plastics. At SemBioSys Genetics Inc., created by Moloney and University Technologies International Inc., the University of California's commercial technology transfer company, Moloney was interested in adding value by one means or another to the seeds of canola and related oilseed crop species. He developed methods whereby a variety of proteins could be produced:

– low-value, commodity end-of-the-scale proteins for the improved nutritional value of seeds;

– intermediate value proteins such as industrial and food enzymes required in bulk but which were, nevertheless, specialty products; and

– high-value proteins, mainly of interest to the pharmaceutical industry (transgenic canola producing the anti-coagulant hirudin was developed; also a human cytokine, interleukin-1, used experimentally as a modulator of the immune system, was produced by a transgenic canola) [Moloney, 1995].

Also, some of the specialty oils to be produced by oilseed crop species were an example of molecular farming; they would address a commodity-based market as hundreds of thousands of hectares might be planted with crop species. Calgene Inc. had registered a lauric acid-producing canola (*Brassica napus*) which was being grown commercially in Georgia in 1995.

By the end of the 20th century, the first protein products to be registered would either be in the feed-meal area or possibly industrial enzymes requiring some registration information but nothing like the degree of testing that a pharmaceutical would require. It would also be possible to produce a range of interesting pharmaceutical proteins in plants by the end of the century but it might take longer before these were registered due to the intensive testing that would have to take place, including human clinical trials (Moloney, 1995).

If we looked to the use of molecular farming for commodity-based proteins, such as in feed-meal improvement, this would involve introducing an enzyme that would not be purified, but which would improve the quality of the meal, for instance through the expression of phytase. Crop species or varieties modified in this manner would be cultivated on a very large scale. Ultimately, we would be talking about millions of hectares simply because some of these modifications would become standard for feed-meals (Moloney, 1995).

On the other hand, one could also expect a large volume production of more specialized products, such as enzymes of interest to the food industry. For instance, with a glucose isomerase that could be used in the process of fructose syrup production, one would envisage planting between 20,000 and 50,000 acres to meet world demand. In this case we would be down a couple of orders of magnitude from immense planting, although one could imagine 20 different specialty enzymes, each taking up between 20,000 and 50,000 acres; in total, these acreages would be sizeable. At the very high end, the high value but lower volume pharmaceutical proteins, one could literally produce the world's supply of a specific product on a single farm because 2,000 to 3,000 acres would be sufficient in some cases (Moloney, 1995).

In addition to canola, Moloney (1995) was interested in using flax for molecular farming. There was also a potential for some cereal species now that transformation procedures were available. In particular, wherever small to medium-sized acreages were required, a foreign or novel species might be desirable; these crop species might provide advantages in terms of sexual isolation of the crop or in terms of product yield and disease resistance (Moloney, 1995).

Molecular farming was assisted by the research work being carried out on tissue-specific genetic promoters. Moloney's work at SemBioSys Genetics Inc. was a by-product of research on a particular gene expressed in canola seeds encoding a protein known as oleosin: how this protein was targeted to oilbodies in cells. It was also realized that these proteins could act as an efficient carrier of other proteins. The molecular farming programme was a spin-off from that research on oleosins. Greater efforts needed to be made to isolate new promoters of potential value for plant genetic engineering. Some of the commonly used promoters were protected through patents. Any isolation of a strong constitutive promoter, which was comparable to plant viral promoters like the 35S promoter from cauliflower mosaic virus, would be extremely helpful and should be given high research priority[11] (see p. 249) (Moloney, 1995).

According to Arntzen of the Boyce Thompson Institute for Plant Research, edible vaccines produced in plants would obviate many hurdles associated with the cell-culture systems currently used in large-scale vaccine production. These hurdles included the need for relatively sophisticated fermentation technology, strict purification protocols, refrigeration during shipment including the 'cold chain', the risk and pain associated with parenteral injection and high costs. In addition, vaccine production in plants would not entail risks associated with the use of live pathogens and sterility requirements for injected vaccines. The basic idea behind the development of edible vaccines was that the consumer would be immunized against a specific disease simply by eating a certain plant (Mason and Arntzen, 1995).

Thanavala *et al.* (1995) of the Boyce Thompson Institute for Plant Research had successfully developed tobacco plants producing the hepatitis B virus surface antigen (HBsAg) which could immunize against this viral disease. The antigen thus produced had the same structure and function as that extracted from the serum of disease carriers or produced by transformed yeast and provoked a strong immune response when injected into mice. Researchers of the same Institute had developed transgenic tobacco and potato plants containing a highly active immunogen of *Escherichia coli* heat-labile enterotoxin (LT-B), which was structurally similar to cholera toxin. Mice orally immunized with transgenic plant extracts exhibited a strong immune response. Human clinical trials with volunteers were to be conducted with this plant-derived vaccine against diarrhoea using fresh potatoes (Haq *et al.*, 1995). McGarvey *et al.* (1995) of Thomas Jefferson University in Philadelphia had produced tomato plants that expressed rabies antigens. See also Moffat (1995).

In contrast to the above-mentioned examples of 'active immunization', 'passive immunization' was also being explored through the production of protective antibodies in plants. Use of plant tissue rather than hybridoma cells to produce antibodies had several advantages associated with the relatively simple nutrient requirements of plants. Researchers at Guy's Hospital, London, and Salk Institute, California, had used tobacco hairy roots to synthesize a complete and fully-assembled murine IgG1 monoclonal antibody; the antibody expressed was Guy's 13, which recognized the 185 kDa cell-surface protein of *Streptococcus mutans*, a principal causal agent of dental caries in humans. Antibody expression in the root cultures was stable, with antibodies continuing to accumulate over a 19-month monitoring period. In an unmodified medium, titres of fully-assembled antibody were up to 18 mg per litre, with a maximum of 14% of the accumulated antibody being secreted into the medium. Total antibody amounts were increased by adding nitrate, polyvinylpyrrolidone and gelatin to the cultures; polyvinylpyrrolidone and gelatin also markedly improved extracellular antibody concentrations corresponding to up to 43% of the antibody present. Antibody accumulation was growth-associated, with a constant specific accumulation rate at the beginning of the culture; however, degradation of the antibody was significant after 14 days and the amount of assembled antibody declined. Antibody accumulation in hairy roots was more stable and less prone to protein degradation than in suspended cells of tobacco.

At the Department of Biotechnology, University of New South Wales, Sydney, eight antibody-producing hairy root clones were also established from transgenic tobacco seedlings carrying genes coding for Guy's 13 antibody. The hairy roots were initiated by transforming the seedlings with *Agrobacterium rhizogenes*. The presence of heavy and light chains and fully-assembled antibody was confirmed by Western blot analysis of root extracts. The hairy roots were shown to produce assembled antibody over a period of 19 months.

Further work was required to determine the sequence of antibody assembly in roots, glycosylation characteristics and the factors affecting degradation of the antibody in extracellular and intracellular environments.

The U.S. biotechnology company Agracetus Inc. (Middleton, Wisconsin) had developed transgenic soybeans producing a tumour-reactive monoclonal antibody called BR96, which could be used as a drug-carrier to treat breast, colon, ovarian and lung cancers. These transgenic soybeans were being grown in Puerto Rico and clinical trials were planned to test the antibodies derived from these plants. Tobacco plants had been developed by Crop Tech Development Corp. in Virginia to produce glucocerebrosidase, an expensive human enzyme for treating Gaucher's disease. Currently, this enzyme was derived from human placentae. It took 2,000 to 8,000 placentae to produce a single dose of the enzyme, raising the cost of a single treatment to $300,000 per year (1995). It was expected that the production of this enzyme by plants would bring down the cost of the drug a thousandfold (Prakash, 1996).

Genetically-engineered plant viruses were also being used to produce vaccines and other medicinal compounds in infected plants. At the Scripps Research Institute, La Jolla, California, tobacco mosaic virus had been engineered to contain mouse zona pellucida ZB3 protein, which was an immuno-contraceptive as it covered the unfertilized egg preventing fertilization. In the long run, the outcome of this research might serve as a cheap source of oral contraceptives. Researchers at the John Innes Institute, Norwich, United Kingdom, had engineered cowpea mosaic virus (CPMV) to contain a surface protein of the human immuno-deficiency virus (HIV-AIDS); chimaeric coat proteins of the CPMV that expressed the material and foot-and-mouth disease epitopes had also been produced. Other novel compounds, including an anti-viral protein inhibiting the HIV *in vitro*, trichosanthin (ribosome inactivator) and angiotensin-1 (an anti-hypertensive drug) had also been expressed in infected plants through engineered virus inoculation (Prakash, 1996).

A plant would be suitable for oral vaccine production if it:
– produced edible parts that could be consumed uncooked since the vaccine antigens were heat-sensitive;
– was rich in protein because vaccine protein would only make up a small proportion of the total protein content of a plant;
– could be transformed by genetic engineering;
– could be grown widely;
– was fast growing; and
– did not produce toxic compounds.

Tobacco, often used as a model plant because of its easy transformation and regeneration of transgenic plantlets and on which the initial work on vaccine production took place, did not meet many of the above requirements. The research group of Arntzen had thus chosen banana for delivery of edible vaccines in developing countries. The goal was to have vaccine-producing banana processed in baby-

237

food jars. At the Center for Plant Biotechnology Research, Tuskegee University, Alabama, musk melon (cantaloupe) was used for edible vaccine production as it was fast growing, could be propagated by seed and was easy to transform with foreign genes (Prakash, 1996).

Despite the achievements already obtained, the commercial application of plant transgenesis to the production of oral vaccines, antibodies and medicinal compounds was at least a decade away. There were several problems to be solved. Firstly, most inserted genes needed to be expressed more strongly and, consequently, research focused on the isolation of efficient promoters that could enhance this expression in edible parts of the plants. Thus, the Arntzen group had shown that a synthetic cholera vaccine gene, which was more 'plant'-like in its sequence, was four times more productive than the original gene. Secondly, the stability of vaccine proteins when transgenic fruits or leaves were stored under ambient conditions was another concern. Antibodies in leaves had to be extracted immediately or they would decay with the leaves themselves. German researchers reported that, by linking antibody genes to a genetic 'switch', antibodies could be produced in the seeds instead of in the leaves. These antibodies in the seeds did not deteriorate significantly after a year of storage at room temperature; this could imply that antibodies would be preserved until extraction or consumption of the seed at a later stage. Thirdly, there was also concern about oral tolerance in case greater amounts of vaccines became ineffective when consumed orally by supressing systemic immunity. Further research might identify useful adjuvants enhancing oral immunogenicity. Fourthly, the dosage was a major problem, as vaccine content in plants might vary depending on when and where they were grown. Further collaborative research between plant and medical scientists might resolve these and other issues. In the short term, edible vaccine-producing plants might be better targeted at animals. This approach would greatly benefit livestock husbandry as billions of dollars were spent currently on vaccinating farm animals and poultry (Prakash, 1996).

9. Biosafety regulations

The WHO was probably the first United Nations specialized agency to be involved in biosafety. By 1975, it had initiated the Special Programme on Safety Measures in Microbiology, in order to review safety-related subjects and the conjectural risks posed by recombinant DNA research. Some examples of programme results were the Safety

Guidelines for Diagnostic and Research Laboratories working with the AIDS virus (HIV) and the Minimum Biosafety Guidelines for Workers engaged in producing vaccines and biologicals (De Groot, 1991). A new edition of the WHO Laboratory Biosafety Manual was published in 1992.

The Codex Alimentarius Commission (CAC) was established in 1962 to implement the joint Food Standards Programme of the FAO and WHO, whose purpose was to protect the health of consumers, ensure fair practices in the food trade and co-ordinate all food standards work undertaken by international governmental and non-governmental organizations. Once the General Agreement on Tariffs and Trade Uruguay Round had been completed, the CAC announced its intention to develop international guidelines for assessing the safety of food produced by modern biotechnologies, so as to minimize potential barriers to trade in biotechnology-derived foodstuffs, which might otherwise arise from the application of different safety assessment procedures in different countries.

In 1990, the FAO and WHO convened a consultation meeting in Geneva on the use of biotechnologies in food production and processing with relation to food safety. The consultation concluded that there was no reason to assume that foodstuffs produced by biotechnologies were inherently less safe than those made by conventional means, although this needed to be demonstrated through comparative evaluations covering both safety and nutritional value. The same year, the Group of National Experts on Safety in Biotechnology, set up by the Committee for Science and Technology Policy of the Organisation for Economic Co-operation and Development (OECD), agreed to establish a food safety working group to give priority to the elaboration of scientific principles for assessing the safety of novel foodstuffs or food components produced by biotechnologies. In line with the FAO/WHO consultation, this working group concluded that the most practical approach to determine the safety of foodstuffs and food components developed through the application of modern biotechnologies was to consider whether they were substantially equivalent to analogous conventional foodstuffs where these existed. The way in which the food would be processed needed to be taken into account as did the intended uses and intake. This approach would allow an evaluation of both safety and nutritional value.

The main United Nations body on biosafety was the UNIDO/WHO/UNEP/FAO Informal Working Group on Biosafety (IWGB). The OECD had been co-operating with the IWGB ever since its inception in 1986. In 1992, on behalf of the IWGB, the UNIDO issued an Annotated Voluntary Code of Conduct for the Release of Organisms into the Environment, which covered biosafety aspects concerning public health and the environment at all stages of research and development, as well as the use and disposal of genetically modified organisms (GMOs). Intended as a general framework that could be adapted by countries with no regulations in this area, the Code was not designed as a manual on how to handle GMOs. Risk assessment, for instance, was to be carried out case-by-case regarding 'relevant information' and 'relevant attributes of the site'. To help solve the problem of what to consider 'relevant', the IWGB recommended setting up an International Biosafety Information Network and Advisory Service. There was no substantial difference between the IWGB's Code of Conduct and documents published by the OECD (Nilsson, 1992).

The safety of some of the marker genes inserted in genetically-modified organisms to facilitate their identification from amongst the many unmodified organisms produced in attempts at genetic modification, were examined at a workshop convened by the WHO in 1993 in Copenhagen. It was concluded that: there was a need for marker genes in plant biotechnologies and it was impractical to remove them from modified plants once they had fulfilled their function; the presence of marker genes *per se* in food crop species was not a safety concern; in judging the safety of the expressed proteins (coded by the marker genes), the assessment needed to focus on the function of the protein rather than its structure, since there was no reason to suppose that marker gene proteins posed a greater allergenic problem than other proteins; and there were no characteristics of marker genes or their products that suggested that their site of insertion into the plant genome would give rise to additional secondary and/or pleiotropic effects. The workshop also concluded that there was no recorded evidence of the transfer of genes from plants to micro-organisms in the human gut. However, if it did occur, unless the gene was under the control of a bacterial promoter, there was no mechanism for its expression in gut bacteria.

Government officials from the United Kingdom and Dutch Departments for the Environment had decided to support the development of voluntary guidelines for safety in biotechnology. These guidelines were expected to assist governments to develop their own policies concerning the introduction of safety mechanisms. In two subsequent meetings in March 1994 in the United Kingdom and May 1994 in the Netherlands, a proposal drafted by both government officials was discussed. At these meetings, experts from Brazil, Canada,

Colombia, Costa Rica, Denmark, Egypt, Hungary, India, Kenya, the Netherlands, Russia, South Africa, Spain, Sweden, Switzerland, Thailand, Uganda and the United Kingdom, were representing governmental organizations, academic institutions, industry, non-governmental organizations and international agencies. They agreed on a draft text and on its further discussion in various international fora to promote its adoption (Visser, 1994*b*).

These draft guidelines contained the following proposals:

– identification of a national administration focal point for the international exchange of information;

– establishment of regional groups to make arrangements for routine reciprocal exchanges;

– encouragement of governments and international agencies to provide technical assistance in order to increase awareness and expertise in assessing and managing risks associated with the use of genetically-modified organisms;

– assistance from companies to train local people in the safe handling of these organisms.

These draft guidelines drew heavily on previous documentation and endeavours, such as the United Nations Industrial Development Organization (UNIDO) Voluntary Code of Conduct or the Inter-American Institute for Cooperation on Agriculture (IICA) Guidelines. The draft guidelines aimed to be practical, broadly applicable, to cover more aspects than previous texts and to pay particular attention to the position of developing countries (Visser, 1994*b*).

Many delegations present at the meeting of the Intergovernmental Committee on the Convention of Biological Diversity (Nairobi, June 1994) supported the initiative. Previously, in 1993, in Harare, the African Regional Conference for International Cooperation on Safety in Biotechnology had stressed the need for international support for information exchange and capacity-building in this area. Donors would also play an important role in providing adequate funding to allow developing countries to implement the guidelines (Visser, 1994*b*).

Notes

1. Arthur Klausner, principal of a U.S. venture capital firm, listed the 1993 big four independent world biotechnology companies: Amgen Inc., Chiron Corp., Synergen and Biogen Inc. He pointed out that back in 1983, the four were: Genentech Inc., Genex, Biogen Inc. and Cetus Corporation. Klausner also listed the big product successes of the 1980s in dollar terms (world sales, 1992) as:

alpha-interferon	$565 million
erythropoietin	$125 million
factor VIII	$253 million
G-CSF	$405 million
anti-hepatitis B vaccine	$105 million
human growth hormone	$575 million
human insulin	$625 million
tissue plasminogen activator (tPA)	$230 million.

2. On 23 October 1995, Glaxo plc concluded an amicable agreement with Genpharm, a subsidiary of Merck & Co. Inc., so as to settle out of court a legal battle raging over the patent protection of Zantac. Genpharm committed itself to not marketing a molecule similar to form 1 of Zantac before July 1997, when the patent protecting form 1 expired, and to not marketing form 2 of Zantac before expiration of the latter's patent protection in 2002. Glaxo plc was to pay Genpharm financial compensation over three years. Glaxo plc was thereby defending the composition of its drug, after winning a court appeal against the Canadian drug company, Novopharm, and sueing the German firm Boehringer Ingelheim.

3. The main leading pharmaceutical groups were: 1. Glaxo-Wellcome plc (United Kingdom, $9.7 billion of annual turnover in 1994, 4.9% of world pharmaceutical market); 2. Hoechst-Marion-Roussel (Germany, $7.5 billion);3. Merck & Co. Inc. (USA, $7 billion); 4. Bristol-Myers Squibb Co. (USA, $6.6 billion); 5. American Home Products Corp./American Cyanamid Co. (USA, $6.5 billion); 6. Roche Holding Ltd.-Syntex (Switzerland, $5.6 billion); 7. Johnson and Johnson-Ortho Pharmaceutical Corp. (USA, $5.3 billion); 8. Pfizer Inc. (USA, $5.2 billion); 9. Pharmacia & Upjohn Inc.(Sweden, $5.2 billion) 10. SmithKline Beecham plc (United Kingdom, $5.1 billion); 11. Ciba-Geigy AG (Switzerland, $4.9 billion); 12. Rhône-Poulenc Rorer-Fisons (France, $4.4 billion); 13. Eli Lilly & Co. (USA, $4.3 billion); 14. Bayer AG (Germany, $4.2 billion); 15. Sandoz AG (Switzerland, $3.8 billion); . . . 23. Sanofi Winthrop (France, $2 billion).

   In 1996–1997, the ranking was: 1. Glaxo plc ($12.6 billion of annual turnover in 1995); 2. Novartis AG (Ciba Geigy AG + Sandoz AG; $30 billion of annual turnover in 1995, including $11.8 billion for pharmacy); 3. Merck & Co. Inc.; 4. Hoechst-Marion-Roussel; 5. Bristol-Myers Squibb Co.; 6. American Home Products Corp.; 7. Roche Boehringer Mannheim Diagnostics.

   The ten leading cosmetics groups were: 1. L'Oréal (France, $7.88 billion of annual turnover in 1993); 2. Procter & Gamble (USA, $5.76 billion); 3. Unilever N.V. (Netherlands, $5.32 billion); 4. Shiseido (Japan, $4.05 billion); 5. Estée Lauder (USA, $2.74 billion); 6. Avon (USA, $2.54 billion); 7. Sanofi (France, $1.9 billion); 8. Beiersdorf (Germany, $1.62 billion); 9. Revlon (USA, $1.6 billion); 10. Wella (Germany, $1.56 billion).

4. In 1996, while Hoechst AG's turnover decreased by 2% to 50.9 billion Deutschemarks, net profits reached 2.8 billion Deutschemarks (a $1.9 billion record), a 24% increase over that of 1995.

5. Sanofi (with 85,500 employees, including 55,000 in France) was the pharmaceutical branch of the French oil group Elf Aquitaine, privatized at the beginning of 1994, which ranked eighth among the world's leading oil companies. The 1995 turnover of Elf Aquitaine amounted to $41.6 billion, distributed as follows: 58% for exploration and production of oil, 17% for chemistry (Atochem), 15% for pharmacy (Sanofi) and 10% for refinery and distribution. The Stock Exchange value of the group was $19.2 billion.

In 1996, Sanofi's turnover amounted to $4.729 billion (+3% over that of 1995) for a net profit of $348 million, an 11% increase over 1995.

6. Rhône-Poulenc Rorer, the world's seventh-biggest chemical company and thirteenth-biggest pharmaceutical group in 1996, with 81,500 employees, had been founded in 1858 as Poulenc Frères in France (Heissler, 1994).

In a book published by Rhône-Poulenc for its centenary, entitled *Innover pour la vie - Rhône-Poulenc 1895–1995 (Innovate for life - Rhône-Poulenc 1895–1995)*, it was shown that each phase of international expansion of the French chemical group had occurred while it was still controlled by the State. The company had been nationalized in 1981 and privatized 12 years later. The State had brought $340 million to the company between 1982 and 1993 and made a capital gain of almost twice this amount ($600 million). Regarding staffing, the number of employees in France had decreased by 38% over that period, from 56,614 to 35,152. Conversely, staff had numbers increased outside France and, since 1993, had remained stable. Lastly, three years after privatization (1996), there had been no increase in capital through inputs from the financial market, due to the poor appeal of the company shares (Gallois, 1996e).

A pragmatic approach prevailed at each major stage of development. In 1979, the textile issue was resolved by centering on specialty chemicals and selling off all the petrochemical activities. In 1982, the company's new President pursued the trend and did away with fertilizers; he also restructured the textile sector by closing down plants and laying off staff. In 1986, another President was entrusted with the task of internationalizing the group in order to make it one of the leading companies in the world. He made two costly, but symbolic, decisions: the purchase of the German laboratory Natterman and of the agrochemical division of the U.S. Union Carbide company. Other acquisitions followed over the next five years; $8 billion was devoted to purchasing about thirty societies, including 15 in North America (e.g. the Canadian Connaught Laboratories and the U.S. Rorer). The State, the major shareholder, did not participate in funding these purchases because of lack of funds and the group became indebted. On 18 October 1993, Rhône-Poulenc was privatized (Gallois, 1996e).

The State was replaced by a group of stable shareholders who held 20.6% of the capital and guaranteed the perennity of the group. Most of them were close to the company's President, e.g. the insurance company Axa and the bank Société générale. On the other hand, Rhône-Poulenc's employees held 4.3% shares.

With its partly state-funded Bio Avenir programme, the company had become one of the world's biggest spenders on biotechnology research. Initiated in 1991, Bio Avenir designated an ambitious five-year biotechnology research programme linking Rhône-Poulenc with major research institutions like the National Institute for Agricultural Research (INRA), the National Centre for Scientific Research (CNRS) and the Pasteur Institute. With a total budget of about $233 million, of which 40% was contributed by the French Government, and a staff of 500 scientists, the research programme focused on three areas:

– human health, which received 50% of the research budget, and concentrated on atherosclerosis, cancer and diseases associated with ageing (Alzheimer's disease);

– agrochemistry, with a view to developing crop protection products active at tiny doses and with a limited impact on human health and the environment;

– chemistry, focused on enzymatic catalysts (Heissler, 1994).

The company had three core activities: chemical intermediates; applied chemistry and specialty chemicals; and life sciences (including health- and agro-divisions). The life sciences component was the strongest, the health sector alone accounting for 80% of Rhône-Poulenc's net income (Heissler, 1994).

In 1993, Rhône-Poulenc (RP) spent about $1 billion on research and development, of which nearly 20% went on biotechnologies. RP's research activities were spread over 13 research centres in Europe, North America, Japan and Brazil. In the mid-1980s, the company's management had decided to aim for a position among the five world leaders in its areas of business. In keeping with this decision, RP began internationalizing production and marketing by applying an aggressive expansion-through-acquisition policy. Between 1986 and 1993, it spent $7 billion on acquisitions, thereby doubling sales world-wide. The company had become a true transnational, with affiliates in 140 countries and more than 83,000 employees world-wide. International operations accounted for 79% of RPR's revenues. Its biggest market was North America: between 1986 and 1993, company sales in this region had increased by 25%, resulting in a larger turnover than its domestic market. Africa, Asia and Latin America accounted for only 16.8% of net sales (Rhône-Poulenc, 1993; Ward, 1993; Heissler, 1994).

With its 1990 acquisition of a 67% share in the U.S. company Rorer (changing the company's appellation to Rhône-Poulenc Rorer), RPR had become a major actor on the pharmaceutical world stage. In 1995, it occupied third position on the European market and fifteenth position on the U.S. market. RPR was rapidly expanding its activities in biotechnologies, as illustrated by the setting up of a special biotechnology unit in its research-and-development centre in Vitry, France, to develop new ways of treating cancer and AIDS. Together with the Institut Curie, Paris, RPR had developed a topoisomerase II inhibitor, an important enzyme in the control of tumour growth and cell division. The company also produced a recombinant human identical granulocyte colony stimulating factor ('Granulocyte'), used in cancer therapy and developed in co-operation with the Japanese pharmaceutical corporation Chugai. In a joint venture with Immune Response Corporation (USA), RPR was developing a therapeutic vaccine against AIDS; it consisted of an inactivated HIV cultivated in human cells before its re-injection into patients. Clinical tests showed that this vaccine slowed down the rate of viral infection and stimulated the immune response (treated individuals had a greater number of antibodies in their bloodstream) [Heissler, 1994].

RPR's goal was to play a major role in developing gene therapy. On 18 October 1995, RPR and the Santa Clara (California)-based company, Applied Immune Sciences, concluded a fusion agreement for a $84.4 million deal. In 1993, RPR had acquired 46% of the American company's capital and with the deal concluded in October 1995 the French group was consolidating its presence in gene therapy. A subsidiary of RPR, Armour Pharmaceuticals (USA), was also involved in the development of gene therapy technologies. Combined with the research alliance with the CNRS for gene therapy vectors, the company expected to gain a strong position on the future gene therapy market. By the year 2010, this market was estimated at $3.8 billion annually (Rhône-Poulenc, 1993; Heissler, 1994).

In January 1994, RPR introduced a new anti-malaria drug named Paluther, which was expected to overcome resistance to conventional drugs in African countries. RPR owned the Institut Mérieux which controlled about one-third of the global vaccine market. Institut Mérieux's earlier achievements included prodution of the first European polio vaccine and the first commercial vaccine against a specific form of meningitis. In 1986, it also introduced the first genetically engineered human vaccine on the market: Recombivax against hepatitis B. Two years earlier, Institut Mérieux had become the majority shareholder in Pasteur Vaccins, which included all the serum and vaccine activities of the Institut Pasteur; this had led to the setting up of

Pasteur Mérieux Sérums et Vaccins, which linked the Institut Pasteur's basic research and Institut Mérieux's manufacturing capability. In the late 1980s, Institut Mérieux had strengthened its position on the vaccine market through the acquisition of several biotechnology-based companies, such as the American company, Virogenetics, and the French, Transgène, Europe's first biotechnology start-up. In 1989, Institut Mérieux took over the Canadian human vaccine developer, Connaught Laboratories, an acquisition giving the French corporation a strong foothold on the North American vaccine market. Today, Institut Mérieux focused research efforts on AIDS and hepatitis B (Heissler, 1994).

RPR's veterinary division, Rhône-Mérieux (RM), a subsidiary of Institut Mérieux, was the world's biggest animal vaccine producer. It was the world leader for marketing vaccines against rabies and foot-and-mouth disease, which accounted for 30% to 35% of total net sales of animal vaccines. In addition, Rhône-Poulenc Animal Nutrition maintained a leading position on the world market of feed additives, such as vitamins and methionine. In 1990, RM produced the first recombinant anti-rabies vaccine for animals, Raboral, in collaboration with several subsidiaries; the vaccine obtained European Commission approval for release. The German Federal Health Organization, however, expressed concern because the vaccine was based on a smallpox virus strain named Copenhagen; according to the Organization, RM could not prove that Raboral was less pathogenic than the conventional medicine, with its well-known side-effects. Today, RM was directing research efforts toward developing new recombinant vaccines, e.g. one against Newcastle's disease, which was the most important viral disease affecting poultry in the world, especially in Asia, where poultry meat and eggs formed a major part of the human diet; broad vaccination against the disease was considered a top priority. Recombinant vaccines were, however, often too expensive for small farmers in developing countries (Heissler, 1994).

On 3 February 1997, Rhône-Mérieux announced the sale of its diagnostics division to the U.S. company Synbiotics, the second world leading firm in veterinary diagnostics.

Regarding food additives, Rhône-Poulenc (RP) was the world's biggest producer of artificial vanilla (vanillin), the most widespread flavouring, found in chocolate, candies, desserts and cakes. Owing to its high price, natural vanilla was an easy candidate for substitution through synthetic production. In 1876, the German scientist, Reimer, had discovered vanillin, RP beginning production only in 1920. Nowadays, vanillin was about 200 times cheaper than natural vanilla, which was mainly produced in Madagascar and the Comores. Vanillin was however still not comparable with the superior aroma of natural vanilla. By 2000, RP was expected to double its turnover in the food sector to $800 million. The company had discovered the new market of low-fat and low-cholesterol products; RP's first launch in this line was Oatrim, a fat substitute (Heissler, 1994).

Although the agro-business only accounted for 12.4% of RP's total net sales, the company ranked fourth on the world's agrochemical market. It was primarily concentrating on crop protection products, which accounted for 80% of agro-division sales. In 1986, Rhône-Poulenc purchased Union Carbide's agrochemical division after the Union Carbide disaster in Bhopal, India (Heissler, 1994).

RP had also entered the seed business, as had many other agrochemical companies. It had begun by buying the U.S. company Callahan Seeds, specialized in improving maize and soybeans. Subsequently, it acquired the French grain seed corporation, Cérès. In 1989, the company married its seed interests with those of Lafarge-Coppée's seed subsidiary, Orsan, in the new firm, Artois, currently a leading corporation in the world vegetable seed business. Clause, the French market leader in vegetable and ornamental seeds, and Harris Moran Seeds, the third-biggest seed company in the USA, were party to this venture. Clause and Harris Moran had business operations in Asia, South America and the Middle East (Heissler, 1994).

In 1984, Rhône-Poulenc concluded a research partnership with the U.S. biotechnology company, Calgene Inc. This collaboration would lead to engineering resistance in cotton to the company's bromoxynil herbicide, Buctril. In 1986, a gene encoding an enzyme that detoxified bromoxynil within the engineered plant was discovered. The U.S. Department of Agriculture had approved Calgene's genetically modified cotton; a first for a genetically engineered herbicide-resistant crop species, the new transgenic cotton variety was to be marketed in 1995. In addition, Callahan Seeds was conducting research on herbicide tolerance for soybeans. In 1986, Rhône-Poulenc had been involved in a project of the European research programme, Eureka, to develop artificial tomato seeds (somatic embryos) in bioreactors (Heissler, 1994).

Rhône-Poulenc was joining a new trend in agro-industry by developing biopesticides, which were considered more environment-friendly. However, the company was still producing highly dangerous pesticides, such as lindane and aldicarb. The industrial area of Cubatao, Brazil, where the company's subsidiary, Rhodia, had a chemical plant, was known as the 'Valley of Death'; it was one of the most polluted areas in the world and had the highest infant mortality rate in Brazil. It was obvious that not only one factory was responsible for the disastrous environmental situation in Cubatao; Rhodia's plant, however, produced chlorinated chemicals and, until 1978, also pentachlorophenol (PCP). According to *Pesticides News*, soil probes taken around the factory had shown a concentration of poisonous chemicals in excess of 7,840 times the permitted level. In addition, blood tests taken from Cubatao residents showed high amounts of toxic substances, such as PCP. In June 1993, a Brazilian court ordered the company to close its Cubatao factory, so as to halt the continued exposure of plant workers to residues. RP lodged an appeal against the factory's shutdown; in its defence, the company stated that, since 1984, the factory's incinerator, a $20 million investment, had eliminated all its organochlorine waste products (Heissler, 1994).

Rhône-Poulenc was also making efforts to develop more environment-friendly insecticides. In its laboratories located in the Research Triangle Park, Raleigh, North Carolina, which the company occupied since 1986 when it purchased the agrochemical division of Union Carbide, 130 researchers and 75 technicians (in 1995) were researching more environment-friendly substitutes for current insecticides that would also be effective in lower doses. On the basis of data showing that insect pests, diseases and weeds destroyed every year 50% of the rice, 35% of the maize and 25% of the wheat grown in the world, Rhône-Poulenc developed in 1981 a new molecule, called Fipronil, at its Ongar research centre in the United Kingdom. Fipronil was patented in 1985 and commercialized in 1993 in Colombia and Indonesia under the trademark, Regent. In 1995, it was being tested in Thailand on termites and, in the Sahel countries, on grasshoppers and locusts (these insects had destroyed 400,000 tonnes of cereals in 1987). Trials with Fipronil showed that a dose of 10 g per hectare could destroy 95% of the grasshopper population. The product had a wide range: it could protect rice from leaf-hoppers (Cicadellidae), cotton or the banana tree from weevils and potatoes from Colorado beetles. For large-scale crops, the dose varied from 25 g to 120 g per hectare, while other insecticides were used at a dose of 1,120 g per hectare. Rhône-Poulenc had also demonstrated the effectiveness of Fipronil against ticks, cockroaches, lice and ants, which could have interesting prospects for the household market (Alberganti, 1995).

In 1994, RP's distribution of sales by markets was the following: 25% USA, 22% Europe without France, 21% France, 8% Asia, 6% Brazil and 18% other (Rhône-Poulenc, 1993).

In 1995, RP's net profits amounted to $426 million (+ 11.4% compared to 1994) for an annual turnover of $16.92 billion (– 1.8% compared to 1994) distributed as follows: 43% in pharmacy, 30% in chemistry, 15% in fibres and polymers, and 12%

in agrochemistry. Ten years earlier, the annual turnover of $11.22 billion was distributed as follows: 68% in chemistry and 32% in pharmacy, animal health and crop protection. In 1995, the Stock Exchange value of the group was $8.06 billion.

Regarding the pharmaceutical sector of the group, the 1995 turnover reached $7.66 billion, a record since the merger in 1990 of Rhône-Poulenc and Rorer; it was distributed as follows: Rhône-Poulenc Rorer ($4.5 billion); Fisons (since the autumn of 1995, specialized in pharmaceuticals against asthma and allergy; almost $800 million); Centeon, created by Rhône-Poulenc Rorer, specialized in plasma derivatives, and co-managed with Hoechst AG ($1.2 billion); Pasteur Mérieux Connaught, the world's biggest vaccine-production group ($560 million); and Connaught-Merck & Co. Inc. joint subsidiary ($600 million). However, due to the acquisition of Fisons and Applied Immune Sciences, the 1995 net profit decreased by 3% to $337.8 million. The overall debt of the group rose to $7.2 billion (Gallois, 1996*a,b*).

Since 1995, the main shareholders ('hard core') had realized that the share price was lower than the purchase price; they had become more demanding and some of them were questioning the group's strategy, which consisted of keeping together four sectors (chemistry, health, agrochemistry, fibres and polymers). Although the big European groups such as Sandoz AG and Hoechst AG were separating their pharmaceutical and chemical activities, Rhône-Poulenc was reluctant to adopt this approach, despite the pressure exerted by financial experts who stressed that the return rates of the two activities were totally distinct. The return rate was low in chemistry, but high in pharmacy which demanded an important research input. Remaining in both sectors might lead the group to an arbitration that would be made at the expense of one or the other sector. After a heated debate among the group's administrators, the directorate was given two years to find an appropriate solution. With regard to chemistry, in January 1995, RP announced that it would be focusing on high value-added products, which implied the abandonment of basic commodities. Of a total 115 activities listed by the mid-1980s, only 45 represented the main focus in 1995 and this figure was expected to drop further (Gallois, 1995*k*).

In 1996, Rhône-Poulenc's turnover amounted to $17.16 billion, a 1.2% increase over that of 1995. Net profit rose 28.4% to $540 million, mainly due to the growth of pharmaceutical and plant and animal health activities, which represented 87% of the results associated with the group's exploitation. Net profit per share amounted to $17 approximately, a 25.8% increase over 1995. The ratio net debt: proper funds equalled O.61 at the end of 1996, compared to 0.72 at the end of 1995, the objective for the end of 1997 being less than 0.5.

The group's structures would be clarified in order to highlight the weight of health activities within the group. In November 1996, all these activities were grouped under the heading of 'Health Activities'. The following step was poised to establish closer relations with Pasteur-Mérieux Connaught. Rhône-Poulenc's President did not hesitate to describe the group as a pharmaceutical one: of the $17.16 billion annual turnover, health activities represented 55% (35% for pharmacy and 20% for animal and plant health) [Gallois, 1996g].

Motivated by the low investment capacity in France and by a desire to anticipate a possible withdrawal of some partners, Rhône-Poulenc's President decided to find new partners outside France. A U.S. investment fund, Wellington, took a 5% share of the capital at the beginning of 1996 and was expected to become the most important shareholder; the fund was not excluded from the possibility of increasing its share, especially when the share value had increased by almost 50% since Wellington became a partner. It was also expected that this new partner, like the other investors, would press Rhône-Poulenc to raise its productivity. It seemed, therefore, that financial logics was prevailing over industrial logics (Gallois, 1996*e*).

7. According to the managing director of Hoffmann-La Roche AG (1993), around 20 new proteins, interferons, colony-stimulating factors, thrombolytic enzymes and peptide hormones were registered as drugs. The future portfolio was for 40 monoclonal antibodies and 150 recombinant proteins under current clinical development. He estimated that by the year 2003, recombinant proteins would form 10% of the total pharmaceutical market worth $250 billion (in *Bio/Technology*, 11 March 1993, pp. S-16–20).

8. The CIGB also produced and marketed a recombinant vaccine against ticks, named Gavac[R]. This new vaccine was effective in the immunization of cattle against ticks, in reducting tick populations in livestock husbandry units and it decreased the number of dippings into acaricide baths. The vaccine could be injected into both pregnant and lactating cows and did not interfere with other vaccines or drugs.

9. At the end of 1994, Ciba-Ceigy AG became one of the world's leading groups on the market of 'over the counter' (OTC) non-prescription drugs, by purchasing the OTC branch of Rhône-Poulenc Rorer (RPR) in North America for $407 million. Prior to the acquisition (according to 1992 statistics), the Swiss group's OTC activities had been distributed as follows: 61% in Europe, 29% in the USA, 4% in Asia and 6% in the rest of the world. With the purchase of RPR's OTC branch, Ciba-Geigy AG moved into the top ten OTC groups on the American market, the largest in the world, estimated at $12 billion. In 1993, Ciba-Geigy AG's OTC turnover amounted to 1 billion Swiss Francs world-wide, its OTC division representing 4% of the company's total annual turnover and 10% of its health sector sales.

10. In contrast to a number of toxins and drugs, such as the *Catharanthus* alkaloids, which disrupted the microtubule function by inhibiting the assembly of tubulin filaments, thereby inducing disaggregation and microtubular breakdown, taxol (and its derivative taxotere) promoted microtubule assembly and resulted in unusually stable and disorganized aggregates of tubulin. This unusual stability inhibited the dynamic organization of the cellular microtubule network. These aggregates might either take the form of abundant arrays or abnormal microtubules aligned in parallel bundles or as excessive numbers of abnormal mitotic asters. The precise cytotoxic events accompanying these changes were not known, although 'bundle' formation had been associated with a slowing of cell cycle and increased toxicity.

At the Johns Hopkins Oncology Center, Johns Hopkins University School of Medicine, phase-I trials initiated in 1983 explored a number of schedules of administration of taxol. These studies, as well as the early phase-II studies, provided information about the toxicities associated with taxol. Neutropenia had been the dose-limiting toxicity on all schedules of administration, the maximum tolerated dose being 200-250 mg/m^2. Those toxicities not limiting dosing included alopecia, myalgia and anthralgia, mild peripheral neuropathies and thrombocytopenia. Mucositis and nausea were rare. Development of the drug was threatened by the occurrence of severe 'hypersensitivity' reactions predominantly on short infusion schedules. These reactions, which could be cardiac, pulmonary, cutaneous or other, were felt to be due to the formulation vehicle. They had been minimized by the use of longer infusions (24 hours) and promedication.

Enthusiasm for taxol had been growing since the demonstration of a 30% response rate in 40 patients with refractory ovarian cancer at Johns Hopkins Oncology Center. This data had been confirmed in subsequent studies at Albert Einstein and at Johns Hopkins' Gynecologic Oncology Group. Modest activity (20% PR) was also seen in malignant melanoma in phase-I and several phase-II studies. The next provocative study was the report from M.D. Anderson in 1991 of a 50% response rate in metastatic breast cancer patients.

Further development of the drug was proceeding along several lines. Broad phase-II trials had started in a variety of diseases including cancers of the colon, lung, neck, cervix, etc. Studies were being carried out in Europe and Japan. In anticipation of use in combination therapy for ovarian cancer, a phase-I trial of taxol and cisplatin had been completed which yielded no dose limiting non-haematologic toxicity and had allowed further dose escalation with growth factors. Taxol and cisplatin were compared to standard cyclophosphamide and cisplatin in a phase-III trial in ovarian cancer at Johns Hopkins' Gynecologic Oncologic Group.

Taxol was the only anti-tumour drug known to stabilize microtubules and was the prototype for a new class of cancer chemotherapeutic drugs.

11. A plant gene is a dormant source of information until a message (mRNA) is transcribed from its protein coding region. The transcriptional machinery comprises several protein factors that interact within the promoter part of a gene. These interactions determine the characteristics of gene expression, i.e. where and when genes are expressed. Regulatory elements (discrete DNA sequences) present within promoters specify, for instance, if a gene is active only in the seeds when they are about to mature or if gene expression is induced when the plant is attacked by pathogens. These elements interact with a number of regulatory proteins and transcription factors, and together bring RNA polymerase to a contact point in the promoter region. The nucleotide sequence of this portion is highly conserved in nearly all promoters – hence the phrase 'TATA box' to denote the four nucleotide present here – and mRNA synthesis is intiated within a short distance downstream of this point. Based on the pattern of gene expression dictated by the sum of all regulatory elements present upstream of the TATAbox, promoters are classified as cell-, tissue-, organ-, or developmental-specific, and as constitutive (widely active) or inducible (in response to certain stimuli) [Datla and Selvaraj, 1995].

There were many examples of successful swapping of entire promoters between different genes resulting in hybrid genes whose expression patterns obeyed the 'rules' laid down by the promoters. In some cases, inserting a single regulatory element of less than 20 nucleotides from one promoter into an area upstream of the TATA box of another promoter conferred on the second promoter the activating or silencing effect of the regulatory sequence. For instance, the promoterless segment of a bacterial gene coding for the enzyme beta-glucuronidase (*gus*) was expressed under the control of a plant promoter. Regardless of its origin, a gene could be manipulated to express in a new environment with the aid of a suitable promoter. In order to derive the intended benefits from genetic engineering, any newly introduced genes must be regulated appropriately. For instance, a microbial gene whose product directed synthesis of an industrially important oil could be used productively in plants only if its coding region was expressed under the control of a plant promoter active in particular seed tissues involved in oil synthesis. Some well-known examples included:

– the use of a fruit-specific promoter in Flavr/Savr™ tomatoes to delay ripening and, hence, improve their shelf-life (Calgene Inc.);

– an anther-specific promoter to subvert pollen formation, resulting in male-sterile plants which could then be used for hybrid production (University of California in Los Angeles, and Plant Genetic Systems, Ghent, Belgium);

– tuber-specific promoters to produce lauric and stearic acid oils in oilseed rape (Calgene Inc.).

Constitutive promoters like the 35S promoter of cauliflower mosaic virus had been widely used to express genes which needed to be active throughout a plant as in the case of, for instance, herbicide-resistant plants (Datla and Selvaraj, 1995).

In April 1994, the Plant Biotechnology Institute (PBI) of the National Research Council of Canada, in Saskatoon, set up the Promoter Technology Group, whose objective was to identify, isolate and characterize useful promoters. It was establishing a bank of promoters from a number of plant species, including some Brassicas in collaboration with the PBI Brassica Biotechnology Group. In co-operation with other groups at the PBI, the Promoter Technology Group planned to expand the bank to include promoters from cereals and other plants. PBI scientists had engineered a novel *gus* construct in which the capacity to inactivate kanamycin was incorporated by fusion in another bacterial enzyme, neomycin phosphotransferase. When a promoterless version of this gene was activated by an upstream plant promoter, it produced a protein that protected the cells from kamamycin-mediated killing and, furthermore, allowed detection of the *gus*-producing cells by chemical staining. A collection of T-DNA (the DNA segment transferred from *Agrobacterium*-based genetic transformation vectors into plant cells) tagged plants obtained using this approach included plants with *gus* expression localized to pollen, embryo, cotyledon, stigma, root tip, xylem or phloem tissues. Plants showing a constitutive reporter expression had also been obtained (the bacterial *gus* gene was one of the best-known examples of such reporters; the plants in which the *gus* gene was activated were identified on the basis of their blue staining; the location of the stain within the plant provided the first clue as to the specificity of the putative promoter tag). While assembling a promoter bank and characterizing useful ones further, PBI scientists were also working with internal and external partners to isolate promoters for specific applications, such as modifying seed composition (Datla and Selvaraj, 1995).

International Atomic Energy Agency

The International Atomic Energy Agency (IAEA) was set up in the mid-1950s for the purpose of accelerating and enlarging the contributions made by the peaceful use of atomic energy throughout the world. To assist developing countries to establish a modern and safe technological base, the IAEA required laboratory support; this was provided mainly by its laboratories in Seibersdorf, some 30 km south of Vienna, and in Vienna itself. In addition, the Agency was served by its Laboratory of Marine Radioactivity in Monaco, by the International Centre for Theoretical Physics in Trieste, managed by UNESCO and funded through an important Italian Government subvention, and by many national laboratories under research contracts or other agreements. The nucleus of the Laboratories had been formed in 1959; these were transferred to Seibersdorf in 1961. From the very beginning, training had been an important part of the Laboratories' activity; it included in-service training of fellows for periods varying from a few weeks to up to one or two years; formal training courses, each course lasting approximately one month and involving lectures as well as practical work; and group training in specific practical topics for three to six months through technical tutoring, hands-on experience, periodical lecturing and direct experimental supervision. Every year in the Laboratories, in-service training of about 60 fellows from developing countries was complemented by three to four training courses organized for a similar number of trainees.

The Laboratories were organized in three branches: the Agricultural Laboratory; the Physics, Chemistry and Instrumentation Laboratory; and the Safeguards Analytical Laboratory. Together, these Laboratories occupied a floor space of more than 7,000 m^2 and employed a total staff of 180. In addition to the Agency's regular budget resources and FAO contribution, the Laboratories had access to funds for specific projects from individual governments.

In 1964, a Joint FAO/IAEA Division of Nuclear Applications in Food and Agriculture (called Joint FAO/IAEA Division for short) had been set up. The IAEA's Agriculture Laboratory with its five Units dealing with Soil Science, Plant Breeding, Animal Production, Entomology and Agrochemicals, was working on projects originating in the Joint FAO/IAEA Division, including biotechnology research-and-development activities. The Joint FAO/IAEA Division had a staff of some 40 scientists from more than 25 countries, including those working its its allied laboratory. Most served for fixed terms of two to five years before returning to their home institutions. This turnover allowed for flexibility and a constant input of up-to-date know-how. Continuity was provided by long-term staff members, who comprised about one-quarter of the total. The Joint FAO/IAEA Division was located at the IAEA headquarters in Vienna and the associated Laboratory in Seibersdorf; operated by the IAEA Department of Research and Isotopes, the Laboratory provided the Joint FAO/IAEA Division with the necessary support for condcuting experiments.

The Joint FAO/IAEA Division operated through six specialized Sections and was assisted by corresponding Units at the Seibersdorf Laboratory. The specialized Sections were:
- Soil fertility, irrigation and crop production;
- Plant breeding and genetics;
- Animal production and health;
- Insect and pest control;
- Agrochemicals and residues;
- Food preservation.

The Joint FAO/IAEA Division had scientific and technical responsibility for all FAO and IAEA activities concerned with applying nuclear techniques and related biotechnologies to food and agriculture, and for projects within the research programmes executed using the facilities of the founding partners. Thus, it had main responsibility for all scientific and technical meetings, special missions, training courses and publications in its designated area of expertise, and responsibility for technical co-operation programmes, research-contract programmes, and the laboratory activities in Seibersdorf in the field of nuclear techniques in food and agriculture.

The FAO/IAEA Agricultural Biotechnology Programme of the Seibersdorf Laboratory was designed to support the Joint FAO/IAEA

Division activities. Through the Laboratory's Units, this facility specialized in research, development and technology transfer in soils and crop production, plant breeding and genetics, animal husbandry, entomology and agrochemicals. Food preservation activities were supported by an international training network under the auspices of the International Consultative Group on Food Irradiation (ICGFI). Seibersdorf and the ICGFI trained a total of 30–50 fellowship holders annually, as well as a greater number of participants in four to six training courses held each year.

Approximately 400 universities and research institutions in FAO and IAEA Member States co-operated annually in some 35 co-ordinated research programmes, each dedicated to solving a scientifically and economically significant problem, and involving collaboration among 10–20 institutions from different countries. Those in developing countries were awarded research contracts providing for nominal IAEA financial support, while those in industrialized countries participated through research agreements without financial support. The Sections organized regular meetings of programme participants for the purpose of reviewing results and determining subsequent steps, and to draw conclusions from the results of the Co-ordinated Research Programmes.

Each year, the Joint FAO/IAEA Division evaluated requests from over 100 Member States for technical assistance involving services, equipment, training and experts. Advisory missions aimed to assist governments in designing technical co-operation requests. Improving national expertise was also a major goal of technical co-operation projects. Training was provided either in Seibersdorf or at research centres elsewhere in the world, individual training lasting from a few weeks to a year. In addition, there were regional or inter-regional training courses for groups of scientists at appropriate facilities in a Member State or at the Seibersdorf Laboratory. In the mid-1990s, the Joint FAO/IAEA Division was responsible for managing over 220 technical co-operation field projects, several of which were regional in scope, in almost 65 developing countries. Most of the funding for these activities was provided by the IAEA Department of Technical Co-operation, while the Joint FAO/IAEA Division Sections arranged for the provision of experts and supply of equipment and services.

Over the five-year period from 1988 to 1992, almost 1,500 agricultural scientists were trained under the Joint FAO/IAEA Division supervision, either as beneficiaries of individual fellowships or as participants in special training courses.

The Sections regularly published scientific results of practical importance obtained in the Joint FAO/IAEA Division projects. Up to

1992, more than 100 special technical documents had been produced, in addition to a high number of papers published in international scientific journals. The Sections also maintained contact with scientists in Member States through the publication of periodically newsletters and bulletins. They prepared other materials, such as films, audio-visual programmes and brochures, for the purposes of promotion and general information.

Among the Co-ordinated Research Programmes supported by the Soil Science Unit at the Seibersdorf Laboratory, the following related to biological nitrogen fixation and aimed to:

– increase the yield and nutritive value of pastures by incorporating high nitrogen-fixing legume species;

– assess nitrogen fixation and nitrogen cycling in the *Azolla/Anabaena* system and the usefulness of the water fern *Azolla* as a biofertilizer in paddy fields;

– examine genetic variation in symbiotic nitrogen fixation by the common bean to improve nitrogen fixation in order to save fertilizer and increase food production (in Latin America);

– improve yield and nitrogen fixation in several grain legumes in subtropical and tropical regions of Asia.

As part of an FAO/IAEA Co-ordinated Research Programme, field experiments had been carried out in Austria, Brazil, Chile, Colombia, Guatemala, Mexico, Peru and the USA to investigate the nitrogen-fixing potential of several cultivars or breeding lines of *Phaseolus vulgaris*. Each experiment included approximately 20 genotypes of common beans compared using the ^{15}N isotope dilution method. Gaping differences in nitrogen fixation had been observed both between and within experiments, with average values of 35% nitrogen derived from the atmosphere (Ndfa) or about 25 kg of nitrogen fixed per hectare and highest values of 65% Ndfa or more than 110 kg of nitrogen per hectare, far above that previously reported for common bean. Values as high as this were only recorded when environmental factors were favourable. Lines of high nitrogen-fixing common bean were therefore available for use in breeding programmes seeking to enhance nitrogen fixation in other cultivars.

Technical assistance projects covered such topics as biological nitrogen fixation, basic studies in soil microbiology and plant physiology, fertilizer use efficiency. The Unit performed ^{15}N determinations on plant samples. It also offered its analytical services to research contractors and to some technical co-operation projects.

A general training course on Isotope and radiation techniques in soil-plant relationship studies was held at the Laboratory every second year. In alternate years, an advanced course on special topics was offered. Each course was open to approximately 20 scientists from developing countries. There was also individual fellowship training available in a specific technique for periods of two to four months (e.g. ^{15}N assay by emission spectroscopy) and six- to twelve-month research fellowships; on average, ten fellowships were offered annually.

The Plant Breeding Unit was supporting the Joint FAO/IAEA Division's programme in genetic crop improvement, in particular in the following research areas: comparison of genetic variation arising in tissue culture (somaclonal variation) with that induced either by irradiation or by chemical agents, using maize as the model crop species; improvement of disease resistance in banana and plantain by mutation breeding using *in-vitro* culture techniques; improvement of environmental stress tolerance in *Azolla* by mutation induction to create mutants tolerant to high salinity, toxic aluminium amounts and certain herbicides; investigation of methods of mutation breeding of cassava and yam, the most important staple food crop species in the tropics.

Modest genetic variation and sterility handicapped genetic improvement of banana and plantain (*Musa* spp.) by conventional breeding techniques. Consequently, shoot tip culture and *in-vitro* plant regeneration were being investigated for use in mutation induction and selection; in addition, somatic embryogenesis and plant regeneration from cell suspensions of *Musa* spp. aimed to develop somatic cell manipulation procedures for banana and plantain breeding. In cassava and yam, mutation breeding techniques were being developed to increase variation in plant habit, cyanide toxicity, disease and pest resistance; *in-vitro* culture techniques were used for propagation of healthy plants and improved clones; somatic embryogenesis was being developed for cassava and yam improvement.

Contributions were also being made to: increasing variation within the currently available cocoa cultivars, through the use of somatic embryogenesis for propagation of the desired genotypes and for *in-vitro* mutagenesis; inducing mutations in citrus and date-palm tissue cultures; regenerating *in-vitro* and inducing mutations in garlic.

The FAO/IAEA Programme on research in the use of DNA fingerprinting techniques for detection and characterization of genetic variation in vegetatively propagated plants was dealing with such crop species as banana, plantain, sweet potato, yam, sugar-cane and cassava. From 1990 to 1993, two new DNA fingerprinting techniques were introduced; they could be transferred to laboratories of developing countries, in order to characterize genetic diversity induced by mutagenesis or by *in-vitro* culture and the discrimination between mutants. Institutes and laboratories from developing countries had been invited to send proposals for research contracts under this Programme.

The Plant Breeding Unit had greenhouses and experimental fields, as well as facilities for aseptic *in-vitro* manipulation of plant cell and tissue cultures. A plant cytology laboratory and specialized facility for chemical mutagen application with a bio-hazard cabinet were available, as were a ^{60}Co gamma cell for *in-vivo* and *in-vitro* irradiation of plant material and facilities for radioisotope work. The swimming pool-type Astra reactor of the Austrian Research Centre, in Seibersdorf, was used for fast neutron irradiation. Walk-in growth chambers with controlled temperature, humidity and artificial illumination were used for culturing plant material. A mutagen treatment service was provided free of charge to plant breeding institutes in FAO and IAEA Member States.

An inter-regional training course on Induction and use of mutations in plant breeding was held every year for 20 participants. In addition, about eight three- to twelve-month fellowships per year were awarded to junior scientists from developing countries involved in plant breeding for in-service training in mutation breeding on crop species cultivated in their home countries; training activities were individually designed to assure direct application of the techniques learnt upon return to the home institution.

The Animal Production Unit was supporting activities to improve the productivity and health of livestock in tropical and subtropical countries by way of research and development, the production of quality-control services, standardized diagnostic kits, training and other ancillary services. The rumen stimulation technique (RUSITEC) aimed to evaluate with the help of isotopic tracers the fermentative digestion of crop residues and agro-industrial by-products by rumen micro-organisms maintained *in vitro* in an artificial rumen under normal physiological conditions. If the results indicated satisfactory fermentation with regard to digestibility, production of end products of fermentation, such as volatile fatty acids and ammonia, and the synthesis of microbial protein, then the feedstuff could be of potential value for ruminants and would be further tested by nutritionists in Member States.

The Unit's activities focused on the use of enzyme linked immunosorbent assay (ELISA) in diagnosing animal diseases. The kits developed for the diagnosis of rinderpest, brucellosis, babesiosis, infectious bovine rhinotracheitis and trypanosomiasis were designed for use under conditions found in laboratories of developing countries.

Each kit contained a detailed protocol and information on kit contents and assay trouble shooting, and sufficient reagents to carry out 40,000 assays. Development work was underway on the use of radioactively labelled DNA probes for detecting disease agents and the production of monoclonal antibodies for use in disease diagnostic kits.

At the Entomology Unit, the sterile insect technique (SIT), consisting of the repeated release of high numbers of laboratory reared and radiation-sterilized insects in the infected area to suppress the indigenous insect pest population, had been successfully used since 1954. As mating between the sterile and wild insects produced no viable offspring, continuous release of sterile insects over successive generations led to a gradual decrease and finally to eradication of the pest. Regarding the Mediterranean fruit fly, which attacked more than 200 varieties of fruits and vegetables, a SIT programme developed at a 500-m² pilot rearing facility in Seibersdorf had been successfully implemented in Mexico where eradication of the Mediterranean fruit fly saved approximately $500 million annually.

With respect to the tsetse fly (*Glossina* spp.), advances in rearing techniques had been made in Seibersdorf by replacing living hosts as food sources with an artificial system using blood obtained from a slaughterhouse; the diet, when freeze-dried, could be stored for many months and easily shipped anywhere in the world; artificial diets to replace blood by commercially available ingredients were being developed. A successful SIT project on the tsetse fly had been completed in Nigeria, a backup colony being kept at the Unit. The natural low reproductive rate of the fly and resultant low density field populations made the tsetse a good target for SIT control. Work was being carried out on improving feeding and rearing procedures of several *Glossina* species.

In addition to finding more effective large-scale rearing procedures, the Entomology Unit was carrying out research on various insect species and strains for expanding application of the SIT. Gamma radiation was commonly used to render sterile treated insects by inducing dominant lethal mutations in their sperm; experiments were performed to determine the optimal doses and application time during the insect's development, so that somatic damage to the insect was negligible.

Since sexually sterile males were the active components in a SIT project, females produced along with the males had to be eliminated; genetic sexing of the insect populations was therefore suitable, but not easy. One research project attempted to use genetic manipulation to eliminate Mediterranean fruit fly females at an early stage of the rearing process; when the manipulation was successful, males would carry genetic traits making them exclusively resistant to some lethal factor which would eliminate females.

Research was also being carried out to reduce the number of native fertile females through the isolation of *Bacillus thuringiensis* strains for use in bait sprays for suppressing wild populations of the Mediterranean fruit fly. This bacterial species was safe for beneficial insects and higher forms of animals, and was therefore more environmentally acceptable than chemical insecticides.

Approximately six fellows at a time were being trained in entomology under fellowship arrangements for periods lasting from a few months to two years. An average of 12 fellowship holders were accepted each year.

In the Agrochemicals Unit, microbial strains were being screened for their ability to degrade lignocellulose; this research aimed to develop cultures capable of bioconverting agricultural wastes to animal feeds and industrial chemicals. To that end, the Unit was supporting a Co-ordinated Research Programme.

Other United Nations specialized agencies and other bodies

1. World Intellectual Property Organization

The work of the World Intellectual Property Organization (WIPO, Geneva) was of great relevance to the issue of gene and genotype patenting, as well as to breeders' rights. While there seemed to be a significant amount of technology transfer activities among firms and institutions in developed countries, it also seemed true that, in developing countries, access to technology under favourable conditions was difficult.

Since technological innovation was a key competitive factor in bio-industry development, innovative enterprises were not generally willing to share their technology, particularly when it was very new and provided them with a competitive edge over competitors. However, three circumstances contributed to opening sources of technology to potentially interested parties. Firstly, innovative start-ups generally needed to license technologies they had developed so as to generate revenue and continue financing research-and-development activities. Indeed, technology transfer (or research-and-development work under sub-contract) accounted for the lion's share of revenue from start-ups which, in fact, operated as 'technology enterprises'. There were nevertheless some limitations to this potential technology transfer. On the one hand, since transnational corporations had taken over a large number of biotechnology firms, or established joint ventures, they restricted technology transfer in order to preserve their competitiveness. On the other hand, specialized firms tended to form strategic alliances with other enterprises with assets to offer in exchange, in terms of technological capabilities or market access. This was not generally the case for firms in developing countries, which lacked personnel, as well as the technological and marketing strength that would induce innovative firms to enter into partnership (Correa, 1991*b*).

Secondly, it was not uncommon for a number of enterprises and university laboratories to be carrying out research and development on the same subject at the same time. Scientific publications and contracts with researchers at these laboratories might enable access to valuable information and, indirectly, technology transfer. Furthermore, university policies in developed countries increasingly favoured the licensing of research-and-development results in order to recover expenses and fund new activities (Correa, 1991*b*).

Thirdly, a significant number of small enterprises willing to license technologies they could not exploit by themselves had emerged in several countries. Technical advice might also become available from experts in a personal capacity or as part of more comprehensive services (Correa, 1991*b*).

Licensing in biotechnologies took several forms. Originally, biotechnology start-up firms had licensed their inventions to large corporations out of a lack both of the ability to undertake successful market operations themselves and of financial resources to pursue their research-and-development activities. This situation had changed as some biotechnology start-up firms followed the path of inventing, developing and marketing the products themselves. On the other hand, large pharmaceutical companies had decided to upgrade their in-house expertise by recruiting outside specialists or taking over smaller start-up firms.

Two major types of licensing contracts existed in biotechnologies. The first related to 'generic' technologies, i.e. those required for most production activities in biotechnologies. Examples were the Genentech Inc. patent concerning the use of a recombinant DNA cloning vehicle for transformation into a host and a Hybritech patent on the use of monoclonal antibody technology. In these cases, a license agreement only authorized the practising of a patented technology, generally under non-exclusive conditions. The second type covered numerous specific technologies (for producing a given product or applying a process with particular results) that might be transferred under license. In these cases, biological material (e.g. a microbial strain) containing the necessary genetic information needed to be delivered. This was the main means of technology transfer. The material could be reproduced, in general, without limitation and applied in a variety of fields (typically in human health and veterinary medicine). Often, however, the licensors set up field-of-use restrictions that limited the commercial exploitation by the licensee to a specified area (Correa, 1991*b*).

Licensing fees in biotechnologies were likely to be higher than in other industrial sectors. High royalties might, in practice, prevent access by firms in developing countries to protected technologies and know-how. Royalty rates might range from 1% to 5% for research tools (expression vectors, cell cultures, microbial strains) to from 5% to 10% for therapeutic products (monoclonal antibodies, cloned factors, etc.) and vaccines. Rates might even be higher (10% to 15%) when the licensed product was sold in bulk (Correa, 1991*b*). These were all issues for debate by the WIPO.

The World Intellectual Property Organization (WIPO) had convened the following committees of experts:

– Committee of experts on Biotechnological Inventions and Industrial Property – from 1984 to 1988, four Committee meetings had been convened to consider whether the existing systems of legal protection for inventions were satisfactory as far as biotechnological inventions were concerned and, if not, to make suggestions for improving these; the International Bureau of WIPO prepared a report on the industrial property protection of biotechnological inventions and suggested solutions in this regard, both of which were reviewed and commented on by the Committee of Experts; the report and suggested solutions addressed availability of protection, the scope of protection and deposit of micro-organisms;

– Committee of Experts on the Interface between Patent Protection and Plant Breeders' Rights – from 29 January to 2 February 1990, this Committee of Experts was convened under the joint auspices of WIPO and the International Union for the Protection of New Varieties of Plants (UPOV) to consider issues concerning the relationship between plant breeders' rights and patent protection, the extent to which these rights meet, conflict, overlap or present gaps in protection. The issues discussed concerned: whether patents and plant breeders' rights should both be available with respect to plant varieties; limitations on rights granted to take into account the general nature of biological material and the agricultural and horticultural industries; how the phrase 'plant variety' should be defined; the question of dependent varieties and essentially derived varieties; whether protection of processes for producing plant varieties should extend to a plant variety directly obtained by such a process.

In this respect, one should recall that in the early part of the 20th century, plant breeding became an activity completely separate from farming in Europe and North America as seed companies and public research institutes became specialized in crossing and creating new plant varieties. The USA enacted a Plant Patent Act in 1930 and after the Second World War the Europeans worked out an intellectual property regime for developers of new crop varieties called Plant Breeders' Rights (PBR). An international convention establishing the Union for the Protection of New Varieties of Plants (UPOV) and laying out common rules for PBR was signed in 1961. The convention was administered by a small secretariat, housed within the World Intellectual Property Organization (WIPO). As of January 1996, the UPOV had 30 member States, while an additional 14 countries also had some type of PBR system in place. The original convention had been revised several times, the last revision being in 1991 (*Seedling*, the Quarterly Newsletter of Genetic Resources Action International – GRAIN, vol. 13, no. 2, June 1996, pp. 23–30).

In essence, plant breeders were given a limited monopoly over the reproductive material of the variety; this entailed an important difference with patents, whose holders claimed ownership to the germplasm, technology and industrial processes, while breeders -in the original UPOV concept- could only control multiplication and sale of seeds. Farmers had been allowed to continue with their ancestral costume of saving seeds for the following seasons and informally exchanging them with other farmers, even from protected varieties, this right being called the farmers' privilege. Breeders had also been allowed to make use of protected varieties' genetic material to develop new lines without having to pay royalties or ask permission. This right was included in UPOV as breeders' exemption. Without the possibility to freely exchange germplasm there could be agribusiness, but not agriculture (*Seedling*, vol. 13, no. 2, June 1996, pp. 23–30).

The 1991 version of UPOV was tougher, as it brought plant breeders' rights (PBR) closer to patents. The most important change was the virtual elimination of the farmers' privilege and breeders' exemption. Member countries accepting this new version might permit farmers to keep seeds and other propagation material from protected varieties for use on their own farms, but it would no longer be an automatic right. At the same time, breeders faced new restrictions in the free use of genetic material, since the holder of a variety might limit the right of another breeder to develop, produce, sell, stock or simply use any variety which was 'essentially derived' from a previously protected variety. Other important changes in the 1991 version of UPOV included the elimination of the ban against double protection, and countries might provide for simultaneous PBR and patents on everything from genes to entire crop species; the extension of UPOV rights to the import and export of protected varieties, and the control of the harvest produced from those varieties without breeder authorization; extension of UPOV protection up to 25 years in some cases and to new genera (*Seedling*, vol. 13, no. 2, June 1996, pp. 23–30).

Plant breeders' rights and the UPOV convention had been the subject of debate in both developed and developing countries since the establishment of the Convention. PBR had little to do with the local varieties small-scale commercial farmers and peasants usually cropped, since they did not meet the distinctiveness, uniformity and stability requirements. Furthermore, it was generally held that 80% of the seeds used by farmers in the tropics were saved from their own fields or freely exchanged with neighbours; these practices, disseminating biological diversity all the time, were an essential component of agroecosystem sustainability. Seed companies were rather interested in promoting hybrids and homogenous modern varieties, often through government agricultural extension services, and they naturally pushed for stronger PBR laws. But despite the doubts on the relevance of PBR for developing countries, the pressure on them to enact PBR legislation and join the UPOV was growing (*Seedling*, vol. 13, no. 2, June 1996, pp. 23–30).

With the closing of the GATT Uruguay Round, the member countries accepted an agreement on Trade-Related Aspects of Intellectual Property Rights (TRIPs); the TRIPs agreement stated that member countries of the new World Trade Organization must provide for the protection of intellectual property rights over plant varieties either by patents or an effective *sui generis* system. This agreement had spurred a number of initiatives in developing countries aimed at adopting a PBR legislation, e.g. the five member countries of the Andean Pact -Bolivia, Colombia, Ecuador, Peru and Venezuela-, Brazil (approval in early 1996 of a law which allowed patents on transgenic plants, and introduction of a PBR Cultivars Act), The Philippines, Argentina (which ratified the 1978 UPOV Convention. Many of the laws approved or under discussion in Latin America followed UPOV 1991 criteria for length of protection and scope of genera; the Costa Rica draft included the extension of protection to production, adopted UPOV 1991 'essentially-derived variety' clause and emphasized that farmers should apply for a permit from the national seeds authority to benefit from the farmers' privilege (*Seedling*, vol. 13, no. 2, June 1996, pp. 23–30).

Alternatives to the IPR scheme were being worked out and would be presented to the World Trade Organization as effective *sui generis* systems required by the TRIPs. Third World Network had developed and was promoting a Collective Intellectual Rights (CIR) system which aimed to redress the injustice done in the Convention on Biological Diversity, which recognized indigenous people and local communities, but fell short of accepting the rights of these communities to the protection of their intellectual achievements in knowledge and technology. In India, Vandana Shiva and a coalition of farmer groups and non-governmental organizations were proposing alternative Community Rights (CR) to counter IPRs as imposed by the TRIPs. The M.S. Swaminathan Research Foundation (Madras) was working on the implementation of a farmers' rights regime that would simultaneously deal with breeders' rights. Thailand had also been discussing a PBR law with a multisectorial group, proposing a farmers' Rights Law that departed from PBR but tried to meet the country's obligation with TRIPs. Thailand's draft Plant Protection Act, modelled after the 1978 UPOV Convention, was supported by the Ministry of Commerce and transnational corporations, which thought that it would help Thai agriculture to become more advanced, to attract funding from transnational corporations and to strengthen the country's competitivity on international markets. Public breeders, farmers' organizations and non-governmental organizations were opposing the law and claimed that progress in Thailand's agriculture was not the result of plant variety protection laws but because of the contributions of innumerous farming local communities and the public breeders who had backed them. Some officials of the Ministry Agriculture were also on that side. However, a working group composed of people from the Thai Traditional Medicine Institute of the Ministry of Public Health, lawyers' associations, universities, farmers' groups and non-governmental organizations, was trying to reconcile both positions. In Colombia, an Ad Hoc Group on Access to Genetic Resources had also worked extensively on developing *sui generis* options; they insisted that any IPR regime must recognize community rights as a distinct framework that should not meet patent law requirements; such *sui generis* regimes must lead to control by the communities over their resources and rights (*Seedling*, vol. 13, no. 2, June 1996, pp. 23–30). See also GAIA Foundation (1996).

The broad-coverage patents was also a thorny issue, as exemplified by the patents granted to the U.S. biotechnological company Agracetus Inc. The latter was founded in 1981 by Winston J. Brill, a renowned plant geneticist from the University of Wisconsin, who was at that time a consultant for Cetus Corporation, the first-ever biotechnology company formed. He convinced Cetus Corporation to create a plant biotechnology company in Madison, Cetus Madison Corp., on 21 August 1981. In 1984, Cetus Corp. sought a major partner for its Madison agricultural subsidiary. W.R. Grace & Co., a world leading company in specialty chemicals, with interests in energy, manufacturing, service and biotechnology businesses, purchased nearly half of Cetus Madison Corp., and the partners agreed to change the name to Agracetus Inc. (a superimposition of Grace and Cetus, designating an agriculture focus). With Grace's investment, the company's technology productivity accelerated, driven by two major inventions in 1986: genetic engineering of cotton and a process for gene transfer known as electric-discharge particle transformation. Administration of Agracetus Inc. was shared until W.R. Grace & Co. acquired sole ownership of Agracetus Inc. in 1990. Since then, the company has been operated as a unit of Grace Specialty Businesses. Agracetus Inc., located in Middleton, adjacent to the capital city of Wisconsin and the University of Wisconsin, employed more than 70 scientists and supporting staff. A variety of collaborations and consultation arrangements were established with University of Wisconsin faculty.

W.R. Grace & Co., founded in 1854, with headquarters in New York City, employed approximately 50,000 people in 46 States, the District of Columbia and 44 countries. Annual sales exceeded $6.7 billion in 1990. Under the Grace Specialty Businesses umbrella, Agracetus Inc. was associated with other agricultural specialty companies such as American Breeders Service, a leader in dairy and beef cattle genetics; Farr Better Feeds, a central plains supplier of cattle feed supplements; and Walnut Grove, a leading supplier of hog feeds in the Middle West. The Grace Washington Research Center in Columbia, Maryland, provided expertise to complement Agracetus Inc.'s own research efforts. As an example of the synergy made possible through this co-operative research, Agracetus Inc.'s microbial research programme, directed at developing biopesticides for controlling seed ans soil-borne diseases, was transferred in 1990 to the Grace Research Division as part of a consolidation with a complementary biocontrol programme operated in Columbia, Maryland. The combined programme was developing new products for marketing in horticulture through Grace Sierra, a supplier of horticultural and turf products.

Agracetus Inc. was considered a world leader in applying biotechnologies to agriculture. Crop species of long-standing interest to Agracetus Inc. included maize, soybeans and cotton. These target species represented about 45% of total U.S. crop land and produced commodities valued annually at about $30 billion in the USA at the farm level by the early 1990s. Improvements to additional crop species, such as wheat, rice, legumes, vegetables and forest species, were also being researched.

The world's first field test of a genetically-engineered plant was conducted by Agracetus Inc. in 1986. This was a field evaluation of a tobacco plant that had been modified to be resistant to crown gall disease. This experiment, while not commercially important, clearly demonstrated for the first time that genetic engineering could be used to improve agricultural crop species.

Agracetus Inc.'s most significant accomplishment had been the invention of an improved method of plant transformation that involved accelerating DNA-coated gold beads into plant cells via an electrical discharge instrument. The coated particles were spread uniformly onto a carrier sheet, which was placed above a chamber containing two electrodes electrically connected by a suspended droplet of water. Application of a high-voltage electrical current across these electrodes generated a spark which vaporized the water and created a shock wave. The latter accelerated the sheet and particles toward a retainer screen which stopped the sheet but allowed the particles to strike the target tissues. If the proper conditions were met, the DNA on the gold beads migrated into cell chromosomes once they had entered the plant tissue. Using this device patented under the name ACCELL™, new genes were introduced into soybeans, other legumes and cotton. Additionally, in collaboration with other researchers, Agracetus Inc.'s scientists introduced new genes into alfalfa, orchard grass, cranberry, red alder, Douglas fir and poplar. This method had the advantage of bypassing the lengthy tissue culture process and interfered less with the plant own metabolic systems, thereby reducing the likelihood of abnormalities in the regenerated transgenic plants.

Using the proprietary particle-method transformation technology, Agracetus Inc.'s scientists developed transgenic beans. This was the first report of transformation of this crop species, achieved by Russel, McCabe, Christou, Martinell and their colleagues in March 1991. Soybeans were also transformed using the same technique in May 1991.

In 1987, Agracetus Inc. developed the world's first cotton plants containing foreign genes through *Agrobacterium*-mediated transformation. With more than 10 million acres grown in the USA and 75 million acres world-wide, cotton was one of the world's most significant crop species, valued at more than $4 billion annually in the USA alone by the early 1990s. Cotton accounted for use of more chemical insecticides than any other U.S. crop species except maize ($500 million in pesticides and herbicides were being applied annually by the early 1990s to control insects, fungal diseases and weeds). The Agracetus Inc. programme focused on developing cotton resistant to the cotton bollworm and tobacco budworm, which both accounted for nearly half of cotton insecticide expenditures. Agracetus Inc.'s initial insect-resistant cotton plants were field-tested in Mississipi in 1989 in co-operation with the U.S. Department of Agriculture Agricultural Research Service (U.S.DA-ARS). This world's first field test of insect-resistant cotton confirmed expression of the insect-resistant trait in the field and showed that yield was not adversely affected by the new genes.

In 1991, using proprietary-mediated gene transfer technology, McCabe and Martinell genetically engineered the leading cotton seed varieties in the USA: Deltapine 50, Deltapine 90, Pima S-6 and Sea Island. The first two varieties, products of Delta Pine Land Co., were the top two commercial upland varieties grown in the USA, with over 25% market share. Pima S-6 was a leading extra-long fibre variety and Sea Island was a variety with premium fibre characteristics. In addition to being the first reported development of a variety-independent method of cotton transformation, the technique reduced the time needed to generate transgenic cotton by more than 50%.

Collaborative arrangements were made between Agracetus Inc. and researchers throughout the USA to genetically engineer plants toward resistance to disease and virus attack. On average, 12% to 14% of U.S. crops were lost each year to the various disease pathogens. Thus, in collaboration with Maxwell, Department of Plant Pathology, University of Wisconsin, Madison, and Gilbertson, Department of Pathology, University of California, Davis, Agracetus Inc. was developing coat protein-mediated virus resistance in beans to resist attacks of bean golden mosaic virus and bean common mosaic virus.

In 1991, Christou, Ford and Kofron of Agracetus Inc. also succeeded in transforming both a long-grain Asian rice variety, IR-54, and the important U.S. commercial variety, Gulfmont, to deliver a gene for herbicide tolerance. The trait was stably passed to subsequent generations and the gene delivery method took less than five months from gene delivery to testing of first-generation plants, providing clear product development advantages for the evaluation of novel genetic traits. This achievement represented a breakthrough in monocot transformation and underscored the extensive skills of Agracetus Inc.'s staff and the broad potential of the company's proprietary gene transfer technology. The rice long-grain varieties represented around 75% of rice trade; rice was also the single-biggest global market for agrochemicals, with annual expenditures approaching $3 billion by the early 1990s.

Agracetus Inc. was working on transgenic cotton plants with brightly coloured cotton bolls. Although several naturally-coloured cotton varieties had been obtained by conventional breeding, no blue variety existed. As blue was in great demand in the textile industry, particularly for jeans production, synthetic fabric dyes were used. Natural blue cotton fibre would have a great market potential, and genetic engineers intended to insert into cotton plants the genes coding for the production of the blue colour in the indigo plant, formerly the source of natural blue dye, until it was substituted by aniline dyes (Christou *et al.*, 1990; Bijman, 1994*b*).

In addition to programmes in agricultural biotechnologies, Agracetus Inc. was developing a mammalian research programme, with potential to impact numerous areas, such as gene therapy of various human diseases, novel cell culture products and production of transgenic animals with increased immunity to diseases or greater production efficiencies. In December 1990, Yang of Agracetus Inc. developed a new method to insert foreign genes into mammalian somatic cells in culture or to tissues within live organisms. The method was based on the company's proprietary ACCEL™ technique.

In conjunction with American Breeders Services (ABS), research focused on methods for genetically engineering bovine species. A programme with ABS to clone embryos from superior cows was related to Agracetus Inc.'s molecular capabilities to develop technology for inserting new genes into cows. The programme objective was to select cows with improved disease resistance and other traits enhancing overall productivity of the dairy industry.

Another co-operative project with Grace's Washington Research Center concerned the development of an artificial pancreas. This implantable device contained live mammalian cells that functioned to maintain excellent glucose control in insulin-dependent diabetics. Frequent monitoring of blood sugar amounts and daily injections of insulin would no longer be necessary. The potential for further optimizing cultured cells used in an artificial pancreas through genetic modification of hormone-regulating cells was being explored in this co-operative project.

On 2 April 1991, Agracetus Inc. had been granted a U.S. patent (no. 5,004,863) covering plant genetic engineering technology using *Agrobacterium tumefaciens.* Also in April 1991, Agracetus Inc. received a U.S. patent (no. 5,015,580) covering a method for genetically engineering soybeans using its gene gun. The ACCELL™ technique had been patented in 1992 (no. 5,120,657, issued in June 1992). In October 1992, Agracetus Inc. was granted a U.S. patent (no. 5,159,135) covering all genetically-engineered cotton plants. Similarly, in March 1994, the company had been granted a European patent (no. 0,301,749, B1) on all transgenic soybeans. The cotton and soybeans patents had broad coverage. This was due largely to a precedent set in Scripps Research Institute versus Genentech Inc. In 1991, the Scripps Research Institute successfully challenged Genentech Inc. for infringing its patent for a purified clotting factor made from blood; the courts ruled that Genentech Inc. must obtain a license from Scripps although Genentech Inc. was producing the factor via genetic engineering, thus using a different process. Originally, Agracetus Inc. filed for all its claims in one patent; at that time, the U.S. Patent and Trademark Office rejected the broader claim focussing on the matter instead of the process. Only the product by process claim was awarded (U.S. patent no.5,004,863, 2 April 1991). Then Agracetus Inc. filed a continuation application stating that because of the Scripps versus Genentech Inc. case the process language was meaningless; therefore it wanted to drop this useless process language and keep the product claim. Thus, a patent for composition of matter was awarded on appeal by the Court of Appeals, Federal Circuit; this patent (no. 5,159,135) was granted on 27 October 1992 (Mestel, 1994).

A similar broad cotton patent had been granted in India and patent applications were filed in Brazil and China. Together, the USA, Brazil, China and India accounted for 60% of world cotton production. In addition, through non-exclusive licenses, others could use the genetic-engineering technique. For its transgenic cotton, Agracetus Inc. already had non-exclusive commercial license agreements with Calgene Inc. and Monsanto Co. Calgene Inc. was developing a herbicide-resistant cotton variety, while Monsanto Co. was marketing an insect-resistant variety, transformed with a gene from *Bacillus thuringiensis* coding for an entomotoxin. For companies unable to develop transgenic plants, Agracetus Inc. provided a service to improve soybeans under contract. Agracetus Inc. stated that its broad patents would not affect public-funded research, because research licenses were available, free of charge, to all academic or governmental researchers. European Union patent law included a research exemption, allowing the use of protected intellectual property for true research purposes, without infringement of patent rights. In the USA, however, utility of industrial patent law (the type of patent granted to Agracetus Inc.) had no research exemption, although judicial decisions appeared to provide such an exemption for non-commercial research (Bijman, 1994*b*).

These broad-coverage patents had initially met with the opposition from non-governmental organizations which were concerned that patents might lead to monopoly positions for companies or nations, thereby adversely affecting cotton production in developing countries. The Rural Advancement Foundation International (RAFI), in its communiqué of July-August 1993, concluded that the Agracetus Inc. patents on cotton would stiffle, rather than stimulate, innovations on genetically-engineered cotton outside the three to four major corporations and plant biotechnology companies that dominated transgenic cotton research and development. Other biotechnology companies as well as seed corporations had also expressed their concern, even though in general they supported patentability. Even if Agracetus Inc. did want to license, it could exert considerable control over production and sale. The terms of the license covered the height of the fees, but might also hold restrictions on special applications of the technology and on commercial activities in certain markets. For instance, for improving special fibre qualities, Agracetus Inc. was not likely to grant any license, as developing and selling specialty natural fibres was part of its core business (Bijman, 1994*b*).

Yet, other companies would not take action against the broad-coverage patents, as some had obtained or hoped to obtain similar patents. For instance, Calgene Inc. had filed a patent covering all genetically-engineered vegetables in the *Brassica* family, including cauliflower, broccoli and kale. Plant Genetic Systems (PGS) N.V. had filed patents covering all transgenic plants containing *Bacillus thuringiensis* genes, and genes inducing nuclear male sterility (Bijman, 1994*b*).

The criticism of the U.S. Department of Agriculture (U.S.DA) was much broader: the patents might give Agracetus Inc. virtual control over all applied research on transgenic cotton; the U.S.DA attorney also believed that the inventions patented by Agracetus Inc. were taught in the prior literature, and the claim of non-obviousness did not hold (Holzman, 1994).

Agracetus Inc. contended that it had not set a precedent, pointing out that the very broad Cohen/Boyer patent covered all DNA transfer. But the latter did not claim any rights to matter produced by using the patented technology. Agracetus Inc. case was clearly unprecedented in that it gave the company rights to all genetically-engineered products from an entire crop (Bijman, 1994*b*).

The Indian Council of Agricultural Research and the Department of Biotechnology were trying to revoke Agracetus Inc.'s patent, because it might restrict India's access to a crop line produced by this method or harm the interests of Indian cotton industry. Through the working of this patent, Indian scientists focusing on transgenic cotton (even with totally different techniques) were in a stranglehold by Agracetus Inc. Another example of difficult relation was the exorbitant license fee demanded by Monsanto Co. for its insect-resistant transgenic cotton varieties, so that the Indian Government had to put off the deal (Bijman, 1994*b*).

2. International Labour Organization

The International Labour Organization (ILO) was conducting case studies on the socio-economic impact of biotechnologies and particularly their implications for employment. Ahmed (1992*a*), of the ILO, provided information on the potential impact of genetic engineering and new biotechnologies on employment opportunities. According to Ahmed (1992*a*), biotechnologies could help cross the yield threshold apparently already reached for major crop species produced and consumed largely by the poor. Simple biotechnologies, such as micropropagation, were within the reach of even the poorest of developing countries. These biotechnologies needed to be more closely targeted to respond to the needs of the poor, e.g. focusing on subsistence food crop species, limiting the use of purchased inputs, higher cropping intensity, risk reduction, etc. The new biotechnologies could have a net positive effect on the intensity of labour use. Labour displacement in some traditional operations, like pest and disease control, could be compensated by gains in labour absorption for cropping practices newly created by the application of biotechnologies. The latter could make a major contribution to increased labour use and agricultural production growth by facilitating multiple cropping.

Agricultural biotechnologies appeared to be potentially more scale-neutral at the farm level for two reasons: their use reduced farmers' production costs; they lowered farmers' risks resulting from previously uncontrollable production variances (Ahmed, 1992*a*).

There appeared to be a false presumption that all private sector biotechnology developments were anti-poor. On the contrary, evidence suggested that achievements in genetic engineering by private industrial corporations were most certainly oriented toward the poor. The crucial issue was in fact how to improve developing countries' access to such pro-poor but often patented biotechnologies. Urgent policy intervention was needed to restructure the economics of developing countries, which lost or were losing markets for their traditional exports through the application of biotechnologies in industrialized countries. Such a loss of export markets was detrimental to the livelihood of small producers and plantation workers. There was therefore a need to restrain and redeploy redundant workers (Ahmed, 1992*a*).

Ahmed (1992*b*) stated that concrete data on the socio-economic impact of current biotechnological developments had to be generated, if *ex-post* definitive confirmation was to be obtained of the *ex-ante* forecasts made. The following rural labour market issues needed investigating: did workers made redundant in conventional agricultural operations by biotechnology applications possess the skills required by the new job opportunities created? what was the effect of biotechnology applications on family and hired labour? what kind of support services were needed to enable small farmers to adopt biotechnologies simultaneously with the larger farmers? what specific domestic policies and types of economic restructuring were needed to mitigate or avoid the negative effects of changing international trade patterns on developing countries' employment? what concrete measures were needed at the national and international levels to encourage the free flow of socially beneficial biotechnologies and prevent the entry of socially harmful biotechnologies into developing countries? Furthermore, three aspects of Third World science and technology capacity deserved attention: what country-specific measures were needed to strengthen the existing research capacity (e.g. in plant micropropagation)? how could existing capability, however limited, be channelled to address improvements in plant or microbial traits which could contribute to poverty alleviation? how could the scale of biotechnology processes be increased to significantly reduce per unit costs?

In a study for the International Labour Organization, entitled Employment and income effects of biotechnology in Latin America: a speculative assessment, Galhardi (1993) concluded that improved new crop varieties could help increase physical output and, by implication, the income and employment opportunities of rural workers/producers. However, results seemed to nuance this appraisal, especially where the small, poorer farmers and wage workers restricted to marginal areas in developing countries were concerned. A qualitative estimate of the costs of production and employment requirements for some current or expected biotechnology applications in selected Latin American crop production suggested that not all of these were 'pro-poor' in character and that many of them would barely be adopted by small farmers.

Biotechnologies might offer, however, an alternative for reducing production costs. Biofertilizers, biological control of pests, diseases and weeds, appeared to be less costly than chemical and energy-intensive fertilizers, pesticides and herbicides. It seemed that the main contribution biotechnologies could make to the small farm in developing countries was not only an improvement in productivity but also a reduction in production costs, through the substitution of chemical inputs with biological ones. Therefore, an evaluation of the increased net income of farmers would have to take into account both the increased productivity achieved and the reduction in costs, as well as the net earnings obtained through any expansion of cultivated land (Galhardi, 1993).

Biotechnology developments might lead to changes in the international trade pattern by enhancing the possibilities for crop substitution. If this occurred, small farm producers would lose more than big farmers, because they could not always take advantage of improved varieties or other agricultural inputs to increase yields and quality of their production. Considering, however, the current stage of biotechnology developments, the possible trade shifts might not occur in the short run and developing countries with a minimum level of technological capability in this area might have time to take advantage of some biotechnological developments to improve production and provide income gains to small farmers and rural workers. Crop diversification from export crops to food crops might benefit the poor rural worker-producer made redundant by biotechnology-induced changes in the international trade pattern of tropical products. The replacement of export crops by a more labour-intensive production of selected basic grains might generate a net gain in employment (Galhardi, 1993).

A shift from the production of traditional export to 'non-traditional' export crops was also an employment-generating option for those threatened by the depressed demand for their crops. Diversification of production toward 'potential' export crops was another possibility stimulated by the advances of plant biotechnologies. Alternative uses for export crops was another possibility proposed to help the small-scale producer/worker to mitigate the negative effects of possible substitution of their crops. Biotechnologies could help produce diversified products with a high value added. Diversification of end-products to processed, value-added exports seemed to generate employment and income through linkages with the processing sector (Galhardi, 1993).

The United Nations Centre for Science and Technology for Development (UNCSTD) began, in 1990, a series of national and regional workshops on biotechnologies for development. Emphasis was placed on the social, economic and biosafety aspects. Priority was also given in the ATAS (Advanced Technology Alert System) Bulletin to opportunities available for the marketing of biotechnology innovations and products.

3. United Nations Development Programme

Another example of international collaboration in biotechnologies was the UNDP (United Nations Development Programme)/WHO (World Health Organization)/TDR Initiative for Biotechnology Implementation, the second stage in the Programme for Research and Training in Tropical Diseases (TDR), set up in 1979. It aimed to effect real transfer of relevant medical biotechnologies to affected regions or countries.

To illustrate the involvement of the UNDP in biotechnology projects, one could cite the setting up of a National Agricultural Genetic Engineering Laboratory (NAGEL) in Egypt. The work plan formulated by a panel of experts contained three research projects on: tissue culture, DNA diagnostics and genetic engineering. The three chosen areas were considered sufficiently documented to reduce the risk of failure within the four-year time frame of the project. Great importance was given to training and technology transfer. The UNDP contribution totalled $3.1 million.

A five-year project was initiated in January 1988 with a UNDP contribution of $1,123,950 and executed by the FAO. Its purpose was to strengthen the Bose Institute of Calcutta, in order to: genetically engineer crop species; generate new plant types that could not be developed via conventional breeding techniques; and develop new genetic resources relevant to plant breeders through recombinant DNA techniques. The project also aimed to create a training centre with the appropriate teaching aids for plant biotechnology researchers. The cultivars chosen for research (mung bean, jute and mustard) had previously been extensively studied at the Bose Institute, using tissue culture, protoplast fusion and some molecular biology. This experience provided a strong basis for more advanced research, using genetic engineering.

A project budgeted at $2,225,400 aimed to improve the crop species under the mandate of the ICARDA (International Center for Agricultural Research in Dry Areas, Alepo, Syria). Biotechnologies were to be used to develop wheat, barley, chickpea and lentil cultivars more tolerant of environmental stress and resistant to pathogens.

In the period 1977–1990, more than 100 biotechnology projects had been financed by the UNDP at a cost of $98 million.

4. World Bank

In the 1950s, the World Bank's agricultural focus was on cash crop species (such as cocoa, rubber and palm oil). From the 1960s onward, World Bank agricultural projects acted as an extremely effective conduit for the spread of 'green revolution' agriculture. The Bank worked closely with the growing network of International Agricultural Research Centers (IARCs), under the umbrella of the Consultative Group on International Agricultural Research (CGIAR). To attract farmers' attention, seeds were often given away, and loans were made for fertilizers and equipment. As a result, high-yielding varieties spread considerably. In Mexico, for instance, the first semi-dwarf wheat varieties were released in 1962, and by 1966 they had taken over 95% of the country's wheat lands. India's New Agricultural Strategy, adopted in the mid-1960s, proved so efficient that by 1968, nearly half the wheat planted in the country came from the semi-dwarf varieties. Similarly, strong governmental policies in The Philippines meant that by 1982, 93% of irrigated lowlands were planted to 'green revolution' varieties. The government's 'Masagana 99' programme, which began in 1981, only gave loans to farmers who agreed to plant a government-recommended variety. Only ten varieties were on the programme's list for the whole of The Philippines (Bell, 1996).

The impact of the 'green revolution' on agriculutral biodiversity led to the establishment in 1972 of the International Board for Plant Genetic Resources (IBPGR) as a World Bank-FAO joint venture to address genetic erosion. But, by 1976, 44% of all wheat lands and 27% of rice lands around the world were planted to new varieties. The Bank's involvement in biological diversity rapidly gathered momentum during the years of Robert McNamara's presidency (1968–1981). McNamara introduced a welcome new focus for the Bank: poverty and agriculture became a major emphasis of Bank lending. Ambitious land-clearing and settlement projects were another important component of the Bank's supported poverty alleviation strategy in the McNamara era. These often involved the felling of vast areas of prime biological diversity habitats, particularly tropical rain forests. For instance, during the 1970s, the World Bank approved a series of loans that cleared 1.3 million acres, or 6.5% of Malaysia's rain forests, mainly to install monocultural plantations for the production of palm oil. Plantation forestry systems were covering some 11 million hectares today, and they were still expanding (Bell, 1996).

This trend continued into the 1980s. Brazil's Polonoreste 'agricultural development' programme, funded by the World Bank to the tune of $443 million, increased the deforestation of the Brazilian Amazon from 1.7% in 1978 to 16.1% in 1991. More than half the loans financed the paving of 1,500-kilometer track through the rainforests of Rôndonia; most of the rest went into constructing feeder and access roads, and the establishment of 39 rural settlement centres to consolidate and attract settlers who were to raise tree crops (mainly cocoa and coffee) for export. Instead of the tens of thousands of settlers anticipated, half a million arrived in the space of five years. Agricultural extension services and credit did not materialize and resettlement officials were overwhelmed. In order to survive, the settlers tried, largely unsuccessfully, to grow rice, maize and beans on the poor soils, which would become exhausted in a year or two. Slash and burn went out of control, as the settlers were constantly forced to move on. In Indonesia, between 1976 and 1986, $630 million were lent by the World Bank to support the movement of millions of Javanese people to the outlying islands (Transmigration programme). It provided an additional $734 million for agricultural development, which either did not materialize or was used to provide rice which people tried, and failed, to grow in totally inappropriate environments. By the late 1980s, transmigration was responsible for deforestation rates in the fragile forests of the outer islands reaching a rate of 5,000 km^2 a year. This impact was particularly devastating in Irian Jaya, one of the world's great reservoirs of biological and cultural diversity (Bell, 1996).

The World Bank had also funded some of the world's most notorious environmentally damaging dams. Ghana's Asokombo dam flooded more land than any other dam in the world, submerging 8,500 km^2 for an industrial development project which apparently never came close to achieving its rate of return. The Tucurui and Balbina dams together drowned 6,400 km^2 of rain forests in the Brazilian Amazon, while Zimbabwe's Kariba dam soaked up 5,100 km^2. Not only land was lost, but also some of the best wildlife habitat and richest ecosystems found along river valleys (Bell, 1996).

Bell (1996) considered that in the 1970s and 1980s the majority of the World Bank's projects in forestry, agriculture, industry and energy had serious impacts on biological diversity.

When Lewis Preston became President of the World Bank in late 1991, he appointed a task force to survey the overall performance at Bank loans. More than a third of Bank projects completed in 1991 were judged failures. The worst affected areas were water supply and sanitation, where 43% of the projects had major problems, and the agricultural sector, where 42% of the projects were failing. The establishment of the Inspection Panel in 1994 provided non-governmental organizations and affected communities with a channel through which they could challenge the Bank for violating its own policies (Bell, 1996).

Another important shift in the World Bank's policy was the increasing emphasis laid on the private sector. In late 1995, in the face of threats from the U.S. Congress to cut U.S. contributions to the Bank, the latter embarked on a high-profile advertising campaign to underline its importance to the economies of donor countries. The Bank announced that 'it does not just lend money, it helps developing countries become tomorrow's markets'. The Bank shifted from project lending to 'policy' lending in the form of loans for removing trade barriers, privatizing government-owned companies and restructuring whole sectors of the economy in order to allow the entry of multinationals. Some analysts thought that this shift might mean that private sector projects could be less accountable and less stringent with respect to environmental policies (Bell, 1996).

The Bank was in fact in a tight situation: it needed to be seen to doing projects for people, but at the same time it felt forced into endorsing privatized, industrialized agriculture as the provider of those projects. The Bank's action plan for the rural sector was based on the following criteria and objectives:

– rural growth is widely shared, with private and competitive agriculture and agribusiness as the main engine of growth;

– family farms and non-farm enterprises provide ample remunerative employment opportunities to men and women;

– rural people manage the soils, water, forest, grasslands and fisheries in a sustainable manner;

– rural people are linked to well-functioning markets for products, inputs and finance;

– rural people have access to medical care, clean water and sanitation, educational opportunities, and sufficient nutritious foods;

– essential legal frameworks, public investment, productive and social services are provided and financed in a pluralistic, decentralized and participatory manner.

In late 1993, the International Finance Corporation (IFC, established in 1956 as an affiliate to the World Bank) and the Global Environment Facility (GEF) met with private foundations to discuss their interest in investing money in venture capital funds to 'exploit the knowledge stock' of traditional communities. These discussions led to the $30 million 'Biodiversity Enterprise Fund for Latin America', which aimed to support private companies undertaking sustainable uses of biological diversity in Latin America. The areas for investment included sustainable agriculture, bioprospecting activities, sustainable forest management, non-timber forest products and ecotourism. The Fund was being managed by the IFC, and the GEF contributed $5 million in grant funds for 'biodiversity-related projects screening and monitoring costs'. Another GEF/IFC initiative, known as the 'Small and Medium Scale Enterprise Program', was also created 'to stimulate greater involvement of small-and medium-scale enterprises in preserving biological diversity and reducing greenhouse gases' (Bell, 1996).

The World Bank was still the biggest international funder of agricultural development and research, despite the fact that the Bank spending on agriculture had dropped considerably since 1988. This spending had fallen from 30% of its budget in 1980 ($5.4 billion per year) to 20% in the early 1990s ($3.9 billion per year). The 1990s saw further erosion of agricultural investment. By 1996, the agriculture portfolio had dropped to third position in the lending ratings, with commitments to agriculture amounting to only $2.6 billion, or 12% of the budget. Nevertheless, despite its falling status, the Bank's agricultural portfolio still consisted of 377 projects representing $25 billion in loans (18% of the Bank's lending). The World Bank also continued to provide 15% ($45 million) of the Consultative Group on International Agricultural Research (CGIAR)'s $300 million annual budget (Bell, 1996).

Of a total of 377 agricultural projects carried out since 1988, only 19 contained biological diversity components and ten of those were in the forestry subsector. Of the remainder, seven were agriculture sector loans, while fisheries, irrigation and drainage accounted for one each. Less than 2% of the agricultural projects dealt explicitly with biological diversity issues (Bell, 1996).

In 1996, at the request of the new World Bank's President, James Wolfensohn, the Agriculture and Natural Resources Department produced a new agricultural action plan entitled 'From Vision to Action in the Rural Sector'. This document described the Bank's strategy to improve the quality of agricultural development programmes in general and the performance of its agricultural portfolio in particular. It also outlined the World Bank's strategy tackling lender countries' 'weak commitment' to rural development and proposed 'three complementary high-profile initiatives at the international level'. The Bank's proposal to eliminate what it saw as the myth of food self-sufficiency as a path to development in favour of trade dependence, and the roles of biotechnologies and the CGIAR were also outlined in the document:

'. . . All too frequently developing countries have equated food security with agricultural self-sufficiency and have pursued highly-distortionary policies, leading to inefficiency and resource degradation. However, to develop an open-economy food policy, countries must be assured of access to, and stability in, international markets. The challenge to the global community was to maintain a stable and open trading environment so that the developing countries can rely on international markets in developing their domestic food strategies. In the area of technology, revolutions in molecular biology and information have the potential to reduce the location-specificity of applied agricultural research.'

The World Bank played a high-profile role in the World Food Summit, held in FAO headquarters in Rome in November 1996, as well as in the 1996 World Trade Organization (WTO) round on behalf of the CGIAR and other multilateral actors in order to promote further agricultural trade liberalization (*Seedling*, the Quarterly Newsletter of Genetic Resources Action International-GRAIN-, vol. 13, no. 3, October 1996, pp. 2–11).

'Vision to Action' did not address the issue of biological diversity directly and did not recognize it as an important indicator of rural and agricultural well-being. However, the Bank launched an initiative called 'Mainstreaming biodiversity in development', in which agriculture was considered a main focus. The principal output of this initiative was a spurt of technical papers, including a couple that addressed biological diversity in agriculture. One of these, 'Biodiversity and agriculture: implications for conservation and development' acknowledged that 'little attention has been given to biodiversity in the Bank's agricultural development projects', and outlined some important changes in strategy that were needed in the agricultural portfolio. However, non-governmental organizations were of the opinion that the World Bank was still blind to the fact that local communities had the best record in biological diversity conservation, management and use, and that there was a need to look to them for the way forward. They were also of the view that the agrobiodiversity of existing farms was bound to decrease even further as industrial agriculture would increasingly prevail for global food production (Bell, 1996).

Consequently, the non-governmental organizations suggested some fundamental steps the Bank must take in its agricultural projects if its commitment to biological diversity management was to gain credibility:

– recognize that biological diversity was a pressing issue in agriculture, and that the main cause of genetic erosion in agriculture was the very intensive, monoculture-based practices that its agriculture sector was promoting;

– acknowledge that biological diversity was important in agriculture not just because of its importance in securing the gene pool on which global food security was dependent, but also as indicator of sustainable production systems and sustainable livelihoods;

– introduce agrobiodiversity appraisals as a mandatory part of the environmental assessment procedure;

– develop agricultural and biological diversity management projects with the full participation of the local communities and on the basis of their priorities;

– discontinue its support for corporate bioprospecting activities, which stripped communities of their resource base, livelihoods and knowledge (Bell, 1996).

In 1988, the International Service for National Agricultural Research (ISNAR), the World Bank and the Australian Government, through the Australian International Development Assistance Bureau (AIDAB) and the Australian Centre for International Agricultural Research (ACIAR), decided to undertake a joint study to consider the opportunities for, and constraints on, the use of agricultural biotechnologies in fostering the agriculture of developing countries. The study was summarized in a book by Persley (1990*b*). One of its conclusions was that biotechnologies were not likely to lead to 'green revolution' style increases in agricultural productivity and output over the next 10 or 20 years. Biotechnologies could, however, lead to more balanced growth and a reduced use of agrochemicals. Realizing this potential would depend on whether biotechnology research were directed toward meeting Third World needs. The success of new biotechnologies depended on how well they were integrated into current applied agricultural research.

One of the trends identified was the private sector's growing role in biotechnological research. This involvement had led to the availability of large research-and-development resources, but also to a concentration on research and products with a high rate of return. Research and development would thus focus on well-to-do farmers with the capacity for purchasing expensive inputs. There was therefore a need for additional investments in biotechnologies on so-called orphan commodities,[1] (see p. 288) important as food or cash crops in the Third World, but not likely to yield high profits for private investors.

The suggested Orphan Commodities Programme aimed to promote the early application of biotechnologies to those commodities important to developing countries. Investments in biotechnologies by developing countries were low in the early 1990s, due to the minor role played by these commodities in the industrialized world.

It was also concluded that the possibility existed of producing compounds by tissue culture and thereby replacing crops currently grown in developing countries. The development of an 'early warning system' to identify their negative effects was indispensable.

The International Agricultural Research Centers (IARCs) could play an important role in adapting the tools of modern biotechnologies to the needs of developing countries' agriculture, so as to prevent an increase in the productivity gap between industrialized countries, as well as among developing countries. The IARCs could become involved in the application of new scientific advances and, eventually, develop new knowledge. Therefore, innovative methods for acquiring technologies from the private sector needed to be considered. The IARCs could also perform a negotiating role for acquiring technologies on behalf of National Agricultural Research Systems (NARSs), particularly for the smaller countries. The key issue was how to integrate biotechnologies into the existing agricultural research systems. According to Persley (1990*b*), new initiatives were needed, rather than new institutions. Furthermore, there was a need both for the IARCs and NARSs to engage in commercial and marketing skills, with regard to the acquisition of technology and distribution of the final products.

In 1991, the World Bank published a paper on agricultural biotechnologies (World Bank, 1991). In summarizing the findings from earlier studies, the World Bank's purpose was to clarify socio-economic policy and management issues whose non-resolution could impede the successful application of biotechnologies in developing countries. According to the World Bank, developing countries needed to become more familiar with the role of intellectual property rights in stimulating technology transfer and local research. They also needed to develop a clear understanding of the limitations involved, particularly with respect to the use of progeny of plants and animals protected by intellectual property agreements. There was a conflict of interest between technology sellers and buyers, which prevented countries in the latter group from recognizing as a 'natural right' the intellectual rights requested by industrial countries (in the General Agreement on Tariffs and Trade-GATT – and World Intellectual Property Organization-WIPO). The patent issue of most concern to the World Bank pertained to the restricted rights of foreign firms selling technologies. Licensing arrangements and contractual agreements were proposed as a means of providing developing countries with access to biotechnologies, while simultaneously protecting the interests of its inventors. Each country, however, was advised to weigh up costs and benefits and frame policies accordingly (Knudsen, 1991*a*).

281

In order to guide its future strategy, the World Bank had completed a study on the likely impact of modern biotechnologies on agriculture and natural resources management. The study reviewed the World Bank's future role in supporting the application of these biotechnologies in its member countries. The study considered: the socio-economic issues which would affect the successful application of modern biotechnologies; the changing roles of public and private sector research; intellectual property management; regulatory and institutional issues; human resources and institutional arrangements. The study concluded that the application of modern biotechnologies would be essential if constraints on the productivity of many tropical commodities were to be eliminated and to maintain their competitive position on international markets. The strategy chosen by an individual country depended on its size, the strength of its scientific and technological sector and whether it was primarily a developer or importer of technology.

The creation by the World Bank of a Biotechnology Transfer Unit was suggested in order to facilitate the transfer of new biotechnologies from industrialized to developing countries by acting as a broker and advisor to countries interested in acquiring new technologies, and to public and private sector institutions wishing to expand their activities in the developing countries (Persley, 1989, 1990*a,b*).

The World Bank had various instruments at its disposal to help developing countries achieve capability in biotechnologies and cope with the new pattern of biotechnology protection, increasingly in the hands of the private sector. Loans and credits could help developing countries acquire and adapt the new technologies; joint ventures with the International Finance Corporation (a World Bank branch) could help local private companies participate in the commercial development of biotechnologies. The World Bank was providing some support for research in agricultural biotechnologies and for agricultural projects with biotechnology components. In addition, to overcome the problem of patents as an obstacle to acquiring new technologies, the NARSs were counselled on negotiating the procurement of biotechnologies, just as they had learnt to facilitate interdisciplinary collaboration (Knudsen, 1991*a*).

The World Bank pointed to the need for making biotechnologies serve sustainable and poverty-alleviating development. While recognition of the Bank's lesser emphasis on agriculture, large poor countries and poor people was still controversial within the Bank, Lipton and Paarlberg (1990) emphasized a decline in so-called narrow agriculture and rural development lending, from 29.6% of total Bank lending in 1978 to 15.6% in 1988.

Between 1982 and 1990, the World Bank supported ten agricultural projects with specific biotechnology components. These were located in Brazil, Cyprus, Hungary, Indonesia, Madagascar, Malaysia, Rwanda, Senegal, Sri Lanka and Sudan. Additional support was provided for biotechnologies through the education, science and technology sectors for projects in Brazil, Indonesia and Portugal. The total estimated loans and credits for all these projects from 1982 and 1990 came to approximately $100 million. The projects included support for infrastructure, laboratory facilities and equipment for biotechnology training, research and development activities.

In Indonesia, for instance, an agricultural research management project provided support for the application of biotechnologies to selected crop species and financed laboratories, equipment and supplies for research. Another project supported post-graduate biotechnology programmes at three Inter-University Centers for Biotechnology, located at the Institute of Technology (Bandung), Agricultural University (Bogor) and Gadjah Mada University.

In India, a significant biotechnology component had been included in the World Bank National Agricultural Research Project in September 1992. This provided approximately $8 million over three years to support the further development of plant and animal biotechnologies at the institutes of the Indian Council of Agricultural Research. It also supported collaborative research on oilseed biotechnology with the Tata Energy Research Institute in Delhi, as an example of public-private sector research collaboration.

Regional development banks like the Inter-American Development Bank, Asian Development Bank and African Development Bank, were supporting activities in biotechnologies.

5. United Nations Conference on Environment and Development

At the United Nations Conference on Environment and Development (UNCED), held in Rio de Janeiro, Brazil, from 3 to 14 June 1992, *Agenda 21* was a plan of action document specifying projects to be undertaken by intergovernmental organizations, industrialized and developing countries. *Agenda 21* included the following objectives: to increase plant and animal productivity by 25% by the year 2000; to reduce dependence on pesticides for food, feed and fibre by 25% by the year 2000; to increase productivity on marginal lands through the use of biological nitrogen fixation and mycorrhizae, and reduce dependency on chemical fertilizers. Some activities aimed to achieve the environmentally sound management of biotechnology.

The proposed activities entailed, among others:

– use of conventional technologies and biotechnologies to develop transgenic plants resistant to biotic and abiotic stresses;

– use of techniques of nitrogen fixation and mycorrhiza inoculation, in conjunction with advanced molecular biology techniques aimed at improving the efficiency of the process in legumes and grasses, as well as phosphorus uptake by crop species;

– acceleratation of animal breeding through conventional techniques and reproduction and health biotechnologies, and rescue of endangered native livestock for breeding purposes;

– provision of an adequate institutional infrastructure;

– addressing issues related to germplasm resources, intellectual property rights and harmonization of biosafety procedures.

With regard to human health, five areas for action were adopted:

– universal immunization (development of new and improved vaccines against major communicable diseases, these vaccines being efficient and safe and offering individual protection with the minimum dosage; vaccines stable at higher temperatures and preferably orally delivered in a single dose for multiple disease protection);

– development and use of specific diagnostics (new diagnostics based on monoclonal antibodies and DNA probes for the early, accurate detection of diseases, enabling prompt treatment; use of diagnostics by semi-skilled personnel under unsophisticated conditions);

– development of new therapeutic and growth-promoting agents (use of hormones and their agonists or antagonists); cell growth promoters and immune-system modulators; new drugs based on molecular design, using computer simulation and modelling; new drug delivery systems to target sites);

– development of safe and effective methods of detection and treatment of genetically inherited and in-born diseases, using DNA probes and gene therapy;

– development of new population control agents, using biotechnologies leading to safe, reversible and long-lasting methods.

Biotechnologies encompassing a wide range of techniques, it would be difficult to assess the impact of new biotechnologies on plant breeding. Firstly, all insertions or deletions of genetic material carried out so far had been on simple genes, predominantly in one plant family only, the Solanaceae. Secondly, most desirable yield-increasing traits, for instance, tolerance, quick ripeness or an increase in photosynthetic efficiency or nutrient absorption, were controlled by gene clusters. Such polygenic traits could, at the present time, only be transmitted by conventional breeding methods. Thirdly, there was consensus that these traits were close to optimally developed in modern varieties. In general, the single gene additions carried out thus far had used genes conferring resistance against pests and genes altering plants and products by modifying, for example, the composition of starch and lipids. In the short term, the outcome of such gene additions would increase productivity and supply new raw materials. In the long term, there would be problems with pests that gradually became resistant to the introduced toxin (Zeckhauser and Viscusi, 1990; Nilsson, 1992).

An Inter-Agency Committee for Sustainable Development (IACSTD) in charge of implementing *Agenda 21* assigned the UNIDO task manager for Chapter 16 of the Agenda (Environmentally sound management of biotechnology); the UNIDO was to provide, in collaboration with other relevant organizations, co-ordinated technical inputs on the United Nations system-wide implementation of *Agenda 21*, as the follow-up to the United Nations Conference on Environment and Development. In this context, the UNIDO convened an *ad hoc* United Nations inter-agency consultation at its headquarters in Vienna, from 15 to 16 September 1994 with the participation of the relevant intergovernmental and international non-governmental organizations. The meeting reviewed developments since the signing of *Agenda 21* in June 1992, but also intended to be forward-looking by identifying gaps and/or overlapping activities and initiatives, and suggesting inter-agency efforts to overcome these problems. The UNIDO's report was presented for discussion at a New York meeting of all task managers on cross-sectoral issues called by the Department for Policy Co-ordination and Sustainable Development in December 1994. It was then finalized before the April 1995 meeting of the Intergovernmental Commission for Sustainable Development.

The Programme on Environmentally Sound Management of Biotechnology formulated for the United Nations Conference on Environment and Development (UNCED) contained a biosafety component including the following principles: primary consideration of the organism, including genetically modified organisms (GMOs); application of the step-by-step procedure; complementary consideration of risk assessment and risk management; classification into contained use or release into the environment; a framework for safety in biotechnologies. The USA rejected the step-by-step procedure and asserted that the risk was exaggerated. The proposed regulation would hamper the development of biotechnologies in industrialized countries, while the developing countries stressed the risk that they might become testing grounds for the release of GMOs (Nilsson, 1992).

Even if all nations agreed on the terms of an international code of conduct, there would still be problems with its interpretation and implementation. For this reason, the establishment of independent international advisory panels was proposed. In addition to the advisory services recommended by the UNIDO/WHO/UNEP/FAO Informal Working Group on Biosafety (IWGB), the Stockholm Environment Institute had prepared a proposal for setting up an independent Biotechnology Advisory Commission (BAC), whose task would be to give advice, upon request, to authorities in developing countries on the potential risks and benefits expected as a result of introducing a GMO, and on the appropriateness of the product for a particular need. It would also review specific agricultural projects to advise on risks, particularly those related to biosafety. It was also suggested that the BAC might provide advice on the socio-economic effects of biotechnologies (Nilsson, 1992).

Taylhardat and Zilinskas (1992) suggested that, instead of setting up new networks for training scientists in biotechnologies, those already in existence should be strengthened (e.g. the MIRCEN network, the Consultative Group on International Agricultural Research-CGIAR-Network, the ICGEB-affiliated countries network, regional networks, such as the Regional Biotechnology Programme for Latin America and the Caribbean, and sectoral networks such as the Cassava Biotechnology Network). In addition, measures were needed for raising additional support for organizations providing training, to cover the escalating costs of scientist training and upkeep.

Taylhardat and Zilinskas (1992) stated that, to bridge the gap between research and applications, universities and research institutions needed to market their research through transfer units like those existing in the USA. These units had four objectives: to identify research being carried out at university with a commercial future; to obtain patent protection for inventions resulting from university research; to present inventions to potential users in appropriate industries; and to make contractual arrangements between the university and the technology user wishing to apply an invention. *Agenda 21* was expected to promote the concept of technology transfer units among governments and universities in the developing countries and make available seed funding for setting up these units.

In addition, entrepreneurship needed to be promoted in developing countries. For instance, support would be provided for such groups as the Biofocus Foundation, incorporated in the Netherlands. An initiative of the World Academy of Art and Science, the Biofocus Foundation sought to identify target areas and potential entrepreneurs, in order to stimulate the development of private enterprises in developing countries. It was expected to assist in preparing business plans and submit these as viable projects to potential investors. The Biofocus Foundation sought co-operation with the biotechnology programme of the International Federation of Institutes for Advanced Studies (IFIAS, Maastricht, Netherlands) and the African Centre for Technology Studies (ACTS, Nairobi, Kenya), in order to strengthen the research arm of Biofocus and seek donor support jointly. Pre-projects were identified in microbial starter cultures, coastal biotechnology and bagasse as a chemical and microbial feedstock.

It was therefore felt that the UNCED's *Agenda 21* could help transform promises into reality by promoting capability-building, strengthening existing networks of scientific communication and encouraging the formulation of international biosafety programmes.

At the invitation of the United Nations ACC (Administrative Co-ordination Committee) Task Force on Science and Technology for Development, the UNIDO commissioned an article on the contribution of biotechnologies to sustainable development within the United Nations system. Among the recommendations was the proposal to organize a Consultative Group on Biotechnology to accelerate research and development and commercialization, stimulate support for, and the spread of, environmentally sound biotechnologies world-wide. Another related article on intellectual property rights in relation to commercialization of biotechnologies was prepared for the ACC.

According to M.S. Swaminathan, Chairman of the Centre for Research on Sustainable Agricultural and Rural Development, Madras, India, the time had come for a bold and imaginative International Initiative for the Application of Biotechnology for Sustainable Development. Such an initiative could be supported by an arrangement similar to that of the Consultative Group on International Agricultural Research (CGIAR), where membership was open to governments, multilateral donors, foundations and private and public sector industry. A 'CG-Biotech' would bring about the necessary convergence and synergy among academia and the business, government and international sectors. The major aim would be to assist developing countries in crossing the threshold essential for deriving economic and social benefit from the wide range of biotechnologies.

Note

1. An analogous situation existed with orphan drugs in the USA, i.e. drugs which were needed by a limited sector of the population, but not commercially viable propositions in their own right. The Orphan Drug Act of 4 January 1983 aimed to stimulate the manufacture of non-profitable drugs. Some of them were destined for patients suffering from rare diseases, i.e. whose prevalence was less than 1%, as well as for those unable to pay for medicines used to cure tropical diseases in the developing countries. These orphan drugs could be used in prevention, diagnosis or treatment of a rare disease, or as antidotes in the treatment of exceptional acute intoxications. The Orphan Drug Act was the result of joint action by patients' associations, Congress members, as well as of a partnership between the pharmaceutical industry and government. Since promulgation of the Act, five committees or specialized bodies had been created; the lists of orphan drugs, instructions for use and name of each manufacturer were updated four times a year; a 50% tax exemption was granted on clinical study costs; and from the time authorization was delivered, the manufacturer enjoyed an exclusive right to commercialize the product for seven years (Folléa, 1995).

Between 1983 and 1994, 64 orphan drugs were commercialized in the USA, compared to authorization for only 34 specialty drugs during the 15 years preceding the Orphan Drug Act. In March 1992, a total of 488 substances were classified as orphan drugs, while another 189 were being developed. The seven-year exclusivity was being questioned because some drugs had become profitable and provoked the anger among manufacturers producing similar products but were not benefiting from the orphan status; this was the case for growth hormones. It was true that some orphan drugs had been patented, but without finding a purchaser; others had been withdrawn from the market, despite their therapeutic interest, for economic reasons (low selling price, low consumption rate), or because they were not patentable (e.g. natural substances). Others had been withdrawn due to their negative side-effects, but were shown to be effective in the treatment of other diseases (e.g. thalidomide was very effective in the treatment of leprosy) [Folléa, 1995].

In Japan, an Orphan Drug Act was adopted in October 1993. A special fund allocated subsidies and fiscal exemptions were granted to cover research costs. As a result, 212 requests from 54 enterprises had been filed one year after establishing the procedure. Of these requests, 40 were declared acceptable by the Japanese Bureau of Pharmaceutical Affairs and another 15 subsidized by the special fund (Folléa, 1995).

The European Union was lagging behind the USA and Japan in orphan drug legislation and practice. However, while acknowledging this situation, a report prepared by the French National Institute for Health and Medical Research and issued in early November 1994 strongly recommended appropriate measures, especially for rare diseases. About 5,000 rare diseases had been identified, half of them being of genetic origin (e.g. myopathies, cystic fibrosis, multiple sclerosis, Charcot disease, Turner syndrome, haemophilia, etc.). It was also recommended that a 'European Observatory of Rare Diseases' be created, which would allow for the exchange of data between Europe and the USA. The report also underlined the necessity of following up the products after their commercialization and of granting fiscal exemptions and incentives to the manufacturers of these drugs; the optimal duration for commercial exclusivity was estimated at ten years (Folléa, 1995).

With respect to orphan drugs for developing countries, there were no initiatives to help these countries control the numerous tropical diseases, often communicable, lacking effective treatment or vaccine prophylaxis. These diseases could be qualified as 'orphan' because the world's manufacturers were not interested in developing drugs to cure them; this was the case for the six major tropical diseases designated by the World Health Organization: malaria, trypanosomiases, leishmaniases, filariasis, schistosomiasis and leprosy. The pharmaceutical industry had ceased supporting research on anti-parasite drugs, because the countries affected by these diseases represented only 10% of the world drug market. Activities carried out under the World Health Organization's Tropical Disease Research Programme and the European Union's Life Sciences and Technologies for Developing Countries Programme had not resulted in any commercial product (Folléa, 1995).

The overall bleak situation was aggravated by the 1994 devaluation of the CFA currency in French-speaking sub-Saharan countries: the doubling of drug prices resulting from this devaluation made the mostly-imported drugs even less accessible to people. The AIDS epidemics was another aggravating factor; the disease was still classified as rare in the USA, endeavours by the pharmaceutical industry in research-and-development being made at the expense of activities devoted to parasitic diseases (Folléa, 1995).

Part II
International agricultural research

Consultative Group on International Agricultural Research and related issues

1. Goals, mandate and objectives

Largely engaged in the health sector after the Second World War, the Rockefeller Foundation's fight against the 'population bomb' focused on the distribution of contraceptives and family planning in the Third World. When, in the late 1950s, it decided to fight the 'food problem', this time the solution would be the development and wide dissemination of high-yielding crop varieties and their seeds. The first country selected was Mexico. In 1941, in a premonitory move, the Rockefeller Foundation had placed scientists from Cornell University to raise the yield of wheat production. After Mexico, the Foundation turned to Asia, considered a priority region with respect to the population issue. In 1960, the Rockefeller and Ford Foundations together set up the International Rice Research Institute (IRRI) at Los Baños in The Philippines, so as to repeat the wheat success story with rice but this time at global level. The IRRI was to be the prototype International Agricultural Research Center (IARC): a politically neutral centre of excellence supported by rich donors, which transferred technologies as a means of supplying food to the poor (GRAIN, 1994c).

Within a few years, scientists at the IRRI came up with a promising cross of two rice varieties, called IR-8, which offered an important leap in yields. The IR-8, dubbed 'miracle rice', set in motion the 'green revolution'. Encouraged by this result, the Rockefeller Foundation set up three other international centers: the CIMMYT for wheat and rice in Mexico; the CIAT for beans, cassava, rice and forages in Colombia; and the IITA for maize, cassava, cowpea, rice and others in Nigeria (GRAIN, 1994c). See Table 4.

Table 4. International Agricultural Research Centers (IARCs) funded through the Consultative Group on International Agricultural Research (CGIAR)

Acronym	Est.	Full name	Focus	Location
ADRAO	1971	Association pour le développement de la riziculture en Afrique de l'Ouest	Rice sector of 15 Member States of West Africa	Monrovia, Liberia, then Bouaké, Côte d'Ivoire
WARDA	1971	West Africa Rice Development Association		
CIAT	1967	Centro Internacional de Agricultura Tropical International Center for Tropical Agriculture	Cassava, common bean, maize, rice; pasture crops; livestock. Emphasis on lowland tropical regions, especially in Latin America	Cali, Colombia
CIFOR	1991	Center for Internacional Forestry Research	Sustainable development of tropical forests	Bogor, Indonesia
CIMMYT	1964	Centro Internacional de Mejoramiento de Maiz y Trigo International Maize and Wheat Improvement Center	Wheat, maize, barley and triticale	El Batán, Mexico
CIP	1971	Centro Internacional de la Papa International Potato Center	Potato and sweet potato	Lima, Peru
ICARDA	1976	International Center for Agricultural Research in Dry Areas	Farming systems of West Asia and North Africa, with emphasis on wheat, barley, chickpea, lentil, faba bean and pasture and forage crops	Aleppo, Syria
ICLARM	1977	International Center for Living Aquatic Resources Management	Fisheries and aquaculture	Manila, Philippines

ICRAF	1977	International Council for Research in Agroforestry	Agroforestry techniques	Nairobi, Kenya
ICRISAT	1972	International Crops Research Institute for the Semi-Arid Tropics	Farming systems of the semi-arid tropics with emphasis on sorghum, millets, chickpea, pigeonpea and groundnut	Hyderabad-Patancheru, India
IFPRI	1975	International Food Policy Research Institute	Food policies and programmes	Washington, D.C., USA
IIMI	1984	International Irrigation Management Institute	Improved irrigation management	Colombo, Sri Lanka
IITA	1967	International Institute of Tropical Agriculture	Farming systems of lowland tropical regions, especially in Africa; emphasis on rice, maize, cowpea, pigeonpea, common bean, soybean, cassava, yam and sweet potato	Ibadan, Nigeria
ILCA	1974	International Livestock Center for Africa	Animal production systems and improvement of agropastoral economies in tropical Africa	Addis Ababa, Ethiopia
ILRAD	1974	International Laboratory for Research on Animal Diseases	Trypanosomiasis (sleeping sickness) and theileriosis (East Coast Fever)	Nairobi, Kenya
INIBAP	1984	International Network for the Improvement of Banana and Plantain	Banana and plantain	Montpellier, France
IPGRI	1974	International Plant Genetic Resources Institute (formerly International Board for Plant Genetic Resources, IBPGR)	Conservation of plant genetic resources, including forestry species	Rome, Italy

IRRI	1960	International Rice Research Institute	Rice, with emphasis on Asia	Los Baños, Philippines
ISNAR	1979	International Service for National Agricultural Research	Research policy, organization and management issues	The Hague, Netherlands

In 1971, the Consultative Group on International Agricultural Research (CGIAR) was created. It was an informal coalition of donors (governments, intergovernmental agencies and private foundations) co-sponsored by the World Bank, the FAO and the United Nations Development Programme. At its inception, the CGIAR counted 15 donors providing $20 million for four international centers. In 1995–1996, there were more than 41 donors contributing $300 million annually to 18 IARCs (Table 4), which had a staff of 1,700 scientists of MSc. level and above (1,200 of these 1,700 scientists were internationally recruited).

Even though Africa's total population of 500 million was only a small fraction of that of Asia, the CGIAR spent 45% of its budget on Africa in 1990 (Eicher, 1993).

The CGIAR annual budget amounted to only about 3.5% of the global agricultural research expenditure of $9 billion (1992). The IARCs had surprisingly limited budgets compared to state agricultural research stations in the USA. It should also be noted that Pioneer Hi-Bred International, Inc. $70 million research budget in 1991 was twice as big as CIMMYT annual budget for maize and wheat research combined (Eicher, 1993). Although the bigger IARCs each had 80–120 scientists and annual budgets of $32–36 million (1992), these resources were modest relative to the regional and global mandates of the Centers.

Germany was the third-biggest national donor of the CGIAR, with annual funding of $19 million (1995), of which only a small part was reserved for biotechnologies. Obstacles to additional support of the IARCs could arise from a decision of the Budget Committee of the German Parliament to put a ceiling on multilateral contributions from the Federal Ministry for Economic Cooperation and Development (BMZ) budget. Funding was allocated to the core budget of the CGIAR, specific projects at the IARCs and to special projects between the IARCs and German research institutions. In 1995, German institutes received about $2.3 million to facilitate this kind of co-operation.

About ten industrialized countries alone accounted for 57% of all CGIAR Board seats. More than three-quarters of all key committee

Chair positions were held by industrialized countries. In fact, four countries – Australia, Canada, the United Kingdom and USA – held half or more of all key staff positions and nominated posts in 1995 (GRAIN, 1994*c*).

The CGIAR goal was to increase food production in developing countries in a sustainable way, so as to improve the nutritional status and economic welfare of low-revenue populations. The general orientations of the CGIAR's programmes were:

– sustainable improvement of agriculture through resource conservation and management;

– increased productivity of food production systems;

– greater research potential in developing countries;

– a better economic environment for agricultural development (Rives, 1987).

Whereas the CGIAR, as an informal club, had neither legal identity, statutes nor by-laws, each of the IARCs was an autonomous institute with its own Board of Directors. The IARC autonomy was of course tempered by dependency on the CGIAR for funding. Each member of the CGIAR allocated its annual contribution to the IARC(s) of its choice, the World Bank filling the gap between the approved system-wide budget and that year's donor pledge. The CGIAR had a small permanent secretariat in the World Bank in Washington, D.C., which provided its chairmanship through one of the World Bank's vice-presidents. On technical issues, the CGIAR was guided by a Technical Advisory Committee (TAC), a group of 14 agricultural scientists (in 1995) from around the world. The TAC secretariat was based in the FAO headquarters in Rome and TAC met three times a year. TAC members were overburdened with preparing priority papers, special studies, medium-term plans and quinquennial reviews, and they seemed to have little spare time to reflect on the key issues facing global agriculture 10 to 25 years down the road (Eicher, 1993). The IARC autonomy was also tempered by the recommendations and findings of the TAC concerning research priorities and resource allocation (GRAIN, 1994*c*).

The 1990 and 1992 decisions to add five new Centers to the CGIAR network were motivated by a combination of political, scientific and technical forces. This expansion from 13 to 18 Centers without adding the necessary resources to implement the new programmes and maintain the scientific momentum of the system was perceived as controversial by scientists and administrators alike in the 13 original Centers because they had been forced to downsize their programmes (Eicher, 1993). However, at the October 1993 meeting of the CGIAR in Washington, D.C., it was decided that the INIBAP (International Network for the Improvement of Banana and Plantain) should become a programme of the International Plant Genetic Resources Institute (IPGRI), without losing its identity and specificity, or its headquarters in Montpellier, France. At the same October 1993 meeting of the CGIAR, the Rockefeller Foundation was requested to study, with the assistance of a group of experts, the feasibility of a new programme combining in one Center, the International Livestock Research Institute (ILRI), the ILCA (International Livestock Centre for Africa) and the ILRAD (International Laboratory for Research on Animal Diseases).

Research supporting the 'green revolution' could generally be characterized as follows:

– improved germplasm distributed through National Agricultural Research Systems;

– research primarily conducted downstream or applied and adaptive research carried out by the IARCs;

– minimal use of patents and plant variety protection;

– conventional research technologies considered sufficient to sustain agronomic progress;

– minimum involvement with regulatory bodies concerned with biological manipulation and transportation, except in the case of quarantine;

– strong reliance on advanced breeding research based at the IARCs;

– little commercial involvement required for technology dissemination;

– dependence on germplasm to achieve genetic gains.

Shiva (1991), director of the Research Foundation for Science, Technology and Natural Resource Policy in India, provided an integrated socio-economic and ecological assessment of the modernization of agriculture in developing countries, based on experiences in Punjab. Shiva held that the benefits of the 'green revolution' were often overestimated. The high-yielding varieties (HYVs) and the exotic dwarf varieties introduced by the 'green revolution' yielded more grain than the local varieties, but such comparisons did not take into account the diverse crop outputs in the traditional rotation systems; the HYVs depended on large amounts of chemical fertilizers and appeared to be more susceptible to new pests and diseases. In addition, they produced much less biomass compared to local varieties and their introduction had reduced genetic variability. Intensive agriculture also led to an increased demand for water in two ways: crop species that were relatively water-economic, such as millet and oil-seeds, were replaced by wheat and rice, which needed water throughout the year. These new varieties needed more water than local relatives. Shiva (1991) argued that the need for water had provoked countless conflicts between Punjab and the neighbouring States over water-sharing and between Punjab and the central government over the management of water reservoirs. Many farmers suffered from irrigation systems which destabilized the natural drainage process, leading to waterclogging and salinization of farmers' land. The creation of canals and water reservoirs made hundreds of families homeless and dispossessed farmers of their land.

The 'green revolution' was, according to Shiva (1991), in fact a strategy for creating cheap food surpluses for the growing urban industrial centres. Furthermore, moving away from staple foods for export markets created a new dependence on imports of biotechnological inputs and on volatile world market prices. Shiva (1991) favoured an agricultural policy that moved away from resource- and capital-intensive agricultural technology toward low-cost agriculture, by making food production economically and ecologically viable once again, through reduced input costs.

In response to this critical appraisal of the 'green revolution', Von Loesch (1996) stated that one should remember that in 1965 India had harvested 12 million tonnes of wheat, while thirty years later it achieved a fivefold increase in output, i.e. 63 million tonnes. Thereby India had overtaken the USA, becoming the world's second-biggest wheat producer after China. Whatever the shortcomings of the early years of the 'green revolution', mainly in environmental terms, it was and remains tremendously successful. It was supported by millions of small farmers whose livelihood benefited and will benefit from the productivity and hardiness of high-yielding crop varieties.

Farmers tended to clash with the environment when their technology levels were operating below effective population and economic demands. This had been the situation in developing countries since about 1950. Massive forest losses in tropical and subtropical areas, salination of irrigated lands, erosion of hill sides, pollution from intensive farming and livestock production were the results of inappropriate technology and farm management. However, had technology not developed as it did, environmental strain would have been unimaginably stronger. Had crop technologies in developing countries remainded at 1970–1974 levels, they would additionally need the equivalent of the combined arable lands of the USA, Brazil and Canada to produce current harvests. Clearly, not even a fraction of this additional land would be available for cultivation in the developing regions, not to mention the need for its even distribution throughout all four regions. Population and technology gaps must be closed if agriculture was again to become part of an environmentally stable system (Von Loesch, 1996).

The first major impact of the CGIAR was in breeding: aside from building up major germplasm collections of their priority crops, the IARCs had developed plant varieties that today played a key role in world agriculture, whether grown directly by farmers or channelled through National Agricultural Research Systems for future fine-tuning. The second important impact was the sheer influence of the CGIAR on agricultural research world-wide: despite a modest budget (the CGIAR accounted for less than 4% of public agricultural spending world-wide, whereas the U.S. bio-industry spent annually more than twice the CGIAR budget on crop research), the CGIAR and its IARCs had gathered considerable support for otherwise unglamourous agricultural research, thereby earning the right to direct that research, as well as the training of national scientists (GRAIN, 1994c).

The CGIAR claimed credit for the approximate increase of $50 billion in the Third World's production of rice and wheat since the 1960s. It pointed to the more than 750 new varieties of wheat, rice, maize, pearl millet, sorghum, potato, cassava and field bean released by or through its IARCs since their establishment. Also, it stated that between 20,000 and 45,000 scientists from developing countries had been trained or retrained. Most importantly, it pointed to the tremendous amount of germplasm – 745,000 seed samples, both unaltered and 'improved' in 1987–1991 – which had been distributed to support national and international research programmes (GRAIN, 1994b).

According to the Barcelona-based non-governmental organization (NGO) Genetic Resources Action International (GRAIN, 1994b), these results should be tempered by the additional costs of external inputs required for increasing production from higher-yielding varieties, as well as by harvest losses for 'minor' crop species or varieties and other major food supplements from the farm largely ignored by the 'green revolution'. The NGO recognized nevertheless that the most important function of the CGIAR network was the supply of germplasm to scientists working in the developing countries. Of the 745,000 seed samples sent out to researchers upon request, 45% were distributed within the CGIAR network and its associated international institutions, one-third was distributed within respective host countries of the individual IARCs and one-fifth went to other countries, with a small but growing proportion going directly to the private sector.

On the other hand, just over 35% of all the CGIAR germplasm collections had been duplicated for safety storage elsewhere. The other two-thirds had either not been duplicated or the CGIAR was not informed of it. Of the 78 back-up collections currently detailed, only 12 (i.e. 15%) were held by the national gene banks in developing countries, the CGIAR germplasm donors. The rest were being held in industrialized countries or by the IARCs themselves. Genetic Resources Action International also pointed out that only 9% of the total CGIAR collections duplicated were backed up by a formal written agreement with the recipient institute. This, according to GRAIN (1994*b*), fell short of the CGIAR expectations. For those duplicates held in co-operating gene banks for which no written agreement existed, governments might interpret these as having been received prior to the coming into force of the Convention on Biological Diversity and, thus, as forming part of the national collections.

2. Biotechnologies and conventional breeding

The 'green revolution' was launched during the 1960s in India, Pakistan and The Philippines, markedly increasing rice and wheat output on irrigated land and generating support for a major expansion of global agricultural capacity. By the mid-1990s, modern varieties added more than 50 million tonnes of grain each year to Third World grain output, enough to feed an additional 500 million people. Asia's 'green revolution' results encouraged donors to support research: the World Bank initiated this support with a loan to Spain in 1972 and it invested $2.1 billion in agricultural research projects over the 1981–1987 period (Eicher, 1993).

The rapid build-up of National Agricultural Research Systems (NARSs) in the Third World since 1970 had been characterized by growth cycles and erosion of research capacity. In India, for instance, a task force recommended, in 1988, sweeping changes to revitalize the Indian Council of Agricultural Research, the NARS of India. In Africa, the annual outlays on agricultural research increased from $103 million in 1970 to $380 million in 1984. In Nigeria, the number of agricultural researchers increased from 100 at independence in 1960 to 1,000 in 1985, but then declined to around 800 by 1990. Despite this increase in financial support from donors and the parallel increase in the number of scientists, the productivity of many NARSs in Africa had declined since the mid-1980s because of ineffective management, lack of donor co-ordination, political unrest and lack of government support for research (Eicher, 1993).

The 17 countries in the Asia-Pacific region were characterized by sharp variations in the size of their NARSs. With over 55,000 scientists and nearly 30,000 technical support staff in the late 1980s, China's NARS dwarfed the NARSs in Asia. Excluding China, seven NARSs in Asia employed more than 1,000 agricultural researchers in 1981–1985 (India, Indonesia, Pakistan, Republic of Korea, Taiwan, Thailand and The Philippines), while nine had more than 500 researchers. On the other hand, the 11 countries in the Pacific collectively employed only 260 agricultural researchers (Eicher, 1993).

Plant breeding research on basic food crop species was well advanced in many Asian countries relative to research on livestock and secondary crops, such as grain legumes and crop management. Increased attention was needed on crop and resource management research on rice and wheat, the two food staples in the Asia-Pacific region, in order to improve the efficiency of input use and address emerging problems in sustaining the quality of the resource base. Hybrid rice, which was cultivated on a large area in China, was expanding slowly in other Asian countries (Eicher, 1993).

Three NARSs (Argentina, Brazil and Mexico) employed two-thirds of agricultural researchers in Latin America and the Carribbean by the late 1980s. The majority (12 of 21) of the NARSs fell into the range of 100–999 researchers. The first expansion phase of public agricultural research in Latin America had occurred around 1930, with the establishment of NARSs within ministries of agriculture. However, these national systems failed to flourish because of over-centralization, poorly trained scientists and unstable financial and institutional support. The second phase, beginning in the 1960s, focused on the introduction of semi-autonomous NARSs, including INTA (Argentina), ICA (Colombia), INIFAP (Mexico) and EMBRAPA (Brazil), which promoted the decentralization of research and upgrading of staff through massive overseas training programmes in the 1960s and 1970s. The short-term results of the semi-autonomous model were impressive; hundreds of scientists were trained but many NARSs were unable to generate stable domestic financial support. For instance, in Mexico, the research system was frequently reorganized and the INIFAP budget declined by 50% in real terms during the 1980s. Despite decades of experimentation with alternative research models, many NARSs were under stress (Eicher, 1993).

The International Service for National Agricultural Research (ISNAR, The Hague) was established in 1979 to strengthen the weak link in the global agricultural system: the NARSs. During the 1980s, much of research within the NARSs focused on how to organize and manage a NARS, how to carry out on-farm experiments and how to develop master plans. There was little in-depth research on the political economy, or the size and financing of research and on how NARSs fared in the political process, including the art of building grass-root support from farmers and commodity groups. Since the mid-1980s, many donor agencies, consulting firms and universities had designed over-sized projects, too overloaded with hardware (buildings, vehicles and equipment) and too little concerned with the factors that shaped the scientific discovery process and the productivity of NARSs. Donors, while assessing this experience, needed to design a new mode of assistance that concentrated on strengthening the productivity of NARSs, mobilizing financial support from national sources, increasing farmer participation in research priority setting and developing new modes of public-private co-operation in research (Eicher, 1993).

An ISNAR study of 152 countries reported that 39 NARSs employed fewer than 25 agricultural researchers. For the next generation, it was almost certain that the countries with small (fewer than 50 scientists) and medium-sized (50–250 scientists) NARSs would comprise about half of the nations in the world. Eicher (1993) was of the opinion that most nations in Africa with a population of less than 5 million should strive for a NARS of 25–150 researchers; and that many African NARSs should pursue a decompression strategy to reduce the number of scientists and concentrate instead on increasing operating budgets per scientist. More time and resources would be necessary before mature NARSs in the Third World would have the capacity to generate technology that could be of use to other NARSs in the same ecoregion. For instance, the 1988 evaluation of the Indian Council of Agricultural Research urged the Council to intensify research in frontier areas such as tissue culture, genetic engineering, computer modelling, environmental education and energy management (Eicher, 1993).

While two-thirds of Third World nations had local graduate programmes in agriculture, most of the programmes were weak and lacked funds for rigorous field research. There was an atmosphere of tension and competition rather than co-operation between the NARSs and local universities in both research and graduate training. To make matters worse, donors had been slow to support long-term human capacity programmes in agriculture. For instance, the World Bank had included a small research fund in agricultural research projects in several countries in Africa that could be tapped by local university researchers (Eicher, 1993).

To sum up, the size of the NARSs and the politics of research financing needed to be the subject of vigorous debate in ministries of agriculture and of finance, in NARSs and among donors during the 1990s. Unless the issues of size, political support and financing were addressed simultaneously, the sustainability of many NARSs, particularly in Africa, would turn out to be a mirage (Eicher, 1993).

Following the achievements of the 'green revolution' in the 1960s, national and international breeding programmes targeted the breeding and popularization of a few varieties as their major goal. Breeders did not see a need to involve farmers because the required major characteristics of the new varieties were well-defined dwarf plant height to prevent lodging and increase the proportion of grain in the plant; the ability to flower about the same period of time whatever the latitude and time of sowing; and post-harvest qualities that satisfied many consumers. In addition, despite different socio-economic circumstances, developing countries adopted from the USA and Europe a regulatory framework designed to release few, widely-adapted cultivars for intensive, mechanized, monoculture cropping systems. In developed countries, farmers were regarded only as growers and not direct consumers, because grain was rarely consumed on farm, but was sold to industrial food processors. To set breeding objectives for grain quality, the grain purchasers rather than the farmers, were consulted. These purchasers were also the arbiters of the post-harvest traits of newly-finished products (Witcombe, 1996).

Even after release, extension services did not need to involve farmers in a very 'hands on' way. The literate farming community was completely aware, through printing media, of the availability and characteristics of new cultivars. Farmers could rely on varieties performing in their fields in the way described in promotional literature because of the similarity between the management of the crop on reseach stations and on the farms (Witcombe, 1996).

Production was generally stagnant or increased slowly in marginal areas. Most farmers in these areas had not adopted new cultivars in favour of their local landraces. Farmers might not have access to varieties adapted to less favourable conditions, or recommended varieties had not the attributes, such as high straw yield, that low-resource farmers needed, or did not appear as productive as expected (Witcombe, 1996).

In the 1980s, to encourage the adoption of higher-yielding varieties by low-resource farmers, scientists initiated farmer participatory research in plant breeding in several countries. All of this research was devoted to the latter stage of the plant breeding process: the selection among finished, or nearly finished, varieties. These participatory varietal selection (PVS) programmes had several characteristics in common. The needs of farmers were identified by discovering what crops and varieties they grew, and what traits they considered important. Scientists selected new varieties with the traits desired by the farmers and matching farmers' land races for such traits as maturity, plant height and seed type. Farmers visited research stations to select material from the wide range of varieties in breeders' trials. Once selected, the varieties were given to farmers to grow alongside their local varieties with conventional management. Instead of complex trial designs, farmers were the unit of replication and each farmer grows one, or few, of the new varieties. However, in every village, each of the new varieties was grown by at least one farmer (Witcombe, 1996). See also Eyzaguirre and Iwanaga (1995).

Evaluation methods were also participatory. The participating farmers visited all of the plots of all the new varieties. They could then make judgements, as a group, on the relative value of the new varieties. Additionally, in many programmes, yield per unit area was assessed to provide data for variety release committees and to test the agreement between farmers' perceptions of yield and quantitative yield data. Small quantities of seeds of named varieties were distributed to farmers, but no instructions were given on how to grow them, and no attempt was made to undertake formal evaluation of their relative performance. Instead, adoption rates were monitored after several seasons to see which varieties proved to be most popular with farmers. For a more rapid evaluation, informal discussions with farmers after a single season was expected to lead to the identification of highly-preferred varieties (Witcombe, 1996).

PVS programmes were described in many countries, including Colombia, India, Namibia, Nepal and Rwanda, in grain legumes, rice, pearl millet and maize. A number of lessons were drawn from these programmes.

1. Farmers evaluated varieties for multiple traits and did not place an overriding emphasis on grain yield. For instance, farmers traded off early maturity against yield, and yield from crop residues, such as straw, against grain yield. Hence, the most preferred varieties were often not amongst those selected by breeders for grain yield alone.

2. Farmers, particularly women, could give detailed information on post-harvest traits such as grain milling characteristics, taste and the ability of the cooked grain once eaten to delay the onset of hunger. Farmers could describe the market value of the grain and how it differed from that of the local varieties. It was feasible for a plant breeder to evaluate many of these traits without farmers, but it would be more expensive and could not provide data on how the traits traded off against each other.

3.   The spread of new varieties could be promoted in other ways that involved farmers' participation. However, sometimes less participatory approaches were required such as the contracting of local farmers to multiply the seeds. To promote the varieties, local distribution channels could be used such as non-governmental organizations, seed merchants and co-operative societies. In India and Nepal, networking among NGOs had been a most effective method for scaling up the seed distribution of preferred varieties (Witcombe, 1996).

A number of criticisms of these participatory methods were commonly voiced by scientists who had not used them.

Firstly, some scientists claimed that participatory approaches by extension services were already being used. However, although conventional extension methods could involve farmers, they often relied on demonstration of a few rcommended varieties, grown by extension workers with a recommended package of practices. Usually, this package of practices was beyond the limited resources of farmers in marginal areas.

Secondly, it was said that PVS entailed an unnecessary risk to farmers. The latter managed risk exceptionally well and their risk avoidance strategies became more sophisticated the fewer resources they had. Low-resources farmers never grew a new variety on a large area the first time they cultivated it, and rarely grew it on their best land. Only after the first season will they grow a very promising variety on better land as a pure stand. A less preferred variety might be grown as a pure stand on poorer land, mixed with seed of a local variety, intercropped with other species, or not grown at all. Several seasons of evaluation passed before farmers grew a new variety on much of their land.

In mistakenly attempting to protect farmers from themselves by limiting their access to new varieties there was a risk that the great economic benefits offered by new varieties might be foregone. If farmers were not given new varieties, then old varieties remained under cultivation longer and became more susceptible to evolving pathogens.

Thirdly, the lack of credence given by scientists to farmers' perceptions was a result of training in scientific methods that used formal statistical designs and objectively obtained quantitative data such as yield per unit area. Studies had shown a remarkable consistency in farmers' perceptions, a consistency that was often lacking in the results from more formal replicated designs.

Fourthly, it was asserted that farmers might reject varieties after one season of testing. However, in formal trials, entries were always rejected after a single year testing in a multilocational trial, no matter how atypical the season. Farmers could make judgements that were not permitted in a formal trial. For instance, a variety which had not yielded well might be tried for a second season because farmers had logical explanations for its poor performance. It might be a low yielding, short-duration variety that farmers had grown in a wet year, but they assumed that in a drought year it would have an advantage.

Fifthly, many scientists worried about the costs of involving farmers. To maximize the effectiveness of a non-participatory approach, research station sites for varietal trials were chosen for the availability of good infrastructure and fertile, uniform land. In a participatory approach, farmers must also be carefully chosen. For instance, it would be more effective and cheaper to select villages and farmers with the help of a local non-governmental organization which had already built up relations with local communities (Witcombe, 1996).

Participatory methods for marginal areas could be adapted to the socio-economic environment of more favourable production systems in developing countries and used to speed up varietal replacement. It was simpler to offer farmers in high-potential areas many new varieties as more varieties were bred for these areas than for marginal ones. Conventional extension approaches could be adapted easily to provide farmers with more choice. In high-potential areas, farmer-managed demonstrations of many varieties were simpler to organize when farmers were literate and had large, uniform fields. In marginal areas, however, the literacy rate was often low, but farmers would still grow small plots of the experimental varieties on their own fields, alongside their regular crops. There was a great potential to increase yields by reducing the average age of cultivars grown in high-potential areas. The more recently released the varieties that farmers grew, were, the greater advantage they took of the genetic gains made in breeding programmes. The United Kindgdom's Overseas Development Administration had funded projects in India and Nepal to test the hypothesis that PVS would be effective in increasing production in high-potential areas (Witcombe, 1996).

When participatory varietal selection succeeded, the farmer-preferred cultivars were the ideal parents for a participatory plant breeding (PPB) programme. In consultative programmes, farmers were consulted at every stage to set goals and choose parents that were entirely appropriate. In collaborative programmes, farmers grew the early, variable generations and selected the best plants among them on their own fields. Collaborative programmes were reported for rice in Nepal and for beans in Colombia and Brazil. In Colombia, a comparison was made between farmers' and breeders' selections. It was concluded that breeders tended to select for yield and stress tolerance, while farmers placed greater emphasis on quality traits (Witcombe, 1996).

Consultative methods could be easily incorporated into decentralized breeding programmes targeted at specific environments. Breeders could consult farmers to chose parents which could be both landraces and modern varieties. Farmers were also consulted to incorporate appropriate traits in the selection targets and farmers visited the breeders' research plots and commended on the new material. In consultative breeding, once finished products were available, collaborative research was employed. Farmers, perhaps those who had been consulted earlier, evaluated the finished products in their own fields. However, in collaborative programmes, there was no discontinuity between the end of breeding new products and the start of selection among finished products (Witcombe, 1996).

Despite the demonstrable value of farmer participation, there had been a disappointing failure to adopt the approach widely. In part, this was because institutional support and training had been aimed at conventional approaches. Fortunately, the situation was changing: four International Agricultural Research Centers had undertaken some form of participatory breeding programme, e.g. in pigeonpea and pearl millet in India, barley in Syria, rice in Viet Nam and Côte d'Ivoire. The International Center for Tropical Agriculture (CIAT, Cali, Colombia) had been the strongest advocate of participatory approaches and carried out pioneering work on beans in Rwanda and Colombia. In addition, there had been an encouraging response from the National Agricultural Research Systems which had been exposed to participatory approaches. For instance, in Nepal a variety bred by using participatory methods had been released officially; in India, at least four State Agricultural Universities had initiated participatory breeding programmes. The support of both the International Agricultural Research Centers and National Agricultural Research Systems offered a great opportunity to increase agricultural production; an opportunity perhaps no less important than that afforded by biotechnologies to improve the food security of the world (Witcombe, 1996). See also Eyzaguirre and Iwanaga (1995).

The IARCs had an important role to play in adapting biotechnologies to the demands of developing countries' agriculture. They could facilitate access to advanced biotechnologies for national agricultural services. In order to play this role, shifts in research strategies and the reallocation of resources and staff would be necessary. Plucknett and Cohen (1989) identified a sequence of steps to be followed, as the IARCs sought to adapt biotechnologies to new objectives. Firstly, expertise needed developing at each Center to provide an internal capability for observing, choosing and utilizing biotechnologies that might prove useful in crop or livestock improvement. Secondly, various means needed to be explored for acquiring new technologies from both the public and private sectors. Thirdly, the Center's research team would need to verify the performance of the acquired technology in a developing country environment. Fourthly, the applied technology would need to be tested in small-scale experiments designed in conformity with agricultural biosafety guidelines (Cohen *et al.*, 1988*a*). Only then could the Centre assume the role of extending the technology's use. Furthering the 'green revolution' would therefore require the IARCs to consider the following modifications:

– distributing improved germplasm through the private sector and national agricultural research systems;

– encouraging the IARCs to move research upstream toward more strategic or basic programmes;

– relying on patents or other property rights for processes and products, with like protection for proprietary lines prior to use;

– integrating molecular and cell biology with conventional breeding to achieve new agronomic advances;

– complying with national and international regulatory standards, especially those involving genetic engineering;

– maintaining and enhancing alliances for collaborative research required to increase centre-oriented research;

– considering more commercial involvement as national programmes and IARCs collaborated with the private sector;

– depending on germplasm to achieve genetic gains (Cohen *et al.*, 1987; Cohen, 1988; Cohen *et al.*, 1988*b*; Cohen 1989*b*; Plucknett, 1989; Plucknett and Cohen, 1989; Plucknett *et al.*, 1990).

Four segments of conventional cultivar development are presented in Table 5, as are potential biotechnology contributions.

Table 5. Potential applications of biotechnologies for integration with conventional cultivar development (Plucknett and Cohen, 1989)

Components of conventional cultivar development	Conventional time span	Potential biotechnology contributions
1. Germplasm		
a. Acquisition and exchange	1 year	*In-vitro* culture, disease indexing and eradication, micropropagation
b. Conservation	On-going	*In-vitro* conservation, gene libraries
c. Evaluation	2 seasons	Molecular diagnostics, RFLPs
d. Germplasm improvement	3–5 seasons	Embryo rescue, molecular diagnostics, selection in tissue culture, somaclonal variation, gene transfer
e. Wide hybridization	2 years	Embryo rescue, somaclonal variation, anther culture, protoplast fusion
2. Breeding		
a. Selection of parental germplasm – Elite lines – Adapted populations – Exotic materials		Molecular diagnostics, tissue culture-derived lines, gene transfer
b. Initial development cross (F1)	1 year	
c. Production and selection of segregating lines (F2-F3)	2 seasons	Somaclonal variation, anther culture, molecular diagnostics, RFLP mapping
d. Controlled inbreeding (F4-F7)	3–4 seasons	
e. Bulk increase of finished lines	2 seasons	Pathogen elimination, micropropagation
3. Testing		
a. Observational trials and/or preliminary testing	2 seasons	
b. International trials	2 seasons	Molecular diagnostics
c. Advanced testing in national co-ordinated trials	2 seasons 2 seasons	
d. Farmers' field trials	2 seasons	
4. Distribution		
a. Bulk increase	1–2 seasons	Micropropagation
b. Certification	1 season	Disease indexing and eradication
c. Quarantine	1 season	Disease indexing, molecular diagnostics, micropropagation

Donor agencies or potential public and private sector collaborators would have the opportunity of supporting individual segments closest to their particular interest. Support for these various segments of research using new technologies would ensure the developing countries access to the products of biotechnology research (Plucknett and Cohen, 1989).

The Technical Advisory Committee (TAC) of the Consultative Group on International Agricultural Research (CGIAR) drew up a policy document entitled *The role of biotechnology in the CGIAR* in 1988. The document stressed the need to use biotechnologies almost as much in germplasm-based research as in breeding activities. It emphasized the relationship between genetic resources, biotechnologies and the genetic improvement of crops, an interaction of primary importance if breeders and biotechnologists were to reinforce their reliance on germplasm accessions for the isolation and cloning of desired genes (in Peacock, 1989).

To sum up, Knudsen (1991*b*) was of the opinion that the IARCs needed to develop their own biotechnology programmes, if they wished to remain at the forefront of tropical agricultural science. A reallocation of resources and additional targeted funds were a prerequisite for this. They should move their research upstream, i.e. from applied toward more strategic programmes.

3. Intellectual property policy

The IARCs of the CGIAR embodied, on the one hand, an important part of the public breeding sector in developing countries while, on the other hand, co-operating with the private biotechnological companies from industrialized countries. Some thought that the IARCs should actively seek patents for their inventions in order to facilitate collaboration with private companies. Others considered that the acceptance of patenting could seriously hinder the free distribution of plant genetic material and innovations among developing countries' breeding institutes and therefore insisted on maintaining the CGIAR's current 'open door' policy (Van Wijk, 1992).

An open controversy dated back to 1991 when a draft policy statement on intellectual property rights for the ICRISAT was leaked by the Barcelona-based non-governmental organization, Genetic Resources Action International (GRAIN). In that statement, the ICRISAT claimed that 'the Center will assert control over intellectual property only where it appears necessary to make technology transfer effective or to protect the interests of intended beneficiaries'. The statement went on to claim that ICRISAT-held germplasm containing useful genes would be distributed to users in developing countries 'in accordance with any agreement we have with that country'. The need to take out licences and the possibility of delaying publication of research results were also mentioned. It was the first time that an IARC – a public institution, after all, dependent on the germplasm and financial support of its donors – admitted that it was considering applying intellectual property restrictions on its gene bank and research materials (GRAIN, 1994*b*).

However, in 1993, the CGIAR released a 'working document' stressing that 'Centers do not seek intellectual property rights unless it is absolutely necessary to ensure access by developing countries to new technologies and products'. Another CGIAR Statement on Plant Genetic Resources presented to the Second Session of the Intergovernmental Committee for the Convention on Biological Diversity, held in Nairobi from 20 June to 1 July 1994, assured that the Centers 'should not seek to benefit financially from the commercialization of germplasm, but should help developing countries obtain financial benefit when opportunities occur' (GRAIN, 1994*b*).

Therefore, the IARCs would neither seek intellectual property protection for income-generating purposes, nor view potential returns from intellectual property protection as a source of operating funds. Should exceptional cases arise where an IARC might receive financial return, appropriate means would be used to ensure that these funds were used for the conservation of genetic resources and related research. On a case-by-case basis, the IARCs were expected to carefully consider the advantages and disadvantages, and the costs and benefits before deeming it necessary to seek and maintain any form of intellectual property protection on their inventions (Komen, 1992*d*).

The latest proposal on intellectual property rights stated that the CGIAR Centers will neither claim legal ownership nor apply intellectual property protection to the germplasm they held 'in trust' – meaning seeds 'as such' stored in gene banks for conservation purposes. Once those seeds were taken out of the gene bank and used in a research programme, however, the story changed. Regarding outside users of the germplasm, the Centers will allow outside users to patent genetic material such as genes or molecular constructs isolated from the original seed samples that they provided upon specific agreement with the Center. The agreement will be accorded after consultation with the country of origin of the germplasm, if this is known. The new proposal for guiding principles made also clear that the benefit-sharing mechanisms of the Convention on Biological Diversity will be applied only to those germplasm collections that were collected *after* the coming into force of the Convention (29 December 1993).

In the case of an outside user seeking plant breeders' rights or other *sui generis* monopoly right on a variety developed through germplasm provided by a Center, the light was green as well, provided that such a monopoly did not cover the original germplasm itself. As to internal use of the germplasm at the Centers themselves and to their research, the door was slightly swinging open to intellectual property protection of the research results and products at the CGIAR Centers. As the policy stated, 'the Centers will not assert control over intellectual property or derivatives except in those rare cases when this is needed to facilitate technology transfer or otherwise protect the interests of developing nations'.

For instance, the transfer of technology between the International Agricultural Research Centers and the Belgian biotechnology company, Plant Genetic Systems (PGS) N.V., had been the subject of contractual agreements covering scientific and budgetary matters, as well as issues of biosafety, ownership and exploitation of results. As to the ownership of results, project know-how was owned by both partners. In the case of patentable technology generated by the project, ownership of the patent would belong to the company, since it was best qualified to pursue its application. As to the exploitation of results, commercial rights were assigned on the basis of the client countries of each partner, i.e. developing countries for the IARCs and developed countries for the company (Bijman, 1994*a*).

4. Future of the CGIAR system

By the mid-1990s, the CGIAR was struggling to cope with both external and internal pressures. Internal pressures included: a flattening out of funding in the early 1980s that was to turn into a stagnation by the end of the decade; a shift in donor concern toward sustainability, equity and natural resource management; and no or little impact in subSaharan Africa, where nearly half of the CGIAR budget was going. The U.S. Agency for International Development was threatening to cut 40% of its support in 1995 and Canada's International Development Agency was also pondering cuts. More and more, donors tied funding to those specific projects they liked most: the Swedes wanted more focus on Africa, the Swiss were pushing for on-farm work, the Rockefeller Foundation was emphasizing biotechnologies. Furthermore, a whole set of new Centers had been pulled into the network: ICLARM, ICRAF, CIFOR and IIMI. All of this was happening in a period of dissension over new priorities and shrinking funds (GRAIN, 1994c).

External pressures related to the need for: transparency and accountability to the public; democratizing participation in the system, as well as its governance; addressing the impending demise of public research in the face of the increasingly important role the private sector was playing; and an adequate response to the critiques of the 'green revolution' (GRAIN, 1994c).

There were obviously conflicts between donors and the Technical Advisory Committee (TAC) on priorities, approaches and even the long-term prospects for international agricultural research. With respect to the apparent conflict between agriculture and the environment, natural resource management (including germplasm conservation) was kept separate from production systems in the IARCs' work programmes. It was because of this that a number of donors had been bandying about the phrase 'natural resources management' to convince the IARCs to work more toward protecting and utilizing the natural resources base of agriculture. This meant conservation of genetic diversity but also resource management approaches to production systems as a whole. The IARCs – at least some of them – riposted that their main job was to feed people and not to protect the environment (GRAIN, 1994c).

It was true that alleviating poverty was ultimately the raison d'être of the CGIAR and this figured prominently in the system's mission statement. The CGIAR rejected the criticism that the technologies developed and promoted by the IARCs benefited the rich at the expense of poor and 'low-income people'. The CGIAR retaliated that the latter were the explicit targets of CGIAR research, the income of rural poor having increased in tandem with the supply of cheaper food to urban poor. However, the CGIAR limit to dealing with the broader aspects of equity and poverty was a fundamental one. The architects of the CGIAR were convinced that science was superior to politics: rather than waiting around for political leaders and conscious citizens to agree on better distribution systems for relieving poverty and inequity, it was the duty of science to produce more food and generate income through effective technologies (GRAIN, 1994c).

Another problem with an impact on CGIAR functioning was the situation of the National Agricultural Research Systems (NARSs). In the mind of the CGIAR founders, the NARSs were to be strengthened through close association with the IARCs. Thirty years later, however, many NARSs were weaker rather than stronger (see p. 301). While this was due to factors beyond the control of the CGIAR, it was a major issue because, in many cases, the relationship between the NARSs and individual Centers was more one of dependency or competitiveness than a partnership. The CGIAR was therefore debating whether to set up 'ecoregional mechanisms' to strengthen co-operation (GRAIN, 1994c).

By the mid-1990s, the CGIAR was at a stage of maturity comparable to that of many big universities in the USA. However, alternative management models needed to be studied for the CGIAR in the 21st century. The new management model would have to reward excellence in research, retain flexibility and demonstrate the ability to make difficult decisions on a broad range of system-wide issues such as: the CGIAR agenda for the following 25 years, the size of the system, generating political support for long-term funding, a commodity versus a resource management focus, the relationship between the CGIAR and mature NARSs, and the CGIAR/multinational seed company relationship (Eicher, 1993).

Another step in revitalizing the CGIAR was to protect the real (inflation-adjusted) budgets of such proven Centers as the CIMMYT, IRRI and IFPRI. Despite the growth of private seed companies and mature NARSs, global commodity Centers had a crucial role to play in germplasm and information exchange and in complementing the CGIAR expanded research agenda on natural resource management (Eicher, 1993).

One could envision generating annual savings of 10%-15% ($20–$30 million) of the current core funding of the 13 original Centers by phasing out several of these, merging others and by cutting out programmes in the remaining Centers. Eicher (1993) suggested that the ICARDA should be required to generate 80% to 90% of its budget in the Middle East; ICRISAT, which had largely fulfilled its mission in India, could phase out its programme in India over a five-year period and shift its headquarters to Africa; the CIMMYT wheat programme in Latin America could be scaled down to a barebones germplasm exchange programme because most of the wheat in the region was produced by big wheat farms in Argentina, Brazil and Chile, and these farmers could help make a case for expanded wheat programmes in their own NARSs; the CIAT rice research programme needed to be directed toward poor consumers, the Latin American NARSs assuming more responsibility in serving big rice farms; the WARDA might be merged with the IITA, an attractive possibility particularly if the latter took on the responsibility for the subhumid warm tropics; the IITA should be restricted to working in West and Central Africa for the next 25 years, all the other programmes should be terminated (IITA cowpea programme should be turned over to the

ICRISAT) and the IITA should develop a scientific partnership with tree crop research centres in the NARSs.

There was evidence that the CGIAR system was experiencing difficulties in reproducing itself in terms of the quality of its scientific staff, especially among the top 5%-10% of its scientists. One reason was that career prospects in areas such as social sciences, biotechnologies and plant breeding were more attractive in the private sector and universities in developed countries than in many of the IARCs. One way of dealing with the human resources issue was for the IARCs to develop more active partnerships with universities in industrialized countries. This would enable academic staff from overseas universities to be secunded for two to four years to an IARC. These visiting scientists could help carry out the Center research agenda and guide doctoral students and post-doctoral researchers. The IARC scientists could then spend their sabbatical leaves at the overseas universities and research institutes (Eicher, 1993).

When looking ahead, one should remember that six major research systems made up the global agricultural research system:

– public international agricultural research organizations like the CGIAR;

– private multinational seed, chemical and biotechnology firms engaged in conventional plant breeding and/or biotechnology research, and in the sale of proprietary products;

– universities in industrialized nations engaged in graduate training and research on conventional plant breeding, biotechnologies and the sale of proprietary products and services;

– mature NARSs in the Third World (Brazil, China, India, Malaysia) with a strong national research capacity in conventional plant breeding and some biotechnology capacity;

– NARSs with 50–250 scientists that generated and imported technology;

– small NARSs (25–50 scientists) in countries with 1 to 5 million people, which imported the bulk of their agricultural technology (Eicher, 1993).

Over the coming 25 years, global agricultural research was expected to be characterized by the growth of biotechnology research and development, and the privatization of research. Multinational corporations would be aggressive competitors in conventional plant breeding and seed sales in the Third World. Mature NARSs in the Third World would be unable to generate the required technology for 'developing' NARSs over the coming 25 to 30 years and/or uninterested in doing so. This explained why the CGIAR would continue to play an important role in international germplasm and information exchange for both high-income and Third World nations (Eicher, 1993).

One compelling conclusion emerging from the assessment of the NARSs throughout the world was that they were the weak link in the global agricultural research system. For instance, it would take decades of effort to develop productive and locally-financed NARSs in Africa. The current approach to providing project assistance to NARSs and faculties of agriculture needed to be replaced by a long-term institution-building strategy that would be pursued over the coming 25 to 30 years (Eicher, 1993).

Part of the current stress in the CGIAR system was caused by donors, as they committed the CGIAR to a broader array of activities without adding the required financial resources to maintain the esprit de corps of the system. Part of the stress was caused by the CGIAR decentralized management model, which was unable to make difficult system-wide decisions quickly. It was an open question whether the CGIAR could regain its institutional distinction and luster of the 1970s and 1980s when it had enjoyed a narrower mandate and greater real resources. A new management structure was needed for the CGIAR system in the 21st century; the CGIAR would have to move quickly on this issue because it needed to 'protect the proven IARCs', which were being forced to lay off scientific and support staff as their core budget was being trimmed in real terms (Eicher, 1993).

When ministers of agriculture and other high-level policy-makers met in Lucerne, Switzerland, in February 1995, to discuss the future of the CGIAR, non-governmental organizations called for: a rebirth rather than a renewal, based on a full and effective external review of the system, since no system-wide review had been conducted since 1981; a truly consultative process at the local, national, regional and global levels involving farmers and their organizations, indigenous peoples, governments and the scientific community; and a debate over existing policies on research goals and processes, and intellectual property rights (*Seedling*, the Quarterly Newsletter of Genetic Resources Action International -GRAIN-, vol. 13, no. 2, June 1996, pp. 14–22).

In November 1995, at the CGIAR Centers Week in Washington, D.C., the CGIAR embraced the vision of the International Food Policy Research Institute (IFPRI) as its own. The IFPRI argued for another 'green revolution', with the help of biotechnologies, to feed the world and protect the environment (see p. 319). The main challenge was still to keep one step ahead in the race with population growth, which would be achieved by a steady flow of improved technologies for food production. The CGIAR documents pointed out several more areas where new policies had been accepted or new action proposed (*Seedling*, vol. 13, no. 2, June 1996, pp. 14–22).

With respect to membership and governance, the CGIAR had, in 1996, 16 developing countries (including the Russian Federation) and 21 industrialized countries as members. An Impact Assessment and Evaluation Group set up during the renewal process was expected to become active later in 1996; a fully fledged external review was on the cards. During the period of renewal, seven Director-General posts for the IARCs were open for recruitment, as was the Technical Advisory Committee (TAC) chair. Of these eight positions, only one went to Egypt. Four went to Australia and New Zealand, and the rest to U.S. citizens. In addition, during 1995, seven of eight vacant Board positions went to representatives of industrialized countries. To explain this trend, it would seem that the IARCs used the contacts of Board members to approach advanced-research organizations in industrialized countries and to secure funding from certain donors. The CGIAR secretariat at the World Bank was requested to improve the present representation of developing countries in IARC boards, which had declined from 53% in 1991 to 45% in 1995 (*Seedling*, vol. 13, no. 2, June 1996, pp. 14–22).

Regarding its research agenda, the CGIAR stated that this had been refocused on: increasing productivity and protecting the environment; increasing sustainable yields in low-potential areas and intensifying production in high-potential areas; an ecoregional approach to natural resources management; and linkages with other public and private organizations for research and programme implementation. It seemed, however, that the system continued to ignore greater farmer participation in its research work (*Seedling*, vol. 13, no. 2, June 1996, pp. 14–22). See also p. 304.

The renewal process helped blow away the clouds of financial gloom in 1994; the CGIAR research agenda was fully funded in 1994, 1995 and 1996, with an annual overall budget of roughly $300 million. The FAO Global Plan of Action to conserve and use genetic resources saw the CGIAR as one of the major players; also, the Convention on Biological Diversity and the Conference of the Parties to the Convention (CoP-3), in November 1996 in Buenos Aires, agreed that the CGIAR had an important role to play in agricultural genetic resources management. Its parent agency, the World Bank, was positioning itself to expand its role in agriculture and become the lead manager for financial and genetic resources important to agriculture (*Seedling*, vol. 13, no. 2, June 1996, pp. 14–22). See p. 275.

The non-governmental organizations were still calling for a full consultative process that would culminate in a new research agenda oriented toward the world's poor with the following characteristics: a focus on the well-being of the farming communities, which should be empowered and participate at every level of the research process; broadening the mission from narrow commodity-based research to work addressing the issues of food security and livelihood systems; greater diversity in the governance structure of the CGIAR, as well as in the actual activities of each of the Centers; more receptive ear to governments of developing countries, farmers' organizations, other non-governmental organizations and the private sector; decentralized action at local, national, subregional and regional levels, and financial support to initiatives not involving centers or where centers did not take the lead responsibility (*Seedling*, vol. 13, no. 2, June 1996, pp. 14–22).

During the IARC week (28 October-2 November 1996) in Washington, D.C., the CGIAR which was 25 years old, initiated a forum on the global system of agricultural research, aimed at better defining the priorities in this area, identifying projects and establishing the ways and means to strengthen partnerships. This forum was to involve non-governmental organizations, farmers' associations from developing countries, national and international institutions, as well as the private sector.

5. '*2020 Vision*' of the International Food Policy Research Institute

In October 1995, the International Food Policy Research Institute (IFPRI)[1] (see p. 348) published the policy document *2020 Vision*. According to the latter, world population was expected to grow to a total of 8 to 12 billion between 1990 and 2020. About 94% of the population increase was expected to occur in developing countries, whose share of the world population would increase to 82%. The projected growth of 1.4% of the world population between 1990 and 2020 was however lower than the growth in the 1960s, when populations grew at a rate of 2.1%. Together with population growth, urbanization and displacement of people would continue, contributing to greater risks of food scarcity and poverty (Van Roozendaal, 1996).

On an aggregated level, *2020 Vision* estimated that between 1990 and 2020 the global effective market demand for food grains would increase by 55%, for livestock products by 75% and for roots and tubers by 50%. These rises were not only due to population growth and urbanization, but also to rising incomes and related diet changes. The IFPRI expected that, if no decrease in current investments in agricultural research and infrastructure occurred, the global food supply would still be sufficient. Even though the per capita grain production had fallen and the availability of other food resources such as marine fisheries was also declining, the current projections foresaw enough supply to meet demand. In the case of world food grain production, supply would even be sufficient to decrease real prices, according to the IFPRI (Van Roozendaal, 996).

However, at the regional level, the picture was different. Based on the criterion of a minimum income of $1 a day, more than $1 billion people in the developing countries, or 30% of the population, were living in absolute poverty by the mid-1990s. Without vigorous action, poverty would remain entrenched in South Asia and Latin america, and would significantly increase in sub-Saharan Africa. Only East Asia would witness a decline in absolute poverty. The IFPRI recognized that in South Asia and sub-Saharan Africa, the gap between production and effective demand was expected to increase. Aid was to decline due to reduced food surpluses as a result of the abolition of price-support mechanism in Europe. Those regions that were particularly dependent on food aid were bound to be hit hardest (Van Roozendaal, 1996).

The purpose of *2020 Vision* was to impose access to and availability of food (food security) and nutrition. The required investments should come from public sources, since developing countries knew from experience that the investors' interest in most developing countries, especially the African ones, was limited. Nevertheless, the IFPRI saw a greater role for the private sector once the appropriate laws on intellectual property rights were designed and implemented (Van Roozendaal, 1996).

In *2020 Vision*, the IFPRI clearly indicated on the one hand that a second green revolution should pay attention to women as food producers and as household caretakers; to the developmental role of non-gouvernmental organizations; to sustainability, diet patterns, nutrition, markets and resource mobilization. It called for relieving the foreign debt of developing countries. On the other hand, the IFPRI expressed that private markets should be developed and competition assured, structural adjustment programmes continued (though with more attention to the needs of the poor), and nations should be integrated in the global market. By taking this position, the IFPRI avoided conflict with the majority of donors. It had integrated in its analysis the 'soft side' of development, while at the same time it reproduced the neoliberal discourse of structural adjustment, open markets and privatization (Van Roozendaal, 1996).

Some criticism had been expressed with respect to *2020 Vision*. During an international conference on this programme in 1995, it was said that the IFPRI seemed to have no alternatives to high-science and high-technology approaches. For instance, while a growing number of people moved to marginal lands, modern science had not come up with a solution for adapted food production in these areas. Secondly, *2020 Vision* was criticized for its failure to set priorities. Thirdly, it was pointed out that the programme would only be realized if the IARCs took a more interdisciplinary development approach, not only horizontal (i.e. scientists with different disciplinary background), but also vertical (i.e. the inclusion of farmers, representatives of the poor). Despite the criticism, the IFPRI message was loud and clear: an agenda for development should be set, and, above all, agricultural funding should be maintained and hopefully even raised (Van Roozendaal, 1996).

With funding from the U.S. Agency for International Development (U.S.AID), the IFPRI had co-ordinated the activities relating to nutrition of the CGIAR Centers since 1993. One of the pressing problems *2020 Vision* addressed was the micronutrient deficiencies of diets. It estimated that nearly 2 billion people world-wide were iron deficient; this had resulted in 1.2 billion people with anaemia, of whom many were pregnant women. In addition, 125 million infants had vitamin A deficiency, while more than 600 million people had iodine-deficiency disorders. The World Bank stated that iron, iodine and vitamin A deficiencies undermined productivity and education; the developing world's gross domestic product was 5% lower than it would have been without micronutrient deficiencies. The spread of these deficiencies was thought to be related to the high-yielding rice, wheat and maize varieties released during the 'green revolution', as these varieties were low in micronutrients and also displaced previously grown crop species such as pulses, vegetables and fruits (Van Roozendaal, 1996).

An IFPRI project led by Graham and Welch of University of Adelaide and Cornell University respectively aimed at indicating ways and means for correcting micronutrient deficiencies. It was noted that much of the arable land was low in plant nutrients. On the basis of the results of soil surveys conducted in India and China, it was estimated that about 50% of the arable land used world-wide for crop production was low in availability of one or more of the essential micronutrients. Although in most soils the supply of trace minerals was large, they were not easily available for plants because they were chemically bound to soil particles (Van Roozendaal, 1996).

The fact that certain genotypes were more efficient in the uptake of trace minerals from soils than others was an important impetus for the

IFRRI project. Research had been directed toward zinc, iron and vitamin A; iodine was excluded for all crop species with the exception of cassava, because the supplementation programmes with the cheap iodized salt had proven to be effective. In addition, this micronutrient was almost absent from plants, while little was known yet about genetic enhancement. The main crop species under study were wheat, rice, maize, beans and cassava, the first three species representing 54% of global food production (Van Roozendaal, 1996).

Research over the five-year period 1997–2001 was expected to determine: the range of genetic variability available for exploitation by future breeding programmes; the bioavailability of the micronutrients (i.e. those actually absorbed and utilized by the human body) of the best selections; the genetics and biochemistry/physiology of the selected traits; and the screening protocols for use in breeding programmes. However, the $9.4 million needed for this phase (excluding the costs of human bioavailability studies) was partly available. The Danish Development Cooperation Agency, DANIDA, committed $1.1 million. Besides the University of Adelaide and Cornell University, the CGIAR Centers, CIMMYT, IRRI and CIAT, were collaborating. When all funding was obtained, collaborative agreements with national programmes would be negotiated. Contacts were already established with Bangladesh, Brazil, China, Colombia, Egypt, India, Nepal and Turkey. The IFPRI estimated that the countries' contribution to the project would be less than the conventional approaches, such as fortification (Van Roozendaal, 1996).

Although attempts to improve the nutritional characteristics of crop species (mainly vitamin and protein content) had been plagued by the conflict between high nutritional quality and yield, Graham and Welch were of the opinion that breeding for trace mineral-dense seeds might not only improve the nutritional quality of plants, but in many cases also improved yields and profits on trace mineral-deficient soils. Additionally, they did not expect that consumers' behaviour would be changed, because of the small portion micronutrients represented of the total physical mass. Seeds with higher concentrations of particular micronutrients had other advantages, such as higher germination rate, better seedling vigour and improved resistance in soils deficient in that micronutrient. The breeding strategy could also improve the stress tolerance of a plant species: at Cornell University, it was found that the higher the concentration of zinc in the root cell membranes of a plant, the higher the tolerance to environmental stresses, such as salinity. Regarding the financial advantages of that breeding strategy, it was estimated that Turkish farmers growing zinc-dense wheat varieties would save between

$75 million and $100 million annually in reduced seedling rates alone. However, more research was needed to determine whether the agronomic advantages were high enough for the seeds to be adopted, and whether the additional nutrients contained in the seeds would have a durable impact on human nutrition (Van Roozendaal, 1996).

A member of the CGIAR Technical Advisory Committee (TAC) stated that it might take at least ten years and a substantial amount of money before the first results would be ready for the market. Meanwhile, the development of other, more efficient strategies might make the quality crops obsolete. The encouragement of balanced diets, the increase in vegetable production, or the enhancement of food and income security through agricultural diversification might be as good methods as this breeding strategy. These alternatives were low-technology in nature. For instance, after the processing phase, some cereals, such as rice, might lose much of their nutritional quality. If rice consumption habits changed (i.e. consumption of white rice), the processing would change and some of the mineral deficiencies would already have been overcome. However, continuing consumption patterns would complicate the research since it should not just enhance the nutrition quality of the seed as such, but should also concentrate on those parts that were actually consumed. Regarding the overall support provided by the CGIAR to this project, it was generally assumed that this support would be very weak or even nil if the micronutrient enhancement were to be achieved at the expense of crop yield (Van Roozendaal, 1996).

6. Task Force on Biotechnology

The CGIAR Task Force on Biotechnology (BIOTASK) held its first meeting in May 1989. The activities of BIOTASK encompassed:
- regulatory issues and environmental release of modified organisms;
- collaboration between the public and private sectors;
- cross-Center collaboration;
- an inventory of the above and of information systems.

In 1990, the BIOTASK sponsored two seminars. The first, Cassava and Biotechnology, held in Amsterdam in March 1990, reviewed the priority constraints in cassava production which the application of biotechnologies might remedy. The second, held in Canberra in June 1990, introduced new techniques in genetic mapping to experienced plant breeders from the IARCs and National Agricultural Research

Systems (NARS). In 1991, BIOTASK focused on informing scientists of recent developments. This included an assessment of the needs of scientists at national institutions regarding access to biotechnology information and the provision of selected books and journals. The BIOTASK was also investigating the setting up of a computer-based *Biotechnology Bulletin Board*, with a view to facilitating rapid communication amongst scientists in IARCs and national institutions.

The secretariat of the BIOTASK was located at the International Service for National Agricultural Research (ISNAR, The Hague), where a seminar was organized from 2 to 4 September 1991. Financed by the Directorate-General for International Co-operation of the Dutch Government, the seminar was attended by some 70 participants from international agencies, IARCs, universities, public institutes and private companies, with a view to identifying the needs of the National Agricultural Research Systems (NARSs) in the areas of biosafety and intellectual property rights, as their position might differ from those of the international institutes (Komen, 1991*f*).

A number of IARCs were operating in accordance with biosafety host-country guidelines, where these existed. In the absence thereof, the centres followed self-imposed, internationally accepted guidelines. All Centers with crop improvement programmes had established institutional biosafety committees. In many developing countries, the difficult economic situation had led to budget reductions for regulatory services, which were costly to maintain. However, uncertainties in biosafety regulations might hinder the transfer of biotechnologies to developing countries or, conversely, favour the use of developing countries as testing grounds in conditions judged unacceptable in industrialized countries. It was therefore recommended that the IARCs should encourage their national partners to adopt a regional approach to biosafety, in order to harmonize the relevant guidelines (Komen, 1991*f*)[2 (see p. 348)].

The seminar revealed that: many developing countries were likely to adopt or strengthen intellectual property protection over the coming years; and that a policy on intellectual property protection would substantially modify the CGIAR's current 'open-door policy', i.e. the free distribution of plant genetic material and innovations (Komen, 1991*f*).

The ISNAR also organized a workshop on a Global Biotechnology Programme: providing a framework for assistance, in The Hague, from 5 to 7 October 1993. The main purpose of the workshop was to familiarize participants with the subjects, areas and approaches of programmes being carried out by various agencies for the applying and developing biotechnologies in Third World countries.

Another workshop entitled International agricultural biotechnology programmes: providing opportunities for national participation, was organized by the ISNAR in The Hague from 9 to 11 November 1993. The meeting's main purpose was to analyze the needs of National Agricultural Research Systems, the challenges they faced and how international programmes could support them. In particular, discussions focused on increasing opportunities for developing countries to integrate international research programmes and networks, and on analyzing what financial backing was necessary for full use to be made of biotechnologies in meeting developing countries' needs. The meeting was attended by 48 participants from 19 developing countries in Africa, Asia and Latin America, and 21 industrialized countries and representatives from national and international programmes, regional networks, IARCs and donor agencies. The surveyed organizations were supporting collaborative biotechnology research directed at the food or economic needs of developing countries. Additionally, they provided opportunities for strengthening national programmes through training or networks, or linkages for scientists in developing countries. These organizations requested information on overall goals and priorities, agricultural and regional focus, training opportunities, research management, research-and-development progress, funding and expenditures. The information collected had been entered into the Intermediary Biotechnology Service data-base (see p. 327). Other data-bases, such as REDBIO/CATBIO, were being considered for merging.

The meeting provided an excellent opportunity to reflect on: the challenges national programmes in developing countries faced in implementing biotechnology initiatives; the possibilities offered by international programmes, networks and donors for meeting these challenges at national level; and the harmonization of these national and international programmes and activities to better address these challenges. The analysis of data on available expertise in international biotechnology programmes and the conclusions and recommendations of the regional working groups were very useful for region-specific recommendations regarding such key elements as priority setting, human resources development, programmme design, research collaboration (crops and livestock), technology transfer and funding, biosafety and intellectual property protection, information and communication (*REDBIO Circular Letter*, 8 June 1994, pp.12–13).

In April 1996, co-operation between ISNAR and the French Centre for International Co-operation in Agricultural Research for Development (CIRAD) was initiated on several topics, such as a typology of national agricultural research systems taking into account the modalities of functioning and co-operation of these institutions, the evaluation of research findings and the setting up of systems for evaluating farmers' organizations. A memorandum of understanding was signed by the two institutions and one CIRAD researcher was secunded to the ISNAR (*CIRAD Information*, no. 62, 23 May 1996, p. 5).

7. Intermediary Biotechnology Service

Plans for setting up an Intermediary Biotechnology Service (IBS) were discussed at the Task Force on Biotechnology (BIOTASK) of the Consultative Group on International Agricultural Research (CGIAR). The BIOTASK had conducted an in-depth investigation into the problems and potential benefits of applying biotechnologies to agricultural research in developing countries. It recommended that a demand-driven, problem-oriented advisory service be set up to make available the expertise of advanced biotechnology institutes to the developing countries. The IBS would therefore function as a clearing-house between the priorities of developing countries and expertise in the industrialized countries. It would represent a continuation of activities begun in 1988 under a four-year joint programme of the ISNAR, World Bank and the Australian Government, entitled 'Agricultural biotechnology: opportunities for international development' (see p. 280).

In September 1991, a founding group consisting of representatives from the Norwegian Centre for International Agricultural Development (NorAgric), the World Bank, the Overseas Development Administration (ODA, United Kingdom), the U.S. Agency for International Development (U.S. AID), the Swiss Development Council (SDC, Switzerland), the Directorate-General for International Cooperation (DGIS, Netherlands), and from developing countries was set up. The founding committee met again in February 1992 to discuss the following issues: in-house capacity for policy advice versus clearing-house for technical advice; networking; demand-driven methodology; complementarity to the existing biotechnology research networks and other international initiatives. The Dutch Government provided funding to set up the International Biotechnology Service (IBS) in late 1992, which was to act as an independent advisor to national programmes in developing countries in biotechnology research policy and management. The IBS was headquartered at the International Service for National Agricultural Research (ISNAR) in The Hague.

The IBS was guided by a steering committee composed of representatives from participating countries, contributing donors and the implementing agency, the ISNAR. Its three main functions were to:

– assist National Agricultural Research Systems in developing countries with biotechnology research programme management and policy formulation;

– carry out country studies to identify priority problems amenable to being solved through biotechnologies;

– identify international biotechnology expertise and enhance its availability to national programmes in developing countries;[3] (see p. 348)

– provide services on socio-economic subjects, regulatory issues, intellectual property management and access to information;

– assist developing countries in implementing biosafety regulations and in the development of staff and research capacity.

The IBS advised bilateral and multilateral development agencies on biotechnology issues affecting developing countries. The IBS would also provide an early warning system for countries and commodities experiencing negative implications of biotechnologies, such as the substitution of certain tropical export commodities by bio-industrial products manufactured in industrialized countries.

The ISNAR/World Bank Biotechnology Country Data-Base provided a regularly updated, consolidated set of data on the status of biotechnologies in about 18 countries. The following areas of information had been selected: general country information; government policy, including information on national programmes, public sector research, public-private collaboration, human resources management, intellectual property rights, biosafety; private-sector activities; international collaboration; current applications in plant production, plant protection, biofertilizers, animal production and health, diagnostics and other applications; specific data on national, bilateral and multilateral programmes; institute profiles; bibliographical data on key documents; addresses of contact persons. The data-base software was a user-friendly package called Q&A, which could handle large text fields, as well as quantative data. Q&A easily imported or exported data from or to almost any data-base or word processing package. Two persons were responsible for the data-base, one at the ISNAR's Intermediary Biotechnology Service and the other in the World Bank's Agricultural and Natural Resources Department.

Brenner and Komen (1994) reported extensively on the results of an Intermediary Biotechnology Service survey among some 45 organizations involved in international agricultural biotechnologies. The IBS survey revealed that international biotechnology initiatives were focusing on a limited number of countries with relatively advanced scientific capabilities. Moreover, the great majority of the research programmes supported were designed by scientists and administrators from industrialized countries. Consequently, these programmes were not necessarily most relevant for achieving food sufficiency or sustainability in developing countries. Biotechnology programmes could not afford the dispense with the participation of the countries themselves at all levels and phases of design and implementation. The authors underlined that more attention needed to be given to product development and even distribution of these products in some cases, rather than solely, to research. Owing to the limited funding available in most developing countries, it was crucial to stimulate private sector and design a legal framework to guarantee biosafety and protect intellectual property rights.

Some 45 representatives from Indonesia, Malaysia, Singapore, Thailand, The Philippines and Viet Nam attended a regional policy seminar, the first in IBS series of Agricultural Biotechnology Policy Seminars designed to strengthen the capacity of developing countries in the planning and management of agricultural biotechnologies. Held in Singapore from 25 to 29 September 1994, the seminar was organized by the Intermediary Biotechnology Service (IBS), in collaboration with a local organizing committee including representatives from Singapore's Economic Science and Technology Board and Primary Production Department of the Ministry of National Development. Financial support was provided by the Dutch Ministry of Foreign Affairs, through its Special Programme Biotechnology and Development Cooperation, and the Swiss Development Cooperation (Komen *et al.*, 1995).

The IBS had identified four phases in planning and implementing initiatives in agricultural biotechnologies:

– setting policies and identifying priorities that addressed those constraints on agricultural productivity for which biotechnologies offered a comparative advantage;

– formulating a national programme to address these priorities and policies;

– implementing and monitoring the research programme;

– transferring and delivering technologies to end-users (Komen *et al.*, 1995).

The objectives of the Seminar were to: introduce policy-makers, scientists and end-users to a decision-making framework for integrating biotechnologies into agricultural research; identify gaps and needs in biotechnology research management and planning; and develop follow-up initiatives at the national and individual levels, to be reviewed and implemented after the seminar (Komen *et al.*, 1995).

Prior to the Seminar, participating countries had set specific national objectives for agricultural biotechnologies, as an element of broader programmes for agricultural research and biotechnologies:

– Indonesia: Agricultural Research Management Project, which included a component for agricultural biotechnology development, ending in 1995;

– Malaysia: Intensification of Research Priority Areas (IRPA) for agriculture (1990-1995) and National Biotechnology Programme (1996-2000);

– Singapore: National Biotechnology Committee;

– Thailand: National Center for Genetic Engineering and Biotechnology (BIOTEC);

– The Philippines: Biotechnology Action Plan (1990-1995);

– Viet Nam: National Programme in Biotechnology (1991-1995).

The Seminar identified three issues which required special attention when setting priorities for biotechnologies within national agricultural objectives: the limited data available for assessing biotechnology research; the timing of investments in this type of research; and the comparative advantage of biotechnologies versus conventional types of agricultural research (Komen *et al.*, 1995).

In Viet Nam, for the period 1995-2010, the government's first priority for scientific research was biotechnologies; four priority projects in agricultural biotechnologies had been identified:

– development of large-scale micropropagation technology for plants of economic importance;

– application of genetic engineering to plant breeding programmes, with emphasis on rice, vegetables and root crop species;

– research and technology transfer for improving crop varieties and processing agricultural products;

– development of biotechnologies related to environmental protection and reforestation (Komen *et al.*, 1995).

The Seminar debated the constraints on the development of agricultural biotechnologies in South-East Asia, such as a lack of capital, a weak science base and insufficient links between the research, productive and consumer sectors. It was also highlighted that the major scientific breakthroughs needed to meet food production expectations were: breaking the yield barrier; developing durable pest- and disease-resistant varieties; improved plant management; nitrogen-fixing crop species; biological control of weeds; increased tolerance to abiotic stresses; and increased photosynthetic efficiency (Komen *et al.*, 1995).

Regarding the issue of intellectual property rights (IPR), the attitude of governments was affected by the following factors: existing level of national technology and expectations as to its future development; need to encourage technology transfer from developed countries; and desire to induce foreign investment in the country or region. It was argued that a strong patent system was more likely to catalyze technology transfer and foreign investment, but would not in itself ensure that technology transfer took place. In Thailand, although the government had taken important steps toward implementing a national system for biosafety regulation, there was still uncertainty over whether the new regulations for biotechnology research were understandable for all parties concerned, including public and private sector researchers and government officials involved in approving and monitoring experiments. A second private-sector concern related to the loss of critical information and research material to competitors during the approval process, which was the responsibility of several different government offices. Thirdly, regarding IPR, concern was expressed that Thailand's draft Plant Variety Protection Act (PVPA) might not effectively protect new transgenic varieties. In addition, there was also concern about co-ordination, as two different government departments (Agriculture and Intellectual Property) were working on different draft Acts. It was recognized by the participants in the Seminar that implementing IPR policies along the lines of those in industrialized countries might not be appropriate until the industries in developing countries had reached a competitive level comparable to that of their counterparts in the developed countries (Komen *et al.*, 1995).

With respect to financing (mobilizing and allocating resources for biotechnologies), the representative of the National Development Planning Agency of Indonesia (BAPPENAS) presented a summary of the national planning and budgeting process for agricultural research under the Five-Year Development Plans. A new institutional feature in Indonesia were so-called 'tripartite partnerships', in which government, public research institutions and the private sector co-operated in funding, conducting and commercializing research-and-development operations. It was stressed that, when considering investments in agricultural biotechnologies in a situation of limited resources, the following points needed to be addressed:

– setting clear priorities to trim a broad agenda, balancing the needs of agro-industry and those of small farmers;

– establishing time horizons (short-, medium- or long-term), monitoring and accountability mechanisms;

– when attracting donor funding, development of projects addressing the strategic thrust of a particular donor agency;

– pooling resources through regional collaboration;

– creating an environment conducive to attracting private capital (Komen *et al.*, 1995).

Regarding programme management and collaboration, the specific management issue of human resource development was discussed and urgent needs in this area were highlighted: to upgrade the skills of mid-career agricultural scientists; to establish a second tier of training focused on the provision of specialized laboratory technicians and initiate specific courses for research administrators, managers and policy-makers to improve their understanding of the changes and benefits inherent in the introduction of biotechnologies. The subject of biotechnology project management courses came up as a major training need. Training in other technical areas appeared to be increasingly available, but greater efforts could be made to collect and circulate information on training opportunities (Komen *et al.*, 1995).

As a vehicle for analyzing the various issues pertaining to technology transfer and product diffusion to identified end-users, short presentations and discussions took place on private-sector enterprises (e.g. Saigon Biotech; Micro-Biomass International, The Philippines, and Fitotek Unggul, Indonesia) involved in biotechnology research and development. It was concluded that government institutions could influence product development by: offering on-farm demonstrations, pilot-scale production facilities, or science parks; and by procuring and distributing micropropagated planting material (Komen *et al.*, 1995).

As far as follow-up planning was concerned, Indonesia's priorities for agricultural biotechnologies, IPR and biosafety were discussed at the Second National Conference on Agricultural Biotechnology in June 1995. The Philippine Agricultural Biotechnology Agenda was discussed during a national workshop in December 1994. The Singaporean delegation to the Seminar was exploring the possibility of organizing a regional biosafety conference and sharing data-bases on biotechnology research. Identified priority actions for Viet Nam included: propagating elite varieties; development of biofertilizers and biopesticides; conservation of biological diversity; and strengthening the co-ordinating power of the Ministry of Science, Technology and Environment (MOSTE); these priorities were discussed at a national science conference in December 1994 (Komen *et al.*, 1995).

The Seminar conclusions emphasized the need to look farther a field to innovative avenues of funding, especially joint funding (e.g. consortium of private-sector agencies with government acting as a 'catalyst'); an international fund for technology development and the transfer of suitable proprietary technology in areas related to agricultural biotechnologies should require careful examination; a 'consortium of users' could be constituted to negotiate the transfer of proprietary technology to developing countries; intra-country technology diffusion should be need- and market-driven, promoted by international or national intermediary organizations, such as the Intermediary Biotechnology Service, non-governmental organizations, or national biotechnology programmes. With respect to IPR systems, it was concluded that they needed strengthening, but also that 'farmers' rights' had to be respected if the benefits of agricultural biotechnologies were to be spread fairly among the various groups (Komen *et al.*, 1995).

The second seminar in the IBS series of Agricultural Biotechnology Policy Seminars, entitled, Turning priorities into feasible programs: Seminar on planning, priorities and policies for agricultural biotechnology for East and Southern Africa, was held in South Africa from 23 to 27 April 1995. Delegations from six countries of East and Southern Africa and 24 resource persons representing various international organizations and countries in other African regions attended the Seminar. The latter was co-organized by the IBS and a local committee convened by the South African Foundation for Research Development (FRD). Financial support was provided by the Swedish Agency for Research Collaboration with Developing Countries (SAREC), the Technical Centre for Agricultural and Rural Co-operation (CTA), the Netherlands' Ministry of Foreign Affairs through its Special Programme Biotechnology and Development Cooperation, and by the Swiss Development Cooperation (SDC). Full national delegations came from Ethiopia, Kenya, South Africa, Tanzania, Uganda and Zimbabwe, while individual delegates represented Burkina Faso, Burundi, Malawi and Mauritius (Komen *et al.*, 1996).

During extensive preparatory missions, IBS staff had realized that a number of African countries were considering, reviewing and/or implementing research in agricultural biotechnologies through their national scientific and agricultural organizations:

– Ethiopia: National Science and Technology Programme, National Agricultural Research Programme, co-ordinated by Ethiopia Science and Technology Commission;

– Kenya: Kenya Agricultural Research Institute (KARI) Biotechnology Programme (1992-1997), Special Programme Biotechnology and Development Cooperation (DGIS, the Netherlands), co-ordinated by the Ministry of Research, Technical Training and Technology, Kenya Agricultural Biotechnology Platform;

– South Africa: Foundation for Research Development (FRD) Biotechnology Programme for Human Resource Development (1990-1994, then from 1996);

– Tanzania: activities co-ordinated by the Commission for Science and Technology and the Department of Research and Training;

– Uganda: activities co-ordinated by the National Research Organization and National Council for Science and Technology;

– Zimbabwe: Biotechnology Research Institute (1992-1997); Special Programme Biotechnology and Development Cooperation (DGIS, the Netherlands), co-ordinated by Zimbabwe Biotechnology Advisory Commission (Komen *et al.*, 1996).

These developments raised a diverse set of issues and questions for decision-makers, reflecting the fact that African countries were facing many of the same issues and challenges as countries in other regions. The Seminar specific objectives were therefore to: have policy-makers, scientists and end-users examine ways of integrating biotechnologies into agricultural research and the overall objectives of agriculture; identify gaps and needs in research management and planning for agricultural biotechnologies including priorities, policies, financing and programme structure; develop follow-up initiatives for in-country review with regard to their implementation and impact; point out potential regional actions which complemented the needs and capabilities identified by participating countries with regard to utilizing biotechnologies (Komen *et al.*, 1996).

A three-step approach was adopted to stimulate discussion, review and analysis of findings. Firstly, a panel discussion was organized to summarize key findings from plenary sessions as well as to present the panel's own analysis of the plenary discussions. Secondly, national working groups prioritized specific gaps and needs identified from previous working-group sessions then defined national and regional planning actions to address these. Lastly, a special National Coordinators meeting, including delegation co-ordinators, representatives from international agencies and donor organizations, met with the IBS to review the findings from steps one and two above in an effort to determine specific areas for collaboration (Komen *et al.*, 1996).

Regarding needs and priorities, the main issue to emerge was that of how one managed technology transfer from the laboratory to a range of end-users. Technology had to move to the production environment, then to the farmer, through to the food processor and the consumer. The first question was, did the end-user want the product? This question could be addressed through straightforward marketing research. Secondly, what was the size of the market? Both local and export opportunities had to be looked at. Thirdly, what was the customer going to be prepared to pay for the product? Lastly, how much would the project cost? One ought to be looking at research, development and production costs, which were often difficult to determine, but some projections were necessary. Socio-economic input was critical for enhancing sound planning and priority setting. Some of the issues economists might consider were food security, efficient resource utilization, employment, equity, environment, income distribution and sustainability. The involvement of economists was therefore indispensable in research planning and priority-setting teams (Komen *et al.*, 1996).

As far as biosafety was concerned, the issue needed to be addressed in a national and regional context, because the environmental effects of biotechnology applications could transcend national boundaries. The regional standing committee and the regional focal point in Harare needed therefore to be strengthened. The regional focal point was requested to encourage national authorities to have biosafety regulations and guidelines put in place (Komen *et al.*, 1996).

Policy-makers and research planners were invited to examine the following points relating to livestock productivity:

– the precise role of animal production for human nutrition, income and trade;

– opportunities for biotechnology interventions when these were relevant to local production systems;

– the policy environment for research on animal production and health, including national policies to support this type of research and encourage investment;

– potential for regional and international collaboration, including sharing responsibility for some transboundary problems (disease) and the promotion of international technology transfer;

– formal mechanisms for monitoring the changing user needs (Komen *et al.*, 1996).

Considerations on financing highlighted the fact that, for many countries participating in the Seminar, biotechnologies were basically a public-domain activity and that the appropriate infrastructure and equipment were essential. Another overriding requirement was the acquisition of expertise, which was a major deficiency. Investment in visits to countries where biotechnologies were a 'mature' technology and training in these countries was required for scientists to gain knowledge of basic techniques. Thirdly, establishing an information supply system was worth considering. The supply of journals and access to (on-line) data-bases was crucial in a field like biotechnologies. Internet access was still very limited in African countries. Lastly, the selection of projects needed to be approached carefully, especially when resources were limited. Biotechnologies were often presented as a necessity, but many problems could be tackled by conventional techniques. Also worth considering was whether a project could be a 'money spinner' or make a marginal difference. Market intelligence was essential to assessing these considerations (Komen *et al.*, 1996).

Regarding the end-user perspective, it was stressed that farmers needed to be actively involved in as many steps as possible in the research process, e.g. constraint identification and priority setting. Their involvement would ideally be co-ordinated through representative organizations, which made it essential to strengthen these; formal linkage mechanisms needed to be developed between farmers and researchers, policy-makers, private-sector representatives and extension workers; an integrated approach to conventional and advanced agricultural research would be necessary. Adoption of new technologies by farmers could be facilitated by promoting farmers' access to production resources and credit facilities. The setting up of farmer-training institutes was worth considering. Another step in the right direction would be to enhance the evaluation and adoption of existing technology packages (Komen *et al.*, 1996).

The final session of the Seminar reviewed the potential for follow-up activities between the co-ordinators of country delegations and representatives of international organizations and donor agencies. With regard to regional co-operation, delegates did not grasp at overly-optimistic, short-term approaches to regional solutions. It was mentioned that differences among countries with respect to capacity, policies and technological expertise were regularly encountered at African meetings. This made the idea of regional co-operation difficult to entertain. Therefore, relevant follow-up actions would have to be country specific (Komen *et al.*, 1996).

A number of important findings were emphasized by the national co-ordinators with regard to the difficulties African leaders faced when considering decisions on new technology. This was especially true when they found themselves advocating and supporting the introduction of biotechnologies in the face of general perception that such innovations might not be what was most needed to address pressing food, environmental or health objectives (Komen *et al.*, 1996).

Many of the countries attending the Seminar were trying to redouble their efforts in biotechnologies. Changing organizational structures was one of the options under consideration, strengthening the participatory nature of decision-making was another. The relation between areas of national competence and matching support for research provided from international programmes was highlighted by the meeting, although much more could be done in linking national needs and capabilities with relevant international programmes. The need for country-specific testing and development of products from new technologies was acknowledged. The meeting also stressed the advantages of better co-ordination among the limited number of organizations in a position to support biotechnology research. Last but not least, academic-industrial co-operation was emphasized; this would benefit from the organizational changes mentioned above (Komen *et al.*, 1996).

Many co-ordinators stressed the need for awareness campaigns targeted to policy-makers, important in building understanding of the complementarity between biotechnologies and conventional agricultural research and the integration of these to enhance productivity. In this regard, the need for biosafety regulations was reiterated, in order to deal with external requests as well as the material being generated nationally. Carefully thought-out material and information were needed, and it should be underscored that biotechnologies did not replace conventional agricultural research, but were complementary to it (Komen *et al.*, 1996).

A number of countries, including South Africa and Uganda, insisted on the importance of reviewing and planning for the human resource needs of bio-industry. An audit would help determine where gaps existed in certain areas and where new educational and research programmes were called for to address these shortcomings (Komen *et al.*, 1996).

Regional organizations and networks could offer possibilities for collaborative research and assistance to solve the main issues mentioned above. For instance, Kenya, Tanzania, Uganda and Zimbabwe suggested that the creation of a Biotechnology Advisory Commission would provide complementary support to the Regional Biosafety Focal Point in Harare. Tanzania and Uganda mentioned the Cassava Biotechnology Network (CBN), which could support priority research and short-term training through the CBN small-grants programme. Kenya and Zimbabwe referred to the DGIS Special Programme Biotechnology and Development Cooperation (the Netherlands) and provided details on the Zimbabwe-Kenya Project on Disease and Drought-Tolerant Maize Varieties. Participating countries indicated that the United Nations Economic Commission for Africa (ECA) would bring forward findings and conclusions from the Seminar to the ECA Conference of Ministers and the ECA Biennial Programme. All country delegations, while identifying technology transfer and biosafety as priority areas, suggested that the International Service for the Acquisition of Agri-Biotechnological Applications (ISAAA) Afri-Center

(Kenya) should expand its support in African countries to include technology transfer, project implementation and commercialization, and should continue to assist in developing biosafety guidelines, specifically in relation to cotton and *Bacillus thuringiensis*. Uganda and cereal-growing African countries proposed that the Rockefeller Foundation support the development of tissue culture of vegetatively-propagated food crop species (banana, cassava, sweet potato) and research on maize resistance to streak virus and *Striga*. The Southern African Centre for Co-operation in Agricultural & Natural Resources Research & Training (SACCAR) could support training in biotechnologies, with possible priority for the Regional Project for the Strengthening of Agriculture, Forestry and Veterinary Medicine; and incorporate biotechnologies into the Long-Term Strategy for Research in Food, Agriculture and Natural Resources. Lastly, Ethiopia, Kenya and Uganda suggested that the U.S. Agency for International Development initiate activities to strengthen the East African capacity to shift biotechnologies from the laboratory to commercial products (Komen *et al.*, 1996).

A fourth IBS Seminar was planned for West and Central Africa in 1997.

In the meantime, the third IBS Agricultural Biotechnology Policy Seminar was held in Lima, Peru, from 6 to 10 October 1996, to review and take stock of investment and research results in selected countries of Latin and Central America, looking back to whether research lined up to expectations, and looking forward to determine whether anticipated decisions in the coming years would make investments effective and consistent with broader policy decisions. In developing the programme for this Seminar, the IBS worked closely with the ISNAR and the Canada-Latin America Initiative on Biotechnology for Sustainable Development (CAMBIOTEC). In addition, collaboration involved the International Agricultural Research Centers of the region (CIAT, CIP, CIMMYT) as well as the International Development Research Centre (IDRC, Ottawa), Inter-American Institute for Cooperation on Agriculture (IICA) and the FAO Plant Biotechnology Network (REDBIO).

The Seminar specific objectives were to: have policy-makers, scientists and end-users examine planning, investments and priorities for biotechnology research addressing agricultural needs for Latin America; analyze case studies (which reviewed financial, planning and research efforts) with regard to future needs in research management and planning for agricultural biotechnologies; and determine needs among participating countries for follow-up initiatives and suitable collaboration on these initiatives.

Delegations from Chile, Colombia, Costa Rica, Mexico and Peru, representing diverse stages of development for biotechnology programmes, included policy-makers from agriculture, science and technology, and finance/planning; researchers from national agricultural research organizations and universities; research managers of public and private (commercial) institutions; representatives of farmers' groups, producers' associations, or other end-users. In addition, resource persons from other countries in the region and regional organizations attended the Seminar in order to facilitate regional comparisons and follow-up activities.

The Seminar sessions covered: the needs and priorities for biotechnology research in the context of agricultural objectives; national policies for productivity and environment; socio-economic considerations for biotechnology policy and planning; financing, product development and international technology transfer; reviewing the issues; working at the national level (summary and follow-up planning).

Follow-up opportunities (in collaboration with CAMBIOTEC) included: compiling and publishing country profiles on priorities, policies and research management; developing national plans and research collaboration on biotechnologies; and initiating proposals for funding and implementation. This reflected the IBS strategy to provide a systematic means of addressing issues and building collaboration globally, followed by regional policy seminars and, as the last link in the chain, to work at national level on the implementation of specific activities.

8. Biotechnologies used for commodity crops

Table 6 provides a summary of biotechnologies used at the International Agricultural Research Centers (IARCs) for a number of commodity crops. The IARCs had established interdisciplinary research teams, incorporating conventional, cellular and molecular biologists, good examples of the technology integration beneficial to developing countries. These teams were also collaborating with partners throughout the world, e.g.:

– wheat, CIMMYT and Tissue Culture for Crops Project (TCCP);

– potato, sweet potato, CIP, IITA and the U.S. Department of Agriculture, North Carolina State University, University of Braunschweig, Cornell University (New York), the Weizmann Institute

of Science, Swiss Federal Agricultural Research Station;
- rice, IRRI and Rockefeller Foundation;
- cassava, CIAT and Louisiana State University, University of Manitoba, Washington University;
- common beans, CIAT and University of California, University of Florida, TCCP;
- cowpea, IITA and University of Naples, Purdue University, Canadian Department of Agriculture.

Table 6. Current applications of biotechnologies for commodity crops in the International Agricultural Research Centers (Plucknett and Cohen, 1989)

Commodity	Biotechnology	IARC and collaborator	Conventional crop component
Wheat	*Somaclonal variation* Somaclone selection from spring wheat for tolerance to salinity	CIMMYT and Tissue Culture Crops Project (TCCP)	Breeding, selection of segretating lines
	Regeneration and somaclone selection in durum and bread wheats		
	Tissue culture for alien gene introgression Use of *Aegilops* as source of karnal bunt resistance Use of *Agropyron* for tolerance to *Helminthosporium* Wheat x disomic addition lines containing rye chromosomes	CIMMYT and TCCP	Germplasm, prebreeding
	Monoclonal antibodies Detection of barley yellow dwarf virus (BYDV)	CIMMYT	Testing
	Biochemical markers Electrophoresis used to mark alien germplasm in wide cross programme	CIMMYT	Germplasm, prebreeding

Rice	*Anther culture*		
	Selection of stress-tolerant lines	IRRI	Breeding
	Rapid achievement of homozygous lines from F1 sexual crosses	IRRI	
	Homozygous diploids for testing in the southern cone of South America	CIAT	Testing
	Monoclonal antibodies		
	Diagnostics for rice tungro and rice grassy stunt viruses	IRRI	Testing
	Nucleic acid diagnostic probes		
	Rice blast and bacterial blight	IRRI	Testing
	Protoplast fusion		
	Hybrid production between species with incompatibility barriers	IRRI	Germplasm, prebreeding
	RFLP (restriction fragment length polymorphism) mapping		
	Nuclear and cytoplasmic variation determined in breeding material	IRRI	Breeding
	Somaclonal variation		
	Selection for tolerance to salt and aluminium	IRRI	Breeding
	Embryo rescue		
	Resistance to brown planthopper	IRRI	Germplasm
Potato	*Anther culture*		
	Haploid plantlets from pollen and production of homozygous tetraploids	CIP and ENEA (Italy)	Distribution
	Electrophoresis		
	Phanerograms to verify duplicate accessions in potato gene bank	CIP and University of Braunschweig (Germany)	Germplasm

In-vitro propagation

Induction of *in-vitro* plantlets	CIP	Distribution

Meristem culture/thermotherapy

Virus/viroid elimination	CIP	Distribution ·
In-vitro use of chemotherapy and thermotherapy	CIP and Cornell University (New York)	Distribution

Monoclonal antibodies

Detection of viruses Y, A and leaf roll	CIP and Swiss Federal Agricultural Research Station	Testing

Nucleic acid diagnostic probes

Potato spindle tuber viroid (PSTV)	CIP and USDA	Testing
cDNA probes for virus detection	CIP and North Carolina State University	Testing

Protoplast fusion

Transfer of mitochondria-coded male-sterility traits	CIP and Weizman Institute of Science (Israel)	Breeding

RFLP mapping

Construction of a molecular map for use in introgressive backcrossing	CIP and Cornell University	Breeding

Somaclonal variation

In-vitro selection for salt and drought tolerance in wide crosses	CIP and ENEA (Italy)	Germplasm, prebreeding

Transformation

Insertion of synthetic genes to increase amino-acid production in tubers	CIP and Louisiana State University (LSU)	Breeding (added-value)
Resistance to leaf roll virus and PSTV through anti-sense constructs	CIP and LSU	Breeding
Resistance to fungal and bacterial diseases	CIP and LSU	Breeding

Cassava	*Electrophoresis* Germplasm characterization *in situ* and *ex situ*	CIAT and University of Manitoba	Germplasm
	In-vitro conservation Clonal depository, in-vitro gene bank	CIAT	Germplasm
	Somatic cell culture Regeneration through embryogenesis from leaf cell culture	CIAT, IITA	Breeding
	Shoot-tip culture/thermotherapy Elimination of viral and bacterial diseases	CIAT	Distribution
	Anther/microspore culture Achieving homozygozity to express recessive traits	CIAT	Breeding
	Transformation Insertion of synthetic genes to increase selected amino-acid production	CIAT and LSU	Breeding (added-value)
	Insertion of viral coat protein to confer virus resistance	CIAT	Breeding
Sweet potato	*Embryo rescue* Crosses of sweet potato cultivars with wild *Ipomoea* species	CIP	Germplasm
	In-vitro conservation Clonal depository for over 1,500 clones	IITA	Germplasm
	Monoclonal antibodies Indexing of viral diseases	CIP	Distribution
	Nucleic acid diagnostic probes Detection and characterization of viruses	CIP	Testing
Plantain/ cooking bananas	*Embryo rescue*	IITA	Breeding
	In-vitro conservation	IITA	Germplasm
	Micropropagation	IITA	Distribution
	Somaclonal variation	IITA	Breeding

Legumes	*Electrophoresis* Characterization of storage proteins in wild relatives of chickpea, lentils	ICRISAT	Germplasm
	ELISA Detection of groundnut viruses, aflaxotin B	ICRISAT	Testing
	Embryo rescue Wide hybridization in groundnut, chickpea, pigeonpea	ICRISAT	Germplasm
Common beans	*Electrophoresis* Germplasm characterization using phaseolin and isoenzymes	CIAT	Germplasm
	Gene pool relations and evolution	CIAT	Germplasm
	Screening resistance to bruchids	CIAT	Breeding
	Embryo rescue *P. vulgaris* x *P. acutifolius* crosses	CIAT	Germplasm
	RFLP mapping Resistance to bacterial blight	CIAT	Breeding
	Somatic cell culture Plant regeneration from cell suspensions Plant regeneration from callus culture	CIAT	Breeding
Cowpea	*Embryo rescue* Resistance to insects	IITA	Breeding
	Monoclonal antibodies Virus strain detection	IITA	Testing
	Somaclonal variation *In-vitro* screening for tolerance to aluminium and cold	IITA	Breeding
	Transformation Insertion of genes for resistance traits	IITA	Breeding

Efficient plant regeneration from tissue cultures had been achieved for most major crop species. All IARCs working on root crop species had obtained cell cultures from them and their rapid multiplication *in vitro*.

Somaclonal variation, e.g. at the IRRI, had the following objectives:
– plant regeneration from long-term calli;
– incorporation of salt and aluminium tolerance into modern rice varieties through *in-vitro* selection;
– identification of salt- and aluminium-tolerant variants;
– improvement of agronomic characteristics of local rice varieties.

Two somatic cell culture lines from an *indica* rice variety, selected from 125 lines in yield trials, were compared with the parent in advanced yield tests and screened for resistance to pests and diseases. One line had a significantly higher yield and greater resistance to rice tungro virus than the parent (Plucknett and Cohen, 1989).

At the CIAT, co-operative work of the Biotechnology Research Unit and the Tropical Pastures Programme resulted in the identification of a wide range of variability in the progeny of the forage legume *Stylosanthes guyanensis* regenerated from leaf-derived callus cultures. In addition to high rates of polyploidy, somaclonal variation in tissue culture was found for such traits as growth habit, anthracnose resistance, seed production, chlorophyll deficiency and leaf morphology (Plucknett and Cohen, 1989).

Disease and virus freeing relied on thermotherapy (heat treatment) and shoot-tip culture, but thermotherapy did not eliminate most viruses, but it could reduce virus multiplication and translocation in plants. In some cases, higher temperatures increased infectivity and, in others, low-temperature treated plants showed evidence of some viroid elimination.

Regarding chemotherapy, work at the CIAT with the nucleotide analogue, virazole, produced promising results. With cassava, virazole was far more phytotoxic to sand-grown cuttings than *in-vitro* cultures; consequently, large shoot tips were cultured in media containing 40 ppm virazole; after 30 days, the terminal bud was taken from each culture to be grown in virazole-free media, and frog-skin virus disease-free plants were recovered. The IITA evaluated the efficiency of using virazole in eliminating yam mosaic virus, in comparison with heat treatment: yam meristems with one-two leaf primordia were grown on culture media containing virazole (5–20 ppm) for two to three months and thereafter transferred to culture media without virazole for further growth and development (Plucknett and Cohen, 1989).

Most common indexing methods involved one or more of the following procedures: sap inoculation, serology, aphid transmission, graft transmission, electron microscopy and enzyme-linked immunosorbent assays (ELISA). Agricultural diagnostics based on biotechnologies included monoclonal antibodies, nucleic acid probes and biosensors. Of several monoclonal antibody test methods, the enzyme-linked immunosorbent assay, or ELISA, was commonly used in agriculture, in particular for spotting a pathogen or a disease in its early stages. The use of nucleic acid probes and biosensors was moving out of the research laboratories of industrialized countries. One application had been in the field survey of coconut diseases in the Philippines and Pacific Island States; one of their great drawbacks was their reduced sensitivity (Miller and Williams, 1990; Smits, 1992).

Agricultural diagnostics were being used to detect specific nucleic acid sequences or specific gene products, so as to accelerate progeny selection following hybridization or other gene transfer operations. Furthermore, the detection of pathogens in plant tissues could be useful in breeding for resistance, e.g. to screen varieties resistant to viruses from those sensitive to them. Diagnostics could facilitate the identification of pathogens, elucidation of the relationships between these pathogens in different hosts and/or in different locations (Smits, 1992).

The availability of rapid and accurate means of detecting plant pathogens in plant tissues or seeds would make quarantine measures more efficient. They could be used in detecting viruses and bacteria in vegetative propagation material of such crop species as cassava, white potato, sweet potato and yams, in grain legume seeds, cereals and oil seeds. The rapid detection of mycelium in seedling tissues could accelerate tests on the efficacy of seed treatment (e.g. diseases like smuts and bunts in cereals, which were seed-borne, but which did not induce symptoms for a long time after the seeds were sown) [Smits, 1992].

Agricultural diagnostics could also be used in seed certification services, i.e. for selecting high-quality planting material; to monitor pathogen occurrence in soil (e.g. in the USA, diagnostic kits had been developed to determine the density of *Phytophthora* in the soil so as to indicate to growers whether soil treatment was necessary); in crop management, through the accurate knowledge of the occurrence, density and spread of pathogens, thus enabling farmers to make appropriate decisions concerning control measures (Smits, 1992).

In the developing countries, diagnostics developed in the industrialized countries against similar pathogens (e.g. *Fusarium, Rhizoctonia, Phytophthora*) could be used directly, or with some adaptation to environmental conditions. They could, however, experience the following difficulties in relying on these diagnostics:

– lack of investment in the diagnostic sector and of appropriate manufacturing equipment and highly trained manpower;

– the specificity of some plant pathogens in the developing countries made local development of diagnostic kits compulsory, which entailed necessary, often lacking inputs (e.g. the African cassava mosaic virus, the maize streak virus, the wheat karnal bunt fungus *Neovissa indica* and several downy mildews of the *Sclerospora* and *Peronosclerospora* genera);

– effective follow-up to the diagnosis, i.e. treatment of the disease and control measures could raise problems due to the lack of funding and expertise;

– the need to adapt diagnostics developed in industrialized countries to tropical environments (e.g. higher temperatures, higher dust amounts and lower availability of refrigerated storage) [Smits, 1992].

In addition to buying diagnostic kits (when they had the means to do so) from private specialized biotechnology corporations (e.g. Agri-Diagnostics Associates, Cinnaminson, New Jersey) or multinationals, developing countries could rely on assistance from the International Agricultural Research Centers and some research centres in developed countries whose work was geared toward tropical agriculture.

At the ICRISAT, nucleic acid hybridization techniques were used to diagnose isolates of peanut clump disease because serological techniques proved unreliable. The work was carried out at the Scottish Crops Research Institute using ^{32}P-labeled complementary DNA, a technique enabling detection of picogrammes of clump RNA. At the CIP, recombinant DNA technology had replaced electrophoresis as the standard method for identifying the potato spindle tuber viroid (PSTV). The technique developed in co-operation with the U.S. Department of Agriculture (Beltsville) allowed detection of a trillionth gramme of viroid RNA. A letter-size piece of nitrocellulose membrane which could accommodate up to 100 plant samples was mailed by the CIP to a developing country for spotting of samples and then returned to the CIP. The samples were hybridized with a ^{32}P-labeled DNA probe and hybrids were detected by autoradiography. Results could be cabled to the sample source in the developing country. DNA probes were used in virus detection for both potato and sweet potato. At the IRRI, non-radioactive (biotin-labeled) probes were used for identification and early detection of pathogens, namely the rice blast fungus (*Pyricularia oryzae*) and bacterial blight (*Xanthomonas campestris* pv. *oryzae*). At the IRRI also, species-specific DNA probes were developed to follow the introduction of DNA from wild species into cultivated rice varieties.

The International Board for Plant Genetic Resources (IBPGR), in collaboration with the Queensland Department of Primary Industries, Australia, had worked on the development of a DNA probe for banana bunchy-top virus that detected the pathogen in crude sap of infected plants (Plucknett and Cohen, 1989).

Meristems and shoot tips provided the greatest security against genetic instability during *in-vitro* conservation. Cryopreservation offered the most security in long-term storage of germplasm. It was applied to meristems, zygotic and somatic embryos, suspension cultures of a number of species, and the method was expected to be applied to any materials held as *in-vitro* cultures. Experiments had proved successful for two-year storage of potato and chickpea. The technique required a liquid nitrogen refrigerator and reliable supply of coolant. At the CIAT, the feasibility of cryopreservation had been demonstrated through a collaborative project with the Plant Biotechnology Institute, Saskatoon, Canada, and with the IBPGR (Plucknett and Cohen, 1989).

The principles of *in-vitro* inoculation could be adopted in field collection of germplasm. The IBPGR had tested the idea for cocoa using a fungicide and water purifying tablets to surface sterilize explants, and inoculation into tubes of culture medium containing fungicides and antibiotics. The technique was also used for avocado and cotton. In a joint IBPGR/IRHO[4] (see p.348) project in Côte d'Ivoire, an *in-vitro* collecting approach for coconut was developed; in this case, excised embryos with or without a plug of endosperm were inoculated in the field; within the three-year time-span of the original project, it had been possible to apply this method during a coconut germplasm collecting mission in Indonesia (Plucknett and Cohen, 1989).

Quarantine regulations permitted only clean germplasm to be moved internationally. It was easier to satisfy these phytosanitary regulations through the use of disease-free tissue cultures in test tubes, particularly with respect to viruses.

Notes

1. The IFPRI, which was part of the Consultative Group on International Agricultural Research (CGIAR), was set up in 1975 to identify and analyze policies aimed at meeting the food needs of the developing countries. The motivation for its establishment was the need to respond to the mounting criticism of the technological bias of the 'green revolution'. The mandate of the IFPRI, therefore, included not only technology issues, but also health, gender and other socio-economic issues. Half of IFPRI's funding was provided by the CGIAR, the other half being contributed by the individual CGIAR donors, for which funds the IFPRI had to compete with the other IARCs. Besides autonomous research on food-related issues, the IFPRI initiated research projects (System-Wide Initiatives) in order to increase the collaboration with the other IARCs and with the National Agricultural Research Systems (NARSs).

2. The ISNAR had prepared a manual (*Biosafety*) offering guidelines for research managers on the safe use of biotechnologies in developing countries. The manual dealt with biosafety from different perspectives and suggested a series of steps for setting up national biosafety systems, starting with local committees for establishing policies and procedures. The manual assigned maximum importance to utilization of human resources in national institutions through five main principles: regulatory review; identifying the risks *per se* of biotechnological products and not emphasizing the process whereby they were developed; process of review on the protection of health and the environment; regulatory requisites for advanced biotechnologies integrated into the global regulatory system (pesticides, quarantine), including the launching of new products; extent of understanding of the behaviour of organisms similar to that of transgenic organisms; flexible regulatory programmes capable of rapidly adapting and adopting the new knowledge and understanding of the product and technologies.

3. For instance, in February 1995, the French Centre for International Co-operation in Agricultural Research for Development (CIRAD) was approached by the Intermediary Biotechnology Service of the ISNAR to examine the feasibility of transferring biotechnologies concerning the commercial production of coffee vitroplants to Uganda (*CIRAD Information*, no. 50, 13 March 1995, p. 7).

4. Institut français pour les huiles et oléagineux, belonging to the French Centre for International Co-operation in Agricultural Research for Development (CIRAD), now part of the CIRAD's Department of Perennial Crops.

International Agricultural Research Centers and Institutes

1. Biotechnologies at the CIMMYT

In 1996, wheat and maize were the second and third most important staple foods in developing countries, both supplying about one-fourth of the populations' caloric intake. In the early 1990s, production of the various cereal crops was: 48.3% for rice, 22.6% for wheat, 19.4% for maize, 6.6% for sorghum and millets, and 3.1% for others. With an annual world production of more than 550 million tonnes, wheat occupied a unique position among the important grain crop species of the world. It was also the single largest commodity traded in the world, accounting for more than 40% of the total world export market.

In Africa, per capita cereal production had fallen since the 1970s, and consumption of millet, sorghum, root and tuber species was declining. Most African governments initially responded to the growing food deficit by importing increasing amounts of cereals, primarily wheat and rice, either commercially or through food aid[1] (see p.509). Nigeria, for instance, placed a full ban on wheat imports in 1987, resulting in an increase in local wheat production from 50,000 tonnes to an estimated 90,000 tonnes in 1990. However, this was produced under relatively favourable and irrigated conditions (Komen, 1992*a*).

Maize was the world's third staple crop species in terms of production, with 502 million tonnes produced in 1995. The USA accounted for more than one-third (38%) of global production, far ahead of the other five top producers: China (21%), Brazil (7%), Mexico (3%) and France (2%). As a block, the North's share was not a great deal bigger than the South's (58% to 42% between 1989 and 1991, according to the FAO).

According to the CIMMYT, 99% of the maize sown in industrialized countries in 1992 came from commercial hybrids. In the developing counrries, commercially-marketed maize seeds accounted for only 46% of the total maize sown. But the situation was more contrasted: in China, all marketed seed was of public origin and was publicly distributed; in other countries, such as Brazil, Kenya and Zimbabwe, a big share of commercial hybrids were of public origin. As an average, multinational corporations accounted for nearly 34% of all commercial maize sales in developing countries, excluding China.

The introduction of maize hybrids, especially commercial varieties, had led to the displacement of local varieties and the introgression of alien genetic material into local populations. For instance, only 20% of local varieties reported in Mexico in 1930 were still known. In the industrialized countries, even fewer maize varieties were available. Monocultures of maize hybrids were mainly derived from six inbred lines. As was the case for most widely grown crop species in industrialized countries, genetic uniformity was a major plague in maize production, as illustrated by the vulnerability of Pioneer Hi-Bred International, Inc.'s hybrid to the gray leaf spot disease. In 1996, drought conditions in Southern and Central USA created erosion conditions that had been characterized by climatologists as being worse than the Dust Bowl of the 1930s; and Pioneer Hi-Bred's best-selling maize variety, Pioneer 3394, was shown to be highy susceptible to this fungal disease. This variety held 15% of the maize market and the disease tended to become an epidemic due to the genetic uniformity of maize varieties (*Seedling,* the Quarterly Newsletter of Genetic Resources Action International – GRAIN, vol. 13, no. 3, October 1996, pp. 23–32).

Differences between industrialized and developing countries also existed with respect to the way maize was grown. In the former maize was grown in intensive, external input-led monocultures that might cover up to millions of hectares, as found in the U.S. 'corn belt'. In the latter countries, maize was cultivated in a high number of different agricultural systems, which included both monocultures and traditional systems based on intercropping with legumes such as beans, and other crop species like squash. But perhaps the biggest difference concerned the use of maize. In the North with the USA in the front line, it was mainly, and increasingly, used as a raw material for the livestock industry. In Central America, South America and Eastern and Southern Africa, it was the basis for food security for families and communities. Maize was the single most important U.S. crop species. According to the U.S. National Corn Initiative, maize generated

$20 billion in farm value and more than $4 billion in exports annually. However, only 1% to 3% of the crop was used for human domestic consumption. In contrast, 62% of maize was used for feed (for beef, pork, chicken and fish production) and 20% was exported to compete on international markets mainly as feed (*Seedling*, vol. 13, no. 3, October 1996, pp. 23–32).

With the aid of biotechnologies, maize was becoming a cheap, reliable and controllable raw material for all kinds of industrial applications. The fastest growing market was for high-fructose corn syrup, which replaced sugar as sweetener in soft drinks and many other food processes. Also widely used were maize ethanol and starch to finish paper and clothes. Up to 15% of the U.S. maize crop was used as a raw material for more than 3,500 products, and a great deal of research and development was being carried out to increase this proportion (*Seedling*, vol. 13, no. 3, October 1996, pp. 23–32).

Since the first hybrid maize was introduced in the market by Funks (now part of Novartis AG) in 1928, maize had been the most commoditized crop species. Ever since the introduction of high-yielding hybrids from crossing pure inbred lines, farmers using them had been obliged to purchase new seed for every planting season, because the seeds saved from the harvest did not retain the high-yielding traits of their parents. These *de facto* 'property rights' created the financial security which enabled the development of current big seed companies, most of which (with the exception of the leaders in the field, Pioneer Hi-Bred International, Inc. and De Kalb) were acquired by petrochemical and agrochemical corporations in the 1970s and 1980s. Nowadays, transnational corporations alone accounted for 56% of the hybrid maize seed sold in the industrialized countries, and 34% of all commercial maize seed sales in developing countries, according to the CIMMYT. Pioneer Hi-Bred International, Inc. alone was responsible for 46% of U.S. maize seed sales. The 1995 estimated sales of the top ten seed companies were: $1.5 billion for Pioneer Hi-Bred International, Inc., $900 million for Novartis AG, $500 million for Limagrain, $500 million for Seminis, $400 million for Cargill Inc., $300 million for KWS, $300 million for De Kalb, $300 million for Coopérative de Pau, $200 million for Zeneca plc and $200 million for Van der Have (*Seedling*, vol. 13, no. 3, October 1996, pp. 23–32).

In its drive to maximize hybrid sales, the seed industry had influenced maize research and development more than any other staple. This was especially true for industrialized countries where, according to the CIMMYT, only 20% of maize breeders worked in the public sector (compared to 65% or more in the developing countries). Another difference was that while hybrids were the only type of maize commercialized in the North, in the South 10% of the sales were of open pollinated varieties (OPVs), which allowed farmers to replant and further develop them (*Seedling*, vol. 13, no. 3, October 1996, pp. 23–32).

The challenge facing cereal research was to develop varieties adapted to a wide range of agricultural environments prevailing in tropical areas, especially to adverse soil and weather conditions. The principal limitations on wheat production in tropical areas were:

– diseases such as spot blotch (caused by the fungus *Helminthosporium sativum*), rust and *Fusarium*; spot blotch was the most widely distributed and major disease in warm and humid environments;

– abiotic stresses like heat and drought, and acid soils with associated aluminium toxicity; about a third of wheat acreage in the developing countries suffered from moisture stress, while acid soils occupied approximately one billion hectares in the tropics and subtropics (Komen, 1992*a*).

In 1943, acknowledgement by the Government of Mexico and the Rockefeller Foundation of the world-wide importance of wheat and maize co-incided with the launching of a joint research programme on these and other crop species. The origins of the International Maize and Wheat Improvement Center (CIMMYT), founded in 1966, dated back to this initial programme. By the mid-1960s, thanks to high-yielding wheat varieties produced by CIMMYT researchers, the needs of many Asian countries could be met. This was the origin of the 'green revolution' which culminated in the Nobel Peace Prize being awarded in 1970 to Norman Borlaug, a pioneer in wheat research at the CIMMYT.

The CIMMYT, which came under the CGIAR, aimed to reduce poverty by increasing both productivity and the sustainability of wheat and maize production systems in developing countries and thereby promoting food security among the poor.

In 1996, CIMMYT staff was made up of more than one hundred scientists from 40 countries and a further 600 support staff. While CIMMYT headquarters was located in Mexico, there were affiliated offices in another 16 developing countries and collaboration extended to 100 States world-wide. Its annual operating expenditures amounted to $22.4 million toward the end of the 1980s (Komen, 1990*a*). See also Sasson (1990).

The CIMMYT had five main research groups: maize, wheat, economics, natural resources and biotechnologies. About two-thirds of the scientific staff was employed at headquarters, while the rest was assigned to African, Asian and Latin American countries. Regional staff served as a crucial link with national programme specialists, because they participated in joint research, facilitated the exchange of improved germplasm and experimental results, and ensured that technologies developed at the CIMMYT corresponded to the needs of the countries concerned.

The CIMMYT set out to:

– develop wheat and maize varieties resistant not only to disease and pests but also to other adversaries;

– conserve and use wheat and maize genetic resources throughout the world;

– develop more sustainable wheat and maize production systems;

– implement research on the conservation of germplasm, economics, biotechnologies, crop physiology and ecosystem management;

– design more efficient research approaches;

– generate new scientific information;

– offer training at various levels;

– provide technical advisory services to a wide range of collaborators.

Among the most salient CIMMYT achievements, one could cite:

– more than 50 million hectares in low-income countries were sown with wheat varieties derived from CIMMYT germplasm, i.e. 70% of the whole area cultivated with wheat in the developing world (excluding China where at least 1 million hectares were sown with wheat derived from CIMMYT germplasm); in 1982, CIMMYT wheats developed by Borlaug and their offspring were grown on 125 million acres and the use of the dwarfism gene from the Norin 10 variety was having an important impact on the food supply of more than one billion people;

– almost all the original varieties developed during the 'green revolution' of the 1970s had been replaced by more productive varieties, which required little or no pesticide, due to the incorporation of durable resistance and the more efficient utilization of nutrients, water and solar energy;

– more than 13 million hectares (i.e. 50% of the total area devoted to improved varieties) were sown with maize varieties derived from CIMMYT work in temperate-climate zones of low-income countries;

– more than 5,000 researchers from all over the world had been trained at the CIMMYT;

– CIMMYT scientists had made numerous contributions to agricultural sciences, from designing practical research techniques to discovering the genetic basis of disease resistance in maize and wheat.

According to an IFPRI (International Food Policy Research Institute) Food Policy Report, published in September 1996, the U.S. economy gained at least $3.4 billion and up to $13.7 billion from 1970 to 1993 from the use of improved wheat varieties developed by the CIMMYT. Since the U.S. government support of wheat improvement research at the CIMMYT had amounted to less than $71 million since 1960, the country's investment amounted to less than 2 cents for every $100 of U.S. wheat production. The benefit/cost ratio for U.S. government support of the CIMMYT was as high as 190 to 1.

Together with the Commonwealth Agricultural Bureaux (CAB International), the CIMMYT published the *Wheat, Barley and Triticale Abstracts*, and *Maize Abstracts*.

Research under the CIMMYT Wheat Programme sought to improve the productivity and sustainability of the developing world's agricultural systems in which bread wheat, durum wheat, triticale and/or barley were major crop species. Bread wheat, especially spring bread wheat, was by far the most important of these species in developing countries and therefore received the bulk of CIMMYT attention and research resources. Yet, durum wheat, used mainly for making pasta, and triticale, a hardy man-made cross between wheat and rye, were now gaining favour in harsher environments and fed millions of people. Work related to barley was carried out in close collaboration with the International Center for Agricultural Research in Dry Areas (ICARDA).

CIMMYT research work, all of which was done in partnership with national wheat programmes and other centres of research excellence, focused on a dozen very large but relatively homogenous production environments. As the first link in the chain, genetic breeding research produced experimental varieties able to withstand the major production limiting factors existing in each of these environments (such as heat or drought, or prevalent diseases). National programme partners then took these varieties and refined them for more specific production zones in their own countries. CIMMYT agronomic research was currently being organized around a complementary set of large or mega-environments, and the Wheat Programme breeders and agronomists would soon begin to jointly test the suitability of new varieties and production techniques for these environments.

In 1996, the CIMMYT Wheat Programme involved 30 senior scientists, 19 of whom were based at CIMMYT headquarters in Mexico, with the remaining 11 outposted to various locations in Africa, Asia and Latin America. Staff at headquarters conducted most of their research in experiment stations located in Mexico, but this work was closely linked to the activities of outreach staff. The latter were assigned to the following six regional and two bilateral programmes:

- Turkey (winter and facultative wheat breeding);
- Uruguay (breeding wheat for high temperatures and long-production cycles);
- Syria (CIMMYT/ICARDA bread and durum wheat breeding programme for semi-arid areas);
- Ethiopia (agronomy, wheat breeding and pathology, networking);
- Zimbabwe (breeding and networking);
- Nepal (assistance to national research systems of South Asia, pathology and breeding);
- Bangladesh (agronomy);
- Bolivia (agronomy).

CIMMYT Wheat Programme concentrated on breeding for high-yield potential and resistance to the four main wheat diseases: stem rust, leaf rust, stripe rust and yellow dwarf virus. Research was also being carried out on improving environmental stress tolerance (drought, soil acidity), as well as resistance to other diseases striking wheat (spot blotch, karnal bunt, septoria, *Fusarium*). The CIMMYT had co-ordinated several research projects at institutes in developed and developing countries included in a programme financed by the United Nations Development Programme (UNDP) entitled Increasing wheat production in warmer and stressed environments, initiated in 1982. It aimed to develop wheat varieties tolerant to stress due to heat, drought and acid soils with associated aluminium toxicity, which were some of the most important constraints for wheat cultivation in the tropics. Some success had been achieved in developing varieties for acid soils and a wider base of rust resistance (Saunders, 1991; Jaffé and Rojas, 1994*a*).

Wheat germplasm conservation responsibilities were shared with the ICARDA, in charge of maintaining a base collection for durum wheat and wild relatives of wheat; the CIMMYT maintained a base collection for bread wheat and triticale (in the mid-1980s, triticale covered some 750,000 hectares in thirty countries). The wheat germplasm bank contained more than 60,000 accessions (Komen, 1990*a*).

The newer CIMMYT wheat varieties of the post-green revolution era had raised developing countries' yields by nearly 25% since the early 1970s, at a steady pace of about 1% annually. Over this same period, the area planted to these wheat varieties had also grown steadily, especially in rainfed regions, to the point where they were sown on over 50 million hectares, more than 70% of the total wheat area in the developing world, excluding China, and, even in China itself, at least one million hectares were planted to CIMMYT-related varieties. Over 80% of the hundreds of commercial spring bread wheat varieties released by national programmes in developing countries came directly from the CIMMYT, or had a CIMMYT parent.

To cite only one example of environmental impact, the CIMMYT-related wheats widely grown by Indian farmers today had prevented tremendous damage to the country's more vulnerable environments. Were India to produce its current wheat harvest using the technologies of thirty years ago, more than 40 million hectares of additional land would have to be brought into production.

The greater pest resistance built into the genome of modern wheat varieties helped protect the environment by reducing the need for pesticides. This enhanced genetic resistance, combined with greater tolerance to environmental stresses, such as poor soil fertility, soil toxicities and drought stress, had greatly increased the reliability of yields. Contrary to popular opinion, wheat genetic diversity on the farm had grown, rather than diminished since the early 1970s, thanks to the development and release of a high number of ever more genetically diverse commercial varieties.

Farmers were not the only beneficiaries of new wheat varieties and modern agronomy. In countries like India and Pakistan, the average real price of wheat had dropped steadily over the past 20 years, helping poor consumers (many of them urban dwellers) to stretch their meagre food budgets. Estimates of the rate of return on investment in national and international wheat research indicated that payoffs were to the order of 60%.

The Wheat Programme aimed to strengthen national research capabilities by providing training in Mexico to wheat breeders and to those specializing in milling and baking-quality research. The CIMMYT co-sponsored crop management research training courses at a regional training centre in Pergamino, Argentina. Visiting scientists were hosted for one to three months to work with Programme staff on projects of mutual interest. To provide training at a higher level, mid-career courses were being multiplied and upgraded for researchers from developing countries occupying more senior positions in national programmes.

At the present rate of some 90 million additional mouths to feed each year, the world population was projected to reach more than 8 billion by the year 2020. This was expected to fuel an explosive demand for wheat, projected to double by 2020. Wheat would become the number one cereal grain in the developing world in the next ten to fifteen years. Since there was little room to expand cultivated area, greater wheat production would have to come from higher yields. This demand could be met through genetic manipulation of wheat varieties and the development of more sustainable production systems. CIMMYT wheat researchers, in collaboration with many others, were developing strategies for breaking the yield barrier in wheat, and were focusing on agronomic practices that improved the efficiency with which soil nutrients and water were managed, while combining these practices with new varieties that were more efficient in the uptake and use of nutrients, water and solar energy. These varieties, better adapted to the new cropping systems, would produce both higher and more reliable yields.

The CIMMYT Maize Programme arose from a joint Mexico-Rockefeller Foundation project through which improved varieties and farming practices were developed and promoted in Mexico from 1943 to 1961. Among the notable achievements of the project was the collection, characterization and preservation of native maize seed from Mesoamerica. Beginning in 1966 and continuing through the 1970s, the CIMMYT Maize Programme had expanded the scope of its predecessor to an international scale, with the following key developments:

– setting up experiment stations in Mexico to represent the major maize growing ecosystems in developing countries;

– forming genetic pools of maize for the tropics;

– launching a world-wide network for testing and distributing experimental seed;

– locating scientists who focused on prevalent maize types or combating disease and pests in key maize-producing regions;

– conducting research to develop high-protein maize varieties known as 'quality-protein maize (QPM)'.

During the 1980s, hybrid maize research was initiated in response to the growing demand from CIMMYT partners.

The CIMMYT Maize Programme was divided into five subprogrammes: four focused on the major production ecosystems in developing countries; one concerned research on stress-tolerant maize; several additional sections, such as entomology, pathology and the germplasm bank, provided cross-Programme support for this work. Approximately two-thirds of Programme staff were based at CIMMYT headquarters and several research stations in Mexico. The remainder were based at regional offices throughout the developing world, where they conducted breeding and other research activities and served as CIMMYT contacts to national programmes.

In Mexico, the locations for the CIMMYT Maize Programme were: CIMMYT headquarters at El Batán (highland tropical), Ciudad Obregón, Sonora (property of the Mexican Government and the State Farmers' Association; tropical desert), Poza Rica, Puebla (lowland tropical) and Tlaltizapán, Morelos (subtropical).

The regional offices were located in: Guatemala City (hillside and lowland tropical maize systems of Central America and the Caribbean); Cali (maize varieties and hybrids for the arid savannas and hillsides of South America, Africa and Asia); Bouaké, Côte d'Ivoire (incorporation of streak virus-resistance into maize varieties adapted to lowland tropical areas of West Africa and dissemination of these varieties); Kumasi, Ghana (strengthening the research capability of the Ghanaian maize programme); Nairobi/Njoro (crop management to fully exploit the potential of improved germplasm for East Africa; crop management research training for the maize specialists of East and Southern Africa); Harare (development and dissemination of streak virus-resistant varieties and hybrids for Southern Africa); Bangkok (research on maize resistant to downy mildew, aimed at meeting the growing demand for improved varieties and hybrids for Asia; crop management research training for regional maize specialists).

The CIMMYT Maize Programme provided an array of experimental varieties, hybrids and inbred lines that were high yielding and able to overcome major hurdles to maize production in developing countries – including infertile or acid soils, drought, insect pests and disease. Maize, teosinte and tripsacum seed were freely available to researchers world-wide so as to reach as many farmers in the developing world as possible. The main means of distribution was an international testing programme in which experimental seed was sent to hundreds of co-operators in dozens of countries each year.

Research was being carried out on crop and natural resource management to improve productivity while sustaining natural resources in maize-based cropping systems. For instance, in Central America and the Caribbean, work aimed to refine and spread conservation tillage, residue management and the green manure cover cropping technique for hillside maize systems. Research goals in Southern Africa were to identify and solve soil fertility problems affecting the productivity of more than 5 million hectares of maize lands.

Knowledge and techniques were being generated to increase the effectiveness of research by CIMMYT scientists and their partners. Programme physiologists, for instance, had found that the ability to maintain synchronous male and female flowering under arid conditions was a reliable indicator in tropical maize of tolerance to late season drought. A CIMMYT maize physiologist was helping breeders in drought-prone East and Southern Africa to apply this finding to developing drought-tolerant varieties and hybrids. CIMMYT researchers were working with advanced institutes world-wide to test and apply crop modelling, geographic information systems, DNA marker-assisted selection, genetic transformation, etc.

At CIMMYT headquarters, training courses on crop improvement were offered for young researchers and for experienced scientists and research managers. Visiting scientist appointments and post-doctoral fellowships were also available. For crop management research, the Programme supported three courses intended for maize researchers in Thailand (for Asia), Kenya (for East and Southern Africa) and Brazil (for Latin America and Portuguese-speaking African countries). Finally, the CIMMYT offered a range of regional and international conferences, in-country workshops and short courses on selected topics.

The Programme included advisory services to national scientists on the planning and execution of their research programmes. CIMMYT partners were assisted in improving priority setting and financial management, implementing gender-informed research approaches and in using scarce resources efficiently by sharing activities and outputs with peers.

The CIMMYT Maize Programme contribution was reflected in more than half the improved maize seed released to farmers in developing countries over the past three decades. This included more than 400 maize varieties and hybrids sown on at least 13 million hectares and contributing an estimated 7% to maize harvests in the developing world each year. The value added from this seed was some 15 million tonnes of grain, enough to meet the annual maize needs of 270 million people.

Along with the International Plant Genetic Resources Institute (IPGRI), the CIMMYT was setting up a global network for maize genetic resources. In 1994, the CIMMYT's 11,322 maize accessions originated from 53 countries, in the following proportion: 31.1% from Mexico, 23.9% from various developing countries, 19.8% from Brazil, 7.6% from Uruguay, 4.9% from Ecuador, 4.2% from Guatemala, 0.4% from industrialized countries and 8.1% from unknown sources (GRAIN, 1994*b*). By making available on CD-ROM (compact disc, read-only memory) complete data for these accessions, the CIMMYT provided researchers in developing countries with means of obtaining useful germplasm. With funding from the Technical Centre for Agricultural and Rural Co-operation (CTA, Ede-Wageningen, the

Netherlands), the CIMMYT and CGNet Services (California, USA) had developed the software required to operate the data files on CD-ROM. Although it had cost $5,000 to manufacture the master disc, the price of copies was only $5–$10, depending on how many were made. In 1989–1990, an initial batch of 300 copies was produced, of which about a third were distributed by the CTA, along with disc readers, to selected developing countries (Komen, 1990*a*).

The CIMMYT Economics Programme generated information about how germplasm and management practices were being used and how they could be used more efficiently.

One on-going project safeguarding genetic diversity intended to clarify global trends in wheat germplasm diversity. By analyzing pedigrees and other data sources, researchers showed that international plant breeding programmes had not reduced genetic diversity in the major production areas of developing countries. In fact, several measures suggested that diversity had increased over time. Another project was exploring the prospects of on-farm improvement of maize landraces as a strategy for conserving maize diversity in farmers' fields. Researchers were determining whether this kind of improvement could provide sufficient incentives for farmers to conserve and grow landraces in the face of mounting economic pressures.

As effective agricultural policies and research strategies had a clear prerequisite, that of reliable estimates of supply and demand, the CIMMYT was refining its ability to develop supply scenarios by region and by crop. It was also evaluating and modifying global projection models developed in other advanced- research institutions.

The part of the CIMMYT Economics Programme devoted to technology assessment and forecasting helped to answer the following questions: What impact was a new technology likely to have by 2005 and beyond? How would that impact vary across regions? How did projected payoffs from germplasm research compare to those for crop management research? Targeted policy workshops would foster social changes that accelerated the adoption of improved practices. Partners in this initiative included the International Center for Tropical Agriculture, the International Food Policy Research Institute, the International Potato Center and various National Agricultural Research Systems.

CIMMYT economists were also helping to foster a productivity-enhancing, resource-conserving maize revolution in Africa. On-going research focused on policies that affected fertilizer availability and use, germplasm improvement from a user's perspective and the application of geographic information systems to reassessing maize production environments and research priorities.

A world-wide technology inventory for maize and wheat, extending to years 2000, 2010 and 2020, was being developed. Researchers were to assess the potential impact of those technologies across developing regions and across similar ecological, agricultural and social environments.

The Economics Programme was monitoring the diffusion of improved germplasm and clarifying its impact on the poor and on the environment and with respect to various gender issues. Case studies of maize seed industries, for instance, were clarifying paths by which public and private sectors could complement one another. In subSaharan Africa, researchers were identifying policy changes that would increase the use of inorganic fertilizers, thereby boosting food production and protecting the environment. In individual countries, CIMMYT economists had collaborated with local scientists to assess returns on maize and wheat research. Future work would monitor the diffusion of CIMMYT germplasm by region and across similar ecological, agricultural and social environments. Researchers would assess the impact of new technologies on farmers and on the environment. They would also address policy and institutional hurdles that prevented farmers from adopting new technologies.

By integrating information from the research topics outlined above, the CIMMYT Economics Programme had developed procedures for efficiently allocating maize and wheat resources, both on a global and regional basis. Future efforts would aim to develop models for setting research priorities at the institutional, programme and problem levels.

The CIMMYT Natural Resource Group did not function as a separate programme. Rather, it was a cross-cutting activity that supported and complemented the Maize, Wheat and Economics Programmes. Problems tackled by the Natural Resource Group included threats associated with resource degradation and untapped opportunities for environmentally-safe production gains. The Group had four inter-related objectives: overcoming resource-management problems, refining research methods, improving maize and wheat productivity, and strengthening national research programmes.

Administered by an independent group manager and funded from a separate budget, Natural Resource Group staff were in charge of developing research methods, conducting research and, most important, backstopping CIMMYT programme staff and their research partners as they addressed productivity and sustainability issues. The staff were linked to designated programme associates, who worked within established national programmes on issues with crucial natural resource components.

As resource degradation was reducing the productivity of South Asia's rice-wheat systems, with sobering implications for the 150 million farmers who depended for their livelihoods on this cropping sequence, the Rice-Wheat Consortium for the Indo-Gangetic Plains was striving to better understand and resolve the systems productivity and sustainability problems. Participants included national programmes from Bangladesh, India, Nepal and Pakistan (with China as an associate member), as well as universities and international institutions. The CIMMYT was leading work on land management and tillage, as well as on crop establishment; it also contributed to work on nutrient and water management and ecology.

Across Central America's hillsides, land degradation caused primarily by erosion affected 40%-50% of the agricultural area along these slopes. Productivity-enhancing, resource-conserving maize systems were one means of mitigating this problem, since the area devoted to hillside maize was three times the combined area devoted to other domestic food crop species. The CIMMYT was promoting the use of cover crops and conservation tillage (with crop residues as mulch) to reduce erosion, enhance moisture retention and improve soil fertility; farmers were being encouraged to adopt relevant new technologies. The CIMMYT's main partner was the Regional Maize Programme, a National Agricultural Research System-managed Central American research network. Other collaborators included the International Center for Tropical Agriculture, International Food Policy Research Institute, Inter-American Institute for Co-operation on Agriculture (IICA), Tropical Agriculture Research and Training Centre (CATIE), Central American Institute for Administration of Enterprises, Programme for Sustainable Agriculture in Central American Plains, Pan-American School of Agriculture, and several non-governmental organizations.

In Southern Africa, productivity would need to increase from about 1.1 tonnes of maize per hectare to 2.5 tonnes per hectare to meet food needs into the first quarter of the next century. At present, declining soil fertility prevented this kind of increase in the wetter agro-ecosystems and was a major handicap in semi-arid maize zones. Together with the Rockefeller Foundation, the CIMMYT had organized a research and extension network to overcome declining fertility. The network linked multidisciplinary groups in Malawi and Zimbabwe to their colleagues in Kenya, Mozambique and Zambia. Network members were developing technologies compatible with the socio-economic environment of small-holding farmers.

The Fourth Concertation Meeting between the CIMMYT and the French CIRAD, ORSTOM and INRA was held at CIMMYT headquarters from 24 to 26 April 1996. Several co-operative research topics were defined, such as natural maize resistance to viruses, genetic engineering of maize for insect and disease resistance, and tolerance of maize to acid soils and aluminium. One CIRAD researcher was secunded to the CIMMYT to work on sustainable agriculture involving conservation tillage systems and rainfed maize crops (*CIRAD Information*, no. 62, 23 May 1996, p. 5). In accordance with the terms of a contract signed with the CIMMYT, a synthetic gene coding for *Bacillus thuringiensis* toxin Cry1B was constructed by CIRAD researchers, i.e. it was modified to achieve its correct expression in the plant; it was to be incorporated into vectors used in transgenesis. A vector adaptable for different toxins and target plant species was developed for dicotyledonous species; it was used for transforming coffee plants and making them resistant to the insect *Perileucoptera coffeella*. A similar vector was being constructed for monocotyledonous species.

Biotechnology had been part of CIMMYT research since the early 1980s. Techniques at the time had included rescuing embryos resulting from 'wide crosses' involving maize or wheat and their wild relatives, and the use of antibodies to diagnose viral diseases in wheat. In the maize wide cross programme, emphasis was laid on crossing maize with *Tripsacum*, a wild maize relative with broad tolerance in extreme soil conditions and resistance to several leaf diseases and insect pests. The wheat wide cross programme focused on bread wheat improvement, through the incorporation of broad stress tolerance and disease resistance. The maintenance of several hundred inter-specific *Triticum* germplasm accessions was receiving substantial attention in connection with the breeding of durum and bread wheats (Bajaj, 1990; Komen, 1990*a*).

With the advent of DNA-marker technology and other advances in plant genome manipulation during the late 1980s, the CIMMYT began working with leading biotechnology groups and building specialized facilities at its headquarters in El Batán, Mexico. The latter was completed in 1990, at which time the CIMMYT established the Applied Biotechnology Laboratories (ABL). From the outset, the group had sought to: address immediate concerns of the crop research programmes; acquire and adapt useful products and techniques from advanced research; establish proper biosafety procedures and containment facilities; and transfer technologies to developing countries.

The Applied Molecular Genetics Laboratory (AMGL) evaluated and adapted marker techniques for the molecular characterization of plant, pathogen and pest genomes and for tagging chromosome segments associated with traits of interest. The AMGL focused on multigene traits, such as insect resistance and drought tolerance in maize or durable rust-resistance in wheat, in collaboration with CIMMYT crop programmes. Its achievements included the adaptation of non-radioactive marker detection, the refinement of marker techniques for long-scale analyses, the development of detailed cost structures for marker experiments, and the creation of software to support all aspects of such experiments.

The CIMMYT had developed marker-assisted breeding programmes in maize for drought tolerance (Visser, 1994*a*). RFLP-markers for wheat[2] (see p. 510) were identified at Cornell University, Ithaca, New York. Sponsored by the International Triticeae Mapping Initiative[3] (see p. 510), Pioneer Hi-Bred International, Inc. and CIMMYT, a three-week training workshop was organized at CIMMYT headquarters from 14 October to 1 November 1996 on the techniques and applications of genome mapping of wheat and maize. The audience included geneticists, plant breeders, graduate students and post-doctoral scientists wishing to apply these techniques in their own institutions. The workshop included lectures and hands-on exercises in DNA analysis using non-radioactive RFLP (restriction fragment length polymorphism), microsatellite and AFLP (amplified fragment length polymorphism); molecular and field data collection, verification and analysis using current statistical tools; and the use of molecular data for marker-assisted selection of simple and complex agronomic traits.

Breeding disease resistance in wheat was also supported by the use of wide hybridization and double haploid line production. At the CIMMYT, resistance to spot blotch and *Fusarium* was being transferred from several wild wheat relatives to cultivars, through wide hybridization. Also, Canadian researchers were working on the transfer to wheat cultivars of resistance to the leaf spot complex. The latter included *Septoria nodorum* blotch, tan spot and *Septoria tritici* blotch. Tests conducted at the University of Saskatchewan in central and northern Saskatchewan showed that yield losses in spring wheat averaged almost 15% annually. Occurrence of this disease complex had increased throughout the prairies in recent years, owing to reduced tillage, which left more infected crop debris – and thus greater inoculum potential – on the soil surface than did conventional tillage systems (Hughes, 1995).

Septoria nodorum was the target of on-going research at the Crop Development Centre of the University of Saskatchewan. Research had confirmed crop rotation as one partial means of control. It had also identified a type of resistance which was effective in adult plants but could be determined in seedling tests. In 1993, field tests at Saskatoon revealed that wheat lines with this resistance showed a 5%-8% yield loss as compared to 31% in the susceptible check. This resistance showed lesion development and spore production, thus delaying the rate of both leaf damage and disease spread through the crop. In addition to common wheat, it also occurred in wild and cultivated tetraploid and diploid wheats (Hughes, 1995).

Genetic studies had identified two genes for resistance and determined their chromosomal location. Additional resistance genes had been found but their relationship to these two genes was yet to be defined. The resistance genes were being used in the Crop Development Centre wheat programmes to develop leaf spot-resistant wheat cultivars through identifying suitable molecular markers for them (Hughes, 1995).

At the Brazilian National Research Centre for Wheat (EMBRAPA/CNPT), anther culture was applied for the production of haploid lines derived from crosses between wheat and a wild relative belonging to the genus *Aegilops*. Poor regeneration rates of wheat plants from anther cultures was the major limiting factor. They also hampered the regeneration of transgenic wheat plants either from transformed tissues or protoplasts.

Wheat had been a target for genetic engineering since the first demonstration of successful gene transfer in dicotyledonous species in the mid-1980s. Progress toward wheat transformation remained disappointingly slow because of two major hurdles:

– finding an alternative method of gene delivery into wheat target cells, since wheat had proved recalcitrant to both *Agrobacterium-*mediated transformation, routinely used for dicotyledonous species, and protoplast gene transfer; and

– developing efficient plant regeneration systems for recovery of fertile plants from transformed wheat cells.

In 1985, the Plant Biotechnology Institute (PBI) of the National Research Council Canada, located in Saskatoon, committed itself to improving cereal crops, especially wheat and barley, using biotechnological means. The Cereal Biotechnology Group had been created as part of the then Cell Technology Section, under the leadership of Kartha. Initial efforts were directed at establishing suitable plant regeneration protocols from various explants for use in biotechnological manipulations. The production of genetically-engineered wheat and other cereals had been given a boost in 1989 with the acquisition of a Du Pont's biolistics particle gun as a means of delivering DNA directly into cells and organized tissues which could be regenerated into complete plants. Subsequently, considerable time was spent constructing suitable vectors for gene expression in cereal cells and establishing the best conditions for efficient delivery and expression of foreign genes in wheat and barley cells and tissues. This work resulted in the production of stably transformed cell lines carrying various marker genes (*Plant Biotechnology Institute – PBI- Bulletin*, Saskatoon, May 1993, pp. 1–3).

In 1993, the Cereal Biotechnology Team successfully produced fertile transgenic wheat plants carrying various marker genes. The key to this research breakthrough was the development of an enhanced regeneration system (ERS) with the capacity to produce high numbers of somatic embryos and plants within a short period. This transformation technology had been used by the team to incorporate three marker genes driven by different promotors into the wheat genome. The marker genes were:

– the *gus* gene coding for beta-glucuronidase activity, which could be scored by the presence of a characteristic blue colour in the transformed cells and tissues when incubated with an appropriate substrate;

– the *npt II* selectable marker gene encoding neomycin phosphotransferase activity, which conferred resistance to antibiotics;

– a *bar* gene encoding phosphinothricin acetyltransferase which inactivated the commercial non-selective broad-spectrum herbicide Basta, thus conferring on transgenic wheat plants resistance to the application of this herbicide (*PBI Bulletin*, Saskatoon, May 1993, pp. 1–3).

The explants used for ERS were bombarded with DNA-coated gold particles and selected either on media containing antibiotics or the active ingredient of the herbicide to recover fertile transgenic plants. The transgenic nature of primary regenerants (Ro plants) was confirmed by analyzing functional enzyme activity in leaf tissues using enzymatic assays and localized topical applications of herbicide. The integration of marker genes into wheat genomic DNA was confirmed. Analysis of R1 progeny plants obtained from self-pollination of Ro plants also confirmed the Mendelian inheritance of introduced genes. Further evaluation of these plants in successive generations was performed, lines of transgenic wheat being field-tested in 1994 at various locations in Western Canada and the USA. Two other laboratories in the USA and one in Germany had reported genetic transformation of wheat. This transformation technology was used to incorporate Roundup resistance into commercial Canadian wheat cultivars in collaboration with Monsanto's researchers. The technology also provided an opportunity to introduce genes for other value-added agronomic traits, such as insect and disease resistance, stress tolerance and the modification of nutritional quality of Canadian wheat varieties (*PBI Bulletin*, Saskatoon, May 1993, pp. 1–3).

Vasil *et al.* (1993), at the University of Florida, Gainesville, succeeded in transforming wheat cells belonging to calli that could be maintained more than two years and could regenerate wheat plantlets. Protoplasts derived from these calli were bombarded with particles and glyphosate-resistant plantlets (containing also the *gus* marker gene) had been obtained, as well as Basta-resistant transformed wheat plants.

The Applied Genetic Engineering Laboratory (AGEL) focused on inserting and obtaining expression, in maize and wheat, of useful DNA segments from other organisms. The group had identified elite maize and wheat lines from which single cells could routinely be regenerated in whole plants, a prerequisite for genetic transformation. Research in wheat and tropical maize involved genes for resistance to insect pests and to fungal and viral pathogens. Attention was given to the inheritance and stability of transferred genes and to the efficiency of transformation procedures. In collaboration with the University of Illinois, the CIMMYT developed a transforming DNA technique for incorporating small segments of alien DNA into maize.

The Applied Molecular Biology Laboratory (AMBL) was in charge of acquiring and developing new gene constructs for transformation research, monitoring inserted genes in transformed plants, DNA sequencing and synthesis, and advising on the development of PCR (polymerase chain reaction)-based markers for selection.

In August 1986, the CIMMYT initiated an International Collaborative Network on Maize Biotechnology involving public and private sector institutions from both industrial and developing countries[4] (see p. 512). The network promoted the use of RFLP markers in maize breeding as a selection tool. In Europe, in addition to those universities and public research institutes participating in the network, the following companies were committed in France, Germany, the Netherlands and Italy respectively: Limagrain[5] (see p. 514), Kleinwanzlebener Saatzucht (KWS) AG, van den Have and AMI. In developing countries, the following institutions were involved in the maize RFLP network: CINVESTAV (Centre for Advanced Research and Studies) at Irapuato, Mexico, for the construction of a restriction fragment length polymorphism (RFLP) map for maize; EMBRAPA (Empresa Brasileira de Pesquisa Agropecuária, Brazilian Agricultural and Livestock Research Enterprise). Furthermore, the CIMMYT was striving to broaden the network to include American institutions and private corporations, such as Agrigenetics Corporation and Pioneer Hi-Bred International, Inc.[6] (see p.514) (Komen, 1990*a*).

Releasing new higher-yielding hybrid varieties[7] (see p.516) would not be enough to increase crop production in order to match the growing food needs of developing countries; these varieties would continue to represent a prohibitive investment for most farmers from these countries. According to the FAO, the cost of a kilogramme of hybrid seed could be as high as $4, when 20 kg to 30 kg were needed to sow one hectare, while the annual income of an African farmer was about $100 (Savidan, 1995). One solution to this problem might be the transfer of apomixis to the new hybrid varieties.

In 1965, ORSTOM (French Scientific Research Institute for Development in Cooperation) researchers initiated a programme of genetic improvement of Guinea grass (*Panicum maximum*), the challenge being how to improve through crossings a plant species which apparently never crossed in natural conditions? Guinea grass is an aposporic species, i.e. a new plant is derived from a non-reproductive cell (a cell from the tissue that feeds the ovule, or nucelle). This type of apomixis (i.e. non-sexual reproduction via seeds, where the seeds give rise to plants which are identical to their mother plant), as well as the diplosporic type (where a new plant is derived from a reproductive cell that does not achieve its normal division) found in *Tripsacum*, close wild relatives of maize, are finally similar to cloning. The choice of Guinea grass, a weed difficult to eradicate, was a good one and the collections made in East Africa showed that while sexually-derived plants were all diploid, the apomictic ones were all polyploid. Crossing these plants led to a very surprising result with major impact: apomixis seemed to be governed by a single gene. This simple genetic control was thereafter confirmed in other species, such as a buttercup of temperate regions and two other tropical grasses (Savidan, 1995).

On the basis of these results, other research programmes were launched such as the *Brachiaria* programme, carried out since 1986 by the ORSTOM and Brazilian Enterprise for Agriculture and Livestock Research (EMBRAPA). This is the most important fodder grass present in tropical countries throughout Africa and Latin America. More than 30 million hectares were cultivated in Brazil with one apomictic variety belonging to the species *Brachiaria decumbens*, for which no sexual form was known and consequently no genetic improvement was feasible. In addition to the research project carried out by the ORSTOM and EMBRAPA under the European Commission's Science and Technology Development programme (STD-3), the Brazilian institution was pursuing its research on Guinea grass and two varieties were released: Tanzania-1 in 1990 and Mombasa in 1993 (Savidan, 1995).

Results obtained from the Guinea grass programme led a U.S. team to launch, in 1985, a new programme aimed to transfer apomixis to wheat. Moreover, the ORSTOM signed an agreement with the CIMMYT in 1986 which led three years later to a project meant to transfer the apomixis gene to maize from its wild relative *Tripsacum dactyloides*. The apomictic hybrid, obtained from a single cross between a sexually-derived plant and an apomictic plant (of which the pollen was used), would be immediately fixed. The achievement would open the way, in developing countries, to local selection of improved varieties, better adapted than those which are nowadays selected in a single research centre for a whole region or even a continent (Savidan, 1995).

Wheat, sorghum, millet and maize had apomictic relatives, but it was with maize that the experience of hybrids between a cultivated plant species and its wild relatives was the widest: since 1931, numerous hybrids between maize and *Tripsacum* had been produced, mainly to try to elucidate the mystery of maize origin. In Mexico, it is possible to grow maize all the year round; consequently, crosses and backcrosses could be made throughout the year; furthermore, apomixis of *Tripsacum* was easy to identify in both the wild plants and hybrids (maize and *Tripsacum*). A series of crosses and backcrosses were carried out with a view to gradually eliminating all the chromosomes of the wild species and to keeping only the part of the genome which carried the apomictic trait (Savidan, 1995).

Maize has 20 chromosomes and the apomictic *Tripsacum* 72 chromosomes. The F1 generation resulting from the first cross had 46 chromosomes (10 from maize and 36 from *Tripsacum*); 1,200 F1 hybrids were produced between 1990 and 1992; some of these perennial plants were still in production after four years. The following backcross led to a collection of 3,000 plants which were in production between the end of 1992 and mid-1994; the plants had 56 chromosomes (20 from maize and 36 from *Tripsacum*). A dozen of haploid offspring were produced in 1993 and 1994 from the first backcross; they contained 28 chromosomes (10 from maize and 18 from *Tripsacum*). By early 1995, 1,700 apomictic plants were field grown as a result of a third backcross and they had 38 chromosomes (20 from maize and 18 from *Tripsacum*). In April 1995, 28 plants were produced as a result of a fourth backcross; they contained between 22 and 34 chromosomes (20 from maize and the rest from *Tripsacum*); their reproduction was being studied using molecular markers of apomixis (Savidan, 1995).

Molecular genetics was playing a crucial role in this work, from gene maps of crop species and markers that could ascertain the presence or absence of the gene at an early stage, to transposons for isolating the apomixis gene in *Tripsacum*. Four markers linked to apomixis were identified; they enabled the researchers to know at a very early stage of the hybrids resulting from the fourth backcross whether the plant contained the *Tripsacum* chromosome bearing the apomictic gene. The identification of markers specific to each of the remaining 18 chromosomes of *Tripsacum* would allow the determination of those present in each hybrid resulting from the fourth backcross. When combining this marker technique and *in-situ* hybridization, one could recognize in a hybrid with 21 chromosomes the additional chromosome and, then in the offspring of this plant, whether recombinant forms were produced. It was thus becoming possible to know and quantify the exchanges between chromosomes belonging to the wild and cultivated plant genomes (Savidan, 1995).

Another technique, particular to maize, which could be transferred to other species, used *Mu* transposons in order to mark and isolate genes of interest within the cultivated species. About 100 genes had been isolated in this way. These *Mu* transposons had the property of being incorporated throughout the genome, even far away from the point of origin. ORSTOM and CIMMYT researchers, because of the homology between maize and *Tripsacum*, were trying to induce the incorporation of these transposons from maize chromosomes onto *Tripsacum* chromosomes, the final objective being the incorporation of the apomictic gene(s). The latter would therefore change the reproduction modality in the apomictic hybrids. One could isolate the ADN fragment to which the transposon was incorporated, so as to isolate the apomixis gene (Savidan, 1995).

Other groups were working on apomixis:

– Hanna and colleagues of the U.S. Department of Agriculture Agricultural Research Service (Coastal Plant Experiment Station, Tifton, Georgia) were making substantial progress on introgressing apomixis into pearl millet;

– Miles and Tohme at the International Center for Tropical Agriculture (CIAT, Cali, Colombia) had made a breakthrough in mapping a gene or gene complex associated with apomixis in *Brachiaria*;

– in New Zealand, at the Crop and Food Research Institute, Christchurch, Bicknell had pioneered the use of the important model apomictic genus, *Hieracium*, to develop the necessary laboratory tools for studying and transferring apomixis, including genetic transformation, anther culture, tissue culture, transposon mutagenesis; in collaboration with Koltunow of the Commonwealth Scientific and Industrial Research Organisation (CSIRO) Division of Horticulture, Adelaide, strides were being made in molecular and cell biology of autonomous apospory – the most promising mechanism.

Australian researchers at the Commonwealth Scientific and Industrial Research Organisation (CSIRO) Division of Plant Industry, Canberra, were also working on the transfer of the apomictic trait from natural apomicts to related crop species. Their approach was to identify key components of apomixis in an experimentally more tractable system that also provided an opportunity to isolate the key genes. These genes could then be transferred to crop species to trigger the apomictic trait. This strategy was based on their earlier hypothesis that apomixis might be controlled by a simple genetic mechanism and there might be key regulatory control points in ovule development that were altered in apomictic plants, presumably by an untimely activation of the apomictic genetic programme, without any cue from sexual fertilization. They designed a genetic/morphological screen in *Arabidopsis* to detect mutants that formed seeds without fertilization (*fis*) and isolated several *fis* mutants. In the latter, several steps of seed development occurred without fertilization, including autonomous development of diploid endosperm cells, sporadic development of embryos up to the globular stage, and the development of seed in size and external morphology undistinguishable from those produced by pollination. Three independent mutants mapped in three different locations of the *Arabidopsis* genome; several other putative mutants were being characterized further, and map-based cloning was under way for mutants that had already been mapped.

The Center for the Application of Molecular Biology to International Agriculture (CAMBIA), Canberra, through its International Molecular Apomixis Project (IMAP), in which many of the researchers mentioned above were participating, was securing funding to carry this work forward; the FAO was working with CAMBIA in bringing together the necessary expertise in all fields to analyze possible outcomes and to shape future research, ownership and application.

Results achieved by the ORSTOM/CIMMYT team as well as by other research teams led to the establishment of an international network following an initiative by the ORSTOM which was publishing a newsletter circulated to some 300 researchers in 1996, with the support of the Rockefeller Foundation (Savidan, 1995).

The first international conference on apomixis was held at College Station, Texas, from 25 to 27 September 1995. It was attended by 125 scientists from 20 countries (five continents) and representatives of seven multinationals (e.g. Pioneer Hi-Bred International, Inc., Monsanto Co. and Limagrain), the FAO and Rockefeller Foundation. The French Scientific Research Institute for Development in Cooperation (ORSTOM) was the co-organizer and cosponsor of the conference with the University of Texas A & M. The conference took stock of the results obtained in the transfer of apomixis to a crop species and of the advances made in this respect by the ORSTOM team, International Center for Tropical Agriculture (CIAT, Cali) and University of Georgia, Tifton. It was also agreed that these three teams meet in January 1996 with the International Rice Research Institute at CIMMYT headquarters to design a major inter-institutional programme on apomixis that could start in 1997. A synthesis in two volumes on the state of knowledge and techniques, edited by Savidan (ORSTOM) and Carman (State University of Utah) was published by the FAO in 1996. Regular update on progress in apomixis could be found in the *Apomixis Newsletter.*

Triticale, a cross between wheat and rye, was already grown on arid and sandy soils in temperate climates. It was also cultivated in the arid tropics, mainly in China, Brazil and Tunisia. In these regions, triticale yields were unmatched by wheat, because of its broad disease resistance, tolerance to acid soils and drought, and its efficiency in assimilating available nutrients. Its good grain quality and high lysine content made it an interesting alternative to bread wheat (National Research Council, 1989; Komen, 1992a).

By the 1960s, the CIMMYT had initiated research on triticale. Embryo rescue was used to obtain primary hexaploid triticale, as well as intergeneric and interspecific hybrids. A spontaneous outcross of triticale with an unknown Mexican bread wheat resulted in a new triticale line, known as the Armadillo line, with several desirable traits, including improved yields and good nutritional quality. The crop variety was considered to be suitable for commercial production on a large scale. Triticale could be used to improve both wheat and rye because it could be backcrossed to either of its parents. For instance, rye genes were transferred from rye to wheat via triticale, thereby producing wheat cultivars that grew better in copper-deficient soils (Komen, 1992a).

2. Biotechnologies at the IRRI

Since its domestication 6,000 years ago (as witnessed by traces discovered in Thailand at Non NoK Tha, rice importance in human food had grown considerably. World-wide, rice was harvested on 148 million hectares, more than 10% of the Earth's arable land. Unlike wheat, 95% of the world's rice was being grown in less developed nations; cultivated mainly in Asia, the first consuming region, rice was there the staple food of more than half the world population. In 1995, its production – 550 million tonnes of paddy or 330 million tonnes of bleached rice – was superior to that of wheat (Galus, 1997).

Asian farmers tilled 90% of the world's harvested rice area and accounted for 92% of global rice production. In the humid and subhumid tropics, rice was the primary source of human caloric intake: in Bangladesh, Cambodia, Indonesia, Laos, Myanmar, Thailand and Viet Nam, rice provided 55% to 80% of the calories consumed daily.

In most Africa and Latin America, rice was less important. On average, rice contributed 10% or less of total caloric intake. But in Guinea, Guyana, Liberia, Madagascar and Sierra Leone, 29% to 50% of the caloric intake came from rice.

Rice production and consumption were often associated with low income and poverty. Of the 23 countries in the world that produced more than 1 million tonnes, almost half had a per capita income of less than $500 per annum. These were the countries categorized by the World Bank as 'least developed'. Globally, rice-consuming population was growing at 2% per year. In humid and subhumid Asia, where rice was the primary staple food, population was expected to increase by 18% during the 1990s, and by 58% over the next 35 years. Projections indicated a world rice food need of about 758 million tonnes in 2025 – 70% more rice than was consumed by the mid-1990s. In South Asia, where poverty was extensive, the food need for rice was expected to double over the next 40 years. Production needs could be expected to be even higher, to provide stocks, seed and non-food uses.

In most of Asia, rice was being grown on small, one to three-hectare farms. A typical Asian farmer planted rice primarily to meet family needs; less than half went to market and even that was mostly sold locally. In Brazil, 70% of paddy fields were in commercial farms of more than 50 hectares. International rice trade accounted for only 4% of world production, and was mostly in quality rice. For instance, Basmati, the high-quality, scented rice produced in Pakistan and Northwest India, commanded an international market price four times higher than the domestic price of the coarse local rice low-income people ate. Major exporters were Thailand (36% of the world market), the USA (19%), Viet Nam (10%) and Pakistan (7%). Australia, China, India and Uruguay each accounted for 1% to 3% of the market.

Most countries could not depend on imports to meet the food needs of their people. The world market was thin and volatile. For instance, if China wanted to meet just 10% of its domestic consumption through imports, the demand for rice in the world market would increase by more than 80%, and that would dramatically affect international prices. In addition, few countries had adequate foreign exchange for major international purchases.

Therefore, an important political objective in most rice-dependent countries was self-sufficiency in rice production, in order to maintain stable prices (in particular for rapidly increasing numbers of urban consumers). But variable natural contidions caused year-to-year shortages and surpluses, and that meant wide variation in the amount farmers could send to market. This also made domestic prices highly unstable. Price controls through maintenance of big stocks could benefit urban consumers, but often kept farm prices below a profitable level.

Scientists had incorporated many yield-stabilizing traits into modern rices: greater pest resistance, shorter crop duration, better grain quality. Improved varieties were being grown on more than 70% of paddy fields in Asia, 37% in Latin America and the Caribbean. Average yields had increased 72% and rice production had doubled since 1966. During the same period, populations in major rice-consuming countries had increased by 66%. It was estimated that at least 600 million people were being fed by the mid-1990s by the additional rice supplies made possible by diffusion of modern rice varieties.

Rice ecosystems were characterized by elevation, rainfall pattern, depth of flooding and drainage, and by the adaptation of the crop species to these agro-ecological factors:

– upland rice was seeded in non-flooded, well-drained soil on level to steeply sloping fields; crops suffered from lack of moisture and inadequate nutrition, and yields were very low; upland rice was being grown on about 19 million hectares world-wide, it was dominant in Africa and Latin America;

– rainfed lowland rice was transplanted or directly seeded in puddled soil on level to slightly sloping, bunded or diked fields with variable depth and duration of flooding, depending on rainfall; yields depended on rainfall, cultivation practices and use of fertilizer; rainfed lowland rice was being cultivated on 37 million hectares world-wide, it was dominant in the humid and subhumid tropics;

– flood-prone rice was directly seeded or transplanted in the rainy season on fields characterized by medium to very deep flooding (50 cm to more than 300 cm) from rivers and tides in river mouth deltas; soils cycled from dry to flooded and might have severe problems of salinity and toxicity; the crop grew as flood waters rose, with harvest after the floods receded; flood-prone rice was being cultivated on more than 10 million hectares, predominantly in South and South-East Asia;

– irrigated rice was transplanted or directly seeded in puddled soil on leveled, bunded fields with water control, in both dry and wet seasons in the lowlands, in the summer in higher elevations, and during the dry season in flood-prone areas. The crop was heavily fertilized and yields could reach 5 tonnes per hectare in the wet season, more than 8 tonnes per hectare in the dry season. Irrigated rice was being planted on 81 million hectares world-wide, accounted for 55% of the world's harvested rice area, and contributed 76% of global rice production. Irrigation agro-ecosystems in Asia were concentrated in the semi-arid and subhumid subtropics.

In the study entitled '*Vision 2020*', the International Rice Research Institute (IRRI) estimated that rice production would have to increase by 70% to meet the needs of world population in 2020 (about 8.5 billion people). In addition to boosting the production of rainfed rice land (18% of total rice land) and that of flooded rice (32% of total rice land), the IRRI focused on raising yields of irrigated rice. IRRI researchers therefore conceived a new Super-rice the expected yield of which was 15 tonnes per hectare, i.e. a 50% increase in the potential yield of rice varieties derived from the 'green revolution' (Galus, 1997).

With respect to rainfed rice, which was prevailing in Africa and South America, a number of specialists were of the opinion that it needed to be boosted rapidly and that South America where 230 million hectares of land and savannas could be sown with rice, might become the world rice granary. This would become a reality if risks associated with random rainfall could be minimized. Consequently, one of the breeders' objectives was to select drought-tolerant plants, as the same time as cultivation practices needed to be designed to stimulate the development of roots in depth. Potential yields were estimated at 4 tonnes per hectare (Galus, 1997).

Flooded rice covered an area in Asia equal to that of irrigated rice. Experts thought that its potential could be better exploited. Thus, Thailand, first leading exporter of rice, particularly scented rice, was producing three-quarters of its rice in flooded paddy land. Mastering water supply without substantially increasing production costs, e.g. through low-cost hydraulic systems, as well as the breeding of adapted rice varieties were supposed to give its full potential to flooded rice cultivation. This was being done in West Africa and Asia (Galus, 1997).

To meet future food needs, a 'double green' revolution was considered the appropriate solution by an increasing number of experts, i.e. a revolution that would impact on all types of rice cultivation and would be based on a greater sustainability and higher yields that would not harm the environment. In this respect, there was the unknown issue concerning China. This country, with almost 1.3 billion inhabitants (about 22% of the world population), had only 9% of arable land. Consequently, would China be food self-sufficient in the 21st century? In 1996, China produced 30% of world rice output and was meeting its needs. However, some analysts underlined that if China was to become deficitary, it would be almost impossible to meet its demand, owing to the strained rice market; rice surpluses represented only 3% to 5% of world production (Galus, 1997).

The International Rice Research Institute (IRRI) was established in 1960 by the Ford and Rockefeller Foundations with the approval and help of the Government of The Philippines.

The mandate of the IRRI focused not only on rice, but on virtually all rice-related activities. Conservation of germplasm, education and training, and information exchange were also important activities. The IRRI published about 25 scientific books annually and three major periodicals (e.g. the *International Rice Research Newsletter*). It had a scientific staff of approximately 120 and its total annual revenues amounted to some $47 million by the early 1990s, including $28 million for the core budget and $18.7 million of complementary funding.

Among the major achievements of the IRRI, one could cite:

– IRRI's Medium-Term Plan for 1994–1998 entitled Rice Research in a Time of Change;

– sixteen IRRI breeding lines had been named as varieties in nine countries, bringing the total number of IRRI breeding lines named as varieties throughout the world to 252;

– two IRRI-derived salt-tolerant cultivars identified by the Philippine Seed Board for release;

– IRRI Genetic Resources Center had become responsible for the international rice genealogy data-base; 2,900 records on crosses in the Republic of Korea and 18,000 hybrid records from Latin America had been added to the data-base;

– gene-bank collections had increased to 74,700 *Oryza sativa* samples, 1,330 *O. glaberrima* and 2,216 wild species; accessions of *Oryza sativa* were being distributed to more than 30 countries during biennial periods;

– successful transfer of disease resistance into existing high-yielding rice lines through genetic engineering;

– emphasis on using computer modelling to design new plant types with higher yield potential;

– evaluation of 880 breeding lines by scientists of the Rainfed Lowland Rice Research Consortium for the variable environments of the rainfed lowland ecosystem;

– important chemical processes improving the tolerance of rice to excess water had been revealed by the Rainfed Lowland Research Consortium and use of indigenous fungal pathogens for biological weed control had been suggested by the Upland Rice Research Consortium;

– improved upland rice varieties showed considerable promise, particularly in Indonesia and Viet Nam;

– elite lines developed for use in flood-prone areas and provided to Cambodia, Myanmar and Viet Nam, showed great promise.

IRRI five research programmes concentrated on the four major environments in which rice was being grown: irrigated rice, rainfed lowland rice, upland rice, flood-prone rice. A fifth, termed cross-ecosystem research programme, focused on research that would generate knowledge applicable to all, or several, ecosystems. In addition, the five international support programmes aimed to strengthen research capabilities of rice research institutions and scientists; they covered: germplasm conservation, dissemination and evaluation; crop and resource management networks; information and knowledge exchange; training; and national research services. Finally, IRRI Medium-Term Plan for 1994–1998 was focusing on four key challenges: increasing rice productivity; achieving sustainability; protecting the environment; and addressing social equity.

World-wide research collaborative mechanisms, promoted by the IRRI included research consortia, networks, technology evaluation networks, joint ventures, shuttle research, etc.

Consortia involved a group of selected institutions that mutually agreed to accept different responsibilities to contribute to achieving a common objective. Two ecosystem-based consortia were active by the mid-1990s:

– the Rainfed Lowland Rice Research Consortium, whereby the national agricultural research systems of Bangladesh, India, Indonesia, Thailand and The Philippines were conducting with the IRRI targeted research in seven key sites representing different rice production constraints in subecosystems of the rainfed lowlands;

– the Upland Rice Research Consortium, whereby the national

agricultural research systems of India, Indonesia, Thailand and The Philippines, and IRRI, had targeted five key sites, each of which representing a subecosystem and a major production constraint. Research was being carried out on the impact of drought, adverse soil conditions, weeds, land degradation and blast disease on rice productivity, environmental safety and the well-being of upland farm families. Improving rice productivity was considered the entry point to alleviating inter-related problems that contributed to upland degradation and damage to the lowland watersheds.

The first higher-yielding rice variety, IR-8, had been released in 1965. Over the following years, 27 IRRI varieties and more than 100 IRRI-parented varieties were released by national research programmes. The higher-yielding, early maturing, stress-tolerant, multiple-disease resistant variety IR-36 was released in 1976. Thirteen rice varieties from six countries and a wild species related to cultivated rice were used in the breeding process. Resistance to grassy stunt was one of its qualities. An extensive search for material resistant to this disease was conducted at the IRRI's gene bank in 1970; after screening 5,000 accessions and 1,000 breeding lines, only one accession of a wild rice was found to be resistant and, within this single accession, only three plants containing the gene resistant to the disease. IR-36 had become the world's most widely cultivated rice within a few years. Another release, IR-66, included 20 landraces in its pedigree (Komen, 1990*b*).

Higher-yielding varieties were grown across more than 50% of the Asian rice-growing area by the early 1990s. During the 1965–1985 period, Asian rice production had increased by 66%. These results, however, were also due to productivity gains in more favourable rice production areas, i.e. irrigated lowland paddy fields and favourable rainfed lowlands. Under less favourable conditions, such as deep water, uplands, tidal wetlands, or drought-prone areas, the higher-yielding varieties (HIVs) offered scant advantages over local varieties. Production gains in irrigated rice fields resulting from the use of HIVs appeared to have reached a high level and increased production was expected through augmenting agrochemical inputs (Komen, 1990*b*).

In Asia, 24% of the increase in rice production from 1965 to 1980 was attributed to better crop nutrition due primarily to the increased use of nitrogen fertilizers. By the mid-1990s, more than 20% of all nitrogen fertilizers produced world-wide were applied to the paddy fields of Asia. In most cases, inefficient plant recovery of applied nitrogen was the most important constraint to high agronomic efficiency: for irrigated rice, uptake efficiency ranged from 2% to 60%

of the applied nitrogen, although average efficiency was between 30% and 40% in most areas. Usually at least two split applications of nitrogen were needed to achieve a nitrogen supply that was synchronous with plant demand. Vigorous root and shoot growth, healthy plants, agronmic practices providing adequate nutrients other than nitrogen, weed control and proper water management contributed to efficient uptake of nitrogen inputs. In the harsher environments, nitrogen uptake efficiency was primarily governed by environmental stresses (drought, flooding, phosphorus deficiency and aluminium toxicity on acid soils) beyond the farmers' control.

On irrigated land in most Asian countries, rice farmers applied 100 to 150 kg N per hectare to the dry season rice crop and 60 to 90 kg N per hectare to the wet season crop. At these inputs, the cost of nitrogen fertilizer often represented 10% to 20% of total variable production costs. Nitrogen inputs to the irrigated system from biological nitrogen fixation ranged from 25 kg to 45 kg per hectare for each rice crop cycle, which was sufficient to sustain rice yields of 2–3 tonnes per hectare. To achieve a yield of 6 tonnes per hectare in the dry season required actual crop uptake of approximately 100 kg N per hectare. If nitrogen fertilizer uptake efficiency was only 36%, a more representative value for irrigated rice, the required rate would rise to 150 kg N per hectare.

Nitrogen uptake efficiency from applied nitrogen was needed so as to reduce the non-renewable fossil fuels used to manufacture inorganic nitrogen fertilizers, as well as gaseous emissions of nitrogen from irrigated systems to the atmosphere which contributed to global climate change. Rice-diazotroph associations were well known, but their contribution to nitrogen supply was minor. An intimate association between rice and free-living or loosely associated diazotrophs might be achieved. Another possibility would be examining the capacity of rice to support endosymbiosis or nodulation by rhizobia and other microsymbionts from different plant species.

The IRRI estimated that world's annual rice production would increase from 458 million tonnes in 1991 to 556 million tonnes by the year 2000, and to 758 million tonnes by 2020, a 65% increase in thirty years. For the leading rice-growing countries of South and South-East Asia, the required increase by the year 2020 would be about 100%. With little scope for expanding the irrigated area, this requirement could only be met by increasing production from existing rice land, improving rice production in vulnerable environments, collaborative research in biotechnologies and strengthening National Agricultural Research Systems (Komen, 1990*b*). See also the publication *IRRI toward 2000 and beyond* (1989).

The first hybrid rice had been developed by Chinese researchers and released to farmers in 1976. In the early 1990s the amount of land in China planted with hybrid rice was nearly 18 million hectares of a total 33 million hectares of harvested paddy fields and contributed to 66% of the country's rice output. As the Chinese hybrids and cytoplasmic male-sterility lines were not suitable for tropical regions, they had been adapted by the International Rice Research Institute (IRRI) and national institutes in India, Indonesia, Malaysia, The Philippines and Viet Nam. The hybrids derived from these lines had shown a 15%-20% yield advantage compared to rice open-pollinated varieties under irrigation, both multiple disease and insect resistance and acceptable grain quality. The IRRI reported that in 1987 the net return on hybrid rice cultivation in China was $444 per hectare, compared to $322 for conventional rice cultivation. Countries with a high labour-land ratio and a large proportion of irrigated area, such as India, Indonesia, Sri Lanka, The Philippines and Viet Nam were more likely to have the greatest potential demand for hybrid rice technology. Agronomic management appeared to be very important for maximizing the hybrids' yield potential.

It was reported that the Chinese Government had exclusively licensed its hybrid rice technology to Cargill Seeds and Ring Around Products Inc. (Occidental Petroleum). The licensing agreements interrupted the exchange of hybrid rice breeding materials between China and the IRRI, but did not drastically reduce the exchange of information. Chinese literature on hybrid rice had been fairly well circulated outside China and Chinese scientists had been communicating with rice scientists in various international fora, which kept information flowing. The licensing contracts were terminated in 1992, Cargill Seeds and Ring Around Products Inc. having been unsuccessful in commercializing Chinese rice hybrids outside China owing to their weak adaptability to the tropics and/or poor grain quality.

In India, nearly 20–25 hybrid rice varieties had been chosen for commercial trials after an evaluation of 350 experimental hybrids researched at 12 centres in the country over the period 1991–1993. These hybrid varieties were based on the parental paddy lines (breeding material) which were well adapted to tropical conditions. During the summer of 1994, 200 tonnes of hybrid rice seeds were produced to sow circa 10,000 hectares. Since the 1980s, several research projects on hybrid rice had been conducted:

– in 1989, the Indian Council for Agricultural Research (ICAR) started sponsoring the hybrid rice research project, which was strengthened by the financial and technical support of the United

Nations Development Programme; during the summer of 1994, several hybrids were released for cultivation; parent lines were supplied free of charge to all the interested private and public sector seed agencies, along with the requisite technical guidance, with a view to expanding the area under hybrid rice cultivation from 10,000 hectares in 1994 to 2 million hectares by the year 2000. The corresponding increase in seed requirements would rise from 200 tonnes to 40,000 tonnes;

– using several new cytoplasmic male-sterile lines, including two from the International Rice Research Institute and two male-sterile lines from Punjab, scientists evaluated over 400 hybrid combinations in trials over the period 1984–1993;

– at the Southern Petrochemical Industries Corporation (SPIC) Foundation, Madras, cytoplasmic male sterility (CMS) and its use for developing hybrid rice varieties was studied; the research was directed at rearranging specific DNA sequences in the mitochondrial genomes of the rice CMS lines IR 62829 A, its maintainer, and the restorer line IR 9761-19 R and a single cross hybrid (AxR); the mitochondrial genome was responsible for maternal inheritance;

– in a project at the Central Rice Research Institute, Cuttack (south-eastern India), research was directed toward wide hybridization, with special reference to diversification of cytoplasm and use of alien genes for imparting resistance to biotic stresses; 13 wide-cross hybrids had been obtained through embryo rescue;

– the world's first Basmati rice hybrid, developed by the Indian Agricultural Research Institute (IARI), was expected to be available in 1997 or 1998.

Research in other countries also indicated that hybrid vigour or heterosis in rice could increase yields by 15%–20% over the best available semi-dwarf inbreds under irrigation. Photoperiod-sensitive male sterility and thermosensitive male sterility systems showed promise, whereas the use of chemically-induced male sterility was not efficient enough to be applied on a large scale. Well-developed hybrid seed production practices gave average yields of 2 tonnes seed per hectare.

According to an IFPRI (International Food Policy Research Institute) Food Policy Report, published in September 1996, during the 23-year period, 1970–1993, the U.S. economy realized at least some $30 million and up to $1 billion through using improved rice varieties developed by the IRRI. Total U.S. government support of the IRRI had cost about $63 million, an investment equal to about 9 cents per $100 of U.S. rice production. The benefit/cost ratio for U.S. government contributions to the IRRI was as high as 17 to 1.

As partners in National Agricultural Research Systems (NARSs) of rice-growing countries were undertaking more and more of the needed strategic and applied research, the IRRI was conducting more anticipatory research in new partnerships. These included joint ventures on specific research projects; shuttle research consisting of exchanging scientists between the IRRI and another institution to undertake specific phases of a project; bilateral collaboration on a joint work plan for specific activities of mutual benefit; and direct consultation and training by the IRRI to assist a national programme in strengthening its own research and ability to participate in networks and partnerships.

IRRI megaprojects focused on emerging and evolving issues of major concern to growth and sustainability of rice production. The nominated megaprojects were focal points within the research and international services programmes. While the IRRI was guaranteeing the megaprojects core funding, it was also seeking additional support for the following megaprojects: raising the irrigated rice plateau; reversing trends of declining productivity in intensive irrigated rice; improving rice-wheat systems; conservation of genetic resources; exploiting biological diversity for sustainable pest management.

IRRI new-frontier projects aimed to explore exciting opportunities to stretch the horizons of rice research; their chances of success might be difficult to predict, but the returns on success would be high. The IRRI could only provide limited funding from its core budget for the following exploratory projects and was therefore seeking support from donors: apomixis – ensuring equity in use of hybrid rice; assessing opportunities for nitrogen fixation in rice; managing weeds using fewer chemicals -the role of allelopathy and biological control; developing a perennial rice plant – a sustainable agricultural system for the uplands.

With respect to increasing yield potential, the target for intensively-cropped irrigated systems was a higher experimental yield ceiling by up to 50%. The increased yield potential achieved in the 1960s with semi-dwarf varieties was attributable mainly to an increase in the harvest index (HI) of from 30% to 50%. The IRRI aimed to increase HI from 50% to 60% by further increasing sink size, reducing unproductive tillers and achieving a more efficient partitioning of biomass between grain and straw. Desirable traits included three to four large panicles (200–250 grains per panicle); no unproductive tillers (harvest index 0.6); very sturdy stems, dark green, thick leaves and a vigorous root system; 90-cm tall; and 110–130 day-growth duration; and a yield potential of 13–15 tonnes per hectare.

Development of the new plant type (NPT) rice began in 1989 and progress was rapid. NPT lines having short stature (90–100 cm), sturdy stems, thick dark-green erect leaves, five to eight productive tillers, no unproductive tillers, more than 200 grains per panicle and high harvest index, were superior to the elite inbred *indica* variety IR-72 in terms of grains per panicle. The IRRI researchers were still checking biomass and the harvest index. However, the NPT rice showed incomplete grain filling: 60% of grains were filled (mainly the superior spikelets), 20% of grains were half-filled and the remaining 20% were empty (mainly inferior spikelets). In IR-72, only 10%-15% of grains were partially filled or empty.

Competition between superior and inferior spikelets for assimilates was well known. The most inferior spikelets of the rice panicle did not begin to accumulate dry biomass, nitrogen, glutelin messenger RNA or glutelin protein until the most superior spikelets had almost completed development about twenty days after flowering. Removal of the superior spikelets led to immediate accumulation of dry biomass and nitrogen in the inferior spikelets, irrespective of the stage of ripening. Delayed development of the inferior spikelets was due to limited partitioning of nutrients to them at an early stage of ripening.

In a proposed research project to be conducted jointly with the Norman Borlaug Institute for Plant Science Research (see p. 678), the filling of inferior spikelets would be increased by prolonging the production of assimilates by flag leaves, the transport of assimilates from leaves and stem to grain and the capacity of inferior spikelets to convert assimilates to starch and protein. The objective of the research project was to modify the concentrations of phytohormones in rice using biolistic transformation to introduce cytokinin and auxin biosynthesis genes from *Agrobacterium tumefaciens* under the control of appropriate promoters. Three genes were to be transferred: isopentenyl transferase (*ipt*) gene for cytokinin biosynthesis, tryptophan monooxygenase (*iaaM*) and indolacetamide hydrolase (*iaaH*) genes for auxin biosynthesis. It was expected to raise cytokinin concentrations in senescing leaves and cytokinin and/or auxin concentrations in developing endosperm. Leaf senescence would be delayed, plant biomass would increase, assimilate supply to the grain would be strengthened and endosperm formation enhanced, especially in inferior spikelets.

Arabidopsis thaliana contained genes that were switched on during leaf senescence, known as senescence-associated genes (SAG). Some of them were cloned and characterized. The most senescence-specific SAG gene was *SAG-12*, encoding a cysteine proteinase. When the *SAG-12* promoter was fused with the *gus A* reporter gene, *gus* expression in transgenic tobacco was observed only in senescing leaves.

When the same promoter was fused to the *ipt* gene, cytokinin biosynthesis was stimulated, senescence was delayed, and both plant biomass and seed weight increased by 50%. At the IRRI, the rice homologue of the *SAG-12* promoter was to be isolated and its performance in transgenic rice compared to that of the *A. thaliana* promoter. It was expected that expression of the *SAG-12: ipt* construct in rice would delay senescence in all leaves, increase total plant biomass, raise carbohydrate storage in the stem, prolong photosynthesis in the flag leaf as well as carbohydrate supply to the grain, especially the inferior spikelets and, lastly, increase yield.

Endosperm development in cereals was accompanied by the successive rise and fall of cytokinin, auxin and abscissic acid concentrations. The wave of cytokinin was associated with mitosis of endosperm cells, the wave of auxin with massive accumulation of protein and carbohydrate and the wave of abscissic acid with dehydration, ripening and dormancy. The strategy for increasing grain filling in the inferior spikelets of NPT rice included prolonging their capacity to synthesize starch and protein. This capacity was probably determined during the first two waves of phytohormone production in the endosperm. Spraying of cytokinin was known to increase grain yield in cereals, but the genetic approach would consist of using endosperm-specific promoters from rice and wheat to raise the concentrations of cytokinins and/or auxins and determining which was the most apropriate combination of hormones and the most effective promoter. The promoters would originate from the rice glutelin (*Gt1, Gt2* and *Gt3*) and prolamine genes and from the wheat high- and low-molecular weight glutenin (*HMWG* and *LMWG*) genes. These promoters were expressed exclusively in the developing endosperm of rice, wheat, barley and tobacco.

The research project objectives were therefore to:

– construct and test chimaeric cytokinin and auxin biosynthesis genes in which the *ipt*, *iaaM* and *iaaH* genes of *A. tumefaciens* were controlled by promoters specifically expressed in senescing rice leaves or the developing endosperm;

– transfer these genes to elite rice varieties including IR-72 and NPT using the biolistic procedure or the *Agrobacterium*-mediated approach;

– determine the effect of the genes on cytokinin and auxin concentrations in rice leaves and endosperm, as well as on leaf senescence, endosperm development, yield and seed viability.

The project was intended to run for three years from April 1997 to March 2000. It was a collaboration between the Norman Borlaug

Institute for Plant Science Research and IRRI Division of Plant Breeding, Genetics and Biochemistry.

A controversial issue raised by some non-governmental organizations concerned whether soils could support rice varieties producing 15 tonnes per hectare. To achieve current yields of four tonnes to six tonnes per hectare, farmers were applying 120 kg of nitrogen per hectare. To obtain a yield of 10 tonnes per hectare, like on IRRI's experimental farm, the rice plants needed 200 kg of nitrogen. Even if the efficiency of absorbing nitrogen was improved, the super-rice variety (15 tonnes per hectare) would need between 240 kg and 400 kg of nitrogen per hectare. This was considered a huge amount and one was wondering how soils would cope and whether farmers could afford it. Another controversial issue related to pest and disease-resistance which was supposed to be engineered into the super-rice varieties in order to do away with pesticides. It seemed that pests and pathogens might adapt to the narrow genetic base of modern cultivars. Furthermore, the new varieties would be sown directly into the soil rather than transplanted and this might lead to increase in herbicide use in South-East Asia because it made mechanical weeding difficult; in addition, herbicides were cheaper than labour in the short term (*Seedling*, the Quarterly Newsletter of Genetic Resources Action International - GRAIN, vol. 13, no. 3, October 1996, pp. 12–16).

The super-rice varieties were aimed at irrigated farms, which represented 40% of South-East Asia's rice land in area, 75% of grain output and represented the higher echelons of agricultural income. The new plants were being bred for the 'better off' farmers and would probably enhance their status relative to poorer farmers. It was nevertheless true that the IRRI was also developing rice varieties for the uplands, rainfed lowlands and flood-prone rice land. A number of non-governmental organizations, scientists and farmers' groups involved in alternative rice research programmes throughout South-East Asia were not hopeful that developing the 15-tonne rice would minimize chemical fertilizer use and eliminate the need for pesticides. The sustainability issue of this 'rice revolution' was questioned, particularly with respect to its beneficiaries (*Seedling*, vol. 13, no. 3, October 1996, pp. 12–16).

Potentially harmful organisms to rice included microbial pathogens, insects, molluscs and rodents; some were herbivores feeding on the rice plant, others were parasitic disease organisms:

insect pests

stem borers	yellow stem borer (*Scirpophaga incertulas*)
	white stem borer (*Scirpophaga innotata*)
	striped stem borer (*Chilo suppressalis*)
	dark-headed rice borer (*Chilo polychrysus*)

defoliators	rice leaffolders (*Cuaphalocrocis medinalis*)
	rice caseworm (*Nymphula depunctalis*)
leafhoppers	green leafhopper (*Nephotettix virescens,*
	N. nigropictus, N. parvus, N. cincticeps)
planthoppers	brown planthopper (*Nilaparvata lugens*)
	white-backed planthopper (*Sogatella frucifera*)
rice bugs	Malayan black rice bug (*Scotinophara coarctata*)
	rice grain bug (*Leptocorisa oratorius*)

rodents
rice field rats (*Rattus rattus argentiventer, R. r. mindanensis*)

diseases of rice
viral diseases and their vectors
rice tungro (*Nephotettix virescens, N. nigropictus*)
ragged stunt (*Nilaparvata lugens, N. acuta*)

bacterial diseases and their causal agents
bacterial blight (*Xanthomonas oryzae* pv. *oryzae*)

fungal diseases and their causal agents
blast (*Pyricularia oryzae*)
sheath blight (*Rhizoctonia solani*)

weeds
Echinochloa colona, Cyperus iria, Monochoria vaginalis, Echinochloa crus-galli, Fimbristylis miliacea, Cyperus difformis.

Potential losses of up to 55% before harvest were estimated, but these estimates often represented only the top of the scale rather than mean losses. Actual losses were much lower. There had been massive invasions by insects like the brown planthopper and serious outbreaks of blast, tungro virus and sheath blight, among others, over large areas. In 1975, the brown planthopper infested nearly 80% of paddy fields in the Republic of Korea and crop losses in affected fields reached 20%-30%; this insect pest destroyed 200,000 hectares of rice between 1975 and 1980. In Indonesia, a viral disease destroyed 100,000 hectares between 1972 and 1975 in South Sulawesi alone. Calamities of this kind encouraged crop protection approaches emphasizing eradication and prevention, with the resulting dramatic increase in agricultural pesticides.

Despite the introduction of insect pest- and disease-resistance genes into rice cultivars, pesticide use had not declined. Modern approaches to crop protection relied on management rather than control or eradication. A species was considered a pest only when it reached numbers that could cause yield reduction. Natural factors, such as natural ennemies, that prevented a pest species from multiplying were emphasized. Pesticides were used only as a last resort to bring abnormal pest densities down when crop losses were expected to exceed the cost of treatment. In addition, the use of rice cultivars resistant to major pests was encouraged. Using a combination of control tactics instead of relying on just one, such as host-plant resistance or pesticides, and basing the decisions for controlling pests on sound economic grounds was referred to as integrated pest management (IPM).

In 1983, the IRRI Board of Trustees reorganized the genetic resources programme of the IRRI as the International Rice Germplasm Center (IRGC), to broaden its working base. The IRGC's principal objective was to be the central repository of the world's rice genetic resources, for use by rice researchers and growers throughout the world. More than 90% of the accessible rice-growing areas in the tropics had been covered by collecting missions (Komen, 1990*b*).

The IRRI held collected rice germplasm in trust and safeguarded it by storing this germplasm in the IRGC and by dispatching duplicate sets to other safe centres. The main phase of renovation of the IRRI gene-bank began in 1993 with the construction of a seed-drying room and improved seed-processing facilities. The gene-bank contained 74,700 *Oryza sativa* samples, 1,330 *O. glaberrima* and 2,216 wild species, originated from 110 countries in the following proportion: 19.5% from India, 10.7% from Indonesia, 9.4% from China, 7.1% from Thailand, 7.0% from Bangladesh, 39.4% from various developing countries, 5.6% from industrialized countries and 1.3% from unknown sources (GRAIN, 1994*b*). Several thousands of *O. sativa* samples were being characterized in the field and several more thousand were being distributed to some 30 countries. Collaboration with the regional gene-bank of the Southern Africa Development Council had led to the first comprehensive collection of wild rices from Zambia and Botswana. A satellite-based global positioning system was used for the first time to locate sampling sites accurately.

The International Network for Genetic Evaluation of Rice (INGER) was promoting the world-wide exchange of seeds of different rice varieties and evaluating promising cultivars, elite breeding lines, local cultivars and genetic donors through a network of trials at many sites in different environments where they were grown under various environmental stresses (diseases, drought or adverse temperatures). Each year, the INGER prepared nurseries (catalogued sets of seeds) and participating institutions were provided with appropriate selections from these for testing and evaluation under local conditions and for use in national breeding programmes. For instance, in 1993, 776 sets of 15 types of nurseries were sent to 46 countries – about 600 of these went to 18 Asian countries and the remainder to four countries in West Asia, two in North Africa and five in Latin America, to Papua New Guinea, the USA and Italy.

The Genetic Resources Center, which included the IRRI International Rice Germplasm Center and the INGER, took over responsibility for the international rice genealogy data-base during 1993. A rice genome data-base called RICE GENES had been created jointly by researchers from the IRRI and Cornell University, Ithaca, New York, to accommodate the wide range of information generated by genetic research on rice and other crop species. Evaluation of wild rice accessions had identified some resistance to the two viruses causing rice tungro. Similar efforts were being made to identify any suitable resistance to rice grassy stunt virus among wild species, after screening of some 12,000 cultivated rice accessions failed to detect any such resistance. Evaluations of wild rice accessions from eight species for resistance to sheath blight suggested that resistant varieties did exist.

In addition to the cultivated species *Oryza sativa* and *O. glaberrima*, the genus *Oryza* had 24 wild species, which might prove to be important sources of useful genes for rice improvement. Many wild *Oryza* species, however, failed to hybridize with cultivated rice because of differences in the number or in the genetic constitution of their chromosomes. Fertilization might occur, but the embryo was later aborted. It was, however, possible to rescue hybrid embryos containing extra chromosomes and maintain them through several cycles of backcrossing and tissue culture until their chromosome number declined to that of cultivated rice ($2n = 24$) and fertility was restored. The 12 chromosomes of the haploid set of these new lines closely resembled the chromosomes of the cultivated parent, but with small regions replaced by segments of the wild genome through random crossover events. Hybrids between cultivated rice and 12 wild species had been produced using embryo rescue.

The wide cross inter-specific programme aimed to: increase the yield potential of rice through the introgression of genes from wild into cultivated rice; transfer genes for resistance to major diseases and insects from wild to cultivated rice; incorporate genes for stress tolerance (drought, stagnant flooding, unfavourable soils) from wild to cultivated rice (Plucknett and Cohen, 1989). Supported by the Rockefeller Foundation within the framework of the International

Programme on Rice Biotechnology, this programme resulted in the transfer of genes for resistance to brown planthopper, white-backed planthopper, bacterial blight and blast from wild species to elite breeding lines of rice.

Repeated selfing of a hybrid could also generate new varieties. At least five cycles of selfing were required to produce stable lines. In places where only one generation was possible per year, anther culture was advantageous because homozygous plants could be produced in two generations.

The objectives of anther culture were:

– to reduce the time required to produce cold-tolerant, blast-resistant and salt- and aluminium-resistant rice varieties from sexual crosses between *japonica/japonica*, *japonica/indica*, and *indica/indica* rices;

– to reduce the time necessary for producing homozygous lines from crosses for upland conditions;

– to study yield and yield components of plants regenerated from anther culture of F1 sexual crosses;

– to examine the variability in adverse soils and environmental stresses among anther culture-derived plants under screenhouse and field conditions;

– to conduct studies on increasing both the efficiency of pollen grain to undergo androgenesis and plant regeneration;

– to carry out studies on isolated pollen cultures.

Protoplast fusion had been tried out on three *japonica* and two *indica* rice varieties. Green plant regeneration was obtained in one *japonica* variety while albino plants were regenerated from an *indica* variety. Protoplast fusion was expected to produce hybrids of those species isolated by strong incompatibility barriers (Plucknett and Cohen, 1989).

Marker-aided selection was being used when an important trait that was difficult to assess was interwoven with an easily-measured trait. For instance, a gene for resistance to brown planthopper was close to a gene specifying the purple coleoptile colour in some local rice varieties grown in northeast India. When a resistant plant with a purple coleoptile was crossed with a susceptible plant with a green coleoptile, more than 95% of F-2 plants showing purple coleoptile were also resistant to brown planthopper. In this case, the coleoptile colour was a morphological marker aiding selection for brown planthopper resistance. Unfortunately, few morphological markers were known. The advent of molecular markers had considerably heightened the relevance and usefulness of marker-aided selection. Isozyme and DNA markers were more common than morphological markers; they were available for any cross and were co-dominant, meaning that both parental markers could be observed in the hybrid. Additionally, the environment did not affect them, nor did it interact with other genes. They were, however, more difficult to measure or score than morphological markers.

The most commonly-used DNA markers were restriction fragment length polymorphisms (RFLPs). The difference in length of restriction fragments (obtained from cutting DNA with restriction enzymes or endonucleases) could be used as a marker in much the same way as a difference in coleoptile colour. More than 900 RFLP markers had been placed on the genetic map of rice through co-segregation analyses. Morphological and isozyme markers were also placed on the map. The first DNA-based map of rice chromosomes had arisen from a population of 53 F-2 plants derived from an *indica/javanica* intraspecific cross. The map had since been refined with additional mapping populations, including a population of 120 vegetatively-propagated inbred plants derived from an *O. sativa/O. longistaminata* interspecific cross. Gene mapping and tagging had been possible rather rapidly because rice had a small haploid genome, was a true diploid (2n = 24) and contained relatively little repeated DNA that could interfere with map construction; another contributing factor had been the organization of the International Programme on Rice Biotechnology by the Rockefeller Foundation.

The RFLP map could be used to locate genes of agronomic importance relative to DNA markers with known locations on rice chromosomes. If a marker very tightly linked to a gene was identified, the gene was said to be tagged and the marker could be useful for indirect selection of the gene. A technique called bulked segregant analysis was particularly powerful for gene tagging and could be used with RFLP markers and with RAPD (random amplified polymorphic DNA) markers. With this technique, a linked marker was found then located relative to other markers on the RFLP map. This allowed the genomic location of the gene to be efficiently determined. Over 20 single genes for disease and insect resistance had been located relative to RFLP markers. Among them were several genes for resistance to bacterial blight, rice blast fungus and three insect pests (brown planthopper, whitebacked planthopper and gall midge). Genes determining photoperiod sensitivity, aroma, wide compatibility and fertility restoration had been mapped as well. Mapping results could be immediately applied to breeding programmes.

Many important traits were governed by multiple genes with relatively small effects. In addition to single genes with strong phenotypic effects, genes governing quantitative traits could be identified and characterized by RFLP mapping. While single major genes for disease and insect resistance often were soon overcome by pest/pathogen populations, it was believed that combining resistance genes might contribute to longer-lasting resistance. Durable resistance was associated with multiple major and minor resistance genes. In the presence of multiple resistance genes, there would be little or no gain in fitness for a pathogen variant that could overcome only a fraction of the genes. Many rice improvement programmes aimed to incorporate multiple resistance genes, including genes for partial resistance, into rice varieties.

DNA markers could also be used as tools for population genetic studies aimed at understanding the diversity and structure of pest and pathogen populations. For the blast and bacterial blight pathogens of rice, repetitive DNA markers had been used extensively to evaluate pathogen diversity, determine the evolutionary relationships between pathogen strains and understand how pathogen races evolved. If the local pathogen population structure was understood, potential sources of resistance could be screened with isolates or populations that included the major phylogenetic and pathotypic groupings of the pathogen. For blast, the diversity of pathogen populations in screening nurseries was being optimized based on DNA typing data. Known resistance genes were being characterized in relation to the pathogen lineages for which they were effective.

Several laboratories could produce transgenic rice plants via the uptake of DNA into protoplasts, either by adding the neutral polymer polyethyleneglycol or by electroporation. Rice was the first agronomically important monocot to be transformed from protoplasts to yield viable, fertile plants. Protoplasts prepared from suspension cells appeared to give the best regeneration frequencies, with *japonica* varieties responding better than *indica* varieties. Chromosomal abnormalities might occur, however, during the four to six months of tissue culture required to produce suitable suspension cells before transformation then to regenerate whole transgenic plants.

The first foreign genes expressed in rice plants were bacterial genes conferring antibiotic or herbicide resistance. Reporter genes, such as the bacterial beta-glucuronidase (*gus*) gene, had been used to optimize the transformation protocol and to study the properties of some plant promoters that might eventually be used to control the expression of useful genes in transgenic rice. IRRI researchers aimed to develop suitable transformation systems for selected new plant type (NPT) rice lines. They used both protoplast and biolistic methods of transformation. Up to the end of 1996, about 60 plants had been regenerated from transformed calli. Plants transformed with reporter genes (e.g. *gus* gene) were fertile with normal morphological features. Different *Bacillus thuringiensis* (*Bt*)[8] (see p. 517) constructs driven by constitutive and tissue-specific promoters had been introduced into NPT rice and molecular analysis demonstrated the integration of the *Bt* genes. Biological assays for insect resistance of the transgenic lines were carried out by the Plant Breeding, Genetics and Biochemistry Division, and Entomology Division.

Resistance to the rice stripe virus had been engineered into rice by expressing the virus gene encoding its coat protein. The *bar* gene for resistance to the herbicide phosphinothricin could be used to develop herbicide-resistant rice varieties where direct seeding led to competition with weeds. Such varieties, however, were unlikely to be released because of the danger that cross-pollination would allow the herbicide resistance gene to escape into local populations of weedy and wild rices and negate the original strategy. It might be necessary to place such genes in the chloroplastic DNA, which was not transmitted through pollen.

In collaboration with the University of Wisconsin and Kansas State University, research was being conducted on the development of DNA probes for bacterial blight and blast. The resistance of cultivated rice was often short-lived as these pathogens adapted rapidly. The longer-term goal was to use the knowledge generated to produce more durable resistance in rice. The IRRI also collaborated with the John Innes Institute (Norwich, England) and Washington University in order to identify genes for resistance to rice tungro virus.

The IRRI and U.S. Environmental Protection Agency (EPA) were co-operating to determine the effects on rice production of a likely global climatic change. Under study were the direct and indirect effects of ultraviolet-B radiation on rice and of increased carbon dioxide and temperature on this crop species. With financial support from the EPA, the IRRI was carrying out baseline research on methane fluxes in paddy fields in collaboration with the Fraunhofer Institute for Atmospheric Environmental Research (Germany) and the Westland Biogeochemistry Institute of Louisiana State University. Other collaborating institutions were the Wageningen Agricultural University, Laboratory of Microbiology of the French Scientific Research Institute for Development in Cooperation (ORSTOM), the University of Provence, France, and the University of Georgia, USA. The IRRI was also co-ordinating an inter-regional research programme on methane emission from paddy fields funded by the Global Environmental

Facility of the United Nations Development Programme, comprising collaborative research on irrigated, rainfed and deepwater rice in China, India, Indonesia, Thailand and The Philippines.

On 2 April 1993, the IRRI's Board approved the following policy regarding rice genetic resources and intellectual property rights:

- the rice genetic resources maintained in the IRRI gene bank were held in trust for the world community;
- the IRRI adhered to the principle of the unrestricted availability of the rice genetic resources it held in trust, including any information on these;
- the IRRI was opposed to protecting the rice genetic resources it held in trust with any form of intellectual property protection;
- the IRRI was opposed to the application of patent legislation to plant genetic resources (genotype and/or genes) held in trust;
- the rice genetic resources held in trust by the IRRI would be made available on the understanding that the recipients would take no steps to restrict their further availability to other interested parties.

The IRRI had adopted a separate policy on intellectual property rights relative to its hybrid rice breeding programme, which reflected a conviction that the private sector had a positive role to play in delivering hybrid rice research results to farmers, but that such research should not be monopolized (Pearce, 1990).

Current networks co-ordinated at the IRRI included the Integrated Pest Management Research Network, International Task Force on Hybrid Rice, Asian Rice Biotechnology Research Network, and Systems Analysis and Simulation for Rice Production (SARP). Two technology evaluation networks, which were a voluntary, open, informal association of scientists and research organizations exchanging and evaluating technologies, as well as sharing experience and information, were also co-ordinated at the IRRI: the International Network for the Genetic Evaluation of rice (INGER), the objective of which was to evaluate promising cultivars, elite breeding lines, local cultivars and genetic donors through a network of multi-location trials in different environments subject to various stresses; and the Crop and Resource Management Network, the purpose of which was to evaluate prototype technologies for sustainable production systems in different agro-ecological and socio-economic situations.

For a number of years, the Centre of Agrobiological Research (CABO) and the Department of Theoretical Production Ecology in Wageningen, the Netherlands, in collaboration with the IRRI, had executed the Systems Analysis and Simulation for Rice Production (SARP), a project funded by the Directorate-General for International

Co-operation of the Dutch Ministry of Foreign Affairs. The long-term objective was to enhance the efficiency of agricultural research to support sustainable rice farming systems, with emphasis on rainfed rice. Sixteen teams from nine Asian countries were participating in the project, whose research topics were: cropping systems; potential production; nutrients, water and roots; and pests, diseases and weeds. Research institutes in China and India already incorporated the SARP methodology into their activities (Komen, 1990*b*).

In Asia, the IRRI collaborated with a network of about 20–25 National Agricultural Research Systems (NARSs). Some of them had advanced technical facilities, while others were restricted to routine or even occasional work (e.g. the IRRI was rebuilding a totally war-devastated laboratory in Cambodia in 1989). It was expected that the stronger NARSs would take over part of the IRRI's maintenance research, e.g. adapting modern rice varieties to ever-changing local conditions. Maintenance research was very important, because it was only by maintaining the gains already achieved in irrigated and favourable rainfed areas that future demand for rice could be met. However, as stated in the IRRI's publication, *Implementing the strategy: work plan for 1990–1994* (Manila, June 1989), many NARSs would have difficulty taking over part of the IRRI's activities, due to 'decreasing public investments in irrigation in many major rice-growing countries'.

The German Ministry for Economic Cooperation and Development (BMZ) had supported the Asian Rice Biotechnology Research Network at the IRRI since its inception in 1992, with the aim of transferring technologies developed at the IRRI to the biggest rice-producing countries in the region – China, India, Indonesia and Thailand (Heissler, 1996*b*). The Government of Germany had joined the Asian Development Bank in providing a $2.28 million to the Network. Early in 1993, Germany had granted an additional $1.38 million to the IRRI to fund the second phase of the project for a three-year period.

The IRRI had been running training programmes since 1962 to boost the capacity of scientists in developing countries to solve domestic rice production and utilization problems. Training courses had evolved from relatively basic courses in rice production and research methods to courses and fellowhips devoted to highly sophisticated techniques. Current major programmes emphasized training opportunities that paralleled IRRI research priorities, sharing responsibilities for training and collaboration among national rice research institutes and universities. Increasingly training was being provided jointly by the IRRI and national trainers at institutions outside the IRRI, or in-country by IRRI-trained personnel with IRRI support.

In March 1992, the International Rice Research Institute strengthened its collaboration in rice breeding with the French agricultural research institutions (INRA, National Institute for Agricultural Research; CIRAD, Centre for International Co-operation in Agricultural Research for Development; and ORSTOM, French Scientific Research Institute for Development in Cooperation), by signing another five-year co-operation programme. In addition to the French researchers (three from ORSTOM and one from the CIRAD) stationed at the IRRI in 1992, the CIRAD had sent two other researchers to the IRRI in 1993.

Research carried out on cyanobacteria since 1980 by ORSTOM microbiologists in collaboration with the IRRI had led to the conclusion that inoculation of paddy fields with cyanobacteria to increase rice yields was hindered by many constraints and that other solutions had to be found.

Cyanobacteria living in paddy fields could fix 10 kg to 30 kg of nitrogen per hectare and per cultivation cycle; when they died, the released nitrogen was absorbed by rice plants. At one time, Asian rice growers used to supply 30 kg and 90 kg of chemical nitrogen fertilizers per hectare of paddy fields. In addition to fixing nitrogen, cyanobacteria had other interesting features: they limited weed development, supplied organic matter to the soil and facilitated the uptake of phosphorus by rice plants. To benefit from all these advantages, an inoculation technique had been developed from laboratory cultures by the late 1970s and applied to some paddy fields (Egypt, India and Myanmar). However, the technique was never adopted on a large scale and ORSTOM and IRRI researchers had shown that introduced cyanobacteria were inhibited by a number of factors, such as phosphorus deficiency, the presence of predators (micro-crustaceans and insect larvae) or the presence of chemical nitrogen fertilizers. The inoculant death knell was sounded when it was observed that indigenous cyanobacteria could be 10 to 100 times more numerous than those contained in 10 kg of inoculant required to fertilize one hectare.

It was therefore concluded that stimulating the development of autochtonous strains in paddy fields by using such management tools as phosphorus input and predator control would be preferable to inoculating the paddy fields with strains grown in the laboratory. *In-situ* studies showed that one could draw benefit from indigenous cyanobacteria by embedding nitrogen fertilizers in the soil of the paddy fields. This practice had the following advantages: it enabled indigenous cyanobacteria to fix nitrogen (some 5 kg to 30 kg of nitrogen per hectare); it decreased nitrogen losses due to volatilization of ammonium (these losses could amount to 50% of the nitrogen fertilizer input); and it prevented the proliferation in the paddy field water of mosquito larvae and vectors of parasitic diseases.

The first international upland rice breeders' workshop was held from 6 to 10 September 1993 at the CIRAD's facilities in Montpellier, France. Participants in the workshop included representatives from the IRRI, CIAT and WARDA, national institutes, such as the CRRRC in India, the ICA in Colombia, the IDESSA in Côte d'Ivoire, the IRI in Hungary, as well as universities (e.g. Los Baños in The Philippines), regional organizations (e.g. CORAF in Africa) and the ORSTOM. Delegates put forward ideas for improving breeding and standardizing both testing procedures and genetic resource management practices. The most important recommendation was the adoption of a common variety nomenclature, which was expected to simplify data-base exchanges and lead to a greater transparency in variety creation (*CIRAD News*, October 1993, 6).

3. Biotechnologies at the IITA

The International Institute of Tropical Agriculture (IITA) had been established in 1967 to increase productivity of major food crops and develop sustainable agricultural systems replacing bush fallow or slash-and-burn cultivation in the humid and subhumid tropics. Nigeria had provided 1,000 hectares of land for the IITA headquarters and an experimental farm at Ibadan, while the Ford and Rockefeller Foundations had provided initial financial support. Since 1971, as in the case of the other IARCs, funding was provided through the CGIAR. The IITA employed about 180 scientists and professional staff from more than 40 countries, and 1,100 support staff, most of whom were from Nigeria. The annual budget amounted to $33.6 million at the end of 1980s (Komen, 1990*c*).

One major achievement of the IITA was development of the maize varieties TZB and TZPB, resistant to lowland rust and blight. These varieties made the rapidly expanding production of maize into the humid savannas possible, especially in Nigeria. Expansion was curbed by the outbreak of another disease caused by the streak virus which devastated crops whenever epidemics occurred. A ten-year research programme had been launched in 1975 to identify sources of resistance to this virus and breed new resistant maize varieties. In addition to streak virus-resistant maize, the IITA had developed hybrid maize well adapted to Nigeria and other African environments. The innovation led to the forming of commercial seed companies in Nigeria (IITA, 1990; Komen, 1990*c*).

In the ITTA's *Strategic Plan 1989–2000*, research focused on:
- three primary commodities – cassava, maize and cowpea;
- three secondary commodities – yam, plantain and soybeans;
- the lowlands, humid and subhumid tropics of West and Central Africa;
- the biological control of crop diseases;
- the African small holder or family farmer;
- biotechnologies.

A tissue culture laboratory had been set up at the IITA as early as 1977. It produced large numbers of virus-free clones of cassava, sweet potato, yam, cocoyam, plantain and banana. A biotechnology unit established at the IITA with the financial support of the Italian Government started work in mid-1989. An external biotechnology advisory committee was formed to help ITTA focus its activities and strengthen collaboration with advanced laboratories and institutions. In addition, an internal biotechnology committee and a biosafety committee was set up (Komen, 1990*c*; Ng *et al.*, 1990). The IITA new Biotechnology Unit formed a link between laboratories in the advanced countries and the National Agricultural Research Systems in Africa. The unit was developing strategies to increase the efficiency of breeding programmes by finding solutions to problems that could not be solved by conventional methods.

A meeting of African scientists working on cassava, yams and plantain/cooking bananas was held at the IITA in August 1988. An agreement was reached on a set of recommendations which would guide the IITA in developing biotechnology applications. A similar meeting was held in February 1989 at the IITA to devise priorities in cowpea biotechnology research. A conference entitled Biotechnology: enhancing research on tropical crops, held at the IITA in November 1990, attracted 130 participants. An African Plant Biotechnology Network (APBNet) was initiated with the IITA as its secretariat. The conference also identified the constraints in various crops that could be handled through plant biotechnologies (Thottappilly *et al.*, 1992*a,b*). In collaboration with the FAO, a Biotechnology Workshop/Training for African Scientists was also organized in November 1990. Assistance in the development of tissue culture laboratories was provided by the IITA to a number of African countries (Komen, 1990*c*).

Research work on plantain and banana deserves special mention, because of the importance of plantain as the staple food of about

60 million people in West and Central Africa, where 60% of the world's plantain was produced and consumed. African banana and plantain production was affected by the spread of the virulent sigatoka leaf spot disease, which could cause yield losses of up to 50%. The black sigatoka disease was emerging as a pan-African epidemic and, due to the apparent lack of resistance in the African *Musa* gene pool, it was becoming a major threat to food security in the plantain- and banana-growing regions of Africa. The IITA addressed this problem through a short-term and a long-term strategy, i.e. distribution of resistant starchy alternatives and plantain/banana breeding respectively. Low clonal multiplication rates, lack of genetic variability and barriers to sexual hybridization impeded genetic improvement. Hence the considerable potential of novel, biotechnological approaches to plant improvement (Thottappilly *et al.*, 1992*a*).

The banana bunchy-top virus (BBTV) was confined to relatively small areas in Burundi, Gabon, Rwanda and Zaire; although it caused serious damage in Asia and the Pacific, for unknown reasons, it was not spreading rapidly and had not provoked much damage (Thottappilly *et al.*, 1992*a*).

A plantain/banana tissue culture laboratory was set up at the Onne High Rainfall Substation of the IITA in 1983. A breeding strategy targeting the creation of resistant plantain hybrids was developed and achieved success within three years. Tissue culture research and applications played an important role in this success. An *in-vitro* micropropagation technique for plantains and cooking bananas, developed in the 1980s, was routinely applied to obtain large numbers of plants. Increases in the number of plantlets ranged from 10–30 every two months, compared to 6–12 months using conventional field multiplication techniques. Shoot tip culture was applied successfully in the propagation of over 400 *Musa* germplasm accessions. These materials could be distributed to national programmes through plant quarantine systems because they were considerably lighter and less bulky than conventional propagules, amenable to rapid multiplication, if required, and, most importantly, free of pathogens (Thottappilly *et al.*, 1992*a*).

Embryo culture techniques were applied to enhance seed germination rates, with the aim of improving the 4%-12% germination obtained *in vitro*, as compared to the 1%-2% germination rate in soil. An improved embryo culture protocol had been developed, whereby germination rates ranged from 10% to 25% (if calculated on the basis of the number of embryos cultured). On average, about 700 plantain seeds were handled *in vitro* each month, resulting in the production of one plantain hybrid per working day (Pistorius, 1992*a*; Thottappilly *et al.*, 1992*a*).

Plant regeneration by somatic embryogenesis in cell suspension cultures had been achieved in *Musa*, but only in wild species (from zygotic embryo explants) and in a few clones of AA and AAA dessert bananas and ABB cooking bananas. As of 1993, no success had yet been reported in any of the African bananas and plantains (Thottappilly *et al.*, 1992*a*). In collaboration with the Catholic University of Leuven, Belgium, the IITA was conducting research into the regeneration of *Musa* plants through somatic embryogenesis. Embryogenic cell suspension cultures of the widespread cooking banana clone, 'Bluggoe' (*Musa* spp., ABB group) were developed by culturing meristematic 'scalps' taken from proliferating shoot-tip cultures. Plant regeneration proceeded through the development pathway of somatic embryogeny, which at all stages showed conspicuous morphological and histological resemblance with zygotic embryogenesis in a wild *Musa* species. Somatic embryos were produced directly from cells in suspension and not via callus. Germinated banana somatic embryos were successfully established in soil. The relative simplicity of this cell culture protocol was in favour of the integration of biotechnological approaches into conventional banana and plantain breeding schemes (Thottappilly *et al.*, 1992*a*).

Owing to the fact that *in-vitro* propagation was a frequently used technique for handling *Musa* germplasm in IITA's plantain improvement programme, it was necessary to determine the nature and extent of somaclonal variation among a wide range of plantain cultivars. Factors influencing the incidence of somaclonal variation were being investigated in order to identify guidelines for control of *in-vitro* instability (Thottappilly *et al.*, 1992*a*).

Over 300 new *Musa* accessions had been introduced, thereby quadrupling the number of accessions held in the IITA collection. These genetic resources were introduced in a joint effort with the Nigerian Plant Quarantine Service and the International Network for the Improvement of Banana and Plantain (INIBAP). At least 33 of these introductions showed resistance to black sigatoka. Among these, several AA diploids were useful sources of black sigatoka resistance in IITA's plantain breeding programme. Five black sigatoka-resistant ABB cooking banana cultivars were being rapidly multiplied *in vitro* and distributed at an annual rate of 5,000 plants to Nigerian national programmes and farmers as an alternative to the susceptible plantains. No cloned genes were available that might directly confer host resistance to black sigatoka and *Fusarium* wilt. There were a number of genes available associated with expression of resistance that could be used experimentally in attempts to confer fungal resistance (Thottappilly *et al.*, 1992*a*).

As screening in the field for useful banana/plantain somaclonal variants (e.g. with disease resistance) was unfeasible, screening at the cellular level with a selection pressure applied *in vitro* was a more practical approach. Pathologists were purifying extracts from the fungus *Mycosphaerella fijiensis* (sigatoka agent) that could be tested as a screening agent (Thottappilly *et al.*, 1992*a*).

The IITA had contacted the USDA/ARS Laboratory at the Regional Plant Introduction Station, Griffin, Georgia, to initiate research on molecular biology techniques like RFLP and RAPD (random amplified polymorphic DNA) aimed at enhancing the efficiency of plantain breeding schemes.

Cassava was affected by viral diseases and also attacked by two major insect pests: the cassava mealy bug and the cassava green mite. Together, these pests could cause yield losses as high as 80%, with an average 30% considered a conservative figure. The world's largest biological control programme had been launched against these pests by the IITA with the help of many collaborators and donors in Africa and in other regions: the Africa-wide Biological Control Program (ABCP). Exploration of thousands of square kilometres resulted in identification of more than 60 natural enemies of the two pests, 14 of which had been released in Africa. However, only one parasitoid, *Epidinocarsis lopezi*, proved effective against the mealy bug. The parasitoid was released by the IITA, by air and on the ground, in 18 countries across Africa's cassava belt, thus reducing mealy bug damage substantially (Komen, 1990*c*).

The battle against the cassava green mite (*Mononychellus tanajoa*) had taken the turn for the better and the pest was in retreat. After 13 years of painstaking research, scientists were confident that they had found the right natural enemies to control the green mite.

In 1971, cassava green mites were found in Uganda. Within eight years, they had spread across the continent, causing crop losses as high as 80% in some places. In 1983, national and international scientists began their search in South America for biological agents to control the pest. A predatory mite, *Typhlodromalus manihoti*, was released by the IITA in Ghana and Benin in 1990; it gradually fanned out and reduced populations of the cassava green mite. Three years later, a second predatory mite, *Typhlodromalus aripo*, was released in Benin and, subsequently, in other countries of East and West Africa. Initially, it dispersed at a rate of about 12 km per year but in later years would spread like wildfire. One reason for this rapidity was that *T. aripo* had remained on planting material moved from one farm to another, probably unbeknown to farmers. From a release site in Benin, it had quickly penetrated 400 km into Nigerian territory, including a migration of some 350 km from the coast up to the northern limits of the cassava green mite. Once *T. aripo* had become established, it had reduced pest populations by two-thirds, which scientists expected would translate into a 30 % increase in cassava yields. The advantage of using *T. aripo* was that it did not require a mass breeding programme. It could be transferred to new locations on the shoot tips of plants picked only once the mite had had the time to multiply in the field. The mite would then ride piggyback on the cut shoot tip to the release site. On the cassava plant, *T. aripo* spent its productive life within the shoot tips, but in areas where cassava lost its leaves due to low temperatures or drought, the predatory mite was unable to survive. To overcome this drawback, scientists were going back to South America to areas that were climatically similar to search for more natural enemies. In the meantime, the IITA was testing a fungal pathogen, *Neozygites floridana*.

The international project to control the cassava mealy bug in Africa had led to a decade-long partnership between the International Institute of Tropical Agriculture (IITA), the International Center for Tropical Agriculture (CIAT) and the Brazilian Centre for Research on Cassava and Fruticulture (CNPMF), part of the EMBRAPA (Brazilian Enterprise for Agricultural Research). Cassava cultivation in West Africa and Northeast Brazil was practised under similar environmental agronomic and socio-economic conditions and constraints. In both regions, demand for cassava was increasing, resulting in intensified production which, sometimes, degraded already marginal areas and multiplied pests and pathogens and the risk of pesticide abuse (*Cassava Newsletter*, vol. 19, no. 1, March 1995, pp. 1–4).

The United Nations Development Programme (UNDP) was funding a four-year project expected to become a model for other cassava-growing countries and regions in Africa and South America. The two branches of the UNDP project were the Ecologically Sustainable Cassava Plant Protection (ESCaPP) in Africa and Proteção Fitossanitária Sustentável da Mandioca (PROFISMA, Sustainable Phytosanitary Protection of Cassava) in South America. Initiated in January 1993, the ESCaPP was implemented by the IITA's Plant Health Management Division in collaboration with national plant protection programmes in Benin, Cameroon, Ghana and Nigeria. The PROFISMA was run jointly by the CIAT and the CNPMF, with agricultural research and extension agencies in six States of Northeast Brazil (*Cassava Newsletter*, vol. 19, no. 1, March 1995, pp. 1–4).

The research activities were:

– Plant pathology. Determination of cassava varietal response to diseases caused by fungi, bacteria, viruses and mycoplasmas. Identification of alternate hosts, vectors and dispersal mechanisms of specific pathogens. Development of controls for major pathogens causing, for instance, root rot in growing plants and dry rot in cassava chips. Development and implementation of quick diagnostic procedures for cassava vein mosaic virus (CVMV) and for African cassava mosaic virus (ACMV). Multiplication of uninfected planting material and promotion of farmer-managed multiplication methods and sites for virus-free planting material.

– Weed science. Identification of major weeds and determination of critical periods of competition between weeds and cassava for optimal use of labour in small-scale production units. Study of interactions between major weed species and biological control agents, especially phytoseiid predator mites.

– Entomology and acarology. Suitability of introducing new natural enemies of the cassava green mite (*Mononychellus tanajoa*). Decentralization of mass-rearing and field release of biological control agents such as phytoseeid mites, cassava mealy bug parasites, cassava hornworm baculovirus and a fungal pathogen (*Neozygites floridana*) of the cassava green spider mite. Mass production of natural enemies of the cassava green spider mite and cassava mealy bug for farm trials in Brazil. Import, quarantine, mass production and distribution of these natural enemies (predatory mites and pathogenic fungi) in the four West African countries.

– Support activities. Shipment of natural enemies from South America to Africa via quarantine in the Netherlands, and from the CIAT to Brazil via quarantine at the EMBRAPA's National Research Centre for Improvement and Evaluation of Environmental Impact, in Jaguariuna, Brazil. Update of the taxonomy of African Phytoseiidae in cassava agroecosystems and establishment of reference specimen collections of pests, natural enemies, weeds, and diseased plants in Brazil and the four West African countries (*Cassava Newsletter*, vol. 19, no. 1, March 1995, pp. 1–4).

The UNDP project was developing training materials and syllabi, and was conducting courses on the principles and practices of sustainable crop protection. Farmer participatory techniques and how to adapt them to regional conditions were also taught. The IITA provided a special training programme to help enhance the status and influence of African women within national agricultural programmes, thus fostering the role of women in contributing to food security and to solving environmental problems in Africa. In each of the four countries, 14 professional women received post-graduate training (MSc.) to equip them with the technical, research and leadership skills necessary for effective sustainable plant protection (*Cassava Newsletter,* vol. 19, no. 1, March 1995, pp. 1–4).

The IITA developed high-yielding cassava cultivars resistant to the African cassava mosaic virus and cassava bacterial blight, tolerant to the cassava mealybug and cassava green spider mite, and with low cyanide content (linamarin and lotaustralin). It was observed that shy flowering in some cassava cultivars, particularly those with the desirable traits, had limited the choice of parents for genetic recombinations (Ng, 1992; Thottappilly *et al.,* 1992*a*).

In view of the high degree of heterozygosity in cassava and *Musa* spp., the production of homozygous breeding lines through haploidy would be of use in genetic improvement programmes and would be a tool for studying the genetics of disease resistance. Anther culture from a spontaneous tetraploid cassava led to a protocorm structure and roots. Unpollinated ovary cultures were also used to explore the possibility of obtaining haploid plantlets (Ng, 1992).

Though somatic embryos and plantlet formation had been obtained from Latin American cassava materials, similar work on African cassava explants was not successful. However, in 1991, somatic embryos developed up to the green cotyledon stage were obtained from leaf cultures of six IITA cassava clones; plantlets were derived from some of these clones (Ng, 1992).

The IITA researchers were able to germinate seeds of wild species related to cassava, but the germination rate was low in some species. Embryo culture was an important tool used to germinate isolated embryos from seeds difficult to germinate. The immature embryo culture technique was also used to rescue hybrids which could not be obtained via conventional methods. Several culture media formulations were developed for these techniques (Ng, 1992).

The biosynthesis of cassava glucosides, their translocation and accumulation in specific tissues, particularly in edible root tissue, were being studied in collaboration with the Royal Veterinary and Agricultural University of Denmark. The wide varietal differences in linamarase activity (which hydrolyzes cyanogenic glucosides) observed by the IITA scientists in cassava tissues made it possible to improve the crop species for this trait by conventional breeding methods. Molecular biology techniques were needed to establish the biochemical basis of these differences and to develop appropriate screening tools (DNA probes, RFLP markers) [Thottappilly *et al.,* 1992*a*].

The IITA was a member of the Cassava Biotechnology Network (see p. 738).

Diseases and pests striking yams (*Dioscorea alata* and *D. rotundata*) included the yam mosaic virus, water yam chlorosis, yam storage rot, yam anthracnose, yam tuber beetles and nematodes. Shy flowering and the non-synchronization of male and female flowers were bottlenecks in yam breeding; thus, the choice of parents for hybridization and recombination of desirable traits was limited. Cytogenetic studies on the ploidy levels, tissue culture and genetic engineering would assist in introducing desirable traits into selected plant materials (Thottappilly *et al.*, 1992*a*). Yam was amenable to infection by *Agrobacterium* and transgenesis could lead to disease- or pest-resistant plants.

The IITA developed and adopted meristem culture media for cassava, yams, sweet potatoes and cocoyams. It was found that the combination of heat treatment on the mother plant followed by meristem culture was effective in eliminating African cassava mosaic virus (ACMV) from cassava and yam mosaic virus (YMV) from white yam (Ng, 1992). For white yam, which was less tolerant to thermotherapy, chemotherapy in *in-vitro* cultures using virazole was being explored. Meristem culture followed by virus indexing was effective in eliminating sweet potato virus disease complex. About 100 clones of cassava and its related *Manihot* spp., 500 clones of sweet potatoes, 1,500 clones of yams and 100 clones of cocoyams were regenerated from meristem cultures (Thottappilly *et al.*, 1992*a*).

Plantlets of selected improved clones produced from meristem cultures were virus indexed. Methods for indexing ACMV and YMV included sap inoculation of a sensitive test plant, *Nicotiana benthamiana* and ELISA (enzyme-linked immunosorbent assay). An approach graft to *Ipomoea setosa*, complementary grafting to pre-infected clones, ELISA and electron microscopy were used for sweet potato virus complex detection (Thottappilly *et al.*, 1992*a*).

A laboratory attached to the U.S. Department of Agriculture (USDA) at Beltsville, Maryland, was collaborating with the IITA in the production of monoclonal antibodies and cDNA probes for the detection of viruses affecting root and tuber crop species. A project funded by the International Development Research Centre (IDRC, Ottawa) aimed to produce monoclonal antibodies for detecting viruses and their strains in food crop species in various African countries. This would enable the identification of viruses within each country, with a resulting simplification of quarantine regulations and the possible incorporation of virus resistance into plants (Thottappilly *et al.*, 1992*a*). The IITA collaborated with the Nigerian Quarantine Service for inspection and certification of their *in-vitro* materials; the Inter-African Phytosanitary Council approved these methods.

Media for rapid multiplication and germplasm preservation of cassava, yams, sweet potatoes and cocoyams had been developed. A multiplication rate of five-fold could be obtained within four to five weeks using single node cuttings. For yams, *in-vitro* microtubers and aerial microtubers were also obtained by increasing the sucrose concentration in the culture media. They could be stored for at least three months, sprouted and planted directly in soil. Virus-free plantlets in sterile containers with culture media were used for international distribution. A total of 39 clones of cassava, five clones of white yam and 38 clones of sweet potato, all of them virus-free, were available for distribution. Virus-tested cassava clones were distributed to 43 countries in Africa, sweet potato to over 50 countries throughout the world and yam to 19 countries in Africa, as well as to India and the Fiji islands (Ng, 1992; Thottappilly *et al.*, 1992*a*).

A germplasm conservation method based on reduced growth *in vitro* was being used to maintain root and tuber crop species at the IITA: over 1,500 accessions of yams, 200 of cassava and related *Manihot* spp., over 1,000 of sweet potatoes and 100 of cocoyams were maintained (Ng, 1992). Under a lower incubation temperature, these accessions could be kept for more than a year when cultured on a normal culture medium. With the addition of 3% mannitol in the culture media and by lowering the incubation temperature, sweet potato germplasm could be stored for one or two years. Cryopreservation for the long-term storage of germplasm was considered a priority research topic, which would benefit national research institutes involved in germplasm conservation (Thottappilly *et al.*, 1992*a*).

In-vitro microtuber formation had been obtained from 300 accessions of white yam and water yam. The number of microtubers and aerial tuber formation was being increased. Microtubers were successfully produced by transplanting *in-vitro* yam plantlets in sterile soil under greenhouse conditions. The average number of tubers produced per plant ranged from two to three. Mean weight per tuber and tuber weight per plant ranged from 9.51 g to 18.72 g and from 17.82 g to 57.09 g respectively. The tubers were hand carried or mailed to the requesting national programmes. They were kept under ambient conditions before being roused from their dormant state and planted directly in the field or seedbed (Ng, 1992).

Some African rice accessions (*Oryza glaberrima*; *O. longistaminata* and *O. barthii*) had important traits for rice improvement in Africa, in particular, immunity to the rice yellow mottle virus and resistance to the stem borer *Diopsis*, both stresses being specific to Africa. Transferring the desirable traits from African species to the high-yielding *O. sativa* background was not satisfactory, due to insufficient recombination. Biotechnology approaches to solving the problem were being investigated in collaboration with advanced laboratories (Pistorius, 1992a; Thottappilly *et al.*, 1992a).

In maize breeding, an African target was to utilize biotechnological approaches to solve the *Striga* problem. Linkage projects were being developed between the IITA and advanced laboratories in the USA and Europe already working on molecular aspects of maize streak virus. The viral coat protein transfer approach could be explored for all important African viruses in maize. Research on genetically engineered endophytes (inocuous bacteria living in maize xylem) was a major private sector activity and this approach to delivery of resistance compounds to maize was worth considering (Thottappilly *et al.*, 1992a).

In collaboration with the University of California, Davis, USA, the IITA had initiated a project to study variability in tropical maize downy mildew fungi using molecular markers (Thottappilly *et al.*, 1992a).

Cowpea (*Vigna unguiculata*) is an important food legume crop in the semi-arid regions of Africa. It is cultivated as a mixed crop species, mostly with sorghum and millet, and forms an integral part of most Africans' diet.

The cowpea lines TVx3236 and TVx82D-716 with high-yield potential were also resistant to anthracnose, bacterial blight, brown blotch, web blight and scab. Resistance to fungal and bacterial diseases was also available in the cowpea germplasm. Several cowpea lines with resistance to as many as five viruses had been developed. Among the cowpea's most destructive insect pests were the legume pod borer (*Maruca testulalis*) and three pod-sucking bugs (*Clavigralla tomentosicollis*). The legume pod borer infected stems, floral buds, flowers and green pods; the greatest damage was caused to flowers, while the most obvious damage appeared on the pods. Cowpea bruchid was a serious pest of cowpea in storage; complete infestation often occurred within six months of storage at the farm (Thottappilly *et al.*, 1992a).

Resistance to cowpea bruchid was extensively studied at the IITA. A moderate level of resistance had been identified in the cultivar TVu 2027. After three months in storage, TVu 2027 showed about 20% infestation, compared to 66%–96% infestation among other cowpea varieties. By the end of a six-month storage period, TVu 2027 was about 71% infested, while the other varieties had been completely destroyed. This resistance had been incorporated into most advanced breeding lines (Thottappilly *et al.*, 1992a).

After screening over 8,000 cowpea accessions, no resistance to the legume pod borer was found in the cultivated *Vigna* but very good sources were identified in wild species, particularly in *Vigna vexillata*. Research by both the IITA scientists and collaborators in institutes in Italy (Universities of Naples and Tuscia, Viterbo), at Purdue University and the University of California, Davis, aimed to transfer the resistant gene(s) from the wild species *Vigna vexillata* to cultivated cowpeas. This research included wide crosses, cytogenetics, embryo culture and regeneration of plantlets (Thottappilly *et al.*, 1992*a*).

In collaboration with the University of Ibadan, Nigeria, it was possible to rescue hybrid embryos after wide crosses between cowpeas and *Vigna pubescens*. In another collaborative project with the Universities of Naples and Tuscia, protoplast isolation and multiplication techniques were developed; somatic fusions were made and cowpea tolerance to abiotic stresses (e.g. low soil pH and aluminium toxicity, and drought) was being studied on protoplasts and free cells (Thottappilly *et al.*, 1992*a*). The IITA collaborators in Italy and the USA were able to generate roots from calli derived from several explants including leaf discs. They were also able to obtain fast dividing protoplasts with the capacity to fuse with *Nicotiana* protoplasts. Research was being pursued with a view to reducing losses caused by insect pests (Thottappilly *et al.*, 1992*a*).

The IITA was collaborating with the University of Frankfurt to study restriction fragment length polymorphism markers. An RFLP map of the cowpea genome was expected to help identify specific markers for traits relating to pest resistance and to ultimately aid in the selection of desirable genotypes.

Striga gesnerioides and *Alectra vogelii* were two major parasitic weeds infesting cowpea. *Striga* was more common in West Africa, where it provoked severe yield losses. *Alectra vogelii* was reported in West and Southern Africa; it caused damage similar to that of *Striga*. B301, a cowpea line from Botswana, showed resistance to a number of *Striga* populations in laboratory tests. The existence of various physiological strains of *Striga* made breeding for resistance a difficult task. The use of isozymes and RFLPs could help in strain identification and in developing an understanding of population genetics in *Striga*, so as to follow the genetic basis of the epidemics (Thottappilly *et al.*, 1992*a*).

There were about 15,000 accessions of cowpea in the germplasm collection at the IITA, although some might be the result of duplication. RFLP analysis was an effective classifying tool.

The IITA and the Nitrogen Fixation by Tropical Agricultural Legumes (NifTAL) Project (Hawaii, USA) were carrying out a collaboration study of the symbiosis between promiscuously nodulating soybean genotypes and their affiliated *Bradyrhizobium* spp. strains. Scientists from both institutions were expected to examine the indigenous bradyrhizobia nodulating the IITA lines. The project's goal was to determine the potential of indigenous bradyrhizobia for providing sufficient nodulation and nitrogen fixation to meet the yield potential of the promiscuously nodulating lines of soybeans selected at the IITA. This two-year programme was initiated in September 1991. Extensive sampling of *Bradyrhizobium* populations from several environments and field inoculation trials were be compared to the introduced *B. japonicum* (in *NifTAL BNF Bulletin*, vol. XI, no. 1, 1992, p. 4).

IITA scientists had transferred the ability to nodulate with African *Rhizobium* from an unimproved Nigerian soybean variety to high-yielding, imported varieties. The IITA was maintaining a collection of over 700 *Rhizobium* strains. The IITA's research work also focused on tree legume genera, such as *Leucaena*, *Sesbania* and *Tephrosia*, and on mulches, such as *Psophocarpus palustris*. Microbial research related to strain selection, competitiveness and persistence, and inoculant production (Pistorius, 1992*a*). See also West Africa MIRCEN, p. 97.

A concertation meeting between the IITA and the French Centre for International Co-operation in Agricultural Research for Development (CIRAD), French Scientific Research Institute for Development in Cooperation (ORSTOM), National Institute for Agricultural Research (INRA) and the University of Nantes was held on 30 and 31 January 1996 in Montpellier. The meeting prepared the groundwork for collaboration on ecoregional programmes in humid and subhumid tropics. CIRAD research on perennial crops in forest areas and on agrofood was considered complementary to that of the IITA on food crop systems. The terms of collaboration were summarized in a note presented to the CGIAR meeting in Jakarta in mid-1996. The objective was to set up an ecoregional programme in the humid tropics involving the National Agricultural Research Systems (*CIRAD Information*, no. 59, 13 February 1996, p. 1).

With a view to implementing the ecoregional programme initiated by the CGIAR, ten African countries had joined forces with the IITA and CIRAD to create two consortia, Humid Forest and Moist Savannah. The first line of research was devoted to the analysis of regional problems prevailing – in the case of the Humid Forest Consortium – in Cameroon, Ghana and Nigeria. On the issues of deforestation and man's relation with forests, reliable indicators would be developed, as would evaluation methods involving the use of remote-sensing techniques, to see how the situation was evolving and to monitor the impact of such projects as buffer zones/protected areas. The second line of research proposed by the CIRAD concerned thematic studies, including the regeneration and replanting of old coffee, cocoa and oil-palm plantations for the consolidation of commercial subsectors, and agroforestry, which enhanced the security of the small-holder farming systems by combining annual crop species and tree crops. The CIRAD was also willing to take part in initiatives on periurban cropping systems and associated processing, an area which had so far attracted dismally inadequate resources. The third African forestry sector in which the CIRAD was hoping to step up its efforts concerned collaboration projects and research and development, e.g. the production and acceptability of improved plant material for forest planting and replanting, post-harvest and preliminary processing techniques and the development of settled agriculture in buffer zones around protected forests (*CIRAD News*, no. 13, July 1996, p. 6).

4. Biotechnologies at the CIAT

The International Center for Tropical Agriculture (CIAT) had grown out of the collaborative rice programme supported by the Rockefeller Foundation and the Colombian Ministry of Agriculture in the 1950s, whose objective was to bring the 'green revolution' to Latin America with regard to rice cultivation. In 1967, an agreement had been signed between the Rockefeller Foundation and the Colombian Government for creation of the CIAT. In 1973, the latter had been brought under the aegis of the CGIAR, its mandate being to conduct research on common beans and cassava, as well as on rice and tropical pastures in Latin America and the Caribbean.

The annual CIAT budget amounted to about $34 million in the late 1980s. It had a staff of more than 1,600, of whom 260 were scientists and professionals (Komen, 1991*a*).

The global mandate of the CIAT being centred on common beans and cassava, its endeavours were directed toward the small farmer. Beans were the staple food legume for over 500 million people in Latin America and the highlands of eastern and southern Africa. Demand was growing fastest in Africa where production growth lagged behind population increase. Cassava also played an important role in the marginal agro-ecological zones largely untouched by the 'green revolution', and it was the staple food of hundreds of millions of people, as well as the only alternative of poor farmers. The CIAT's rice programme had shifted toward opening new production possibilities in less favoured areas, while the Tropical Pastures Programme aimed at developing legume-based pastures for the acid soils of the humid and subhumid lowland tropics (Komen, 1991a).

In the CIAT, socio-economic research had long been integrated into commodity programmes, contributing to the setting of priorities in biological research. For instance, the beans economic section provided socio-economic guidelines for technology development and release, also assessing the degree of success obtained with new technology. Furthermore, a Farmer Participatory Research Project had been initiated in 1987, with funding from the Kellogg Foundation, and the contribution of sociologists and agronomists. The project's main activities involved farmers in research design and evaluation, monitoring and evaluation of farmers' own experimentation, and training (CIAT, 1989, 1990).

In Latin America, new rice technology yielded annual benefits of some $600 million, mostly in the form of lower prices for the region's 460 million rice consumers. Rice prices had dropped by 40% in real terms since 1967. As for research on irrigated rice in the International Agricultural Research Centers, there had been a decline in support, despite huge financial returns (*CIAT International*, vol. 14, no. 1, April 1995, pp. 6–7).

That is what prompted the setting up of the Latin American Fund for Irrigated Rice (FLAR) on 16 January 1995, at the CIAT. The cofounders were official and private entities of Brazil, Colombia, Uruguay and Venezuela, working with the CIAT and the Inter-American Institute for Cooperation in Agriculture (IICA). Together the members pledged $315,000 yearly to the Fund for the period 1995–1997. Delegates from the Dominican Republic attended the signing of the agreement, and Argentina and Ecuador were considering membership (*CIAT International*, vol. 14, no. 1, April 1995, pp. 6–7).

The FLAR had been endorsed by the International Rice Research Institute (IRRI), which held the world mandate on rice research. The IRRI was interested in joining the Fund and had already agreed to participate in the Fund's technical committee meetings. The FLAR aimed to make irrigated rice more competitive and profitable in the region, while also reducing environmental risks. The technical work plan assigned top priority to ensuring the region's access to the best rice germplasm available world-wide. Activities in plant breeding, integrated crop management, biotechnologies and market development were also planned under the Fund (*CIAT International*, vol. 14, no. 1, April 1995, pp. 6–7).

In *CIAT in the 1990s: a strategic plan* (CIAT, 1989), an important role was envisaged for biotechnologies. The CIAT set up the

Biotechnology Research Unit (BRU) in 1985, the key functions of which were assess the potential of new techniques using information and materials from advanced laboratories; and to make biotechnologies available to plant breeders and other agricultural researchers. Co-operative research projects were implemented with a view to putting biotechnology specialists in contact with scientists from other disciplines. Up to December 1994, the CIAT had carried out ten such projects with support from various donor agencies (Komen, 1991a; Roca, 1991).

The early biotechnological work on cassava focused on the use of tissue culture for virus elimination, germplasm exchange and conservation. Thus, over the 1980–1991 period, the CIAT contributed to the elimination of viruses (common mosaic, Caribbean mosaic, X, frogskin and latent cassava viruses) from 650 clones in 12 countries. Cassava micropropagation techniques were extended to several developing countries for the production of clean material and this resulted in significant increases in root yield under field conditions. Trials with micropropagated disease-free cassava clones had resulted in yield gains of up to 100% for many local cultivars. For instance, using 16 cassava clones sent by the CIAT as *in-vitro* cultures, the South China Institute of Botany had developed a high-yielding cassava cultivar, Nan-Zhi 188, which was quickly distributed to farmers via tissue cultures at low cost.

In co-operation with the International Plant Genetic Resources Institute (IPGRI), the CIAT had developed an *In-vitro* Active Cassava Gene Bank in 1991, after a three-year study of its technical and logistical requirements. It contained more than 5,900 clones representing over 95% of the world collection of cassava germplasm. The Center's Genetic Resources Unit maintained these clones under slow-growth conditions (i.e. at a reduced temperature in a special medium). Even so, the accessions had to be renewed every 12–18 months. The entire *in-vitro* bank occupied 35 m^2 of laboratory space, about one-thousandth of the area needed to maintain the same materials in the field. From this active collection, the CIAT had distributed nearly 2,000 pathogen-tested cassava clones to the national research institutions of 35 countries in Africa, Asia and Latin America up to the end of 1994.

An even more ideal approach was cryopreservation, or ultrafreezing of the cassava cultures. The CIAT had been working on the cryopreservation of cassava shoot tips since 1989. By 1991, CIAT scientists were able to recover complete cassava plants from shoot tips frozen in liquid nitrogen (-196 °C). Further improvements in the technique (involving changes in tissue dehydration treatments, the rate of cooling and culture media) enabled the CIAT scientists to consistently recover plants from frozen shoot tips with a success rate of more than 60%. The CIAT was developing a simple protocol for more efficient and less costly freezing, which would open the way to long-term conservation of a base gene bank of cassava clones in liquid nitrogen.

The cassava collection at the CIAT comprised nearly 6,000 accessions from the species' primary centres of diversity in the Americas and secondary centres in Africa, Asia and Australasia. One of the CIAT's tasks was to identify duplicates in the collection, which contained several local clones (each with a different name) of the same genotype; this was expected to increase the cost-effectiveness of germplasm conservation and management. Analysis of isozyme profiles, along with morphological and agronomic descriptors, showed that about 20% of the collection consisted of duplicates. Among varieties already screened on the basis of morphology and isozymes, DNA fingerprinting techniques were being used to detect genetic differences more precisely. For instance, in a sample of 100 apparently similar accessions, the CIAT scientists determined that 20 were genetically unique (and the remainder duplicates), using the gene for protein III of the bacteriophage M13 as a probe. The RAPD markers confirmed these results.

In previous work at the CIAT, cassava plants had been regenerated from somatic embryos. This system was used for transformation experiments using the plasmid construct pGV 1040 provided by Plant Genetic Systems (PGS) N.V., Belgium. Intense gene expression was obtained on globular cassava somatic embryos one-three days after microprojectile bombardment (in *Proceedings of the 1992 Miami Bio/Technology Winter Symposium, Advances in Gene Technology: Feeding the World in the 21st Century*, Miami, 20–24 January 1992, vol. 1, p. 87).

The 26,500 *Phaseolus* accessions stored in the CIAT's Genetic Resources Unit by the end of 1994 had not been thoroughly characterized. The CIAT researchers (including specialists in bean genetics, biotechnologies and agricultural geography) had formed two *core* collections. The first, containing 1,420 accessions, represented cultivated common beans (*Phaseolus vulgaris*), while the second, with 100 accessions, covered wild *Phaseolus vulgaris*. The core collections were intended not to replace the complete holdings, but to give researchers a preview of them as a guide to further investigation.

Core collections were useful, however, only if they accurately represented the genetic diversity of the species sampled. To meet this requirement, the composition of the core collections was based on a combination of factors related to the evolution of common bean and to the agro-ecological conditions in which it was found. For instance, in forming the collection of cultivated *P. vulgaris*, CIAT scientists included more accessions from primary than from secondary centres of diversity and gave more weight to primitive seed types and growth habits than to modern, commercial ones. To guarantee that the core collection covered the crop's whole range of adaptation, they had developed a simple agro-ecological classification. It was based on four factors (such as soils and rainfall) and included a total of 54 distinct agro-ecologies. Using map co-ordinates for the sites where seed of bean landraces were collected, the CIAT scientists identified the agro-ecology to which each accession belonged. In co-operation with the University of Wisconsin, they were using RAPD markers to verify that the genetic variability of the cultivated *P. vulgaris* core collection truly represented that of the base collection. One example of the use of core collections was the screening of the cultivated bean collection for phosphorus use efficiency and selection of desirable genotypes.

In addition, the characterization of wild accessions was using phaseolin and other polymorphic seed proteins as biochemical indicators of genetic diversity as well as molecular markers. These techniques helped the CIAT scientists study the genetic structure of the wild germplasm, determine the extent to which cultivated beans evolved from only a limited fraction of wild populations (referred to as the founder effect), and trace the gene flow between wild and cultivated germplasm and between the Andean and Mesoamerican gene pools of common bean.

In 1991, after many years as pioneers in the collection and selection of efficient strains of *Bradyrhizobium* and *Rhizobium* for tropical forage legumes, the Soil Microbiology Section of the CIAT's Tropical Pastures Programme changed direction: the new focus was on the role of the legume in nutrient cycling of sustainable pasture-based systems, including crop-pasture alternatives for the acid soils of tropical savannas. A multidisciplinary group which included an ecophysiologist, a plant nutritionist, a soil scientist and an animal nutritionist, was undertaking a long-term experiment on nutrient cycling which was open to participation from other parties. The CIAT collection of *Bradyrhizobium* and *Rhizobium* bacteria included some 4,000 strains, with emphasis on strains for the most frequently requested forage legume species and *Phaseolus vulgaris*. The inoculants were supplied free of charge.

Other research projects included:

– the use of ELISA to screen *Rhizobium phaseoli* germplasm for nitrogen-fixing potential and for the ability to survive and compete in the soil; strains superior to indigenous ones had been identified for some regions and were being used as inoculants in on-farm trials;

– the construction of genetic maps using RFLP markers in collaboration with the University of Florida, with a view to identifying and locating genes conferring resistance to bean common mosaic virus and bean common bacterial blight;

– the use of tissue culture for rescuing hybrid embryos and for regenerating plants from cell suspensions; cross breeding between *Phaseolus acutifolius* (tepary bean) and *Phaseolus vulgaris* (common bean) had become possible through embryo rescue, in order to transfer the resistance to bean common bacterial blight and the *Empoasca* leaf hopper, as well as tolerance of drought (Roca, 1991). See also Allavena (1984); Muñoz *et al.* (1987).

Research was also being carried out on: the transfer of traits between the two major gene pools of *Phaseolus vulgaris*, e.g. the transfer of the high-yield potential of small-seeded germplasm (Central America) to large-seeded cultivars (southern Andes); screening methods for disease resistance (e.g. common bacterial blight) and sensitivity to high temperatures in most *P. vulgaris* germplasm. Transfer of drought tolerance from tepary bean to common bean was assisted by molecular genetic markers (RFLPs) as part of the bean improvement programme (Visser, 1994*a*).

By screening thousands of accessions of wild *P. vulgaris*, the CIAT entomologists identified some resistant to Mexican bean weevil (*Zabrotes subfasciatus*), others resistant to bean weevil (*Acanthoscelides obtectus*), the two major pests of stored dried beans in Africa and Latin America, and a couple resistant to both insects.

Among Mexican bean weevils that died in resistant seed, studies conducted in co-operation with the University of Wisconsin pointed to a single cause of death – the protein arcelin, which the insect apparently could not digest well. The protein was named after a town in Mexico, Arcelia, where wild bean accessions containing the gene were collected. Since the biosynthesis of arcelin in resistant genotypes was a monogenic or simply inherited trait, the CIAT bean researchers were able to breed resistance to *Z. subfasciatus* into experimental lines of domesticated beans, which were tested in Africa and Latin America.

Arcelin had no effect on *A. obtectus*. With support from Belgium's General Administration for Development Co-operation, CIAT scientists were trying to determine which factors accounted for resistance to this pest in wild *P. vulgaris* germplasm. They had identified a protein fraction that inhibited larval development in resistant accessions of wild beans. Another fraction also contained general resistance factors limiting insect growth. These results accounted in part for the quantitative or complex genetic character of resistance to *A. obtectus.* The scientists expected to develop a biochemical assay or molecular probes permitting efficient selection for multigenic, durable resistance to this important pest. If successful, these experiments would lead to cloning of the relevant genes and their transfer to common bean.

With funding from Belgium's General Administration for Development Co-operation, scientists at the University of Ghent were cloning the arcelin-5 gene, to impart resistance to the Mexican bean weevil on common bean and other crop species. Brazil's National Centre for Genetic Resources (CENARGEN) was also investigating this possibility. At the CIAT, alternative approaches were also being explored for developing resistance, including antinutritive factors such as avidin and cystatin.

The CIAT had set up the *Phaseolus* Beans Advanced Biotechnology Research Network (BARN). During a workshop held at the Center in 1993, 50 scientists from 16 countries identified a range of topics around which co-operative projects could be developed. The workshop was funded by the German Agency for Technical Co-operation (GTZ).

New biotechnology projects included the use of RFLPs to identify and select single-gene traits associated with stress tolerance (such as osmotic adjustment, photoperiodic response and water use efficiency) in the CIAT's mandate crop species -cassava, rice, bean and fodder species (Jaffé and Rojas, 1994*a*).

The CIAT was participating in the International Programme on Rice Biotechnology supported by the Rockefeller Foundation. Co-operation of the Biotechnology Research Unit with this Programme focused on the production of thousands of doubled haploid lines obtained through anther culture. The Programme aimed to accelerate the development of improved varieties for areas where only one rice crop per year could be grown. Two years after the crosses had been made, new materials were ready for testing in farmers' fields: superior cold-tolerant and high-quality grain lines selected by Latin America's Southern Cone breeders were evaluated in yield trials (Plucknett and Cohen, 1989). A course-workshop for Latin America and the Caribbean was held at the CIAT from 13 to 16 February 1994 in a move to integrate the use of haploids obtained from anther culture into rice breeding programmes in Latin America. Working teams were formed, comprising one plant breeder and one expert in cultivation of anthers from each national rice breeding programme (*REDBIO Circular Letter*, 8, June 1994, p. 14).

Caused by the fungal pathogen *Pyricularia grisea*, rice blast was the most widespread and damaging disease attacking rice – the staple food of 2.5 billion people in the mid-1990s. The fungus produced a high number of pathotypes, whose extreme diversity complicated the development of resistant cultivars. Most rice varieties released contained single resistance genes effective against certain pathotypes. Invariably, this resistance lost its effectiveness after only two or three years, as a result of shifts in the frequency of pathotypes, immigration of existing compatible races, or the rapid emergence of new ones through mutation or other mechanisms. In the absence of varieties with durable blast resistance, many farmers relied heavily on fungicides.

In 1989, an experimental line of rice developed by CIAT researchers at Santa Rosa, a blast 'hot spot' in Colombia, was released as Oryzica Llanos 5 by the Colombian Institute for Agricultural Research. In six years of commercial production, the blast resistance (immunity) of this variety had shown no sign of breaking down. Scientists at the IRRI reported that Oryzica Llanos 5 had also shown resistance at several blast hot spots in Asia. To explain the durability of this resistance and facilitate the development of similar varieties, an interdisciplinary group at the CIAT, in co-operation with colleagues from Purdue University, Lafayette, Indiana, carried out virulence studies and characterized the genetic structure of the pathogen, using a DNA molecular probe developed at E.I. Du Pont de Nemours & Co., Inc. and designated *Magnaporthe grisea* repeat – MGR-586. Certain combinations of virulence genes were absent or occurred at a low frequency where resistance genes in the host plant were specific to a given lineage or family of pathotypes. On the basis of these results, the CIAT scientists were ameliorating the precision of breeding for durable blast resistance. Their strategy was to match combinations of resistance genes in the host plant with the combination of virulence genes either absent or occurring at a low frequency in the pathogen population. This would render the various genetic lineages of the pathogen incompatible with the host plant.

With funding from the Rockfeller Foundation, rapid progress was being made in using the lineage data derived from MGR-DNA fingerprinting, together with molecular markers (RFLPs, RAPDs) to identify chromosome segments carrying resistance to the lineages found in Colombia. Within a few years, the CIAT scientists expected to have markers enabling them to identify combinations of resistance genes more efficiently.

The IRRI and CIAT were promoting international co-operation for the development of germplasm with durable blast resistance, so that developing countries could more easily reap its benefits (estimated at $210 million annually, on average, in Latin America in 1994). While the

IRRI was co-ordinating research globally, the CIAT focused on needs in Latin America. Together with scientists from Cornell and Purdue Universities, staff of the two international centres had agreed on a joint breeding strategy. The work carried out in Santa Rosa (Colombia) was critical, because the fungus was extremely variable there.

The CIAT held a rice blast workshop in October 1994 in co-operation with the PROCISUR (Co-operative Programme for the Technological Agricultural Development of the South Cone). It focused on molecular marker-aided analysis of pathogen diversity and virulence diversity studies. The participants were multidisciplinary teams of scientists (each consisting of a breeder, pathologist and biotechnology specialist) from the five countries of South America's South Cone.

Research was also being conducted on the development of resistance to the *hoja blanca* virus, a serious limiting factor to rice production; because conventional breeding schemes were unsuccessful, a gene conferring resistance to the virus had been tagged with RFLP markers at Cornell University, with a view to transferring it to rice plants.

Brachiaria and other tropical forage grasses were among the few economically important species able to reproduce by means of apomixis. At the CIAT, scientists had identified molecular markers (RAPDs) linked to a single, dominant gene that appeared to control apomixis in *Brachiaria*. By allowing rapid identification of apomicts among progeny of crosses between apomictic and sexual types, it was reasonable to assume that the markers would help breeders at the CIAT and in Brazil combine desirable traits from different *Brachiaria* species in apomictic cultivars. In Brazil alone, more than 50 million hectares were sown to *Brachiaria* pastures and, in Latin America as a whole, these were by far the most widely grown commercial forages.

There were three prerequisite steps to genetically engineer apomictic plants: densely mapping the *Brachiaria* chromosome region on which the apomixis gene was located, using molecular markers; isolating and cloning the apomixis gene; and genetically transforming target plants. By identifying a molecular marker linked to the apomixis gene, the CIAT had embarked on the first task and, by regenerating *Brachiaria* plants from tissue culture, it had also made progress in developing a transformation protocol. This technique would allow the expression of the apomixis gene to be tested against different *Brachiaria* backgrounds. See also p. 368. for the work carried out by CIMMYT/ORSTOM scientists on the development of apomictic maize.

Techniques for plant regeneration from protoplasts had been developed for three species of the tropical forage legume *Stylosanthes*. Fusion experiments between *S. guianensis* and *S. capitata* had resulted in fusion products (callus level), from which plants were regenerated; isoenzyme electrophoresis revealed hybridity in several of the regenerated plants; the objective of this work was to transfer some *S. capitata* traits to *S. guianensis* (Plucknett and Cohen, 1989).

Transgenic plants of *Stylosanthes guianensis* had been obtained via *Agrobacterium*-mediated transformation[9] (see p. 517). The plasmid pGV1040, a typical transformation cassette provided by Plant Genetics Systems NV, Belgium, was one of the gene constructs used by the CIAT in *Agrobacterium*-mediated transformation; between its right and left borders, the plasmid contained two selectable marker genes: the *bar* gene coding for phosphinotricin resistance and the *sept II* gene for kanamycin resistance; it also possessed a screenable marker, the *gus* gene, which encoded the enzyme beta-glucuronidase. Through particle bombardment-mediated transformation, the CIAT's researchers obtained transgenic plantlets of the rice variety CICA 8.

The CIAT was developing Material Transfer Agreements (MTAs) for all exchanges of biotechnology products and methods to guarantee their availability to national institutions in developing countries.

Training in biotechnologies had started in the early 1980s under the Training and Communications Support Programme and was expanding rapidly to facilitate biotechnology transfer to developing countries (CIAT, 1990). Over the five-year period 1990–1994, more than 100 scientists took part in biotechnology training at the CIAT. In 1994, with the Rockefeller Foundation's support, the CIAT initiated a series of courses on rice improvement through anther culture. Participants formed teams, consisting of a tissue-culture specialist and a rice breeder from the same institution, to focus on how to integrate anther culture into rice breeding. In October 1994, the CIAT and the Co-operative Programme for the Technological Agricultural Development of the South Cone (PROCISUR) organized a similar course for breeders and pathologists; it dealt with molecular marker-assisted analysis of pathogen diversity, and identification and tagging of genes for host plant resistance to rice blast.

In November 1994, the CIAT offered its first international course on biotechnology for the conservation and use of agrobiodiversity, in co-operation with the Organization of American States, Instituto Colombiano de Crédito Educativo y Estudios Técnicos en el Exterior (ICETEX, Colombian Institute for Educational Credit and Technical Studies Abroad) and the Fondo Colombiano de Investigaciones

Científicas y Proyectos Especiales 'Francisco José de Caldas' (COLCIENCIAS, Colombian Fund for Scientific Research and Special Projects). Seventeen scientists from universities, national research institutes and environmental agencies in ten Latin American countries participated in this course. The objectives of the course were to: contribute to the strengthening of institutional capacities in Latin America in modern biotechnologies for the implementation of the Convention of Biological Diversity; train national professionals in the genetic/ecological interpretation of agrobiodiversity, utilizing molecular and cell biology tools; and to promote effective research-and-development collaboration mechanisms at subregional and regional level for the conservation and use of agrobiodiversity (*REDBIO Circular Letter*, 9 October 1994, p. 17).

In 1991, the CIAT set up the International Biosafety Committee to oversee all research at the Center involving recombinant DNA techniques and to monitor the release and testing of transgenic organisms. In addition, the CIAT co-organized a regional workshop on biosafety in Latin America with the Inter- American Institute for Cooperation in Agriculture. Participants in this workshop called for partnerships in the Andean countries to develop biosafety guidelines and co-operate in the properly controlled experimental release of transgenic organisms.

The second concertation between the CIAT and the inter-organization committee, including the CIRAD, INRA and ORSTOM, was held in Montpellier, France, from 6 to 8 June 1995. French researchers at the CIAT were working on several programmes, e.g. molecular biology, plant disease control, nitrogen fixation, phosphorus assimilation in soils, biological activity in soils and post-harvesting processing of agricultural products. In particular, the long-standing partnership with the CIAT on starch products was to be extended (*CIRAD Information*, no. 54, 13 July 1995, p. 6).

5. Biotechnologies at the CIP

The Centro Internacional de la Papa (CIP, International Potato Center) was established in 1971. In 1990, the CIP's professional staff totalled about 100 scientists and administrators and 500 support staff. Its total annual budget amounted to approximately $22 million.

The CIP was the first International Agricultural Research Center to set up regional programmes on its core funding. A decentralized policy of this kind had a number of advantages: the CIP's central plant had been built at a cost of no more than $3 million and maintenance costs were a fraction of those borne by other centers. The CIP maintained eight regional offices – two in Latin America, three in Africa and three in Asia. Approximately 40% of its research staff was located in these regional offices. Together with the various regional research networks initiated by the CIP, this decentralized structure could be the main channel for transferring results of advanced research to developing countries (Komen, 1992*e*).

The CIP's mandate was initially limited to research on potatoes, with a view to solving priority problems inhibiting production in developing countries. In April 1985, the CIP's mandate expanded to include sweet potatoes, due to the growing importance of this crop species neglected by research funding (Komen, 1992*e*).

Potato (white) was the fourth most important food crop species after rice, wheat and maize in developing countries, both in terms of yearly production and in value. Potatoes belong to a group of over 200 tuber-bearing, and a few non-tuber-bearing, species, all classified in the genus *Solanum* section *Petota*. Cultivated potatoes were subdivided into eight species comprising many different varieties and forms, all of which were endemic to the Andean region. Only one of these cultivated species, *Solanum tuberosum*, was cultivated world-wide. Wild potato species grew from Chile to Colorado in the USA, but a major centre of potato diversity was located in the Lake Titicaca region of southeastern Peru and southwestern Bolivia. The region harboured some 120 wild potato species and was the only known place where all cultivated potato species might be seen growing together (Bijman, 1992*b*).

Since 1980, potato production in developing countries had risen by 39%. Most was concentrated in Asia, China and India being by far the largest producers (33.05 million tonnes and 15.137 million tonnes respectively out of a total production in developing countries of 78.71 million tonnes and a world production of 190.851 million tonnes in 1990). Production was also high in Latin America and the Near East: Turkey 4.3 million tonnes; Argentina 2.5 million tonnes; Iran 2.475 million tonnes; Colombia 2.464 million tonnes; Brazil 2.219 million tonnes (in Bijman, 1992*b*).

The potato harvest was almost entirely consumed domestically, with only small quantities being exported. In 1990, the major exporting developing countries were: Egypt 180,000 tonnes; Lebanon 160,000 tonnes; Cyprus 146,000 tonnes; Syria 109,200 tonnes, China 90,500 tonnes; Indonesia 76,800 tonnes; Morocco 59,900 tonnes; Pakistan 20,300 tonnes; and Tunisia 17,000 tonnes (in Bijman, 1992*b*).

Average potato consumption in most developing countries was approximately 20 kg per capita annually, while it was about 80 kg in Western European countries. While one hectare of potatoes produced twice as much protein as one hectare of wheat, the major constraints to expanding potato production in developing countries were the limited supply and high cost of seed tubers, particularly in warm areas where viral diseases spread rapidly and storage facilities were scarce. Furthermore, the big volume of tubers to be produced, harvested, handled, stored, hauled and often desprouted before planting the following season made potato production costly. Due to the complexity of handling this perishable and bulky commodity, the private sector in many developing countries was reluctant to tackle potato production and distribution. Consequently, governments had always played a major role in developing potato seed programmes, in industrialized, as well as in developing, countries (Bijman, 1992*b*).

In addition to buying seed tubers, farmers also invested massively in fertilizers and pesticides, as potato yields were heavily dependent on seed quality, tillage, irrigation, fertilizers and pest control. Storage, processing and transportation involved additional risks, particularly in tropical regions where higher temperatures, insects, fungi and bacteria could cause severe post-harvest losses (Bijman, 1992*b*).

At the CIP, seeds were maintained from more than 1,000 accessions of about 100 different wild potato species. The *in-vitro* cultivated potato germplasm collection originally consisted of more than 13,000 samples. Through the application of electrophoresis, duplicate accessions could be identified and the collection reduced to 3,500 samples. Accordingly, management of the collection was significantly simplified. The sweet potato collection consisted of more than 2,300 accessions; duplicates were identified through electrophoresis and training in this area was provided by the CIP to scientists from Latin America and the Caribbean (Komen, 1992*e*). See also p. 505.

In addition, in co-operation with national institutions in Bolivia, Ecuador and Peru, the CIP was developing a gene bank for the less known Andean tuber crop species of oca, olluco, mashua and arracacha. In collaboration with the Research Centre of Andean Crops (CICA) of the University of Cuzco, Peru, for instance, a collection of more than 700 accessions of Andean tubers from southern Peru was maintained and characterized. Electrophoresis was applied to determine the genetic variation in such a collection and the genetic diversity in some of the Andean root and tuber crop species was found to be much smaller than the diversity existing in potatoes and sweet potatoes. This was confirmed through interviews with local farmers, showing that crop diversity in Andean tubers had decreased over recent decades (Komen, 1992*e*).

The CIP emphasized the creation of 'seed' systems in developing countries, since the cost of imported seed tubers could represent over

50% of production costs in these countries. Relatively simple biotechnologies provided opportunities for national programmes to produce quality 'seed' at reduced costs (Dodds and Horton, 1990; Dodds and Tejada, 1990).

Rapid multiplication of pathogen-free stocks through stem cutting, often combined with heat treatment (thermotherapy) or chemical treatment (chemotherapy), to clear it of pathogens, was widely used throughout the developing countries. Through the CIP training programme, the ability of national teams to handle *in-vitro* material had steadily increased.

In-vitro micropropagation could be simple enough for use by small farmers. For instance, in Burundi, a CIP project involving a seed tuber production scheme based on an *in-vitro* method of propagation combined with improved cultural practices had been launched for bacterial wilt control, with the resulting decrease in bacterial wilt infection from 60% to less than 1% (Komen, 1992*e*).

In-vitro germplasm collections, based on *in-vitro* multiplication of pathogen-free plant material, offered a number of advantages over collections maintained in the field: the material was available all year-round, it was protected from environmental and pathogen risks and could easily provide multiple copies to enable the maintenance of duplicates in different geographical locations (Bijman, 1992*b*).

Research carried out at the CIP also improved production of *in-vitro* tuberlets from pathogen-free plantlets, in order to comply with international quarantine requirements. The main advantage of *in-vitro* tuberlets was that they survived longer transit times than *in-vitro* plantlets, thus facilitating germplasm exchange. However, the production cost of a tuberlet was significantly higher than than of an *in-vitro* plantlet. The CIP collaborated in the production of *in-vitro* tuberlets with a number of institutes in the Andean countries. The CIP aimed to find ways to reduce the cost of *in-vitro* multiplication techniques: for instance, by replacing some of the basic imported chemical components of the growth media with common sugar and fertilizers, or by multiplication in bioreactors (this technique was developed at the University of Wisconsin, Madison, and licensed to the U.S. company, Small Potatoes) [Bijman, 1992*b*].

There were more than 200 wild species of tuber-bearing *Solanum*, considered as potential valuable sources of germplasm for potato improvement. Resistance to bacterial wilt, root-knot nematodes and potato tuber moth was transferred into cultivated germplasm from two diploid wild species, *S. chacoense* and *S. sparsipilum*. Successful transfer had been achieved for resistance to cyst-nematodes from the wild species *S. verneii.* A more remotely-related species such as *S. etuberosum*, which does not tuberize, was exploited through a CIP research contract with the Agricultural University of Wageningen, the Netherlands, to tap the resistance to potato leaf roll virus in this wild species. At the CIP also, a high number of hybrids between sweet potato and the wild *Ipomoea trifida*, believed to be an ancestor of the cultivated species, were produced using manual crosses and embryo rescue; resulting double hybrids could be directly crossed with cultivars, making a new gene pool of wild sweet potato species available to breeders (Plucknett and Cohen, 1989).

In collaboration with the Weizmann Institute of Science, Israel, protoplast fusion was used to transfer mitochondria-coded male sterility traits from a donor to a recipient plant. This technique was designed for low-cost production of hybrid true potato seed. Potato plants were regenerated from fused protoplasts and evaluated in the CIP's highland experiment station (Plucknett and Cohen, 1989).

The CIP had adopted collaborative networking for carrying out more complex research such as gene mapping and genetic transformation (CIP, 1991). The use of restriction fragment length polymorphism (RFLP) markers was applied to potato with a view to locating specific resistance genes, such as those coding for resistance to potato viruses X and Y (Bijman, 1992*b*).

In collaboration with the Biochemistry Department at Louisana State University (LSU), the CIP had developed a project to insert synthetic genes into potato plants, so as to enhance the nutritional value of the potato by obtaining the production of a synthetic protein rich in essential amino-acids. Although the nutritional value of potato protein was relatively high, it was deficient in certain essential amino-acids, such as lysine and methionine. In this research project, *Agrobacterium* plasmid vectors were utilized and the synthetic gene was reported to have been successfully inserted (Vayda and Park, 1990; Komen, 1992*e*).

The CIP screened and selected potato cultivars which resisted temperature shocks of − 4°C. Some 2,000 cultivars had been screened and 537 clones selected at CIP's research station in Cajamarca, Peru. This research was carried out using conventional breeding (Jaffé and Rojas, 1994*a*).

A research co-operative programme between the CIP, Louisana State University (LSU), the Central University of Venezuela and the Potato Research Programme (PROINPA, Programa de Investigación en Papa) at the Bolivian Institute for Agricultural and Livestock Technology (IBTA, Instituto Boliviano de Tecnología Agropecuaria), had been funded by the Andean Development Bank to engineer cold resistance in potato cultivars through the transfer of the gene for a flounder anti-freeze protein. It had been known since the early 1980s that a flounder, *Pseudo-pleuronectes americanus*, could survive temperatures of − 1.5°C. Several genes coding for different anti-freeze proteins (APs) had been isolated from this fish. Found in the fish's blood, these proteins protected the animal from freezing; their concentration in the bloodstream varied at different times of year, production of the proteins starting in the autumn and reaching the highest concentration in winter, before falling again in the spring. The University of Louisiana group had constructed a plasmid containing a gene coding for one of these proteins and placed it between two marker genes, thereby enabling identification of the plants transformed with a strain of *Agrobacterium rhizogenes* containing the chimaeric plasmid. The Venezuelan group introduced the plasmid supplied by the University of Louisiana into strains of *Agrobacterium rhizogenes*, which were used as vectors for carrying the genetic information into potato plant cells. Thus, the AP gene had been transferred to a group of potato clones subsequently transported to Bolivia for multiplication (Jaffé and Rojas, 1994*a*).

Since 1993, the PROINPA Group had been testing the new transgenic varieties in a confined greenhouse, the next step being that of field trials, which required a biosafety evaluation and go-ahead from national regulatory authorities. Bolivia having some experience of field trials for transgenic plant species, national biosafety guidelines had been drafted (Jaffé and Rojas, 1994*a*).

Potato is susceptible to a great number of diseases, the causal agents including viruses, bacteria, fungi, mycoplasms and nematodes. Late blight, caused by the fungus *Phytophthora infestans*, was the most damaging disease world-wide. Genetic resistance to late blight was hard to obtain and, consequently, big amounts of fungicides were applied, resulting in environmental pollution. Another fungal disease was early blight, caused by *Alternaria solani*. In developing countries, particularly those in warmer climates, the most important bacterial diseases were bacterial wilt (brown rot), caused by *Pseudomonas solanacearum*, and soft rot and blackleg, both caused by *Erwinia* bacteria. Total losses from these diseases ranged from 30% to 100% during cultivation and the two-six months of storage, when temperatures hovered between 27°C and 32°C. Genetic engineering of potatoes to obtain resistance to bacteria and fungi could use several routes: insertion of insect-derived genes coding for antibacterial peptides, or of genes coding for proteins, like osmotin, that could breakdown fungi. Several infections of complete potato plants with *Agrobacterium rhizogenes* and co-cultivation of leaves and stems with *A. tumefaciens* were made at the CIP in order to obtain transgenic plants containing antibacterial genes. Research had been initiated through contracts with the ENEA (National Atomic Energy Agency, Italy) and the University of Tuscia, Viterbo, to obtain potatoes resistant to bacterial wilt (*Pseudomonas solanacearum*) and *Erwinia* spp. (Bijman, 1992*b*; Komen, 1992*e*).

In 1990, ELISA kits produced at the CIP headquarters and distributed to national programmes were sufficient to assay more than 900,000 potato samples, with a view to detecting a broad range of potato viruses. The NASH (nucleic acid spot hybridization) test for detecting potato spindle tuber viroid (PSTV), which had a higher sensitivity and cost than ELISA, was also distributed free of charge to official seed programmes in developing countries (Komen, 1992*e*).

Efforts were made to use molecular breeding techniques to obtain virus-resistant potato plants. Obtained by genetic engineering, these plants were field-tested, their resistance resulting from the expression of viral coat protein (CP) genes, which protected the potato from being infected by the virus from which the CP gene was obtained. Although protection from several important viruses was thus conferred, this approach might only be an intermediary stage in engineering resistance. Reports indicated that resistance conferred by naturally occurring resistance genes was far superior to CP-mediated resistance, especially in vegetatively propagated crop species like potato (Bijman, 1992*b*).

The main insects causing potato crop losses were aphids, Colorado potato beetle and potato tuber moth. Aphids were very serious pests, not so much for the direct damage they caused, but because they acted as vectors for viruses. Potato tuber moth was a pest in warm, temperate and tropical regions. The potato tuber worm damaged both tubers and leaves, threatening potatoes both in the field and in storage. The Colorado potato beetle and potato tuber moth were susceptible to toxins from *Bacillus thuringiensis*. Transgenic potatoes with genes coding for these toxins were being tested in the USA (beetle resistance), Belgium and the Netherlands (moth resistance) [Bijman, 1992*b*]. In 1992, the International Potato Center and the Belgian biotechnology company Plant Genetic Systems (PGS) N.V. initiated a three-year collaboration on the production of transgenic potato clones with resistance to the potato tuber moth, supported by the Belgian Agency for International Development. Potato germplasm was supplied by the Center, the *Bacillus thuringiensis* genes and genetic engineering expertise being provided by PGS. The Center carried out field trials of the tuber moth-resistant transgenic potatoes (Bijman, 1994*a*).

Finally, transgenic potatoes with herbicide resistance had been developed by, among others, PGS. These potatoes were resistant to the herbicide Basta (active ingredient: phosphinothricin) produced by the German agrochemical company Hoechst AG (Bijman, 1992*b*).

Regarding risk analysis of transgenic potatoes, the main research issue was to ascertain how these plants would interact with wild varieties in South America, as it was possible that these would hybridize with their transgenic relatives (Bijman, 1992*b*).

Sweet potato (*Ipomoea batatas*) is an ancient crop species originating from South America; archaeological evidence from Peru showed that domestication of sweet potato dated back to 6000 BC. It was adaptable to a wide range of agro-ecological conditions and fitted in low-input agriculture. It was grown in more than 100 countries as a valuable source of food, feed and industrial raw material. About 114 million tonnes of sweet potato were produced annually in the early 1990s, almost all of it in developing countries. China alone produced 80% of the world's sweet potatoes, followed by Viet Nam.

Sweet potato was a staple caloric source in many South-East Asian and sub-Saharan African countries, the Caribbean and Pacific Islands. It provided significant quantities of ascorbic acid, riboflavin, iron, calcium and protein; in addition, orange fleshed sweet potatoes were rich in beta-carotene. Among food crop species, sweet potato had the highest recorded net protein utilization (based on percentage of food nitrogen retained in the body) [Prakash, 1994].

Sweet potato had a very high genetic variability and thousands of varieties existed in germplasm collections. The International Potato Center, which had the global mandate for sweet potato research, possessed nearly 4,000 accessions in its collection. The Asian Vegetable Research and Development Center in Taiwan (see p. 505) and the Agricultural Research Service of the U.S. Department of Agriculture also had extensive, if smaller collections. At all three locations, sweet-potato germplasm was stored *in vitro*, as tissue cultures contributed to the storage of disease-free collections and facilitated easier maintenance and distribution of germplasm (Prakash, 1994).

With funding from the U.S. Agency for International Development, U.S. Department of Agriculture and National Aeronautics and Space Agency (NASA), scientists at Tuskegee University (Alabama) had embarked on an ambitious programme to understand and manipulate the genome of sweet potato. NASA assistance was justified by the fact that the Agency had chosen sweet potato as one of eight crop species to be grown for long-term space missions. The collaborating institutes had so far succeeded in developing a tissue-culture system enabling them to quickly produce high numbers of adventitious sweet-potato plants. Somatic embryogenesis had also been achieved, researchers at the University of Florida having designed a system for producing somatic embryos from the sweet-potato cultivar, White Star, encapsulated in gels. There were also reports from France and Japan of sweet-potato plants being regenerated from protoplasts. Transgenic sweet-potato plants expressing marker genes had been developed by using *Agrobacterium tumefaciens*. Foreign genes had been introduced and expressed in sweet-potato cells using the particle gun technique (Hill *et al.*, 1992; Prakash and Varadarajan, 1992; Prakash, 1994).

The transfer of a cecropin gene from the giant silk moth had been achieved in tobacco and potato, and the resulting transgenic plants had demonstrated measurable resistance to bacteria and fungi. Synthetic versions of this gene, with improved stability and expression, were being introduced into sweet-potato cultivars at Tuskegee University (Jansson and Raman, 1991; Prakash, 1994).

Sweet-potato feathery mottle virus caused 'russet crack' disease and affected sweet potato production, particularly in Africa. Experiments were carried out to develop resistance to this virus using the coat-protein gene and anti-sense RNA genes. Research at Monsanto Co. and Tuskegee University aimed to develop transgenic sweet-potato plants using these genes. As part of this project, African scientists received training in genetic engineering of sweet potato and cassava. The U.S. AID and Monsanto Co. had both invested around $150,000 in the project. In Cuba and China, scientists had cloned the coat-protein gene of sweet-potato feathery mottle virus and were attempting to develop virus-resistant plants (Prakash, 1994).

Sweet-potato weevil was by far sweet potato worst enemy, especially in the tropics. Production losses due to this insect could reach 60% to 100% in certain areas. The weevil fed on stored roots, thereby reducing their yield and quality; secondary compounds produced by roots in response to an attack by weevils made even slightly damaged roots inedible. Unfortunately, minimal resistance to weevil could not be found in sweet-potato germplasm stored in collections. Therefore, the British Agricultural Genetics Company (AGC) had signed a contract with the United Kingdom's Overseas Development Administration (ODA) Plant Research Programme to produce transgenic insect-resistant sweet potato and potato. Since being founded in 1983, the AGC had isolated and cloned, often in collaboration with the University of Durham, 15 different plant genes whose products were insecticidal. The gene to be used in developing transgenic insect-resistant sweet potatos was the cowpea trypsin inhibitor gene. The latter was found initially in a variety of cowpea that was highly resistant to bruchid infestation. Scientists at the University of Birmimgham subsequently isolated, characterized and transferred this gene to tobacco which became resistant to many pests. It was not yet clear whether the trypsin inhibitor could protect sweet potato against the weevil, especially considering that trypin inhibitors were already present in many sweet-potato varieties. Another strategy was to search for *Bacillus thuringiensis* strains that attacked the weevil and to insert the endotoxin gene into sweet potato. The AGC had granted the ODA a non-exclusive royalty-free licence to its proprietary technology, to allow the ODA to distribute any transgenic germplasm resulting from the research programme to plant breeders in the developing world. The AGC carried out the research programme within the financial guidelines laid down by the ODA, which was responsible for co-ordinating field trials and incorporating the novel transgenic lines into conventional breeding projects. The transgenic germplasm was expected to be tested at the University of Durham and at the CIP, so as to select those lines showing the greatest resistance to the targeted pests (Barfoot, 1993; Prakash, 1994).

The most useful application of genetic engineering in sweet potato might be in the improvement of nutritional and quality traits. Sweet-potato protein was deficient in many essential amino-acids. Research at Tuskegee University aimed to introduce a synthetic gene coding for a storage protein rich in essential amino-acids. As the leaf tips of sweet potato were also consumed as a green vegetable, targeting improved protein gene expression in young leaves would also be nutritionally beneficial. Genes coding for sulphur-containing proteins, such as those found in the Brazil nut, might also be useful (Prakash, 1994).

The use of restriction fragment length polymorphism (RFLP) markers had been instrumental in assessing the relationship between cultivated sweet potato and wild *Ipomoea* species at the Agricultural Research Service of the U.S. Department of Agriculture. In addition, collaboration between the Tuskegee and Auburn Universities employed a new approach to genetically fingerprinting sweet-potato varieties. The technique of DNA amplification fingerprinting used the polymerase chain reaction to define polymorphic DNA markers and was fast enough to enable a single technician to screen 200 sweet-potato varieties in one day. Analysis of preliminary results revealed considerable genetic variation in sweet-potato germplasm collected across the globe, but little variation among U.S. varieties. DNA fingerprinting techniques could thus be employed to assess genetic variation and also to identify duplicates in germplasm collections. It also facilitated germplasm collection by identifying those geographic areas with greatest genetic diversity (Prakash, 1994).

6. Biotechnologies at the ICRISAT

The mandate of the International Crops Research Institute for the Semi-Arid Tropics (ICRISAT) was to:
– improve the yield and quality of its mandate crop species, sorghum, millet, chickpea, pigeonpea and groundnut;
– act as a repository for the genetic resources of these crop species;
– develop improved farming systems in the semi-arid tropics;
– identify constraints to agricultural development in the semi-arid tropics and evaluate means to alleviate them through technological and institutional changes;
– assist in the development and transfer of technology to the farmer through co-operation with national research programmes.

The ICRISAT research programme was organized around three multidisciplinary areas: cereals (42% of overall research resources), legumes (32%) and resource management (26%). In addition, specialized servicing units and facilities supported ICRISAT research activities. Due to the decentralized system of research management, half of the ICRISAT resources were allocated to regional operations in sub-Saharan Africa. The ICRISAT primary target group was the small-scale farmer in the semi-arid tropics (ICRISAT, 1988; Knudsen, 1991*b*).

In 1989, the ICRISAT received a $1.25 million grant from the Asian Development Bank for setting up a Plant Biotechnology Research and Training Unit. The Bank wanted the ICRISAT to maintain a leading role in crop improvement, but also its position as a 'centre of excellence' (Knudsen, 1991*b*).

Some biotechnological methods were not new to the ICRISAT. For instance, embryo rescue was being applied to the improvement of groundnut, pigeonpea and chickpea, in crosses occurring between cultivars and their wild relatives, so as to select new lines with acquired resistance to pests and disease, and with higher grain quality. Desirable genes were transferred from diploid wild groundnut species into tetraploid lines crossable with groundnut, enabling breeders to incorporate wild species genes into locally adapted material. Triploids, hexaploids, amphiploids and autotetraploids were produced and backcrossed with the cultivated groundnut. Some lines demonstrated disease resistance and good agronomic traits, including high seed yield, and were entered in the All India Co-ordinated Oilseeds Project trials. Resistant materials developed from wide crosses were being used extensively in the ICRISAT breeding programmes for India and Africa (Plucknett and Cohen, 1989).

Organized by the ICRISAT and South Africa's Agricultural Research Council in Pretoria from 18 to 20 March 1996, a workshop on groundnut viral diseases reviewed recent research work on these diseases, particularly clump and 'rosette'. Molecular biology data on these viruses had been accumulating since 1990 when the Centre for International Co-operation in Agricultural Research for Development (CIRAD) and French National Centre for Scientific Research (CNRS) jointly initiated their research, and also thanks to the work by the Scottish Crop Research Institute (SCRI). A project presented by the SCRI, CIRAD, CNRS and the University of Leuven (Belgium) was to be submitted to the European Commission for funding (*CIRAD Information*, no. 61, 19 April 1996, p. 5).

As it happened, the Asian Development Bank's grant was spent on creating a facilitating unit, servicing several ICRISAT research subunits, under ICRISAT's cereal or legume programmes. Part of the grant was used to build a monoclonal antibody producing unit, in order to manufacture tests needed for plant virus identification. Whereas this unit was located at the ICRISAT, mentor institutions were using the RFLP (restriction fragment length polymorphism) technique to locate genes or gene clusters, so as to be able to genetically identify the lines used for breeding purposes. The RFLP technique proved very promising in tracing the so-called recessive genes (e.g. resistance genes). Selection in cell cultures for resistance or tolerance to fungal toxins, viruses and some abiotic stresses was being performed at the Plant Biotechnology Research and Training Unit (Knudsen, 1991*b*).

A facility was expected to be available for growing transgenic plants, while the production of these plants was to be contracted by the ICRISAT to a specialized or private institution. The ICRISAT could then use its comparative advantage in the applied aspects of this new technology, to grow and test the transgenic plants at the new facility for reaction to semi-arid environments. The transfer of virus coat proteins to induce resistance to viruses in legumes (e.g. groundnut stripe virus) was given priority. Induction of pathogenesis-related proteins (e.g. for downey mildew resistance of millet) was also considered (Knudsen, 1991*b*).

Drought tolerance was a breeding objective for sorghum, pearl millet, chickpea and pigeonpea. Sorghum was grown on more than 40 million hectares world-wide. Pearl millet could be successfully cultivated in areas too dry for sorghum and was a good source of fresh and dried fodder for livestock. Finger millet was a food crop species in the highlands of East and Southern Africa. Pigeonpea, like chickpea, was a protein-rich crop species important in South Asian small-scale agriculture (ICRISAT, 1993).

In collaboration with several international partners, a genomic map for sorghum had been developed using maize markers, whereas mapping for drought tolerance in sorghum and pearl millet had been identified as a priority. Similar research on chickpea, pigeonpea and groundnut had been initiated (Visser, 1994*a*). See also Parleviet *et al.* (1991); Ruivenkamp and Richards (1994).

The ICRISAT collaborative research work with the Australian Centre for International Agricultural Research (ACIAR) had demonstrated that the carbon isotopic composition of groundnut leaves was well correlated with water-use efficiency. There was a correlation between the carbon isotopic composition and the thickness of leaves, the latter being an easily identifiable criterion in the selection of drought-tolerant varieties. Unfortunately, groundnut varieties that used water efficiently failed to adequately partition dry matter among their pods. Therefore, the ICRISAT, in collaboration with the ACIAR and Indian Council of Agricultural Research (ICAR), was currently studying selection possibilities for efficient water use and dry matter partitioning in groundnuts. This initiative also included testing the stability of the selected genotypes across a range of environments in India (Chaturvedi, 1994). Research on groundnut drought tolerance was also being carried out at the Central Research Institute for Dryland Agriculture, Hyderabad, India. By exposing suspension cultures to drought stress, this Institute had developed variant clones of two existing groundnut cultivars with 15% greater drought resistance (Chaturvedi, 1994).

In India, in 1992, the Water Technology Centre at the Indian Agricultural Research Institute (IARI) took up a World Bank-supported project for understanding the tolerance mechanisms of crops in drought and thermal stress environments. The project sought to evaluate the importance of stress proteins, osmotic adjustment and the ability to keep green leaves in wild and cultivated wheat, chickpea and sorghum. The relationship between drought tolerance and drought-induced proteins was also studied, the latter comprising both dehydrins, the responsive to abscissic acid (RAB) protein and water stress proteins (WSP). This four-year project had a $7 million budget (Chaturvedi, 1994).

Production of drought-tolerant varieties was also studied at the IARI Nuclear Research Laboratory, where it was reported that relative drought tolerance of wheat genotypes could be assessed quickly by measuring the leaf water spin-lattice relaxation time (a method used to determine the plant water status and water availability in different tissues) at tillering stage under irrigated or stressed conditions. The relaxation times of 20 wheat varieties with different drought tolerance levels had been measured *in vivo* with the help of low-resolution nuclear magnetic resonance (Tiwari *et al.*, 1993).

For rice, the Indian research institutes were focusing more on avoiding rather than resisting drought. For drought-prone, rainfed upland, a new hybrid variety (PNR-570) had been released which matured in 65–67 days, with a yield potential of 4,500 kg per hectare. The United Nations Development Programme had provided $3 million for the network on Development and Use of Hybrid Rice Technology at 12 Indian institutes (Chaturvedi, 1994).

The emphasis laid by Indian research institutions on drought tolerance, along with the work carried out at the ICRISAT, was in relation with the fact that nearly 50% of the 141 million hectares of India's cropped area was mainly dependent on the South-West monsoon for its water requirements. This monsoon, from June to September, contributed almost 80% of India's total precipitation. According to a survey conducted by the Indian Ministry of Agriculture covering the 1987–1988 drought, the most severe since the mid-1960s, India's GDP had decreased by 7% on account of crop loss. Nearly 286 million people had been affected, whereas the total loss of crop production accounted for 36 million tonnes, mainly of wheat, rice and coarse cereals (Chaturvedi, 1994).

A strong private sector, associated to solid National Agricultural Research Systems, would allow the ICRISAT to reduce the proportion of work carried out to produce finished crop varieties. The ICRISAT had already experienced increasing interest shown by the private sector seed industry in multiplying and marketing ICRISAT mandate crop seeds. For instance, the Centre had developed a new hybrid pigeonpea requiring only 100 days to ripen, i.e. half the time needed for conventional varieties. This reduced the maturation period so that viral and fungal diseases could not establish themselves sufficiently. It was estimated that this might save pea growers $100 million a year. The new hybrid pigeonpea, called ICPH8, also increased yields by a reported 30% to 40% and could tolerate growing conditions from abnormally dry to abnormally wet. The breeding of ICPH8 involved the screening of more than 5,000 germplasm accessions stored at the ICRISAT gene bank. It had taken 18 years to develop the hybrid, which was approved for release to Indian farmers in June 1991 (90% of world pigeonpea production came from India and it was a major source of protein in the diets of millions of people in the semi-arid zones) [Knudsen, 1991*b*].

While this development had been welcomed by the Federation of Indian Chambers of Commerce and Industry (FICCI), because it would boost the private seed industry in India (over 30 companies wished to produce and market the hybrid seeds), some ICRISAT scientists argued that the hybrid variety might be totally inappropriate for small farmers by creating greater dependence and crop insecurity that outweighed the short-term yield gains (Knudsen, 1991*b*).

In the ICRISAT strategy for the nineties, entitled Pathways to progress in the semi-arid tropics, the issues of intellectual property rights and free use of research findings needed to be considered. For instance, the Mexican agricultural department proved reluctant to exchange germplasm with the ICRISAT, because the latter made germplasm available to the private sector. The ICRISAT was therefore devising means of obtaining cash royalties from any private company using national germplasm (ICRISAT, 1991).

The ICRISAT also intended carrying out technology assessment, including of the effectiveness of ICRISAT input into strengthening National Agricultural Research Systems (NARSs). For that purpose, scientists involved in generating and exchanging technologies were expected to participate in assessing these, particularly the social implications of induced technological change in terms of growth and equity, food security and sustainability. The ICRISAT Resource Management Program (RMP) was already identifying constraints on production associated with scarcity and inefficient use of resources, studying the adoption of new technologies, outlining specifications for research. While the ICRISAT allocated less than 3% of its resources to social science research, other centres or institutes belonging to the CGIAR network used between 5% to 10% of their resources to that end. It was suggested that the RMP focus on the socio-economic effects of technology application through devoting more attention to *ex-ante* and *ex-post* technology acceptability problems (Knudsen, 1991*b*).

On 18 and 19 September 1995, in collaboration with the West and Central African Network on Sorghum Research and the Institute of Agricultural Studies and Research (INERA, Burkina Faso), the ICRISAT organized a workshop for the research group on sorghum in the North-Guinean zone of West and Central Africa in Bobo Dioulasso. About 30 researchers from ten African countries attended the workshop, which identified the priority research topics for each country participating in the Network (*CIRAD Information*, no. 56, 23 October 1995, p. 7).

The Fourth Concertation Meeting between the French CIRAD, ORSTOM, INRA and ICRISAT was held in Hyderabad from 30 November to 1 December 1995 to review: co-operation between the French research institutions and the ICRISAT, including with the

ICRISAT Sahelian Centre in Mali; the new project on groundnut in West Africa and the CGIAR ecoregional initiative 'Desert Marches', which was co-ordinated by the ICRISAT (*CIRAD Information*, no. 57, 19 December 1995, pp. 5-6).

7. Biotechnologies at the ICARDA

In 1975, the Consultative Group on International Agricultural Research (CGIAR) appointed the International Development Research Centre (IDRC, Ottawa) to set up an International Center for Agricultural Research in Dry Areas (ICARDA). The Center began operations in Aleppo, Syria, in 1977. The ICARDA mandate covered dry areas in West Asia and North Africa (WANA). This region comprised some 24 countries stretching from Morocco in the West to Pakistan in the East and from Turkey in the North to Sudan and Ethiopia in the South. The WANA region included the primary centres of diversity of the ICARDA mandate species: barley, lentils and broad bean (global mandate), and wheat, chickpea and a number of forage species (regional mandate). These crop species were the subject of four research programmes: farm resource management; cereals; legumes; pasture, forage and livestock management (Komen, 1991*d*).

Scientific information from the ICARDA and from outside sources was being spread through the *Faba Bean Information Service* (FABIS), *Lentil News Service* (LENS), and RACHIS (for cereal crop species).

In the West Asia and North Africa (WANA) region, approximately 8% of land was thought to be arable, 22% steppe and 70% desert, some of it at high altitude. The WANA region was characterized by temperature extremes: plants at the same location might suffer both from pre-flowering cold stress and pre-harvest heat stress. Soil erosion caused by run-off was potentially severe at the onset of the rainy season, while wind erosion occurred during the summer, especially in the drier areas. Despite these unfavourable conditions, the region had produced a surplus of cereals in 1950, but over three decades this situation had been reversed, the WANA becoming the largest food-deficit region in the world (Komen, 1991*d*).

In the ICARDA Medium-Term Plan for 1990-1994, it was stated that, although food self-sufficiency would prove impossible during this century in the WANA region, self-reliance for food would be enhanced through a combination of new technology, better farm practices, more favourable government policies and a more rational land-use pattern. While acknowledging that major increases in food production would come from its higher rainfall lowlands (over 350 mm of rain annually), the ICARDA focused its work on the highlands and driest areas (Komen, 1991 *d*).

Several biotechnologies had been integrated into ICARDA research programmes. Regarding immunodiagnostic techniques, polyclonal antisera had been used effectively since the early 1980s for the detection and field survey of a number of plant viruses; these antisera were produced and purified at the ICARDA to manufacture the ELISA kits for the detection of the barley yellow dwarf virus, broad bean stain virus, broad bean mottle virus and bean leaf roll virus, seed-borne *Tilletia* species, and for the differentiation between pathogenic and saprophytic species of *Fusarium*; the kits were being supplied to scientists of national research institutes.

Wide crossing in wheat and barley was carried out in collaboration with the University of Cordoba, Spain. The transfer of desirable genes from wild species of *Aegilops* was carried out at the ICARDA as well as in collaboration with the University of Tuscia, Viterbo. Interspecific and intergeneric hybridization in winter cereals aimed to: transfer genes for abiotic stress tolerance such as drought, cold, heat and salinity from wild types to cultivated forms; expand the genetic base against biotic stresses such as diseases; improve the quality and total biomass of *Triticum* and *Hordeum* in moisture-stress areas; provide specific genetic stocks to national programmes for use in their breeding programmes (Plucknett and Cohen, 1989).

In the case of barley and wheat, following anther culture, interspecific crosses and embryo rescue, the first double haploid lines were tested under field conditions (Komen, 1991 *d*). The *bulbosum* technique was used for this purpose. *Hordeum bulbosum* is a wild barley species found throughout West Asia and North Africa; it is crossable with wheat and barley (for barley only in the diploid form); however, after crossing, the *bulbosum* chromosomes are eliminated and the young embryo is cultured to produce haploids. After selection against biotic and abiotic stresses, double haploids are produced. These techniques could skip a number of intermediary breeding generations.

An ovule-embryo rescue technique was developed in order to cross the cultivated lentil species, *Lens culinaris*, with *Lens nigricans*, a wild species adapted to dry environments (Komen, 1991 *d*).

In addition to a special biotechnology project financially-supported by the United Nations Development Programme (UNDP) and France, which aimed to strengthen the institutional and scientific capabilities of the ICARDA, two major projects involving biotechnological research and application were carried out under the co-ordination of a

Biotechnology Committee, comprising members of the different crop programmes (Makkouk *et al.*, 1991; Weigand and Lashermes, 1991).

DNA marker techniques were being used to identify and characterize genetic variability within varieties, land races and wild species. In collaboration with the University of Frankfurt, DNA typing, including polymerase chain reaction (PCR) and randomly amplified polymorphic DNA (RAPD), was applied to develop single locus, trait-specific probes. The German Agency for Technical Co-operation (GTZ) was supporting the application of DNA fingerprinting techniques in the ICARDA project concentrating on developing the chickpea's resistance to the fungal disease *Ascochyta* blight. An inventory of the different strains of the noxious fungus *Ascochyta rabiei* provided insights into their geographical distribution and the degree of genetic variability (Heissler, 1996*b*).

In co-operation with institutions involved in the North American Barley Genome Mapping Network Project, the ICARDA was working on the development of RFLP markers for barley breeding in low-rainfall environments. This would allow a more efficient and accurate selection of drought-tolerant barley germplasm. Drought tolerance (DT) was not a single trait, but the collective result of many traits of a plant of which several influenced each other, positively or negatively. RFLP markers could be used for the identification and selection of single-gene traits associated with DT (such as osmotic adjustment, photoperiodic response in wheat, water use efficiency). These were the main findings of a technical study carried out at the request of the Dutch Government's Directorate General for International Co-operation (Parlevliet *et al.*, 1991). Another project supported by the GTZ aimed to develop molecular markers (RFLP and RAPD/PCR) for barley breeding, in order to effectively select disease-resistant barley germplasm (Heissler, 1996*b*).

At the ICARDA, research was being carried out on the role of rhizobia in ley farming. Ineffective or insufficient nodulation was a major constraint in establishing integrated farming systems based on the rotation of annual *Medicago* (alfalfa) species with cereals in the Mediterranean countries. Ineffective populations of *Rhizobium meliloti* in the soil often hindered effective inoculant strains, thereby affecting the exploitation of annual pastures and the improvement of livestock production. The overall objective of the *Rhizobium* research work was to increase nitrogen fixation and thereby reduce fertilizer needs for cereals in legume rotations. Research aimed at introducing a superior *Rhizobium* strain into an existing, less effective, indigenous soil population. The introduced strain would have to compete successfully with native *Rhizobium* populations for nodulation sites on the legume root and, subsequently, colonize the soil so that repeated inoculation was unnecessary. More refined methodologies for *Rhizobium* identification for use in *in-vivo* studies, including RFLP markers and enzyme polymorphism, were being developed in co-operation with the Microbial Ecology Department of the University of Lyon, France. In addition, a collaborative effort was being focused on the classification of chickpea rhizobia, involving the Universities of Lyon, Ghent (Belgium) and the French National Institute for Agricultural Research (INRA) [Komen, 1991*d*].

In collaboration with American universities, a project was being carried out to introduce the delta-toxin gene from *Bacillus thuringiensis* into rhizobia, the objective being to control the nodule feeding larvae of the *Sitonia* beetle. A complementary effort on selecting competitive lentil rhizobia strains (engineered to produce the toxin) was being made with Egyptian scientists (Komen, 1991*d*).

In 1990, the ICARDA first training workshop on the application of biotechnologies in food legumes was dedicated to the potential uses of the RFLP markers (Komen, 1991*d*).

8. Biotechnologies at the WARDA

Rice was becoming a staple food in Africa: a survey in Burkina Faso, typical of several other West African States, had shown that the poorest third of urban households obtained 33% of their cereal-based calories from rice. Consumption was rising by 5% a year and although this was a decelerating increase compared to the 1970s, there was an ever-widening gap between demand and local supply. Availability and price were major issues for consumers, and therefore also for rice producers, in West Africa (in *Spore*, the bi-monthly bulletin of information for agricultural development, Technical Centre for Agricultural and Rural Cooperation-CTA, no. 64, July-August 1996, pp. 1–3).

The effect of devaluation (1 CFA = 0.01FF instead of 0.02FF) had been to strengthen rice production in areas where it was already successful, such as in Mali. Where production was weaker, e.g. in Senegal where production had been in decline since 1991 and in Niger where the public sector had been experiencing some difficulties, devaluation had made the situation worse. Structural adjustment had loosened the grip of government on pricing, as it affected both producers and consumers (*Spore*, no. 64, pp. 1–3). Results of recent research by the West Africa Rice Development Association (WARDA) showed that it was unrealistic to believe that local rice production could ever meet the demand of the coastal capital cities. Even if it were possible to raise production sufficiently, the cost transporting rice from the hinterland to the coast, for the most part on inadequate roads, would quickly price it above imported rice. However, there were viable opportunities for local farmers to supply the many cities and towns away from the coastal ports. This meant that the cost of transport was transferred to the imported rice, favouring the competitive edge of the local supplier (*Spore*, no. 64, pp. 1–3).

Throughout much of Africa soil fertility was in decline. Pressure on land in the last two decades had the effect of reducing the fallow period of forest bush from 12–15 years to 3–5 years in high-population areas, 5–7 years elsewhere. In the savannah, similar pressures were forcing farmers to double (four to six from two to three) the number of croppings between fallow periods. Not only this had the effect of depleting the soil of nutrients, reducing organic matter and increasing soil erosion, but farmers currently had an even greater struggle with what had always been a major problem with rice production: weeds. The upland soils on which rainfed rice had traditionally been grown were vulnerable. Currrently, upland rice represented nearly 60% of the total regional rice area. Forced to intensify cultivation without access to improved inputs, farmers' practices were degrading these soils and contributing to declining productivity (*Spore*, no. 64, pp. 1–3).

In the first place, farmers needed upland rice varieties yielding more for less: any new varieties must have the capacity to reward farmers with much higher yields in return for modest improvements to their farming systems. In the second place, there were areas of land that were underexploited so that increasing rice production on these surfaces would have a positive impact on the vulnerable upland environment on which the demand for rice production currently fell (*Spore*, no. 64, pp. 1–3).

The West African Rice Development Association (WARDA/ADRAO) was formed in 1970 with the assistance of the United Nations Development Programme, the Food and Agriculture Organization of the United Nations and the United Nations Economic Commission for Africa. Its mandate was to assist member countries in becoming self-sufficient for rice. In 1992, the 16 member countries were: Benin, Burkina Faso, Chad, Côte d'Ivoire, Gambia, Ghana, Guinea, Guinea-Bissau, Liberia, Mali, Mauritania, Niger, Nigeria, Senegal, Sierra Leone and Togo. In 1986, the WARDA became a member of the Consultative Group on International Agricultural Research (CGIAR), thus converting the association into a fully-fledged

International Agricultural Research Center (IARC). Its headquarters were relocated from Monrovia, Liberia, to Bouaké, Côte d'Ivoire, and a new research programme was formulated. In 1991, the WARDA Research Division initiated the first year's work as set out in the Medium-Term Implementation Plan 1990–1994. While this Plan called for a total of 22 senior scientists and senior technical support staff in 1992, budgetary constraints limited this number to 14 (WARDA, 1989, 1991). The WARDA total funding for 1992 amounted to $6.3 million (Komen, 1992*b*).

The WARDA's initial approach to improving rice production in West Africa was to introduce the higher-yielding rice varieties developed at the IRRI, but it was soon realized that such a transfer was not feasible: irrigation was too limited in extent and small farmers in West Africa seldom had access to the necessary inputs, particularly fertilizers. The WARDA therefore decided to initiate its own breeding programmes in 1983, in all ecosystems its addressed. Research focused on three priority programmes relating to the three major rice-growing environments in West Africa:

- the Upland/Inland Swamp Continuum Rice Research Programme, located at Bouaké;

- the Sahel Irrigated Rice Research Programme, located in Senegal;

- the Mangrove Swamp Rice Research Programme, located in Sierra Leone.

A Mangrove Swamp Rice Network, which sought to assist national scientists in conducting an intensified programme of adaptive on-farm trials and maintaining and multiplying the improved cultivars, was expected to take over full responsibility for the mangrove swamp programme; partly due to financial difficulties, the WARDA phased down the programme at the end of 1992 (Komen, 1992*b*).

Throughout Africa, it was the Asian rice species, *Oryza sativa*, that had predominated in modern times, because it had much higher yield potential than the indigenous African rice, *Oryza glaberrima*. The latter was being grown only in small pockets of land for domestic consumption, because many people preferred its taste. The main reason for the greater yield of *O. sativa* was the number of grain-holding spikelets that formed on the panicle. Unlike *O. glaberrima*, which had only primary branching, *O. sativa* formed secondary, grain-holding spikelets. The more spikelets there were, the more grain the panicle could produce. This said, *O. glaberrima* was not without advantages of its own: it had droopy leaves which shaded the ground and reduced competition from weeds; it also had very rapid seedling growth and produced many more tillers than *O. sativa*, which reduced the space in which weeds could grow. Not only was weeding labour intensive, but the three-week window in the farming calendar when it was to be done was too short for most farmers to finish the job. Rice which was weeded late did not recover, even if it was cleared of weeds later in the season. The droopy leaves of African rice also helped to conserve soil moisture and, because it had evolved over 3,500 years in the African environment, *O. glaberrima* was better adapted to the biotic stresses and poor soils and was therefore more robust than Asian varieties (*Spore*, no. 64, pp. 1–3).

The work of WARDA breeders had led to successful crossing of African and Asian rice species. The new progeny developed like *O. glaberrima* in the early growth stages, with thin droopy leaves which helped smother weeds. As the rice plant grew, it became more like *O. sativa*, the leaves becoming thicker and more upright and therefore capturing solar radiation more efficiently, a trait critical for high yield potential. The new varieties also inherited the thicker stem of the *sativa* parent and were less susceptible to lodging. Their panicles developed with secondary spikelets and most of the new progeny had substantially bigger panicles than either of their parents. These new varieties, like their *O. glaberrima* parent, continued tillering even under drought conditions (*O. sativa* increased its height in preference to tillering when under stress). The new progeny was a good starting material for subsequent breeding programmes (*Spore*, no. 64, pp. 1–3).

There were 20–30 million hectares of inland valleys in West Africa, of which less than 15% was cultivated and less than 5% was used for rice. In a single decade, lowlands had the potential to produce ten crops of at least twice the yield compared to the three crops (allowing for fallow) achievable on uplands. The new varieties developed by the WARDA had the genetic potential to resist some of the agronomic constraints experienced in lowland cultivation, particularly rice yellow mottle virus (RYMV), blast and African rice gall midge (*Spore*, no. 64, pp. 1–3).

First described in Kenya in 1966, RYMV was Africa's only known rice viral disease and had spread throughout most of sub-Saharan Africa where rice was grown in lowland, humid conditions. It affected the improved rice varieties cultivated under irrigation and derived from *O. sativa*. At its worst, RYMV caused 100% loss. If inoculation by the virus occurred early in the life of the plant, its height was reduced by 60% and the number of tillers was curbed. The panicles did not open up properly and the percentage of filled grain was dismal. Sites where the virus was most presistent had been identified and varieties that were similar to those preferred in the region were being tested at these 'hot spots' with the help of national scientists through the WARDA Task

Force, which involved the National Agricultural Research Systems (NARSs) of its member States. About 112 varieties were being tested in special screen houses. These varieties had been challenged with the virus by the simple process of grinding leaves from infected plants and wiping the crushed residue, by hand, onto the leaves of the varieties to be tested. The most resistant ones had been selected and, provided they proved suitable in all other respects, would be available for release in 1997. Perhaps most promising of all were the new varieties, some of which carried not only resistance but also natural immunity to the virus (*Spore*, no. 64, pp. 1–3).

Advances in rice research had the potential to deliver real improvements to the rice production sector in Africa that would be beneficial to rural producers, urban consumers and those in-between who were involved in milling and trading. African rice farmers needed continued support from the agricultural research community in order to respond to the demand while protecting the region natural resource base (*Spore*, no. 64, pp. 1–3).

The African rice germplasm collection was expected to be transferred from the IITA to WARDA, which would then take a greater responsability for rice biotechnology research in West Africa. The WARDA therefore intended to expand its biotechnology research capacity through close co-operation with the IRRI during the 1995–2000 period (Komen, 1992*b*).

On 26 June 1992, the WARDA and the inter-organizational committee representing the CIRAD (French Centre for International Co-operation in Agricultural Research for Development), INRA (French National Institute for Agricultural Research) and ORSTOM (French Scientific Research Institute for Development in Cooperation) signed an agreement to undertake joint research programmes in areas of common interest.

9. International Plant Genetic Resources Institute (IPGRI)

Established in 1991, the IPGRI was an autonomous international scientific organization operating under the aegis of the Consultative Group on International Agricultural Research (CGIAR). The international status of the IPGRI was conferred under an Establishment Agreement which, by December 1992, had been signed by the Governments of Belgium, China, Denmark, Egypt, India, Italy, Jordan, Kenya, Switzerland, Syria and Turkey. After ratification by the Italian

Parliament of an agreement to locate the IPGRI in Rome, the IPGRI commenced operations as an independent international organization, benefitting from strong programme links with the FAO, under which the IPGRI had previously operated as the International Board of Plant Genetic Resources (IBPGR). Financial support for the core programme of the IBPGR/IPGRI was provided in 1992 (and in subsequent years) by the Governments of Australia, Austria, Belgium, Canada, China, Denmark, France, Germany, India, Italy, Japan, the Republic of Korea, Mexico, the Netherlands, Norway, Spain, Sweden, Switzerland, the United Kingdom, the USA and the World Bank (IPGRI, 1993).

The IBPGR was set up in 1974 in response to calls for international action to stem the loss of irreplaceable plant genetic resources. It was administered as a unit within the FAO but reported to, and received funds from, the CGIAR. From an organization reacting to an emergency in the early 1970s and heavily involved in collecting plant germplasm, the IBPGR had evolved to provide a wide range of services supporting national, regional and global efforts in plant genetic resources. This development was made possible by structural changes, by a broader research programme to foster scientific and technical knowledge, by an information programme, and by opening regional offices to ensure greater contact with national activities (IPGRI, 1993).

SUMMARY OF ACHIEVEMENTS

From its first effective year of operation (1975), the IBPGR scientific and technical support to national genetic resources programmes had contributed to the establishment in over 100 countries of *ex-situ* national and international storage facilities for the conservation of germplasm of particular crops.

The IBPGR had always been heavily involved in collecting germplasm, especially in the early years when massive genetic erosion was occurring as local cultivars were replaced by new crop varieties. By 1991, almost 200,000 samples had been collected on missions sponsored by the IBPGR to 120 countries; three Seed Handling Units had been set up at Royal Botanic Gardens, Kew, United Kingdom, the University of Singapore and the Tropical Agriculture Research and Training Centre (CATIE, Turialba, Costa Rica). Over time, emphasis moved from broad collecting of cultivated material to specific cultivars either threatened by genetic erosion or needed to fill gaps in existing collections.

The IBPGR training efforts were initially concentrated on supporting a post-graduate course on the conservation of plant genetic resources, at the University of Birmimgham. Soon however, activities were to expand to cover short courses, individual training and internships for qualified scientists and technicians. Since its creation, and up to 1992, the IBPGR had sponsored 1,700 scientists and technicians on different aspects of plant genetic resources.

The IBPGR work on the documentation of plant genetic resources had resulted in a standardized system for characterizing germplasm samples. The system had been adopted by institutions throughout the world and the IBPGR had published almost 70 standardized descriptor lists. Seven volumes in a series of Directories of Germplasm Collections had been produced listing the germplasm holdings of specific crops and food plants held in institutes around the world. Data-bases were established to cover: profiles of national genetic resources systems, *ex-situ* germplasm collections world-wide, germplasm collecting carried out with IBPGR support and training activities sponsored by the IBPGR.

The IBPGR had produced over 200 publications, from informative newsletters to research-level textbooks and conference proceedings. In connection with the IBPGR Communications and Library Services Programme, 40 publications were issued in 1989–1990, including the *FAO/IBPGR Plant Genetic Resources Newsletter* and several issues of the *IBPGR Regional Newsletters*. A public awareness project on genetic resources in Latin America sought to educate journalists from influential Latin American journals and newspapers as a means of reaching the project's target audience, i.e. policy-makers and those who influence them. Carried out in collaboration with the International Center for Tropical Agriculture (CIAT), the International Potato Center (CIP), the International Center for the Improvement of Maize and Wheat (CIMMYT), *Diversity Magazine* and Interpress Services, the project consisted of training exercises and visits by journalists to the Latin American CGIAR centres, as well as the production of specific information materials. Another example of inter-center collaboration in the area of public awareness was the publication in 1989 of *Partners in Conservation*, a booklet describing the plant genetic resources activities of each of the CGIAR centers. An important public affairs initiative in 1989–1990 was the publication of the first two issues of *Geneflow*, a magazine targeting policy-makers and non-governmental organizations concerned with the Earth's plant genetic resources. The IBPGR Library provided information, basic documents and bibliographic data on plant genetic resources, as well as storing, preserving and disseminating project documents. The Library served the immediate information needs of staff through the provision of a current awareness service, a bibliographic research service and document supply and reference services.

The IBPGR had pioneered the concept of networks dealing with the genetic resources of individual crop gene pools as a mechanism to ensure better conservation and wider use of underexploited genetic resources, provide support to crop improvement programmes and to strengthen links among and between developed and developing countries. This concept had been rapidly accepted and an ever-increasing number of such networks were being set up. An international crop networks programme initiated in 1988 by the IBPGR brought together germplasm collectors, curators, researchers, breeders and users, in networks based on crop gene pools. The programme promoted activities on 11 crop species: barley, maize, rice, buckwheat, groundnut, alfalfa, sweet potato, okra, beet, banana and coconut. Seven international crop data-bases had been established or strengthened.

The IBPGR had supported ground-breaking research to improve conservation technology, particularly seed storage methods and standards for storage, monitoring and management in gene banks that were employed world-wide. The IBPGR-sponsored research projects on ultra-dry seed storage studied the effects of moisture and temperature on seed longevity, preservation techniques for recalcitrant seeds, genetic stability during storage and regeneration, and seed dormancy. A number of widely accepted guidelines and handbooks on basic seed conservation had resulted from these early efforts. The programme had expanded into fundamental research on *in-vitro* conservation, particularly the development of a pilot *in-vitro* active gene bank with the CIAT, which had led to the practical application of these techniques in a number of developing countries. Research on genetic diversity, conservation technology, regeneration and evaluation had resulted in significant advances in conservation strategies and techniques. Collaboration between the FAO and IBPGR on plant pathology and quarantine as it affected the movement of germplasm had led to the publication of widely used guidelines on the safe exchange of germplasm. The FAO and IBPGR had published guidelines for transporting germplasm of cocoa (1989), edible aroids (1989), *Musa* (1989), sweet potato (1989), yam (1989), legumes (1990), cassava (1991), citrus (1991), grapevine (1991), vanilla (1991), coconut (1993) and sugar-cane (1993). Guidelines were being published for potato, small grain cereals, nuts, *Fragaria, Rubus, Ribes* and *Vaccinium* (*REDBIO Circular Letter*, 9, October 1994, p. 16).

The IBPGR co-ordinated the European Cooperative Programme for Crop Genetic Resources Networks which had stimulated the development of European Crop data-bases (IPGRI, 1993).

FRAMEWORK OF ACTION

Developments in the political, economic, environmental and scientific arenas were impinging on plant genetic resources and biological diversity in general. It was therefore important to identify those areas where changes would affect what the IBPGR could achieve and for it to be able to adapt accordingly, while maintaining flexibility to respond to unforeseeable developments.

The United Nations Conference on Environment and Development (UNCED, Rio de Janeiro, June 1992) had on its agenda the item of biological diversity. The Earth Summit approved the global environment and development programme, *Agenda 21*, which depended on many hundreds of millions of dollars of new funding (see p. 283). The Keystone International Dialogue Series on Plant Genetic Resources had earlier proposed a global initiative for the sustainable use of plant genetic resources, the cost of the suggested measures being estimated at $300 million a year (see p. 43).

The IBPGR contributed to developing the Convention on Biological Diversity. About 150 countries at the UNCED had originally signed the document, other countries, like the USA, following suit. It was important that awareness of these critical issues and the momentum generated by the UNCED be maintained during the 1990s (IPGRI, 1993).

More intensive medium- and high-input farming methods were expected to contribute to increasing productivity in many parts of the world but, for a large number of developing countries, self-reliance in food production would only come with improvements in low-input agriculture in difficult environmental conditions. Plant genetic resources would play a key role in achieving these new production levels (IPGRI, 1993).

Biotechnologies had already made a significant contribution to the preservation and utilization of genetic resources. Examples included:
- *in-vitro* collecting (techniques had been developed for a wide range of crops including oil-palm, coconut, temperate fruits and forage grasses);
- conservation using tissue culture (both slow-growth and cryopreservation techniques offered effective and sometimes unique options for conserving species which could not be stored as seeds);

– evolution and the relationship between species (molecular genetic techniques provided new insights into the relationship between species in crop gene pools and on the amount of variation in individual species, which had led to more effective collecting, maintenance and use of germplasm);

– genetic diversity (techniques such as RFLP – restriction fragment length polymorphism – and RAPD – random amplified polymorphic DNA – provided high-quality assays of the extent and distribution of genetic diversity in target populations or species, a priority now being to adapt these methods to large numbers of accessions);

– identifying useful genes (DNA probes could be used to determine useful genes and new alleles in large batches of samples; PCR (polymerase chain reaction) techniques would enable desired genes to be detected in segregating populations and in bulk tests of gene bank material);

– disease indexing (reliable and sensitive procedures using antibody and molecular techniques for such diseases as banana bunchy top virus were improving and tranforming the safety of germplasm storage and transfer);

– genetic engineering (the practical methods being used for the routine transfer of genes across natural reproductive barriers were widening the range of species useful in plant improvement and greatly extending the usefulness of conserved germplasm);

– DNA storage (long-term storage of DNA samples provided a viable option for maintaining useful genes or security storage of extremely rare plant material and would take its rightful place among the tried and tested procedures necessary to an integrated conservation strategy for the different crop gene pools) [IPGRI, 1993].

Changes in legislation dealing with intellectual property protection, especially patenting applied to plants or plant genes, were likely to influence the availability of plant genetic resources in the future.

Throughout the world, ever since the birth of agriculture, farmers, plant breeders, foresters and gardeners had used the genetic variation in plants to develop new types and varieties of crops. They had developed an extensive range of different plant genotypes adapted to a broad gamut of environments and providing a wide array of useful products. As land use patterns changed or land was degraded by erosion, as forests were cleared or the desert encroached, so the genetic diversity contained within wild species and cultivated varieties was lost.

Thus, despite greater conservation efforts, it was estimated by the early 1990s that at least 17 million hectares of forest were being destroyed every year. According to the FAO report published on 10 August 1993 on the Global evaluation of tropical forest resources,more than 150 million hectares of forests had disappeared in tropical countries between 1981 and 1990, equivalent to an annual deforestation rate of 15.4 million hectares. The heaviest losses were to be found in Latin America and the Caribbean (7.4 million hectares per annum), followed by Africa (4.1 million hectares per annum), Asia and the Pacific (3.9 million hectares per annum). Brazil and Indonesia were the greatest culprits, with 3,670,900 hectares and 1,212,000 hectares respectively deforested during the period of the evaluation. Conversely, only 43.8 million hectares had been replanted in the countries under review, 30.7% of efforts proving a success according to the FAO. The FAO Director-General warned that if the destruction of forests continued at the same pace, irreplaceable biological wealth would disappear. Among the main reasons for deforestation, the FAO cited the conversion of forest into crop land, slash-and-burn agriculture, grazing land extension and the sprawling of urban and industrial areas. Tropical countries still possessed abundant forest resources, but population growth combined with economic stagnation and the increasing demand for land to meet subsistence needs would likely lead to more deforestation. The basic cause of deforestation was indeed proverty; as the FAO Director-General put it: how could we expect from people who were starving to protect forests and care about the well-being of future generations, when their immediate survival was threatened?

Conservation and development were linked both biologically and logistically. Development and the enhancement of human well-being were partially dependent on agriculture, which in turn relied on the sustainable use of plant genetic resources, i.e. using components of biological diversity in a way and at a rate that did not lead to its long-term decline. Modern plant breeders relied on the genetic variation in primitive forms and wild species, landraces and traditional varieties to produce better adapted and higher-yielding crop plants. In turn, development was needed to provide the incentives and material resources for conservation to take place. Countries rich in biological diversity were currently looking for practical ways to draw monetary value from their assets. Plant species used for food, timber, fuelwood or medicine and genetic resources to be used in the future improvement of plants were elements of biodiversity of long-standing economic value (IPGRI, 1993).

IPGRI PARTNERS

National programmes on plant genetic resources were the building blocks of a global effort. Some national programmes were confined to a national plant genetic resources unit; others included non-governmental organizations, seed companies, university researchers, plant breeders, herbaria and botanic gardens, co-ordinated through a national plant genetic resources committee. In yet others, the various groups were linked informally. National programmes ranged in size from one or two persons collecting seeds for storage in a domestic freezer, to a wide array of research centres with hundreds of scientists conserving and studying germplasm to support large plant breeding programmes. Each was an important national facility with the potential to make a growing contribution to national development.

A national programme survey carried out by the IBPGR in 1992 showed that, throughout the world, there were 26 countries with one collection, 45 countries with two to five collections and 48 countries with six or more collections; there were 195 institutions with long-term storage facilities, 242 institutions with medium-term storage facilities, 22 institutions holding field collections and 23 institutions with *in-vitro* storage facilities, four gene banks holding 100,000 or more seed occasions, 61 gene banks holding between 10,000 and 100,000 seed occasions, and 877 gene banks holding between 1 and 10,000 seed accessions (IPGRI, 1993).

Some of the older national programmes had made substantial contributions to crop improvement and agricultural research. Among the newer ones, several – including some in developing countries – had important collections, good facilities and activities in germplasm study and distribution. Many national programmes were, however, very weak and depended heavily on external support. The way in which national programmes would develop during the 1990s to meet their own needs would be crucial to the future conservation and use of plant genetic reousrces world-wide (IPGRI, 1993).

The majority of the CGIAR International Agricultural Research Centers had plant genetic resources programmes. Every commodity center had a well-established genetic resources unit and was entrusted with the major responsibility of assembling and maintaining collections of germplasm of its mandate crops including, in most cases, related wild species. Some were engaged in advanced research on germplasm conservation and had characterized and evaluated large numbers of accessions. An Inter-Center Working Group on Plant Genetic Resources, set up in 1987, co-ordinated collaboration between the individual Centers. The CGIAR had enlarged its scope to encompass agroforestry and forestry; consequently, two additional institutions, the ICRAF and CIFOR, had expanded the CGIAR's role in plant genetic resources work. Among the non-commodity centers, increased collaboration with the ISNAR in support of national programmes, and with the IFPRI on policy issues opened up new avenues to the IPGRI (IPGRI, 1993).

The CGIAR Centers located in or near areas of agricultural origin and diversity of crop species had built up over 600,000 accessions, the world's largest collection of genetic resources. It was CGIAR policy for collections assembled as a result of international collaboration to be held in trust for researchers throughout the world. Well over 100,000 samples of materials held in CGIAR collections were distributed over a two-year period (IPGRI, 1993).

During the 1990s, the CGIAR was reorienting some of its efforts on an eco-regional basis. Eco-regional activities were proposed which focused on strategic and applied research to enhance the development of sustainable production systems, and on greater collaboration with national partners. Global activities would focus not only on key commodities, but also on policy, research management, irrigation management and the conservation of genetic resources (IPGRI, 1993).

Regional programmes oriented toward plant genetic resources were generally dictated by the importance of a particular crop or geographical area, for instance the Regional Committee for South-East Asia and the Southern African Development Community regional genetic resources programme. They could be highly effective in promoting co-operation between countries and the IPGRI was envisaging a close partnership with them.

In 1992, the IPGRI signed a co-operation agreement with the French agricultural research institutions: the National Institute for Agricultural Research (INRA), Centre for International Co-operation in Agricultural Research for Development (CIRAD) and the French Scientific Research Institute for Development in Cooperation (ORSTOM).

Nine countries from Asia, the Pacific, Africa and America were represented at the first meeting of researchers responsible for coconut germplasm collections. Organized under the aegis of the IPGRI and held from 18 to 22 May 1992 at the CIRAD premises in Montpellier, the meeting discussed the principle of setting up and managing the data-base of the new Coconut Genetic Resources Network (COGENT). It should be pointed out that, in 1991, a CIRAD-ORSTOM research team had achieved a world first by obtaining somatic coconut-palm embryos from young leaves and inflorescences, and for diverse varieties. The Montpellier-based researchers were striving to improve the process of somatic embryogenesis so that it could be scaled up. The first *in-vitro*-derived plantlets were planted in an experimental station in Africa. Owing to the genetic improvement resulting from this propagation technique, 25% to 30% increases in plant yields were forecast. This technique was therefore of prime importance for certain Asian and Pacific countries where coprah was the primary export commodity.

From 8 to 10 September 1993, around 100 researchers from some 20 countries in Europe, Africa, Latin America, Asia and the Pacific took part in EUROCOCO, the first international seminar on European coconut research, held in Montpellier. The seminar was organized by the CIRAD Bureau for the Development of Research on Tropical Perennial Oil Crops (BUROTROP). Topics covered by the seminar included genetic improvement of coconut, biotechnology applications, crop protection, chemistry and technology. In addition, a round-table was devoted to international co-operation and, in particular, research networking.

From 11 to 15 September 1995, the management committee of the Coconut Genetic Resources Network (COGENT) met in Kasaragod, India, at the Central Plantation Crops Research Institute (PCRI). The committee, funded by the Asian Development Bank, included the 13 participating countries of the Asia-Pacific region, as well as the associated regional and international organisms (IPGRI, the World Bank, Australian Centre for International Agricultural Research-ACIAR, Max Planck Institute, CIRAD Department of Perennial Crops, Bureau for the Development of Research on Tropical Perennial Oil Crops – BUROTROP). The Network activities were reviewed and an action programme was designed for 1996. Emphasis was laid on the ways and means to improve coconut cultivation and performance in order to enhance its competitivity (*CIRAD Information*, no. 56, 23 October 1995, p. 7).

The genetic resources network named TROPIGEN was set up during a meeting held in Brasilia at the end of 1993, on the initiative of participants in the PROCITROPICOS[10] (see p. 517) programme. Tropigen was expected to co-ordinate research on the genetic resources of eight countries in the Amazonian basin. Joint activities were to be conducted on peach-palm, semi-domesticated cocoas, pineapple and papaya. The CIRAD Departments of Perennial Crops and Fruit and Horticultural Crops (CIRAD-CP and CIRAD-FLHOR) elaborated a project on peach-palm for funding by the European Commission within the framework of the Science and Technology for Development programme (STD-3).

COLLABORATION BETWEEN THE IPGRI AND FAO

On 21 September 1990, the IBPGR and FAO had signed a Memorandum of Understanding on Programme Co-operation which was to remain in force after the IBPGR was renamed the IPGRI a year later. The main elements of the Memorandum were:

– the IPGRI subscribed to the principles of the International Undertaking on Plant Genetic Resources and was committed to implementing the Undertaking together with the FAO;

– the FAO and IPGRI recognized the intergovernmental authority of the Commission on Plant Genetic Resources;

– the FAO and IPGRI agreed to co-operate to ensure complementarity of effort and optimal use of resources;

– the FAO would focus mainly on the political, legal and technical issues contained in the Undertaking, supporting the work of the Commission on Plant Genetic Resources and assisting Member countries;

– the IPGRI would act within and outside the CGIAR system to sustain a viable international plant genetic resources programme, especially through enhancing national and international capabilities;

– the IPGRI would provide scientific and technical advice to the FAO and, through the FAO Secretariat, to the Commission;

– the FAO would assist the IPGRI in its work and facilitate its access to the FAO Member States;

– the FAO and IPGRI agreed to co-operate on the preparation of a periodical report on the State of the world's plant genetic resources, which the FAO would submit to the Commission on Plant Genetic Resources;

– the FAO Network of Base Collections and the IPGRI's register of base collections would be merged as far as possible;

– the FAO and IPGRI would prepare crop-specific protocols and guidelines for use by quarantine officials and scientists involved in the exchange of plant germplasm;

– the two organizations would develop various programme activities of common interest and would keep each other informed of relevant programme initiatives;

– an FAO representative would be a trustee of the IPGRI and a representative of the IPGRI would be invited to the Commission meetings;

– the IPGRI would provide the Commission with a report on its activities through the FAO Secretariat (IPGRI, 1993). See also p. ...

THE IPGRI MISSION AND STRATEGY

The IPGRI mission was to encourage, support and engage in activities to optimize the conservation and use of plant genetic resources worldwide, with special emphasis on the needs of developing countries. The IPGRI differed from most other CGIAR institutions in that its work was executed principally through supporting and facilitating the work of others. That is why it acted in partnership with other national, regional and international organizations, when undertaking research and training or providing scientific and technical advice and information (IPGRI, 1993).

Significant advances had been made in conserving the genetic resources of the world's major crop species, but conservation efforts had barely begun for a wide range of plant biodiversity, particularly for many minor crop species and trees. Gaps existed in the world's collections of plant genetic resources; some had redundant accessions, while in others accessions had not been duplicated for safety. Many lacked legal protection under national legislation or international arrangements to ensure their long-term security. Existing conservation methods needed to be improved and adapted to suit developing countries (IPGRI, 1993).

It was necessary to evaluate conserved material so as to ascertain which characteristics users were looking for. An adequate amount of good material would need to be put at their disposal. It was also important that samples be made widely available, which meant increased movement of germplasm, with the consequent need for more work on plant health. In the meantime, a trend was emerging toward greater restrictions on germplasm accessibility. A key challenge was to assure co-operation at the national, regional and international levels, while securing the increased funding required to develop and maintain an adequate system of conservation (IPGRI, 1993).

The IPGRI long-term strategy set four objectives. The first objective was to assist countries, particularly developing countries, to assess and meet their needs for the conservation of plant genetic resources, and to strengthen links with users of plant genetic resources. The IPGRI was paying special attention to those countries lacking the capacity to develop a fully objective system themselves. It was helping them to assess their own needs for genetic resources conservation, exchange and use. Increasing emphasis was being laid on surveying genetic resources through collecting missions, early warning systems for genetic erosion, appropriate sampling strategies, and the handling characterization and evaluation of accessions (IPGRI, 1993).

The IPGRI work with national programmes took various forms including:
   – assisting with assessing national needs and inventorying national plant genetic resources;
   – advising on the development of national priorities, plans and strategies for plant genetic resources conservation and for setting up and maintaining strong links with users;
   – co-operating on setting up national co-ordination systems and early warning mechanisms;
   – stimulating and facilitating international linkages;
   – providing scientific and technical advice and access to information;
   – identifying and providing suitable opportunities for training;
   – contracting research out to appropriate national institutions;
   – participating jointly in certain key activities, e.g. in genetic resources surveys, data-base development and germplasm rescue missions;
   – encouraging the adoption of international standards and guidelines for various aspects of plant genetic resources and taking an active part in preparing, evaluating and revising them;
   – collaborating in securing adequate resources, both through targeted awareness building in the countries themselves and through assistance in the design and submission of projects for external funding;
   – promoting the importance of appropriate national genetic resources policies and activities among policy-makers and those who influenced them (IPGRI, 1993).

The second objective was to build international co-operation in the conservation and use of plant genetic resources. To that end, the IPGRI was encouraging and supporting the formation of networks, both on a crop and geographical basis. Networking efforts focused on those plants of key importance to regional agriculture and forestry. The CGIAR Centers were important partners in this respect. The IPGRI was working toward a system ensuring that the diversity of useful plants was safely conserved and that accessions in gene banks were documented, conserved, whether *in situ* or *ex situ*, under safe conditions, duplicated in at least one other location and accessible for use via active collections (IPGRI, 1993).

The FAO remained a special partner of the IPGRI, especially with regard to the implementation of the programmes and initiatives of the FAO Commission on Plant Genetic Resources. The IPGRI had collaborated closely with the FAO for the Fourth International Technical Conference on Plant Genetic Resources. Other opportunities for collaboration included activities in support of national and regional programmes, advice to FAO technical assistance projects and joint activities in forestry genetic resources. Collaboration with the United Nations Environment Programme and UNESCO was to be strengthened through the IPGRI's membership of the Ecosystem Conservation Group, a joint intergovernmental agency/international NGO forum, which also included the FAO. As a member of this Group, the IPGRI would be in a position to place genetic resources in the broader context of biological diversity conservation, particularly in the follow-up to the United Nations Conference on Environment and Development (IPGRI, 1993).

The Convention on Biological Diversity made specific provisions for the conservation and exchange of genetic resources. These included the development of *ex-situ* approaches to conservation as a complement to *in-situ* conservation. The recognition by the Convention of the central importance of national programmes and its placing of an obligation on signataries to integrate the conservation and sustainable use of biological resources into national decision-making was in accord with the IPGRI's mission and strategy. The Convention also emphasized the need to facilitate the exchange of information relevant to conservation and use of genetic resources; this was directly in line with the IPGRI's objectives. Also, the free exchange of plant germplasm, emphasized in the Convention, was fundamental to the strategy of both the IPGRI and the CGIAR (IPGRI, 1993).

The third objective was to develop and promote improved strategies and technologies for plant genetic resources, and integrated methods of conservation. Retention of diversity in collections, conservation technology and plant health were major topics.

Rarely would it be feasible or safe, or cost-effective to conserve the full range of the diversity of a crop, forage or forest gene pool *ex situ*, under base collections conditions. As a general rule, the most effective option would be a combination of methods including *in-situ* conservation of natural populations that would continue to evolve and adapt to environmental change, and *ex-situ* collections in gene banks. The latter should be well described, readily available for distribution to users and protected from the natural disasters that threatened field populations. For material difficult to store as seed, *ex-situ* collections might be conserved in field gene banks or as tissue cultures, embryos, pollen or perhaps in DNA banks (IPGRI, 1993).

There were several types of collection:
– a base collection comprised a set of genetically different accessions of a given gene pool conserved for the long term, ideally

under long-term storage conditions; the international base collection of a gene pool could be regarded as the sum total of all genetically different accessions conserved *ex situ* in gene banks throughout the world; base collections were not normally used as a routine distribution source;

– an active collection was a collection of germplasm used for regeneration, multiplication, distribution, characterization and evaluation; ideally, germplasm in the active collection should be maintained in sufficient quantity to be available on request; active collection germplasm was commonly duplicated in a base collection and was often stored under medium- to long-term storage;

– a working collection was generally for short-term use by the holder of the collection; such collections were commonly used by breeders or researchers;

– a field collection or field gene bank was a collection of living plants (e.g. fruit trees, glasshouse crops and perennial field crops); germplasm which would be otherwise difficult to maintain as seed could be kept in field collections;

– an *in-vitro* collection was a collection of germplasm kept as plant tissue or organs; in some cases the tissue was stored at very low temperatures such as in liquid nitrogen (cryopreservation);

– a core collection attempted to combine the maximum genetic variation of a species within a manageable number of samples; core collections were a means of improving the accessibility and increasing the use of collections; they were not a substitute for base and active collections (IPGRI, 1993).

The two basic approaches to conservation were *in-situ* and *ex-situ* methods, which should always be considered complementary. *In-situ* conservation maintained plants and animals in their original habitats; it was appropriate for many wild species, including relatives of crops and particularly trees, for which no adequate *ex-situ* methods were available. *In-situ* conservation preserved evolutionary processes and had low direct costs (IPGRI, 1993).

Ex-situ conservation maintained organisms outside their original habitats in facilities such as botanic gardens, seed gene banks, *in-vitro* gene banks and field gene banks. Seed gene banks were considered safe and cost-effective for the majority of seed-producing agricultural crop species. Field gene banks were useful for species with seed that was difficult to store, including rubber, cassava and potato. *In-vitro* gene banks conserved material in a nutrient medium; for certain species, *in-vitro* conservation was the only currently viable method for long-term conservation. *Ex-situ* conservation made it easier for scientists to access, study, distribute and use plant genetic resources (IPGRI, 1993).

The IPGRI had published a list of institutions providing a virus cleansing service for germplasm of several crop species (*REDBIO Circular Letter*, 9 October 1994, p. 16). Some of these institutions were:

Institution	Country	Crop species
CSIRO	Australia	Grapevine
CENARGEN	Brazil	Grapevine, potato, garlic
CIRAD	France	Sugar-cane, banana, yam, groundnut
IRG	Germany	Grapevine
ISPV	Italy	Almond, peach, plum
CIP	Peru	Andean roots and tubers
NRI	United Kingdom	Cassava, yam, banana, *Citrus*
SCRI	Scotland	*Rubus* and *Ribes* spp.
University of California	USA	*Citrus*
Washington State University	USA	Caduceus-leaved fruit trees
AVRDC	Taiwan	Alliaceous crop species

The IPGRI was expected to play an important role in CGIAR programmes on forestry and agroforestry dealing with genetic resources in partnership with the ICRAF and CIFOR, and in close collaboration with the FAO. The IPGRI was responsible for maintaining an information base on the status of conservation and use of genetic resources in forestry and agroforestry, and an inventory of existing information systems. It was also working to define a research agenda on forestry/agroforestry genetic resources. Several aspects of the IPGRI's work on crop genetic resources could be readily extended to forestry and agroforestry species; they included field sampling techniques, investigating population structures and breeding systems, *ex-situ* conservation methods, *in-vitro* techniques and taxonomic studies (IPGRI, 1993).

The IPGRI was addressing the need to develop and improve computerized techniques of storage and retrieval of information on gene bank accessions, and to facilitate data exchange. It was also initiating research on conserving traditional knowledge about plant characteristics and local practices for using and conserving plant genetic resources. The IPGRI was interested in using gender analysis (i.e. the activities and responsibilities of men and women, and the differential impact that policies, programmes and project activities had on them) in the planning and execution of its projects. Women who in most parts of the developing world were playing a key role in agricultural production (up to 60% of all farm work) and therefore had intimate contact with their environment, were the primary custodians and users of crop varieties and land races, forest genetic diversity and medicinal plants. In the field of *in-situ* conservation, they were a good source of information concerning the feasibility and social acceptability of establishing reserves or introducing conservation practices in areas held as common property (IPGRI, 1993).

The fourth objective was to provide an information service to the world's genetic resources community. Evaluation data, essential to the use of plant genetic resources, was seldom readily available to all potential users. Mechanisms were needed to ensure that all evaluation data was deposited with the gene bank supplying the material and was provided to other users. This was a responsibility of both those working primarily in conservation and those using the germplasm. The IPGRI was therefore studying methods to facilitate the gathering and sharing of evaluation data and other information pertinent to current and potential use of plant genetic resources, such as local knowledge (IPGRI, 1993).

The IPGRI was monitoring and evaluating the effectiveness of different mechanisms for disseminating information, including audio-visual tapes, CD-ROMs, etc. Publications in printed form were expected to continue as the key medium for disseminating the information on the world's genetic resources (IPGRI, 1993).

The CGIAR Public Awareness Association, a consortium of donors and center information officers, was set up in 1987 to increase public knowledge of international agricultural research, primarily through the outlet of the media. The IPGRI was participating in the Association's projects dealing with plant genetic resources (IPGRI, 1993).

STRATEGY IMPLEMENTATION: PROGRAMME AND BUDGET

In 1992, as part of its new strategy, the IPGRI restructured its programme into five regional and three thematic groups. The Regional Groups were based in: sub-Saharan Africa; West Asia and North Africa; Asia, the Pacific and Oceania; the Americas; Europe. The Regional Groups were responsible for developing and reviewing regional strategies, providing assistance to national and regional programmes, formulating and, where appropriate, being directly involved in research, collecting, training, documentation and information services. The IPGRI headquarters in Rome also served as the Regional Office for Europe; the Regional Office for West Asia and North Africa was located in Aleppo, Syria; the South Asia Office in New Delhi; Beijing was chosen for the East Asia Office; Singapore for the Regional Office for Asia, the Pacific and Oceania; Cali, Colombia, for the Regional Office for the Americas; Niamey, Niger, for the West Africa Office; and Nairobi for the Regional Office for sub-Saharan Africa (IPGRI, 1993).

The three Thematic Groups were established at IPGRI headquarters in Rome. They were responsible for developing and co-ordinating research and information work of inter-regional or global relevance in their respective areas. They were also in charge of providing the regions with scientific and technical support. The three Groups were organized around the following themes:

– genetic diversity (extent and distribution of genetic diversity, its measurement, *in-situ* conservation and *ex-situ* collecting, forest genetic resources conservation, and socio-economic aspects of plant genetic resources conservation and use);

– germplasm maintenance and use (strategies and techniques of conservation and use, germplasm management, seed, pollen and *in-vitro* conservation, and germplasm health);

– documentation, information and training (germplasm documentation, documentation technology, library and bibliographic services, publications, training co-ordination, impact assessment and public awareness).

The 1994 budget amounted to $11.9 million allocated by the IPGRI donors. Of this total, $6.9 million was allocated to the research programme, approximately $1.7 million to information services, $602,000 to conferences and training, about $1.6 million to general administration and $1.55 million to general operations. Expenditure by region with respect to the IPGRI core budget was: 26% for sub-Saharan Africa, 21% for West Asia and North Africa, 24% for Asia, the Pacific and Oceania, 22% for the Americas and 7% for Europe (IPGRI, 1994).

In 1994, IPGRI staff numbered 115, including INIBAP staff. There was a planned increase in the number of internationally recruited scientific and technical staff to be sent to the regions, in addition to locally recruited professionals. Staff could also be assigned to other IARCs, especially where they had fully functional genetic resources units.

The Programme, Planning and Review Committee, comprising the Group Leaders, and chaired by the Deputy Director-General-Programme, was responsible for programme planning (including the formulation of projects and overall allocation of resources to these) and on-going review of programme activities. An annual joint programming meeting between the IPGRI and FAO ensured that the programmes of the two organizations complemented and reinforced each other (IPGRI, 1993).

IPGRI programme was built on a set of projects, each designed to contribute to one or more of the Institute's objectives. A project was most commonly multidisciplinary, involving a number of the different areas of specialization available within the IPGRI (e.g. genetic diversity, training and information). A project nearly always involved the participation of a member of the IPGRI staff and one or more partner institutions. A typical project might thus involve institutions in several countries and comprise activities such as collecting, research to develop and test new methods and techniques, training, scientific and technical advice, exchange of germplasm and information and public awareness. All projects would ensure that adequate dissemination mechanisms existed, or were built into the project, and that they were adequately monitored and evaluated (IPGRI, 1993).

At the Consultative Group on International Agricultural Research (CGIAR) Mid-Term Meeting in New Delhi in May 1994, it was agreed to establish the System-wide Genetic Resources Programme (SGRP) with the IPGRI serving as Secretariat. Six months later, conceptual work began on a System-wide Information Network on Genetic Resources (SINGER). Over the same period, the IPGRI was playing an important role in negotiations to place the CGIAR in-trust germplasm collections under the auspices of the FAO. These negotiations culminated in agreements being signed during the International Centers Week in Washington, D.C., in October 1994 (IPGRI, 1994).

In sub-Saharan Africa, 1994 was marked by the IPGRI signing a formal agreement with the Government of Kenya to operate the Regional Office in Nairobi. A project on improving the conservation and use of forages and fodder species in Africa studied the spatial and temporal distribution of genetic diversity within five annual forage grass and legume species in Niger. National fora attended by crop scientists, policy-makers and non-governmental organizations were organized in Cameroon, Congo, Côte d'Ivoire and Ghana. Each set up a national committee for the co-ordination of plant genetic resources and a national plan of action. The IPGRI supported research concerning on-farm conservation of yam germplasm in its natural environment in Côte d'Ivoire. Three regional crop working groups were constituted: forage and fodder, food crops and *in-situ* and underutilized plants (IPGRI, 1994).

In 1994, the number of member countries of the West Asia and North Africa Plant Genetic Resources Network, with formal committees on genetic resources, rose to ten. A Regional Rangeland Seed Information Network was established, with two Subregional Documentation Units in Jordan and Morocco. A project on the conservation and use of fruit trees and nut species developed co-operation with national programmes in Iran, Jordan and Pakistan for collecting wild and domesticated germplasm of almond. An *in-vitro* collection was initiated by Jordan's University for Science and Technology. Courses were given on different aspects of genetic resources of fruit trees (IPGRI, 1994).

In Asia, the Pacific and Oceania, the Coconut Genetic Resources Network (COGENT) was expanded in 1994 to a membership of 24; its up-dated data-base was to contain information on 500 coconut accessions. The IPGRI Regional Office in Singapore collaborated in a survey to identify priority fruit species for research and development in Asia, and finalized regional priorities for genetic resources work on the major (mango, citrus and rambutan) and minor (jackfruit, durian and litchi) fruits. A three-week documentation course trained 27 gene-bank managers from 12 countries on computer and data-base systems for *ex-situ* gene bank management. The Regional Office was collaborating with partners to develop a bamboo and rattan genetic resources working group, facilitate germplasm exchange, assist Viet Nam in collecting *Musa* genetic resources and evaluate *Musa* germplasm (IPGRI, 1994).

The Regional Office for the Americas, based at the International Center for Tropical Agriculture (CIAT, Cali), was responsible for conserving and researching plant genetic resources in Latin America and the Caribbean, in liaison with the USA and Canada. The Office identified two main problems: the accelerated rate of genetic resource erosion (i.e. the conservation problem) and the lack of knowledge and resources on how to use native germplasm (i.e. the utilization problem). To address these problems, the following networks were established in partnership with the Inter-American Institute for Co-operation in Agriculture (IICA) and leading national agricultural organizations: the Central American Network of Plant Genetic Resources (REMERFI), the Andean Network of Plant Genetic Resources (REDARFIT) and the Amazonian Network of Plant Genetic Resources (TROPIGEN).

In 1994, IPGRI staff implemented a project on Sapotaceae and Passifloraceae in association with national programmes in Meso-America and the Andes, and the Meso-American and Andean Networks on Plant Genetic Resources. In the Caribbean, a meeting was held to develop a plan of action for fruit trees, food legumes and root crops being considered a priority. The main training event was the first course on Documentation of plant genetic resources (IPGRI, 1994).

In Europe, Phase V of the European Cooperative Programme for Crop Genetic Resources Networks was more ambitious than its prdecessors. The first item on a crowded agenda was the launching of the European Forest Genetic Resources Programme with a meeting on *Populus nigra*. Also at the top of the list was the provision of emergency assistance for securing unique collections in some East European countries[11] (see p. 517). Meanwhile, in Olomouc, Czech Republic, the safety duplication of the European *Allium* collection was pursued. A series of joint missions opened contacts with the Newly Independant States of the Caucasus, Central Asia and the three Baltic states. A meeting on the conservation and utilization of indigenous underutilized species of the Mediterranean established a number of crop-oriented networks focusing on the genetic resources of einkorn, emmer, spelt, *Pistacia* spp., rocket, and medicinal and aromatic species. The first three issues of a new regional Newsletter for Europe were published in 1994 (IPGRI, 1994).

In genetic diversity (first thematic group), projects were developed on the socio-economic and cultural aspects of conservation and the *in-situ* conservation of crop plants, particularly ethnobotany. International collaborative efforts were initiated, such as the international barley core collection and a sesame core collection. Eco-geographic surveys were designed and indicators for genetic erosion developed; areas were targeted for *ex-situ* collecting of germplasm rich in particular traits. The IPGRI was collaborating with other centres and partners to identify areas of interest in a comprehensive conservation programme for tropical humid and dryland forests, timber and non-wood forest products. A new data-base called TREESOURCE provided an overview of the holdings and locations of forest genetic resources on a global basis. A research project was launched in South-East Asia to design effective *in-situ* conservation strategies for tropical forest ecosystems (IPGRI, 1994).

The second thematic group on germplasm maintenance and use focused on research into optimum moisture contents for seed storage and *in-vitro* slow growth protocols that individual gene-banks could adapt to suit their specific requirements. A compendium and a data-base were prepared on seed storage behaviour for about 6,000 species from over 200 families. Projects focusing on the conservation of recalcitrant seeds were continued, in particular cryopreservation techniques (tea and jackfruit embryonic axes were successfully

461

cryopreserved). A first version of a computer programme was produced to assist in the design of seed gene-bank facilities whose size was dictated by predicted storage needs. Studies on the legal aspects of germplasm exchange and international arrangements for the conservation and use of plant genetic resources were also published (IPGRI, 1994).

The third thematic group (documentation, information and training) had distributed a questionnaire on problems linked to documentation to over 500 gene-bank managers and documentation staff. Work had begun on developing a software application as an alternative to printed crop directories. Over 40 publications and over 50,000 copies were distributed in 1994. The same year, a series of films on genetic resources went into production as part of the System-wide Genetic Resources Programme. Progress was made in implementing Master's level courses in universities in Kenya, Zambia and The Philippines, and the potential for establishing courses in West Africa was looked into (IPGRI, 1994).

10. Biotechnologies at the INIBAP

Only 10% of global *Musa* (banana) production was being exported by the mid-1990s. Most bananas and plantains were produced for home consumption or for the local market. Small and large farmers grew *Musa* using different systems of cultivation, from backyard cultivation, extensive cultivation with or without inputs, to intensive cultivation. *Musa* was grown as a monocrop, but was also found in complex cropping systems in various ecoregions (Commandeur, 1994*a*).

Banana was the fresh fruit the most widely consumed throughout the world and the most widely exchanged. More than 95% of banana exports originated from developing countries, 74% from Latin America alone. Europe was the largest banana market (3.6 million tonnes per year), ahead of the USA (3.2 million tonnes) and Japan (about 800,000 tonnes). The European market was supplied by three different production areas: the French Overseas Departments (Guadeloupe and Martinique mainly, with 900,000 tonnes per year); the African, Caribbean and Pacific countries (ACP, with 500,000 tonnes); and Latin America (2 million tonnes). In the case of France, two-thirds of the imported 600,000 tonnes originated from the Antilles and one-third from Africa, primarily Côte d'Ivoire and Cameroon (Varney, 1994).

In 1992, Latin American countries sold 2.4 million tonnes of bananas to the EEC, down from 2.8 million tonnes the previous year.

Consequently, according to several dealers, the multinational corporation, Chiquita Brands International (which, with the two other big American corporations, Dole and Del Monte, exported 6 million tonnes of bananas annually) was forced to adjust its commercial policy. To secure a greater share of the European banana market, it adopted a dumping policy in 1992, driving prices down to 2 FF per kilogramme in Hamburg and sparking violent reactions in the West Indies. In February 1993, the same situation occurred, but in mid-1993 publication of the company's financial results revealed its incapacity to pursue this policy (Varney, 1993).

In July 1993, the European Union decided to set up a Common Market Organization (CMO) for banana, which fixed an annual ceiling of 2.2 million tonnes for banana imports from Latin America (called 'dollar bananas'; this nickname stemmed from the predominance of American multinational corporations, like Chiquita Brands International, Castle and Cook, and Del Monte, in the production of Latin American bananas). The CMO was created to protect banana production in the French Overseas Departments (Martinique and Guadeloupe), the Spanish Canary Islands and, to a lesser extent, those banana exports from most African, Caribbean and Pacific (ACP) Countries. Another agreement concluded in April 1994 in Marrakech, Morocco, during the final stage of the Uruguay Round of the GATT, between the European Union and four Latin American banana producers (Colombia, Costa Rica, Nicaragua and Venezuela) granted several advantages to these countries: higher import quotas, reduced tariffs and the granting of licenses, in exchange for the withdrawal of their complaint against the CMO (Tuquoi, 1995).

Bananas made up half of Martinique's exports, while they represented Guadeloupe's biggest or second-biggest export item, depending on the year. That is why the French Compagnie générale maritime (CGM), which was running four specially-equipped ships between France and the Antilles, had set aside 100 million FF (about $20 million) for co-financing, together with local communities, forwarding agents in the port of Le Havre, a huge warehouse for storing bananas prior to their ultimate delivery to French supermarkets and the Rungis wholesale market near Paris, but also two pre-refrigeration centres at Fort de France and Pointe à Pitre. The refrigeration chain from the banana plantation to the market place had been considerably improved without increasing prices (Grosrichard, 1995).

The protection set up by the European Union also proved advantageous for the English-speaking Caribbean States: one out of three bananas eaten in the United Kingdom was imported from Saint

Lucia. That explained the anger of the multinational American corporation, Chiquita Brands International, at the European Union's decision to create the CMO. A major banana producer in Latin America, Chiquita Brands International linked a loss of several hundreds of millions of dollars to the European Union's reduction in imports. The company took its case to the U.S. authorities, which, in accordance with article 301 of the Trade Act, threatened to retaliate if the European Union did not propose a compromise.

By the mid-1990s, the production cost of Latin American bananas was $245 per tonne; this compared to $333 for the ACP States, $343 for Somalia, $354 for Cameroon, $548 for the Caribbean, $506 for Guadeloupe and $696 for the Canary Islands. According to the results of a study commissioned by the French Ministry of Co-operation, the investment cost for a hectare of banana trees amounted to $8,000 in 1989 in Ecuador, $9,600 in Colombia, $10,500 in Cameroon, $12,000 in Costa Rica and $12,500 in Côte d'Ivoire. The final production cost, including labour, showed a striking difference between ACP bananas and 'dollar bananas'. On the one hand, the modern, heavily mechanized Latin American plantations enjoyed high productivity (in Costa Rica, productivity was equal to 136 days per tonne per hectare, compared to 399 days per tonne per hectare in Côte d'Ivoire). On the other hand, the daily wage in Latin America was nine times lower than in the Antilles. When the Prime Minister of Saint Lucia stated in 1993 that, in the four small Windwards Islands, about 20,000 farmers produced less than 400,000 tonnes of bananas, he rejected any comparison with the Central American and Latin American multinationals, with their thousands of hectares and production of about 2 million tonnes. He asserted that Saint Lucia's farmers were working on small plots located in mountainous regions and producing nevertheless better quality fruits. The Dominica's Prime Minister emphasized that banana production was not a leisure activity, but critical for people's survival (*Spore, Bimonthly Bulletin of the Technical Centre for Agricultural and Rural Co-operation, CTA*, June 1993, no. 45, p. 6).

The banana producers of the European Union and the ACP countries organized a symposium in Paris on 22 February 1995 chaired by Dominica's Prime Minister. The latter suggested the creation of a lobby for pleading their case before the U.S. Government. On 3 March 1995, in Saint Lucia, the same Prime Minister, with other Caribbean political leaders, stressed to the U.S. Trade Representative that the banana producers of the Windwards Islands (Dominica, Grenada, Saint Lucia and Saint Vincent) were not prepared to be the scapegoats of the conflict between the USA and the European Union. They feared that, if the European Commission decided to increase 'dollar banana' imports, this would be to the detriment of their own exports (Tuquoi, 1995).

Within the European Union itself, there was a lack of consensus. Germany, the leading banana consumer in Europe, had brought the Union and France before the European Court of Justice and lost. Its interests were totally opposed to those of France, due to the fact that Germany imported bananas almost exclusively from Latin American countries at highly competitive prices. Increasingly, the point of entry was Antwerp, through which were imported bananas not only from Ecuador, Colombia and Costa Rica, but also from Cameroon or Saint Lucia, before being ultimately re-exported to Düsseldorf, Munich or Copenhagen. Antwerp was therefore the direct competitor of the French port of Le Havre, an observation that led some commentators to talk of a 'banana war' between the two ports and between member countries of the European Union with divergent interests. This antagonism would only be compounded by the European Union's new members, Austria, Finland and Sweden, which were even bigger banana consumers than Germany and therefore likely to prefer imports at good competitive prices (Grosrichard, 1995).

The Arbitration Commission of the World Trade Organization concluded by the end of April 1997 that the banana market and trade in Europe was not in agreement with multilateral trade regulations. The Commission requested that all banana exporters to the European market be treated on equal footing. Although the European Union could appeal to change this decision, the latter could change the whole organization of the European banana market, the biggest in the world with 35% of the demand. Europe was the main outlet of Latin American producers which contributed 76% of the world's supply, as well as for the U.S. multinational corporations (Chiquita, Dole or Del Monte) which controlled a big portion of the commercialization. Implications of this change might be disastrous for some Caribbean countries whose economy was mainly based on banana. They could also be a serious blow to banana producers of Canary Islands, Madeira, Martinique, Guadeloupe and La Réunion (Buhrer, 1997).

This 'banana war' was another episode of the harsh commercial competition between the USA and the European Union. Since the creation in 1995 of the World Trade Organization (WTO), the USA were the country which most often had recourse to WTO's mechanism for solving litigation with their competitors (Buhrer, 1997).

Today's known bananas and plantains resulted from human selection (not breeding) of varieties from *Musa acuminata*

(AA genome) and hybrids between this wild banana and *Musa balbisiana* (BB genome), another wild species of the family Musaceae. Plantains are simply a sub-group of AAB genome bananas. Due to this confusion, bananas and plantains were often referred to as *Musa*. Currently, the most important genome types were AAA (including Cavendish, the export banana), AAB and ABB (Commandeur, 1994*a*).

Initial research in banana had been linked with an outbreak of the fungal disease *Fusarium* wilt (or Panama disease) in export banana cultivation. In the 1920s, the rapid spread of this disease endangered the just a few decades old and highly lucrative banana exports of Central America and the Caribbean. For that reason, the British Government set up a research institute in Jamaica, while the private United Fruit Company initiated banana research in Honduras. The latter initiative was most successful, not only in controlling *Fusarium* wilt in existing varieties, but also in introducing a new, resistant and still common Cavendish banana variety from Asia (Commandeur, 1994*a*).

A new disease, yellow sigatoka, had triggered off a second wave of research in the 1930s. This leaf spot disease, however, was soon sufficiently controlled by fungicides and mineral oil sprayings. The outbreak of black sigatoka in the 1960s was at the origin of a third major phase in banana research. The fact that black sigatoka not only affected the intensive cultivation of export bananas in Latin America, but also invaded locally consumed banana and plantain varieties throughout the world, awakened interest in *Musa* research orientated toward smallholdings (Commandeur, 1994*a*).

The dominance by transnational companies was, to a certain extent, diminished by the emergence of governmental and intergovernmental organizations to protect common national interests. This was the case for one of the most important intergovernmental organizations, the Union of Banana Exporting Countries (UPEB), comprised of Colombia, Costa Rica, Guatemala, Honduras, Nicaragua, Panama and Venezuela. Established in 1974, the UPEB aimed to reduce the dependence of its member states and their national producers on transnational companies for marketing operations. Due to the lack of success after decades of investment in breeding and the political struggles in its producing countries, the United Fruit Company withdrew from banana research in 1983. It donated the breeding programme, related property and *Musa* germplasm to the Honduran Government. The opportunity to internationalize the commitment of the world's most important research institute on *Musa* and expand it to include non-export bananas was seized when the Fundación Hondureña de Investigación Agrícola (FHIA) was funded first by the FAO and the

Canadian International Development Research Centre (IDRC, Ottawa) and later by the U.S. Agency for International Development (U.S. AID), Windward Islands Banana Growers Association (WINBAN), St Lucia, and Ecuador (Commandeur, 1994*a*).

The spread of black sigatoka in Africa and the threat it posed to small holders in the early 1980s had led to establishment of the International Network for the Improvement of Banana and Plantain (INIBAP) in 1984. It was stressed that the INIBAP primary goal was to increase and stabilize production of bananas and plantains grown for domestic consumption within producing countries, while co-ordinating international efforts to increase banana and plantain research in developing countries. The network made use of the resources of existing breeding programmes rather than creating its own research facility. In 1990, the INIBAP became part of the Consultative Group on International Agricultural Research (CGIAR), with the commitment to improve the productivity of small holders growing banana and plantain. With an annual budget of about $3 million and a small staff, the INIBAP was collaborating with the world's main research institutes in *Musa*, including the FHIA, Honduras, IITA, Ibadan, the French Centre for International Co-operation in Agricultural Research for Development (CIRAD) and the Brazilian Enterprise of Agricultural and Livestock Research (EMBRAPA, Empresa Brasileira de Pesquisas Agropecuarias) [Commandeur, 1994*a*].

The goals of the INIBAP were to:
– organize global research on banana and plantain for the development, evaluation and dissemination of improved cultivars and the conservation of *Musa* diversity;
– promote regional research dealing with region-specific problems and help the regions to contribute to global research and share the benefits;
– strengthen the ability of National Agricultural Research Systems to conduct research on bananas and plantains;
– arrange for the exchange of information and documentation among researchers (IPGRI, 1994).

The INIBAP main activities included:
– The Musa Germplasm Exchange System, which included co-ordinating the collection, indexing, inventory and shipment of *Musa* accessions. At the Catholic University of Leuven, Belgium, the INIBAP had an *in-vitro* gene bank and research was being carried out on *in-vitro* techniques, cryopreservation and genetic transformation. For the safe exchange of *Musa* germplasm, the INIBAP relied on two virus-indexing centres, one at the French Centre for International Co-

operation in Agricultural Research for Development (CIRAD), Montpellier, and the other at the Queensland Department of Primary Industries, Brisbane, Australia. Research into developing reliable tests for detecting viruses to be carried out on *in-vitro* cultures was a priority.

– The *Musa* Germplasm Information System, aimed at identifying the biological diversity of *Musa*, so as to facilitate the efficient conservation and utilization of germplasm; the development of an unequivocal taxonomy was given high priority.

– The International *Musa* Testing Programme, which co-ordinated the evaluation of new banana and plantain hybrids for resistance to black sigatoka at the National Agricultural Research Systems and international centres in different ecoregions. In the first phase (1990–1993), seven hybrids of the FHIA had been tested in six sites, out of which three showed a potential for further evaluation at regional and local levels. In the following phase, new material from seven breeding programmes was tested in 18 countries.

– Regional research and training, associated with three regional networks with which the INIBAP was collaborating to elaborate its global activities; the regional networks assisted regional and national programmes in research priority setting, finding donor support, sustaining research on region-specific problems and opportunities, and developing training courses.

– Information and documentation. The INIBAP was running two trilingual data-bases on literature and research on *Musa*, and was organizing thematic workshops, e.g. on biotechnology applications to *Musa* research. It issued the tri-annual bibliographic abstract publication *Musarama* and a bi-annual information journal *Infomusa* in English, French and Spanish (INIBAP, 1993; Commandeur, 1994a).

An external evaluation of INIBAP management and programme had been commissioned by the Technical Advisory Committee of the CGIAR in 1992. A second evaluation, wider in scope, had been carried out in 1993 as a CGIAR Task Force on Banana and Plantain. This Task Force appeared to be opposed to the INIBAP co-ordinating role in international *Musa* research. One of the recommendations made was for the establishment of a consortium of *Musa* research organizations, with a mutually agreed programme on improving *Musa* germplasm. The INIBAP activities would be reduced to running the scientific secretariat of the consortium, facilitating relations between research programmes, information, documentation and training (Commandeur, 1994a).

In May 1993, the CGIAR decided to bring the INIBAP under the governance and administration of the International Plant Genetic Resources Institute (IPGRI), while maintaining the INIBAP identity, location, mandate and programme focus. The Board Chairpersons of the two institutions and the Chairperson of the INIBAP Support Group had signed the appurtenant Memorandum of Understanding in May 1994 in New Delhi. The INIBAP Administration Board then handed over the reins to the IPGRI Board, the Director of the INIBAP becoming a member of the IPGRI Management Committee. The INIBAP was expected to continue to exist as a legal entity, at least until the External Programme and Management Review of the IPGRI in 1996–1997 (IPGRI, 1994). During its September 1995 meeting in Aleppo, Syria, the INIBAP Administration Board approved the construction of a 400-m^2 facility in Montpellier, France, in the Scientific Park area of Montferrier; construction work began in 1996 (*CIRAD Information*, no. 56, 23 October 1995, p. 1).

The first review commissioned by the CGIAR recommended further development of the INIBAP regional networks. But in the second review, the Task Force showed no confidence in the potential of the regional networks and recommended that the INIBAP significantly reduce its involvement in regional activities. The INIBAP rejected the recommendation, claiming that the regional networks had not been given enough time to mature and affirming with confidence that support for regional networks would be continued after the INIBAP integration into the IPGRI (Commandeur, 1994*a*).

Its commitment to small holder production of *Musa* implied that the INIBAP was dealing with a diverse 'group' of small farmers growing different varieties of *Musa*, for several purposes in distinct circumstances. Within this diversity, the INIBAP was giving priority to genetic resistance to major *Musa* diseases, sustained by germplasm collection, conservation and dissemination activities. The INIBAP expected the development of new resistant *Musa* cultivars and their dissemination among small producers to benefit those who could otherwise not afford the costs of chemical protection from diseases and pests, especially black sigatoka. Biological control, integrated pest management and cultivation practices, although not considered priorities in the INIBAP global activities, were, to a certain extent, addressed in the regional networks (Buddenhagen, 1993; INIBAP, 1993; Commandeur, 1994*a*).

The INIBAP-supported research at the Catholic University of Leuven focused on somatic embryogenesis and cell suspension culture before moving on to protoplast culture. Researchers worked in collaboration with the Paris Sud University, at Orsay, south of Paris, and the CIRAD laboratory, with partial support from the European Union, especially with respect to protoplast culture and fusion. At the

IITA, the INIBAP-supported research concerned embryo rescue methods, somaclonal variation and meristem propagation, somatic embryogenesis, and germplasm storage. The introduction of *Musa* germplasm through the Leuven transit centre was made possible thanks to authorization from the Nigerian Quarantine Service. This was of great importance, because the African continent needed a massive introduction of germplasm, firstly for screening cultivars with respect to the rapidly progressing sigatoka disease, before integration into the IITA breeding programme.

Due to the limited potential of somaclonal variation through meristem propagation for obtaining disease-resistant variants, the INIBAP intended further stimulating research on somatic cell culture and consequently on somatic embryogenesis (Plucknett and Cohen, 1989).

The INIBAP and IPGRI stressed that the banana bunchy-top virus (BBTV) could be controlled by transforming *Musa* spp. with viral coat protein. Expertise for this approach was available in Australia, at the Queensland University of Technology. Furthermore, *in-vitro* plant regeneration from transgenic *Musa* cells seemed a genuine possibility.

The INIBAP was expected to help the National Agricultural Research Systems (NARSs) in building up capacity and expertise for *in-vitro* introduction, propagation and dissemination of improved *Musa* germplasm. In addition to Colombia and Uganda, the INIBAP Regional Co-ordinators would play a major role in organizing training courses (for Africa, in collaboration with the IITA) for quarantine officers and tissue culturists and in monitoring the follow-up to these courses.

On 27 March 1992, the INIBAP signed a co-operation agreement with the following French agricultural research institutions: INRA (National Institute for Agricultural Research), CIRAD (Centre for International Co-operation in Agricultural Research for Development) and ORSTOM (French Scientific Research Institute for Development in Cooperation).

From 7 to 9 September 1992, an international symposium on the genetic improvement of bananas for resistance to diseases and pests was organized at the CIRAD facilities in Montpellier, on the initiative of the Department of Fruit and Horticultural Crops (CIRAD-FLHOR), in collaboration with the INIBAP. It brought together researchers from 37 countries.

For the first time in Latin America, the INIBAP, in collaboration with the Tropical Agriculture Research and Training Centre (CATIE) and the French Centre for International Co-operation in Agricultural Research for Development (CIRAD), had organized an international training course on genetic transformation of banana and plantain. On this occasion, a helium particle gun manufactured by the CIRAD Biotechnology Unit was installed at the CATIE. The course was attended by 20 researchers from Colombia, Costa Rica, Cuba, Honduras, Panama and Venezuela (*CIRAD Information*, no. 56, 23 October 1995, p. 8).

On the INIBAP initiative, the first global International *Musa* Testing Conference and the first meeting of the *Musa* Breeders Network were held in Honduras from 27 April to 3 May 1994. About 60 participants, including six researchers from the CIRAD Department of Fruit and Horticultural Crops, reported on their results in genetic banana improvement and their contribution to the second phase of the international *Musa* assessment programme. These meetings also provided an opportunity to discuss future co-operation between the various improvement programmes and biotechnology research teams. In preference to a consortium, most of the participants advocated an informal network co-ordinated by the INIBAP and involving breeders and biotechnologists with common interests. The priority research topic in one joint project was the development of genetic nematode resistance (*CIRAD News*, no. 11, December 1994, p. 2).

Also in 1994, important steps in INIBAP programme development included a workshop on nematodes and weevil borers in the Asia-Pacific region; a safety duplicate of the Asia-Pacific *in-vitro Musa* germplasm collection was established; *Musa* Germplasm Information System for rationalizing information on *Musa* genetic resources and making it available to collaborators, began to function. The INIBAP was playing a key role in regional *Musa* training and research, including priority setting and collaborative activities (IPGRI, 1994).

The number of Musa germplasm samples exported from the INIBAP Transit Center in Belgium (at the Catholic University of Leuven) amounted to 900 in 1994, compared to 606 in 1993. By the end of 1994, the active *in-vitro* collection of this Center included 1,050 accessions representing a large proportion of genetic diversity within the genus *Musa* (IPGRI, 1994).

11. Biotechnologies at the ICRAF

Created in 1977 as the International Council for Research in Agroforestry with headquarters in Nairobi since 1978, it became the International Center for Research in Agroforestry (ICRAF) in 1991 and member of the CGIAR network. Its mandate was to promote, initiate and support, in developing countries, research on a more productive and sustainable utilization of soils through the integration or better management of trees and shrubs within land-use schemes. The three-pronged ICRAF strategy was to develop agroforestry as a discipline and to maintain its leading role in this area; to help regional and national bodies to develop their creative capacities and their ability to implement agroforestry research projects, and to collaborate with these bodies in mastering appropriate agroforestry techniques; and finally to promote the use of agroforestry techniques and systems within national development schemes (Baumer, 1992).

With regard to rangeland management, research on selecting fodder species for the dry areas of Africa was bearing fruit. Many of these species had a good potential for improving soils, when the latter were utilized correctly, or for either restoring or maintaining soil fertility. For instance, in the semi-arid zones of West Africa and in Sudan, as well as in subhumid zones, especially in Ethiopia, Malawi and Senegal, *Acacia albida* was highly appreciated by farmers and cattle breeders. Increases of 50% to 100% in soil organic matter and nitrogen had been observed under this legume tree species, as compared to unplanted soil, as well as a greater water retention capacity. These improvements could lead to a 100% increase in millet, sorghum and groundnut production. In addition, for the cattle breeder, each of the 40 trees found on one hectare could produce 30 kg to 300 kg of pods each year (but usually every two years), a feed rich in protein, which could be stored for a long period (Baumer, 1992). It was now generally accepted that tree species made a precious contribution to domestic animal breeding, because they often offered the only feed available during the driest months, especially to browsing animals.

The ICRAF launched a germplasm bank of forest trees and shrubs in 1993. In addition, the Center had prepared and disseminated: a handbook enabling farmers and cattle breeders to be associated with the identification of problems they faced and with the research needed to cope with them; information on trees and shrubs used in agroforestry and stored in the Center's data-base, which comprised more than 1,600 species; the survey of agroforestry systems, published in the periodical *Agroforestry Systems;* the evaluation of soil conservation under agroforestry, which gave information on the changes in the soil induced by agroforestry practices; reference books; and the computerized programme Mulbud on the budgets of multiple cultivation. With the assistance of Australia, the ICRAF had created a special team and a unit of seeds and germplasm on its campus which the Kenyan Government had decided to enlarge via a 40-hectare plot added to the ICRAF's research station at Machakos, near Nairobi (Baumer, 1992).

If many international training courses had been run for specialists from 40 or so countries, the numerous workshops organized were oriented solely toward participants in the African Network for Agroforestry Research comprising Burkina Faso, Cameroon, Côte d'Ivoire, Mali, Niger and Senegal among others. Fellowships had been awarded to scientists from developing countries for a duration of between three months and one year (Baumer, 1992).

Lastly, the ICRAF was developing its information base, storing thousands of references it retrieved for a wide range of users. It replied annually to thousands of requests from institutions and individuals. It contributed to the specialized literature by publishing or supporting the publication of documents, conference or symposium proceedings, handbooks, reference materials and articles. It co-published two international reviews in English, entitled *Agroforestry Systems* and *Agroforestry Abstracts*, and was instrumental in the launching of an international magazine in French and English, *Agroforestry Today*, for a wide readership (Baumer, 1992).

12. Biotechnologies at the CIFOR

The Center for International Forestry Research (CIFOR) was officially created at the annual meeting of the CGIAR, held in Washington, D.C., in October-November 1991. It was the fruit of three years of intensive study and international meetings starting in 1988. At the first Bellagio Conference organized in 1987 by the United Nations Development Programme, World Bank, FAO, Rockefeller Foundation and the World Resources Institute, it had been recommended that the somewhat neglected on-going tropical forestry research be regrouped and completed without delay. In early 1991, the CGIAR had entrusted the Australian Centre for International Agricultural Research (ACIAR), in Canberra, to prepare the groundwork, including recruiting CIFOR initial staff.

With headquarters in Bogor, Indonesia, the CIFOR was to be home to a multidisciplinary team of foresters, agronomists, ecologists, sociologists, anthropologists and economists headed by a director nominated for a renewable three-year mandate. In order to accelerate research, the CIFOR would not create its own facilities, but rather engage in co-operative and contractual research, and support networks of existing institutions. The requisite funds to launch the CIFOR were provided by the USA, Canada and Japan. The foreseen budget for the early 1990s was $10–12 million per year. Total funds devoted to forestry via the CIFOR, ICRAF, IFPRI and other international agricultural research centers amounted to some $50 million per year in 1995.

Under the guidance of an international administration board comprising 12 to 15 persons chosen in their personal capacity and on the basis of their professional ability, the CIFOR was focusing its action on:

– understanding the physical, biological, economic and social environment of forest systems in developing countries;

– providing advice and information to assist in decision-making regarding the use of forest land (in collaboration with other competent institutions);

– enhancing the national forestry research capacity, including through the exchange of personnel and the supply of equipment.

The CIFOR approach for strengthening National Forestry Research Systems (NFRSs) involved: the participation of NFRS staff in the Center research projects; training young scientists from the NFRS through projects or their own activities; and a communication and information programme. In general, the NFRS were weaker than their agricultural counterparts in the developing countries. It was therefore challenging to organize and implement an efficient programme meeting the expectations of developing countries. Technology transfer was as important as research, and implied relationships among scientists, between scientists and users, and between users and forest managers or land owners.

The Australian Centre for International Agricultural Research had entrusted the Australian Bureau of Rural Resources with the initial preparation of the TROPIS project, i.e. the Information System on Tree Growth Potential, which was expected to become a key component of the CIFOR information systems programme. TROPIS was supposed to meet the needs of foresters in charge of introducing new forest species, or working on growth rates in artificial stands and agroforestry in developing countries. This would gain them rapid access to information (published or not) on the growth features of species and their climatic and location needs. The behaviour of individual species according to climatic zones and locations (i.e. soil and humidity conditions) could be evaluated.

The CIFOR organized an expert group meeting from 4 to 6 November 1993 to prepare a state-of-the-art on the management of tropical humid forests.

Launched on the initiative of the French Ministry of Co-operation, the French Centre for International Co-operation in Agricultural Research for Development (CIRAD) and the CIFOR, in association with the relevant institutions of Cameroon, Central African Republic, Congo, Côte d'Ivoire and Gabon, the Regional Project for Capitalization and Transfer of Forestry Research in African Humid

Tropical Zones (FORAFRI) aimed to find practical applications for the knowledge accumulated since the mid-1980s on natural forests of these five countries. The ultimate goal of the project was the sustainable management of the resource. For forest managers, the most important challenge was to maintain forest natural capacity for regeneration, i.e. to determine how tree felling interferred with regeneration processes. In some countries, data had been gathered over a 20-year period, covering a variety of situations ranging from natural forest to plots on which 40% of trees had been felled. The time had come to make a synthesis of these results, after quality checks to confirm the consistency of data from the different countries concerned.

The initial workshop, held in Bangui from 7 to 9 May 1996, focused on the products resulting from these syntheses. All participants – scientists, representatives of the relevant authorities and of the non-governmental organizations – highlighted the importance of developing forest tree population simulation techniques in an operational forum for decision-makers, administrators and managers. Geographical information systems (GIS) had a promising role to play in the establishment of management plans; spatial information provided managers with a precise knowledge of the resource at all times and enabled the administration to monitor inflows and outflows. The representatives of the five African countries emphasized the urgent need for training so that these new tools could be used for densely-forested areas. They stressed the need for practical manuals, synthesis documents, CD-ROMs and other knowledge transfer and communication media. In addition to a scientific committee responsible for checking the quality of the Project final product, the FORAFRI framework foresaw the appointment of national correspondents to run the Project as a network to ensure its long-term effectiveness (*CIRAD News*, no. 13, July 1996, p. 7).

13. Biotechnologies at the ILCA

Since 1970, meat consumption in the developing world had rapidly shifted from beef and mutton to poultry and pork, a tendency likely to accelerate as income and urbanization increased. Between 1963 and the end of 1980s, the number of cattle increased by 50%, that of pigs by 70%. This had put pressure on limited land resources, causing environment degradation. Sustainable livestock development, therefore, would need to focus on higher productivity per head. Livestock systems varied in the relative importance of livestock in the system (animal based, mixed crop-animal, crop based), in the intensity of resource requirements (intensive versus extensive), in the scale of operation, in the utilization of output (subsistence versus commercial), in the levels of development (traditional versus modern) and in the source of feed (uncultivated versus cultivated lands). In small-scale farming systems, livestock provided milk, meat, eggs, wool, hides (i.e. means for subsistence), and generated additional income through the sale of animal products. With extensive pastoral systems and small-scale intensive systems, livestock utilized marginal lands and/or crop residues not used by humans. Animals also supplied draught power and were used for transport, processing harvests and irrigation. Manure was utilized as fertilizer, fuel (dried or to produce methane through anaerobic fermentation) or feed in fish ponds. The latter were often integrated into duck or pig production in Asia. Other important functions of livestock were risk spreading, investment and security, and social status (Bijman, 1992*a*).

In developed countries, breeding programmes based on the recording of individual animal performance had annually improved economically important traits by 1% to 2%. In developing countries, the infrastructure required for performance testing was often lacking, because of frequently small herd sizes and large variability between farms, farming systems and seasons. Furthermore, reproductive efficiency was often limited by low quality forage, particularly in cattle. It was thus crucial to increase reproduction rates. The reproductive state of an animal could be determined through measuring reproductive hormones, by radio-immuno-assay or enzyme-immuno-assay (EIA). For instance, the measuring of progesterone in the milk or blood of cows was a widely used technique for monitoring ovarian functioning and for pregnancy tests. For developing countries, particularly in Africa, such assay systems had been developed by the Joint FAO/IAEA Division. Asian countries were also developing hormonal tests for reproduction studies; in Pakistan, for instance, EIA-tests developed by the Veterinary Research Institute in collaboration with veterinary scientists from the Netherlands were used to study the reproduction of Nili-Ravi dairy buffaloes (Bijman, 1992*a*).

Although not for use on the small farm, embryo transfer technology could greatly contribute to research work or genetic improvement of local breeds. Advances in embryo technology were mainly to be found in cattle reproduction and breeding. The reasons for this emphasis lay in the possibility of producing more calves from a female animal than would be possible with normal reproduction, just as artificial insemination produced more offspring from the male animal. While a cow normally would give birth to four calves in an average lifetime, this could be increased to 25 calves. Increasing the reproductive rate of selected cows had important benefits for breeding schemes:

– genetically outstanding cows could contribute more to the breeding scheme, particularly if their male offspring were being selected for use in artificial insemination;

– the rate of genetic change could be enhanced if breeding schemes would take advantage of the increased intensity of female selection combined with increased generation turnover.

Other advantages were even more important for developing countries:

– international transportation of breeding stock, transportation of embryos being much less expensive than that of live animals and avoiding the risk of importing diseases;

– rapid expansion of rare or exotic genetic stocks, for instance, if a new breed was introduced;

– the shock to imported genotypes could be avoided by having them born to dams of local breeds, rather than importing them as live animals (this was particularly important when farmers in the tropics wanted to import breeding stock from temperate climate zones). Furthermore, indigenous breeds with special adaptive traits, like disease resistance, climate stress tolerance, ability to use poor-quality feed and to survive with reduced and/or irregular supplies of water and feed, could be preserved through embryo transfer to surrogate animals of less interest (Bijman, 1992*a*).

Before embryos could be transferred to foster cows, they had to be obtained from donor cows. Two routes were possible for this purpose: superovulation through hormonal treatment and artificial insemination, before flushing the uterus to collect the embyros; *in-vitro* fertilization (IVF), whereby ovocytes recovered from the ovaries of a cow then matured and fertilized outside the body were further developed until ready for implantation into foster cows (after about a week). The advantages of the IVF over embryo transfer were the following:

– a larger number of embryos could be recovered from a single female animal, thereby reducing the cost of embryos and making embryo transfer techniques economically feasible on a large scale;

– a larger number of embryos from cows with important production traits could increase the efficacy of breeding shemes;

– the availability of a large number of relatively cheap embryos would facilitate research in genetic engineering;

– *in-vitro* fertilization made available embryos at the one- or two-cell stage, i.e. the phase suitable for embryo manipulations like cloning (Bijman, 1992*a*).

Embryo cloning aimed to obtain a large number of identical embryos which would give rise to identical production animals. Most research in industrialized countries was being carried out on producing clones for more uniform beef production. These clones could be used for further research, e.g. on the sex and quality of embryos and on genetic engineering. For developing countries, embryo cloning might be of importance for research institutes and the large modern farms, but not for small-scale livestock farming directly (Bijman, 1992*a*).

Sexing of embryos, and possibly semen, was important for the efficient application of embryo transfer and IVF techniques. As more embryos were implanted, it became necessary to know beforehand the offspring's sex, since there was a limited number of foster cows. Genetic markers were used in breeding schemes by analyzing the relationship between genetic variance at the molecular level and variance in production traits. Genetic markers were also a necessary tool for genetic engineering, enabling the identification of genes for commercially important traits (Bijman, 1992*a*).

With respect to animal feeding, most of the advances for ruminants would come from improving pasture management. In African and South American subhumid savannas, the focus was on developing agropastoral systems, rotating pasture and crops and including legumes or legume/grass mixtures to maintain soil fertility and alleviate the dry season protein deficiency. Crop residues could be used in tropical ruminant nutrition, after their nutritional quality was improved through chemical and enzymatic treatment, plant breeding and eventually rumen microfauna manipulation. Grain prices having fallen faster than livestock prices, use of concentrate feed had grown considerably. Between the late 1960s and the mid-1980s, concentrate feed use in developing countries had grown at an average of 4.8% per year, more than double the growth rate in the developed world. The main focus in concentrate feed technology was on improving protein contents, e.g.:

– adding essential amino-acids (lysine, methionine and trytophan) to concentrate feed made of raw materials lacking these amino-acids; the efficiency of the bacteria used in the industrial production of these amino-acids could be improved through genetic engineering;

– the amino-acid composition of certain cereals could be enhanced through genetic engineering;

– enzymatic pre-treatment of feed components could improve the digestion of cellulose-rich feed by pigs and poultry, and could decrease the anti-nutritional factors in certain feed crops, like anti-trypsin, lectin and tannins in legumes.

The use of cereal substitutes like cassava meal, sweet potato meal and maize gluten feed would increase in animal feeding in developing countries. Cereal substitution was well advanced in the European Union, but was also improving in Thailand, the world's largest exporter of cassava meal. At about half the price and at 70% of the feeding value of coarse grains, cassava was also attractive for the producing countries themselves and their neighbours (Bijman, 1992a). A promising technology consisted of using urea-molasses mixtures and bypass protein for supplementation of low-quality fibrous feeds (like dry season pastures). Progress in productivity were reported from Pakistan, Bangladesh and Indonesia, but research was also being carried out in Latin America (Bijman, 1992a).

Research on genetic engineering of rumen bacteria, particularly to improve their efficiency in breaking down lignocellulose, was being carried out in several places around the world, but it would take considerable time before results could be applied.

To sum up, increased productivity from ruminants through biotechnologies and other technologies would be achieved slowly, which prompted developing countries to turn increasingly toward pigs and poultry to increase meat production (Bijman, 1992a).

Forage grasses of the genera *Pennisetum, Cynodon, Digitaria, Panicum, Chloris, Cenchrus, Setaria* and *Brachiaria*, which formed the major components of native African pastures, were a major feed resource. Indigenous tree legumes such as *Sesbania, Erythrina, Faidherbia* and *Acacia*, together with introduced genera like *Leucaena*, had considerable forage potential in the African environment (Hanson and Ruredzo, 1992).

Although conventional management of forage germplasm relied on seeds, some important species of forage grasses rarely produced seeds and other slow-growing trees might be outcrossing and take several years to produce seeds, thus inhibiting rapid dissemination of selected germplasm. An important constraint to the rapid development of these forage species for utilization was the long time they took to reach maturity and produce seeds or, in the case of grasses, inadequate production of seeds for collection, multiplication, dissemination and utilization. *In-vitro* culture techniques provided solutions and alternative approaches to overcoming constraints in the management of tropical forage legumes and grasses (Hanson and Ruredzo, 1992).

Work on *in-vitro* culture techniques had been in progress at the ILCA since 1986 when the International Board for Plant Genetic Resources and ILCA agreed to collaborate in a two-year project to develop minimal facility methods for *in-vitro* collection and *in-vitro* slow growth methods for the conservation of *Cynodon aethiopicus, C. dactylon* and *Digitaria decumbens*. A suitable basal medium for grass species was identified for growing these species *in vitro* and suitable exogenous growth substances (auxins, cytokinins and gibberellins) and carbon source for normal growth rates were determined. Cultures of *Cynodon* and *Digitaria* spp. were successfully initiated, multiplied and rooted, and slow-growth conservation techniques using low temperature were developed for these species. It was possible to maintain cultures at 15°C for up to 18 months without subculturing and to recover them into normal growth conditions. A minimal facility method for transferring these species to soil was developed (Hanson and Ruredzo, 1992).

In 1989, the work was expanded to multipurpose tree legumes in a project supported by the International Development Research Centre (IDRC, Ottawa); *Sesbania sesban, Leucaena leucocephala* and *Erythrina brucei* were successfully cultured *in vitro* from embryo-derived cotyledons, hypocotyls and embryo axes of *Sesbania sesban*, and from embryo-derived explants in *Faidherbia albida* and *Acacia tortilis*. Non-adventitious regeneration was sucessfully achieved from shoot tips in *Erythrina brucei, Faidherbia albida* and *A. tortilis* (Hanson and Ruredzo, 1992).

The ILCA anticipated advances in livestock production based on biotechnologies encompassing: the use of monoclonal antibodies in identifying endocrine changes and disease status in domestic animals; blood typing for paternal half sib identification; induced multiple ovulation; oestrus synchronization and embryo transfer/embryo splitting techniques (Plucknett and Cohen, 1989).

In 1991, one year after launching of the programme on embryo transfer, the first 34 kg-bull calf was born at the Research Station of the ILCA, Debre Zeit, Ethiopia. This promising achievement showed that Boran cows, used as donors, were very receptive to treatments aimed at triggering superovulation in a synchronized way. The surrogate mothers were heifers resulting from a cross between Boran and Friesan breeds. In the medium term, research carried out aimed to conserve African livestock germplasm and increase cattle productivity.

14. Biotechnologies at the ILRAD

The International Laboratory for Research on Animal Diseases (ILRAD) was established in 1973 by the CGIAR in Nairobi. The ILRAD was focusing on basic research concerning the immunological and related aspects of controlling trypanosomiasis (sleeping sickness) and theileriosis (East Coast fever), two major constraints on livestock production in sub-Saharan Africa. These diseases killed about 3 million domestic animals annually and prevented (especially trypanosomiasis) livestock husbandry over an area of about seven million square kilometres.

With an annual budget of about $13.2 million in the early 1990s, the ILRAD employed nearly 50 scientists. It was estimated that, in 1990, half of the CGIAR funds for biotechnology research (totalling $14.5 million) went to animal biotechnologies, primarily conducted at the ILRAD (Collinson and Wright Platais, 1991; Komen, 1992*c*).

The ILRAD estimated that control of trypanosomiasis would make it possible to raise a further 20 million head of cattle in sub-Saharan Africa (Sudanian and Guinean zones) without additional environmental stress. Of a total stock of about 160 million cattle in Africa, only about 45 million were located in areas infested with tsetse flies, the main vector of trypanosomiasis. The tsetse belt was located in sub-Saharan Africa's humid and subhumid areas, which had the greatest potential for cattle production on the continent. The only means available in 1993 of controlling African trypanosomiasis were control of the vector and drug treatment of livestock. Methods included low-level insecticide application, the use of insecticide-impregnated traps attractive to the flies and the release of sterile male flies. Drug treatment of infected livestock was hampered by the resistance developed by the parasites to the lethal effects of drugs (Komen, 1992*c*).

Development of a vaccine was proving extremely difficult. Trypanosomes had come up with a sophisticated counter-mechanism against the immune system, termed antigenic variation. The parasites were able to change their surface membrane structure, so as to avoid being destroyed by the immune response, and held their capacity to multiply in the infected host. The ILRAD was following three complementary research pathways toward controlling the disease:

– treatment of the disease was facilitated by the development of new diagnostic tools; an ELISA test developed at the ILRAD proved helpful in detecting the three major tsetse-transmitted trypanosome species infecting livestock; a set of nucleic acid probes enabled ILRAD scientists to identify precisely the different strains of trypanosomes (*Trypanosoma congolense* and *T. vivax*) and their use was accelerated through the application of the polymerase chain reaction (PCR) technique;

– chemotherapy research aimed to improve the efficacy of drug treatments used to prevent and cure trypanosomiasis; techniques were developed for the *in-vitro* cultivation of eight strains of *T. congolense*, so that they could be easily screened for resistance, the levels of which were determined by using biochemical markers;

– breeding trypanotolerant cattle; N'Dama cattle were able to tolerate trypanosomes, but they produced only one-quarter to one-tenth of the milk and meat of breeds kept in industrialized countries. An ambitious project was initiated in 1990 to locate the genes for trypanotolerance; several genetic marker techniques were applied for the generation of the bovine genome map. To support this programme, the ILRAD was carrying out an embryo transfer programme for generating high numbers of crosses between N'Dama and Zebu cattle, from which both trypanotolerant and susceptible cattle could be generated (ILRAD, 1991; Komen, 1992c).

Already in 1984, several frozen embryos of N'Dama cattle had been transferred from Gambia to the ILRAD, where they were implanted into foster mothers of an East African Zebu breed called Boran. Since 1990, embryo transfer had been used to produce N'Dama-Boran cross-bred calves (Bijman, 1992a).

East Coast fever, caused by the parasite *Theileria parva* transmitted by ticks, affected cattle in eastern, central and southern Africa. ILRAD scientists estimated that 24 million of the 63 million cattle present in this region were at risk of infection. Control measures for the disease were based on acaricidal control of the vectors: cattle had to be treated with acaricides by dipping or spraying as often as twice a week to control tick infestation. Not only was it a very costly operation, but tick populations had become resistant to some acaricides. Drugs to control the parasite were available, but they were expensive and most effective when the disease – which often became apparent when the infection had reached an advanced stage – was diagnosed early (Komen, 1992c).

A major achievement of the research conducted at the ILRAD was the mapping of the genome of *Theileria parva* comprising four chromosomes. ILRAD researchers could also identify the cells infected by the parasite and develop monoclonal antibodies against the intra-lymphocytic stages of the pathogen; this had led to the detection of distinct strains of *T. parva* (Clark and Juma, 1991).

Cattle that survived East Coast fever (ECF) exhibited immunity to the disease for long periods, which suggested the feasibility of vaccination as a means of combatting the disease. The ILRAD already applied a vaccination-like 'infection-and-treatment' method to immunizing cattle against ECF, involving the infecting of cattle with live parasites, while simultaneously injecting them with drugs. The major disadvantage of this technique was its reliance on live parasites, which had to be cryopreserved to remain infective; cattle needed to be treated simulaneously with drugs and, even after immunization, the cattle might remain carriers of the infection (ILRAD, 1991; Komen, 1992c).

According to ILRAD publications, the prospects for developing a vaccine against ECF were good. Two antigenic proteins had been identified that could be the basis of such a vaccine. In 1989, ILRAD researchers cloned the gene for one of these proteins and filed a patent in the USA covering its potential use for vaccination against ECF. This patent filing was done in order to facilitate collaboration with a major vaccine-producing company, SmithKline Beecham plc (United Kingdom), for the joint development of a vaccine. In co-operation with this company, the ILRAD produced large quantities of the recombinant protein, so that the vaccine could be tested for effectiveness (Komen, 1992*c*).

15. Biotechnologies at the ICLARM

The International Center for Living Aquatic Resources Management (ICLARM), set up in 1977 in The Philippines with the support of the Rockefeller Foundation, aimed to conduct and stimulate research on all aspects of fisheries and other living aquatic sources. An autonomous, non-profit international scientific and technical centre, the ICLARM's priority target groups were small-scale fishermen and traditional fish farmers. Four basic programmes were supported by a number of private foundations and by governments. Specific programme-related newsletters (*Fishbyte* and *Aquabyte*) supplemented the general magazine, *Naga*, the ICLARM quarterly (Komen, 1991*b*).

In the late 1980s, the ICLARM employed about 60 scientific and support staff, with an annual budget of $3.8 million. Most funds had been allocated to Asia, the ICLARM's programme being implemented in collaboration with existing national facilities. The Five-Year Plan 1988–1992 called for a doubling of the staff and budget, with a 1992 budget of about $7.57 million (ICLARM, 1988; Maclean and Dizon, 1990). The proposed expansion was reflected in the setting up of regional offices such as the South Pacific Office and Coastal Aquaculture Centre (both at Honiara, Solomon Islands). The ICLARM was also constructing a project office in Malawi, at Lilongwe. Furthermore, a thorough study of African farming systems was being conducted, with a view to applying modified and adapted Asian aquaculture technologies in African environments. The ICLARM also planned to set up an office in Latin America (ICLARM, 1988).

Emphasis was being laid on building up in-house research capability in fish genetics and integrated farming systems. Biotechnologies could contribute to such priorities. Thus, within the framework of the research

483

project on the Genetic Improvement of Farmed Tilapias (GIFT), initiated in 1988, various biotechnological marker techniques were used for the evaluation of strain performance and to provide a detailed picture of the genetic structure of the various *Tilapia* strains involved in the project. The main objective was to produce better *Tilapia* breeds by selection for high growth rate and other, economically important traits. In order to broaden the genetic base, the project had started with the documentation of *Tilapia* genetic resources in Asia and Africa and the creation of a collection of promising strains from new *Tilapia* imports from 'wild' African and existing Asian cultivated stocks. This collection was kept in a 'live gene bank' at the national Bureau of Fisheries and Aquatic Resources, at Nueva Ecija, Philippines (Komen, 1991*b*).

As the GIFT project had reached the stage where the fish were ready for distribution, the ICLARM convened a meeting on International concerns in the use of aquatic germplasm in The Philippines, in June 1992. The international distribution of farmed fish strains might affect the wild stock and other aquatic organisms. The experts participating in the meeting recommended that the ICLARM promote information gathering on resident biota, focusing especially on trophic interactions between fishes by improving knowledge of fish ecology. An activity of this type would be an appropriate supplement to the ICLARM's on-going work of establishing and improving international fish data-bases, such as FISH BASE.

A crucial issue concerning international fish germplasm distribution related to whether it might be better to export know-how about breeding methodologies rather than the breeding stock itself. Nile tilapia seemed to be 'cornering the market' in an increasing number of developing countries. The ICLARM, therefore, was encouraging countries to set up their own breeding programmes to respond to particular local needs and use the GIFT project experience as a model for genetic improvement of other tropical species. National control of germplasm dissemination seemed most appropriate in reaching small-scale distribution and facilitating compliance with environmental regulations, as well as in introducing new fish strains.

An issue raised by the ICLARM meeting was that of how to reward Africa for its past contribution to international tilapia breeding. It was important that Africa conserve the wild tilapia relatives for future use, some of the benefits accruing from utilization of tilapia germplasm needing to be returned. The expert panel concluded accordingly that, considering that the genetic resources tapped were African in origin, it seemed equitable to encourage the ICLARM to recognize this by increasing its commitment to African aquacultural development.

484

Methods and approaches to fish genetic improvement, defined on the basis of work on *Tilapia*, would be applied to other fish species. Potential donors had been approached on a scheme to create an independent Aquaculture Genetics Research Unit. The ICLARM was also developing the concept of a global finfish genetic improvement network, following a request from the United Nations Development Programme (Komen, 1991*b*).

Oreochromis niloticus was the most widely bred species of tilapia; it had one of the best growth potentials and was particularly adaptable to the environment. Tilapias were cichlids of African origin comprising some 50 species belonging to three genera: *Tilapia*, *Oreochromis* and *Sarotherodon*. Tilapia's reproduction process, unlike that of other fish-breeding species, had to be interrupted to enable the fish to develop flesh: the species was so prolific that it could hamper its own growth. *Tilapia* reproduced all year round, laying eggs up to once a month; it scattered its eggs to protect them from parasites and oxygenate them, unlike *Sarotherodon* and *Oreochromis*. The female *Oreochromis* laid its eggs in a nest and, once they had been fertilized by the male, took the eggs in her mouth to incubate them at 27°C; they hatched four days later. Over the ensuing week, up to 2,000 fry hustled about in her mouth until they had exhausted their vitellus. Driven out by hunger, they left their mother to feed, sheltering timidly in groups, only to dash back at the slightest sign of danger. The mortality rate was low and the fingerlings reached maturity early, at between three and four months. This partial mouthbrooding behaviour gave the female time to eat; but only after three weeks, when the fry finally became independent, would she begin to feed normally, until the next laying. If males and females were left together in a pond, the fish multiplied rapidly. Overpopulation induced dwarfism, especially in the female, and accelerated reproduction (CIRAD, 1994).

In Asia and some African countries, such as Côte d'Ivoire, tilapia buyers were not interested in fish smaller than 250 g. Owing to the period of forced fasting which it underwent at the time of incubation and the energy spent in reproduction, the female of *Oreochromis niloticus* was always smaller than the male and uninteresting for the fish farmer. Therefore, a farmer usually separated the sexes to avoid reproduction, keeping only the males, who could then grow (CIRAD, 1994).

The males could be sorted from the females manually when their sexual dimorphism became apparent at between two and three months. This was time-consuming and only possible on a small scale. It also meant that, until sorting, the fish farmer was feeding twice as many fish as he would actually rear. Furthermore, the method was far from foolproof, since 3% to 10% of the females were not sorted out. So, several months after the first sexing, the females and the already hatched fry had to be fished out again. The second technique, hormonal sex inversion, was being used mainly by big producers (Israel, Taiwan and The Philippines). An artificial steroid, 17-alphamethyl-testosterone, was added to the fry's food for a month once it had exhausted its vitellus, to masculinize the fry regardless of their sexual genotype. The fish farmer's infrastructure was thereby fully utilized from the very first months. This technique, however, had its detractors, including consumers who were wary of hormone-treated animals. Although used throughout Asia and Israel, it was banned in Europe because it released into the environment about 30 derivative products whose effects were unknown (CIRAD, 1994).

There was a need for another sure and non-polluting method for obtaining exclusively male progeny. In co-operation with the Savanah Institute of Côte d'Ivoire and the Laboratory of Fish Physiology of the French National Institute for Agricultural Research (INRA), The CIRAD was exploring the physiological, genetic and environmental factors of sex determinism in tilapia. The present assumption was that sex determinism in the tilapia was mammalian: the females were homogametic (XX) and the males heterogametic (XY), the Y chromosome determining the male sex. CIRAD researchers created parents of monosex female progeny, i.e. genotype XX males, by hormonal inversion; their progeny was divided into two groups and reared under constant temperatures, one group at 27°C, the average temperature for tilapia fish farms, and the other at 36°C. Thermal treatment was applied from the 10th to 14th day after fertilization for 21 days, the period when the fry seemed most sensitive to external factors (CIRAD, 1994).

Between 27°C and 34°C, there was no significant change in sex-ratio as compared with that observed at 27°C. When the temperature rose above 34°C, however, the percentage of males obtained at the end of treatment increased. But there was no temperature threshold above or below which the population became 100% monosex, unlike for turtles or crocodiles. Furthermore, the progeny was differentially thermosensitive. Deviations from the norm in the sex-ratio were variable; among the progeny, the male population could be as high as 91% under the same experimental temperature of 36°C, which suggested parental influence. The experiments gave the same results with conventional populations. The maximum obtained was a 98.3% male population. Differing thermosensitivity among individuals of the same population and among populations of the same species was being studied to select the best fish. Thermal treatment was also being improved: the length of treatment could be shortened if applied at the right time. The objective was to obtain a 100% male population at the end of treatment, since a 5% female population in a pond could cause considerable economic loss (CIRAD, 1994).

In the project on giant clams (*Tridacna gigas*) at the Central Aquaculture Centre (CAC), experiments were being conducted on artifically-induced spawning and mass rearing of giant clam larvae, using an artificial diet and antibiotics. The produced juveniles were transferred first to ocean nurseries then to growout sites in villages in the Solomon Islands. Clam meat constituted part of the diet of many islanders in the Indo-Pacific region. However, populations of *T. gigas* in Pacific countries had dwindled and giant clams were listed as a threatened species. Giant clams are phototrophic, like plants, and therefore self-feeding potential farm animals. Clam farming could provide a source of protein and income in Pacific countries, with a yield potential of as much as 60 tonnes of meat per hectare per year. A major giant clam genetics project was planned at the ICLARM, whose goal was selective breeding from broodstock with favourable traits (particularly growth), the development of homozygous strains of giant clams by self-fertilization and the creation of fast-growing triploid stocks (Komen, 1991*b*).

Co-operation between the ICLARM, the Freshwater Aquaculture Center (FAC) of Central Luzon State University (Philippines), the International Rice Research Institute (IRRI) and national rice-fish research programmes within the IRRI-based Asian Rice Farming Systems Network (ARFSN) had generated several collaborative projects in India, Indonesia and Thailand. Experiments on small fish ponds on irrigated and rain-fed rice farms showed that increases in net returns over rice monocropping occurred in all cases. *Tilapia*, common carp and silver barb were confirmed as the most appropriate species for rice-fish systems. These encouraging results led to an increasing adoption of the technique in Indonesia and Thailand, with involvement of governments and non-governmental organizations. For instance, the Government of Indonesia had announced a plan to expand rice-fish farming in West Java by 20,000 hectares and in North Sumatra by 2,500 hectares (Komen, 1991*b*).

At the invitation of the CGIAR, the ICLARM was developing a strategic plan for international fisheries research, including aquaculture. The activities of the ICLARM were considered particularly relevant in the context of the alarming decline in marine living resources.

Since January 1994, many international conferences had drawn world attention to the dwindling living resources of the ocean. According to data provided by the Consultative Group on International Agricultural Research, between 1950 and 1989, the total fish catch (both at sea and in freshwater) had multiplied by five throughout the world, amounting to up to 100 million tonnes of fish, crustaceans and molluscs in 1989, the record year. The world fishing fleet had grown from 585,000 vessels in 1970 to 1.2 million in 1990 and 3.5 million in 1995, not counting the millions of unregistered small boats, pirogues and canoes (Cans, 1995).

The unprecedented exploitation of seas and freshwaters explained the numerous conflicts over fishing areas: the cod war between the United Kingdom and Iceland, disputes between French and Spanish fishermen in the Gulf of Gascogne, the black turbot war between Spain and Canada in 1995. An increasing number of countries were fiercely defending their fishing grounds on their continental shelf and beyond it. For instance, Iceland, where fish exports represented 80% of the total value of exports, had agreed to reduce its cod quotas from 400,000 tonnes in 1987 to 155,000 tonnes in 1994, thereby inducing its fishermen to explore new territories to compensate. Consequently, in 1994, according to the non-governmental environmentalist organization Greenpeace, Icelandic boats confronted Norwegian coast-guards in the Spitzberg area during a week of a so-called cod war. Chinese fishermen had been killed by a Russian vessel which found them fishing in the Okhotsk Sea. Russian and Japanese factory-ships were present off the coasts of Mauritania, Senegal, India, Indonesia or The Philippines. Japanese fishermen were even harvesting holothurias around the Galapagos Islands to supply their markets with this delicacy, regardless of this Ecuadorian territory's status as part of the World Heritage (Cans, 1995).

Some fishing zones were considered on the verge of exhaustion, e.g. the Gulf of Thailand, South-East Asian seas, the southern part of the North Sea and the northern coasts of the Mediterranean Sea. The World Bank considered that nine of the 17 main fishing areas of the planet were showing a fast production decline. With the present catch regime in certain coastal zones, more than one-third of the fishing resources would disappear if conservation rules were not respected (Cans, 1995).

On 4 August 1995, the representatives of 99 countries gathered in New York adopted by consensus an international convention to preserve fish stocks and avoid conflicts between countries over fishing grounds. The conference, which had been studying the problem since

1992, stressed the need for international co-operation to reach the goals of the convention adopted, which included strict control measures even on the high sea's by coastal States. The agreement on the management of overlapping fish stocks, i.e. those found at the 200-mile limit (cod and black halibut) as well as on migrating fish species (tuna and swordfish), was to be adopted formally by the United Nations Assembly by the end of 1995. The agreement would then be open to ratification by Member States, before coming into force once signed by 30 countries. The European Union's representative welcomed the convention and, at the same time, warned against the abuse of power by coastal States, which would be contrary to international law.

While some 5,000 species of fish, hundreds species of crustaceans, molluscs and urchins were available, the fishing effort was concentrated on a few dozens only. It was estimated in 1991 that 40% of the catch was provided by only 24 species. In 1993, five fish species provided the bulk of the world catch: anchovies (8.3 million tonnes), Alaska pollack (4.6 million tonnes), Chilean mackerel (3.4 million tonnes), pilchard (2.3 million tonnes) and caplin (1.7 million tonnes) [Cans, 1995]. A recent *Issue in Science and Technology* revealed that the swordfish population had halved in twenty years and that the catch of groupers had decreased by 80% during the 1980s. Overall, the FAO calculated that about 44% of the world's fish stocks were already at their yield limit. Consequently, the return on fishing today was no more than half of its cost; hence the rising number of requests for subsidies to cover the deficit.

Fishing was accompanied by tremendous waste: it was estimated that more than one-third of the fish catch (27 million tonnes) was returned to the sea, because the fish were too small, altered or did not correspond to the categories sought by the fishermen. Furthermore, the smaller size of the net mesh retained younger fish, which constituted a threat to the maintenance of future stocks (Cans, 1995). In October 1994, the FAO published a study on the 'wastes' of industrial fisheries in a *FAO Fisheries Technical Paper*, which confirmed that about 27 million tonnes of fish and crustaceans caught in the nets, but not commercialized, were rejected every year into the sea and that only 11% of the rejected animals could survive. This figure was all the more striking in that the overall annual world catch was 86 million tonnes (Tardieu, 1995).

The most sacrificed species was the shrimp, which represented more than one-third of the world's waste. It was fished mostly in the centre-west of the Pacific by Thai, Indonesian and Philippine fleets, in the Indian Ocean by the Indians and Pakistanis, and in the Atlantic Ocean and Gulf of Mexico by the Americans. Then came the crabs and halibut wasted by American fleets. The north-west of the Pacific was undoubtedly the area overexploited by 'Western' boats, which threw overboard about 9 million tonnes of crabs, mackerels, cod and shrimps every year. Even though the error margin was still wide (more or less 10 million tonnes), the wastage was huge (Tardieu, 1995).

Scientists interpreted these figures in different ways. According to an FAO consultancy institute in The Philippines, the FAO study illustrated the ecological plundering by 'Western' fishing fleets. Another group of scientists, while acknowledging that waste represented more than one-third of the annual catch, claimed that small fish and crustaceans were being partly recycled and eaten by carnivorous fish and sea birds. However, this reintegration in the food cycle was contended and difficult to evaluate. Estimated at several billion dollars, this wastage highlighted the deadlock in industrial fisheries: on the one hand, it was a scandal to waste so many resources, but on the other, if the catch were kept and brought back, the market cost of fish would rise considerably (Tardieu, 1995).

In 1995, half of humankind lived near the seashore, a proportion which would be closer to two-thirds in 2020, according to World Bank data. Most fish species also multiplying near coastal zones, these were therefore the site of conflicts between nations. That was why a number of fishing boats were being equipped to explore very deep waters, from which they extracted strange fish species with names like 'emperor' or 'grenadier'. However, these rare and expensive catches could supply only exclusive markets and never replace herring stocks or other common species. They were even fears that these very deep species might disappear before those living in the continental-shelf waters, due to their very slow growth and difficult reproduction (Cans, 1995).

Our knowledge of deep-sea fauna was indeed scarce: between 500,000 and 1 million species, but there had been numerous discoveries of new fish, crustacean, coral and microbial species over the last four decades. As a result, the old taxonomical lists had been rewritten and a number of preconceptions invalidated. For instance, it was not always true that biological diversity in deep habitats was greater in the tropics than in the boreal regions; this depended on the kind of species; for macro-algae, the most diverse ecosystems were found in the temperate zone around California, Japan, the south of Australia, the North Atlantic and the coast of Brittany. One should also bear in mind that only 7% of the globe's oceans had been sampled by the mid-1990s (Tardieu, 1995).

Aquaculture was the only way to match the disappearance of 'wild' fish. In 1993, total world aquacultural production amounted to 16.5

million tonnes, i.e. 16% of the total aquatic production (fisheries and aquaculture). It is interesting to compare these figures with the world production of meat, which amounted to approximately 170 million tonnes almost totally derived from stock raising. According to FAO statistical data, the world aquacultural production represented a value of $28 billion. Wild fish production was a stable 85 million tonnes, which meant that the increase in world demand due to population growth and in individual consumption would be met only by a steady rise in aquacultural production, which had reached an average 11% per annum since 1984. It was forecast that aquacultural production would reach 35 million tonnes in 2000, 52 million tonnes in 2010 and 77 million tonnes in 2025 (Billard, 1995).

The leading countries in this field were China (8.6 million tonnes in 1992), India (1.4 million tonnes), Japan (800,000 tonnes), Indonesia (600,000 tonnes), and the USA (400,000 tonnes). The share for Asian countries was 80% of total production, including fish, shellfish and macro-algae. Norway led Europe and Chile led South America for salmon culture. Japan, New Zealand and France were considered leaders for scallop cultivation, while the Solomon Islands were the production site of the giant clam *Tridacna gigas*, exported to Japan (Cans, 1995).

Of the global shrimp production (from aquaculture) of 0.9 million tonnes in 1992, 75% was produced in Asia, China being the biggest producer (0.2 million tonnes), followed by Thailand and Indonesia (0.15 million tonnes each). India was the world's fifth-biggest producer of farmed shrimps, with an annual production of 40,000 tonnes (World Bank, 1993).

Several of the big producers had experienced declines in production: excessive use of chemicals and toxic substances adversely affected the coastal environment and therewith aquaculture productivity. In Taiwan, for instance, shrimp production plummeted from about 100,000 tonnes in 1987 to 30,000 tonnes 12 months later. In China, shrimp production had fallen dramatically, mainly because of viral, bacterial and protozoan diseases. Other countries, such as Viet Nam and India, were increasing their market share. In a joint venture with the Thai private company CP Foods, Viet Nam had developed an infrastructure to cultivate 1,000 hectares of shrimps. In 1993, CP Foods exported $96 million worth of shrimps, or about 40% of Viet Nam's total shrimp sales (Pandey and Chaturvedi, 1994).

In the case of France, annual aquatic resources production in 1991 was of the order of 600,000 tonnes from fisheries and 250,000 tonnes from aquaculture (including 200,000 tonnes of molluscs, mainly oysters). Production could not meet national needs. The balance of trade was negative, the deficit being 500,000 tonnes for a value of $2 billion. Part of the deficit was due to the popular demand for such aquacultural products as salmon, prawns, scallops and various molluscs (Billard, 1995).

Some 200 species were being cutlivated world-wide, including 110 fish species, 25 crustaceans, 50 molluscs and eight algae, but 80% of world aquacultural production was derived from only a dozen species. In many cases, one was dealing with the growth of juveniles captured in natural environments. The dozen or so species fully domesticated – in other worlds, whose life-cycle was completely mastered – were perfectly adapted to captivity and to production goals. Domesticated species included oysters (already raised by the Romans), common carp (*Cyprinus carpio*) whose breeding dated back to the VIth and VIIth centuries B.C. in China (followed by the creation of several breeds, especially in Europe) and the red fish (*Carassius auratus*) raised as an ornamental fish for more than 1,000 years in China. Breeding of the rainbow trout (*Oncorhynchus mykiss*) had been initiated in the mid-19th century. Other species had been raised since the 1950s–1970s, due to progress in research to accelerate the domestication rate: the seabass (*Morone labrax*), American catfish (*Ictalurus punctatus*), several species of salmon, tilapia and gilt-head seabream (*Sparus auratus*), and oyster. However, the intensification of aquatic resources production, including the domestication of species and the mastering of environmental conditions, was not as advanced as for terrestrial species. Fisheries had gradually shifted toward the exploitation of primary and secondary production (extensive stock breeding) and toward intensive stock breeding dependent essentially on the physical environment (water, temperature, etc.). Extensive systems were still predominant in the world with a gradient from forced recruitment, to the harnessing of all development stages in mono- or polyculture systems in fertilized ponds (Billard, 1995).

Regarding the raising of stock in open marine or freshwater environments, juveniles were being reared in hatcheries to the size that would enable them to resist predators, before being released into the natural environment. This was the case for the Pacific salmon, which was a highly developed industry in Japan: 150,000 tonnes of salmon were captured every year in the coastal zone to replenish fishing areas. The sturgeon, *Huso huso,* was one of the biggest freshwater fish (record weight: 1,100 kg in 1912); restocking operations with juveniles in the Black Sea and Caspian Sea were common, brood stock fish being caught in the wild, artificially reproduced and the juveniles reared.

Similar activities were carried out in lakes for several Salmonidae and Coregonids in France (Lake Leman) and in Central Europe. A system of cage rearing for juvenile coregons was being practised in northern Poland: after capture of wild brood stock fish and production of gametes, the eggs were fertilized and the embryos incubated in hatcheries; some days after hatching, the larvae were transferred to cages located in a lake, where they were reared until big enough for release (Billard, 1995).

This system implied the respect of size limits and capture quotas. In the former Soviet Union, these conditions did not seem to be fully respected for sturgeons, which came to sexual maturity very late (aged between ten and twenty years). For this reason, a great number of age classes needed protecting so as to enable the fish to reach the reproduction age. In the absence of these conservation measures, overfishing could lead to the extinction of exploited sturgeon species (Billard, 1995).

Another form of lake ranching was practised in China (e.g. a lake close to Wuxi producing about 1 tonne of fish per hectare per year): larvae were put in pens in the lake and fed artificially; on reaching the required size, they were released into the lake where they continued to grow. During regular catches, individuals of market size were removed, the others being returned to the lake (Billard, 1995).

In Europe, by the early 1990s, about 45 fish species were subject to stock replenishment in open environments. One could place in this category the rearing of species threatened with extinction; in this case, the approach consisted of capturing genitors in their natural environment, rearing them and attempting to reproduce them before releasing their adult or juvenile offspring into open environments or, alternatively, capturing juveniles and releasing them once they were of an age to reproduce. To illustrate this approach, one could cite attempts made to safeguard the sturgeon (*Acipencer sturio*) in the Gironde, in France; this species was threatened with extinction and the few existing genitors were almost impossible to trap for the purposes of reproduction in captivity. Juveniles were easier prey. French researchers were trying to rear them to the reproduction stage to constitute a stock of genitors. Other species threatened with extinction like *Zingel asper*, could be multiplied in the same way (Billard, 1995).

Another form of fish stick replenishment was the setting up of artificial reefs, which were considered havens for reproduction and development of primary production, which in turn increased food availability. Such reefs, made of trunks and branches, were common in Benin and Côte d'Ivoire: bamboo sticks were planted in a pen or in a lagoon, allowing a larger surface area for periphyton development and increasing productivity; this was called the acadja system, adapted to pisciculture. Concrete structures or even various kinds of wrecked boats or structures were increasingly being set up in coastal zones, particularly in Japan and the USA (Billard, 1995).

An example of stock rearing directly in open environments was that of molluscs: the breeder captured juveniles in the natural environment and reared them in the coastal zone, in an open medium, the best example being that of oyster culture. Innovative procedures included the setting up of hatcheries that allowed the regulation of juvenile inputs and also the genetic improvement of the species reared. These systems were subject to the vagaries of weather and environment (e.g. availability of algae, growth of toxic algae). In the conventional cultures of molluscs, there was a permanent introduction of species and populations from the environment and, in the case of oysters, there were frequent exchanges between the rearing places world-wide. This could introduce new pathogens and cause breeders serious problems (Billard, 1995).

Many non-domesticated species were reared in captivity but from eggs, larvae or juveniles derived from wild populations, and grown in a controlled environment. In the case of *Esox lucius*, brood fish from the wild or extensive breeding in ponds were stored in tanks prior to reproduction in hatcheries or were left to reproduce naturally in small ponds. Eggs taken from wild fish were also incubated in hatcheries. Larvae were returned to the wild or, after rearing, to semi-protected zones or tanks. This type of production, although quantitatively low, gave a good if unstable revenue, due to predators and weather vagaries (Billard, 1995).

The rearing of other species depended entirely on the capture of juveniles in their natural environment, followed by their growth in cages or ponds: *Seriola quinqueradiata* in Japan (162,000 tonnes in 1991), milkfish (*Chanos chanos*) in South-East Asia (490,000 tonnes in 1991) and carps in India (1,114,000 tonnes in 1991). This meant that a large portion of world aquatic resources production was still derived from wild species. It should be emphasized that the production of seriola and milkfish was tending to stabilize or even decrease, due to the ups and downs in the capture of juveniles and to the very negative impact on the environment in the case of seriola (Billard, 1995).

Fish rearing in captitivy was carried out in ponds, basins, raceways or cages, but the water needed for such systems was taken from the natural environment (i.e. sea, lake or river) and returned to it (in the case of cage rearing, water was just passing through the cages). Feed could be provided by the ecosystem itself (extensive form with annual production fluctuating from 100 kg to 10 tonnes per hectare) or by artifical means (various by-products, grains, concentrates and pellets), which led to the most intensive forms with densities between 10 kg and 100 kg of fish per m³ and production of up to several hundred tonnes per hectare per annum (Billard, 1995).

Fish-rearing freshwater ponds were commonplace in Europe; they represented very extensive forms of fish rearing, with minimal organic or mineral fertilization and with annual production of several hundred kilos of fish. In China, ponds received high organic fertilization in the form of stock effluents (pigsties, poultry and cattle manure) and even domestic residues; they produced about 4 million tonnes of fish annually. This system was extremely productive, because it combined several species belonging to different levels of the food web, the development of which was strongly stimulated by the organic input; the species were therefore feeding on phytoplankton, zooplankton, molluscs, or plants; production was generally greater than 5 tonnes per hectare per annum, without any other exogenous feed. Air was insufflated into the ponds by aerators or paddle wheels, which brought in oxygen and CO_2 to a lesser extent (Billard, 1995).

It should be emphasized that, in China, animal production was taking place around the water (pigs and sheep), on the water (geese and ducks) and within the water (fish). Complex relationships existed between these three compartments which underlined the highly integrated nature of aquaculture in Chinese agriculture. There were also brackish-water ponds in the coastal regions (e.g. the tambacks of South-East Asia), where milkfish was reared, among other species. A characteristic feature of these systems was that the faeces of fish were recycled *in situ* and contributed to the fertilization of the pond. One should not underestimate the risks of some pathogens which could cause serious diseases among the workers (e.g. leptospirosis, schistosomiasis and malaria). Other parasites infecting fish could be transmitted to humans consuming raw or insufficiently cooked fish. In Asia, intestinal parasites affecting man could be transmitted by fish reared in ponds receiving human effluents or night soil. Another risk was that of botulism in pond sediments, due to contamination by mammals dying on the pond banks; water contaminated by ducks could prove fatal to man but generally not to fish, which were solely carriers of pathogenic bacteria. The overall epidemiological situation remained an enigma. More studies were needed to elucidate the relation between the pond environment, pathogens and parasites (Billard, 1995).

The advantages of Chinese pisciculture were perceived by the USSR in the 1950s and fish species such as the silver carp (*Hypophthalmichthys molitrix*) and herbivorous carp (*Ctenopharyngodon idella*) were imported to the USSR and via the USSR to Eastern Europe (Hungary, Rumania and Yugoslavia); however, the results compared unfavourably with those obtained in China, due to an insufficient harnessing of organic fertilization in much larger ponds (in China, ponds extended over less than 1 hectare and their aeration systems were more easily controlled than in European ponds whose surface area was often greater than 10 hectares and which were deprived of aeration). In Israel, efforts were made in the 1970s to integrate the Chinese system but, due to the lack of outlets for Chinese carps, less appreciated than tilapias, nothing came of it (Billard, 1995).

Cage fish rearing was carried out in China. Fish were grown in cages and fed only on the plankton brought by the water passing through the cages; oxygen was nevertheless brought in through aeration systems. Annual production could reach 1 tonne per hectare (Billard, 1995).

When feed was brought in in the form of pellets, this fish rearing system resembled the hydroponic systems of plant culture (i.e. without soil). It was practised in developed countries for salmonids, seriola, American catfish, and carp in Japan. Freshwater trout were generally grown in raceways where a water stream circulated; water was recycled after going through several successive basins, before finally returning to the river into which drained the fish faeces, which posed environmental problems. This system was widespread in Europe, North America and Japan, the annual production of rainbow trout amounting to some 280,000 tonnes by the early 1990s (Billard, 1995).

Salmon from the Atlantic or the Pacific were reared in cages, in the sea or in coastal regions; this system was widespread in the 1980s, particularly in Norway (about 200,000 tonnes per year by the early 1990s), Scotland and Chile. Cage-rearing was also practised in Japan for seriola. In all cases, faeces and metabolic products were rejected into the natural environment, which altered the latter and caused problems for the fishes themselves when the concentration of wastes was high or in zones where currents were weak; hence the idea to transfer the cages to the open sea. Cage-rearing had also become widespread in lagoons and lakes in Japan, The Philippines, Côte d'Ivoire, or even in rivers (Central Europe), with subsequent eutrophication of the water and decrease in water quality (Billard, 1995).

The production of shrimps, both in seawater and freshwater, was exclusively the result of this intensive system, with artificial feed and return of the water to the natural environment; the negative impact on the environment was visible in the destruction of mangroves to give way to cultivation areas and in the diminished water quality, the consequence of which was a drop in total production (Billard, 1995).

American catfish were being reared on abandoned cropland converted into ponds. Feed was entirely supplied as pellets and water was pumped off from the water-table and returned to the river. In order to save water and mitigate the impact on the environment, ponds were emptied and cleaned every five or six years. Similar systems existed in Israel, where water pumped off the fish ponds was used in irrigated areas and not returned to the hydrographic network (Billard, 1995).

To meet environmental standards being imposed in many countries, particularly in Europe, fish-rearing in captivity with total water recycling was being developed. This system did not return any water to the natural environment, or any medicinal substances, pathogens or animals that escaped from the rearing facilities and were alien to the local fauna. This system was expected to develop in the future, due to the pressing demand for clean aquaculture. It was already being applied in hatcheries for the production of larvae and juveniles (whose market value was high), but was not always feasible for growing fishes due to economic contraints. There were, however, success stories, like that of the African catfish (*Charias gariepinus*) in the Netherlands. A system called 'Dekel', combining extensive and intensive production approaches, had been set up in Israel for carp and tilapia, and was also practised in France for rearing catfish in the Sologne: a rearing system both 'offground' and removed from the natural environment, including a battery of highly intensive production tanks (15–20 kg fish/m^3); water was pumped into a conventional purification pond, a ditch preventing water from the watershed from spilling into the pond; water losses were compensated by input from streams, springs or pumped underground water. The purification pond demanded efficient management so as to recycle effluents without accumulation of organic matter. The solution lay in a 'polyculture' system including burrowing fish species which aerated the sediments and zooplanktonophagous fishes to limit the growth of zooplankton and let micro-algae eliminate ammonium nitrogen (Billard, 1995).

Combined production systems were particularly developed in Asia. In China, for instance, one could find on the same lake ranching, intensive and extensive cage-rearing: juvenile fish produced in inland hatcheries were put into lakes to maintain fish stocks, in land tanks, or pens or cages in the lake where they grew until reaching market size; fish in pens, cages or inland tanks were fed on plant matter (itself grown in pens or harvested from the lake), molluscs harvested from the natural environment, pellets or various agricultural by-products. Fish breeding in and around cages was carried out in oxbow lakes in Hungary; due to the input of nutrients from the watershed and intensive rearing cages, these highly eutrophic waters were used for polyculture (associations of various fish species feeding at different levels of the food web: plankton, benthon and plants); free-living fish in the lakes were stocked and captured by fishermen. The association of rice cropping and fish rearing also pertained to this category, as well as the cultivation of water hyacinth and fish rearing with pig husbandry (Billard, 1995).

A major handicap to aquaculture development was its voracious appetite for water: to produce one tonne of live weight, 252,000 m^3 of water were needed for inland salmon rearing in basins, and between 50 and 200 m^3 for the rearing of African catfish in ponds. In the case of Salmonids, water was returned to the river after use while, in the case of pond rearing, some water evaporated (30 to 40 cm per year, particularly in the summer in Europe). Cage-rearing in the natural environment did not consume water, but could alter its quality according to the production system, the degree of intensification, the quality of food and temperature. Pond systems were generally considered as slightly polluting but could in certain cases improve water quality. The Chinese system of recycling pigsty effluent in aquatic environments had been adopted in Italy and France to directly process pigsty effluent. To sum up, water was either a simple physical support for the aquatic animal, bringing oxygen and eliminating wastes of closed systems, or a biological medium (like a cropland) that supplied primary or secondary production (Billard, 1995).

Reared organisms determined qualitative and quantitative water needs, the type of rearing system and their geographical distribution, because of their oxygen needs, tolerance of temperature or pH, food regime, resistance to diseases and predators. As the number of species that were domesticated or easy to adapt was limited, there had been many introductions in the history of aquaculture: oysters had been the subject of broad intercontinental exchanges in recent centuries; rainbow trout had been transplanted in 82 countries, the common carp in 59 countries and the so-called Chinese carp in 113 countries. Risks relating to the introduction of alien species included the introduction of pathogens, the escape and uncontrolled population growth of species in the natural environment and the contamination of wild local populations by domesticated species. These risks, although they could be limited, were at the origin of stricter regulations on the introduction of alien species, such as the ban on introducing live organisms into certain ecosystems, particularly into continental waters. It was likely that, in the future, the diversification of reared species would utilize mainly autochtonous species (Billard, 1995).

The reduction of wastes in closed rearing systems could result from the use of highly digestible feed, e.g. fish meal, which was becoming costly. In particular, many studies showed that, in Salmonids, fatty feed could decrease nitrogen wastes. Feed with a lower concentration of phosphorus was also being developed. Other approaches consisted of atuning the food habits with the biological cycle and improving the biological value of proteins. For cage-rearing, effluent treatment consisted of a mechanical filtration system which retained suspended solids, whereas for the elimination of dissolved matter, like nitrogen wastes, biological filtration on a bacterial substrate was needed. In salmoniculture, trials were being carried out to optimize both processes of mechanical and biological filtration, so as to completely recycle water and insufflate oxygen. For cage-rearing in the sea, it was important to choose sites where currents could dilute wastes. Water quality in open environments could be altered by aquacultural activities, but it could also be guaranteed by them: fish rearing was indeed a good indicator of the biological quality of water. Any alteration of the latter required bioremediation measures. Good examples of protection measures were those to combat the negative impact on oyster rearing in the region of Arcachon, in France, consisting of the suppression of toxic painting on boats, or in the lake of Thau, in the south of France (Billard, 1995).

In developing countries, particularly in Asia, where aquaculture was a well-established activity, the social basis of aquatic resources production and development was very strong. In addition, a large part of production was devoted to feeding local populations, which also found employment opportunities in a labour-intensive activity. The techniques used did not produce irreversible alterations of the aquatic environment and the management of aquacultural systems integrated into other production systems resulted in stable productive ecosystems, whose sustainability was crucial. Overall, the social and natural components of the environment were preserved (Billard, 1995).

In industrialized countries, aquaculture was technology-based with important inputs from research, the main objective being to reduce production costs to a minimum and to maximize profits, or in other words to reduce the labour force; consequently, the social impact of aquaculture was limited. This model which, with the exception of carp and trout, was unrelated to any tradition or local know-how (it was the researchers themselves who domesticated marine species like shrimps, turbot and seabass), had been transferred to developing countries lacking aquacultural traditions (e.g. Ecuador, a leading shrimp producer), resulting in major alterations to the natural environment. The world-wide trend of delocating production and processing activities was pushing modern aquaculture toward traditionally aquacultural countries in Asia (e.g. Thailand and Taiwan), where it was having a negative impact on both the natural and social environment. It was therefore imperative to reverse this process if aquaculture was to fit within a sustainable development (Billard, 1995).

Prospects: the various aquacultural productive systems had been characterized to a large extent by local marketing networks, with small (often family) enterprises in charge of producing live fish. But the aquacultural sector could not escape the globalization of markets, with the setting up over recent years of large production systems, linked to processing and marketing (e.g. for salmons, trout and shrimps). This trend was expected to become widespread, due to the increasing demand for aquacultural products in industrialized countries. In developing countries, traditional approaches would prevail, although the industrial approach would gradually permeate, with the negative impacts on the natural and social environment that went with it (Billard, 1995).

The pursuit of research was indispensable, for there was still room for technological innovation in production and transformation processes, as well as in the harnessing of the aquatic ecosystem, especially in the case of pond fish rearing. The latter had a considerable output, particularly in Asia, but was lesser known in other regions; it needed to be rehabilitated in Europe and developed in African countries. Research also needed to be oriented toward reducing the negative environmental impact of aquaculture through the use of less polluting feed, effluent treatment, definition of the best quality of water compatible with the production of a high-quality product, the regeneration of water in lagoon systems and the reduction of water consumption. As with any other agricultural production, aquaculture would need to become 'cleaner' and was expected to supply two major types of product, at least in the industrialized countries: on the one hand, standardized-quality products at low cost and supplied regularly to meet a massive demand for a small number of species whose rearing was well harnessed; on the other hand, high-quality products from a wide range of well-known species, but in small quantities and derived from extensive rearing systems. In addition, production systems would deal with non-food species and seek to meet the needs of recreation fishing or angling, conserving species threatened with extinction and rearing ornamental fish. It was very likely that the most sought-after aquacultural products would develop independently of natural aquatic networks to ensure their share of a highly competitive market. With respect to fish rearing in open environments, despite its high-risk features, it deserved to be maintained and encouraged, because its extensive nature did not alter water quality, but, on the contrary, maintained it. The overall situation of aquaculture by the mid-1990s meant that, with the spread of fish rearing in confined environments, one was making a gradual transition from fisheries to stock rearing, as had been done for livestock husbandry in terrestrial ecosystems a long time ago (Billard, 1995).

16. Asian Vegetable Research and Development Center

The Asian Vegetable Research and Development Centre (AVRDC), created in 1971 and based in Taiwan, was initially the brainchild of the U.S. Agency for International Development. From the beginning, the goal of the AVRDC had been to increase production and quality of vegetables through improved varieties, increased disease and pest resistance/tolerance, increased heat tolerance and better cultivation practices. Research concentrated initially on six vegetables: tomato, soybeans, mungbean, sweet potato, white potato and Chinese cabbage.

The AVRDC Genetic Resources and Seed Unit (GRSU), constructed in 1984, was a big cold-storage facility capable of keeping some varieties of seed viable for as long as a century. By the end of 1995, the GRSU had a total of 37,938 accessions of its principal crops and 5,404 accessions of non-principal but regionally important crops. The Unit held the world's base collection of mungbean and pepper. The material provided a broad genetic base for vegetable breeding and safety backups against the risk of a limited and highly uniform gene pool.

On-going research aimed to establish sets of core collections and to generate information that would lead to better management of vegetable genetic resources. This included the use of statistical, cytological, biochemical and molecular tools in the analysis of genetic diversity and genetic changes at different phases of germplasm maintenance. The germplasm was made available to researchers. Collaboration with similar centres or institutes in the USA, Japan, France and the Netherlands aimed to increase application of plant biotechnologies for improving vegetable crop species.

An overview of some of the research projects is given below:

Chinese cabbage

diamondback moth	bio-insecticide (*B. thuringiensis*) production, in collaboration with the National Development Centre for Biotechnology (DCB, Taiwan) and National Taiwan University (NTU); transformation for insect resistance (insertion of *B. thuringiensis* toxin gene), in collaboration with Plant Genetic Systems (PGS) N.V. (Belgium);
turnip mosaic virus	detection with monoclonal antibodies.

Mungbean

beanfly, powdery mildew (PW)	wide cross/embryo rescue for insect and disease resistance, in collaboration with Oregon State University;
bruchid, *Cercospora* leaf spot, PW	molecular markers to select for resistance, in collaboration with the University of Minnesota;
gene mapping	restricted fragment length polymorphism (RFLP), in collaboration with the University of Minnesota; isozyme electrophoresis, in collaboration with the University of The Philippines.

Peppers

cucumber mosaic virus (CMV)	insertion of CMV coat protein genes/ transformation for virus resistance, in collaboration with the DCB;
CMV, tomato spotted wilt virus (TSWV), potty viruses	molecular mapping (genetics of resistance), in collaboration with Cornell University;
fruitworm	transformation for insect resistance, in collaboration with the DCB;
pepper mild mottle virus (PMMV), gene mapping	detection with monoclonal antibodies, randomly amplified polymorphic DNA (RAPD), in collaboration with Fujen University;
bacterial spot	*in-vitro* screening for resistance.

Soybeans

vegetable quality	molecular markers to select for quality traits, in collaboration with the Chinese National Academy of Sciences.

Tomato

CMV	insertion of satellite DNA (sDNA) or CMV coat protein genes/transformation for virus resistance, in collaboration with the DCB, U.S. Agricultural Research Service;
fruitworm	transformation for insect resistance, in collaboration with the DCB and Fujen University; wide cross for insect resistance, in collaboration with Cornell University;
nematodes	isozyme electrophoresis to select for resistance;
fruit size, linkage with bacterial wilt	molecular markers to facilitate selection, in collaboration with the University of Minnesota;
heat stress	gene expression and regulation of heat shock protein, in collaboration with NTU, and Texas Technical University.

Source: AVRDC, Shanhua, Tainan, Taiwan.

An eight year-old project supported by the International Development Research Centre (IDRC, Ottawa) attempted to increase the yields of certain vegetables in China, e.g. Chinese cabbage, tomato, soybean, mungbean and sweet potato. Improved lines of these vegetable species developed at the AVRDC headquarters and at its station in Thailand had been tested in various parts of China.

Planted as an important crop species in many regions of China, local mungbean lines were vulnerable to disease, such as *Cercospora* leaf spot and powdery mildew. Two of the new lines developed by the AVRDC were resistant to these diseases and five lines outyielded the Chinese local mungbean lines by 20%. In Shandong province, for instance, one variety of mungbean boasted a yield 55% higher than for the local variety; the accumulated economic profit for Chinese farmers was evaluated at $33.2 million. A particular AVRDC-developed mungbean line, called Zhong Lu no.1, occupied 25% of the total mungbean production areas of China, estimated at more than 253,000 hectares in 1990. Since 1985, over 360,000 hectares of new AVRDC-developed mungbean lines had been planted with an estimated economic benefit to Chinese farmers of over $175 million (in *IDRC Reports,* vol. 19, no. 2, July 1991, p. 16).

Many Chinese cabbage lines had been combined with superior open-pollinated cultivars, generating more than 98 cross combinations. Five superior cabbage lines had been selected, the net yield of these being more than 40% higher than for local cabbage lines. Most of the AVRDC-developed Chinese cabbage varieties attracted the interest of Chinese farmers because of their heat tolerance, early maturity, attractive head shape and excellent eating quality. Between 1987 and 1989, a total of 2.7 tonnes of improved Chinese cabbage hybrid seeds were produced by Chinese scientists co-operating with the AVRDC. The total economic profit was evaluated at more than $2 million (in *IDRC Reports*, vol. 19, no. 2, July 1991, p. 17).

Two diseases hindering Chinese agricultural production were soybean rust disease and tomato viral diseases. According to the AVRDC Thailand Outreach Programme director, the surveys on soybean rust disease in several provinces of Central and Southern China, and on tomato viral diseases were conducted intensively. In 1989, the Oilseed Crops Research Institute of the Chinese Academy of Agricultural Sciences (CAAS) had agreed to be responsible for organizing and leading the soybean rust disease survey in China. Meanwhile, the study of tomato viral diseases had been jointly undertaken by the CAAS and the Jiangsu Academy of Agricultural Sciences (in *IDRC Reports*, vol. 19, no. 2, July 1991, p. 17).

In addition to training activities for Chinese researchers (at Kasetsart University, in Thailand), there was a continued exchange of information between the AVRDC and co-operating institutions in China. Nine agricultural organizations were participating in AVRDC research projects, stretching from the Guangdong Academy of Agricultural Sciences in Southern China to the Xinjiang Academy in the North. The AVRDC regularly exchanged scientific reports, publications, bulletins and newsletters with these academies. Several leading researchers were also able to attend some important AVRDC-sponsored international workshops outside China (in *IDRC Reports*, vol. 19, no. 2, July 1991, p. 17).

Both the AVRDC and IDRC believed that the improvement of Chinese vegetable agriculture could benefit from a two-pronged approach: the development of superior lines of specific vegetables and the training of skilled scientists in crop production and management. This approach had been successful in terms of riper tomatoes, leafier cabbage and bigger mungbeans (Vegetables in China project).

Another AVRDC major achievement was the development of tomato varieties that yielded well under hot, humid conditions. A rich source of vitamin C and carotenoids, tomato was a popular cash crop for small farmers and home gardeners throughout much of the world.

The main problems with tomato in the hot, humid tropics were poor fruit set and disease; the challenge for AVRDC tomato breeders was therefore to combine heat tolerance and disease resistance with desirable cultivation and eating characteristics. The AVRDC relied on its active collection of cultivated tomato and wild relatives which was one of the biggest in the world.

In-vitro screening of sweet-potato plantlets, often challenging the plantlets with the scab fungus, showed a good correlation in tolerance or susceptibility between entire plant genotypes and their cultured plantlets. The AVRDC had also initiated research on *in-vitro* screening and selecting for salt and drought tolerance in sweet potato (see also Villareal and Griggs, 1982). Furthermore, the Center's objectives were to regenerate sweet potato through somatic embryogenesis, identify drought and salt-tolerant somaclonal variants and improve quality traits, such as high starch or low sugar.

Sweet potato was generally propagated vegetatively because it does not flower or set seeds rapidly in the tropics. To maintain its germplasm in the field and keep it relatively disease-free was time-consuming and costly replanting was required each year. Therefore, about one-third of the 1,200 clones comprising the AVRDC sweet-potato collection were tissue-cultured. The *in-vitro* sweet-potato storage at the Center reached 1,200 accessions by late 1990. Research focuses on studying minimal growth conditions for short-term *in-vitro* germplasm storage as well as the method of producing plants on demand by returning to normal growth conditions.

Using shoot-tip culture, the AVRDC had cultured more than 300 sweet-potato accessions. By means of thermotherapy and meristem culture, followed by thorough indexing by ELISA and grafting, nearly 30 pathogen-tested improved clones had been produced and transferred to countries in East and South-East Asia, and the South Pacific. The AVRDC had also induced *in-vitro* storage roots in sweet potato as an alternative method to germplasm distribution to geographically isolated sites ill-equipped to handle *in-vitro* plantlets.

At the AVRDC, monoclonal antibodies were used to identify different strains of turnip mosaic viruses of Chinese cabbage difficult to detect by differential hosts. The strain-specific monoclonal antibodies would be used for the detection of new strains, and for resistance screening. The AVRDC developed monoclonal antibodies for detecting other viruses difficult to purify or present in plant tissues in low quantities, such as tomato yellow leaf curl virus.

The mungbean improvement programme utilized several wild, incompatible *Vigna* species resistant to insects and diseases, and black gram with high sulphur-containing seed storage protein. The embryo rescue technique was used in conjunction with treatments by plant hormones to overcome incompatibility. A collaborative project existed in this area with Oregon State University. Crosses of sweetpotato with wild *Ipomoea* species might offer the potential for using wild materials previously unavailable to breeders. For soybean improvement, wide-cross methods with embryo rescue were used in Australia and the USA to introduce genes for rust resistance and tolerance of adverse soil conditions from wild *Glycine* species[12] (see p. 517).

The AVRDC applied techniques developed by the Agriculture Canada Ottawa Research Station, enjoying some success in the anther culture of Chinese cabbage. Methods elaborated by French researchers for pepper anther culture also suited the AVRDC objectives. For tomato, soybean and mungbean, the potential use of haploid cells and plants for breeding was seldom realized because the frequency of haploid induction in culture was considerably lower than in Chinese cabbage and peppers.

It was possible to regenerate plants from Chinese cabbage and tomato protoplasts. Somatic hybrids involving tomato as one of the fusion partners were reported and suggested as a useful means of transferring desirable chilling tolerance genes into cultivated tomato.

Cytoplasmic male sterility (CMS) was valued for the commercial production of hybrid seeds in Chinese cabbage, tomato and peppers.

Molecular-biology techniques were being used to genetically engineer varieties that might otherwise take years to complete using conventional breeding methods, e.g. the production of mungbean varieties which were highly resistant to bruchids, a major pest of stored beans throughout the world. At National Chunghsing University, Taiwan, with assistance from the AVRDC, the genome of cucumber mosaic virus (CMV) had been genetically modified to develop CMV-resistant tomatoes. Modification of the protein profile of plants might also yield positive nutritional effects, e.g. sulphur-containing amino-acids in legumes or specific peptide or protein for insect resistance, such as for *Vigna* weevil resistance.

Sweet potato and white potato were later dropped from the AVRDC research programme and replaced by pepper, alliums (onion, shallot and garlic) and egg-plant. Cell, tissue and organ cultures were useful for propagating and producing pathogen-free garlic plants and for supplying clonal materials for genetic and breeding purposes. Also, *in-vitro* embryo rescue of the inter-specific hybrids together with callus culture had been demonstrated as a potential means for introgressive breeding of certain *Allium* species.

The production of haploid lines through anther culture would enable early release of eggplant varieties. Protoplast culture had been established and protoplast fusion for the incorporation of resistance to nematodes attempted. A notable case in point was the eggplant variety development in China.

The cucumber was threatened by certain diseases for which no tolerance had been found within the species, although strong resistance was present in wild, related species. Introduction of genes encoding tolerance to diseases by inter-specific hybridization relying on embryo rescue or somatic hybridization, needed to be followed by the development of routine regeneration procedures.

Tissue culture opened new vistas for asparagus breeding: *in-vitro* cloning of meristems or buds was an efficient way of freeing plantlets from viruses A, B, C, and replacing inefficient, conventional crown division. It paved the way to development of a desirable all-male asparagus hybrid.

In August 1992, the AVRDC organized a symposium on Adaptation of vegetables and other food crops to temperature and water stress in Taiwan. The participants felt that selection for gross traits, such as fruit yield per plant, might not be as effective as selection for component traits, such as normal floral bud development, fruit and seed set, and embryo and fruit development. The component traits would be more simply inherited and easier to manipulate than the gross traits. Fresh approaches involved attempts to clone genes for factors relating to stress balance. For instance, proline biosynthesis genes were cloned and introduced into plants, thus conferring drought tolerance on certain crop species. Furthermore, gene constructs incorporating alcohol dehydrogenase promoter caused alcoholic fermentation-related genes to be activated, thus conferring flood tolerance (Kuo, 1992).

Abiotic stresses elevated concentrations of heat-shock, cold- or anaerobic-response proteins for considerable periods of time, but the question remained: would expression of response proteins ahead of stress really protect plants? Efforts to breed for stress tolerance were hampered by the complexity of the phenomenon. Restriction fragment length polymorphism (RFLP), randomly amplified polymorphic DNA analysis or indirect marker selection could be helpful in this respect: molecular markers could serve as a powerful tool to monitor gene introgression from wild and related species. A collaborative network of scientists engaged in heat stress work was also proposed at the symposium; the Director of the International Center for Agricultural Research in Dry Areas (ICARDA) and C.G. Kuo of the AVRDC were nominated to co-ordinate the network (Kuo, 1992).

The AVRDC had established regional networks in South-East Asia, South Asia and Southern Africa. In 1992, the AVRDC signed an agreement with the Southern African Centre for Co-operation in Agricultural Research (SACCAR) to be executing agency for the collaborative Network for Vegetable Research and Development in Southern Africa (CONVERDS). There were ten participating countries: Angola, Botswana, Lesotho, Malawi, Mozambique, Namibia, Swaziland, Tanzania, Zambia and Zimbabwe; the Network was based at Horti, Tengeru near Arusha, Tanzania.

The French Centre for International Co-operation in Agricultural Research for Development (CIRAD) was developing co-operation with the AVRDC, following the visit by the AVRDC Director to the CIRAD Department of Fruit and Horticultural Crops (CIRAD-FLHOR) on 16 June 1995. Researchers from the CIRAD will be posted to the AVRDC to work on bacterial wilt and to co-ordinate the network CLVNET linking Cambodia, Laos and Viet Nam (*CIRAD Information*, no. 54, 13 July 1995, p. 6).

Through its International Co-operation Programme, the AVRDC assisted in strengthening and enhancing national vegetable research-and-development capacity through information and communication services, collaborative research, technology transfer and institution building.

The AVRDC operated a Selective Dissemination of Information (SDI) service for national programmes. It produced and published commodity specific quarterly updates which, abstracted from the latest world-wide horticultural information sources on these commodities, were available at no charge from the AVRDC. In addition, a Tropical Vegetable Information Service (TVIS) project had set up a computer retrieval system using the software MINISIS. Finally, the Center was a leading publisher and distributor of vegetable research information. Publications from the Office of Publications and Communications were distributed to more than 600 libraries and to individuals in 160 countries. The AVRDC bi-annual newsletter *Centerpoint* contained up-to-date news on the Center courses, conferences, research and projects.

Notes

1 In Canada, wheat harvests in the prairies yielded more than 30 million tonnes annually from over 13 million hectares of land. More than 70% of Canadian wheat was exported to other countries, generating billions of dollars for the Canadian economy. That is why this crop was commonly known in the Prairies as 'King wheat' [*PBI* (Plant Biotechnology Institute) *Bulletin* (National Research Council Canada, Saskatoon] May 1993, p. 1).

Wheat exports had been a major source of foreign exchange earnings for Canada. For the past 50 years (1945–1995), Canadian wheat production had accounted for about 5% of world wheat production and some 20% of world wheat trade, national production being valued at $3–5 billion annually (DePauw, 1995).

Sales of Western Canadian wheat had shifted considerably over the last few decades from traditional markets in Europe to newer markets in Asia, the Middle East and South America. Exports to the former Soviet Union and eastern Europe had declined significantly, while markets in North and Central America bloomed (Kruger and Preston, 1995).

It was estimated that an additional $3 million annually for ten years was required to increase wheat yields and quality, and enhance the competitiveness of the wheat industry. The potential return on investment was estimated at about 70:1. The Western Grains Research Foundation, a pool of Western Canadian producer associations, was administering a voluntary producer-levy on wheat to fund the genetic transformation and improvement of wheat varieties. Challenges for biotechnologies included marker-assisted selection and technologies to accelerate the advancement of the inbreeding process, such as doubled haploidy. Transformation technology could be used to direct enhanced accumulation of specific compounds, to synthesize novel compounds, or to add DNA for novel traits and/or new sources of resistance to biotic and abiotic stresses (DePauw, 1995).

Canadian Western Red Spring Wheat (CWRS) was still the choice wheat because of its high quality, cleanliness, uniformity and versatility for a wide range of end-products. Superior-grade, high protein (over 13%, 14.0% moisture basis) CWRS wheat had been generally used for high volume breads and as a blending to improve the processing quality of weaker home-grown or imported wheat with a lower protein content. This continued to be the case in Europe, North America and Japan. More CWRS wheat was being consumed in other Asian, South American and Middle Eastern markets in pan breads. Lower protein (less than 13%) CWRS wheat, including the no.3 grade, was now used extensively in many South American and Middle Eastern countries for health breads and flat breads. There was an increase in the use of CWRS wheat, usually blended with other wheat, for noodles in Asian countries (China and Thailand). Big quantities were also used in China for steamed bread production. Other markets for CWRS wheat included common wheat pasta, gluten production, home-use flour and shrimp/fish feed (Kruger and Preston, 1995).

Canadian Western Amber Durum (CWAD) was recognized for its high quality in pasta. A world-wide trend towards greater pasta consumption had pushed up sales both on the domestic market and traditional markets, such as Italy and Japan. Booming CWAD exports to several South American markets (Chile and Venezuela) and the USA had spurred production. In addition to pasta, this wheat was exported to North Africa for making couscous (Kruger and Preston, 1995).

Canadian Western Red Winter (CWRW) was a medium protein wheat suited to hearth bread, flat breads and noodles because of its 'mellow' dough qualities and excellent flour colour characteristics. Unfortunately, winter wheat production had been insufficient to maintain a consistent supply to markets which preferred the quality of this wheat (Kruger and Preston, 1995).

Canadian Western Soft White Spring (CWSWS) was a soft, lower protein wheat suitable for cakes, cookies and related products. It was also consumed in the Middle East in more traditional flat breads (stone-milled to high-extraction levels) and on the Indian subcontinent in chapattis and related products (Kruger and Preston, 1995).

In addition, there were three classes of Canadian wheat which could meet the challenge of new market demands:

– Canada Prairie Spring red (CPS red) had a medium protein content and strength, giving it a market niche in terms of end-products similar to that of CWRW; because production potential was fairly promising, it had good prospects;

– Canada Prairie Spring white (CPS white) was also a medium protein wheat; its white seed coat made it more suitable for markets where high-extraction flours were used in traditional flat breads (Middle East) and chapattis and related products (Indian subcontinent); many Asian countries, particularly in South-East Asia, preferred white wheat for noodles and steamed breads; considering that noodles alone ranged from around 35% total flour end-usage in Japan to over 80% in Indonesia, there might be a healthy future demand; CPS white wheat had also shown potential for home-use and specialty flours where a lily white, bright flour colour was important;

– Canada Western Extra Strong (CWES) red spring wheat was unique in that it had extremely strong dough properties; it was used primarily in low concentrations as a 'correction' wheat to improve the strength of a wide range of flour types. When mixed with other wheat, it improved the performance of frozen dough, high volume roller-developed pan breads, whole wheat flours and specialty hearth breads (Kruger and Preston, 1995).

2. In 1995, the wheat genome remained largely an uncharted territory. The number of genes governing important traits, their location, spatial organization and the degree to which they varied among different wheat varieties remained largely unknown. A map of the wheat genome would allow the identification and location of these genes and indicate how to maximize their potential to produce better and more adapted wheat varieties.

Bread wheat was probably one of the most difficult organisms in nature to map. The total nuclear complement was composed of three highly related genomes. Most of the genes were present in similar forms in each genome. At least 85% of the DNA was repetitive. Each cell contained ten times more DNA than a human cell. As if these problems were not daunting enough, there were also extremely low levels of DNA sequence variation among varieties (Penner and Laroche, 1994).

3. The International Triticeae Mapping Initiative (ITMI) was an international consortium of researchers from North America, Europe and Australia working on molecular mapping in species of the Triticeae, each group mapping a different population. A key mapping population had been obtained from a cross between the variety Opata and a synthetic hexaploid derived through a combination of a durum genome and a diploid genome from *Triticum tauschii*. Mapping efforts in the USA and Mexico focused on this population (Penner and Laroche, 1994). The primary purpose of the ITMI was to facilitate international collaboration among investigators, maximize the rate of progress in mapping cereal genomes and minimize the duplication of efforts.

The Canadian Wheat Genome Mapping Group, comprising 40 scientists working in plant breeding, plant pathology, cereal chemistry and molecular genetics, focused on the following activities:

– developing a doubled haploid population obtained from a cross between Grandin (strong dough strength) and AC Reed (weak dough strength);

– applying markers mapped on the Opata/synthetic population to their population;

– identifying new markers specific to their population.

This Group was confident that, with the gene mapping tools devised in other research projects as well as the new tools developed specifically for analyzing wheat DNA, they could successfully map the Canadian wheat genome in five years. They intended to raise $2 million from industry and government grants and expected to initiate mapping efforts by late 1995 (Penner and Laroche, 1994).

Most of the Canadian wheat research and varietal improvement effort on end-use quality focused on grain protein quantity and quality and its impact on baked products. Starch, the major component of the wheat grain, had received less attention. Starch was an important commodity whose world-wide use was estimated at more than 20 million tonnes annually in the mid-1990s. Corn starch accounted for 80%-90% of the market but the demand for wheat starch was on the increase. This was mostly directed toward specialty starches such as waxy, amylose extender and others with altered ratios of amylose to amylopectin. Waxy corn starch was used widely in the food industry and fetched a premium price.

Currently, there was a market for semi-waxy wheat, which contained about 20% less amylose then regular wheat. This low amylose 'sticky' wheat was used to make 'Udon' noodles in Japan and other Pacific Rim countries. Approximately half of the wheat consumed in the Pacific Rim region was eaten in the form of noodles rather than bread products. About 16% of the wheat consumed in Japan was used to make Udon noodles. This market was worth an estimated $75-100 million annually (1995).

Stored as granules, starch accounted for almost 70% of a wheat kernel's dry weight. Starch granules from wheat, rye and barley showed a bimodal distribution in size, with large 'A' granules and small 'B' granules. Wheat research had focused on improving the quality and quantity of protein, a major determinant in the bread-making quality of wheat. The change in markets for Canadian wheat had placed new demands on the quality of starch in the grain and refocused research on altering the quantity and composition of starch in wheat (Chibbar *et al.*, 1995).

The biosynthesis of the complex starch macromolecule took place in amyloplasts, where the two fractions (amylose and amylopectin) were formed and deposited as starch granules. An almost linear chain of glucose units formed the amylose, while a highly branched chain of glucose polymers made up the amylopectin. The ratio of the two starch components determined its physical properties and the end-use of the kernels. Wheat starch with a high amylopectin content (waxy and partially waxy) was desirable for the Japanese 'Udon' noodle market, whereas starch with a high amylose content had various industrial uses. The final stages of starch biosynthesis involved the action of three enzymes: ADP glucose pyrophosphorylase regulated starch synthesis, while starch synthases (soluble and granule-bound) and branching enzymes were involved in synthesis of amylose and amylopectin (Chibbar *et al.*, 1995).

Starch with an altered structure (amylose- or amylopectin-rich) occurred naturally in cereals such as maize, barley and rice. The hexaploid nature of the wheat genome, representing three distinct genomes, complicated the detection of such mutations. Genetic engineering became an important tool for altering the starch structure in wheat. Manipulation of one of the three genes involved in final stages of starch biosynthesis had been achieved in potato, resulting in increased starch composed of highly branched amylopectin (Chibbar *et al.*, 1995).

At the Plant Biotechnology Institute (National Research Council Canada) and the Crop Development Centre, University of Saskatchewan, Saskatoon, research focused on the branching enzyme that converted amylose into amylopectin and granule-bound starch synthase (waxy locus). When mutated, granule-bound starch synthase resulted in amylopectin-rich starch or waxy starch. Some of the branching enzyme genes from wheat had been isolated and partially characterized by DNA sequencing and function studies. Gene expression vectors had been constructed to alter the activity of genes present in wheat in order to modify the final structure of starch. These vectors would be introduced into wheat using a genetic transformation protocol developed at the Plant Biotechnology Institute. A research grant from the Saskatchewan Agriculture Development Fund had allowed Canadian researchers to identify wheat germplasm mutated for genes encoding the final two steps in starch biosynthesis. This technology was also to be used to alter the starch granular structure to increase the efficiency of wheat gluten extraction and to identify new markets for wheat in the cosmetics industry (Chibbar *et al.*, 1995).

Wheat starch was used for fuel-grade ethanol in the USA, so a high-yielding wheat with a high starch content could provide farmers with a new alternative crop and additional markets. Soft white spring wheat (SWSW) had high grain yield potential, a low protein content and relatively high starch content compared to other classes of wheat. The SWSW breeding programme at the Agriculture and Agri-Food Canada Research Centre in Lethbridge had developed a number of lines which yielded 10%-20% more than the currently licensed cultivars (Fielder and AC Reed). Although very high yielding, these lines did not meet quality requirements for traditional pastry and cookie markets. They did, however, have potential as a source of starch for ethanol production (Sadasivaiah, 1995).

Starch content could be enhanced further by genetic engineering, as had been achieved with potato. Soft white spring wheat with high yield potential was a good candidate in this respect. Increasing the starch content of high-yielding soft wheat lines through genetic engineering would provide a cheaper raw material for fuel-grade ethanol production and improve the feasibility of this new industry (Sadasivaiah, 1995).

4 As new technologies were developed and breeders' rights and patents turned access to those technologies into the main condition for access to the market, new actors – biotechnology companies and agrochemical giants such as E.I. Du Pont de Nemours & Co., Inc., Dow Elanco (Dow Chemicals and Eli Lilly & Co.), AgrEvo AG (Hoechst AG and Schering AG) and Monsanto Co. – had entered the scene. Research was not necessarily as crop-oriented as it had been before – increasingly, the emphasis was on developing new traits that could be integrated into several species. However, maize continued to be by far the most economically interesting crop species. Maize alone accounted for over 40% of the release notifications for genetically-modified crops and release permits allowed or pending by the U.S. Department of Agriculture Animal and Plant Health Inspection Service until September 1996. According to Derwent Biotechnology Abstracts, between 1982 and June 1996, 138 patents were applied for genetically-engineered maize plants:

Trait	Number of patents	Companies
Starch content	14	Zeneca plc
Oil content	9	E.I. Du Pont de Nemours & Co., Inc.
Protein content	8	E.I. Du Pont de Nemours & Co., Inc.
Pest resistance (not *Bt*-based)	15	Dow Elanco, Pioneer Hi-Bred International, Inc.
Pest resistance (*Bt*-based)	8	Ciba-Geigy AG, PGS N.V.
Disease resistance (including virus resistance)	15	Novartis AG, Pioneer Hi-Bred International, Inc.
Fungal resistance	8	Pioneer Hi-Bred International, Inc.
Herbicide tolerance	13	ICI Ltd
Stress resistance	7	De Kalb, Japan Tobacco Inc.
Crop improvement	4	Miscellaneous
Male sterility	8	Pioneer Hi-Bred International, Inc.

The bulk of the patents (56.5%) were for particular agronomic traits, pest resistance being the commonest. One-third of these patent applications involved *Bacillus thuringiensis* (*Bt*) as the source of resistance. The rest covered a number of options, from antibody fragments to spider venom, with use of lectins being the most abundant. In the case of disease resistance, five out of the 16 applications were related to virus coat protein. Of particular interest for the industry were male-sterility patents, since this trait had the potential to save corporations big amounts of both money and labour required for the detasseling in hybrid variety production. The other focus of research was maize quality (representing 24% of patent applications), with the modification of maize starch content receiving the most attention. This was not surprising, since starch was the raw material for many industrial applications. Because of the low content of essential amino-acids lysine and tryptophan in maize seeds, the latter had always to be complemented with other protein sources, both as food and feed. Improving the protein content of maize was therefore also a research focus (*Seedling*, vol. 13, no. 3, October 1996, pp. 23–32).

Up to September 1996, 1,444 of the 3,534 approved release notifications and release permits - either granted or pending - involved maize. This meant that up to 1,444 legal field tests of genetically-engineered maize had been approved in the USA alone:

Trait	Number	Comments	
Insect resistance	636	*Bt*	316
		not *Bt*	19
Herbicide resistance	557	Phosphinothricin (Basta)	369
		Glyphosate	184
		Sulfonylurea	3
		Imidazolinone	1
Others	251	Mostly agronomic properties and product quality	

There was an important concentration of nearly 83% of the tests upon insect and herbicide resistance. Within insect resistance, at least 49% of the tests had involved the use of *Bt*. On the 557 tests made on herbicide tolerance - apart from four nearly anecdotal exceptions - all had been conducted around only two types of herbicides (*Seedling*, vol. 13, no. 3, October 1996, pp. 23–32).

On the insect-resistance side, Mycogen Corporation (San Diego, California) and Ciba-Geigy AG, and Pioneer Hi-Bred International, Inc. were to market maize genetically engineered with exactly the same *Bt* gene for resistance to the European corn borer. According to the specialized press, Ciba-Geigy AG and Mycogen Corporation's engineered European corn borer-resistant maize would cover 160,000 hectares in the USA in 1997. Two herbicide-resistant maize seeds were reaching commercial release in the USA: one by Monsanto Co. resistant to Roundup, and the other by Pioneer Hi-Bred International, Inc. and AgrEvo AG, resistant to AgrEvo's Liberty herbicide (Basta). De Kalb's Liberty-resistant genetically-engineered maize had already received U.S. approval. The top ten patent-holders owned 60% of the patents and accounted for 93% of the 1,444 maize field tests in the USA:

Company	Patents	Field tests and releases
Pioneer Hi-Bred International, Inc.	21	285
Novartis AG	17	213
ICI Ltd/Zeneca Seeds plc	13	18
E.I. Du Pont de Nemours & Co., Inc.	7	155
Monsanto Co.	7	329
Japan Tobacco Inc.	5	–
DeKalb	4	166

Plant Genetic Systems (PGS) N.V.	4	–
American Cyanamid Co.	3	
Gene-Shears plc	3	
Dow Elanco	3	
Rhône-Poulenc SA	3	
Max-Planck Institute	3	
Berlin Institute for Genetic Research	3	
Holden's Foundation Seeds Incorporated		60
Cargill Inc.		46
AgrEvo AG		41
Great Lakes Hybrids		24

Source: Seedling, vol. 13, no. 3, October 1996, pp. 23–32.

Currently, three corporate blocks were fighting over leadership of the maize seed industry: Monsanto Co. out on its own; Pioneer Hi-Bred International, Inc., Novartis AG and Dow Elanco (Indianapolis) which bought out Lubrizol Corporation shares and a 46% equity stake in Mycogen Corporation;and AgrEvo AG, which had assumed the formerly lonely Plant Genetic Systems (PGS) N.V. position. Transnational corporations were already in control of today's and any future genetically-engineered maize (*Seedling,* vol. 13, no. 3, October 1996, pp. 23–32).

5. Since stepping into biotechnologies in 1984, the French company Limagrain, a co-operative located in Clermont Ferrand, had become the third-biggest seed corporation in the world. In June 1994, Limagrain purchased Kingroup Inc. (Pride Brand Seeds) from Elf Sanofi (France) and created King Agro Inc. in Eastern Canada and Limagrain Canada Seeds Inc. Limagrain's expertise embraced maize, oilseed rape, canola, sunflower, protein peas, cereals and forage crops, with extensive breeding programmes in Australia, France, Germany and the United Kingdom. A transgenic melon, tolerant to tobacco mosaic virus, was developed by Limagrain and was to be approved in 1997 by the French Permanent Committee for the Selection of Cultivated Plants (CTPS, Comité permanent de la sélection des plantes cultivées).

   The canola research centre of Limagrain Canada Seeds Inc. was opened in August 1995 in Saskatoon thanks to a $ million investment by the Saskatchewan Opportunities Corporation. With an annual turnover of $700 million, its annual research budget amounted to $50 million, including 25% for biotechnologies.

   In acquiring the world's second-biggest group in homeopathy, Dolisos, Limagrain initiated a diversification toward pharmaceuticals and plants, which was confirmed in 1994 by the agreement concluded with several laboratories involved in the production of human proteins (albumin and blood-clotting factors) in tobacco and oilseed rape.

6. Pioneer Hi-Bred International, Inc. (Des Moines, Iowa), the world's largest seed company, was set up in 1926 as the Hi-Bred Corn Company. It was the first company to develop and market hybrid maize seed. In 1991, sales exceeded $1 billion, maize seed representing 80% of total sales. However, the company entered into markets for soybeans, wheat, sorghum, canola, sunflower, alfalfa, vegetables, peas and pearl millet (Van Roozendaal and Van Wijk, 1992).

   The company adjusted its policy by:

   – placing more emphasis on developing value-added crops with enhanced protein, oil and starch content, in co-operation with food processors and livestock producers;

   – restructuring of sales, programmes and activities to better accomodate all customers, including the developing 'superfarmer', farmers with large properties and excellent business management skills;

   – increasing the overall profitability by shortening the time-frame between new product introductions;

– expanding activities world-wide, including those in the nations of Eastern Europe and the former USSR;

– acquiring new businesses anywhere in the world, including areas of specialty plant products, microbial genetics and vegetable seeds;

– enhancing and speeding up complex research-and-development projects through joint ventures with other corporate partners.

Central in Pioneer's new strategy was a substantial increase in research-and-development expenditures, amounting to $80 million in 1992. More specifically, biotechnology activities were run on a budget of more than $8 million in 1992. The majority of the company's facilities in biotechnologies were located in Johnston, Iowa, and in Georgetown, Ontario, Canada, for canola seed development (Van Roozendaal and Van Wijk, 1992).

Pioneer had succeeded in transforming maize genetically in 1990, as it had transformed sunflower, soybeans, canola and alfalfa. These transgenic crop species were being tested in a total of 14 locations: twelve U.S. States, Canada and Puerto Rico. The Puerto Rico tests involved multiplying seed of transgenic soybeans during the winter of 1991 for use in field tests in the Midwest of the USA during 1992. These transgenic plants were essentially disease- and insect-resistant, or had a modified oil or protein content (Van Roozendaal and Van Wijk, 1992).

Pioneer's pest resistance activities focused on maize. Plants had been engineered for resistance to the chlorotic dwarf virus. Pioneer was also working on the development of hybrid maize with tolerance to the European corn borer, using a *Bacillus thuringiensis* (*Bt*)-derived insecticide gene, through a licensing agreement with the American company, Ecogen Inc. In 1995–1996, Monsanto Co. licensed its technology for Yieldgard™ insect-protected maize to Pioneer Hi-Bred International, Inc. and Mycogen Corporation (San Diego, California) decided to collaborate with Pioneer on the development of transgenic seeds that expressed *Bt* insecticidal proteins. Pioneer was also able to introduce, through a licensing agreement with the British Agricultural Genetics Company (AGC), a cowpea trypsin inhibitor (CpTI) insect resistance gene into some of its crop species. The incorporation of the CpTI gene into hybrid seed maize would target corn root worms and the European corn borer. Pioneer's researchers had also cloned a gene allowing maize to fight one of the pathogens causing corn blight (Van Roozendaal and Van Wijk, 1992).

In order to overcome the difficulties related to non-transformation of monocots by *Agrobacterium* plasmids, Pioneer was one of the first companies using 'gene gun' to introduce particles coated with the alien DNA, thereby transferring the desired genes into maize plant tissue. Alfalfa was also engineered for disease resistance, against the alfalfa mosaic virus (Van Roozendaal and Van Wijk, 1992).

Herbicide-tolerant maize hybrids were on the U.S. market, Pioneer having three hybrids in 1992. These hybrids were the result of *in-vitro* selection of naturally occurring maize cells by American Cyanamid Co. and backcross breeding activities conducted by Pioneer. The hybrids were tolerant to Cyanamid's herbicide, Pursuit. Pioneer was using other herbicide tolerance, such as tolerance to ammonium glufosinate, as a 'selectable marker' in determining if stable transformation had been accomplished in the laboratory and maintained through field testing (Van Roozendaal and Van Wijk, 1992).

In 1991, Pioneer Hi-Bred International, Inc. purchased the protein modification research programme of the American Plant Cell Research Institute (PCRI), whose researchers had isolated a gene coding for the high methionine amounts in the Brazil nut. Incorporating such a gene into maize would eliminate the need to supplement feed with synthetic methionine. The PCRI had introduced a gene coding for a methionine-rich storage protein of Brazil nut into tobacco plants. Via genetic engineering the gene had also been introduced into oilseed rape, soybeans and sunflower. Pioneer had also developed a stable transforming system for rapidly introducing novel genes into sunflowers: using meristem culture and conventional breeding techniques, this technology was expected to lead to successful routine production of transgenic sunflower. Its main purpose was to develop sunflower hybrids with modified oil and protein quality and better disease resistance. The same approach could be applied to soybeans, which are dicotyledons like sunflowers and difficult to regenerate from cell cultures (Van Roozendaal and Van Wijk, 1992).

In 1996, Pioneer Hi-Bred International, Inc. concluded an agreement with Human Genome Sciences (Rockville, Maryland) to sequence, identify and determine the function of maize genes based on HGS gene sequencing and discovery capabilities.

Pioneer's Specialty Plant Products Division was formed in 1988. Under the logo, Better-Life grains, the company was marketing a range of products grown without the use of pesticides, which met the demand of consumers willing to pay a little extra. The increasing demand for health food in the Northern Hemisphere was also the reason for Pioneer acquiring an exclusive license for the production of a low palmitic acid soybean from Iowa State University; oil from the bean was claimed to be valuable as a health food oil, whose production began in 1993 (Van Roozendaal and Van Wijk, 1992).

A relatively small part of Pioneer's sales (2%) came from microbial products. Pioneer's Microbial Genetics group produced and distributed inoculants to be used in silage, hay and plants, and animal health products. Research and development focused on products containing naturally occurring micro-organisms. This also applied to Pioneer's subsidiary Microbial Environment Services, set up in 1990 to degrade organic contaminants, such as gasoline, diesel fuel, etc. While microbial research was being conducted in the USA and Germany, no bioremediation tests were being done outside the USA (Van Roozendaal and Van Wijk, 1992). It should be mentioned that there was no bio-engineered micro-organism available commercially for cleaning the environment in bioremediation processes, even though these micro-organisms had been produced in the laboratory.

7. Whereas maize is an allogamous species, plant pollen fertilizing the ovary of another plant, wheat is an autogamous species and thus self-fertilized. Wheat hybrids were therefore much more difficult to develop than maize hybrids. The first attempts to make hybrid wheat in the USA dated back to the 1940s. Achieving male sterility was problematic because of the physical and genetic features of wheat. In the 1970s, most public institutes and smaller companies in the northern hemisphere dropped their hybrid wheat programmes, for two reasons: the hybrids produced could not compete with newly developed semi-dwarf varieties which were high yielding; and it had become possible in the USA (as was already the case in Europe) to protect varieties against unauthorized propagation under the Plant Breeders' Rights system. Legal protection apparently weakened the incentive to build in the field of biological protection.

Many seed multinationals which nevertheless persevered with hybrid wheat during the 1970s terminated their programmes later too, for various reasons. Yields of hybrids only barely exceeded those of wheat open-pollinated varieties; the results for hybrid disease resistance and stability were unsatisfactory; and some companies faced problems with the toxicity of the gametocide used to sterilize pollen.

Hybrid wheat research was under way on a small scale by the mid-1990s (e.g. in China and India). Research focusing on commercial hybrids seemed to be limited to two France-based organizations: Orsan and Hybritech (the latter being a company owned by Coop de Pau and Monsanto Co.). The French wheat hybrid variety was the result of a six-year research programme (1986–1992) undertaken with the experimental stations of the French National Institute for Agricultural Research (INRA). The potential market for this new variety was estimated at some $3 billion in Europe and a double figure for China (Augereau, 1995).

In order to obtain male-sterile wheat plants for fertilizing later with the pollen of another plant to give rise to a hybrid, the French researchers had been using gametocide substances capable of selectively inhibiting pollen production while leaving intact the female reproductive organ. The researchers were forced to cease using one of the first gametocides developed by Shell upon discovering that it was inducing tumours. Once having succeeded in identifying other gametocides devoid of this side-effect, they were able to develop a wheat hybrid 110% superior to its genitors (compared to 200% in the case of maize), which proved sturdy and no more necessitous of water and fertilizers than the habitually-cultivated wheat varieties (Augereau, 1995).

8 In 1988, the IRRI and the Belgian biotechnology company Plant Genetic Systems (PGS) N.V. began a two-year project on the isolation, identification and characterization of natural *Bacillus thuringiensis* strains with interesting insecticidal properties against rice pests. The project was supported by the Rockefeller Foundation and IRRI staff received training at PGS laboratories (Bijman, 1994*a*).

9 Transgenic forage legumes were the first to appear but it was not until 1988 that the first transgenic grain legume plants (soybeans) were reported. In 1990, transgenic peas were produced, but they were infrequent, poorly characterized for inheritability or showed abnormal development. However, since 1994, reliable systems for the production of transgenic peas had been described, as well as for transgenic groundnuts, chickpeas and beans (Mahon, 1995).

Grain legumes showed a poor performance in cell and tissue cultures; pea cell suspension cultures grew at one-quarter the rate of alfalfa and one-tenth that of tobacco cells. Moreover, it was much more difficult to regenerate plants from cell or tissue cultures of grain legumes. Delivering foreign genes to the cells of grain legumes seemed to be less of a problem. Functional foreign genes had been detected in these cells after tissue was treated with *Agrobacterium* cultures or bombarded with metal pellets coated with DNA, or after high-voltage treatment of DNA and plant tissue mixtures. Even using specific resistance genes that protected transformed cells from chemicals fatal to normal cells, recovery and verification of transgenic grain legume plants required more than a year. Soybeans and other grain legume species containing genes conferring resistance to broad-spectrum herbicides, such as AgrEvo AG's Liberty (Basta) and Monsanto Co.'s Roundup, were at the stage of advanced field testing. Other genes being examined were those controlling crop damage by insects and viral diseases or producing modified products, such as higher sulphur protein content, industrial enzymes, modified oils and sweeter processing peas. For instance, the Canadian pulse industry listed weed control, fungal pathogens, quality traits and symbiotic nitrogen fixation as major issues in grain legume improvement (Mahon, 1995).

10 PROCITROPICOS: Programa Cooperativo de Investigación y Transferencia para los Trópicos Suramericanos (Co-operative Programme for Research and Technology Transfer in the South American Tropics).

11 Plant genetic resources conservation in Eastern Europe was reviewed at a meeting held at Sadavo, Bulgaria, in September 1990 (Bulgaria had conserved 40,000 accessions, Hungary 44,500, Poland 59,500, the USSR 360,000 and Czechoslovakia 43,800). Programmes for studying the region's cultivated plants and their wild relatives were underway and extensive breeding had been undertaken.

12 Soybeans (*Glycine max*), one of the world's most important sources of edible vegetable oil and protein, were cultivated globally on over 50 million hectares

annually (1995). It had been grown in Asia for over 3,000 years but was a relative newcomer to North America where it had become a significant crop as a result of increased oil demand during the Second World War. In Canada, the early soybeans introduced from China were grown as forage crops because they matured too late to produce seed. Breeding efforts in the 1920s and 1930s had focused on identifying and developing soybean varieties for the short-season areas in southern Ontario, where the first grain quality soybeans were produced. The construction of the Victory Mills crushing plant in Toronto in 1944 fostered the development of soybeans as a grain crop through breeding and improvement in production technology. Currently, 90% of Canadian soybeans were grown in Ontario, with secondary production areas in Quebec and the Maritime Provinces. Most of these were crushing-grade soybeans used domestically to produce oil for further processing and meal for livestock feed. Canada exported crushing-grade soybeans to Europe and the USA, but remained a net importer of soybean meal. A small proportion (less than 10%) of Canadian soybean production centred on high-quality food-grade soybeans exported to Asia and Europe for use in foodstuffs including tofu, soyamilk, natto and miso (Simmonds, 1995).

In Canada, current breeding programmes focused on oil and protein modification desirable for processed soybeans: increased sugar content for some varieties destined for natto, tofu and soyamilk; a higher protein content for full-fat soybeans used in 'on-farm' feed. Improvements in yield, herbicide resistance and tolerance to disease, pests and stress were other targets. Monsanto Co. was transforming a southern-adapted variety of soybeans with a Roundup resistance gene. Although transformation had been achieved in soybeans by several public and private groups in the USA and at the Plant Research Centre (PRC)/ Agriculture Canada, the rate of fertile plant recovery was very low, limiting routine application of this technology to breeding programmes (Simmonds, 1995).

PRC scientists were working on the transformation of northern-adapted Canadian soybean varieties. Two methods of transformation had been tested: using the first, cultured soybean cells were bombarded with DNA-coated particles; plants regenerated from the transformed cultures, however, were sterile; sterility was likely due to the lengthy culture procedure and efforts were being made to reduce the time that soybeans remained in culture. *Agrobacterium*-mediated transformation was the second approach tested. Fertile transgenic plants had been obtained and third-generation plants were being field tested. Although the transformation frequency in soybean explants was high, most of the transformation events resulted in the formation of non-organogenic callus, which resulted in very poor transgenic plant recovery. Work at the PRC therefore focused on increasing the frequency of transformation events at explant sites with produced organogenic tissue (Simmonds, 1995).

Part III

International co-operation for development

Organisation for Economic Co-operation and Development

The Organisation for Economic Co-operation and Development (OECD) was set up in 1961, with the following goals:

– to achieve the highest sustainable economic growth and employment;

– to promote economic and social welfare throughout the OECD by co-ordinating the policies of member countries;

– to stimulate and harmonize its members' efforts in favour of developing countries.

The OECD Development Centre, set up in 1962, was a relatively small and autonomous but integrated part of the OECD. Established as the link between the OECD and the developing countries, its membership was voluntary for the OECD member countries. Its activities included:

– conducting policy-oriented research on emerging issues in international economic relations, development and interdependence, and analyzing implications for member and non-member countries;

– defining national solutions to these issues and suggesting policy directions enabling member and developing countries to deal with them;

– establishing contacts and exchanging information and experience with development organizations and agencies;

– initiating dialogue with developing countries on their development needs, options and policies, and on problems of mutual concern.

Most of the OECD biotechnology activities took place in the Directorate on Science, Technology and Industry (DSTI) of the

OECD proper, while smaller programmes were conducted by the Agriculture Directorate. They concentrated on the interests of Member States and had a technology-centred approach. The OECD biotechnology work started in 1981 with the decision of the Committee for Scientific and Technological Policy (CSTP) to include biotechnologies in its programme. The first report developed a definition of biotechnologies, discussed the sciences and technologies contributing to biotechnologies, devoted a chapter to the constraints on the development of biotechnologies and reviewed major policy issues. The Committee set priorities for subsequent work:

 – safety and regulations;
 – patent protection;
 – long-term economic impacts of biotechnologies;
 – government policies and priorities for biotechnology research and development (De Groot, 1992).

Until 1989, each priority had been worked out by the DSTI in co-operation with research teams and expert groups composed of scientists, policy-makers, specialists from companies and other non-governmental organizations, resulting in several reports. In recent years, biotechnologies had remained on the CSTP agenda. A report on *Biotechnology, Agriculture and Food* was published in July 1992. A new project, Biotechnology for a clean environment, was completed in 1993 (De Groot, 1992).

The biotechnology-related work of the OECD Development Centre was being carried out within the framework of a research programme entitled Changing comparative advantages in food and agriculture, which emphasized interactions between food and agricultural sectors, the rest of the national economy and trends in global markets. The case study on maize examined the capacity of developing countries to acquire and disseminate new biological techniques in agricultural production, both through domestic generation and through the international transfer of technology. The final report synthesized four country studies and a paper on the emerging biotechnologies and their potential impacts (De Groot, 1992).

A second research programme was underway: Developing country agriculture and international economic trends. The research team was focusing on the structural adjustment process and its implications for technology generation and dissemination. Late 1990, a meeting of experts proposed a number of studies:

 – two commodity studies, one on a food crop species (rice) and the other on a cash crop species (cocoa);
 – an investigation into frontier rice and cocoa biotechnology research;

– a country study (Brazil) focusing on agricultural research institutions and the ways in which they were responding to economic crisis and liberalization;

– a study of the supplying of seed to small farmers in three African countries and how it was affected by the structural adjustment process;

– a study on the interaction between changes in economic policy and productivity (De Groot, 1992).

As in the maize study, biotechnologies were not the principal research subject in this project, but were analyzed in the context of international economic processes, national policies and societal structures. The results assessed the extent to which potential benefits of these technologies would be realized, given the international and national circumstances. Common lessons were drawn from the different contributions to the project, while the policy issues with which different actors would be confronted were analyzed. Policy-makers were the principal target group; that is why the dissemination of research results was essential for the Centre's effectiveness (De Groot, 1992).

The survey conducted by the Intermediary Biotechnology Service (IBS) between June and December 1993 was the first systematic effort to review international initiatives in agricultural biotechnologies. The IBS, in consultation with the OECD Development Centre and others, had refined a questionnaire which, in June 1993, was sent to some 45 organizations. The preliminary findings of the survey were presented to an international workshop organized by the IBS in November 1993, attended by some 50 participants involved in different capacities in these activities. The IBS had received completed questionnaires from 28 research and advisory programmes, six networks and five donor agencies. Although the survey did not pretend to be an exhaustive review of international activities in agricultural biotechnologies and some of the growing number of institutions, networks or donor agencies were not included in the survey, the latter had the merit to highlight the wide range of activities and organizations involved in agricultural biotechnologies and to make this information publicly available (Brenner and Komen, 1994).

It was concluded from the survey that since 1985 the various organizations covered by the survey had contributed an estimated $260 million in grant funds to international biotechnology initiatives, including research programmes, advisory activities, networks and specific projects. During the same period, the total biotechnology component of the World Bank loans and credits for national agricultural research projects in developing countries had been estimated at around

$150 million. Consequently, total international investment (grants plus loans) since 1985 could be estimated at $400 million (Brenner and Komen, 1994).

The overwhelming share of funding (40.9%) by foundations was provided by the Rockefeller Foundation, whose major contribution was devoted to the International Programme on Rice Biotechnology. Regarding the 31.6% share of funding by bilateral donors, two countries contributed a big proportion. France through the plant and livestock programmes of the Centre for International Co-operation in Agricultural Research for Development (CIRAD) and the USA through the U.S. Agency for International Development (U.S.AID). The Netherlands was also a major contributor to international initiatives in biotechnologies, but rather than concentrate on research programmes, its efforts encompassed a diversity of activities. The major share of grant funds from multilateral donors was contributed by the United Nations Development Programme (Brenner and Komen, 1994).

For the sake of comparison, it was estimated that in the USA the Federal investment in agricultural biotechnologies reached $207.5 million for the financial year 1993, with U.S. Department of Agriculture investment alone at $119.5 million. The 15 U.S. leading agricultural biotechnology companies spent a total of $68.5 million in 1992. Compared with these research-and-development figures, the total contributions to the various international initiatives in agricultural biotechnologies were quite small. In 1993, when the funding of core activities of all International Agricultural Research Centers combined amounted to $236 million, the budget devoted to biotechnologies was in the order of $23.6 million (Brenner and Komen, 1994).

Within the 25 research programmes for which comparative information was available, 142 discrete research activities were recorded. A very big share of total research activities was devoted to research on plant production and protection (78%). Livestock production and health accounted for 21% of total research activities, with food processing accounting for only 1%. When the relative importance of different crop species in the total research effort was examined, the focus was clearly on food crop species: cereal grains accounted for some 28% of the total, root crops for 19% and legumes for slightly over 14%. The effort devoted to rice (23% of research effort) far outstripped that on maize or sorghum. This again underlined the relative importance of the Rockefeller Foundation International Programme on Rice Biotechnology. Horticulture, essentially for export, accounted for some 10% of total effort. The category termed 'perennial' which included coffee, cocoa, sugar-cane, banana and plantain, also predominantly export crop species, accounted for some 10% of effort (Brenner and Komen, 1994).

Virus resistance and insect resistance and control rated highest as objectives of international research programmes in biotechnologies, with quality characteristics third in order of importance. In terms of the techniques which were being applied to achieve these objectives, transformation accounted for 39% of total research effort, cell and tissue culture 27%, diagnostics 12%, genetic mapping 11% and microbiology (including nitrogen fixation, biopesticides and fermentation) 11%. In the OECD member countries, of the 1,250 field releases of transgenic plants to the end of 1992, herbicide tolerance accounted for by far the greatest number of releases (38,9%), followed by the use of genetic markers (30.4%) and then by traits expected to influence virus resistance, insect resistance, crop quality, male sterility and disease resistance. Between 1986 and 1992, while release approvals had been granted for 30 different crop hosts, seven only accounted for more than 80% of total approvals: oilseed rape or canola, potato, tobacco, tomato, maize, flax and soybeans. Only five countries, the USA, Canada, United Kingdom, France and Belgium, accounted for 94.7% of all releases (Brenner and Komen, 1994).

In research programmes related to livestock, vaccine development and diagnostics for tropical livestock diseases were of almost equal importance, with a very limited number of programmes focusing on reproductive techniques or on productivity (e.g. embryo transfer techniques). The bulk of the effort related to cattle, although one programme was exclusively concerned with small ruminants. The main objectives for the animal health-related research comprised the development of new diagnostics and vaccines for tick-borne diseases (theileriosis, anaplasmosis, babesiosis and cowdriosis), trypanosomiasis, rinderpest and foot-and-mouth disease (Brenner and Komen, 1994).

The survey indicated that most programmes included a human resources development component which involved training in research institutions in the USA, Europe or in institutions in developing countries (e.g. at the International Agricultural Research Centers or IARCs located in developing countries). In a very few cases, opportunities were provided for developing country scientists to receive training in the laboratories of major commercial firms (e.g. Monsanto Co.; Zeneca Seeds plc, former ICI Seeds; DNA Plant Technology Corp.). Almost of the research programmes offered positions at post-doctoral level, while training at PhD. and MSc. level was offered by 18 and 14 programmes respectively (Brenner and Komen, 1994).

A number of international biotechnology initiatives included advice and training on biosafety and intellectual property right issues. In most cases, it took the form of workshops and seminars, to increase awareness in developing countries of the implications of biosafety and intellectual property right protection (e.g. the U.S.AID Agricultural Biotechnology for Sustainable Productivity Project-ABSP had conducted biosafety and intellectual property right workshops in Indonesia, Egypt, Jamaica and the USA; it also initiated a biosafety internship programme in 1993; biosafety workshops had also been organized by the International Service for the Acquisition of Agri-Biotech Applications-ISAAA in Argentina and Costa Rica, in collaboration with the Inter-American Institute for Co-operation on Agriculture-IICA, and Indonesia). The Intermediary Biotechnology Service was itself an advisory service to developing countries on biotechnology research programme management and policy, which included biosafety and intellectual property rights. The Biotechnology Advisory Commission, based at the Stockholm Environment Institute in Sweden, was also providing advice, on request, to government and inter-governmental authorities on field testing and/or on the planned introduction of genetically-modified organisms. The IICA provided support to policy formulation in Latin America and the Caribbean, and encouraged the harmonization of biosafety and intellectual property policies in this region through workshops, technical assistance and policy studies (Brenner and Komen, 1994).

Developing countries were recipient of some 40% of the financial commitment to biotechnology research programmes and networks. Given that the IARCs received over 14% and that a majority of these centres were located in developing countries, the IBS survey showed that more than half of the total financial commitment to international initiatives in biotechnologies was actually spent in developing countries. While a relatively high number of the latter were involved -over 60- efforts were concentrated in a small number of countries within each geographic region: Kenya, Zimbabwe, Egypt and Côte d'Ivoire in Africa; Indonesia, Thailand and India in Asia; and Costa Rica, Mexico and Brazil in Latin America and the Caribbean. For some of these countries, these, and other, donor-funded efforts constituted a big share of their total research effort in agriculture. In Kenya, for instance, donor support in funding agricultural research had increased from 19,6% of total funding in 1986 to 37% in 1991. In Indonesia, donors accounted for more than 75% of all agricultural research financing during the latter half of the 1980s. In Costa Rica, excluding the Tropical Agriculture Research and Training Centre-CATIE, it had been estimated that international agencies provided over 44% of total investments in agricultural biotechnology research-and-development (Brenner and Komen, 1994).

Developing countries had not been closely involved in the planning and design of most international biotechnology initiatives. The most notable exception to this rule was provided by the Dutch Special Programme Biotechnology Development Cooperation, which was not confined to research, in which consultation at the grassroot level and effort to involve small-scale, resource-poor farmers was an essential element of the design and implementation process (see p. 729). Few instances where developing countries contributed matching funds to international programmes were recorded in the survey. The most substantial contributions by participating national institutions emerged in the Rockefeller Foundation International Programme on Rice Biotechnology, to which China, India, Indonesia, the Republic of Korea and Thailand contributed (Brenner and Komen, 1994).

For donors, the broad, long-term objective was to help in creating conditions in developing countries whereby they were able to take advantage of what biotechnologies had to offer, and to integrate biotechnology methods and products within their national innovation systems. This could be done by capacity-building, as in collaborative research programmes and in the training of developing country scientists. It could also be done by providing objective advice and, where necessary, technical and legal assistance in devising workable regulatory frameworks for, for instance, biosafety and intellectual property rights. In some countries, it might be appropriate to provide financial support and technical assistance for capacity-building in techniques needed to underpin biotechnologies (for instance, plant breeding and seed production and certification). Each developing country had its particularities and intimate knowledge of the functioning of the national innovation system, of agricultural priorities and of scientific and technological capabilities needed to be brought to bear if biotechnology initiatives were to be integrated effectively (Brenner and Komen, 1994).

One potential problem which emerged from the analysis of the IBS survey was that of duplication of effort among the various initiatives, for instance in national priority-setting exercises; in the research priorities and objectives of livestock programmes; and in the proliferation of biosafety workshops. This suggested a need for co-ordination of effort both among donors and within 'target' developing countries, as well as exchanges of information like that provided by the IBS survey (Brenner and Komen, 1994).

Public funding for biotechnology research and development was still relatively small in most developing countries and there was also little commercial activity in biotechnologies. Innovative ways of encouraging private-sector involvement should therefore be explored. These might include an expanded role for 'honest broker' intermediaries between private-sector interests and public institutions, or joint ventures between small and medium-sized biotechnology firms (domestic and/or foreign) [Brenner and Komen, 1994].

Developing countries and non-governmental organizations had often expressed concern that private companies might conduct clandestine, indiscriminate field-testing of genetically-modified organisms in developing countries. The lack of established biosafety procedures in developing countries constituted a major constraint to field-testing -and, indeed, to product development- by the public programmes set up to facilitate the introduction of biotechnologies in developing country agriculture; this situation was changing as an increasing number of countries were adopting guidelines for field-testing of genetically-engineered plants. Another policy issue of concern in international biotechnology initiatives, for both donors and developing countries, was that of intellectual property rights. The legal arrangements made thus far suggested that proprietary technology needed not necessarily imply high costs, nor constituted an insuperable obstacle for developing countries in gaining access to a particular technology. Here again, the role of the 'honest broker' might be important, particularly where neither the donor nor the developing country concerned had expert legal knowledge of rapidly-changing developments in intellectual property rights, especially with respect to plants, following the conclusion of the Uruguay Round (Brenner and Komen, 1994).

Finally, lessons drawn from the development co-operation experiences of OECD member countries over the years suggested that the 'top-down' approach had severe shortcomings and that the success of aid programmes and projects depended to a large extent on the participation of developing countries at all phases of design and implementation (Brenner and Komen, 1994).

By far the greatest part of the OECD biotechnology work had been, and still was, devoted to safety considerations for the use of genetically-modified organisms. An historical review had been undertaken into plant breeding in member countries to investigate which safety measures were taken into account in conventional methods and whether these could apply to the release of plants with altered traits (De Groot, 1992).

Perhaps the most influential work on biosafety was done by the Organisation for Economic Co-operation and Development (OECD). The OECD involvement began in 1983 with the formation of the Group of National Experts on Safety in Biotechnology (GNE). The OECD report on *Recombinant DNA Safety Considerations*, published in 1986, defined a Good Industrial Large-Scale Practice (GILSP) applicable to genetically-modified organisms presenting a low risk and used in industry. The report stated that organisms with recombinant DNA handled in accordance with GILSP guidelines could be treated, on a large scale, in the same minimal monitoring and confinement conditions as those applicable to their host strains. The key principle of the GILSP was that an organism with recombinant DNA should be as innocuous as the low-risk organism from which it was derived.

The 1986 OECD report was, until recently, the only international recommendation on biosafety guidelines for the release of genetically-modified organisms (GMOs) and influenced national biosafety policies in the OECD member countries. The recommendations made in the report introduced two concepts in biosafety: the case-by-case risk assessment procedure and the step-by-step approach for release of the GMOs. The basic idea in a case-by-case risk assessment procedure was that, when a release was proposed, national authorities should perform an independent review of the potential risks 'against assessment criteria which were relevant to the particular proposal'. Step-by-step meant conducting the development of a GMO in a stepwise manner (from the laboratory via growth chambers and greenhouses to a limited field test) and evaluating the outcome and potential risks at each step before proceeding with the next (Nilsson, 1992).

In 1988, the GNE met again, this time 'to develop a concept which would identify a generic approach to the safety assessment of low or negligeable risk small-scale field trials'. The result was the document entitled *Good Developmental Principles for Small Scale Field Research with Genetically Modified Plants and Microorganisms* (1990). It was based on the concept that risk was a matter of experimental design. Careful planning and strict practice of various plant breeding methods of reproductive isolation allowed certain experiments to be exempted from the case-by-case assessment (Nilsson, 1992).

In 1991, the GNE undertook to develop principles of safety in the large-scale environmental release of transgenic organisms in order to update the OECD earlier work. The Group completed its task in 1994. The results could be summarized as follows:

– the safety of an organism is independent of the process of genetic modification *per se*; the principles apply to any organism;

– risk/safety analysis comprises hazard identification and, when a hazard has been identified, risk assessment; risk management is based on and should be in proportion to the results of the risk/safety analysis;

– knowledge and experience with any or all of these aspects provide familiarity which plays an important role in risk/safety analysis and risk management; it means having enough information to be able to judge the safety of the introduction or to indicate ways of handling the risks;

– the number and modalities of the stages to be visited from greenhouse to complete release are not fixed, but depend on the outcome of the risk/safety analysis at different stages;

– the detailed design of the developmental stages and the information appropriate to proceeding with any particular stage may vary from one group of organisms to another; the scientific and technological methods for specific groups of organisms were to be dealt separately.

Safety considerations for scaling up field trials on specific groups of organisms (e.g. crop species, biofertilizers, etc.) were thus developed.

More recent OECD publications covered the monitoring of GMOs released into the environment and an International Survey of Biotechnology Use and Regulations, which also led to the setting up of a data-base, BIOTRACK, on the release of GMOs. The OECD document, entitled *Safety Considerations for Biotechnology*, published in 1992, reviewed the first biosafety criteria developed in 1986 for the GILSP concerning biotechnology-derived fermentation products. It also defined good development principles for safe research on a modest scale carried out in the field with plants and micro-organisms bearing new traits.

Japan had adopted since the 1970s voluntary guidelines instead of technology-specific laws as a mechanism of safety assurance for laboratory experiments and environmental applications of recombinant DNA technology. The principles and concepts underlying the Japanese system were generally based on the OECD recommendations. Different ministries and agencies of Japanese Government had their respective guidelines on a product basis according to their jurisdiction. Concerning environmental release, two kinds of guidelines were instituted for safety evaluation of transgenic plants: experiments conducted in closed and semi-closed systems were dealt with by the Science and Technology Agency (STA) guidelines; field testing in both isolated and ordinary fields were covered by the guidelines of the Ministry of Agriculture, Forestry and Fisheries (MAFF); guidelines for safety assessment of foodstuffs and food additives produced by recombinant DNA techniques were revised in February 1996 by the Ministry of Health and Welfare to accomodate whole foods derived from transgenic crop species.

The OECD Environment Directorate had been involved in DSTI activities and co-operation between the two Directorates was increasing. With the current research on Biotechnology for a clean environment, interest was shifting from the necessity to protect the environment against eventually harmful consequences of biotechnology applications to using biotechnologies in environment protection. The Environment Directorate was also increasingly devoting attention to biotechnologies in its own programme of work. In 1990, a report was published reviewing regulatory developments with respect to environmental aspects of biotechnology use in OECD member countries (De Groot, 1992).

European Commission

Biotechnologies were presented at the beginning of the 1980s as the 'new business of the century'. By the early 1990s, according to an Ernst & Young Group study, the world-wide market share of biotechnological product areas was the following:

Product area	Share
Therapy	43%
Diagnostics	27%
Supplies	15%
Agriculture	9%
Chemicals and environment	6%

World sales of biotechnology-derived products would jump from a few tens of billion U.S. dollars in 1996 to $110–220 billion in the year 2006. In the USA alone, the annual growth rate (1996) of medical bio-industry was 12% and sales amounted to $10.8 billion. Although all pharmaceutical groups and companies were concerned by this trend, a survey published in France on 13 February 1995 concluded that half of medical biotechnological research and development was concentrated in 1% of pharmaceutical groups. Of 4,000 companies surveyed in the world, only 39 had a clearcut policy in this area. While the three first groups were Roche Holding Ltd. and Ciba-Geigy AG (Switzerland) and the American Home Products Corp., the French Rhône-Poulenc Rorer was ranked fifth, Sanofi and Synthélabo, also French corporations, ranked 24th and 30th respectively (Gallois, 1995*j*).

The impact of bio-industry, expressed as a percentage of the gross national product, had been assessed at 32% in the Asian countries, 25% in the European Union and 24% in the USA. Bio-industry world-wide, which directly or indirectly employed more than 14 million people, displayed the peculiarity of small companies being absorbed by large ones as soon as they came up with successful products (Viseur, 1993).

It is interesting to analyze the distribution of inventions in biotechnologies by reviewing the licenses granted in the USA between 1988 and May 1993. Of a total of 3,500 licenses, 60% corresponded to North American patents, 19% to European Union companies and 10% to Japanese companies. In other words, more than 95% of inventions came from the Northern hemisphere (Viseur, 1993).

The co-author of an Ernst & Young Group survey (September 1994) stated that in the USA more money was being raised, that they were still great products in the pipeline, that sales for products were increasing and that a lot more products were coming. This comment was vindicated in an earlier report from PaineWebber entitled *Biotechnology Golden Pipeline 1994*, which highlighted that the current biotechnology pipeline provided a wealth of new product opportunities, with two dozen products awaiting U.S. Food and Drug Administration approval for new or expanded uses and another 80 products in advanced phase-III clinical trials.

In fact, in 1996, according to a report by Ernst & Young International Life Sciences and G. Steven Burril & Co., a San Francisco-based private business bank, the U.S. medical bio-industry acknowledged a striking increase in the number of novel drugs at an advanced design stage and made by biotechnology companies and medium-sized corporations. A total of 79 products have been approved, including 20 anti-cancer and 14 anti-infectious drugs, 14 substances used in haematology and seven in metabolic diseases. About 700 products, developed by 167 public corporations, were being submitted to clinical trials (1997).

While the initial spectacular development of biotechnologies had been based on the synthesis of recombinant proteins or polypeptides, used as biomedicines, current work focused on cell and gene therapy to restore the function of a defective or lacking gene. The forecast market in this area would grow to more than $1 billion in 2003 and up to $50 billion in 2010. For the time being, research in this area was highly fragmented, as has been the case for micro-informatics in the 1970s, with dozens of small independent societies offering excellent technologies (Gallois, 1995*j*). In the USA, in 1997, there were more than 20 companies involved in gene therapy and which participated in three out of four clinical trials, while in Europe a dozen corporations were working in this area and participated in only one of two gene-therapy clinical trials (Martin and Thomas, 1997).

In 1996–1997, there were 1,300 biotechnology enterprises in the USA employing some 100,000 persons; of these, 265 were publicly traded companies cited on the Nasdaq, the stock market devoted to high technologies. The U.S. bio-industry was synonymous with small business: of the public companies, 37% had fewer than 50 employees, 18% between 51 and 135 employees and 12% between 135 and 299 employees (BIO, 1995). San Francisco Bay and New England area around Boston remained the dominant locations for U.S. bio-industry.

Company strategy was geared toward acquisition or partnership. In November 1994, Ciba-Geigy AG acquired Chiron Corp. (a biotechnology company located in San Francisco Bay) for $2.1 billion. At the same time, Rhône-Poulenc Rorer chose a less costly strategy: it created a biotechnology consortium, RPR Gencell, which was carrying out research in collaboration with 15 institutions; RPR Gencell, with a staff of 120 researchers, was in fact co-ordinating the work of 800 people and was able to make new alliances according to research and market needs. Pfizer Inc. in the USA had adopted a similar strategy, while Eli Lilly & Co. preferred acquisitions (Gallois, 1995*j*).

In 1994, the U.S. bio-industry spent an overall $7 billion on research and development (+23%). For public companies, R&D spending accounted for 43% of total costs and expenses. R&D expenditure per employee was $68,000 in 1994, compared to $39,000 per employee in the pharmaceutical industry (BIO, 1995). Fifteen agrobiotechnology corporations surveyed by the Journal *Bio/Technology* (vol. 12, August 1994, pp. 755–6) together had spent $85 million on R&D, i.e. an average of $5.6 million per firm. As many agrobiotechnology companies were very close to the commercialization of their products, there was a need for increased R&D spending for regulatory approval, field testing and product introduction.

Venture capital was a major source of funding for the U.S. bio-industry. In 1996, venture-capital amounted to $563 million, while the opening up of biotechnology companies' capital to investors (IPO) concerned $274 million and private investments reached $660 million; regarding alliances, they involved $1.4 billion. The biggest IPOs had been achieved by genomics companies, such as Affymetrix ($90 million IPO in June 1997) or Millennium ($62 million in May 1997). Genomic agreements were also very successful: Corange concluded a first $50 million agreement with Sequana for identifying genes involved in osteoporosis and a second $100 million agreement with GeneMedicine for research on oncogenes. In 1996, biotechnology companies were able to raise 25% more funds than in 1995. See also Gallois (1996*c*).

In 1994, the $4,299.3 million devoted to publicly-funded biotechnology research was distributed as follows: 41% to health, 39% to general foundations, 8% to infrastructure, 5% to agriculture, 4% to manufacturing and bioprocessing, 2% to environment, 0.8% to energy and 0.2% to social impact research. Of this same amount, the research budgets of the eight most important government agencies represented: 78% for the Department of Health and Human Services, 6% for the Department of Energy, 5% for the National Science Foundation, 5% for the Department of Agriculture, 2% for the Department of Defence, 2% for the Department of Veterans Affairs, 1% for the National Aeronautics and Space Administration and 1% for the Agency for International Development (in *Biotechnology for the 21st century: realizing the promise*, 1993, Committee on Life Science and Health, U.S. Government Printing Office).

At the International Bio-Industry Forum (IBF) held in Washington, D.C., on 13–14 April 1994, the Domestic Policy Adviser to the U.S. Vice-President confirmed the top priority the Clinton Administration was giving to biotechnologies. The European Senior Advisory Group on Biotechnology (SAGB)'s chairman, J. Drews, who was also President of International Research and Development at Hoffmann-La Roche AG, concluded after the IBF meeting that 'biotechnology is no longer a distant fantasy. It is a fast-growing industrial, commercial and political reality, and nowhere more so than in the United States. Moreover, success here is clearly due to sustained and vibrant support for biotechnology from America's political leaders'. The IBF had been set up in 1990 and comprised the SAGB, the Japan Bio-industry Association, the Bio-industry Organization (USA) and the Industrial Biotechnology Association of Canada (*European BioNews*, SAGB, no. 6, May 1994).

In 1994, the U.S. bio-industry recorded sales of $7.7 billion. Overall, it was still operating at a net loss: in 1994, the main 152 biopharmaceutical firms reported a loss of $1.3 billion, or an average loss of $8.7 million per firm; only 20 of the 152 firms generated a profit in 1994 (BIO, 1995). The agrobiotechnology companies had reported a total net loss of $140 million in 1993. For the 15 agrobiotechnology companies, the average R&D revenue ratio was 106%. The reason for this high percentage was the low or absent revenue for most of the companies coupled with a heavy, growing investment in R&D (BIO, 1995).

Of the $7.7 billion sales in 1994, the following market segments were: 42% for therapeutic products, 26% for diagnostics, 15% for supplies, 9% for chemical and environmental services and 8% for agrobiotechnologies (BIO, 1995).

In comparison, the total U.S. pharmaceutical industry spent $13.8 billion on research and development, recorded sales of $84.8 billion and employed 353,800 people. Each of the big five U.S. pharmaceutical companies (Merck & Co. Inc., Ortho-Johnson & Johnson, Bristol-Myers Squibb Co., Pfizer Inc. and Eli Lilly & Co.) spent over $590 million on research and development annually (around 12% of sales), whereas the top six biotechnology companies (Amgen Inc., Genentech Inc., Chiron Corp., Biogen Inc., Genzyme Transgenics Corp. and Immunex) spent between $72 million and $299 million each (representing 20% to 95% of sales).

From the financial viewpoint, biotechnologies had proven a much less profitable investment since 1992, a far cry from such success stories of the 1980s as Genentech Inc. or Amgen Inc., which had brought capital flowing into the 'new Eldorado', as it was known. Specialized funds had showed record profits, the Investco fund progressing in 1991, for instance, by more than 90%. In 1992, investors realized that their expectations – including for the success rate of projects – had been unrealistic. Several biotechnology companies, like Centocor Inc. or Gensia, acknowledged failures at the product experimentation stage. Others were forced to abandon a fledgling product in the face of a four- or even ten-fold drop in the company share price. According to the Bloomberg agency, there had been a 68% drop in share values since January 1992. This downward spiral was exacerbated by the U.S. President's plan to limit health expenses, announced in early 1993 (Leparmentier, 1995).

In ten years, investment funds in biotechnologies had dropped from between 200 and 300 funds to between 20 and 30, in 1995. For instance, Sequoia Capital, one of the biggest venture capital companies in the USA with some $600 million in invested funds, had literally withdrawn from the sector; in 1990, one-fourth of their investments had been in biotechnologies; five years later, there was no project they considered profitable enough to warrant investment. Investors had often perceived biotechnologies as a shortcut enabling them to bypass conventional methods and the big pharmaceutical groups in the search for new medicines. But they had overlooked that biotechnological products were insufficiently distinct from other products or necessitated a huge investment of between $200 million and $400 million per product. Furthermore, a depressed stock market impeded the introduction of new companies onto the market; funds sought on financial markets for biotechnologies had plummeted from

$5.4 billion in 1991–1992 to $290 million in 1994 (Leparmentier, 1995).

However, in the USA in 1996, more than $4 billion was raised on the stock market for investment in biotechnology companies, making that year a record for investment in bio-industry. This was indeed an enormous sum, representing the equivalent of one hundred $40 million companies, but for anyone who had travelled in the USA this was not surprising given the maturity of the industry in this country. Europe was also experiencing a surge in investment in biotechnologies. The United Kingdom was especially strong and owing to the fact that Germany was emerging from the 'Green'-imposed *de facto* moratorium on biotechnologies, the German Government made it a priority to significantly strengthen biotechnology ventures. There had also been major initiatives in Asia, including especially in Singapore, Malaysia and the Republic of Korea, while Japan had always been relatively strong.

In general, fledgling biotechnology firms had no choice but to forge strategic alliances with big pharmaceutical groups if they wished to be quoted on the Nasdaq. Sangstat was a prime example. It had given a license for some product distribution to the Baxter Group, an agreement enabling the young company to receive $5.6 million from Baxter (as royalties) by the end of 1994; Baxter also bought 4.2% of Sangstat's capital for $3.25 million (Leparmentier, 1995). In July 1995, Fred Adler, a pioneer in venture capital in the USA, explained that he was not investing in biotechnology corporations because they needed ten to twenty years before being able to sell their products; this was considered too long by financial criteria. Consequently, these corporations looked more attractive for the big pharmaceutical groups, which were rather interested in acquiring a know-how.

However, there were signs that the situation would improve in the future. For instance, on 14 June 1995, when the biotechnology company, Cor Therapeutics, announced that the medicine it had been developing for several years was ineffective, its Stock Exchange shares dropped by 45%, but the new had no repercussions for the overall biotechnology market. One week before the collapse of the Cor Therapeutics shares, another biotechnology company, Cephalon, Inc., published satisfactory results of clinical trials which saw its Stock Exchange capital value jump from $186 million to $320 million; only a year earlier, the same company had recorded a loss of $35 million. The message was clear. Good biotechnology projects were no longer being penalized by bad ones. Companies like Regeneron, Agouron or Autoimmune, which had obtained encouraging clinical trial results, doubled their Stock Exchange share value in a year and specialized investment funds earned between 15% and 30% during the first half of 1995 (Leparmentier, 1995).

Investors and financial analysts concluded it would be no easy task to differentiate veritably promising projects worth funding from dubious ones. This meant that only the most innovative companies capable of effectively marketing good products would have access to venture capital. The mortality rate would be high. Of the 1,300 enterprises existing in 1996–1997 in the USA, only 350 would most probably still be around the year 2000, half of these quoted on the Stock Exchange. If many companies were managing to survive by living off funds raised in the early 1990s, the trend was toward a progressive elimination: for instance, Synergen, one of the biotechnology 'stars' on the Stock Exchange, was purchased at the beginning of 1995 by Amgen Inc. for $260 million at a time when it still had a credit balance of $70 million. Only two years earlier, Synergen had been worth a $1 billion (Leparmentier, 1995). At that time, with a market capitalization of over $8 billion, the stock market was putting a value on Amgen Inc. approaching that of the pharmaceutical giant Hoechst AG.

In February 1997, the shares of Pharmaceutical Proteins Limited (PPL) Therapeutics, a Scottish company specialized in the production of recombinant human proteins for therapeutical use, considerably rose on the London Stock Exchange, following the cloning of an ewe from a somatic cell of the udder of a six-year old Finn Dorset sheep, whose nucleus was transferred to an enucleated ovocyte of the same breed, at the Roslin Institute, near Edinburgh (the company was in charge of commercializing the results of the Institute's researchers). On 26 February, the share value rose to 552.5 pence, a 56.7% increase over its value of 22–23 February 1997. Similarly, by early March 1997, the shares of Pathogenesis Corp. rose by 21% after the company reported a successful treatment during two clinical trials by a drug produced by this company which was supposed to obtain an approval by the U.S. Food and Drug Administration.

These examples showed that the success of a biotechnology corporation on the Stock Exchange was not due to its profits (because most of the companies did not accumulate any profit), but rather to the reported steps of development of its products and acknowledgement of its research results. If only one step of this research-and-development process failed, the share could lose 50% of its value. Conversely, if the research was successful, the share was better known and this acknowledgement lessened its volatility on the stock market.

Analysts were also of the opinion that, in the medium or long term, young biotechnology companies were doomed to join the big pharmaceutical groups. However, it was not forecast that the pharmaceutical groups would take over 100% of all companies, because this would kill the entrepreneurship at the heart of their effectiveness. Furthermore, more than half of new medicines were derived from biotechnologies: several hundred biomedicines were being developed and submitted to clinical trials; those already marketed belonged to the first generation of biotechnology-derived drugs, e.g. interferons, recombinant human insulin and growth hormone, anti-haemophilic factor VIII, etc., a dozen or so products representing an annual market value of $5 billion in 1994 in the USA (Leparmentier, 1995). The Ernst & Young Group survey listed the top ten biotechnology-derived drugs, which accounted for over half the $7.7 billion in sales for U.S. bio-industry in 1994–1995: Neupogen (filgrastim, a recombinant granulocyte colony stimulating factor, G-CSF, which enhances neutrophils production and is used to correct deficiencies in the white blood cells, resulting from genetic defect or from suppressive side-effects of chemotherapy, radiotherapy and zidovudine treatment), Epogen (epoetin alpha or recombinant human erythropoietin, which stimulates the maturation of red blood cells), both by Amgen Inc., which was living up to its mission 'to become the world leader in developing and delivering important and cost-effective therapeutics based on advances in cellular and molecular biology' (e.g. tissue growth factors, brain-derived neurotropic factor, interferon, interleukin-2, anti-hepatitis B vaccine and anti-sense oligonucleotides); Intron A (Biogen Inc.); Humulin (Genentech Inc.); Procrit (Amgen Inc.); Engerix-B (Genentech Inc.); Recombi NAK HB (Chiron Corp.); Activase (Genentech Inc.); Protropin (Genentech Inc.) and Roferon-A (Genentech Inc.).

The $10 million investment by Microsoft Corporation in a small U.S. biotechnology firm, Darwin Molecular Inc. (Seattle), was considered an example of the convergence between information technology and biotechnologies, particularly in pharmaceutical research. In the latter, the use of information technology could save huge amounts of time and money in the development of new drugs, according to industry experts, as the mapping out of molecular structures by computer could be cheaper and quicker than traditional laboratory techniques. Darwin Molecular Inc., which was part of the Gencell consortium created by Rhône-Poulenc Rorer to focus on gene therapy, was using computers to pool vast amounts of genetic data on diseases and to sketch out the genetic make-up of proteins responsible for particular disease factors. The company then used molecular biology techniques in the test tube to produce big quantities of potential drug candidates, which could be matched against the disease proteins on a trial and error basis (*European BioNews*, SAGB, no. 6, May 1994). In 1997, Darwin Molecular Inc. was purchased by the British corporation Chiroscience plc for $120 million.

Researchers of Cornell University (Ithaca, New York) had modified the structure of beta-lactoglobulin (a milk protein found in the lactoserum) through directed mutagenesis, in order to reduce the production of liquid in yoghurt during its storage. Yoghurt with 0.075% of modified beta-lactoglobulin formed a gel six to ten times more easily than ordinary yoghurt. This process also decreased the processing temperature from 85 °C to 70 °C or less, eliminated the need for adding starch to obtain a better gel and reduced the time necessary for the formation of the coagulum. All these advantages helped reduce the production cost of yoghurt. The same researchers were also exploring the use of modified beta-lactoglobulins as transporters of pharmaceutical substances (e.g. L-dopa) through the stomach lining.

A small number of transgenic plants had been authorized for marketing, while hundreds of them were being tested in the field (essentially herbicide-, virus- and insect-resistant crop species or varieties). The market value of plant biotechnologies ($600 million in 1994 in the USA) was therefore much smaller than that of biomedicines (Leparmentier, 1995). However, after having authorized, in 1993–1994, the commercialization of FLAVR/SAVR tomatoes, genetically engineered by the U.S. biotechnology company, Calgene Inc.[1] (see p. 602), so as to impart them with a longer shelf-life, the U.S. Environment Protection Agency (EPA) used the same approach in May 1995 regarding a genetically-engineered potato containing a gene for insect resistance and produced by Monsanto Co. Then came the turn of hybrid maize: in 1992, the Swiss corporation Ciba Seeds was able to create plants resistant to the Lepidopteran pest, *Ostrinia nubilalis* (European corn borer), through the introduction of a gene coding for a bacterial toxin against this pest, which caused annual losses estimated at $1 billion in the USA. The Food and Drug Administration had no objection as to the safety of the food derived from the transformed plants and the U.S. Environment Protection Agency had authorized Ciba Seeds to produce transgenic hybrid maize plants, containing the *Bacillus thuringiensis* (*Bt*) gene coding for the bacterium entomotoxin, on a surface of 180 hectares. This unprecedented decision testified to the favourable evaluation by the EPA of the use of the *Bt* gene. The company, Mycogen Corp., was working with Ciba Seeds to commercialize transgenic maize; it claimed to have the exclusive rights for that purpose, while other corporations like Pioneer

Hi-Bred International, Inc. and Monsanto Co. were testing their own transgenic maize varieties. In Argentina, Ciba Seeds carried out trials on transgenic maize with the *Bt* gene in order to control the stem borer, *Diatraea saccharalis*, and the results were promising.

Analysts underscored the rapidity of the decision-making process at both the FDA and EPA for transgenic crop species, as well as the weaker opposition of environmentalist movements or associations to the release of these plants. The decision-making process was much slower in Europe where, due to unharmonized regulations on the release of transgenic plants, not a single transformed plant had been approved for release up to late 1997 (despite the fact that hundreds of transgenic plants – oilseed rape, maize, tobacco and sugar-beet – had been tested in the field since 1987).

In Canada, there were a number of networking companies across the country which aimed to foster biotechnologies, create and maintain cohesion in the community and across Canada, and provide an opportunity to enter international markets [e.g. BIONET (Ottawa), B.C. Biotechnology Alliance (Vancouver), Toronto Biotechnology Initiative, Québec Biotechnology Association (Laval) and AgWest Biotech Inc. (Saskatoon)].

Several other biotechnology companies, such as Biomir Inc. from Edmonton and Acadian Seaplants from Dartmouth chose a different approach. They emphasized the advantages that could be gained from partnering with the National Research Council (NRC) Canada and its institutes. For instance, a valuable partnership had been developed between Agriculture and Agri-Food Canada (AAFC), NRC/Plant Biotechnology Institute (PBI) and AgrEvo Canada Inc. As a result of Canadian public research support, AgrEvo Canada Inc. had successfully produced a line of herbicide (ammonium glufosinate)-resistant canola. In accordance with the terms of the agreement, Agriculture and AgriFood Canada supplied the needed germplasm, NRC/PBI provided the biotechnology expertise and AgrEvo Canada Inc. took care of product development and regulatory proposals.

Ammonium glufosinate is a non-selective, post-emergent herbicide sold throughout the world. It was manufactured by Hoechst AG under the brand name Basta. It provided exceptional control of both annual and perennial weeds like Canada thistle and quackgrass.

Canola oil was used mainly for salads, cooking and margarine. The meal, left after oil extraction, was a valuable animal feed. The major world markets for Canadian canola oil were Canada, the USA, Japan, Mexico and the European Union. Current supply needed to be expanded to reach full potential. The company AgrEvo Canada Inc. selected canola as a target for research and development for several reasons:

– the most common type grown, Argentine, lended itself to genetic transformation;

– there were no broad-spectrum herbicide options available for this crop, thus creating a need for a new approach to weed control;

– canola was feasible for gene transfer protocols;

– canola was an important crop in Canada (Oelck, 1996).

In 1988, although AgrEvo AG had biotechnology expertise in Europe, the Canadian expertise had to be built up quickly. This could only be achieved through efficient interaction with partner organizations. Agriculture and Agri-Food Canada (AAFC) and Saskatoon Research Station provided the germplasm, while much of the biotech expertise came from the National Research Council Canada/Plant Biotechnology Institute (NRC/PBI, Saskatoon), and the quality analysis of breeding lines was contracted to POS Pilot Plant in Saskatoon. The network of companies and research organizations with similar needs in canola biotechnology and business created an environment for success which helped AgrEvo AG (Oelck, 1996).

Transformation work with *Brassica napus* began at AgrEvo AG headquarters in Germany in 1985. Since AgrEvo AG did not own any canola varieties, co-operation with plant breeders was essential. Agriculture Canada (now AAFC) had developed some of the best and most popular varieties grown, and continued to improve this crop species. In 1987, the first scientific reports were published with evidence that Argentine canola could be used for gene transfer experiments. In 1988, AgrEvo Canada Inc. scientists started to interact with AAFC in Ottawa to transfer the gene that conferred resistance to ammonium glufosinate (*pat*) into their breeding lines. A year later the first successful transformants were produced by AgrEvo Canada Inc. (Oelck, 1996).

Field trials for one of the transformed lines, Innovator™, began in 1992. At the same time, AgrEvo Canada Inc. chose the Prairie Pools (Manitoba Pool Elevators, Saskatchewan Wheat Pool and Alberta Pool) to distribute the seed because of their expertise. Anticipating a 1995 registration, seed was propagated to commercial stocks. As strict guidelines had been set out by the Canadian Government, each field had to be physically-separated from related species and cheked a number of times throughout the growing season. To verify product safety, everything from outcrossing to related weeds and wild species, to effects on bees and honey production was studied. Regular news release on field trials kept the public informed (Oelck, 1996).

In 1994, AgrEvo Canada Inc. needed to increase the seed quantity to prepare for a 1995 launch. Regulatory officials allowed AgrEvo Canada Inc. and the Prairie Pools to proceed under confinement conditions.

In February 1995, the Plant Biotechnology Office of Agriculture and Agriculture and Agri-Food Canada approved the commercial release of AgrEvo Canada's ammonium glufosinate (Liberty) herbicide-tolerant canola HCN92. Health Canada approved Innovator™ for human consumption. In April 1995, the final Canadian approvals -the herbicide label, environmental release, and use of the meal as feed- were granted. In 1997, once the system was available for wide-scale launch, over 500,000 acres were expected to be seeded in the first year. Farmers would be able to seed canola on land previously unsuitable due to difficult-to-control weeds. A post-emergent herbicide allowed for changes in land preparation to allow for optimum germination and rapid growth of the young crop. There were benefits in reduced tillage and enhanced environmental sustainability. The Prairie Pools were promoting Innovator™ under the Ultrabred brand of seeds. They led the way in signing contracts with farmers, and in discussions with crushers (Oelck, 1996).

1995 was the first year in which transgenic products (canola and flax) were available to both farmers and retail consumers in Canada. During the same year, Monsanto Canada, was authorized to release its glyphosate (Roundup) herbicide-tolerant canola GT73.

While Monsanto Co. was commercializing its Nature Mark insect (Colorado potato beetle)-resistant potatoes, Agriculture and Agri-Food Canada was developing (in 1996) potato leaf roll luteovirus (PLRV)-resistant potatoes. Saskatchewan Wheat Pool was working on high-laurate *Brassica napus* with Calgene Inc. and on a herbicide-resistant canola with AgrEvo Canada Inc. Pioneer Hi-Breed International, Inc. was developing: IMI-resistant maize and canola, Roundup-resistant maize, canola and soybeans, European corn borer-resistant maize, *Sclerotinia*-resistant sunflower and canola, new oil profiles and meal improvement in canola, soybeans and sunflower. Zeneca Seeds plc was developing: hybrid sugar-beet, canola, maize and non-hybrid soybeans for fungal, herbicide, frost and shatter resistance, pollination control systems and seed coat colour. Plant Genetic Systems (PGS) N.V. was trying to produce a high-yielding hybrid canola.

The Food Production and Inspection Branch of Agriculture and Agri-Food Canada (AAFC) was the regulatory agency responsible for field trials of plants with novel traits. As of 18 June 1996, approval had been granted for 113 submissions, which represented 747 actual field trial sites. The trials, which were being conducted by 20 organizations, involved the evaluation of 14 genetically-modified crop species. Canola (*Brassica napus* and *B. rapa)* was the most widely tested crop species with 483 trial sites. Substantial increases in trial sites were also reported for alfalfa and maize. While Saskatchewan had the most sites (224), a significant number of trials took place in Alberta, Ontario and Manitoba. Species such as Ethiopian mustard (*Brassica carinata*), cherry and grape vine were being tested for the first time.

Although herbicide resistance was the most widely evaluated trait, during the last few years, there had been substantial growth in trials evaluating insect resistance, viral resistance, stress tolerance and nutritional change. It was important to note that while herbicide resitance was being evaluated on 569 sites, this represented multiple site testing of the same transgenic line. The number of submissions for herbicide resistance was, in fact, only 52. Increased trial sites generally reflected evaluation of advanced lines as part of the commercialization process.

The 1996 trials involved the evaluation of transgenic plants produced through *Agrobacterium*-mediated transformation, biolistic techniques and direct DNA uptake. It was also notable that the number of sites involving lines backcrossed to transgenics had nearly tripled, which was indicative of decisions to advance modified lines into varietal development.

Several crop species, including herbicide-resistant canola and flax, as well as insect-resistant maize and potatoes, had received approval for unconfined release. However, unconfined release did not mean that the crop had been approved for food and/or feed uses. Additional documentation and appropriate tests were required with Health Canada responsible for food uses, and AAFC responsible for livestock feed uses.

Biotechnologies in Canada were forecast to employ an additional 4,000 people by the year 2000, with a big increase provided by scientific research. Although the educational system was expected to be the supply source, capability and skill gaps were likely to exist in the future, which could impede the continued growth and development of biotechnologies in Canada. The challenge facing Canadian biotechnologies, as companies moved from entrepreneurial start-up stages to full commercialization, was the need to match scientific excellence with professional management capabilities. In Canada, there was a shortage of managers with hands-on expertise in building knowledge-intensive companies. In addition, the regulatory process had a major impact on the availability of biotechnology-derived products, which in turn had repercussions on employment. The Canadian regulatory system was perceived as not keeping pace with changes in other countries.

By the year 2000, Canada would have to find 250 additional general managers required with planning, product development and operational experience. In addition to specialists in such areas as X-ray cristallography, bioinformatics, computers and bioprocessing, there was a need for specialists in patenting, regulation, process and product development, finance, human resources and general management. These challenges were going to be met not only by high-quality graduates, but also through on-the-job training, selective recruitment and supportive immigration policies, and, through procedures for incorporating into the team a relatively small group of people with specific highly critical skills, the entrepreneurs.

One could draw up an identikit picture of the latter. Imaginative and not one to go by set rules, the entrepreneur would need to be a visionary. He or she would be a generalist rather than a specialist, their learning coming not from books but from observation. A successful entrepreneur needed a good knowledge of the market and a keen sense of timing. A systematic thinker, he or she would also possess good interpersonal and communication skills.

An important element of the National Research Council Canada's Vision to 2001 was a plan encouraging individual and institutional entrepreneurship to maximize opportunities for the transfer of knowledge and commercialization of technology. Whether by partnerships, co-operative agreements, research consortia, licensing, new business, or another form of technology transfer, an entrepreneurial approach was one which ensured NRC technology ultimately resulted in new products, services and wealth-creating enterprises for the benefit of Canada. The NRC's Entrepreneurship Program was helping to develop an environment in which creativity, innovation, technology transfer and commercialization could flourish. The success of the Programme would be assessed in terms of:

– the efficiency and effectiveness of operational practices;

– the flexibility of human resource policies and practices;

– the quantity, quality and productivity of co-operative research agreements with firms, university partners and other research organizations and the commercial opportunities for innovative Canadian firms that resulted;

– and the social and economic impact of technology-transfer activities.

By the early 1990s, unlike in the USA where start-ups were dominant, the first Japanese companies which invested in biotechnologies were already big established companies, or formed part of a big industrial group. Many corporations conceived biotechnologies as a welcome opportunity to diversify their business, a characteristic activity of Japanese industry in general because of felling profit rates in their core business (e.g. in chemistry). By the mid-1990s, the most successful companies in biotechnologies included food and beverage enterprises, pharmaceutical and chemical corporations. About 800 firms were involved in biotechnology research and development (Heissler and Commandeur, 1995).

The Round Table Conference on the DNA Industries, initiated in June 1995, had published its report on March 1996. While in 1993, the value of the market for biotechnology products was estimated at $5.2 billion, biomedicines accounting for 84% of the sales, the Japan Bioindustry Association (JBA) evaluated the market of all biotechnology-derived products by the year 2000 at about $33 billion of which 44% would be accounted for by pharmaceuticals, 29% by foodstuffs, 12% by chemicals and 8% by agriculture (Heissler and Commandeur, 1995).

The phrase DNA industries covered industries that made use of recent knowledge on biological functions to produce useful products on an industrial scale. DNA industries included the following areas:

– diagnosis and individual identification based on DNA information (DNA sequences could be used to identify individuals and pathogenic micro-organisms, and to determine the risk of specific diseases such as cancers and hypertension);

– stimulation of biological processes based on DNA information (DNA information might be used to reconstruct a biological process using artificial physical and chemical techniques to produce useful products; such knowledge might also be used in computer simulations to design desired features in a product, ensure its safety and evaluate its effectiveness);

– use of DNA technologies (to produce biologically-active substances and biocompatible materials in big quantities using appropriate micro-organisms, biosensors, and to improve the traits of crop species);

– DNA equipment and data-processing (development, production and commercialization of specialty instruments and equipment, and meeting new demand for data processing and technician dispatching services) [*Japan Bioindustry Letters by JBA*, vol. 13, no. 2, July 1996, pp. 2–3].

About 80% of biotechnology research and development was financed by the private sector, while the remaining 20% was funded by the government. The weakest link of the Japanese biotechnology industry was still its lack of basic research. In its early stage, Japanese biotechnology development depended heavily on technology imported from the USA, which was illustrated by the fact that Japanese companies had established at least 375 strategic alliances with U.S. biotechnology firms since 1981. The collaboration was considered profitable for both parties: the U.S. companies, especially the start-ups, were hungry for venture capital and the Japanese corporations needed access to innovative products and new technologies (Yuan and Dibner, 1990; Bullock and Dibner, 1994).

Japanese companies, however, had increased their in-house basic research. This was also reflected in the increasing relative number in 1993, compared to 1992, of early-stage research-and-development agreements together with a decreasing relative importance of later-stage marketing/licensing agreements with U.S. biotechnology companies. Also the share of alliances which included biotechnology transfer agreements from Japan to the USA, was gradually increasing. Nevertheless, in 1993 the number of agreements including technology transfer from the USA to Japan was still four times the number of agreements on technology export from Japan to the USA. The fact that the Japanese bio-industry was a net importer of technology led to an unfavourable position in negotiations on licensing (Bullock and Dibner, 1994).

The reliance on the USA had given rise to many conflicts about supposed infringements of U.S. patents by Japanese companies. U.S. corporations accused Japanese companies of 'inventing around', i.e. making minor changes to protected biotechnological inventions in order to apply for a new patent. An illustrative example was the controversy between the U.S. biotechnology company, Genentech Inc., and the Japanese corporation Sumitomo Pharmaceutical Co., Ltd. around tissue plasminogen activator (t-PA). Genentech Inc. obtained its Japanese patent for its t-PA after filing in 1983. Sumitomo Pharmaceutical Co., Ltd. successfully applied for a patent for its own t-PA, the function of which was the same as that of Genentech's t-PA. In Sumitomo's t-PA, however, one of the 527 amino-acids was different, while the rest of the sequence remained the same. According to the Japanese court's ruling, because of this difference, Sumitomo did not infringe Genentech's patent rights. Despite the pressure of Genentech Inc. and other foreign biotechnological companies to place more stringent patent rules on genetic engineering and derived products, the Japanese Government was not considering revision of patent law or examination standards for industrial patent applications (Heissler and Commandeur, 1995).

It was estimated that in the European Union biotechnologies generated a turnover of 450 billion ECU per annum (1995) and the sectors where they had a direct impact accounted for 9% of gross value added and more than 8% of employment- roughly 9 million jobs in pharmaceuticals, agriculture, food processing, biofuels, chemicals and bioremediation. The biotechnology sector itself employed 180,000 persons and had a market value of about $57 billion. Nevertheless, the European Union position was declining in respect of the USA and Japan, and the challenge was to ensure that such outputs and their associated investment occurred within the European Union rather than the European Union becoming just a market (Meek, 1996; *European BioNews*, SAGB, 8, March 1996).

In the European Union, in 1996, there were 716 biotechnology companies (a 23% increase over 1995) employing 27,500 people (a 60% increase in job creation over 1995). Many of them generally had no more than 50 employees. Predominant biotechnology applications were in the agricultural and food-processing sectors, followed by pharmaceutical and chemical applications (Viseur, 1993). In 1995, among biotechnology-derived products, one could count 40 new drugs, several biopesticides, bio-insecticides and agricultural products.

In 1996, there was an explosive growth in the European bio-industry. Biotechnology companies were able to raise 1.6 billion ECU in new equity (about $2.4 billion) compared to 400 million ECU in 1995. European companies also invested 20% more in research in 1996 than in 1995, spending a record 1.5 billion ECU ($2.25 billion) [*European BioNews-EuropaBio*, June 1997]. According to Ernst and Young Group's First Annual Report on the European Biotechnology Industry, total European venture capital investment rose to $6.1 billion in 1993, but venture capital investment in biotechnologies had fallen from its 1989 peak of over $210 million to just over $90 million in 1992 (*European BioNews*, SAGB, 6, May 1994). The United Kingdom had the most advanced system of venture capital in the European Union: £2.1 billion were invested in the bio-industry in 1994.

InnoGenetics, a Belgian biotechnology company and member of the European Association of Bioindustries (EuropaBio), could be the first company to raise capital on the European Association of Securities Dealers Automated Quotations (EASDAQ), which opened for operations on 30 September 1996. The Brussels-based EASDAQ provided an electronic stock exchange to help high-growth companies raise capital rapidly and more directly from investors. InnoGenetics hoped to raise up to $100 million in its flotation which it would use to build a new plant in St. Niklaas near Ghent. InnoGenetics not only produced diagnostic kits to rapidly detect hepatitis, tuberculosis and AIDS, but was also very strong in the culture of synthetic tissue for seriously-burnt accident victims (*European BioNews,* A review and digest of bio-industry issues from EuropaBio, November 1996).

The different political structures dominating the European Union countries had led to either centralized research and development, like in Spain and France, or to decentralized research and development, as seen in Denmark, Germany, the Netherlands and the United Kingdom. The majority of these countries had developed a national biotechnology programme.

The key role played by innovative technologies, including biotechnologies, in Europe's competitiveness was a major theme at the Bio-Europe '93 Conference in Brussels, on 1–2 June 1993, organized by the Senior Advisory Group on Biotechnology (SAGB) in conjunction with the International Bio-Industry Forum and backed by the European Commission. The Secretary-General of the European Federation of Chemical and General Workers' Unions warned the Conference that 'because of the difficulties in obtaining licenses and authorizations at home, many of our most brilliant brains in biotechnology are forced to leave their countries if they want to work in a more technology-friendly environment. We must warn European decision-makers of the dramatic consequences this will have on our future competitiveness and employment'. The Adviser to the U.S. Vice-President explained how the U.S. Administration encouraged agencies to revise regulatory proposals in the light of public comment, allowing industry and environmental groups to input to the system. He gave the example of the U.S. Department of Agriculture's rule on transgenic crop species. Sumitomo Chemical Co., Ltd.'s adviser outlined the substantial successes achieved by Japanese industry, with the support of the Ministry of International Trade and Industry (MITI), in terms of the development, using biotechnologies, of both new production methods for existing substances and completely new drugs, agrochemicals, plants, livestock and fish. Fot its part, the European Commission's Vice-President emphasized that 'new industrial activities based on new technologies, such as biotechnologies, can play a critical role in the long-term recovery of employment. Increasingly, competitiveness in the global economy is less a function of resource endowment but far more of the level of innovation'. He added that 'if our regulatory framework were at odds with international practice, then severe competitiveness would arise' (*European BioNews,* SAGB, 4, September 1993).

In a letter to each Member State's Industry Minister before the 22 April 1994 Council, the SAGB chairman welcomed the recognition by the December 1993 European Council of the crucial importance of biotechnology for Europe's future prosperity. The European Union White Paper warned that, by the year 2000, with an estimated world market of 100 billion ECUs for bio-industry, the Union growth rate would have to be substantially higher than at present to ensure that the Union became a major producer of bio-products, thereby reaping the output and employement advantages, while at the same time remaining a key player in the related research area. The SAGB chairman told Ministers 'the barriers to European biotechnology competitiveness are not scientific; they are political, industrial and economic; we need mechanisms and actions strong enough to eliminate them'. The SAGB wanted a Special Task Force on Growth and Competitiveness for Biotechnology to include Member States' Ministries of Industrial and Economic Affairs, bio-industry executives, bankers, employee representatives and the European Commission's Biotechnology Coordination Committee. Besides the Task Force, the SAGB outlined to Ministers a full set of proposals for specific follow-up action in a policy document on the White Paper, which included improved regulatory efficiency and predictability, lower barriers to investment in bio-innovation and entrepreneurship, fiscal incentives to encourage investment, better professional skills and flexibility and broad-based leardership for competitiveness based on biotechnologies (*European BioNews*, SAGB, 6, May 1994).

At the Inter-institutional Conference on Biotechnology held on 11 January 1996 in Brussels, the European Commission President reaffirmed the Commission commitment to developing competitive European biotechnology which, he said, 'represented an enormous potential for innovation and growth'. The Farm Commissioner noted how 'biotechnology in agriculture can bring significant benefits to consumers and the environment, as well as to the health and welfare of animals and humans' because the use of genetically-modified crops not only reduced crop losses from diseases, but also entailed considerable environmental benefits by curtailing the use of chemical pesticides. The SAGB welcomed the positive signals emitted by the Conference and considered that its success would be determined by the follow-up aimed in part at reversing the trend which saw $4.2 billion in European investments in the biotechnology sector find their way to the USA between 1986 and 1994. The first follow-up to the January Conference was a European Parliament/Industry Biotechnology Forum held on 16 April 1996 in Strasbourg, which brought together parliamentarians and representatives from SAGB member companies to discuss various issues related to biotechnologies and improve mutual understanding essential for creating a more favourable climate for European biotechnologies (*European BioNews*, SAGB, 8, March 1996).

The European Commission latest annual report on the 'The impact and efficiency of the single market' identified biotechnologies as important for Europe's future competitiveness. The 30-page report represented a call to action for the final push to complete the single market. It reflected concerns that without a renewed commitment to this objective, the single market might simply not survive the challenges of the next decade, such as the continuing globalization of the economy and the possible entry of up to ten new members. The report urged a number of initiatives, such as the effective application of existing European Union rules through national audits and the creation of a registry of market-fragmenting measures, which would allow a review at Community level of national rules obstructing the single market. It also incited Member States to prepare the single market for tomorrow's economy through specific initiatives for the biotechnology sector (*European BioNews-EuropaBio*, November 1996).

The research-and-development of small and medium-sized companies had been reinforced by European programmes fostering co-operation with universities and research institutes (Viseur, 1993). In the USA, in addition to the usual consultancies and research contracts, some universities had signed agreements to train industry staff. In other cases, wide-ranging programmes of assistance to the productive sector, the best known being the MIT Industrial Liaison Program and the Stanford University School of Medicine Affiliate Program, had been established. Another expeditious means was the signature of long-term contracts (Monsanto Co.-Harvard, Bayer AG-Max Planck Institute) or the establishment of consortia (University of Wisconsin Forest Products Laboratory-cellulose firms). Many U.S., Japanese and European universities had set up biotechnology centres as a channel for academic links with industry. One highly attractive arrangement was that of the biotechnology centres set up in the USA on the initiative of universities but funded initially from federal funds (National Science Foundation) in the hope that they would, in time, become self-financing (Duke University, University of North Carolina, Purdue University, University of Texas, University of Minnesota) [Vicuña, 1993].

The biotechnology sector in the European Union was represented by a number of federal organizations. The Senior Advisory Group on Biotechnology (SAGB), funded by several major chemical and biotechnology companies, participated actively with the European Union institutions in defining regulations for Europe. A conglomerate of seven national biotechnology organizations, the European Secretariat for National Bioindustry Associations (ESNBA), sought to defend the interests of European biotechnology companies at the national and European level.

Created through the merger of the SAGB and ESNBA, the European Association for Bioindustries (EuropaBio) was made up of some 500 companies ranging from the biggest bio-industry companies in Europe to the national biotechnology federations representing small and medium-sized enterprises. Launched on 26 September 1996, EuropaBio marked a turning point in the sector's efforts to inform policy-makers and consumers about the benefits of biotechnologies. In addition to its Brussels base, EuropaBio had a network of eight 'branch offices' comprising the national biotechnology associations of Belgium, Denmark, France, Ireland, Italy, Spain, Sweden, the Netherlands and the United Kingdom. This network and the company membership should grow as Finland, Germany, Portugal and Switzerland were expected to complete the creation of their own national associations which would then join EuropaBio. In 1997, Procter & Gamble Co., E.I. DuPont de Nemours & Co., Inc. and the Rothschild Bioscience Unit (a division of Rothschild Asset Management) with funds under management of over $500 million for investments in the biosciences and health care, joined EuropaBio. The latter was governed by a Board of Management composed of equal numbers of representatives from companies and national associations. The Board held its first meeting in November 1996 and set its priorities for 1997, which were developed by its Policy Operations Council, meeting at the end of November 1996 to flesh out EuropaBio's Action Programme (*European BioNews-EuropaBio*, November 1996). Recognizing the need to keep up with technological advances in communications, EuropaBio had introduced electronic mail and launched its own home page on Internet (*European BioNews-EuropaBio*, June 1997).

On the creation of EuropaBio, its new chairman, President of International Research at Hoffmann-La Roche AG, remarked that 'from now on, we will speak with one strong voice when discussing with the European Union and national politicians and legislators the need for regulatory environment in which European bioindustry can grow and expand'. The new organization endorsed a six-point mission statement approved at its creation which aimed at creating a positive climate for competitive biotechnologies in Europe through: the development of coherent and supportive laws; the encouragement of open public debate; transparency in the making of policy; and the promotion of market authorizations based on established codes of safety, quality and efficacy as evaluated by internationally-accepted scientific criteria. EuropaBio's founders also committed themselves to an ambitious work programme in which a pan-European campaign to promote European competitiveness, public awareness, understanding and acceptance of benefits of the bio-industry would play a key role (*European BioNews-EuropaBio*, November 1996).

Putting the biotechnology sector message across to policy-makers was particularly crucial in 1996 when the European Union was in the midst of a major overhaul of its policies affecting the sector as regards both patent protection and marketing authorizations. With global sales in the biotechnology sector expected by the European Commisson to grow from an estimated $12 billion in 1996 to $43 billion in 2006, it was crucial that EuropaBio succeeded in its efforts (*European BioNews-EuropaBio*, November 1996). That was the overall purpose of the first European Bioindustry Congress, hosted by EuropaBio in Amsterdam from 25 to 27 June 1997, 'EuropaBio '97'. A specially-commissioned independent study, 'Benchmarking the competitiveness of biotechnology in Europe', provided a common backdrop for the Congress debates and workshops. It provided the first comprehensive picture of European biotechnologies notably covering both the big, small and medium-sized companies.

One of the first joint efforts by EuropaBio and the European Commission involved facilitating the access of small and medium-sized companies to the European Union research-and-development programmes in biotechnologies. The European Union so-called Fourth Framework Programme on Research and Development, which set the priorities and spending ceilings on European Union-funded research through 1998 provided for ECU 552 million in funds for biotechnology research. At a partnering and access meeting in October 1996, EuropaBio collaborated with the Commission's Life Sciences and Technologies Division of Directorate General XII to interest some 60 small and medium-sized enterprises in the programme. Funding was available for research in eight priority areas including cell factories, genome analysis, molecular and cell biology, and cell communications (*European BioNews-EuropaBio*, November 1996).

Since the mid-1970s, the staff of the European Commission had been arguing for a Community research initiative in genetic engineering and enzymology. The first Forecasting and Assessment in Science and Technology (FAST) programme (1979–1983, 4.4 million ECUs or MECUs) spent over 1 MECU in developing a concept of Community strategy for biotechnology in Europe. This was adopted by the European Commission in its 1983 statement of action priorities for biotechnology and included the launching of a concertation plan. Six priority areas were identified for action:

- research and training;
- pilot agro-industrial projects;
- co-ordination of policies in relation to biotechnologies;
- definition of new regimes for agricultural production and industrial use;
- a European approach to regulation (safety, impact on consumers, etc.).
- a European approach to intellectual property rights.

The Biomolecular Engineering Programme (BEP), adopted by the European Council in November 1981, ran from mid-1982 to mid-1986, with a budget of 15 MECUs ($20 million). Compared to individual government budgets, this was low: in 1982–1983, the total public budget for biotechnology research and development of all European Union member States was $200 million; it was $335 million in the USA and $80 million in Japan.

The European Member States' Ministers for Research invited the Commission to put forward a new proposal and the Biotechnology Action Programme (BAP) was tabled in April 1984. It was adopted by the Council the following year, with a budget of 55 MECUs ($74 million) for 1985–1989, and a promise to review the amount later. It thus overtook and amplified BEP, incorporating some FAST recommendations (e.g. measures concerning data-base and culture collection support), including more industry-related interests (BEP had been limited to agriculture and food) and devoting some 10% of its resources to concertation (Cantley, 1989). The Biotechnology Action Programme (BAP) was both a continuation of BEP and an extension into new areas considered essential for the development of biotechnologies in the EEC, such as enzyme engineering, application of genetic engineering to industrial micro-organisms, *in-vitro* testing systems, bio-informatics, etc. Only 6% of the actors engaged in the projects originated from the industry, and most of them were carried out in single research institutes and not through transnational co-operation. The BAP supported 123 projects, including 413 laboratories, as part of its European Laboratories Without Walls concept.

In November 1987, the BAP review provided a 20 MECU supplement, with a view to financing the participation of Portugal and Spain, following their accession to the EEC in January 1986; reinforcing the support for bio-informatics (especially the European DNA sequence bank); and expanding safety assessment research (to respond to the growing parliamentary and public disquiet about genetic engineering and about the possible release of organisms altered by these techniques).

A favourable evaluation report of BEP and BAP in 1988 gave the go-ahead for the Biotechnology Research and Innovation for Development and Growth in Europe (BRIDGE) proposal (1990-1994) in December of the same year. It received preliminary approval from the European Council in June 1989 (Cantley, 1989). The following tasks were pursued throughout 1990–1994:

– monitoring and interpreting world-wide developments in biotechnologies, with a view to identifying and analyzing opportunities, issues and problems (scientific, technical, economic, social and ethical) related to the development of biotechnologies in Europe;

– initiatives to encourage enterprise formation and growth in biotechnologies, with special emphasis on small and medium-sized enterprises;

– interaction between the European Commission's policies and programmes, and between the EEC and Member States' activities relating to biotechnologies;

– increasing public awareness and understanding about biotechnologies.

Biotechnologies were also promoted in developing countries (follow-up to Biotics' work on collaborative exploitation of phytochemical resources, requirements for training and data-bases, support for, or interaction with, relevant international initiatives).

The BRIDGE budget was about 100 million ECUs ($123 million) for 1990–1993. Two types of transnational projects were foreseen. Those tagged 'N' (networking) were similar to those contracted under the BAP programme in that they were relatively small; the 'N' projects were destined to be integrated in the European Laboratories Without Walls scheme; the EEC contribution to these projects was 400,000 ECUs per annum. Those tagged 'T' (targeted) were larger projects with a budget of up to 3 million ECUs. The 'T' projects were concerned in particular with characterization of industrial lipases; sequencing of the yeast genome; molecular identification of new plant genes; technology of lactic acid bacteria; regeneration of cultured plant cells; automated microbial identification; animal cell biotechnologies (*Biofutur*, no. 83, October 1989, p. 7).

BIOTECH 1, a 189–million ECUs ($229 million) two-year programme, was initiated in 1992–1994 as a supplement to BRIDGE; it included some new research areas, such as the conservation of genetic resources. BIOTECH 2, with a budget of 552 million ECUs ($681 million), was a follow-up to BIOTECH 1 and BRIDGE, and was running from 1994 to 1998.

Under BIOTECH 2, a research project involving 39 scientific teams was dealing with Archaeobacteria, with a view to unravelling the genetic basis of the ability of these micro-organisms to live in extreme environments such as Antarctic frozen soils, acid and sulphur-rich springs, very deep ocean vents. In the USA, the Institute for Genomic Research (Rockville, Maryland), created in 1992 and led by Venter who sequenced the genome of *Methanococcus jannaschii* (discovered in 1977 at a depth of 2,000 m in the Pacific Ocean) which had 1,700 genes, was working on the genetics of Archaeobacteria in association with a private corporation, the Human Genome Sciences, financed by the British pharmaceutical group, SmithKline Beecham plc. The U.S. Department of Energy (DOE) was also funding part of the genome sequencing work at the Institute for Genomic Research and was to share the benefits of the discoveries to be made (Vincent, 1996*d*). It was indeed foreseen to use these micro-organisms or their enzymes in harsh biochemical processes such as mongering of skins in the leather industry, bleaching of pulp and some foodstuff transformations.

In February 1984, the European Commission established internal structures under a Biotechnology Steering Committee (BSC) with, as secretariat, the Concertation Unit for Biotechnology in Europe (CUBE). The Commission's discussions over the following months with 16 bio-industry leaders on the need for a representative voice gave rise to the European Biotechnology Coordination Group (EBCG) in June 1985. Its creation was made possible by the collaboration of five associations (CEFIC for chemicals, EFPIA for pharmaceuticals, CIAA for food, GIFAP for agrochemicals, AMFEP for microbial food enzymes) [Cantley, 1989].

In addition to BRIDGE, two other programmes had been approved: European Collaborative Linkage of Agriculture and Industry through Research (ECLAIR) and Food-Linked Agro-Industrial Research (FLAIR). FLAIR (25 million ECUs, 1989–1994) aimed to apply new technologies to the objectives of quality, safety and nutrition in the food and drink industry. It was thus a programme of central interest to the consumer, at a time when political attention to consumer interests was rapidly increasing (e.g. the creation in February 1989 of the European Commission's new Consumer Policy Service, in line with one of the several recommendations of the European Parliament). The development of improved quality and testing methods was also strongly relevant to development of the internal market (Cantley, 1989).

ECLAIR (80 million ECUs, 1989–1994) promoted biotechnology-based innovations at the frontiers between industry and agriculture, upstream of the farm (better inputs, including more environmentally-friendly products and methods), downstream of the farm (new transformation processes) and on the farm, in all cases from an integrated viewpoint – i.e. the modified inputs might be designed to facilitate later stages in the chain and *vice versa*. The emphasis was on development downstream of programmes such as BRIDGE and on an orientation toward market needs, but still at a precompetitive level (Cantley, 1989).

Between 1987 and 1994, four agro-industrial research programmes with a total budget of 493 million ECUs ($589 million) had been initiated. Their common aim was to stimulate research in plant genetic engineering, animal production and health, processing of new biological materials from agriculture, forestry and fisheries, and food safety. The Agro-Industrial Research and Fisheries (AIR) programme, running from 1994 to 1998, was the follow-up to the previous four agro-industrial research programmes; it had a budget of 684 million ECUs ($844 million).

In the biomedical area, during the 1980s, only human genome research had been conducted. When public health and health research became part of the tasks of the European Commission, the first BIOMED programme (BIOMED 1) was implemented in 1990, with a budget of 135 million ECU ($166 million) from 1990 to 1994. The main objective of BIOMED 1 was to support network-building and training in human genome research, disease prevention, care and health systems, cancer, cardio-vascular, mental and neurological diseases. The budget for BIOMED 2 (1994–1998) was significantly higher than that of BIOMED 1 (336 million ECUs or $415 million). The goal of BIOMED 2 was to improve the partnership between basic and applied research in order to achieve a faster transformation of technological innovation into commercial products. The main difference with BIOMED 1 was the substantial support of research activities on neurological diseases, pharmacy and biomedical technology and engineering.

As part of the Fourth Framework Programme for Research and Development, which was allotted a total budget of $828 million over four years, the European Commission had approved $90 million in funding for 60 research projects in biotechnologies involving 528 laboratories across the European Union and some 77 industrial undertakings (*European BioNews*, SAGB, 8, March 1996).

Lastly, EUREKA (European Research Co-ordination Agency) had funded biotechnology-related projects since its creation in 1985.

European Commission directive 90/219 concerned only micro-organisms – bacteria, yeasts and viruses – of which the genome had been modified. Confined utilization meant any operation through which genetically-modified micro-organisms were grown, stored, used, transported, destroyed or eliminated, and for which physical and/or biological barriers were used. This directive was not dealing therefore with the regulation of voluntary release into the environment of genetically-modified organisms (GMOs, which included transgenic plants); this regulation was spelled out in another European directive, 90/220 (Vincent, 1996*b*).

Hoechst AG and Bayer AG had called for the regulatory system in Europe governing recombinant DNA operations (rDNA) to be replaced by a system 'based on the characteristics and properties of recombinant organisms and their products, and not on the methods by which these are manufactured'. This report made a detailed comparison of the U.S. and European Union systems. In the USA, they noted, regulations governing rDNA had evolved from experiments with micro-organisms and plants, in particular those conducted by the National Institutes of Health and the U.S. Department of Agriculture, which provided 'no evidence that a unique hazard potential existed either through the use of rDNA techniques or through the transfer of genes between unrelated organisms'. As a result, the USA had a 'workable and flexible review system with regard to the construction of working facilities, handling of rDNA organisms and product approval', which was 'pragmatic, scientifically appropriate and thus highly competitive'.

By contrast, Hoechst AG and Bayer AG noted that regulations in Europe reflected the European Commission's view that rDNA techniques required, without exception, surveillance and control mechanisms specifically designed for rDNA operations (i.e. the European Commission 1990 Directives, which stated that no product containing genetically-modified organisms could be commercialized before being submitted to field trials in ecosystems that might be affected by its utilization). They concluded it was 'almost unthinkable' that the existing European Union's regulatory system might allow universities and industry to be competitive and adapt to scientific progress within a short time-span.

The European Commission did not share this view. A December 1992 interim report of the Commission's Biotechnology Coordination Committee (BCC) claimed that the European Union and the USA shared a similar approach. The BCC report maintained that, in practice at the present stage of development, all genetically-engineered plants and most microbial pesticides regulated in the European Union would also be regulated in the USA, and that flexibility was not the prerogative of the U.S. system[2] (see p. 602). However, the Senior Advisory Group on Biotechnology (SAGB, Brussels) wrote to the Commission to challenge the findings of the interim BCC report, claiming that it lacked clear objectives and failed to acknowledge the product-based nature (as opposed to the European Commission's technique-based system) of the U.S. regulatory system, or recognize that the U.S. system focused on risk[3] (see p. 602) (*European BioNews*, SAGB, September 1993).

The European Association for Bioindustries (EuropaBio) believed that changes were long overdue because under Directive 90/220 which took effect in 1994, the European Union had approved only four genetically-modified organism-based products plus two vaccines. In comparison, Japan had approved seven products while the USA had authorized 27 and Canada 11 products – all including Giba-Geigy AG's transgenic maize (Maximiser[R] hybrid maize, resistant to the European corn borer *Ostrinia nubilalis*, as well as to ammonium glufosinate, the herbicide manufactured by Hoechst AG under the brand name Basta). On average, the European Union procedure took some two years compared to the 12-month process in the USA and Canada, and Japan's average of eight months (*European BioNews-EuropaBio*, November 1996). This situation had helped to create a backlog of some 1,000 biotechnology invention requests at the European Patent Office by mid-1997.

Other delays concerned the revision of Directive 90/219 on contained use of genetically-modified organisms. Proposed in December 1995, the revised directive would introduce much needed administrative simplification with a sliding scale of procedural obligations related to the risk of specific products.

The European Commission was sponsoring a newsletter, *Screen* (Swift Community Risk Evaluation Effort Network), on the release and regulation of genetically-modified organisms (GMOs), to facilitate the flow of information between the national authorities of European countries, scientists and regulatory bodies. The Newsletter was also expected to focus, at a later stage, on the safety of GMO-related foodstuffs and intellectual property protection. Although the newsletter focused on European countries, the discussed topics might also be of interest to other parts of the world. *Screen* was disseminated by ProBio Partners, Netherlands.

European Commission directives 90/219 and 90/220 on contained use and deliberate release of genetically-modified organisms (GMOs) had been incorporated in the French bill no. 92-654 of 13 July 1992. Since the mid-1980s, two French Committees had been set up to regulate genetic-engineering activities:

– the Genetic Engineering Committee (CGG) was responsible for evaluating the risks posed by GMOs and the techniques used to obtain them; the Committee proposed the confinement measures suitable for preventing these risks and classified the studies according to their purpose and risks run by humans and the environment;

– the Committee for the Study of Dissemination of Biomolecular Engineering-Derived Products, called shortly Biomolecular Engineering Commission (CGB), was responsible for evaluating the risks associated with the voluntary release of GMOs (field tests, experimentation in open environment and commercialization). The Committee reviewed each field-experimentation file and made very strict recommendations concerning its implementation. In addition, on the basis of already implemented field trials, the Committee had highlighted the actual implications of these tests on human health and the environment (Messéan, 1994*a*)[4 (see p. 602)].

Regarding GMO commercialization, the relevant file was submitted to the authorities of the country where this commercialization was envisaged. These authorities had a delay of 90 days to respond; if their opinion was positive, the file was transmitted to the European Commission, which dispatched it to all other European Union member countries for gathering their views. The latter must be received within a period of 60 days. In case of serious objection or disagreement, an expert committee was entrusted with the task of making a decision based on the majority rule, no other delay being imposed. The product was released throughout the European Union when agreement was reached (Messéan, 1994*a*).

The French Ministry of Agriculture had prepared a circular note that gave precisions on the methods of inscription of genetically-engineered crop varieties on the official catalogue of the Permanent Committee for Breeding of Cultivated Plants (CTPS). The European Commission directive 90/220 concerning the release and commercialization of genetically-modified organisms (GMOs) did not replace the methods of inscription on the catalogue of varieties. The procedure preferred by the French authorities was that the commercialization of transgenic varieties be simultaneously subject to a request in conformity with the European Commission directive and to another request for experimentation addressed to the CTPS. Both requests would be handled by the CTPS which would transmit the file for commercialization to the Biomolecular Engineering Commission. After a positive response, the CTPS would pursue the procedure as with any other variety. In this way, there would be a consistent procedure, based on the principle 'one door, one key', that France wished to see adopted by the European Commission (Messéan, 1994*a*).

If a file for experimentation was submitted to the CTPS before the authorization for commercialization (according to European Commission directive 90/220), official experimentation would be initiated after a favourable advice by the Biomolecular Engineering Commission and a file for commercialization would be assessed during the period of official trials. On the other hand, the Ministry of Agriculture's circular note was pointing out that any variety derived by conventional breeding from a GMO (whose commercialization authorization had been secured) could be disseminated through the official network without taking any particular measure. This was the case of hybrids one parent of which was a GMO, but when both parents were GMOs there was a need to request the approval of the Biomolecular Engineering Commission. All these projects were in conformity with industrialists' wishes, i.e. that their research-and-development efforts should not be hindered by too heavy regulations (Messéan, 1994a).

Regarding herbicide-resistant transgenic varieties, the relevant herbicide must be subject to a request for provisional commercialization authorization, which would generally correspond to an extended use of a new crop (e.g. the case of bromoxynil authorized for cereal crops). The industrialist would therefore be requested to submit a file including elements on the toxicity, effectiveness and selectivity of the active principle. In this case, the competent bodies were the Ministry of Agriculture's committees on toxic substances and homologation (Messéan, 1994a).

The European Commission summoned Belgium, Ireland, Luxembourg, Portugal and Spain to rapidly adopt a legal framework so as to supervise and control genetically-modified micro-organisms (GMMs). This decision, announced on 15 November 1996, requested the five countries to adapt their national laws to European directive 90/219, adopted in 1990 and modified in 1994, and concerning the confined use of GMMs. The time lapse allocated for making this adaptation had expired at the end of April 1995, and consequently these five European Union members had 40 days to respond to the European Commission's request. Otherwise, the Commission would have to go to the European Court of Justice because of non-application of European rules (Vincent, 1996b).

With respect to the environmental risks posed by the release of genetically-modified organisms (GMOs), one should stress that it was the first time that a system for authorizing experimental release and a system for authorizing commercialization were designed before any accident occurred. In other production sectors where a system for authorizing commercialization existed, e.g. the commercialization of medicines and chemicals, regulations and guidelines had been designed after major accidents occurred. This new approach probably meant that a global awareness had developed about new risks following the development of a new technology, and that biotechnologists wanted to give a good image of their behaviour so as to market their products in better conditions. It seemed that the weakest point of the evaluation of risks associated with the release of GMOs was the lack of studies on the long-term impact of these organisms on the functioning of ecosystems.

With respect to transgenic plants, experts thought that there was an exclusively agronomic vision of the risks, that is the dissemination of the transferred gene among the relatives of the transgenic crop species or variety and weeds. One should also study the impact of these weeds on their ecosystems. The reluctance to do so on the part of industrialists could be explained by the lack of an appropriate methodology for this kind of sutdies and by the fact that the latter required a long-term follow-up which was not compatible with the short time-lag required for commercialization.

If a major accident occurred, the regulation authorities might extend the period of field trials, from two to three years to seven to eight years before the request for commercialization, as this was the case for medicines. The major problem here was that the value added of transgenic seeds could not justify such a long period of trials, whereas it was justified for drugs. In general, experts predicted a simplification of current procedures for authorizing the commercialization of GMOs rather than increasing the hurdles.

Rissler and Mellon (1993) reviewed three categories of environmental risks following the introduction of transgenic crop species. Firstly, the newly-introduced traits might enable transgenic plants to become weeds in agricltural ecosystems, or to migrate out of the field to disturb unmanaged ecosystems. The second category of risks concerned the transfer of the transgenes to crop relatives; an example was the transfer of salt tolerance to a wild rice relative, which might then be able to invade a salt-marsh habitat, thereby displacing native plants; if the displaced plants offered a better habitat for nesting birds, the harmful effect could ripple beyond the marsh. A third category of risks was associated with the possibility that virus-resistant transgenic crop species could produce new viruses or alter the host range of existing viruses.

Weediness potential could be predicted, although imperfectly, by comparing the field behaviour of the transgenic plant with its non-engineered parent. The possibility of gene flow could be assessed primarily on the basis of information about the distribution of sexually compatible wild and weedy relatives in the region where the crop species was grown. If no wild and weedy relatives grew in the vicinity, for instance, there was no risk of gene transfer. Where relatives were found in the region, experiments could be done to determine the degree to which the crop species and its relatives interbred. If the transgenes were transferred to relatives, weediness potential experiments could be carried out.

Approval of a transgenic crop species in one country did not assure its safety in another country, because the risks associated with a particular crop species depended, among others, upon the environment in which it was planted. For instance, engineered cold-tolerant potatoes might be approved for commercialization in the USA if they were shown not to be noxious weeds and if there was no gene flow to wild relatives. By contrast, the presence of land races and sexually compatible wild relatives in Peru (the centre of diversity of potato) meant that transgenes were likely to move from the engineered crop species to nearby relatives. Consequently, it was vital for each country where transgenic plants might be introduced to conduct its own risk assessment and weigh the risks of a particular transgenic crop species against its potential benefits.

The release of transgenic plants on a large scale might have unknown implications. For instance, the gene transferred to a plant to make it resistant to a pathogen or to a pest might be introduced into another variety or even into another species. Bacteria and fungi, as well as pollen, could play the role of gene vectors; to what extent could pollen dissemination overcome the species barrier and lead to inter-specific hybrids?

A first approach to studying the environmental impact of transgenic crop species or varieties concerned the assessment of gene flow between these transgenic plants and their wild relatives. Pollen being the major vector of gene transfer between the two groups of plant populations, it was necessary to know pollen dispersion so as to assess the probability of gene transfer. One should qualify gene flow when the formation of fertile inter-specific hybrids could be demonstrated and when their offspring was shown to be composed of parental recombined types. Henceforth the need to carry out several crossing generations before drawing a conclusion of the existence of a gene flow (Gauvin *et al.*, 1994).

Since the 1940s, numerous measurements of pollen dispersion had been made, mainly by the breeders, in order to determine the isolation distances for producing pure lines. These measurements allowed the determination for most large-scale crop species of the distances over which living pollen could travel, but these data were variable from one year to another because of random phenomena (e.g. wind direction and velocity, insect behaviour, etc.) [Gauvin *et al.*, 1994].

All large-scale crop species were confronted with the problem of elimination of weeds belonging to the same family as the crop species. The relative efficiency of the usual weeding processes justified the recourse to herbicide-resistant transgenic plants (HRTP). In the case of oilseed rape (OSR), since the early 1980s, researchers of the French National Institute for Agricultural Research (INRA) and Canadian scientists had introduced genes for resistance to triazines into OSR, after isolating them from the wild species, *Brassica campestris*. Tens of thousands of hectares were currently cultivated with these varieties in Ontario. Other genes encoding resistance to herbicides had been tested, such as the *Bar* gene that conferred resistance to ammonium glufosinate or phosphinotricin (Basta) in OSR; trials had been carried out in the United Kingdom by Dale, in Belgium by Plant Genetic Systems (PGS) N.V. researchers and at the INRA, in Rennes, by Renard and his colleagues (Gauvin *et al.*, 1994).

Trials carried out in Europe within the framework of the BRIDGE Programme aimed to give some answers to the following questions:

– over which maximum distance could OSR pollen travel?

– which was the frequency of inter-specific crosses between the cultivated plant species and its wild relative?

– had transgenic plants a weedy behaviour?

– what was the future of transgenic plants?

The work carried out under the BRIDGE Programme and in particular the experiments made by Renard and his team led to the distinction between continuous systems where the receiving area was contiguous to the pollen source and discontinuous systems where the receiving plots (or trapping plots) were located at increasing distances from the pollen source. In both systems, male-sterile plants were used in order to better evaluate pollen reception: as they could not self-fertilize, male-sterile plants would show a maximum percentage of resistant plants in their offspring and therefore enabled a better assessment of the cloud of transgenic pollen (Gauvin *et al.*, 1994).

In 1989 and 1990, Renard and his team and Dale of the Institute of Plant Science Research in Norwich and his colleagues developed a circular system to test pollen dispersion over a short distance. A central circular plot (nine meter-diameter) containing transgenic spring OSR resistant to ammonium glufosinate was surrounded by sensitive male-fertile and male-sterile plants. At the following generation, seed samples were collected (representing 20% of its circle) on male-fertile and male-sterile plants located at 0.1, 1, 2, 3, 6, 12, 24 and 48 metres from the central plot. The frequency of resistant plants in the offspring of tested plants decreased with the distance of these plants from the central plot. By contrast, the maximum distance of transgenic pollen migration considerably differed during the two years of experimentation: in 1989, resistant plants were found in the offspring of plants located at 50 metres from the central plot, while in 1990 no resistant plant was found in the progeny of plants located at 48 metres or more from the central plot (Gauvin *et al.*, 1994).

Gauvin *et al.* of the Laboratory of Plant Evolution and Systematics, in collaboration with Renard and his colleagues and Plant Genetic Systems (PGS) N.V. scientists, designed another experimental pattern consisting of a square central plot containing OSR resistant to Basta, surrounded by sensitive plants, male-fertile and male-sterile. Four male-sterile, sensitive seeds were sown every three metres, the remainder of the plot being covered by male-fertile plants. All male-sterile plants were harvested, as well as the four male-fertile plants around them. The frequency of resistant plants in the progenies of these four plants was calculated. Like in the circular device, the frequency of resistant plants was decreasing when one was farther from the central transgenic plot, but resistant plant were found in the offspring of plants located at the extremities of the plot (Gauvin *et al.*, 1994).

A discontinuous system was later on developed:
– the 'emitting' plot contained transgenic OSR resistant to Basta;
– the receiving plots were planted with OSR susceptible to this herbicide and located at 200 and 400 metres from the emitting plot, in the four cardinal directions, and separated from the emitting plot by cereal fields. Pollinating insects of OSR had therefore to fly over these fields in order to commute from one OSR plot to the other. Analysis of plants on the receiving plots located at 400 metres from the emitting plot showed that there were Basta-resistant plants in the offspring. In addition, trials carried out at the INRA in Rennes also showed the presence of bromoxynil-resistant plants in the progeny of male-sterile OSR located at more than 800 metres from the emitting plot containing bromoxynil-resistant transgenic plants. It was generally agreed that pollen could travel over long distances (up to 1 kilometre) and consequently total confinement of transgenic OSR seemed very difficult to achieve (Gauvin *et al.*, 1994).

Despite insufficient knowledge, a number of measures had been suggested in order to prevent the multiplication of wild plants which might receive a transgene that would give them a selective advantage. A first preventive measure consisted of planting 'trapping plants' around plots of transgenic plants, i.e. male-sterile non-transgenic plants whose seeds would also be harvested. The dispersion of the transgene would thus be confined to a reservoir of cultivated plants whose populations could be controlled. However, the number of male-sterile plants and the width of the 'trapping rim' had still to be determined. A second measure consisted of imposing to the farmers using herbicide-resistant transgenic plants minimum distances separating the plots weeded out with the tested herbicide. It was not the acreage of herbicide-resistant transgenic plants but rather the total area treated with the herbicide that would determine the propagation of these plants. The latter had a selective advantage only in the presence of the herbicide. This measure would lead to a better management by the farmers of crop distribution and rotation on their farms and in co-ordination with neighbouring farms (Gauvin *et al.*, 1994).

Transgenic crop species could represent a danger only when they were grown in the same regions as their wild relatives. A hybrid between *Brassica campestris* and *Brassica oleracea* (cabbage), OSR probably had its diversification centre at the intersection of the diversity centres of its parents, i.e. Europe and Asia for *B. campestris* and Western Europe and Northwestern Africa for cabbage. OSR was identified in a wild state in Belgium. Introduced in Europe in the 13th century, OSR cultivation was much more recent in Canada (about 1942). Consequently transgenic OSR cultivated in Canada posed less problems because of the absence of wild relatives (with the exception of *B. campestris*); but this was not the case in Europe where inter-specific hybridization was possible. Geographic restrictions could therefore be envisaged regarding the areas for cultivating transgenic OSR and the distribution of transgenic seeds could be regulated (Gauvin *et al.*, 1994).

Finally, one could conceive safety measures for the development of the transgenic organism itself. A cytoplasmic transgene, for instance, would considerably reduce pollen dispersion; this would force seed producers to multiply their transgenic plant material via asexual propagation for producing lines. Gene flow via transgenic pollen could be also reduced through the introduction of male-sterility genes into transgenic plants. Such a measure would limit transgene flow to the dissemination of seeds derived from pollination of male-sterile transgenic plants by wild relatives or by other cultivated varieties. Seed-producing plots or fields could be sown with male-sterile hybrids (80%) and transgenic lines (20%). A last measure of precaution concerned the site of insertion of the transgene into the plant genome. If the transgene was genetically-linked to domestication genes (sometimes clustered on a small number of chromosomes), it could not recombine with them. This would lead to hybrids that integrated the resistance gene but which kept the cultivated phenotype. It was therefore suitable to improve transgenesis techniques so as to limit genetic recombination between the transgene and domestication genes (Gauvin *et al.*, 1994). See also Messéan (1994*b*).

A three-year major field test by a United Kingdom-based team showed that genetically-engineered oilseed rape was no more invasive, or even less invasive, than untransformed rape. The results of the study, led by Crawley of Imperial College, helped to counter one of the strongest arguments used against transgenic plants, i.e. that a new crop species might spread to natural habitats and upset the ecological balance (*European BioNews*, SAGB, 4, September 1993).

However, three geneticists of the Riso National Laboratory at Roskilde, Denmark, demonstrated that in experimental plots, *Brassica napus* (cultivated oilseed rape) and *Brassica campestris* (its wild relative) could hybridize spontaneously. Moreover, after crossing, they observed that a gene transfer occurred: that of the gene coding for resistance to the herbicide ammonium glufosinate, or Basta, which was inserted in *B. napus* genome. In addition, the hybrid offspring carrying this gene was fertile, while many agronomists and biotechnology companies had stated that such an offspring was generally sterile (Tardieu, 1996).

On 11 April 1996, the Scottish Crop Research Institute, after three years of observations carried out in a 480 km²-area in Angus, demonstrated the presence of oilseed rape pollen up to 2.5 km from their plots (having an area of 3 to 10 hectares). Pollen density varied from 0 to 33 grains per cubic metre of air. In this case also, hybrids were found between cultivated oilseed rape and its wild relatives (Tardieu, 1996).

These results showed a striking difference with the figures given in 1991 by McCartney and Lacey of Rothamsted Experimental Station, United Kingdom: they worked on four-hectare experimental plots and predicted that pollen dispersion would not be farther than 100 metres. The same was true of the results of several research teams in Europe (including those of the French National Institute for Agricultural Research – INRA – Rennes and Dijon) who had been working on the hybridization between cultivated and wild oilseed rape since the early 1980s and who predicted that pollen could travel over a maximum 800 metres (Tardieu, 1996).

The new information gathered on 'gene flow' was a subject of concern because a number of transgenic oilseed rape varieties were about to be commercialized in North America, as well as in Europe. In

France ans in other countries of the European Union, rapeseed varieties with genes coding for resistance to herbicides and other traits had been tested in some thirty field trials. For instance, the INRA in Rennes was requesting an authorization for commercializing several transgenic oilseed rape varieties, including some which were resistant to ammonium glufosinate, glyphosate and bromoxynil. That was also true of the companies Monsanto Co., Plant Genetic Systems (PGS) N.V., Rhône-Poulenc and AgrEvo Canada Inc. (Tardieu, 1996).

At the INRA station near Rennes, French researchers were trying to elucidate the transfer rate of the *bar* gene (coding for the resistance to ammonium glufosinate) and to determine the fertility of hybrids between transgenic oilseed rape and its wild relatives. Similar work was carried out at the INRA station in Dijon on a one-hectare plot. The results, published during 1996, showed a rather high production rate of hybrid seeds between transgenic oilseed rape and its wild relatives (Tardieu, 1996).

French researchers, particularly those who participated in the evaluation of risks related to the field release of transgenic plants under the European BRIDGE programme, were concerned about the recent results obtained by the Danish and British teams which, in their view, confirmed the concerns based on 15 years of research. If the genes coding for resistance to glyphosate and ammonium glufosinate which were good biodegradable products, effective against cultivated and wild cruciferous species, were transferred to weedy oilseed rape relatives, the effectiveness of these herbicides might be annihilated (Tardieu, 1996).

The world's first genetically-altered brewer's yeast had been approved by the United Kingdom's Advisory Committee on Novel Foods and Processes. Developed by BRF International in Surrey, the new yeast contained a gene coding for an enzyme from another yeast strain. This enzyme allowed the same amount of ethanol to be produced using less starch. Other genetic modifications of brewer's yeast could improve taste and create new flavours (*European BioNews*, SAGB, 6, May 1994).

It took several years to achieve the genetic transformation of sugar-beet. It was discovered that four out of twenty cultivars could form friable embryogenic calli, which could be transformed, using *Agrobacterium tumefaciens*; two virus-resistant and two herbicide-resistant sugar-beet lines had been obtained at Van Montagu's Laboratory, University of Ghent, Belgium.

In 1993, the Belgian firm Plant Genetic Systems (PGS) N.V. was awarded a U.S. patent on any crop species engineered to contain *Bacillus thuringiensis* genes. *B. thuringiensis*-based products accounted for 90% of the global biopesticide[5] (see p. 602) market, which was expected to be worth $300 million by the end of the century and be the object of one-third of all biotechnology research. PGS claimed paternity for the demonstration that the *B. thuringiensis* genes could actually be engineered into plants, giving them exclusive rights over any methods of transferring the genes into any plant, as well as over any crop species or variety containing the genes. According to PGS, their patent would cover maize, soybeans, rice, wheat, cotton, canola, tomato, cabbage, melons, potato, other vegetables and tree species (*AgBiotechnolgy News*, February 1993).

On 8 June 1994, the European Commission tabled its first approval for the commercialization of a transgenic crop species in the European Union: a tobacco variety carrying a gene for herbicide resistance, developed by the French state-owned cigarette manufacturer SEITA and which had been undergoing field tests since 1988. This tobacco variety had been engineered to tolerate applications of bromoxynil, a herbicide produced by the French chemical group Rhône-Poulenc. The Danish Government opposed the authorization adopted by the other 11 members of the Commission, because it considered the data supplied by the SEITA on the chemical safety to be insufficient. Bromoxynil had been shown to cause birth defects in laboratory animals and was classified as a developmental detoxicant for wild animals, fish and humans. The Danes wanted to ban it as an environmental hazard. In France, this herbicide was only authorized for cereals up to 1994. Once the new tobacco variety passed varietal tests and was grown in the field, it would be up to each European Union Member State to authorize sale of the cigarettes derived from this transgenic variety (*Biofutur*, June 1994; GRAIN, 1994*c*).

In 1994, Plant Genetic Systems (PGS) N.V. applied in the United Kingdom to commercialize as breeding material its oilseed rape (*Brassica napus*), which was genetically modified to become resistant to Hoechst AG's ammonium glufosinate or Basta. The European Commission directive 90/220 required approval from the Council of Ministers. If the majority of members voted for approval, then all European Union countries must allow the commercialization of the GMO. In February 1995, the European Commission authorized the use of PGS' oilseed rape. The conditions attached were that it be used only for breeding purposes, and that it be clearly labelled accordingly, along with an indicator of its resistance to a specific class of herbicides. Labelling of its genetically-modified nature itself was not required.

In 1995, the first commercial crop of genetically-modified tomatoes developed by Zeneca Seeds plc in the United Kingdom was successfully harvested and processed into purée for sale by Safeway plc stores and J. Sainsbury plc at selected outlets in the United Kingdom as of 5 February 1996. The genetic modification of the tomato stemmed from a joint effort by Grierson of Nottingham University and Schuch of Zeneca plc[6] (see p. 602), who had embarked on co-operative research into the biology of fruit ripening ten years earlier. The modification consisted of slowing down the action of polygalacturonase, which caused the fruit to rot. This meant that more of the natural thickening agent, pectin, was retained, and the overall result was less wastage at harvest, higher yields and reduced energy consumption during processing. The product had been cleared for sale following a rigorous safety review by both the United Kingdom and USA government agencies:

– 21 February 1995; the United Kingdom's Government endorses the advice of independent experts of the Adviosry Committee on Novel Foods and Processes and the Food Advisory Committee, and declares that the purée was 'as safe for human consumption as paste from unmodified, conventionally-bred tomatoes';

– 17 March 1995; the U.S. Department of Agriculture gives approval for these tomatoes to be grown as a commercial crop;

– 5 April 1995; the U.S. Food and Drug Administration gives clearance after an extensive evaluation of food safety.

The purée was sold in the United Kingdom under Safeway's and Sainsbury's own labels, which carried a statement informing consumers that the purée had been produced from genetically- modified fruit and that this reduced wastage and enabled less energy to be used during purée production.

In April 1996, the United Kingdom voted against an application for marketing consent for a genetically-engineered crop species for the first time. It occurred in a Brussels Committee of National Competent Authorities on the Deliberate Release of Genetically-Modified Organisms (GMOs). The crop species under consideration was Ciba-Geigy AG's maize, Maximiser[R], which contained a *Bacillus thuringiensis* (*Bt*) gene for resistance to the European corn borer (*Ostrinia nubilalis*), a second gene making it resistant to Hoechst AG's herbicide Basta and yet another one making it resistant to the antibiotic ampicillin. The last gene was linked to a bacterial promoter, and concerns on this resistance trait transferring to pathogens was at the heart of this decision: ampicillin was in clinical use in the United Kingdom. This did not seem to have presented a problem in the USA, which authorized the genetically-modified maize in August 1995. Concerns about the potential environmental and health impact of Ciba-Geigy AG's maize, which were widely publicized by non-governmental organizations, led to this rejection of marketing consent by the Environmental Council of Ministers, where only France, the applicant country, voted in favour.

However, on 18 December 1996, the European Commission approved the commercialization of Ciba-Geigy AG's (now Novartis AG) Maximiser[R] maize for all uses. In early February 1997, Austria and Luxembourg announced that they were implementing the emergency measures foreseen by the European Union legislation and would ban any import and cultivation of Maximiser[R], because of their concern on its impact on human health or the environment. In early March 1997, Italy joined them.

Following the procedures set by European Commission directive 90/220 was the only requirement in order to be able to cultivate genetically-modified seeds in the European Union member countries. Additionally, registering the variety in the European Seed Catalogue was a must. Once a particular variety was approved in one country seed register, it was automatically included in the European Catalogue and then allowed for unrestricted cultivation throughout Europe. In order to qualify, a given variety must show that it was novel, distinct, uniform and stable. Novartis AG initiated the procedures for inscription in national seed catalogues in several European countries. It faced a denial of registering the maize transgenic variety in Italy and France, while Spain seemed to be willing to include two or three varieties of Novartis' Maximiser[R] into the country's seed register. If Spain did so, it would allow for unrestricted planting Maximiser[R] throughout the European Union member countries.

In 1995, the USA requested permission to export to Europe Monsanto Co.'s Round-up-Ready Soybeans (RRS), which were genetically engineered to resist the company's own herbicide glyphosate or Round-up. The application was for all kinds of uses as a product, but not for planting. In France, the powerful Federation of Commerce and Distribution Enterprises (FCD) decided to ban any product containing transgenic soybeans from its shops and supermarkets[7] (see p. 603). It recalled in November 1996 that the two basic principles guiding its action were: the right of the consumer to be informed about the products he or she is buying; and the precaution principle to be applied to the use of new processes, particularly when their effects could be partly irreversible for the ecosystem. The FCD recommended to systematically request the suppliers of foodstuffs to indicate the possible presence of transgenic soybeans in the delivered products. In case this presence was positive, the FCD was requesting to determine the ways and means of labelling the products in order to indicate the exact origin of their ingredients (Vincent, 1996*b*).

In addition, the FCD intended to set up a scientific council in February 1997, comprising recognized experts, as well as a centre for information on food health. The aim was to build up a capacity of reflection and formulation of proposals, independent from the suppliers, in order to facilitate the dialogue with the public authorities in food safety (Galinier, 1996).

Soybean derivatives, such as lecithin, were ingredients of some hundred products, from margarine to baby foods, yoghurts and pasta. The decision made by the FCD aimed to force the industrialists and, upstream, their agricultural suppliers, to assume their responsibility in tracking the origin of products, i.e. their identification along the production chain, as this was the case for meat production. But presently genetically-modified soybeans were mixed with normal soybeans, particularly in the USA which provided 60% of the 15 million tonnes of soybeans used in the European food industry.

The approval of transgenic soybeans from the USA was also delayed because Denmark, Sweden and Austria insisted on labelling the soybeans as 'genetically-modified'. This prompted a very strong reaction from U.S. trade representatives, who argued that before long it would be impossible to distinguish RRS from ordinary soybeans, as they would end up in the same bags or containers. The U.S. representatives noted that there was much more at stake than just the $1.6 billion market for soybeans exported to the European Union. The entire agricultural trade to the European Union could be affected in the long run. The Commission's decision on PGS N.V. oilseed rape compromised its ability to insist on the labelling of Monsanto Co.'s Round-up-Ready soybeans; it could have delayed the decision on the RRS until the Regulation of Novel Foods came into force, but instead it chose to clear the way for Monsanto Co.'s soybeans on 15 March 1996.

Following the campaign launched by Greenpeace, some industrialists and distributors in Austria, Norway and Switzerland, already made the decision to withdraw modified soybeans from their products. However, as the European Commission's experts could not find any public health problem relating to the use of genetically-modified soybeans, the USA could argue at the World Trade Organization that this attitude was a commercial discrimination rather than a scientific approach. The U.S. position was the more justified that more transgenic plants were to be commercialized in the near future, and the FCD could not maintain its stance for a long time (Galinier, 1996).

In its confrontation with the European Commission, and specifically with Denmark in the soybean case, the USA had made clear its position on the trade of genetically-engineered plants. It assumed that if a product had successfully satisfied domestic environmental, health and agronomic standards, there was no scientific ground for its lack of approval in other countries, and any measure that these countries could take that went beyond U.S. requirements (such as demanding the labelling of GMOs) constituted a trade barrier.

On 12 February 1996, the French Prime Minister announced that the cultivation of Ciba-Geigy AG's transgenic Maximiser[R] maize was prohibited in France. This cultivation had to wait for the new variety to be listed on the official catalogue of plant species and varieties cultivated in France. The same day, a press release by the French Ministry for Environment indicated that the government was applying the principle of precaution and recalled its concern about genetically-modified products, especially seeds which, once sown, could be disseminated into the environment. The French Prime Minister obviously wanted to reassure environmentalists and consumers, who tended to transfer on transgenic maize all their fears concerning transgenic organisms and genetically-modified organisms-derived foodstuffs (Vincent, 1997).

The prohibition by the French Government appeared nevertheless paradoxical, because since 1994 France had been requesting the European Commission to commercialize this transgenic maize. On 18 December 1996, the Commission authorized that commercialization and on 5 February 1997 the French *Journal officiel* contained a governmental decision regarding the consumption of the transgenic maize by both animals and humans, but pending a specific labelling of the food- and feed-stuffs derived from this transgenic maize variety, as was required by the European directive on labelling of 'new foodstuffs'. The French Government, while authorizing the import and consumption of this transgenic maize variety and prohibiting its cultivation, was privileging the environmental risks of this crop rather than the risks for human health. Scientists were puzzled by this decision, because most of them were convinced that the environmental risks were non-existent because this transgenic maize variety cannot cross with any wild relative. The chairman of the French Commission of Biomolecular Engineering (Commission du génie biomoléculaire, CGB), who had been leading this Commission since its creation in 1986 and was defending the French position vis-à-vis the European Commission (in favour of the commercialization of Ciba-Geigy AG's transgenic maize), stated that he lost credibility and resigned. The paradoxical nature of the French Government's decision was underscored by the statement of the Minister of Agriculture: the prohibition of transgenic maize cultivation would not prevent 'experimental cultivation assays' (Vincent, 1997; see also Vincent, 1996e). Cultivation was approved by the end of 1997.

In December 1995, the European Commission proposed a new directive that it hoped would win the European Council endorsement. The directive sought to ensure harmonized patent protection for biotechnology inventions in all 15 Member States and replaced the first 'Mark I' directive vetoed in March 1995 by the European Parliament. The European Commission developed a new Draft EU Directive on the Legal Protection of Biotechnological Inventions 'Mark II'. In general, the bio-industry and pharmaceutical corporations in Europe were pleased with the content of Mark II, particularly because of Article 3 which made it clear that isolated genes and proteins were patentable even if they were structurally identical to the natural form. The draft directive was consistent with the present patent situation in Europe where materials derived from the human body, including isolated human genes and proteins, could be protected by patents if the usual requirements for patentability were met (Schouboe and Plougmann, 1997).

The reason why it was important to patent isolated human genes and proteins was that these products could be used in diagnosing and treating diseases. As examples, naturally-occurring DNA sequences could be used as diagnostic tools for the detection of genes involved in genetic diseases. More importantly, significant medical advances would depend on isolating and using products already existing in the human body. Examples of such pharmaceuticals which had already been made available to patients were interferons, tissue plasminogen activator, erythropoietin and factor VIII. Patent protection was necessary in order to ensure that investments made by the industy be recuperated thanks to a sufficient period of marketing exclusivity and that further products would follow to the benefit of patients in need thereof. Therefore, for certain groups of patients, clear legal protection for this kind of invention was vital. According to the drafter of Mark II directive, 'No patent of life' was the slogan of the opponents of the directive, while 'Patent for life' should be that of its supporters (Schouboe and Plougmann, 1997).

Article 3 in Mark II directive reads as follows:

1. The human body and its elements in their natural state shall not be considered patentable inventions.

2. Notwithstanding paragraph 1, the subject of an invention capable of industrial application which relates to an element isolated from the human body or otherwise produced by means of a technical process shall be patentable, even though the structure fo that element was identical to that of a natural element.

In the corresponding article in Mark I, the exclusion of patenting parts of the human body 'as such' led to controversy and uncertainty with respect to the possibility of patenting isolated genes, proteins and cell lines. In this respect, article 3 was a significant improvement (Schouboe and Plougmann, 1997).

Microbial processes and product by process would be patentable, even if the product was a variety. Inventions causing unnecessary animal suffering without substantial benefits to man or animal would not be patentable. A vague concession was made on the non-patentability of inventions that were contrary to public policy and/or morality. As a concession to farmers, Mark II directive included a weak form of a farmer's privilege: farmers would not have to pay royalties for the descendants of patented animals if they were to replace breeding stocks or go to the slaughterhouse; nor for plants if the harvested products were consumed.

On 16 July 1997, the European Parliament adopted Mark II directive by a broad majority (388 votes in favour, 110 against and 15 abstentions). The text which was to be submitted to the European Commission and European Union's Council of Ministers foresaw that there will be only one legislation throughout the Union on biotechnological patents. This legislation will replace the various national laws and regulations. The approved text stated that any biotechnological product or process will be patentable, with the exception of the human body and the embryo. It also excluded from patentability gene interventions on germinal cells as well as cloning of humans.

The European Federation of Pharmaceutical Associations and Industries expressed its satisfaction about the European Parliament's vote, which will stimulate the discovery of new drugs and help European bio-industry to catch up with Japan and the USA. EuropaBio also urged the European Commission to be very careful in any prohibition of cloning so as to avoid interfering with research which might, for instance, permit the growing of new skin for burn patients, replacements for diseased organs or alleviating paralysis by repairing injured spinal cord tissue. EuropaBio pointed out that Mark II directive already provided appropriate safeguards against human cloning, and therefore did not require the modifications requested by the Commission's Group of Advisers on the Ethical Implications of Biotechnology (GAEIB). The latter urged the European Commission to formally express its condemnation of human reproductive cloning and to make sure that this position be reflected in both the Fifth Framework Programme on Research and Development and Mark II directive. EuropaBio defended its position during the GAEIB-sponsored debate on the ethical dimension of the Fifth Framework

Programme on Research and Development, held on 19 June 1997 (*European BioNews-EuropaBio*, June 1997). Conversely, Greenpeace expressed its profound disatisfaction and stated that the approved text, if not modified, will allow the industrialists to patent human genes, animals and plants for the only benefit of multinational corporations.

Another European Commission's initiative involved adapting directive 90/219 regulating the contained use of genetically-modified organisms (GMOs) to reflect scientific, technical and political developments and bring much-needed flexibility into the directive. Reform of the regulatory system, which currently failed to distinguish between high-risk and low-risk areas, was pivotal to the success of European bio-industry. Yet modifications to the European Commission directive 90/219 which included establishing exemptions from legislation for those organisms whose safety had already been established and listing exempt organisms and procedures so that they could be approved by the European Commission Committee rather than having to call in rDNA specialists, were delayed for a year within DG XI, the European Commission Environment, Nuclear Safety and Civil Protection Directorate.

Revisions to directive 90/220, which regulated the deliberate release or marketing of GMOs, needed to retain safety standards while reducing the administrative burden on companies and end the serious delays they faced trying to get their products to the market (*European BioNews*, SAGB, 8, March 1996).

The European Commission Regulation on Novel Foods concerned the following products: foodstuffs or ingredients containing genetically-modified organisms (GMOs) on consisting of GMOs, GMO-derived foodstuffs when they were different from present standard foodstuffs, foodstuffs with a new primary molecular structure or deliberately modified, foodstuffs or ingredients composed of or isolated from micro-organisms, fungi or algae, and proteins derived from these organisms, and foodstuffs originating from new processes and inducing significant alterations of foodstuff composition. The file for commercializing any of these foodstuffs was to be reviewed by the competent body and the assessment was to be submitted to the other European Union member countries. The authorization could include the modes of utilization of the foodstuff, define particular labelling of the product as well as its denomination. Regarding the foodstuffs containing GMOs or derived from GMOs, the debate focused on the importance to be given to the production process: should one only focus on the product characteristics (and on its difference with standard foodstuffs) or should one consider the foodstuff as a new one when it was the result of transgenesis techniques? There were for some time divergent views and several European Union member countries required, on the basis of the right for the consumer to be informed, a systematic labelling of all GMO-derived foodstuffs, even though they were not different from standard foodstuffs (Messéan, 1994*a*).

Consumers' organizations world-wide (including the European Consumers' Organisation and Consumers International) had been demanding compulsory labelling of all products of genetic engineering. However, the European Union Industry Commissioner reflected industry's position when he stated that 'information that was not useful to the consumer should not be included on the label', and that 'informing consumers that a product was genetically modified made no sense if the composition, nutritional value or flavour of the end product was not different from a traditional food'.

The U.S. policy was founded on these principles. Although no formal legislation had been passed on the labelling of novel foods, in practice the U.S. Food and Drug Administration (FDA) considered it 'inappropriate' to label plants that had been modified in a way that did not significantly change their composition. This 'significant change' was analyzed only in terms of nutritional content and organoleptic characteristics (properties that could be apprehended by the senses such as taste, smell and appearance). This excluded from labelling any plants genetically engineered for agronomic purposes, such as making them resistant to stress, herbicides or/and pests.

Conciliation over the proposed Novel Foods Regulation began on 16 October 1996, meaning that representatives of the European Parliament and the Council of Ministers had a maximum eight weeks from then in which to agree on a compromise text. On 16 January 1997, the European Parliament rejected the proposal for a reinforced control and precise labelling of genetically-engineered foodstuffs. By doing so, the European Parliament supported the agreement reached on 27 November 1997 between the Council of Ministers of the European Union and a delegation of European Parliamentarians. The text and directive adopted and to be enforced within three months, were considered a failure of the Parliament's position. According to the members of the Green parties, the legistation adopted gave the European Commission the exclusive power to decide on a case-by-case basis, whether or not the consumer should be informed about foodstuffs derived from genetically-engineered organisms. The legislation did not foresee systematic labelling of 'new' foodstuffs. Those products derived from a genetically-modified plant were not to be labelled when the introduced trait did not affect the agronomic behaviour of the plant; this was the case of the herbicide-resistant crop species or varieties. Also foodstuffs that did not significantly differ from their conventional equivalents, e.g. sugar from a transgenic sugar-beet, oil from a transgenic oilseed rape or ketchup from a genetically-engineered tomato, were not to be submitted to labelling.

However, those in favour of more transparency obtained a concession with respect to the initial proposal submitted to the Parliament: it concerned foodstuffs containing genetically-modified living organisms, e.g. a melon resistant to a virus or seeds were to be labelled. However, a great ambiguity subsisted about the identification of these products. Thus, Monsanto Co. was refusing to separate its transgenic soybeans from the conventional one in its exports. In this case, the European Union's legislation only foresaw the following labelling: 'product that may contain genetically-modified organisms'. This was considered very uncertain. It seemed difficult to have another approach when dozens of transgenic crop species of broad consumption were already grown throughout the USA. All of them could be imported by European countries, and the European Commission could not oppose their entrance on its markets due to the agreements concluded under the aegis of the World Trade Organization.

Consequently, despite the violent opposition of Greenpeace following the vote by the European Parliament (the 'ecological' organization stated that the directive adopted would enable industrial corporations to introduce transgenic foodstuffs into the consumers' plate instead of protecting him), the European Union had to retreat, while at the same time nuancing its initial position about labelling. One would wonder whether the consumers were really benefiting from the new measures, from both the nutrition and palatability viewpoints. According to a poll made by Market & Opinion Research International, quoted by Greenpeace, 77% of the persons surveyed in France, 78% of those in Sweden and Germany, 65% in Italy and the Netherlands, 63% in Denmark and 53% in the United Kingdom were opposed to consuming foodstuffs derived from genetic engineering (Scotto, 1996, 1997).

As several hundreds of transgenic crop species (maize, potato, oilseed rape, sugar-beet, etc.) had been tested since 1987 in both greenhouses and field plots in the European Union member countries, analysts forecast that the European Union would sooner or later follow the example of the USA, where an increasing number of transgenic plants were being authorized for release and consumption.

The first hybrid oilseed rape (rapeseed) variety – a winter rapeseed named Synergy – was registered on the French Catalogue of Cultivated

Species and Varieties. It was marketed by the National Institute for Agricultural Research (INRA) and seed company Serasem, a subsidiary of the Sigma group, in time for the sowing operations in August and September 1995 (Dufour, 1994).

Hybrid maize and sunflower varieties had been welcomed by farmers. Rapeseed was recalcitrant, due to the self-fertilization of this hermaphrodite species. It was therefore necessary to change the plant flower biology. This task had been undertaken by INRA researchers since 1974. A first success had been achieved in the early 1980s: male-sterile rapeseed lines had been selected by crossing rapeseed with male-sterile radish. The male-sterile lines could not self-fertilize because they did not produce pollen which meant that they could be used to obtain hybrid lines throug crossing with selected varieties in the field. This second phase needed another ten years of research (Dufour, 1994).

The importance of this achievement was illustrated by Synergy's 23% increase in productivity over the best rapeseed varieties existing on the market. Synergy was still a 'composite', consisting of 80% male-sterile hybrid and 20% open-pollinated lines, but the researchers believed they could restore the complete sterility of the hybrid (Dufour, 1994).

With Serasem, which had been funding research since 1978, the INRA had launched an intensive programme for the production of new seeds. It was expected to produce sufficient seed to sow 40% to 45% of the 800,000 hectares corresponding to the rapeseed acreage in France, as a first stage. Furthermore, about 30 European and North American companies had concluded licensing agreements for the exploitation, in their respective countries, of the patent covering the new hybrid (Dufour, 1994).

At Horticulture Research International (HRI), United Kingdom, strawberries up to 64 mm in diameter, weighing about 3 ounces, had been produced by conventional breeding. The HRI strawberry programme was focusing on a variety called Bolero which fruited from July until October, yet had the quality found in berries borne in June. Some 20,000 plants were being grown in trials in 1996 and there were 1 million plants available to growers during the winter of 1997 for the variety's first commercial crop. Bolero variety would have a big impact on imports of late-season strawberries. The HRI also introduced the super-sized redcurrant variety called Redpoll. A third development on which British hopes rode was a purple dessert gooseberry called Pax, the principal virtue of which was that its bushes were almost spineless. Scientists of HRI fruit biotechnology group had succeeded in creating cantaloupe melons and tomatoes which could be stored seven weeks longer by inhibiting the function of the gene encoding an enzyme involved in the production of ethylene, which speeded ripening. The scientists were also hoping to transform the Queen Cox apple genetically. This research was being funded by the Ministry of Agriculture, which hoped the results would help the £40 million market for Cox apples fend off the growing threat from imported apples.

In Scotland, a flock of ewes (200 head) could contribute to an important change in the world pharmaceutical market. These transgenic sheep produced milk containing proteins that could be used in therapies against heart stroke and cystic fibrosis, whose cost was evaluated at $1,000 per litre. The company Pharmaceutical Proteins Limited (PPL) Therapeutics, which owned the flock, had signed agreements with several pharmaceutical companies, including the Danish Novo Nordisk, in order to find outlets for its biomedicines. This was not a unique example of transgenic domestic animals transformed to produce new drugs. In Framingham, Massachusetts, the biotechnology company Genzyme Transgenics Corp. owned a flock of transgenic goats which produced several proteins for use as medicines (Nau, 1996a).

Dairy cows naturally produce bovine somatotropin (BST), a protein hormone that plays an important role in the distribution of feed to vital functions like growth and lactation. In the early 1980s, the gene encoding the synthesis of BST in cows had been isolated and cloned by the U.S. biotechnology company Genentech Inc. Since 1982 it had been possible to produce big quantities of BST by genetically-engineered bacteria. The hormone produced in this way was called recombinant bovine somatotropin (rBST). When rBST was administered to lactating dairy cows it resulted in a 10% increase in milk production. Productivity increases varied considerably depending on the particular dairy herd, with larger increases occurring with improved management. This increase in productivity was due to an improved efficiency of feed utilization. Cows treated with rBST needed more feed and for optimal results of treatment by rBST good quality feed and protein-rich feed were required (Bijman, 1996).

Foreseeing the commercial opportunities for rBST, four big pharmaceutical companies had initiated extensive research-and-development programmes to develop a commercial rBST product. These companies were: Monsanto Co., Eli Lilly & Co., American Cyanamid Co. and The Upjohn Co. After several years American Cyanamid Co. and The Upjohn Co. discontinued their research programmes, while Monsanto Co. and Eli Lilly's veterinary pharmaceutical branch, Dow Elanco, had developed commercial products (Bijman, 1996).

Monsanto Co.'s version of rBST, sold under the brand name Posilac, had been sold in the USA since 3 February 1994. It was administered to healthy cows every two weeks, beginning during the ninth week of lactation. Assuring a 310 to 315 days of lactation, this implied 18 injections per cow per lactation period. One injection contained 500 mg of rBST and cost $6.60 ($0.47 per cow per day). Hormone injection led to a 2.5 to 7.5 kg increase in daily milk production (Bijman, 1996).

At least five major issues had been, at one time or another, at the centre of the debate on rBST: food safety, impact on natural environment, socio-economic impact, animal welfare and ethics.

Most scientists agreed that the use of rBST did not pose any threat to human health. Still some of them thought that the increased amounts of insulin-like growth factor-1 (IGF-1) in the milk of cows treated with rBST could exert significant effects on the infant's intestine by stimulating cell division. The environmental concerns were related to the intensification of dairy farming and the concomitant concentrated production of minerals and ammonia. Regarding the socio-economic impact, before rBST was introduced it was expected that increase in milk production of 10% to 15% per cow would benefit big farms more than small farms. Although rBST was administered to cows individually, and therefore its application was assumed to be scale neutral, realization of the productivity enhancement required rather intensive monitoring and management of feed rations, milk production, animal health, breeding schemes and overall system co-ordination. These activities and the equipment needed were not scale neutral: bigger farms tended to have better management and were more likely to have computers for monitoring feed intake, health and production per cow. Many believed that the systematic use of rBST would increase the size and reduce the number of dairy farms, thereby affecting the viability of rural communities (Bijman, 1996).

Numerous studies had been conducted on the impact of rBST on animal health and welfare. The vast majority of these studies indicated that no adverse effects were to be expected. Veterinary advisory boards in both USA and European Union had approved the use of rBST. However, a few studies underlined some negative impact, like a higher incidence of mastitis, an inflammation of the udder; this could be related to the increase in milk production. Another welfare issue was that the hormone was administered to the cow by injection, every two weeks (Bijman, 1996).

With respect to ethical and political issues, both proponents and critics saw rBST as a test case for regulation of agro-biotechnologies in general. The introduction of rBST had therefore become a very politicized issue. Various countries had come up with different regulations on rBST, government officials had to take into account the reserved public attitude toward agricultural biotechnologies in general, the targeted critique by special interest groups and the uncertainty over consumers' reaction to the introduction of milk from cows treated with rBST. At the same time, bio-industrial companies, together with governmental agencies in charge of the promotion of science and technology, did not want the development of biotechnologies to be hampered by too strict regulations. While the use of rBST was not allowed in the 15 member countries of the European Union, Australia, Canada, New Zealand and Norway, the following countries had approved the use of rBST (Monsanto Co.'s Posilac or Dow Elanco's product or a nationally-made product under official license or as an illegal imitation): Algeria, Namibia, South Africa and Zimbabwe; Malaysia, Pakistan, South Korea; Brazil, Costa Rica, Honduras, Jamaica, Mexico, USA and Venezuela; Bulgaria, Czech Republic, Rumania, Russia and Slovakia. In a few U.S. States, special labelling was required for milk and dairy products derived from rBST-treated cows (Bijman, 1996).

In 1994, the European Council decided to ban the use and sale of rBST until 31 December 1999, on the basis of two considerations: first, the introduction of rBST would not be in line with the reform of the Common Agricultural Policy, as it would negatively affect dairy and beef markets (generally excedentary); secondly, a strong aversion to the use of rBST prevailed among consumers. The Council feared, together with the European Commission and the European Parliament, that the consumption of dairy products and beef would decrease considerably and that the image of dairy products would be negatively affected. The future decision on the rBST ban in Europe was closely related to both the public attitude toward biotechnology-derived products (which were to a large extent based on cultural and ethical values) and the milk production quota system. The latter was a system of production rights under which all dairy farmers in the European Union were allowed to produce up to a certain maximum amount of milk (the quota). For every kilogramme of milk above the quota, a levy had to be paid to the European Commission; this levy was prohibitive in nature, as it was more than the price farmers received for their milk (Bijman, 1996).

According to a study of the Agricultural Economics Research Institute in the Netherlands, the abolition of the quota system was expected to result in increased production and exports. Additionally, an acceleration in structural change in the dairy sector toward more concentration of production, on farm as well as at regional level, was predicted. The use of rBST would reinforce these trends: more production and exports, lower internal prices, lower but bigger dairy holdings and more regional concentration of production. This would have a negative social impact, as many farmers would be forced to leave the sector (Bijman *et al.*, 1996).

It was nevertheless true that the abolition of the quota system and widespread use of rBST were likely to contribute to improving the international competitiveness of the European Union dairy industry, as it would benefit from economies of scale in milk production. Such a change would be needed if the European Union wanted to maintain current levels of production, while at the same time it had to lower export subsidies necessary to sell excess produce on the world market. Competitiveness of the European dairy industry also depended on food safety and consumers' perception of the quality of exported products. For instance, in high-income markets like Japan and Switzerland, consumers would be reluctant to accept products derived from milk produced by rBST-treated cows. Furthermore, it would not be easy to separate milk produced with the use of rBST and milk produced without, since the hormone left no traces in the milk, thereby increasing consumers' reluctance. Unfortunately, there was little information on consumers' attitude toward rBST in the major markets for European Union dairy products (Bijman *et al.*, 1996).

In the USA, in November 1993, the Food and Drug Administration approved the commercial use of Posilac, Monsanto Co.'s rBST, and commercial sales began in February 1994. After two years of experience with its use, a little more than 10% of all U.S. dairy farmers were using rBST, who kept around one-fourth of the 9.5 million cows of the USA. There was no evidence of any significant adverse consumer reaction in the USA despite the debate in the news media prior to the approval of the recombinant hormone. In fact, both milk production and consumption continued to increase. Milk prices at the farm remained at or slightly above levels of the period just before the approval of Posilac, while it was expected that the use of rBST would lower milk prices. In some States in the northeastern part of the USA, where labelling regulations had been approved, hardly any rBST was being sold. Most dairy processors in these States were producing high-quality, high-price dairy products, and guaranteed that milk came from untreated cows (Bijman, 1996).

Adoption of rBST was highest among moderate-size farms. In Wisconsin, the second-biggest dairy State, adoption of rBST had been much lower than the U.S. average, 5.5% adoption at the end of 1994 compared to 11% nation-wide. According to a study by the University of Wisconsin, this relatively low percentage of adoption of rBST was the result of the politicization of the debate around the hormone in Wisconsin. In addition, with an average of 51, herd size was much smaller in Wisconsin than in most other States and farmers tended to be slower in adopting new technologies. In California, adoption of rBST had been lower than national average because of the big herd size (on average 305 head per farm) and the corporate style operations. Hence, some Californian dairy farmers had been slow in adopting rBST since their employees had to milk great numbers of cows each day and could not easily monitor the individual performance of each cow, as was done more easily on family farms with smaller herds. In contrast, adoption had been relatively rapid in New York State, where the average herd size was 66 cows. With moderate size herds, and mostly family farm operations that were smaller than corporate farms in California, it was easier to administer rBST and monitor the performance of individual cows. An economic analysis made by Cornell University on a relatively large sample of representative New York State dairy farms showed that farmers adopting rBST had, on average, bigger herds than State average and were more profitable than other farmers. With the adoption of rBST they increased productivity per cow and met farm income. Feed cost per pound of milk sold decreased for farmers using rBST, while it increased for non-adopters. Using rBST was relatively easy, but changes in feeding programme and selection of animals to be treated with the hormone required additional management time (Bijman, 1996).

It could be concluded that in the USA adoption rates of rBST were not the same for all regions and farms, even though regulation by governmental authorities had set a common ground, due to differences in the dairy industry structure as well as to politicization of the debate on the safety of this hormone for the consumers. For the European Union, one could assume, if the ban on rBST were to be lifted, that it might lead to differences in adoption rates and consequently in the impact on the dairy farming industry, given the great structural and cultural differences in agriculture in the European Union member countries (Bijman, 1996).

Science and Technology for Development programme

As early as the first Framework Programme for Research and Technological Development (1982–1986), the European Economic Community (EEC) had responded to the Programme of Action of the United Nations Conference on Science and Technology for Development

(Vienna, 1979), with the Community Programme STD-1 (Science and Technology for Development). The main objective of this first programme was to support Europe's strong tropical research potential. The second programme (STD-2, 1987–1991) sought, in addition, to build up the research-and-development capabilities of developing countries. The third programme (STD-3, 1991–1994) sought, more specifically, to boost the impact of research on development.

The EEC was the biggest importer of products from developing countries, with agricultural products making up a large proportion of trade. It was therefore important for these countries to know what would be the impact of biotechnologies on their exports to the EEC and on their trade relations with it. For instance, within the ECLAIR programme, it was intended to adapt soybeans to suit some European countries, which would affect trade in soybeans with countries like Argentina and Brazil (Bijman, 1990).

Some initiatives within the concertation part of BAP sought to promote co-operation between the EEC and developing countries, e.g. the Seminar on Biotechnology in Europe and Latin America for industrial collaboration. In a document published by the European Commission in June 1986, it was stated that 'It is therefore necessary (in parallel with our evolution toward the new agro-industrial phase of our own development) to continue to reinforce existing Community efforts to assist these countries to improve their agriculture and to secure environmentally sustainable rural development. Biotechnology may well be able to contribute substantially to these aims'.

The main concern of the STD programme was to raise local research potential. The world research-and-development expenditure was divided up as follows in the late 1980s: 20% EEC, 3.1% developing countries and 76.9% others. As a percentage of the gross national product, the average figures were: 2.23% industrialized countries, 0.45% developing countries, 0.36% Africa, 0.27% Arab States, 1.18% Asia, 0.49% Latin America. The number of scientists and research-and-development engineers per million inhabitants totalled in the early 1980s: 850 world average, 2,984 industrialized countries, 127 developing countries, 49 Africa, 207 Arab States, 274 Asia and 252 Latin America (CEC, 1991).

The STD formed part of the Framework Programme for Research and Technological Development. It was not linked to a specific Community co-operation policy (Africa-Caribbean-Pacific, Mediterranean countries, ALA), but sought to stimulate simultaneous study in various parts of the world of specific scientific issues which could contribute to progress in all developing countries. The STD worked according to 'scientific themes', independently of the economic or political contingencies involved in scientific co-operation. From the outset, the STD was opened only to research projects involving at least two teams, one belonging to the EEC and the other from a developing country. Under the STD-3, projects had to pool the potential of at least two EEC teams and at least one from a developing country (CEC, 1991).

Scientists in the developing countries had direct access to the STD programme funds from the EEC budget and could, thus, define their research priorities and choose their partners themselves. In addition to North-North and North-South teams, the STD also supported South-South co-operation. The partnership between teams from the EEC and developing countries raised the potential and value of scientific research conducted in the developing countries. In addition, it enabled researchers from developing countries to carry out research requiring sophisticated equipment which they could find in partner laboratories. Conversely, the contract between European teams and those of the developing countries ensured that the research carried out was of greatest possible relevance to the developing countries and not too far removed from grassroots concerns (CEC, 1991).

There was no maximum limit on the number of institutions allowed to take part in a given project. The results of the STD-2 showed that around 75% of projects involved more than three different laboratories and that 25% brought together more than five. In order to ensure maximum efficiency, the STD programme focused on major development problems: the first STD programme, launched in 1983 and covering the period 1983–1986, concerned two areas of work of crucial importance for developing countries: agriculture and health. Forty million ECUs were allocated to this first STD programme for funding 411 research projects.

The STD was much more than a programme on a specific theme, combining the efforts of the best specialists in a given field. It was a horizontal programme, drawing in as many scientific disciplines as was necessary to achieve its objectives. Thematic networks involved researchers with different specializations. Under the STD-2 (1987–1991), three research networks were set up: Small Ruminants, Tropical Forest and the BUROTROP on perennial oil-seed species.

Following a 1985 study by the French Centre for International Co-operation in Agricultural Research for Development (CIRAD) on the market of vegetable oils and the research-and-development needs concerning these oils, Belgium, France, Germany, the Netherlands, Portugal and the United Kingdom had decided to join forces with the European Commission to support research-and-development activities on oil-palm and coconut. They decided to set up a Bureau for the Development and Research on Tropical Perennial Oil Crops (BUROTROP) open to any donor or producing country. The European Commission contributed to the functioning of this Bureau at the beginning of 1989 under STD-2; this support was renewed in 1993 for a four-year period and for another one (1996–1999). This decision was the major fact of the annual meetings of the programme committee, executive board and general assembly of the BUROTROP, held in Jakarta from 23 to 24 May 1996. This renewed support would enable the Bureau to pursue its activities and seek various sources of funding (*CIRAD Information*, no. 64, 23 July 1996, p. 7).

The BUROTROP began operations in March 1990. Until the end of 1994, the BUROTROP had been functioning with the administrative and logistical support of the CIRAD. On 1 January 1995, the BUROTROP became an autonomous non-profit making association. The Association comprised: an administrative council of 14 members (including seven from Africa, Asia, Latin America and the Pacific, and from donor countries represented by the GTZ of Germany, the Overseas Development Administration of the United Kingdom, the ICCT of Portugal and the French CIRAD); representatives of funding organisms lile the European Commission, the World Bank, the FAO and the CTA, which attended the meetings as observers, as well as several representatives of private corporations (e.g. Unilever N.V.); the International Plant Genetic Resources Institute (IPGRI) was also a member of the Association; a programme committee of six members (including three from the producing countries) which, as a technical advisory body to the administrative council, could rely on external expertise; a small secretariat with a director, administering a budget of $500,000 provided by the European Commission.

The BUROTROP was a network whose specific objectives were to: promote the exchange of information and experience among research organizations and institutions dealing with perennial tropical oil plants; identify the obstacles to producing these plants and the research-and-development needs; initiate and foster research on these plants, and co-ordinate research activities; assess training needs and reinforce current means.

The BUROTROP was not conducting any research, training or information service, but offered a permanent concertation forum for the international and national research institutions of both producing and donor countries; it was not a funding agency, but rather a facilitator, which acted in co-ordination with associations of producers or regional organizations. It promoted the priority activities identified by the forum and reassured the funding sources of the utility of the chosen programmes and their potential impact on the industry of perennial tropical oil plants.

Under its STD-3, the European Commission was supporting six projects identified by the BUROTROP; the GTZ had funded several projects submitted through the Bureau and the World Bank had decided to base its action in Africa on the priorities set for the coconut tree. The BUROTROP and IPGRI had signed a co-operation agreement covering all their activities dealing with oil-palm and coconut. The BUROTROP and the Inter-American Institute for Cooperation on Agriculture (IICA) were linked by a similar convention. The FAO Intergovernmental Group on Oils and Fats was assisted by the BUROTROP in setting the research priorities for oil-palm an coconut. The Bureau was also instrumental in developing the project on heart rot of oil-palm in Latin America.

In addition to the organization of seminars in Africa, Latin America and the Caribbean on current research on oil-palm and coconut, the identification of research priorities based on the producers' assessment and the networking of research, the BUROTROP was publishing a newsletter, the *BUROTROP Bulletin*, every four months, in English and French, with a readership of 1,200 in about 100 countries. This Bulletin aimed to foster the exchange of information and experience among researchers and developers. A Spanish version was published in co-operation with the IICA. Furthermore, a data-base was being set up on research institutions, programmes and teams to answer the question 'who is doing what?', while linking the base to FAO CARIS network. The collection of data, feeding of the data-base and its use were being done in collaboration with regional associations such as the Asian and Pacific Coconut Community and the African Association for the Development of Oil Palm.

The STD-1 and STD-2 budgets amounted to 40 million ECUs and 80 million ECUs respectively, with the following characteristics:

	STD-1	STD-2
projects submitted	1 940	2 527
projects selected	411	339
agriculture projects	228	180
medicine projects	183	159
agriculture (million ECU)	30	50
medicine (million ECU)	10	30
number of countries	73	97
number of developing countries	64	86

Biotechnologies were not explicitly mentioned in STD-2, which dealt with a wide range of technologies. But in fact, several projects supported by STD-2 were biotechnological ones.

In the area of health, the STD-2 sought to create networks dealing with different aspects of a particular disease. Their aim was to attain a 'critical mass' of scientific skills in order to have a lasting impact on the strategies deployed at world level to control the main diseases. Regular meetings were held alternatively, in the EEC or a developing country, on such themes as malaria, schistosomiasis, leishmaniasis, filariasis and health systems. These meetings facilitated the exchange of information and establishement of new links. With respect to schistosomiasis, for instance, networks had been set up on immunology and vaccine development; the research activities involved 28 teams linking scientists from seven EEC-member countries and 12 developing countries (CEC, 1991).

In agriculture, plant production had a 38.6% and 44.5% share in STD-1 and STD-2 respectively, followed by livestock husbandry and fish culture (22.8% and 20.6%), and by soil protection and the environment (20.6% and 13.2%). In particular, five projects had been implemented on cassava for a total amount of 1.4 million ECUs. In these projects, biotechnologies were applied to: improve the post-harvest processing of cassava; improve African cassava cultivars through *in-vitro* conservation, meristem culture, regeneration by somatic embryogenesis, somatic hybridization and the use of enzymatic markers to better characterize the local varieties for breeding programmes; and produce cassava cultivars with acyanogenic roots. In medicine, parasitology received the lion's share, with 81.0% and 50.0%, followed by health and nutrition (13.6% and 20.0%).

With the STD-2, some 630 scientific institutions were mobilized by the European Commission, creating more than 3,000 research links between over 100 countries. The geographical breakdown of the collaborating institutions was: 303 Europe, 188 Africa, 70 Latin America, 66 Asia and 3 Pacific. The EC contribution (in %) was: 65.7% Europe (including the financing of equipment transferred to developing countries), 20.7% Africa, 6.8% Latin America, 6.7% Asia and 0.1% Pacific (CEC, 1991). Under STD-2, over 80 research projects were funded in Latin America in biotechnologies relating to agriculture, medicine, health and nutrition.

The STD-3 had two goals: better living conditions and improvements in health. The main concept underpinning the EC development schemes being sustainable development, this meant that protection of the environment, management of resources and the lasting and non-harmful nature of the solutions studied were decisive criteria for the selection of research projects under the STD-3 (CEC, 1991).

The programme outline was the following:

A. Tropical and subtropical agriculture

1. Improvement of agricultural products
   - Crop production: food and agro-industrial crops; crop genetics; crop protection
   - Livestock production and fisheries: stock farming; animal genetics and reproduction; veterinary medicine; sea and inland fisheries; aquaculture
   - Improved forestry production in humid and arid areas

2. Conservation and better use of the environment
   - Appraisal of resources; water resources and their management
   - Soil management and conservation; better management of vulnerable environments

3. Agricultural engineering and post-harvest technology
   - Agricultural engineering/mechanization
   - Product conservation and processing

4. Production systems
   - Crop systems; production systems

B. Medicine, health and nutrition in tropical areas

1. Medicine
   - Infectious tropical diseases: parasitic, bacterial, fungal and viral diseases
   - Non-infectious tropical diseases; genetic disorders; acquired diseases

2. Health
   - Health services: operational research, organization, management and models
   - Environmental health: water-related diseases
   - Traditional medicine: medicinal plants

3. Nutrition
   - Nutritional deficiencies
   - Impact of agricultural, food and socio-economic strategies on nutrition
   - Relationships between production, storage systems, food habits and health of the population
   - Bio-availability of nutrients.

For the STD-3, 111 million ECUs had been earmarked, including 8 million ECUs for expenditure on staff and administration. The indicative breakdown of funds available for research and accompanying measures was 71.43 million ECUs for agriculture and 38.46 million ECUs for medicine, health and nutrition, i.e. a total of 109.89 million ECUs. The remaining 1.11 million ECUs represented the STD-3 contribution to the centralized scheme for the dissemination (publications, bulletins, seminars, audiovisual resources, etc.) and exploitation (legal protection, technology transfer, market research, pilot projects, partnerships) of the results of the EC research (CEC, 1991).

All types of research (basic, applied, strategic or appropriate) were eligible under STD-3. The selection criteria included the scientific quality of the applicant (researcher and institution) and of the research project; the inclusion of at least two teams from different Member States and one or more teams from developing countries; the projects' end objective, within the five strategic areas and their contribution to strengthening the scientific potential of the developing countries involved; the consistency with the social and economic problems in the developing countries and with the strategies currently implemented to resolve them; the regional impact of the planned solutions; and the complementarity with other EC research-and-development schemes and with the bilateral and/or multilateral activities of Member States (CEC, 1991).

The Commission contributions to research and development were always up to a maximum level of 50% of total research costs, the other 50% being provided by the scientific institution carrying out the research. In the case of universities and higher-education institutes and all institutions in developing countries, the Commission contribution could reach 100% of the marginal costs of a research project (additional costs related to project implementation). The purchase of durable equipment for the participating developing countries might be 100% financed (CEC, 1991).

The most relevant work produced by STD was submitted to other contractors and scientists in the field, in order to increase the focus of research activities on the problems of developing countries, exchange information, equipment and scientific staff and define future research activities. If necessary, research projects could include trips, training courses, theses, post-doctoral studies, research seminars, etc., particularly in the South-North direction. In the case of the young researchers from developing countries involved in research contracts, STD-3 was taking steps to ensure that they maintained links with their original research organization and keep open the possibility of going back (CEC 1991).

STD-3 offered the developing countries' researchers the opportunity to monitor high-level research on the tropics conducted in the European Union. Scientific networks could maintain and reinforce existing links, rapidly disseminating information to specialists and identifying priorities and projects in their fields (CEC, 1991). Interaction was promoted between STD-3 and programmes like

ECLAIR and FLAIR since the latter two were dealing with similar technologies and fields of application (agriculture and food processing). Particularly in agricultural biotechnologies research options for a better integration of these two programmes existed, and all these activities were conceived and managed by the same Directorate-General of the Commission (DG XII: Science, Research and Development) [Bijman, 1990].

Under STD-3, a project had been accepted for increasing knowledge on the physiology of coconut tissues grown *in vitro*, so as to master somatic embryogenesis in this particularly recalcitrant species for *in-vitro* regeneration. The three-year project (1995–1997) involved the Department of Perennial Crops of the French Centre for International Co-operation in Agricultural Research for Development (CIRAD-CP), the French Scientific Research Institute for Development in Cooperation (ORSTOM), Wye College in the United Kingdom, the University of Hanover (Laboratory of Genetic Markers) in Germany, the Centre of Scientific Reseach in Yucatan, Mexico, the Philippine Coconut Authority and the Forestry Institute (Station for Coconut Breeding at Port-Bouët) in Côte d'Ivoire. The participating institutions designated the CIRAD-ORSTOM team as the project co-ordinator (*CIRAD Information*, no. 44, 13 September 1994, p. 7). The first project meeting was held at the ORSTOM Centre in Montpellier from 6 to 10 March 1995.

The third international workshop on *Phytomonas* was also held in Montpellier from 15 to 17 May 1995. The CIRAD Virology Research Unit, organizer of the workshop, welcomed 25 participants from ten countries (Argentina, Brazil, Colombia, Venezuela, Belgium, France, Germany, Russia, Spain and United Kingdom), as well as the researchers involved in the project on plant trypanosomes (carried out under the STD-3) and specialists of both human and animal trypanosomiases.

In addition to the three STD programmes implemented between 1983 and 1994, the European Union had initiated two other scientific development co-operation programmes with developing countries over the period 1991–1996. The International Scientific Cooperation (ISC) programme aimed at enabling scientists from Latin America, Asia and Mediterranean countries to participate in joint research activities with European laboratories. One of these activities was the setting up of the China-European Commission Biotechnology Centre in Beijing, which aimed to improve information exchange on biotechnological research within China, and between China and the European Union. Additionally, it monitored the biotechnology research-and-development activities of STD-3 and ISC in China. The other programme, AVICENNE, promoted scientific and technological co-operation with the Maghreb countries and the countries of the Mediterranean basin; it focused on research on waste-water treatment, basic health care and renewable energy sources (Heissler, 1996*a*).

Since 1994, the European Union had been implementing its Fourth Framework Programme on Research and Development, of which the Cooperation with Third Countries and International Organisations (INCO) formed part. The aim of this $575 million initiative was to strengthen the Union's scientific and technological base and to support the implementation of other Community policies, such as development aid policy. The INCO aimed to concentrate the Union's research-and-development co-operation activities with all Third countries. The financial breakdown of INCO programmes was: 43% for scientific and technological co-operation with developing countries (INCO-DC); 43% for co-operation with the countries of Central and Eastern Europe and with the New Independent States of the former Soviet Union; 8.5% for the co-operation with other fora; and 5.5% for co-operation with non-European Third Countries.

The INCO-DC (Scientific and Technological Cooperation with the Developing Countries) programme aimed to stimulate the generation of knowledge and innovative and appropriate technologies to solve specific problems in a developing region. Additionally, it was expected to enable the European scientific community to maintain and improve excellence in the scientific areas that were relevant to developing countries, in particular environment, agriculture and health. In contrast to the STD programmes, the INCO-DC included the sustainable management of renewable resources and gave explicit priority to regional problems and regional co-operation. The INCO-DC $247 million for 1995–1998 was distributed as follows: 30% for human health, 30% for sustainable management of renewable natural resources, 30% for sustainable improvement of agricultural and agro-industrial production, and 10% for other activities. Opened to all natural persons and national and regional organizations (such as corporations, universities and research institutes) in developing countries, the INCO-DC projects involved partners from at least two different European Union member States and one partner from a developing country. As the overall aim of the programme was to strengthen regional co-operation in the South, there was a strong preference for projects including two or more partners from different developing countries in the same region. The EC contribution was limited to 50% of the project costs. Another form of co-operation between research teams in the European Union and those of developing countries was through concerted actions, where the EC reimbursed co-ordination costs, but not the project costs (Heissler, 1996*a*).

As a result of the first INCO-DC call for proposals in March 1995, 1,164 proposals had been evaluated. In March 1996, the second call for proposals was published in the *Official Journal of the European Communities* as well as on Internet. Particular emphasis was laid on projects which contributed significantly to the solution of problems relevant to more than one developing country. Additional criteria included the estimated impact on sustainable development and the extent to which interdisciplinary approaches were integrated (Heissler, 1996*a*).

The INCO-DC programme did not only address biotechnology applications in the agricultural/agro-industrial sector, but also included socio-economic research such as policy and technology assessment studies, especially with respect to environmental issues. The goal of fostering North-South and South-South co-operation was a commendable ambition but it was perhaps difficult to achieve considereing the small INCO-DC budget. Other programmes in related areas of the Fourth Framework, for instance, had a budget eight times as high (Heissler, 1996*a*).

Project for the establishment of a European Plant Biotechnology Institute for Protection and Valorization of Tropical Forests

The Institute would specialize in the use of molecular and cell biology tools to solve some of the problems encountered in protecting and valorizing tropical forests[8] (see p. 604). It would be integrated into multidisciplinary forest research already going on both in French Guyana (Silvolab, see further) and in all other European centres working on tropical forest ecology. It would function as the out-post where European tropical forest specialists met with molecular biologists to devise ways of spreading knowledge indispensable for sustainable forest management and reforestation. By the same token, research teams in Brazil, Venezuela and other Amazonian countries would make an important input to research subjects and approaches. The presence of a European institute in French Guyana would facilitate technology transfer to Latin American countries.

Although crop species could be engineered for greater resistance to diseases and pests, natural biological diversity was the departure point for picking up the relevant genes. Furthermore there was growing interest among agrochemical, pharmaceutical, biotechnology and other companies to explore natural resources in the search for new medicines, natural pesticides, micro-organisms, food sources, etc. Because natural product-based drug and agrochemical research depended on taxonomy and the reliable supply of biotic material, biological diversity prospecting was best conducted in tandem with biological diversity inventories. This was a good example of how conservation and economic profit could be reconciled and the only way of dispelling developing countries' concern about the conservation and proper use of their natural resources.

Taxonomy of tropical species was far from a *fait accompli*. Often, there were different names for the same species; several species formed complexes of species crossing naturally among each other. While isozyme markers were already an improvement for solving taxonomic problems, they had one important disadvantage: the few genes that could be monitored might not be representative of the whole genome. The existing techniques for DNA sequence analysis were RFLP (restriction fragment length polymorphism), RAPD (random amplified polymorphic DNA), AFLP (amplified fragment length polymorphism), study of the chloroplast genome and ribosomal DNA, and the use of hypervariable markers. All of these had their own specific applications and had been used successfully, but AFLP was the most advanced in terms of reliability. It could be used for DNA fingerprinting and for detecting polymorphisms in genomic DNA, thus revealing genetic differences between individuals. It could be applied to plants and trees, but also to symbiotic and pathogenic micro-organisms (diagnosis).

Up to now, trees with a commercial value (e.g. for timber production) had simply been plucked from forests. Often, whole regions were felled to obtain only a few trees. Even when only the targeted trees were felled, much more forest was destroyed in the process (surrounding area, roads to reach the tree); the latest software programmes were capable of calculating the least harmful tract. It would be a giant step forward if as yet non-commercialized woody species presently being destroyed could be valorized.

For a number of tree species, simple logging was becoming less and less economically viable, due to genetic erosion. Years of injudicious felling had almost completely depleted the exploitation zones of high-quality trees. It had thus become necessary to identify the remaining high-quality trees for use in breeding programmes. Subsequently, they could be used to reforest devastated regions or introduced in peripheral areas of the Amazon forest to form a buffer zone. This was true not only for timber trees but also for trees from which a product was harvested (such as latex and Brazil nuts). By taking into account some conditions of understorey growth, plantations would take over some of the functions of a natural forest (such as nutrient recycling, water cycling and erosion control). These so-called forest analogs might have, for example, a canopy of cacao trees and a diverse understorey of maize, bananas, plantains and other crops. Through agroforestry, these plantations could gain in value both environmentally and economically.

It was amazing that very little was known about the genetic resources and ecological behaviour of even the most commercially important tropical hardwoods, such as mahogany and teak. It should be borne in mind, however, that, even using AFLP, it would not be possible to obtain commercial tree varieties within less than 5 years. In many cases, several crossings would be required and, before the variety could be commercialized, its characteristics would still have to be evaluated in field tests in the same way as other crop species. Compared to conventional breeding, however, decades could be gained.

AFLP mapping allowed the linkage of an interesting trait to a molecular marker which could then be monitored at the seedling stage using tiny amounts of plant material. Before marker-assisted breeding could be performed, markers would need to be isolated. Those traits of interest to breeders (such as disease resistance, genetic and physiological mechanisms influencing adaptation to environmental stress, growth rate, straightness of the trunk, rooting ability, bark thickness, wood specific gravity) were often oligogenic (so-called Quantitative Trait Loci or QTLs). Using the AFLP technique, it was relatively easy to identify linked markers, which could subsequently be followed during breeding in order to obtain the best combinations.

Another, more direct, approach for crop improvement was genetic engineering. Up to now, it had been limited to monogenic traits. Furthermore, it was likely that the transformation procedure would prove a bottleneck for recalcitrant species like (tropical) trees. However, using a variety of DNA transfer techniques and target tissues, all trees should be virtually transformable. Tree species such as poplar, walnut, apple, eucalypt, papaya and *Casuarina* had already been stably transformed. Although genetic engineering of tropical trees would not produce short-term results, it was a potentially powerful tool.

Non-tree tropical forest species might also be of interest, e.g. medicinal plants or plants providing a source of pesticides; harvesting these plants might prove too laborious and the chemical synthesis of the compound highly intricate. This situation could be remedied by cultivating and genetically improving the plants using the above-mentioned molecular approaches. Alternatively, the gene(s) responsible for the biosynthesis of the compound could be isolated and introduced into plants for overexpression in their seeds (molecular farming), or into a bacterium or yeast, which could then be grown in fermenters. In this way, the envisaged compound could be produced in copious amounts, without affecting the forest.

Over the last decade, a considerable amount of research had been compiled on mycorrhiza, although it concentrated mainly on the Northern hemisphere, temperate regions and agricultural ecosystems. Very little had been done on disturbed and natural ecosystems of the tropics. A major drawback was the lack of a proper taxonomy. The unravelling of the complex interaction of the plant root with different mycorrhizal fungi and other micro-organisms in the rhizosphere was a demanding task when based only on morphological characterization. By using molecular markers, however, soil samples could easily be probed for the micro-organisms present; this would enable the dynamics of root colonization by fungi and bacteria to be studied in different circumstances. Ultimately, sufficient knowledge of the best conditions and combinations for plant root inoculation and/or soil treatment would be obtained. This would be important not only for plantations and agroforestry, but also for reforestation.

AFLP markers could be used to identify the symbionts and to study intraspecific variability. Mechanisms concerning host specificity, recognition and differentiation of symbiotic structures can be studied at the molecular level. In the case of mycorrhiza, interesting genes could be isolated and utilized for transforming trees.

The following topics had been proposed for the Institute's research programme:

– isolation of molecular markers linked to interesting traits and QTLs (higher yield, faster growth, improved rooting, better wood quality, stress tolerance) in order to facilitate marker-assisted breeding of:

• (genetically-eroded) timber trees;

• pioneering trees for reforestation (which needed to be stress- and predator-resistant, and preferably deep-rooting);

• multipurpose trees and shrubs for agroforestry;

• non-tree forest species producing useful secondary metabolites (higher production of the interesting compound, stress tolerance);

– study of intraspecific variability of economically and environmentally interesting species for stable reintroduction in reforestation programmes;

– identification of leguminous plants and their nitrogen-fixing bacteria for use in intercropping with trees; study of plant/symbiont interaction;

– identification of mycorrhiza, their mycorrhization helper bacteria and possibly other beneficial soil micro-organisms, plus the fostering of their use (in combination with leguminous trees) for biological restructuring of soils devastated through slash and burn; study of plant/symbiont interaction;

– identification of tropical fruit trees to develop plantations on the edge of the Amazon forest;

– genetic engineering for quality improvement (isolation of new genes, establishment of transformation protocols);

– *in-situ* germplasm conservation of economically important tropical crop species;

– introduction of genes of specific plant species encoding biosynthesis of secondary metabolites in micro-organisms for mass production.

Fifteen species were selected which shared an economical and/or ecological importance and contrasting biological properties (reproductive biology, seed and pollen dispersal, spatial distribution). For each species, the level of diversity was estimated by using molecular markers (isozymes). One person was capable of analyzing 400 samples per week. Installation of a PCR (polymerase chain reaction) machine would make it possible to use DNA markers. Specific primers for chloroplast DNA could be used as universal primers to study gene diversion in tropical plants and soil micro-organisms, including mycorrhiza. The dynamics of diversity would be examined (gene fluxes, population and species dynamics). Genetic engineering and molecular biology-assisted tree breeding would be left for a later stage.

For each research group on biological diversity and microbiology, a team was foreseen comprising: one senior scientist, one post-doctoral fellow, two PhD. students and 2 technicians. The other research groups (including genetic engineering) would start with one senior scientist, one post-doctoral fellow, 1 PhD. student and 1 technician. A number of Third World students would be trained in each laboratory.

The proposed Institute being European, France and other European Union Member States were expected to make a substantial scientific contribution. France had set up a Groupement d'intérêt scientifique (SILVOLAB, with laboratories in Cayenne and Kourou), which included national research organizations in French Guyana to study the functioning and development of tropical rain forest ecosystems. SILVOLAB was a multidisciplinary group composed of 17 researchers divided into five teams including botanists, ecologists, physiologists, microbiologists, geneticists and agronomists, who were studying the functioning and management of tropical humid forest ecosystems. The French participating organizations in SILVOLAB were the CIRAD (Centre for International Co-operation in Agricultural Research for Development), ENGREF (National School for Rural Engineering and Forestry), INRA (National Institute for Agricultural Research), ORSTOM (French Scientific Research Institute for Development in Cooperation), ONF (National Forestry Office), CNRS (National Centre for Scientific Research), the Museum of Natural History and University of the Antilles in French Guyana[9] (see p. 604).

The Institute's objective was to define a common research programme, develop scientific collaboration with both Latin American neighbours and European laboratories, and make know-how in French Guyana accessible to a greater number. The Laboratory of Genetics (University of Ghent, Belgium) intended to co-operate, as its staff of 130 was working on basic plant molecular biology and using AFLP technology to map the genome of several plant species, among them *Petunia* and *Arabidopsis*. In the United Kingdom, the John Innes Institute in Norwich was part of a consortium of four affiliated laboratories carrying out fundamental and applied research relevant to agriculture, horticulture and other industries. It also provided training for researchers in genetics, molecular biology, biochemistry and cell biology.

In French Guyana, in the neighbourhood of Kourou, the Amazonian forest had been relatively undisturbed. Furthermore, being a European territory, French Guyana was the only place where the European Union could invest in tropical forestry research. The establishment of a Plant Biotechnology Institute for Protection and Valorization of Tropical Forests fitted with the European Union policy of a strong commitment to tropical forest conservation. A major importer of tropical timber products, the Union was already involved in the Pilot Programme for the Conservation of Brazilian Tropical Forests (in co-operation with the Brazilian Government and the World Bank) and part of a European Tropical Forest Research Network.

Regarding funding sources, the Global Environment Facility (GEF) set up after the United Nations Conference on Environment and Development could be tapped, as could France. In the European Union, the following Directorates-General could provide funding: DG I, which dealt with forestry development; DGX II, in charge of human resources and mobility grants to large institutions; and DG XVI, which supported the different political regions of the European Union (upon request by the Conseil général de la Guyane, 2 million ECUs was to go toward establishing the Institute).

Funding could come from the European Union's Large-Scale Facilities (LSF) programme. Rather than financing projects or capital, the LSF programme restricted itself to facilitating access by European scientists to specific research facilities outside their home country but located within Europe. One of the criteria imposed on the facility was an adequate infrastructure for accepting international researchers. As SILVOLAB could be considered an LSF, the programme might cover 15% to 20% of SILVOLAB's annual operating costs to enable it to invest the savings in improving researchers' access to the facility; to qualify for the programme, each facility was bound to guarantee access to 10–15 users per year.

Another European Union programme, the Training and Mobility of Researchers Networks Activity, could also make a financial contribution; its purpose was to encourage research teams from a number of countries to work together on high-quality joint research projects and to promote the training and mobility of researchers, particularly young post-doctoral fellows. Networks normally had around ten partners, the minimum being five. One to two million ECUs could be provided for a period of three to four years, with an average of 50,000–80,000 ECUs per partner per year. A researcher could work, for instance, one year in French Guyana and another year in a European laboratory.

Notes

1 In 1995, Calgene Inc. had to reschedule the introduction of its FLAVR/SAVR tomato throughout the U.S. market, because of the bruising and battering suffered by its transgenic tomatoes during shipping. The company had to overhaul its packing methods before distributing the tomato.

2 The London-based European Agency for the Evaluation of Medical Products had granted pan-European market authorization to: recombinant Gonal F, a fertility drug for women manufactured by the Italian-Swiss company Ares-Serono (approval in October 1995); Taxotère, made by Rhône-Poulenc Rorer SA and Betaferon (recombinant interferon beta-1b) by Schering AG, Pharma (*European BioNews,* SAGB, 8, March 1996).

3 At the VIIth Industrial Biotechnology Conference held in Montreal from 4 to 6 December 1995, Calder of Mycogen Corp. (San Diego, California) pointed out that 85% of the calories ingested by humans came from 20 crop species and that 45% came from only rice and wheat. As the world's population would increase from 5 billion in 1995 to 10 billion in the next forty years, more calories had to be produced during that period than had been produced since the beginning of agriculture 10,000 years ago. Calder stated that, in agriculture over time, there had been four crucial developments:
  - domestication of plants and animals;
  - mechanization;
  - plant and animal breeding; and
  - chemistry (e.g. development of pesticides and fertilizers).
He also stated that nowadays the major issue regarding public acceptance of products was the lack of a good regulatory system in place that ensured:
  - the safety of the product;
  - the efficacy of the product; and
  - the quality of the product.
He emphasized that a regulatory system should regulate the product, not the process. Public acceptance of agricultural products was under a lot more scrutiny than public acceptance of human health care products. Most people saw the benefit of a cure for cancer, but were less convinced of the need for a new tomato that would rot more slowly. There was not the same urgency.

4 Since its creation in 1986 and up to the end of 1996, the Biomolecular Engineering Commission had reviewed 450 files, including 376 concerning requests for field trials of transgenic plants.

5 The Cambridge-based Agricultural Genetics Company in the United Kingdom had won the Queen's Award for Environmental Achievement in conjunction with the state-backed Horticultural Research International, for its development of nematode worms acting as natural pesticides. The AGC and HRI had identified strains of the tiny worms that targeted particular pests, then developed means of large-scale production. Of the two commercialized strains, one tackled glasshouse sciarids and the other vine weevils. When the nematodes, sold in packs of 50 million juveniles, were applied to soil around the plants, they targeted insect larvae, which were killed by means of bacteria inside the worms (*European BioNews,* SAGB, 4, September 1993).

6 Zeneca plc's pretax profit in 1996 showed a 15% increase over 1995 to £1,011 million, while annual turnover rose 9% to £5,363 million. Revenue at the

flagship pharmaceutical division rose about 14%, but heavy marketing expenses stemming from launches of several new drugs held the drug division profit rise to about 9% (*The Wall Street Journal Europe*, 29 January 1997, p.3). On 11 March 1997, Zeneca plc obtained the authorization from the British authorities to commercialize its new anti-migraine drug, Zomig, considered a strong competitor to Glaxo plc's similar drug, Imigran.

Advanta was the name of the new company resulting from the merging of Zeneca Seeds plc and Vander-Have, which were the seed subsidiaries of Zeneca plc and the Dutch sugar co-operative Suiker Unie, respectively. With headquarters in the Netherlands (Kappelle) and an annual turnover of about $500 million in 1996, Advanta was ranked among the world's five leading seed corporations (in *Biofutur*, no. 164, February 1997, p. 39).

7 In the USA, on 7 October 1996, Rifkin called for a world-wide boycott of genetically-engineered soybeans and maize. Rifkin's Foundation on Economic Trends in conjunction with the National Family Farm Coalition launched the boycott at a news conference in Washington, D.C., and Chicago. Also at the Washington news conference, Kroener of EuroCommerce, an association of 81 trade associations representing wholesalers and retailers from 20 European countries, called for labelling of genetically-engineered soybeans and maize. Reuters reported that Kroener warned 'that several major members of EuroCommerce would not buy U.S. soybeans without assurance they would not receive genetically-altered ones'.

In response the Institute of Food Technologists (IFT, founded in 1939 as a non-profit making society with 28,000 members working in food science, technology and related professions in industry, academia and government) issued the following press release:

The IFT voiced concern today over the Foundation on Economic Trends' (FET) launching of a world-wide boycott of genetically-engineered soybeans and maize produced in the USA. IFT does not give merit to FET President Jeremy Rifkin's allegation of environmental and health risks associated with gene-spliced soybeans and maize. Rather, IFT asserts that no scientific evidence of such hazards has been found with genetically-engineered plants and that Rifkin's call for labelling of modified U.S. crops in unnecessary to ensure consumers' safety. There is no evidence that genetic transfers between unrelated organisms pose hazards that are different from those encountered with any new plant or animal variety. The most highly publicized method of genetic engineering is recombinant DNA (rDNA) technology, which allows plant breeders to take advantage of genetic sources outside of traditional cross breeding and selection methods. This technology is the most advanced and precise method available to scientists today.

Careful oversight of this technology and other genetic modification techniques, is provided by the U.S. Department of Agriculture, Food and Drug Administration (FDA) and Environmental Protection Agency. FDA ensures the safety of foods developed by genetic engineering through science-based risk evaluations. This requires developers of foods from modified plants to address whether known allergens have been transferred to the modified product; to demonstrate that the new food does not contain increased levels of previously known toxic substances or new hazardous substances; and that the nutritional value of the product has not been compromised.

Plants produced by rDNA technology, such as soybeans and maize, must meet exactly the same safety standards as unmodified plants or those genetically engineered by another method. In addition to complying with U.S. food safety standards, genetic-engineering technologies in agriculture are compatible with conservation and protection of the environment, as well as with sustainable methods of agricultural production. Contrary to Rifkin's allegations, the IFT believes that rDNA technology will enhance public health and environmental protection by:

- increasing biological resistance to specific pests and diseases, thereby decreasing the need for synthetic chemical pesticides;
- improving plant adaptability to harsh growing conditions, such as drought, salinity and temperature extremes;
- augmenting plant tolerance to more environmentally safe herbicides that discourage weeds but leave the desired plant unaffected without harming the environment;
- controlling more desirable nutritional or functional plant traits such as altered fatty acid content or lower water content;
- increasing yields to meet expanding world food needs.

8   There were a few similar projects in the world, all concerning tropical biological diversity. One was carried out by the Smithsonian Institution in Panama, another located in Malaysia was funded by Canada. The FAO supported a third project, in addition to studies on plots in five different countries (among them The Philippines and Indonesia), in order to monitor and compare the dynamics of biological diversity.

9   French Guyana's forest, like many rainforests, is rich in flora, with several hundreds of tree species per square kilometre. French Guyana's economic future seemed inextricably linked to its forest: 9 million hectares, 8 million of which were dense forest. Indeed, timber was the third most exploited natural resource in this French Overseas Department, after fish and shrimps, and gold mines. However, timber exports had seldom risen above 100,000 m³, or the equivalent of the output of one African lumber company (CIRAD, 1994).

There were many tree varieties, but widely dispersed. No single variety dominated, unlike the okoumé in Gabon, or the sipo in Côte d'Ivoire. Four or five species at most could be considered sufficiently prevalent for industrial exploitation by today's standards. For a long time, French Guyana's forests had been exploited solely for rosewood, essential oils and for balata and its gum; nowadays, other more productive species were being exploited. *Dicorynia guianensis* is a beautiful, hard and heavy wood which could be used, like the oak of temperate climates, for flooring, staircases, banisters, etc. Salmon-coloured *Ocotea rubra* could be substituted for mahogany. The violet *Peltogyne venosa* and the red or yellow *Andira coriacea* were used in cabinet making. *Qualea* sp., although devoid of any aesthetic qualities, is a sound wood for building, and accounted for 25% of production by the mid-1990s. *Goupia glabra* is used mainly for construction frames. Finally, the most abundant wood of the French Guianese forest, *Eperua falcata*, is used mainly for the manufacture of shingle boards for the home market (CIRAD, 1994).

Only about 150,000 hectares of forest along the coast were being exploited by the late-1980s. Annual production was 40,000 m³ of sawn timber per year (equivalent to 100,000 m³ of raw timber), 30% of which was exported mainly to the West Indies. However, since 1988, Guianese industries had met with tough and growing competition from Brazil. The arrival of Brazilian wood in the West Indies had caused Guianese exports to tumble to 2,000 m³ of sawn timber. At first, the local market had grown, with the building of the hydro-electric dam at Petit-Saut and the development of the space station in Kourou, thus compensating for the fall in exports. But the boom had been ephemeral, these major projects being completed in 1992. French Guyana was also hit by economic recession. In 1995, timber industries were in a disastrous state: industry in 1993 only produced 60,000 m³ of raw timber and many businesses had closed down (CIRAD, 1994).

To cope with this crisis, the lumberers' union, real estate companies and the government set up a regional economic commission on construction and public works, with the CIRAD as adviser. The commission's objective was to save the timber industries, through giving new impetus to exports (by adapting harbour structures to the timber trade, by building storage facilities and a terminal for wood containers) and by reducing the high freight tariffs so as to make Guianese wood more competitive on the regional and world markets (CIRAD, 1994).

European co-operation institutions for research and development in the tropics

France

NATIONAL INSTITUTE FOR AGRICULTURAL RESEARCH

When the French National Institute for Agricultural Research (INRA) was created in 1946, its goal was to reach food self-sufficiency for France. This was achieved rather quickly and in 1996–1997 France was the world's second-biggest exporter of raw and processed agricultural products. After having given priority to the increase in yields, productivity improvement was the new priority; this was being achieved through reducing the costs of production systems which had become very sophisticated or even artificial. Farmers were trying to overcome the vagaries of weather and pests in order to obtain a produce in all safety throughout the year. For this purpose, it was necessary to control pests and pathogens, as well as to mitigate the impact of weather and soil changes. Consumers, for their part, lost contact with nature; they ignored fruit and vegetable seasons; product standardization was associated with that of social life.

The INRA, with an annual budget of approximately $617 million (1995), of which $176 million were allocated to research programmes, equipment and computational means, and a total staff of 8,615 employees (including 3,852 researchers), comprised 260 research units, 80 experimental units and technological platforms. The INRA also owned 12,000 hectares of experimental lands, farms or stations throughout France and its Overseas Departments; 6,000 cattle head, 16,000 sheep, 2,000 goats and 8,000 swine; and 500,000 plant varieties or crop species (Augereau, 1996).

In 1946, the INRA received the mandate to extend maize cultivation to the whole French territory. Following the example of their American colleagues who, under the Marshall Plan, had introduced hybrid maize in the U.S. South West, they decided to develop their own hybrid varieties (Grall, 1996).

One of the French researchers discovered at that time in his father's garden in Anglès (Tarn Department, in the South West of France) maize plants which grew from the seeds supplied by a livestock breeder who sowed a plot of maize fodder every year. These seeds were bought at the grocer's without any indication of provenance nor variety. Due to the altitude, this maize did not produce ears, except in one occasion. The farmer sowed the seeds and repeated the operation for several consecutive years, thus obtaining a population with low productivity, best cold-resistant and early-maturing. The researcher responsible for the INRA Laboratory of Crop Improvement at Versailles, near Paris, sowed the seeds in 1947 and obtained the well-known F7 and F2 lines which were crossed with American lines and gave birth to the early-maturing maize varieties, grown from North America to Mandchuria (Grall, 1996).

As in the USA, maize hybridization had spurred a very successful industry in France, which was the world's second-biggest seed producer and the second market for maize seeds. The agro-industrial corporations used the income derived from maize seed production to diversify their activities and develop other crop species, like sunflower and oilseed rape. INRA contribution to the breeding of highly-performing varieties had been crucial since the early 1980s and resulted in a profound change in the French agricultural landscape and livestock husbandry.

The INRA, in addition to the creation of new varieties, was involved in their commercialization through its subsidiary, Agri-Obtentions, founded in 1983. Since then, the relations between public research (INRA insuring 90% of this research) and corporations having various legal and financial frameworks were characterized by ups and downs (Grall, 1996).

During the 1980s, the INRA and main commercial groups established the so-called 'groups of economic interest' (GIE) involved each one in one or several crop species: protein and oil-seed species, sugar-beet, straw cereals, soybeans, etc. This partnership policy strengthened companies that had been weakened by lack of investment (generated by family capital) into research and development, as well as by low royalties cashed from non-hybrid crops like wheat (Grall, 1996).

Since then, the INRA had oriented its research toward more basic issues, for instance in biotechnologies which could accelerate breeding methods, identify and patent genes coding for desired traits, i.e. contribute to develop new plants for the next millenium[1] (see p. 689). These plants would respond to the needs and demands by consumers and industrialists, and they would be custom-made (Grall, 1996).

Regarding the quality, cost and health of foodstuffs, INRA researchers predicted that, thanks to the appropriate blending of food technology, plant and animal genetics, as well as tasting knowledge and know-how, these foodstuffs should be more accessible to a wider range of people, less costly and better balanced from a nutritional viewpoint.

The variety of food could be increased through the observation of other cultures or civilizations. For instance, when the Europeans consumed around forty vegetables, the Chinese knew how to cook some 120. According to the researcher responsible for the improvement of vegetables at the INRA research station in Avignon, a lot could be learnt from Asia in this respect. In fact, in addition to the Italian broccoli which appeared on the French tables in the mid-1970s, other vegetables, particularly from the cabbage family, would be consumed due to their tasting and/or nutritional qualities. However, one should not underestimate the variations in consumers' habits which might result in the abandonment of a fruit or a vegetable after enthusiastic adoption. For instance, French consumers rejected the white egg-plant, which nevertheless tasted better, as well as the nashi, an intermediate fruit between the apple and pear (Augereau, 1996).

One of the main efforts made by the INRA was therefore to improve the shelf-life of fruits and vegetables. This was a need expressed by the wholesale dealers and the producers who wanted to reduce wastage, and by the housekeeper who wished to keep its purchased goods as long as possible in the refrigerator. But this policy was not deprived of drawbacks. For instance, in 1991, Israeli geneticists had been able to commercialize a tomato variety with a longer shelf-life (one week), which made the supermarket owners happy, but it lacked aroma and flavour, due to the inhibition of ethylene synthesis following the introduction (by conventional breeding and not by genetic engineering) of the gene that slowed down the ripening process. Ethylene synthesis was necessary to the development of tomato aroma and flavour (Augereau, 1996).

With respect to animal products, research conducted in the 1980s concerned the conditions of slaughtering domestic animals, the freezing of carcasses and electrical stimulation to transform muscle into meat. The current problem was that associated with meat maturation, which involved a series of enzymatic processes giving the final product its tenderness. It was demonstrated that meat quality depended on the psychological status of the animal when slaughtered: excessive stress reduced the quality of meat and favoured its invasion by micro-organisms; it also depended on the capacity to control the biological variability of the animals (Augereau, 1996).

The INRA had financed a three-year programme (1993–1995: $2 million), called Matural, to improve the ripening of fruits and vegetables, the development of cheese aromas, as well as meat tenderness. INRA researchers aimed to develop tools which, at the slaughterhouse, would enable to screen livestock and measure, using physical probes, certain parameters that would predict how meat quality would evolve. These tools had been developed but they were not yet fully utilized by industry. It was, however, generally agreed that a minimum meat tenderness could be achieved, while the difficulties linked to biological diversity remained to be overcome (Augereau, 1996).

This was not the case in the dairy industry which had adopted the results generated by research laboratories and which could therefore offer standardized products to customers from a wide range of raw materials. The task was probably easier, because it was possible to crack and separate the various milk components, and then associate them to meet the demand. Current research was being conducted on the fractioning, manipulation of these components and microfloras involved in the ripening of the final products, in order to improve their texture and aroma (Augereau, 1996).

FRENCH SCIENTIFIC RESEARCH INSTITUTE FOR DEVELOPMENT IN COOPERATION

The Institut français de recherche scientifique pour le développement en coopération (ORSTOM, French Scientific Research Institute for Development in Cooperation) was a public establishment of a scientific and technological nature, placed both under the Ministry for Science and the Ministry for Co-operation. With an annual budget of 1 billion French francs and 2,600 staff, including 1,500 scientists, technicians and engineers, the ORSTOM was carrying out research on tropical and subtropical environments through facilities set up in about 40 countries. Of the 1,500 scientists, technicians and engineers, 600 were French citizens living in Africa, Latin America and the Caribbean, and Asia and the Pacific; they were working in research institutions of developing countries (national, regional or international institutions), or in the ORSTOM's facilities; 500 were technicians from developing countries;

and about 100 were foreign scientists contracted by ORSTOM to work on its programmes.

Although the 1997 budget was decreased to respond to the French Government's decision to drastically reduce the State's deficits, the construction of two units was launched: a Centre for the Study of Micro-organism Polymorphism (CEPM) and a Laboratory of Tropical Plant Genetics (GENTROP).

In 1997, as decided by the French International Committee for Scientific Research, 20% of the funds devoted to research activities were allocated to strengthening collaboration with other research partners. This decision implied for the ORSTOM to associate several research institutions and universities to most of ORSTOM major programmes. Consequently, the latter were not only reviewed and validated with respect to their relevance to the main development issues, but also to their feasibility and interest for the scientific community and co-operation.

The ORSTOM programme comprised four main topics:
– environment and large ecosystems;
– agriculture in vulnerable tropical environments;
– environment and health;
– people and evolving societies.

The ORSTOM's senior researchers were entrusted with the task of training young French and foreign researchers within the programmes carried out in the field, in their own laboratories or in those of either developing countries or partners in the North and the South. Some trainees benefited from research allocations, others came for short periods. Still others participated in university courses or were offered assistance in preparing dissertations.

Teams working in 42 research units implemented programmes in four pluridisciplinary departments:
– Earth, ocean, atmosphere;
– continental waters;
– environment and agriculture;
– societies, urbanization and development.

Seven scientific committees were in charge of evaluating programme results and the staff involved in their implementation; the programmes covered more than 40 scientific disciplines under the following names: geology and geophysics; hydrology and soil science; hydrobiology and oceanography; plant sciences; biological and biochemical sciences applied to humans; social sciences; engineering and communication sciences. The Scientific Council was the body in charge of orientating and assessing the Institute's scientific policy.

In each country where the ORSTOM had a facility (a centre, laboratory or research team), it was involved in a partnership, generally through agreements concluded with the host country's relevant institutions aimed at strengthening its scientific capacities. This partnership belonged to the following three categories:

– implementation of joint research programmes or activities where the ORSTOM afforded logistic support as well as information data (bibliographic data-base, HORIZON, containing more than 30,000 references, ORSTOM's Informatics Network, called Rio), and also facilitated its partners' access to both scientific and technological information, and international research networks;

– support for institutions and researchers in developing countries, through the creation of common structures (e.g. the Plant Tissue Culture Laboratory in Dakar and the Laboratory of Virology at the Faculty of Agriculture, Cairo University), the welcoming of senior researchers to ORSTOM's facilities (short-term stays and advanced training), and backstopping provided to young talented researchers during the first years of their career ('association contracts');

– training for research, associated with the programmes implemented either in the ORSTOM's laboratories (both in the North and South) or in those of its partners, thanks to research grants allocated to young researchers preparing a PhD, or to young researchers, technicians and engineers wishing to improve their knowledge and know-how.

In 1992, a total of 565 scientists from developing countries benefited from the ORSTOM's support. In the same year, the ORSTOM devoted about $3.3 million, including a contribution from the French Ministry for Co-operation, to various kinds of partnership with developing countries.

The ORSTOM laboratories involved in biotechnologies were carrying out research on:

– the genetic diversity of crop species, using molecular markers;

– transgenic plants;

– the diversity of micro-organisms, their ecology and use through biotechnology means;

– fermentations of products or by-products of tropical agriculture, with a view to obtaining nutritionally improved foodstuffs or substances of biological, pharmaceutical or industrial interest;

– waste-water and industrial effluent treatment via anaerobic fermentation (methane production);

– nitrogen-fixing symbiosis by legume and non-legume species;

– genetic study of *Plasmodium falciparum* strains;

– anti-malaria vaccine trials in Senegal.

The ORSTOM Functional Biotechnology Unit was one of the most important research units in the Department of Environment and Agriculture. More than 250 persons, including researchers and temporary workers, were involved in the Unit's activities in plant productivity and the valorization of agro-industrial products. The Unit was composed of a Laboratory of Microbiology, a Laboratory of Analytical Biochemistry and a Unit for Valorization of Scientific Results. Research work focused on three areas:

– microbiology and fermentations (liquid and solid-state fermentations, study of microbial physiology and metabolism, with a view to using by-products of tropical crop species to produce enzymes and value-added compounds, and breaking down several biodegradable polymers) based on lactic bacteria and filamentous fungi strains forming part of ORSTOM's tropical culture collection;

– physiology and biochemistry of the plant cell, with an eye to better understanding the production of economically important metabolites and influencing their regulation mechanisms;

– technical optimization of production processes (in solid-state fermentation, analysis of produced metabolites by high-performance liquid chromatography, electrophoresis, low-pressure chromatography, etc.).

Among the research projects, one could cite:

– edible mushrooms (aroma production, extraction, characterization and microencapsulation);

– sugar-cane bagasse (fungal metabolite production by different strains of fungi);

– coprah (protein enrichment with filamentous fungi, screening and identification of new strains, enzyme production by thermophilic fungi);

– coffee pulp (long conservation with lactic acid bacteria, detoxification by elimination of caffeine and polyphenols, pectinase production with *Aspergillus niger*);

– cassava (research on effective strains of lactic acid bacteria for fermentation, detoxification by these bacteria, physiology and metabolism of *Leuconostoc* cultivated on this material);

– carob (physiology of fungi capable of hydrolyzing polyphenols);

– biodegradable plastics (selection of fungal strains capable of growing on this substrate, isolation of new microbial strains from soil).

The Unit was involved in active training of young researchers, French or foreigners, in co-operation with other French research institutions and universities. It also had relations with several networks and institutions in Brazil, Colombia (CENICAFE and CENICANA), Cuba, India, Mexico, Senegal, etc.

The ORSTOM Laboratory of Microbiology of Anaerobes in Marseille had isolated a new bacterium which could produce L(+) lactic acid by fermentation from palm wine, a local beverage made from palm sap in Africa. L(+) lactic acid is the only lactic acid that could be assimilated by humans and animals; it also had a wide range of applications in industry: anti-acid, aroma and flavour enhancer, texture-improving factor in the food industry; antiseptic in pharmacy and cosmetic production; manufacture of biodegradable plastics. In 1996, world production of lactic acid amounted to 45,000 tonnes and was the result of chemical synthesis and/or fermentation of sugar-rich substrates by bacteria or fungi.

Bacterial strains usually grown by industrialists to produce lactic acid through fermentation needed complex media which raised technical problems, e.g. contamination of the bioreactors and increased production costs. Fungi used for the same purpose had other drawbacks like clogging of filters. The isolation by ORSTOM researchers of the bacterium, called *Bacillus thermoamylovorans*, would enable overcoming some of these problems.

It had a high productivity (100g/litre) in less than 48 hours; it grew between 47 °C and 58 °C, which allowed the elimination of other micro-organisms; it had low nutrient demands, especially with regard to vitamins and nitrogen compounds, which were costly. It was found that by changing the pH, and the concentrations of sugars and nitrogen compounds, it was possible to orient the fermentation toward the production of lactic acid or a mixture of acetic acid, ethanol and formic acid, also used in industry. The bacterium could ferment a wide variety of sugars, in particular starch, glucose, fructose, lactose and sucrose. *Bacillus thermoamylovorans* was therefore considered a valuable alternative to chemical synthesis of lactic acid or to fermentation by the usual lactic acid bacteria or fungi. In developing countries, it could be utilized for the recycling of agro-industrial by-products or wastes containing starch.

Although provisionally placed in the genus *Bacillus*, the new bacterium did not produce spores. Its taxonomic denomination might be reviewed in the near future. ORSTOM researchers were trying to discover bacterial strains belonging to the same group, whose study would clarify its taxonomy and offer new vistas to industrialists interested in commercial fermentations.

The ORSTOM had been collecting wild and cultivated coffee species in Africa and the Indian Ocean and investigating the plant biology, genetics and agronomy since the mid-1960s. Between 1966 and 1987 coffee plants had been collected in Cameroon, Central Africa, Congo, Côte d'Ivoire, Ethiopia, Guinea, Kenya, Madagascar and Tanzania. About 10,000 genotypes had been gathered by geneticists, botanists and phytopathologists not only from ORSTOM, but also from the FAO, the International Board for Plant Genetic Resources, the French Centre for International Co-operation in Agricultural Research for Development (CIRAD) and the French Museum of Natural History.

Conservation of coffee genotypes was distributed between three countries:

– Côte d'Ivoire, which was conserving African diploid coffees;

– Ethiopia, the country of origin of *Coffea arabica*, which was conserving these species;

– Madagascar, which was in charge of preserving coffee species of this region.

The ORSTOM was in charge of managing the existing collection at the Centre for Coffee Genetic Resources of Côte d'Ivoire jointly with the CIRAD and the host country's Forestry Institute. The collection comprised about 7,800 coffee trees belonging to about 20 species. To these natural coffees were added new plant material derived from hybridization between diploid species (55 successful crossings between 13 species), hybridization with *Coffea arabica* (*arabusta* hybrids), intraspecific crossings between groups of *Coffea canephora* of Guinean and Congolese origins, and haploids of *C. canephora* (better known as *robusta*). One thousand haploids had been obtained and transformed into 600 double haploid lines through the use of colchicine (Noirot *et al.*, 1994).

ORSTOM researchers had developed a strategy for evaluating the genetic diversity of their coffee collections. The traits observed in the field related to morphology, phenology, reproduction, ecological adaptation, diseases and pests, productivity and yield, technological value (weight of 100 seeds). In the laboratory, the ORSTOM was the first to develop an analysis of genetic polymorphism and diversity based on isoenzymes. A specialized laboratory had been set up at the Divo Station in Côte d'Ivoire by the mid-1980s, a first in West Africa. Emphasis was also placed on the biochemical compounds of the coffee berry (e.g. caffeine, theobromine, chlorogenic acids). The relevant analyses were carried out in France in collaboration with the CIRAD in Montpellier. Thereafter, the analysis of genetic diversity relied on the use of molecular markers (RFLP, RAPD, PCR).

A data-base had been set up to store observations on the field plots and their management: 62 files containing 120,000 data entries constituted the BASECAFE data-base, which could evolve so as to harbour other data types. Analysis of diversity allowed diploid and allogamous coffees to be classified into two groups:

– the West and Central Africa group comprised species with numerous flowers per node, a long fruiting cycle (nine months), a high content of caffeine and a humid-zone ecology; these species are trees;

– the East Africa group comprised species with few flowers per node, a short fruiting cycle (four months), little or no caffeine and drought-tolerance; these species are bushes (Noirot *et al.*, 1994).

The study of hybrids between different species (inter-specific crossings) had enabled the genetic structure of the subgenus *Coffea* to be elucidated. The genetic affinity of the genomes, i.e. their degree of similarity, was measured by matching chromosomes during the production of gametes and by the degree of fertility of hybrid plants. Consequently, the phenotypic classification was confirmed by genetics (Noirot *et al.*, 1994).

The inter-specific hybridization programmes of the *arabusta* type aimed to improve coffee cultivation in lowland areas. The hybrids, called *Arabusta s.l.*, were produced on a large scale (27,000 hybrids) through the crossing of *C. arabica* with artificial tetraploids of diploid coffee species. Their fertility was highly variable, depending on the species utilized (*C. canephora*: 55%, *C. congensis*: 65% and *C. liberica*: 0 to 45%). Hexaploids were obtained by treating triploid hybrids between *C. arabica* and certain diploids (*C. canephora, C. liberica, C. stenophylla, C. racemosa*) with colchicine. The presence of a high proportion of '*arabica*' genes (2/3) made them poorly adapted to low altitude. Not only that, but they showed as many fertility problems as the tetraploid hybrids (Noirot *el al.*, 1994).

Coffea arabica genetic resources had been valorized through the creation of F1 hybrids between Ethiopian lines and cultivated varieties. Heterosis or hybrid vigour was demonstrated in this way. This approach had been tested in Central America at the Tropical Agriculture Research and Training Centre (CATIE, Costa Rica) within the Co-operative Programme for the Protection and Modernization of Coffee Cultivation (PROMECAFE).

With respect to *C. canephora*, cultivated in lowland areas, the discovery of a strong heterosis among hybrids resulting from crossing Guinean and Congolese coffees was considered a research breakthrough by ORSTOM researchers. The discovery allowed the CIRAD to set up an original breeding scheme called reciprocal recurrent selection. ORSTOM researchers also developed a simple technique for the massive production of haploid plants from supernumerary embryos collected in the berries. This discovery allowed the selection of fixed lines; inter-group F1 hybrids were thus obtained easily (Noirot *et al.*, 1994).

New prospects were opened up by hybridizations between different species. Hybrids of the type *Congusta* (*C. congensis* x *C. canephora* var. *robusta*) showed adaptation to flooded zones and resistance to coffee rust; their palatability was good. ORSTOM researchers had discovered that *Coffea pseudozanguebariae* was the only African species devoid of caffeine and that *C. mouloundou* was the only diploid species which fertilized itself. Hybrids with these species were being studied (Noirot *et al.*, 1994).

Coffee genetic resources were generally conserved *in situ*. However, this means of conservation was costly and plant material remained exposed to diseases, pests and adverse climatic conditions. The ORSTOM had therefore developed an *in-vitro* coffee collection, first at Bondy near Paris, then in Montpellier. Despite the advantages offered by reduced contamination and easy exchange of germplasm, the periodicity of subculturing (every six months to a year) and maintenance costs limited the range of conserved resources. Cryoconservation in liquid nitrogen (-196 °C) was a promising technique, because it allowed plant material to be conserved over long periods in a reduced space, without loss or alteration. Efficient cryoconservation protocols had been developed for embryos of the *C. arabica*, *C. canephora* and *arabusta* hybrid (in collaboration with the CATIE). Cryoconservation had been extended to other species while using apices of *C. racemosa* and *C. sessiliflora*, and relying on a new technique called encapsulation-dehydration (Noirot *et al.*, 1994).

In the early 1990s, ORSTOM researchers started using molecular biology tools for their work on coffee genetics. The first results confirmed those obtained with morphological, cytological and biochemical data. Analysis of chloroplastic DNA sequences and their comparison improved knowledge of the phylogenetic tree of *Coffea* subgenus and enabled fingerprinting of genotypes conserved in collections and the subsequent elimination of duplicates. Cytofluorometric studies demonstrated differences in genome size at intra- and inter-specific level (Noirot *et al.*, 1994).

The following step was genetic mapping. Paillard *et al.* (1996) of ORSTOM Laboratory of Genetic Resources and Breeding of Tropical Plants (LRGAPT) in Montpellier were able to construct a molecular linkage map in coffee. This work was carried out in co-operation with the Nestlé Research Centre in Tours. The map was established on the basis of the molecular analysis of plant material developed at the

ORSTOM Coffee Genetic Station in Man, Côte d'Ivoire, where, since the early 1970s, several thousands of wild, cultivated and hybrid coffee species and varieties, collected throughout Africa, had been stored and studied. This mapping work was done for the species, *Coffea canephora*. It could be transposed to other species, especially to *Coffea arabica*, the most widely cultivated species, because of the slight genetic differentiation among *Coffea* species.

This molecular linkage map was expected to facilitate coffee breeding, which was a long process (ten to fifteen years were needed to correctly evaluate the potential of a coffee species or variety) as well costly work (because of the vast areas needed for field trials and the numerous tests indispensable for the evaluation of coffee quality). With this map researchers could identify the presence of genes of interest at an early development stage of the plant, such as those controlling the size of berries, caffein content and resistance to diseases and pests (e.g. berry anthracnosis, orange rust, nematodes). They would also be able to isolate the most interesting genotypes from the agronomic and technological viewpoints.

ORSTOM researchers were to rely on this map for implementing a programme in collaboration with Kenya's Coffee Research Foundation aimed at controlling the transfer to *Coffea arabica* of the gene for resistance to berry anthracnosis, identified in *Coffea canephora*. Co-operation was also being pursued with the Forestry Institute of Côte d'Ivoire (IDEFOR) and Costa Rica's Tropical Agriculture Research and Training Centre (CATIE).

Future work aimed to refine this first genetic map by increasing the number of markers and defining with greater precision the positions already mapped. In the longer term, ORSTOM researchers intended to use this map for genetic transformation, the markers being used as anchor points in order to isolate and modify the appropriate genes.

All coffee plantations in Central and South America, were threatened by the coffee-berry insect pest, *Hypothemenus hampei*; initially present in Kenya's highlands, this parasite had followed the routes of diffusion of coffee cultivation and migrated from Africa to South America and thereafter to Asia. Hidden in the dried berries, the insect could survive for several months and reproduce inside the fruits. Lines of the insect resistant to endosulfan, the most widely used insecticide against this parasite, had been identified in New Caledonia. Their resistance capacity was so high that they could stand doses that were 500,000 times higher than those which killed sensitive insects.

In 1989, following the multiplication of the coffee-berry insect pest on the east coast of New Caledonia, ORSTOM entomologists were requested to develop a research programme aimed at designing new control methods. This work, undertaken with New Zealand's Horticulture and Food Research Institute and the Universities of Madison and Purdue in the USA, had led to the discovery of a new mode of hereditary transmission of the gene conferring to the resistant insects an 'immunity' toward all insecticide belonging to the cyclodiene group (including endosulfan). Described as 'functional haplodiploidy' by the researchers, the mechanism of gene transmission in this insect pest was similar to that resulting from a 'true' haplodiploidy found in some insects and mammals, when the males received chromosomes only from their mother. In New Caledonia, ORSTOM entomologists observed that in the males the chromosome set received from the father genitor disappeared during cell divisions; they could therefore only transmit the mother's genetic make up to their offspring. Consequently, when a male insect received the resistance gene and mated with a female which received the same gene from both parents, the gene was transmitted to all the female offspring; if the male insect mated with a female which received the resistance gene from its mother and the sensitive gene from its father, half of the female offpsring would possess both genes, while the other half would have only the resistance gene.

In addition, endogamy being the rule among the coffee-berry insect pest, inbreeding lines developed quickly and among them one could find numerous endosulfan-resistant individuals. The results obtained by ORSTOM researchers in Nouméa were associated with the development of a breeding technique that led to the reproduction of the insects on an artificial medium in conditions similar to those prevailing in coffee berries. In addition, a simple, reliable and rapid method of identifying the insecticide-resistant lines was developed; well adapted to developing countries, it was adopted by the FAO as a world-wide reference tool for identifying insecticide-resistance among the coffee-berry insect pests.

In view of the risks associated with the emergence of a resistance similar to that discovered in New Caledonia in the countries relying on endosulfan to control the insect pest, the ORSTOM had created an interdisciplinary research group, involving the INRA and CIRAD Department of Perennial Crops, which was studying different strategies aimed at delaying the emergence of resistance, as well as alternative control methods. An international scientific network, named Scoca, was also set up, with a view to promoting the use of bio-insecticides against *Hypothemenus hampei*.

Scented rice, produced in and exported from Asia, which had the property of freeing a strong aroma when cooked, was in high demand on European and North American markets, as well as in some regions of Africa. Geneticists working at the ORSTOM Laboratory of Genetic Resources and Breeding of Tropical Plants in Montpellier were able to confirm that rice aroma was determined by a major gene, called *AcPy* (2-acetyl-1-pyrroline, the major aromatic molecule of rice). They also could, for the first time, locate this gene on chromosome no. 8 and define two other chromosomal zones that could govern the production of this substance and, henceforth, the variations in aromatic scent of rice varieties.

This discovery resulted from the data produced by using two techniques. One, developed by a joint team of the CIRAD and National School of Agricultural and Food Industries (ENSIAA), consisted of analyzing cooking water through gas chromatography in order to measure the amount of AcPy in each rice variety. The other technique – genetic mapping using molecular markers – enabled the ORSTOM team to determine the location of the aroma genes on rice chromosomes. Genetic mapping of the aromatic trait was done on scent rice varieties developped at the IRRI by a CIRAD researcher. This genetic mapping was expected to enable rice breeders to rapidly select genotypes with good aromatic properties and effective agronomic traits (e.g. productivity, pest and disease resistance).

ORSTOM researchers from the Health Department in Montpellier had succeeded in developing a test for detecting hepatitis B in the infectious phase, with the assistance of the National Agency for Valorization of Research. The test relied on the apoliprotein H, a human glycoprotein secreted by the liver and circulating in the bloodstream. This protein had been identified in the mid-1960s and seemed to be involved in infectious and parasitic diseases. ORSTOM researchers had shown that it could be linked with virus, bacteria and parasites (e.g. leishmania and toxoplasms). In particular, the surface antigen of the hepatitis B virus (HBsAg) which appeared during the acute phase of disease and when the virus was about to replicate, could be linked to apolipoprotein H.

For diagnosing hepatitis B (infectious phase), two tests were being used: one aims to identify another virus antigen, HBeAg, which was present at the beginning of infection, the other serves to detect the viral DNA through the so-called hybridization method. Both tests were considered as partially, effective and sensitive: when they were negative in some patients, it was nevertheless shown that the virus was present and replicating in these patients. ORSTOM researchers proposed the following test: the apolipoprotein H was fixed on a solid substrate and put in contact with a blood sample; if the virus was present, its surface antigen would link to the protein and could be detected by antibodies which would deliver a 'signal' indicating the attachment of the antigen to the protein. After analyzing 500 sera, it was proved that this test could detect the virus in its replication phase, i.e. potentially infectious. The test was more reliable than the two usual tests based on the detection of HBeAg and DNA hybridization. It was also inexpensive and, when commercialized, it would enable clinicians and health workers to make an early diagnosis of a disease which, according to the World Health Organization, caused the death of about 1 million persons annually in the world by the mid-1990s. In addition, ORSTOM researchers were pursuing their work with a view to eventually using apolipoprotein H for detecting other viral antigens.

CENTRE FOR INTERNATIONAL CO-OPERATION IN AGRICULTURAL RESEARCH FOR DEVELOPMENT

The CIRAD (Centre de coopération internationale en recherche agronomique pour le développement; Centre for International Co-operation in Agricultural Research for Development) was a public establishment created in 1985 through the merging of research institutes in agricultural, veterinary, forestry and food sciences for warm regions. Its mission was to contribute to the economic and social development of tropical and subtropical regions through research, experiments, training both in the countries themselves and in CIRAD facilities in France, and the dissemination of scientific and technological information.

The CIRAD budget for 1997 was $205.7 million, compared to $199.4 million in 1996 and $202 million in 1995; in 1996, 35% of this budget was provided by the State budget for research and development and 65% came from CIRAD own resources. The proportion was almost similar in 1997. Priority was given for procuring equipment to the two departments which moved from the outskirts of Paris to the new campus in Baillarguet, near Montpellier.

In French-speaking African countries, the CIRAD was expected to bear an increasing share of the maintenance costs of the programmes to be implemented, due to the weaknesses of national budgets and a political will to change co-operation methods. Priority was also given to the redeployment of staff overseas, training (consisting of welcoming researchers from the developing countries and sending French research fellows into the field), and to the competent centres of the French Overseas Departments and Territories. Finally, emphasis was to be placed on inter-institutional projects (e.g. with ORSTOM, the National Institute for Agricultural Research, the National Centre for Scientific Research and universities), so as to mobilize the scientific expertise previously dispersed.

The CIRAD was co-operating with more than 90 countries in Africa, Asia and the Pacific, Latin America and Europe. CIRAD staff in 1995–1996 totalled 1,800, comprising 528 research personnel and 596 supporting staff in France, most of them located in Montpellier, and 372 research personnel and 304 supporting staff in the French Overseas Departments and Territories and in foreign countries. The staff was distributed as follows: 444 for CIRAD-CA (annual crops), 274 for CIRAD-CP (perennial crops), 277 for CIRAD-FLHOR (fruit and horticultural crops), 183 for CIRAD-EMVT (livestock and veterinary medicine), 170 for CIRAD-Forêt (forestry), 126 for CIRAD-SAR (agro-food and rural systems) and 326 for CIRAD-GERDAT (management, research, documentation and technical support). The 890 research staff was distributed as follows: 518 in France, essentially in Montpellier, 100 in the French Overseas Departments and Territories, 176 in Africa and the Indian Ocean, 53 in Latin America, 42 in Asia-Pacific and 1 in other zones.

On 15 April 1996, the buildings of CIRAD second campus in Montpellier area had been inaugurated. Two research departments, those of forestry, and livestock husbandry and veterinary medicine, were transferred there from their former Paris base. In addition, the research teams belonging to the Unit of Plant Modelling and the Unit for Management of Renewable Resources and Environment (both pertaining to the CIRAD-GERDAT) moved to the new Baillarguet campus. The latter occupied an area of 8 hectares and comprised twelve buildings laid out in semi-circle. Construction began in February 1995 and was completed one year later. The floor area totalled 12,500 m^2, comprising 8,000 m^2 of laboratories, offices, documentation and archives. The cost of building construction associated with the transfers and removals totalled $16 million, of which the Baillarguet campus had the lion's share ($15.06 million). Of this total 25% was provided by the Languedoc-Roussillon region, 25% by the National and Regional Development Directorate (DATAR) and 50% by the CIRAD (*CIRAD News*, no. 13, July 1996, pp. 1–2).

This new settlement aimed to create a strong agroforestry and pasture pole and to facilitate synergy between CIRAD departments. It also aimed to create links with scientific partners in the south of France, as well as with the Australian and U.S. researchers present on campus, thus giving an international dimension to CIRAD research-and-development activities. Some 250 staff members were working on the Baillarguet campus in 1996, bringing to 1,000 the total number of CIRAD staff based in the Montpellier region (*CIRAD Information,* no. 61, 19 April 1996, p. 1).

On 31 July 1996, the fifth contract concluded between the French State and an organism of public research was signed by the Minister for Co-operation, the State Secretary for Research and CIRAD's President of the Administration Council. This four-year contract aimed at initiating the restructuration of the French system of research for development, following the evaluations of both ORSTOM and CIRAD carried out by the National Committee for Evaluation of Research. The contract between the State and CIRAD defined three priority areas for the CIRAD: the improvement of production and processing of crops and their products; the sustainable management of land and natural resources; the inclusion of actors' strategies in agricultural development policies with a view to improving the economic and institutional environment. The contract also mentioned as priority objectives the better involvement of the CIRAD within the French scientific community, the European and international scientific research frameworks, a greater role vis-à-vis multilateral funding agencies, a better support for developing countries' research teams, a consolidation of the relations with French-speaking African countries and a reinforced presence in English-speaking African countries, Latin-America and Asia (*CIRAD Information,* no. 65, 17 September 1996, pp. 1–2).

In 1997, the CIRAD included seven research departments: annual crops (CIRAD-CA)[2 (see p. 689)]; perennial crops (CIRAD-CP)[3 (see p. 689)]; fruit and horticultural crops (CIRAD-FLHOR)[4 (see p. 689)]; livestock husbandry and veterinary medicine (CIRAD-EMVT); forestry (CIRAD-Forêt); food technology and rural systems (CIRAD-SAR); management, common services and laboratories, documentation and technical backstopping (CIRAD-GERDAT).

The CIRAD was working in its own research centres, in agricultural research institutions of the partner countries, or through backstopping development projects.

The former institutes, set up during the colonial era in the French tropical colonies and Overseas Departments and Territories, had been encouraged to direct research toward improving production and developing outlets, especially for export, in their respective areas of competence. This mission was performed in line with the 'development' policy for these colonies and the building, for each commodity, of a series of steps between the producer and the consumer, these being the focus of research. Upon decolonization, the research themes changed, but the main focus remained on training national researchers and on participation, in the mid-1970s, in the creation of National Agricultural Research Systems in most African countries. It was these national systems which were running the stations and programmes formerly in the hands of the French institutes.

In South America, the national agricultural research institutes were often of two types: autonomous and semi-autonomous. In the former case, general policy and management were decided on by a group nominated by the ministry of agriculture. These institutes enjoyed relative independence in managing their budget, even if under supervision (e.g. INTA, Argentina). At the semi-autonomous institutes, on the other hand, the board of directors played an advisory role; orientations were dictated by the government and the institutes' budget autonomy was far more limited (e.g. ICA, Colombia). Latin American institutes had a strong extension service (e.g. Argentina) or technology transfer mechanisms (e.g. INIA, Chile), associated with the ministerial extension service and the agricultural professional organizations.

In French-speaking African countries and some English-speaking ones, the agricultural research institutes, although strongly dependent on the ministries of agriculture or scientific research, enjoyed semi-autonomous status. In some cases (e.g. Cameroon), a council made decisions on general research policy. One could distinguish fragmented national systems made up of a high number of public institutions (e.g. Congo, Côte d'Ivoire, Togo) from those which were not; in the latter case, the smaller institutions were centred around a large public institution with a dominant position (e.g. Burkina Faso, Cameroon, Guinea, Madagascar, Mali, Niger, Senegal). Thus, in Senegal, the ISRA (Senegal's Institute for Agricultural Research) was responsible for more than 80% of the total 'research-years' in agricultural research; the remaining 20% was implemented by higher-education institutions and other public bodies.

In many English-speaking countries, there was a scientific council which decided on general research policy and co-ordinated the research carried out in a number of institutes (e.g. Kenya, Nigeria).

In Asia, responsibility for agricultural research had often been transferred from the division of research at the ministry of agriculture to a semi-autonomous research council. These councils, whose government links enabled them to participate in the overall development policy, could be classified in three categories according to their role:

– organization, management and direction of the network of research centres and universities funded by the government (India, Indonesia);

– co-ordination, orientation and review of results of the different institutes and universities (Bangladesh);

– distribution of government funds to research institutes (public or private) or to university laboratories which needed to present their programme for funding (Philippines).

In North Africa and the Middle East, one could distinguish five types of National Agricultural Research Systems:

– pluralist (absence of financial and scientific co-ordination between the different institutes and universities – Egypt);

– financial (absence of scientific co-ordination, but institutes financially dependent on the same ministry – Somalia);

– co-ordinated (existence of links between ministries and institutions, through advisers in research orientation – Irak);

– financial and co-ordinated (existence of links in the form of a co-ordination ministerial group which received for approval the research proposals of various institutes – Algeria);

– centralized (existence of a centralized administrative authority which decided on the research programme and on the resources of each institute – Morocco).

Many national agricultural research institutions were going through a deep crisis in the early 1990s. Some countries had not yet accorded the right priority to agricultural research; once having created these institutions, some governments could not fund their proper functioning. In addition, many were not managed with sufficient rigour. Their relations with development actors were weak, they were overstaffed and employed underqualified personnel. Therefore, one could not exclude the continuous dysfunctioning of a number of these institutions in French- and English-speaking African countries, as well as in Asia and Latin America. However, in some countries, a dynamic and organized productive sector, a university or a non-governmental organization might take the lead. However, the question remained as to whether these actors could give research the space and time it needed. One could not exclude that some governments, taking into account their lack of means, would abandon agricultural research, limiting their role to managing a directorate for agricultural research while relying on other institutions to supply the research data needed for their rural development. A third hypothesis could be envisaged: the recovery of certain National Agricultural Research Systems thanks to regional co-operation [e.g. the Conférence des responsables de la recherche agronomique africains (CORAF, Conference of African Agricultural Research Executives) in sub-Saharan Africa and such regional initiatives as the Special Program for African Agricultural Research (SPAAR), the Instituto Interamericano de Cooperación para la Agricultura (IICA, Inter-American Institute for Co-operation in Agriculture) in Latin America, the Southern African Centre for Co-operation in Agricultural Research (SACCAR, Botswana) and the three research networks of the United Nations Economic and Social Commission for Asia and the Pacific (ESCAP, Bangkok)].

In 1985, the setting up of the CIRAD led to the redefinition of its missions: the CIRAD became a public establishment with industrial and commercial features (EPIC), responsible for rural development in tropical and subtropical regions. One could draw an analogy between the dramatic changes wrought by redefinition of the CIRAD mission and a State once responsible for the development of its colonies adapting this assistance after decolonization to contribute to the development of the now independent States.

The commercial nature of the CIRAD did not mean that it was profit-oriented. It meant in fact a focus on greater efficiency: the CIRAD could act with flexibility, adaptability and rapidity, using methods operating in the private sector. Furthermore, the creation of the CIRAD clearly meant that this was an instrument of French co-operation, mainly with the governments and public institutions of developing countries. Nevertheless, it had become obvious that the development of tropical regions was not solely the responsibility of governments and public institutions, but also involved a wide range of actors with whom the CIRAD would need to collaborate.

With respect to scientific research, the CIRAD needed to focus on the issues related to the economic, social and agronomic realities of tropical regions and, in particular: the management of agricultural, grazing and forest lands, the means used for such management and their costs, the implications for the environment; plant and animal production, and the conditions for its increase through genetic breeding, appropriate production and protection techniques; the harvesting and processing of products, with particular emphasis on their biological stability. The number and variety of CIRAD facilities throughout the world allowed CIRAD researchers to know the specificity and diversity of environments, production systems, agrarian systems and organization of societies in tropical regions.

Although the CIRAD gave a high priority to the sub-Saharan countries, considered by the French Government as priority targets for its co-operation, the CIRAD policy went further. Its presence on other continents would enable researchers to accumulate knowledge and know-how useful for African countries, but this extension was considered an integral part of the Centre contribution to the development of tropical regions.

The CIRAD research policy aimed to carry out basic research, when deemed necessary and useful, so as to lead to applied research and technological development and participate in economical and social development projects, where research was accompanying innovation among producers, craftsmen and industrialists.

While during the 1970s and 1980s the dominant topics for research and development had related to the struggle against hunger and energy issues, environmental issues emerging in the early 1970s had since become a universal concern in development policies. The 1990s would undoubtedly see the decade consecrated to the environment. Consequently, the CIRAD had to adapt its programmes accordingly: in 1995, about one quarter of its research staff was conducting research on development support work strictly related to the environment.

The CIRAD had adopted a policy aimed at diversifying its partners and funding sources, through:

– increasing requests to the European Commission, the World Bank and the regional development banks, for agricultural research-and-development projects;

– the search for funding in countries with reliable public and private markets;

– the increased sales of CIRAD agricultural products.

There were six main kinds of CIRAD products:

– publications;

– data-bases accessible to the public (e.g. those concerning wood anatomy, mechanical and physical properties of woods, markets and economic data on fruit production and commercialization, soils and mechanization);

– training and retraining of staff in various areas (e.g. nitrogen fixation, watershed management, animal pathology in tropical regions, insect taxomony, genome analysis, analysis and improvement of production systems);

– advisory services (e.g. expert missions, diagnosis, evaluation, engineering) in aquaculture and fisheries in tropical freshwaters, management advice for producers, backstopping for plantations, agro-industrial expertise, rubber production and measurement;

– processing (e.g. production of methane and compost through anaerobic degradation of straw, grating tools for cassava);

– materials (e.g. planting materials and seeds, vaccines, agricultural machinery, scientific equipment, software, bait for tsetse flies, tools for harvesting geraniums, rice harvesting machine, coffee-berry peeling, fruit processing adapted to craftmanship).

The CIRAD strategy for the 1990s was intertwinned with two major issues related to agricultural research in tropical regions:

– which technological innovations should be proposed to those involved in agriculture, livestock, forestry production and agro-industry, so as to meet future needs in a sustainable way?

– which socio-economic conditions were needed for the effective implementation of the proposed technological innovations and for the alleviation of poverty?

A sustainable increase in agricultural production was needed in the following agro-ecosystems:

Africa	West and Central Africa, high-density populated highlands in East and Southern Africa, valleys of great rivers (through irrigation);
Asia	South and South-East Asia (diversification of rainfed agriculture), deltas and valleys of great rivers (new 'green revolution' in irrigated areas);
Latin America	Mexican plateau (new 'green revolution'), Central America (production of basic grains), interior valleys in the Andes, Brazilian North-East and cerrados;
Mediterranean basin	Southern and Eastern Mediterranean countries (large cultivable plains, irrigated areas, hydroponic crops);
Islands	Madagascar and Indian Ocean, Caribbean, South Pacific (intensification, diversification and valorization of agro-ecological complementarities).

The sustainable exploitation and preservation of natural forest ecosystems was considered a priority in:

Africa	Congo basin
Asia	Indonesia, Thailand, Indochinese Peninsula, Papua New Guinea
Latin America	Amazonian basin and Guyana.

The CIRAD had identified several areas where it was able to offer the best services: advanced training, scientific and technological information, research networks and institution- building and management. The CIRAD was laying emphasis on funding the employment of researchers in developing countries and on guaranteeing them satisfactory working conditions. It also aimed to concentrate researchers and means on regional poles, so as to obtain a critical mass and avoid duplicating efforts.

Geographically speaking, the CIRAD intended to maintain important staff numbers in French-speaking sub-Saharan countries, around a few regional poles or acting within the framework of medium-term operations, both in the Sahel-Sudan and humid zones; develop solid co-operation with a few non-French-speaking African countries; strengthen co-operative ties with South-Eastern Asian and Pacific countries, while avoiding dispersion of staff resources; buttress collaboration with Latin America, in particular with the regional institutions; undertake with the INRA (French National Institute for Agricultural Research) joint ventures in the Maghreb and the Near East.

The CIRAD aimed to facilitate the creation of regional concertation frameworks or mechanisms for concluding agreements. With respect to sub-Saharan Africa, the CIRAD had facilitated the creation of the Conference of African Agricultural Research Executives (CORAF) and wanted to extend its membership to include English- and Portuguese-speaking countries. This was also the case with two other research institutions of a regional nature:

– the Southern African Centre for Co-operation in Agricultural Research (SACCAR, Botswana), with membership of nine Southern African countries, focusing on food crop species (sorghum, millet and maize), grain legumes, water management, agroforestry and conservation of forest and cultivated species;

– the Sahel Institute, whose membership included the nine countries of the Comité permanent inter-Etats de lutte contre la sécheresse dans le Sahel (CILSS, Inter-State Permanent Committee for the Control of Drought in the Sahel), focusing on information systems, economic studies and training.

In 1992, the CIRAD signed a co-operation agreement with the Institute for Agricultural and Livestock Research (IRAZ), based in Gitega, Burundi, whose objective was to conduct research for Rwanda, Burundi and Zaire, within the framework of the Economic Community of Countries of the Great Lakes.

In Asia, the CIRAD also wanted to extend co-operation to a number of regional institutions, such as:

– the APCC (Asian and Pacific Coconut Community), with ten member countries interested in coconut improvement and the related information network;

– the CGPRT (Centre for Coarse Grains, Pulses, Roots and Tuber Crops), with eight member countries of the United Nations Economic and Social Commission for Asia and the Pacific (ESCAP, Bangkok), interested in research on production systems, markets, commodity prices and exchanges;

– the RNAM (Regional Network for Agricultural Machinery), with eight member countries of the ESCAP, focusing on the development of machines adapted to small farmers' needs and relevant information;

– the AIT (Asian Institute of Technology), with projects throughout Asia in agricultural machinery, food conservation and processing techniques, agrarian systems, aquaculture systems, environment and rural development planning.

In Latin America, CIRAD regional partners were:

– the Inter-American Institute for Co-operation on Agriculture (IICA), working on the analysis and planning of agrarian policy, the development and transfer of technologies, organization and management in rural development, commercialization and agricultural industries, animal and plant health;

– the Tropical Agriculture Research and Training Centre (CATIE), which included six Central American countries and the Dominican Republic and was involved in plant and animal production, agroforestry and training by teachers-researchers.

In the Mediterranean, there was one institute with regional focus, the IAM (Institut agronomique méditerranéen, Mediterranean Agricultural Institute), which included seven member countries from southern Europe and five North African countries. It was involved in post-graduate training, promoting research and co-operative research networks.

The CIRAD was co-operating with the International Agricultural Research Centers on some priority research themes and was contributing to the advancement of tropical agricultural research by offering some of its facilities as permanent experimental stations.

The CIRAD was also associated with European initiatives related to research networks, like the BUROTROP (Bureau for the Development and Research on Tropical Perennial Oil Crops), REAPER on small ruminants, and tropical forests. In French Guyana, a station on tropical forest research was opened to European researchers. Furthermore, the CIRAD was participating in the exchange of researchers by recruiting and welcoming them from European countries to its own laboratories.

One of the objectives of the reform leading to creation of the CIRAD had been to develop a link with the National Institute for Agricultural Research (INRA). Co-operation between the two institutions for the development of tropical and subtropical agriculture covered genetics, biotechnologies, crop protection, agronomy, social sciences, scientific and technological information and training. In addition, members from both institutions participated in scientific and evaluation committees to strengthen co-operation, while efforts were being made to transfer researchers from one institution to the other in order to exchange experience and know-how.

Similarly, there was on-going co-operation with the French Scientific Research Institute for Development in Cooperation (ORSTOM), which had also been working on tropical environments since its inception in 1943.

CIRAD co-operation policy and strategic alliances were particularly obvious within the framework of Agropolis in Montpellier, in the south of France. The Agropolis Association brought together 18 research and higher-education establishments in the Languedoc-Roussillon region working in agriculture, rural development, agro-industry and the environment, with emphasis on the Mediterranean and tropical regions, and about 2,000 teachers and researchers. All of these establishments had agronomy in common, with particular emphasis on tropical and subtropical agriculture and on food. An association, Agropolis was entrusted with a mission of encouraging concertation, providing information and promoting research; it had a council made up of executives from 18 member establishments and representatives of territorial collectivities, as well as an executive secretariat. Agropolis was also facilitating the transfer of technologies in its region; it ran a scientific park which welcomed industrial laboratories, subsidiaries of research organisms and engineering societies as part of a co-operative agreement with one of Agropolis establishments. Agropolis counted among its partners Montpellier Universities I, II and III and that of Perpignan, seven schools of engineering, four research centres (INRA, ORSTOM, CIRAD, National Centre for Scientific Research – CNRS) and numerous other institutions, including the Mediterranean Agricultural Institute.

CIRAD Departments in Montpellier served the function of knowledge storage and transfer, methodological backstopping, compendium writing, interface with the scientific organizations of developed countries, co-ordination of international programmes and networking. They serviced the expatriate CIRAD teams, through the provision of documentation, analyses, editing and informatics backstopping, conservation of genetic resources, management of data-banks, etc. Finally, they were sites of short- and long-term training: in 1995, 808 researchers had been trained; they came from North Africa

(74), West Africa (126), Central Africa (64), East Africa (19), Southern Africa and Indian Ocean (38), Latin America and the Caribbean (37), Middle East, Asia-Pacific (53) and Europe (397).

The CIRAD had a very good research capacity in the French Overseas Departments and Territories. The latter were interesting for the following reasons:

– they were tropical island systems or small area territories with ecological diversity and, in the case of French Guyana, dominated by pristine forests;

– they had specific problems within the French ensemble;

– they were affording privileged sites for welcoming and training researchers, designing and implementing scientific programmes pertaining to co-operation networks with countries of the neighbouring biogeographical zones;

– finally, these centres offered stability and security often lacking in developing countries and were therefore indispensable for carrying out long-term programmes and managing resources.

In The Réunion, seven stations were working on soil science, sugar-cane, phytopathology of food and horticultural crop species, maize, geranium and aromatic plants, tropical and temperate climate fruit species, livestock husbandry and fodder species, tropical forestry in dry areas and mechanization in mountainous zones.

In Guadeloupe, three stations were working on sweet banana and plantain, fruit diversification, sugar-cane, rice, anthurium and animal production. In Martinique, three stations were interested in banana, pineapple, citrus and other fruits, food and vegetable crop species, mechanization of fodder crops. The CIRAD Department of Fruit and Horticultural Crops (FLHOR) organized several training sessions in Martinique on integrated pest control, mass selection and techniques for rapid propagation of pineapple. These sessions were attended by technicians, researchers and private company representatives from Guyana, Surinam, Trinidad and Tobago, Saint Kitts and Nevis and Dominica (*CIRAD Information*, no. 63, 17 June 1996, p. 8).

In French Guyana, forestry activities were predominant, carried out with other partners and comprising a wide range of disciplines from wood technology to forest management; rice cultivation, cassava, coconut and oil-palm, rubber tree cultivation, genetic resources of coffee and cocoa, and seed production were also subjects of interest. In New Caledonia, seven stations were involved in activities dealing with livestock husbandry (cattle, small ruminants and deer), food and horticultural crop species, forestry, agrarian systems and agricultural machinery.

Vanuatu had entrusted the CIRAD with the management of its agricultural research and training institution. This decision had placed the small Pacific archipelago (fifteen 'high' islands surrounded by one hundred or so smaller coral islets) at the heart of an international co-operation project, supported by the European Commission, on the genetic improvement of coconut in the eight Africa-Caribbean-Pacific (ACP) countries of the region (Papua New Guinea, Solomon Islands, Vanuatu, Samoa, Fiji, Kiribati, Tuvalu and Tonga).

Representing 50% of the country's commodity exports, coconut was a key resource for Vanuatu's 150,000 inhabitants. Although the volcanic highlands of the bigger islands were generally fertile, only coconut palms were growing on the calcium-rich coralline soils of the coastal terraces and islets. The productivity of the local coconut variety was poor and coconut wilt, a viral disease specific to the archipelago, was lethal to all imported varieties. Consequently, to improve the resource, hybrids from indigenous genetic resources which were resistant to the disease should be developed. An intensive selection and varietal development work had been in progress in Vanuatu for many years, conducted in parallel with plant physiology research for intercropping with cocoa or food crop species on the highlands. The CIRAD-CP was assisting the Saraoutou station in its coconut cultivation programme, physiological studies, the development of plant material tolerant to foliar yellowing and its training activities (European Commission, STD-3 project).

The overall aim of the international project was to study the genetic resources of the eight countries, in co-operation with their agricultural services, to train local scientists so that they could perform these studies themselves and to set up a series of station trials for potentially successful hybrids. Each country would then be able to test the most promising hybrids, giving preference to plant material obtained from their own genetic resources. When there were no suitable local varieties, it was better to import high-quality material. In addition, the need for more efficient livestock production in coconut groves was shared by all the eight countries (*CIRAD News*, no. 13, July 1996, p. 8).

In Papua New Guinea, the secundment of a CIRAD-CP phytopathologist aimed to fostering the study of the major cocoa diseases: *Phytophthora*, causing brown rot and trunk canker; and the vascular streak dieback, only known in Asia and Papua New Guinea and caused by a fungus.

Biotechnology research and development

The CIRAD research Unit of Biotechnologies Applied to the Improvement of Tropical Crop Species (BIOTROP) was created on 1 January 1991. As part of the CIRAD-GERDAT Department, it covered the activities implemented up to 1991 by three laboratories of *in-vitro* plant tissue culture, histology and analysis of the genome of tropical species. On 1 January 1993, the Unit was completed by a fourth laboratory of genetic engineering and molecular pathology, called IGEPAM.

About 20 researchers, 25 technicians and some 20 post-graduate students were working in the Unit by the end of 1995. Research centred on supporting the work conducted by the CIRAD other Departments through methodological investigations or through applications to a specific crop species. Part of the senior staff was therefore devoting research to the crop species that were the mandate of the relevant CIRAD departments.

Training was an important part of the BIOTROP Unit work. A number of French and foreign post-graduate students were awarded fellowships to prepare their PhD. degree in the Unit, in connection with the relevant French universities.

The Unit had not only developed and strengthened its supportive and co-ordination work within the CIRAD, in close contact with the Departments interested in its work, but was also relying on partnerships with French universities and research institutions (e.g. the ORSTOM, the National Centre for Scientific Research and the National Institute for Agricultural Research), to respond efficiently to the demand emanating from the CIRAD Departments. Co-ordination was improved through the organization of technical meetings with the Departments and the development of concerted and planned research. As the Unit could not cope with the demand, the Departments were requested to assist in the implementation of the tasks they required, in particular by assigning staff to these tasks.

The CIRAD Department of Annual Crops (CIRAD-CA) chose as a priority the improvement of rainfed tropical rice and Mediterranean irrigated rice[5] (see p. 689), one of the main objectives being the breeding of rice varieties genetically resistant to biotic stresses – the stem borers belonging to the genera *Chilo*, *Maliarpha* and *Sesamia*. The research project carried out by the CIRAD BIOTROP Unit therefore aimed to obtain transgenic rice plants[6] (see p. 689) resistant to lepidopteran insects via the transfer of genes coding for *Bacillus thuringiensis* endotoxins and eventually for protease inhibitors. The chosen transformation method was electroporation of protoplasts or the use of polyethylene glycol to render the protoplasts permeable to DNA. At the same time, trials were made to transform cell suspensions or scutellum of inmature embryos by particle bombardment. Research activities included: optimization of embryogenesis from somatic tissues, microspores and protoplasts to make them prone to transformation; development of effective transfer methods on protoplasts; and development of a transformation technique on scutellum of immature embryos using particle bombardment (CIRAD, 1993).

A method of regenerating rice plants from protoplasts had been improved and successfully applied to various tropical and Mediterranean rice varieties of agronomic interest (Miara, Ariete, Pygmalion, IRAT 177). At the French rice centre, progeny obtained from Miara showed good variation for certain agronomic traits. The method was being extended to include other varieties, like Thaibonnet, cT 53 and IRAT 308 (CIRAD, 1994).

The CIRAD was collaborating with the International Laboratory for Tropical Agricultural Biotechnology (ILTAB, Scripps Research Institute, La Jolla, California) for the creation of transgenic rice resistant to the rice yellow mottle virus (RYMV).

CIRAD researchers had also shown that the aroma component in rice was 2-acetyl-1-pyrroline. The gene coding for the synthesis of this substance had also been localized. This had spawned breeding experiments designed to obtain varieties combining both conventional traits and aroma. The use of gene markers was accelerating the breeding process, which drew interest from several African countries, Laos and Viet Nam (CIRAD, 1994). See also p. 620.

In 1995, the banana tree was the most widely *in-vitro* propagated large-scale crop species, with a world output of about 50 million vitroplants per year. The disease-free plantlets thus produced led to higher productivity and to environment conservation due to a lesser use of nematicides.

The CIRAD Department of Fruit and Horticultural Crops (CIRAD-FLHOR) was working on micropropagation techniques, especially in the French Antilles. The know-how acquired by the CIRAD BIOTROP Unit for massive clonal multiplication was commercialized by the company Vitropic, a CIRAD subsidiary. The main stumbling block to banana-tree micropropagation was the appearance of somaclonal variants or non-true-to-type plants. One formula proving effective in keeping the percentage of variants to a minimum in the field combined good management with the early identification of variants during the acclimatization phase of *in-vitro* plantlet production. The CIRAD BIOTROP Unit had been trying to detect what caused variants in the banana cultivar Grande Naine, with the goal in mind of harnessing massive production. Research included: the study of the metabolism of gibberellins in dwarf variants – the most frequent ones- and in normal vitroplants using mass spectrometry, in collaboration with the National Institute for Agricultural Research at Orléans; the possible strengthening of morphological differences *in vitro* between dwarf variants and normal plantlets using biological tests mainly based on the particular sensitivity of the dwarf variants to an input of gibberellins; the production of vitroplants from the controlled budding of an axillary nature and determination of the true-to-type quality of the resulting products.

In addition to field trials in Martinique and Guadeloupe on banana-tree plantlets derived from *in-vitro* cultures and on the somaclonal variants that could arise during this process, the CIRAD-FLHOR was conducting similar trials in Cameroon.

The CIRAD BIOTROP Unit was also working on somatic embryogenesis and genetic transformation of the banana-tree, with the following three goals:

– harnessing somatic embryogenesis from cell suspensions; for diploid banana trees, embryonic suspensions obtained from zygotic embryos were maintained by systematic elimination of fragments with a diameter over 500μ; a culture medium with modified concentrations of its macro-elements, followed by the spreading of somatic embryos on a medium containing cytokinins, allowed the harmonious development of somatic embryos; for triploid banana trees of the Grande Naine cultivar, suspensions made from young immature male flowers grown using the system of temporary immersion developed by the BIOTROP Unit showed an exceptional proliferation rate;

– developing, with the help of marker genes, direct transformation systems, either by the particle gun or with polyethylene glycol;

– engineering virus resistance through the introduction of the gene coding for the capsid protein of the cauliflower mosaic virus (in the medium-term, resistance would be engineered to bunchy top virus, weevils and nematodes). Field trials were carried out to test the true-to-type qualities of the plants derived from somatic embryogenesis, once the stages of multiplication of the cell suspensions, and the formation and development of embryoids had been harnessed.

CIRAD research on obtaining the genetic transformation of the banana-tree was part of the European Commission's Science and Technology for Development (STD-3) programme relating to the genetic improvement of banana, in which were participating, for the biotechnology component, the University of Paris XI, the University of Leuven (Belgium) and the CATIE (Costa Rica). On the international scene, public research bodies, like the Taiwan Banana Research Center and the University of Taiwan, the Queensland Department of Primary Industries (Australia), the Volcani Center (Israel's Institute for Agricultural Research), the South China Academy of Tropical Crops, the University of Havana, Cuba, or private companies like Monsanto Co., were involved in the transformation of banana.

The conservation and dissemination of sugar-cane varieties benefited from the progress made in plant tissue culture. In collaboration with the ORSTOM (French Scientific Research Institute for Development in Cooperation), cryoconservation was successfully applied to embryogenic calli and to sugar-cane apices. The latter, after being excised from five varieties cultivated *in vitro*, were encapsulated and stored in liquid nitrogen, their survival rate between 40% and 90%. The use of apices was expected to lead to the preservation of genotype stability, a requisite for the conservation of varieties. The *in-vitro* culture collection conserved in Montpellier was supplying similar collections at the CIRAD stations in Guadeloupe and The Réunion. In this way, plant material to be used for genetic studies was being conserved, as were clones for introduction and fast multiplication via micropropagation.

The CIRAD Department of Annual Crops (CIRAD-CA) was in charge of an international quarantine service for sugar-cane in Montpellier: some of the clones going through this service were integrated in a culture collection as cultures of axillary buds, followed by the storage of vitroplants at a low temperature.

Research conducted in Guadeloupe had led to a more reliable means of identifying resistance markers than the observation of the symptoms of sugar-cane leaf blight, caused by *Xanthomonas albilineans*. The resistance level was shown to be directly linked to the population density of the pathogen in the host plant. This new criterion enabled the researchers to make a better differentiation of variety resistance, with or without the disease symptoms. This kind of evaluation was applied to the new sugar-cane varieties produced by the CIRAD in Guadeloupe (CIRAD, 1993).

CIRAD research programme on citrus fruit species included the management and valorization of genetic resources of cultivated species and their relatives, genetic improvement using biotechnologies, the control of diseases and pests, ecophysiology and yield increase, food technology and essential oils. The peculiarities of the reproduction pattern of citrus species (partial apomyxis, auto-incompatibility) as well as the high heterozygosity of cultivars considerably limited the potential for genetic improvement through sexual recombination. That explained the retention of gene transfer as the priority means of improving elite cultivars. The high embryogenic capacity of nucellar calli and of the protoplasts derived from these calli hinted at the direct transformation of these protoplasts through electroporation or using polyethylene glycol.

There were tranformation projects of this ilk in Israel, Japan and the USA, generally using *Agrobacterium*-transformation procedures and protoplast electroporation, as well as in Spain at the Institute for Agricultural Research of Valencia and in Italy at the Experimental Institute for Agriculture. The CIRAD BIOTROP Unit was working on the transformation and regeneration of *Citrus deliciosa* (common mandarin), following a training period in Florida at the Citrus Research and Education Center. Research goals included: the harnessing of somatic embryogenesis with different carbon sources; the transformation of protoplasts with marker genes; the fusion of protoplasts of mandarin and lime varieties; and the cryoconservation of embryogenic calli of various citrus species with a view to building up a genotype bank.

Somatic embryogenesis had been achieved from nucellar tissue of the ovule. More than a dozen *Citrus* cultivars were being preserved as embryogenic calli. Regeneration of plantlets from calli and cell suspensions was well mastered (CIRAD, 1993). The first somatic inter-generic hybrids between *Citrus deliciosa* and *Fortunella japonica* had been obtained in 1994 by electrofusion in the BIOTROP Unit. This method opened new vistas for the short-term creation of rootstock and diversification of tangerine trees. Research was also carried out on the regeneration of the plant material resulting from the fusion of four other inter-specific and inter-generic combinations (*CIRAD Information*, no. 47, 15 December 1994, p. 3).

A new diagnosis technique for the canker (Asian form) had been developed by the CIRAD team in The Réunion, in collaboration with the U.S. Department of Agriculture (USDA, Beltsville, Maryland). A plasmid DNA fragment associated with this canker (PFL 62.42) had been cloned in *Escherichia coli*. A fine detection method, using the PCR (polymerase chain reaction), was applied to epidemiological studies and the certification of planting material health. This high-technology method was considered very opportune at a time when regulations governing the import of citrus fruits into the European Union (especially those from South America) were being reviewed (CIRAD, 1993).

On 9 August 1994, the INRA (National Institute for Agricultural Research) and the CIRAD Department of Fruit and Horticultural Crops signed a co-operative agreement to strengthen the research-and-development work of the Agricultural Research Station of San Giuliano in Corsica, one of the world's leading citrus research centres. Created in 1958 by the former IRFA (Institute for Research on Fruits and Citrus), the Station had been integrated into the INRA in 1964. With a surface area of 105 hectares, a collection of more than 500 citrus varieties and species and an annual budget of $2.5 million, the San Giuliano Experimental Station was poised to play an important role in the production and dissemination of disease-free elite plant material throughout the Mediterranean basin and other citrus-producing regions.

The CIRAD Department of Perennial Crops (CIRAD-CP) research programme on oil-palm[7] (see p. 689) was the follow-up to 50 years of work by its predecessor, the IRHO, i.e. the French Institute for Oils and Oilseeds. This programme was renowned for its selection methods of higher-yielding hybrids with slow trunk growth, reduced density and resistance to fusariosis; its pioneering and advanced research on oil-palm *in-vitro* culture, endorsed by field trials conducted on more than 3,000 hectares at different sites; its studies on the biological control of oil-palm pests and weeds; and its research on the biochemistry of lipids aimed at adding value to palm and kernel palm oil.

In 1996, the CIRAD Department of Perennial Crops (CIRAD-CP) had recruited a molecular biologist to study the so-called 'mantled' anomaly of oil-palm. Some oil-palms obtained via somatic embryogenesis, which had a normal phenotype in *in-vitro* cultures and, when young, showed later on an abnormal flowering pattern; this was a random event. Tree production was thus weak or nil. Since March 1996, the molecular biologist had been working within the CIRAD/ORSTOM team with a view to determining the molecular differences between normal and abnormal palms, originating from a single clone (*CIRAD Information*, no. 61, 19 April 1996, p. 5).

CIRAD-CP research-and-development programme on coconut[8] (see p. 689) included: the study of genetic variability with the goal of coping with a wide range of environmental conditions; biological control of pathogens and pests, as well as their epidemiology; the valorization of products and by-products; the production and dissemination of higher-yielding hybrids.

CIRAD research on coffee strived to improve the know-how on 3 million small exploitations or farms where the coffee varieties *robusta* and *arabica* were grown. The quality of coffee depended on the knowledge and control of those factors determining coffee aroma:

genetics and breeding varieties, soils, harvesting, post-harvesting, processing and torrefaction.

Self-pollinated, tetraploid *Coffea arabica*, which represented three-quarters of world production, was multiplied through seeds; consequently, the breeding and distribution of a new homozygous variety for the desired traits required between 30 and 40 years of work and assays. *Coffea canephora*, of which the variety *robusta* was the most widely known, was diploid, allogamous and cultivated mainly in Africa (75%) and Asia (23%); it was propagated by cuttings; the harnessing of micropropagation allowed for the massive multiplication of F1 or F2 hybrids that combined agronomic traits with resistance to parasites.

With respect to international biotechnology research on coffee, the U.S. DNA Plant Technology Corporation was carrying out micropropagation and analyzing somaclonal variation. In Colombia, genetic transformation of coffee for resistance to berry scolytes had been achieved at the CENICAFE.

At the CIRAD BIOTROP Unit, a first research project aimed to optimize micropropagation through temporary immersion in a liquid nutrient medium. The latter was placed in the lower half of the culture vessel, the plant material in the upper half and a filter in between. When the lower half of the vessel was pressurized via the air ports, the liquid medium rose to the upper chamber. A timer and pump combination could effectively automate the system providing periodic immersion (e.g. 1x1 minute immersion per 24 hours for somatic embryos and 4x15 minute immersions per 24 hours for shoot culture). The system was useful for the application of different phytohormone treatments via the medium. The humidity in the upper chamber was always near saturation, though the gaseous atmosphere was replenishable. The system, which had been patented, enabled culture media to be changed without manipulating plant tissues or cells. It was successfully applied not only to microcuttings of rubber and coffee, but also to their embryogenic suspensions (CIRAD, 1993).

This work relied on the heartening results obtained with the micropropagation on solid culture medium of orthotropic nodes and with the conformity of tissue culture-derived coffee plantlets to their parents, demonstrated by field trials carried out in Central America since 1986. This technique was extended to Uganda via a project funded by the European Commission, as well as to Burundi and Kenya. Other research was dealing with the effect of gibberellin on the growth and multiplication of *in-vitro*-derived plants, root induction in liquid medium, and the commercial feasibility of the micropropagation technique in liquid medium.

The second research project concerned the selection of a coffee tree resistant to the leaf borer; the genetic transformation relied on the harnessing of somatic embryogenesis in liquid medium and the direct transfer of genes using the particle gun. In 1994, the marker *gus* gene was introduced in coffee plants using *Agrobacterium tumefaciens*-induced transformation; the transformation rate was superior to that obtained by the French Nestlé subsidiary FRANCERECO with *Agrobacterium rhizogenes.*

CIRAD cocoa[9] (see p. 690) research programme covered 14 producing countries throughout the world in the early 1990s. Research topics concerned *inter alia*: evaluation of genetic resources and the study of their diversity; development of multiplication techniques based on micropropagation and somatic embryogenesis; improvement of control methods of diseases (swollen-shoot, *Phytophthora* spp.) and pests (rose beetle, pod borer, *Bathycoelia* spp.); control of the chemical composition of cocoa beans during their processing; promotion of higher-yielding hybrids.

The CIRAD BIOTROP Unit was focusing on the physiology of *in-vitro*-derived plantlets so as to optimize the *in-vitro* propagation process; the harnessing of somatic embryogenesis from petals of poliar explants through in-depth knowledge of its biochemical, cytological and physiological processes (including the description of the stages conducive to somatic embryogenesis and the identification of phenolic compounds that might limit somatic embryogenesis).

The Technical Committee for the Study of the Genetic Bases of Cocoa Resistance to *Phytophthora* held its first meeting in Montpellier on 30 January 1996. The project, funded by COABISCO (the European Union's Association of Chocolate, Biscuit and Confectionery Industries), aimed to evaluate the resistance of cocoa clones and offspring and to study the molecular biology of these offsprings. The project involved the CIRAD Department of Perennial Crops, the Coffee and Cocoa Department of Côte d'Ivoire's Forestry Institute (IDEFOR), Cameroon's Institute for Agricultural Research for Development (IRAD) and Trinidad and Tobago's Cocoa Research Unit. COABISCO was represented in this meeting by representatives from Nestlé (France and United Kingdom) and Mars (United Kingdom); a representative of Hershey (USA) was also invited to participate in the debate, which focused on the balance sheet of the first phase of the project, as well as on the administrative and financial measures taken by the various partners. The second meeting of the Committee was held in mid-1996 (*CIRAD Information*, no. 61, 19 April 1996, pp. 4–5).

The CIRAD Department of Perennial Crops (CIRAD-CP) rubber-tree programme was based on the following facts and trends:

– the market of natural rubber was promising and the demand was growing at a faster pace than the supply;

– rubber production was to a large extent (80%) that of small planters, also characterized by the decline of Malaysia's output and a shift toward zones which were not optimal for rubber-tree cultivation but where this tree seemed to play a beneficial role for reforestation and environmental protection;

– a dominant technical position of natural rubber in about 30% of the rubber market, due to its properties which synthetic rubber could not equal; competition between the two types of rubber might become harsher if, in addition to the variability of natural rubber, a deficit in production would induce a rise in prices that would lead industrial consumers to change their habits.

In addition to these facts and trends, the wood of rubber-tree was not considered a by-product, but a real product that could have an important value. This should lead to a fruitful co-operation between the CIRAD-CP and the CIRAD Department of Forestry.

To respond to the rising demand of natural rubber, the need to limit production costs and to deliver a constantly improved end-product to industrial consumers, the CIRAD-CP hevea programme comprised ten research projects involving some 80 operations conducted by the Department itself or in partnership in Montpellier and in a dozen rubber-growing countries in Africa, Asia and Latin America.

Côte d'Ivoire, because of the experimental network developed by the CIRAD-CP till 1991, remained an important research base. A new start for the co-operation was expected to follow the secundment of a CIRAD specialist within the framework agreement linking the CIRAD-CP to the Forestry Institute of Côte d'Ivoire (IDEFOR) and the company Hevego. In Africa, collaboration with the Association of Rubber Producers was expected to lead to the launching of a project for improving rubber quality and the design, in the medium-term, of a regional network on leaf diseases in Central Africa.

In Latin America, the research base established in French Guyana was now being integrated in a regional network involving Brazil (with the French company Michelin), Guatemala and Mexico (where one CIRAD specialist was secunded at the beginning of 1996).

In Asia, the difficulties raised by the co-operation with Malaysia and the reduction of CIRAD implantation in Indonesia were being compensated by the development of new partnerships with Thailand (since 1994), Cambodia and Viet Nam.

For a long time, the rubber tree (*Hevea brasiliensis*) [10] (see p. 690) had
been multiplied by sowing the seeds found at its base. Nowadays, clones
derived from a varietal improvement programme, which yielded about
2 tonnes of dry rubber per hectare, were multiplied by grafting. But the
technique resulted in a two-tiered tree: the bottom, whose root system,
developed from rootstock produced from a seed, was young, unselected
material; and the top, or trunk and crown, which was grafted from a
selected tree at maturity. It was therefore a composite tree, whose top
benefited from selection and whose rootstock contained unknown
diversity. That explained why the grafted tree produced less than the
tree from which the graft was taken and why two *a priori* identical
clones produced different quantities of latex. The tapping yield, i.e.
what each tree produced as latex at each bleeding or tapping, was what
a planter looked at when extending or renewing his plantation. It was
preferable for yield to be the same, if possible, from one tree to the next
so as not to waste the time of increasingly costly labourers (CIRAD,
1994).

By the late 1970s, the French Institute of Rubber had launched a
programme for cultivating *Hevea in vitro* and today the CIRAD-CP, as
well as the BIOTROP Unit, were pursuing this work, building on the
findings of experiments carried out over half a century on thousands of
hectares of rubber plantations in Africa, Asia and Latin America. In
1987, a technique of microcutting stem fragments resulted in the
production of saplings from seedlings. Recognizing the great potential
of this technique, several private firms joined the CIRAD in setting up
the Society for the Microcutting of Hevea (SMH), whose objective was
to improve and micropropagate selected material. The SMH did not get
past the initial stage, being forced to close down in the unfavourable
economic environment of 1993 (CIRAD, 1994).

There were several stages involved in microcutting. For first growth,
stem fragments with latent axillary bruds were cut from the plant to be
reproduced. After disinfection, these fragments were placed on a solid
medium containing growth hormones, cytokinin and auxin. Small-
leafed stems emerged from the buds after a month. For multiplication,
the new stems were fragmented and planted on a new culture medium.
At the stabilized stage, the unselected material had a multiplication
coefficient of 2 to 2.5 every three weeks, while that of clones, such as
IRCA 18 and PB235, was between 1.5 and 2. At the conditioning stage,
stem tissue matured and leaves thickened before roots were induced.
Roots developed in compost in an acclimatization cell. Seventy per cent
of 25,000 seedling-derived saplings and of several hundred clone-
produced saplings were successful. In 1992, the SMH used this method

to produce 23,000 plantlets, 18,000 of which were from selected material. However, once at the greenhouse acclimatization stage, their growth was painfully slow. It did not nevertheless discredit microcutting. In fact, the first microcuttings obtained in the laboratory and planted in Côte d'Ivoire in 1983, as well as the microcuttings from non-selected material which had been planted in field trials since 1988, covered 10 hectares in 1995 and consistently produced well-rooted trees with normal above-ground development; they grew as quickly as trees produced from seeds. Tapping trials were carried out on 2 hectares and, as a world first in 1993, microcuttings of selected clones were planted in the open, with a new series to follow in 1994. The trees were compared with those produced by conventional grafting (CIRAD, 1994).

The CIRAD team was also considered a world leader in somatic embryogenesis of rubber. Research carried out since 1970 in Chinese and Malaysian laboratories on somatic embryogenesis was outpaced by that of the CIRAD. Other laboratories in India, Indonesia, Thailand and Viet Nam were no more successful. Among private research initiatives, the U.S. company Goodyear had made important investments, before suddenly interrupting its research programme after four years, while the French firm Michelin had initiated work on somatic embryogenesis.

The CIRAD team at the BIOTROP Unit chose to use the inner seed coat because this mother tissue retained the selected genotype. Six or seven successive cultures lasting about three weeks each were necessary to obtain a plantlet. The plantlet was then acclimatized in compost, either in a greenhouse or in a protected germ-free nursery, and after four months was planted in the field. Several hundred plantlets had been obtained from four clones of industrial interest - PR107, RRIM 600, PB235 and PB260. The first three of these clones were used in field trials in 1992. They developed normally and other samples were planted in the following years (CIRAD, 1994).

The BIOTROP Unit was encouraged by these results to develop somatic embryogenesis for large-scale production of planting material. However, two problems had to be solved before plantlets could be produced at an acceptable cost. First, the tissue culture had to go through a stage of intensive multiplication of the embryogenic calli; embryogenic suspensions capable of regeneration were obtained for the first time in 1992. Secondly, only 10 to 15 out of 100 embryoids germinated and developed into a plantlet. This yield, the best obtained up to 1994 by any laboratory, was insufficient. The study on endogenous growth regulators conducted jointly by the CIRAD,

ORSTOM and the University of Paris VII, allowed the survey of changes in these regulators in somatic and zygotic embryos of *Hevea brasiliensis*. Consequently, the development of somatic embryos into plants was mastered by adding abscissic acid or a mild dessication. The *in-vitro* cultivation programme focused on adapting somatic embryogenesis to a high number of clones already planted or in final selection and setting up field trials in several rubber-growing countries. Microcutting was still considered a viable solution for those clones not responding to somatic embryogenesis. In this case, research focused on: the comparison between *in-vitro*-derived plantlets and conventional grafted material; field selection of the best clones originating from micropropagation; search for those genotypes best adapted to *in-vitro* culture and to microcutting (CIRAD, 1994).

Rubber-tree plantlets derived from somatic embryogenesis and obtained in the laboratory of the French company Michelin, in Clermont-Ferrand, within the framework of a convention between this company and CIRAD-CP, were transferred to experimental plots in Michelin's plantations by the end of 1996.

In the pace of a growing demand for natural rubber for specialized use, the supply of latex might become insufficient by the beginning of the 21st century, since the acreage given over to *Hevea* was immobile and the existing plantations were ageing. There would be an urgent need for quality plant material. Before this happened, the CIRAD intended to develop techniques for implementing its *in-vitro* cultivation programme on a large scale. Furthermore, genetic transformation of *Hevea* necessitated harnessing *in-vitro* cultivation. These improvements could lead to a yield of 3 tonnes of latex per hectare, a revolution in growing *Hevea* (CIRAD, 1994).

Molecular biology-assisted breeding and genome mapping[11] (see p. 690) was increasingly contributing to the genetic improvement of economically important crop species. Plant breeders had based selections almost entirely on phenotype. On this basis, the breeding process was extremely time-consuming. Many crop species required ten years or more to evolve into an improved variety. Additionally, scientists had gained little understanding of specific genes of agronomic importance. This was especially true for complex (quantitative) traits controlled by the combined action of many genes.

Marker-assisted selection (MAS) could reduce the time required to reach some breeding objectives by 30% to 50%. Consider the case where a breeder wishes to transfer a newly identified disease resistance gene from a line with poor agronomic traits into a high-yielding but disease-sensitive cultivar. The objective is to recover all of the desirable traits of the high-yielding line plus the disease-resistant gene alone from the donor parent. Computer simulations of backcrossing programmes predicted that it would require only three generations to recover the recurrent parent (high-yielding) plant type using MAS, while it would require a minimum of six backcross generations with conventional technology. Additionally, backcross lines derived from the conventional approach would be subject to uncontrolled linkage drag (transfer of large chromosome pieces closely linked to the gene(s) of interest). Through the use of MAS, the plant breeder would be able to observe the plant genetics at the DNA level, which would allow him to minimize the effects of linkage drag (Webster, 1994).

For the first time, plant breeders would be able to design approaches to quantitative traits with a clear understanding of the number and location of the genes associated with individual traits. This ability would be especially useful for unravelling the genetics of polyploid crops, such as oats or wheat. These examples illustrate a shift from a phenotype-based selection to a genotype-based protocol.

In 1984, there were only three laboratories constructing the first molecular genetic maps of plant species (lettuce, maize and tomato). Ten years later, hundreds of laboratories were involved in DNA mapping in plants, including most of the major crop species.

Plants had been relatively late to come into genomics research arena, and *Arabidopsis thaliana* had been chosen as the subject of a plant genomic sequencing initiative. For that purpose, this Cruciferous species offered technical advantages, including a relatively small amount of DNA (120 Mb) that made up its complement of approximately 30,000 genes distributed over five chromosomes. From a crop development perspective, *Arabidopsis* was closely related to other members of the Cruciferae, including the oilseed Brassicas such as *Brassica napus*. Recent evidence indicated that plant species as diverse as tomato/potato and maize/rice had maintained a surprising degree of conservation of the overall organization of the genes on their chromosomes. This suggested that definition of the *Arabidopsis* genome would likely have considerable impact on the study and manipulation of other plant species (Crosby and Hemmingsen, 1996).

Transposon[12] (see p. 692) tagging technology had been developed for *A. thaliana* and plans for generating large populations of plants bearing independent insertions of foreign DNA into the genome were underway in several laboratories. Large populations of tagged lines (250,000 independent insertions) could be generated so that insertions would occur on average every 400–500 nucleotides, resulting in the interruption and thereby the inactivation of numerous genes. This pool of plants could serve as a potential source of gene variability for virtually any gene in the plant. Using sophisticated DNA pooling and *in vitro* PCR (polymerase chain reaction) detection strategies, techniques had been developed that allowed rapid screening and recovery of individual plants bearing insertions in or near specific genes. For instance, selective inactivation of genes involved in metabolism could result in the accumulation of chemical feedstocks, or the alteration of morphology for improved yield or agronomic properties (Crosby and Hemmingsen, 1996).

The DLO-Centre for Plant Breeding and Reproduction Research at Wageningen, the Netherlands, had developed a transposon tagging system in *Arabidopsis thaliana*, which had led to the identification and isolation of genes. New mutants had been characterized, including hairless, male-sterile and wax-free phenotypes. The Centre was involved in the ESSA (European Scientists Sequencing *Arabidopsis*) Project. They had sequenced 45,000 nucleotide pairs of chromosome 4 up to 1995, thus providing a wealth of information on the organization of chromosomes and genes which might be useful in improving cultivated varieties of other plant species.

Transposon tagging and insertion-activation technology in *Arabidopsis* would impact on the state-of-the-art in *Brassica* crop development. The conserved nature of plant chromosomal organization would present new opportunities for the lateral application of *Arabidopsis*-derived information to *Brassica* crop development, since genetic loci identified in *A. thaliana* might share organizational similarity with an equivalent chromosomal region in *Brassica* spp. Exploiting the *Arabidopsis* information would require the existence of an equivalent transposon tagging technology for *Brassica* spp. – preferably one that could be targeted to specific regions on select chromosomes, so that the equivalent disruption might be quickly recovered in the crop species (Crosby and Hemmingsen, 1996).

Further improvement in the technology for linking molecular markers to genes had led to the design of an RFLP potato map at the DLO-Centre for Plant Breeding and Reproduction Research at Wageningen, Netherlands. On this map, 190 molecular and classical markers were located as well as genes for resistance to nematodes and fungi. About 90 maize transposons which had been incorporated into potato via transformation had also been mapped and were being used to find resistance genes.

YAC stands for Yeast Artificial Chromosome. YACs allowed researchers to clone large pieces of the DNA of other organisms and to maintain them in yeast cells. In the yeast, the YAC was copied faithfully each time the yeast cell replicated its own genes, a task that it must perform each time the cell divided. Thus, the cells carrying a YAC were a reliable source of supply for a defined piece of the genome of another organism. To produce a physical map of a plant chromosome, researchers produced a large number of YACs from the chromosomal DNA. They then determined which YACs carried overlapping regions of the chromosomal DNA, which ends of any two YACs were involved in the overlap and the extent of the overlap. The end result was a physical map of a contiguous region of the plant's chromosomal DNA and this was called a 'contig' (Crosby and Hemmingsen, 1996).

Landry (1994) of Agriculture and Agri-Food Canada, Quebec, had constructed detailed molecular genetic maps of several plant species using two classes of DNA markers developed since the mid-1980s. In the RFLP (restriction fragment length polymorphism) approach, cloned DNA sequences were used as probes to detect variations within specific regions of the genome. These variations, or polymorphisms, were identified by restriction endonuclease enzymes that produced fragments of varying length based on genetic differences at the nucleotide level. PCR (polymerase chain reaction)-based DNA markers, such as RAPD (random amplified polymorphic DNA) markers, relied on the amplification of specific DNA fragments from total genomic DNA. Short DNA primers that corresponded to two adjacent regions of a chromosome were used to drive the amplification of the DNA located between these two regions. Genetic differences between individuals were seen as variations in the length of the amplified fragments, or presence/absence of the fragment.

RFLPs remained the best markers with which to construct detailed genetic maps because they could be used in numerous crosses. They were excellent landmarks for identifying and isolating genes of interest. The PCR-based technology was simpler but often required highly controlled conditions and was most useful for targeting several markers in specific regions and for routine genetic diagnosis.

Using the linkage maps created with these markers, Landry (1994) had identified the position of the genes encoding most of the important agronomic traits in *Brassica* species, more specifically in canola. One of these traits was resistance to the fungal pathogen, blackleg, whose precise chromosomal position had been determined. This discovery was expected to ease the work of canola breeders, since it was now possible to indirectly select plants that would breed true for resistance to blackleg simply by monitoring the DNA markers, without the need to inoculate the plants with the fungal pathogen. This was environmentally sound and would speed up the development of resistant cultivars. Landry (1994) had also developed DNA 'fingerprints' for many canola cultivars, which would facilitate certification of seed lots, protect the rights of breeders and guarantee that the producer was buying high-quality seeds.

The CIRAD BIOTROP Unit was involved in mapping the genomes of sorghum, sugar-cane, banana, cocoa and rubber-tree.

Sorghum, which was adapted to semi-arid tropical regions, where rainfall amounted to about 800 mm during the wet season, had been domesticated in Sudano-Sahelian Africa and in India millenia ago. It was still the staple cereal for millions of rural populations, in particular in West Africa between 7° and 14° of latitude North. Sorghum and its derived products were so much part of tradition that one could speak of 'sorghum civilizations'. It was therefore not surprising that researchers were seeking to increase sorghum productivity in the face of a growing food deficit. In 20 years, sorghum varieties had been created which could yield 7 tonnes per hectare. After concentrating on augmenting yields, breeding of sorghum varieties was currently laying emphasis on grain quality, so as to obtain a better dissemination of the improved varieties among farming communities (CIRAD, 1994).

By grain quality, are meant those plant traits which would enable housewives to prepare traditional dishes, the best known being tô, a kind of firm porridge which required the grains being dehulled with a pestle, winnowed, pounded to a fine flour, then cooked with water. The dish could be found under different names throughout southern Africa and India. Researchers reeded to select relatively hard-grain sorghums with high amylose content. As the *guinea* race of local sorghums contained these properties, which were well appreciated by housewives, breeders wanted to include them in variety improvement programmes, despite their low productivity (CIRAD, 1994).

Among the four races of sorghum cultivated as a cash crop, *guinea* possessed the greatest diversity. *Guineas* were polyphyletic. CIRAD researchers had determined at least two centres of domestication, western and southern Africa. A third group with no identified geographic base, the *margaritifera*, was distinguished by early maturity, small very vitreous grains, a rather short stem and abundant sprouting. Breeders were incorporating the *margaritifera* as improvement material into the cross-breeding programmes in Mali (CIRAD, 1994).

Regarding sorghum genetic diversity and genome mapping, eight teams (six in the USA, one in Australia and one in Italy) had launched genome mapping projects in order to compare the genome organization of various plants or analyze different morphological traits, as well as resistance to drought and mildew. Seven teams were using F2 progenies of intra-specific or inter-specific crossings; the DNA probes most frequently used were derived from maize or sorghum, but also from rice and oats; the size of the genome maps obtained was between 400 and 1,756 centiMorgans. One research team was using recombinant lines and RAPD (random amplified polymorphic DNA) markers to map resistance to drought.

The CIRAD BIOTROP Unit had been studying cultivated sorghum diversity using morphological markers, isozymes and RFLPs (restriction fragment length polymorphism); in addition, its researchers were studying cytoplasmic DNA diversity both in cultivated and wild sorghum. A genetic map of sorghum was established from two segregating populations derived from crosses between a *caudatum* line (IS 2807) on the one hand, and two *guinea* lines (379 and 249), on the other. The map comprised (in 1995–1996) 199 loci identified with 190 heterologous probes of maize and sugar-cane, distributed in 13 linkage groups, and covered a genetic distance of 1,095 centiMorgans. When compared with saturated maps developed in the USA, it could be considered as representing 80% of the species genome.

In a second stage, this map was used to localize quantitative trait loci (QTL), which were genomic regions intervening in the expression of quantitative traits, associated with productivity, grain quality and panicle mould. These results would lead to marker-assisted selection, which might enable the breeders to follow the transfer of a small number of QTL in an offspring.

There had already been important repercussions from this work on sorghum improvement: *guinea* sorghum involvement in cross-breeding had increased from zero to 25% in Burkina Faso and to 75% in the CIRAD and ICRISAT joint programme in Mali. It would also be very useful for the European Commission project entitled Diet preference of sorghum products in southern Africa, which aimed to develop semi-industrial food products (CIRAD, 1994).

In the French Overseas Departments, home to the French Centre for Sugar-cane and Sugar (CFCS), the CIRAD was working on improving sugar-cane cultivation. The improvement of sugar-cane varieties was difficult due its complex genetic make-up. Species of the genus *Saccharum* were all highly polyploid. Varieties of sugar-cane grown nowadays stemmed from cross-breeding with a wild species in India and Java at the turn of the century. They were aneuploid with often more than 100 chromosomes, which were derived to a large extent (more than 80) from *Saccharum officinarum* (the 'noble' cane) and to a minor extent from *S. spontaneum*. The hybridization strategies for genetic improvement were not clearcut and the crossing schemes were mainly determined by flowering and the constraints of pollen fertility. On the other hand, selection criteria were lacking, due to the dearth of knowledge on inheritance of plant traits (CIRAD, 1994).

On the international scene, ten research organizations and sugar-cane professional associations representing six countries (Australia, Brazil, Colombia, Mauritius, South Africa and the USA) had set up the International Consortium for Sugar-Cane Biotechnologies in 1991. The consortium was funding projects on genome mapping in *S. spontaneum* and *S. officinarum* and markers of agronomic traits in several U.S. universities.

Two teams had undertaken mapping the genome of a wild clone of *S. spontaneum*; one of the teams, which included Brazilian researchers from COPERSUCAR and American scientists from the Hawaiian Sugar Planters Association, was conducting this study at Cornell University; it had constructed a map including 212 RFLP markers; the second team, located at the California Institute of Biological Research, had succeeded in putting 230 RAPD markers on the map.

The CIRAD BIOTROP Unit had carried out studies in its Montpellier-based laboratory and in Guadeloupe, and was able to tag 88 markers on the 100 chromosomes on the sugar-cane variety SP70 1006. The hypothesis of synteny, i.e. the closeness of sugar-cane and maize genomes (the 20 chromosomes of maize, which belonged to the Andropogoneae family, as did sugar-cane, had been mapped to a large extent), had been validated when the 34 markers involved reproduced the same arrangement in the sugar-cane genome as in maize. Studies on the leading variety R570 from The Réunion were being pursued (CIRAD, 1994).

Application of molecular tools to variety R570 improved our basic knowledge of sugar-cane complex genome structure. The two co-existing genomes, derived from the first domesticated species *Saccharum officinarum* and *S. spontaneum*, could be differentiated by *in-situ* hybridization. They represented about 85% and 15% respectively of the genome of R570 with some chromosomes derived from inter-specific exchanges. Their most likely basic chromosome numbers were $x = 10$ and $x = 8$ respectively, as indicated by physical mapping of the rRNA genes. RFLP mapping allowed to place 408 markers onto 97 cosegregation groups supporting a general colinearity between the chromosomes. Map comparison with other species of the grass family enabled the geneticists to assess a great degree of synteny, especially with sorghum. Linkage between markers and genes of interest was investigated for several traits. A putative major gene for rust resistance was identified. These molecular tools were of great interest for sugar-cane genetics, especially with respect to the inter-specific dimension of sugar-cane breeding.

Co-operation was proving effective both with Australia's Bureau of Sugar Experiment Stations with which the CIRAD was exchanging scientists, and with the West Indies Central Sugar Cane Breeding Station of Barbados on the molecular analysis of inter-generic and inter-specific hybrids produced by this station.

A Symposium on the genetic improvement of banana with respect to the resistance to diseases and pests was held in Montpellier, at the CIRAD facilities, from 7 to 9 September 1992. Representatives from 37 countries attended this symposium devoted to constraints concerning cultivars, pathogens and improvement strategies, and the solutions provided world-wide to overcome them. The participants in the project Life sciences and technologies for developing countries – University of Louvain la Neuve (Belgium), the National Resources Institute (NRI, United Kingdom), the Regional Centre for Banana and Plantain (CRBP, Cameroon) and the Windward Islands Banana Growers' Association (Trinidad and Tobago) – presented the results of their joint project since 1984 (CIRAD, 1993).

In the banana tree, the use of mapped molecular genetic markers would help to understand the genetic determinism of traits, particularly resistance to cercosporiosis, and would offer early markers for breeding. The origin of triploid banana varieties consumed world-wide was still little known; consequently, studies of genetic diversity with the help of morpho-physiological and molecular markers were being made to understand the genome organization within the genus *Musa*. On the international scene, the University of Georgia (USA) was working on the genetic diversity of different species of the genus *Musa* at the level of both nuclear and chloroplastic DNA (CIRAD, 1994).

The first mapping was performed for the diploid banana *Musa acuminata*: two maps were drawn up from two progenies – an F2-type progeny, resulting from the cross-breeding of a cultivar and a wild diploid, and a progeny resulting from the self-pollination of a synthetic hybrid. The first map contained 77 markers which were assembled into 15 linkage groups; 13 other markers segregated independently. The second map contained 56 markers allocated to 14 linkage groups. This map was used as a basis for establishing the chromosomal rgions responsible for variations in quantitative traits, or QTL (quantitative trait loci). CIRAD researchers found ten regions of the genome involved in the expression of those traits. At least two loci appeared to control resistance to black cercosporiosis (CIRAD, 1994).

According to a preliminary assessment, the banana genome was small, like that of tomato. Consequently, about 120 to 170 markers would be needed to locate one in every ten centiMorgans (cM, recombination unit). Work was progressing in the laboratory, especially with the help of microsatellites, which were repetitive genome sequences, very polymorphic since they could present for the same locus up to 20 different alleles. They were useful for the study of large populations, the needed quantity of DNA being small (10 to 50 nanograms). The first functional microsatellites were developed by CIRAD researchers for *Musa acuminata*: about 25 were created in 1995–1996; they could enrich the genetic map of this species and were very accurate for identifying varieties.

Clones of the progeny studied had been planted both in Guadeloupe and Cameroon, with the help of the Regional Centre for Banana and Plantain. They were being analyzed morphologically and agronomically. The results of genome mapping of banana were expected in 1997 once molecular data had been compared with field observations.

The CIRAD was co-operating with the International Network for the Improvement of Banana and Plantain, which acted both as financial sponsor and co-ordinator of the genome mapping activities. The CIRAD was also working in collaboration with Australia's Queensland Department of Primary Industries on the study of genetic diversity among some 200 clones originating from surveys made in Papua New Guinea.

A medium-resolution map of the genome of the progeny of the inter-generic hybrid *Citrus* x *Poncirus* had been established; it linked more than 100 RAPD (random amplified polymorphic DNA) and RFLP (restriction fragment length polymorphism) markers and isozymes. In coming years, the map would enable several genes to be localized for resistance to tristeza, *Phytophthora* and nematodes all present in the genome of *Poncirus* (CIRAD, 1993).

Several research teams were working on the marker-assisted mapping of cocoa genome: the Scottish Crop Institute was identifying cocoa clones and analyzing the diversity of small populations, mainly using RAPD markers; at the University of Pennsylvania, genome mapping was based on RAPD markers, while at Purdue University, the diversity of a limited number of cocoa clones had been demonstrated with a DNA probe; in France, at the Nestlé subsidiary, FRANCERECO, in Tours, the cocoa genome was mapped using RFLP markers. The CIRAD BIOTROP Unit was focusing research on the genetic diversity of cocoa Criollo cultivars, because of their high-quality cocoa. Research included: the study of diversity in nuclear and cytoplasmic DNA of 200 clones of various origins; comparison of diversity as shown by RFLP and RAPD markers on approximately 100 clones. Regarding the mapping of the cocoa genome, the BIOTROP project sought to highlight the major genes (or QTL, quantitative trait loci) involved in the determination of the main quality traits, which were numerous and often complex. Once a map including 200 markers at least was established, the analysis of quality traits would be made on one of the progenies.

As indicated previously (see p. 642), genetic improvement of *Hevea brasiliensis* aimed to create higher-yielding (in latex) and disease-resistant varieties (called graft clones). The approaches followed by the breeders dealt with the rational use of genetic resources, the knowledge of genetic determinism and variability of the traits being bred, as well as the identification of markers for an early selection. At the Rubber Research Institute of Malaysia (RRIM), genome mapping was based on RFLP markers, in co-operation with the Plant Breeding Research Institute in Norwich, United Kingdom.

Three research projects of the CIRAD-CP hevea programme were dealing with genetic improvement and breeding. Their strong components were the following:

– reliable recommendation of high-yielding clones in West Africa, resulting from a regional network of field trials, and regular updating of these recommendations for industrial and village plantations;

– network for the creation and selection of hevea clones resistant to *Microcyclus ulei* (South American leaf disease), in French Guyana, Brazil and Guatemala; results expected in the long term would have an important impact on the development of rubber-tree cultivation in South America; while this project also aimed to prevent the spread of this very serious disease to Africa and Asia, it was the only one of its kind world-wide;

– pursuance of a dynamic policy of exchange of plant material (genetic resources and selected clones), which enriched the existing collections, especially with clones originating from Asia;

– isozyme electrophoresis to enable the planter to check the clonal conformity of its planting material (this technique had become a routine test, adapted to the needs of the plantations, and was used in Côte d'Ivoire, Brazil, Guatemala, Indonesia, etc.);

– molecular-biology techniques which allowed the analysis of the diversity of available genetic resources; hevea genome mapping, a world-wide achievement, was expected to lead to marker-assisted breeding schemes;

– somatic embryogenesis, despite its technical difficulties, was crucial, because it would enable to obtain in plantation the juvenile features of the seedlings in an entirely clonal form, and to considerably increase the possibilities of genetically improving the rubber-tree through the maximum exploitation of genetic variability.

Until the end of 1996, the CIRAD BIOTROP Unit was conducting studies on hevea genetic diversity, under a project within the framework of the European Commission's Science and Technology for Development Programme (STD-3), with the CIRAD station in French Guyana, the Catholic University of Leuven (Belgium), the Forestry Institute (IDEFOR) of Côte d'Ivoire (Department of Latex Plants) and the National Institute for Agricultural Research of Cameroon. The objectives of these studies were to evaluate and characterize the collections of wild clones originating from surveys made in three Amazonian States, considered the place of origin of the species; in addition to the analysis of nuclear DNA using RFLPs, which complemented that of mitochondrial DNA carried out in Leuven, new methods of fast molecular screening were to be used on a large scale and *in situ*, and applied to the other eight species of *Hevea*.

The CIRAD Department of Perennial Crops (CIRAD-CP) was working with the Department of Latex Plants of the Forestry Institute of Côte d'Ivoire (IDEFOR-DPL) to manage and evaluate one of the two international *Hevea* collections. It was a living collection containing 3,500 genotypes of the cultivated species *Hevea brasiliensis*, more than 3,000 of which were wild clones from several international surveys in Amazonia. It included 2,500 clones from 16 districts of three States in Brazil: Acre, Rondonia and Mato Grosso, along with 340 from the Schultes collection in Colombia. The pool of clones, resulting from several decades of selection in Asia for latex yields (Wickham clones), made up virtually all the 8 million hectares of rubber trees planted world-wide. It had a genetic base reputed to be narrow, with no resistance to certain diseases. On the other hand, the wild genotypes, which were potentially worthwhile for these traits, produced very little latex compared to the Wickham clones. The *Hevea* breeding programme implemented by the CIRAD and IDEFOR intended to use these genetic resources in a recurrent selection scheme whose efficiency depended on the knowledge of the genetic organization of *Hevea* germplasm (Seguin *et al.*, 1996).

Analysis by isoenzymatic markers had revealed 14 polymorphic loci, using 12 isoenzymatic systems in *Hevea brasiliensis*. The most wide-ranging diversity study involved 419 clones. Within-population variability appeared to be greater than between-population variability (i.e. between surveyed Brazilian States). However, unlike the morphological data, genetic differentiation appeared between populations depending on their geographical origin. The Wickham population appeared to be genetically closer to Mato Grosso. The Schultes population from Colombia seemed to be divergent from the other Amazonian populations, with a few specific alleles. Thus, genetic structuring between Amazonian populations seemd to be due to differences in allelic frequencies rather than to the existence of alleles specific to each population (Seguin *et al.*, 1996).

An RFLP study was carried out on a smaller number of clones: 92 wild clones from Acre, Rondonia and Mato Grosso, and 73 Wickham clones, but a higher number of loci was involved. The RFLP study confirmed the observations made with isoenzymes, such as genetic divergence between Rondonia and Mato Grosso as well as the similarity between the Wickham and Mato Grosso populations. Both isoenzyme and RFLP results enabled the identification of six genetically divergent groups of populations in *Hevea* germplasm; this classification was important for implementing a preservation strategy based on core collections and for achieving an optimum genetic mixing by selecting parents according to the genetic group to which they belonged (Seguin *et al.*, 1996).

Drawing up a *Hevea* linkage map was useful because it would provide information about the genetic organization of the species; it would be possible to tackle the issue of the assumed tetraploidy of *Hevea*. The ten species of the *Hevea* genus had 2n = 36 chromosomes; karyological and botanical data suggested a basic chromosome number of n = 9, but there was no known species close to 2n = 18 chromosomes that could be an ancestor of *Hevea*. Mapping would reveal whether loci were duplicated in their majority, as in the case of a strict amphitetraploid. Mapping also provided a tool for diversity studies. Lastly, and in the longer term, the aim of mapping was to develop marker-assisted breeding: by drawing up a dense linkage map, this approach would make it possible to localize major genes determining traits of agronomic interest and to identify molecular markers closely genetically linked to these genes (Seguin *et al.*, 1996).

The first *Hevea* genetic map was being established on the F2 progeny using isoenzymatic markers, RFLP and RAPD (random amplified polymorphic DNA). The probes used came from a *Hevea* genome bank, cloned at site Pst1 of vector pUC18 of *Escherichia coli*, and corresponded to single sequences. Up to 1995, 170 markers for the F2 population and 95 for the F1, mainly RFLP, had undergone genetic linkage analysis. The resulting map comprised 30 independent linkage groups, while the expected number was 18, since the *Hevea* genome comprised n = 18 chromosome pairs. The number of linkage groups found could be explained by the genome size of *Hevea*, four to five times bigger than cocoa tree genome for instance. Mapping work was being pursued with a target of at least 300 markers, using other RFLP probes, as the genome probe bank had yet to be completely screened, along with other RAPD primers. All this work was being carried out at the CIRAD BIOTROP Unit, in conjunction with the Forestry Institute of Côte d'Ivoire, with support from the European Commission's Science and Technology for Development programme and Michelin company (Seguin *et al.*, 1996).

The Joint Laboratory ORSTOM/CIRAD for Biotechnology of Tropical Forest Symbioses (BSFT) aimed to increase knowledge of the plant and microbial partners of nitrogen-fixing symbioses of tropical trees in order to achieve an optimal plant production. Two models were studied: an actinorhizian symbiosis between *Casuarina* and *Frankia* and a legume symbiosis between *Acacia mangium* and *Bradyrhizobium*. The following topics were the subject of research:

– setting up of the symbiosis (cytophysiological studies, biochemical and physiological study of the infection process);

– molecular study of the symbioses (identification of the plant genes, role of auxins in nodulation);

– improvement of the host-plant productivity (clonal selection through *in-vitro* tissue culture techniques, genetic engineering of beneficial traits);

– ecophysiology of nitrogen-fixing symbioses (study of the functioning of symbiosis in relation with soil nutritional factors, use of immunological methods and molecular biology tools to study the composition and dynamics of populations of micro-organisms involved in symbiosis with forest legume species).

The actinomycete genus *Frankia* was a most versatile and adaptable group of soil micro-organisms unique in being able to initiate effective, nitrogen-fixing, root nodule symbioses with a wide range of non-legume plants. *Frankia* root nodules had been studied for well over 100 years and the genus was formally described in 1970 solely from observations of bacterial form within root nodules. It was not until 1978 that the first pure culture of *Frankia* was established (Silvester, 1995).

The so-called non-legume root nodule plants, also known as actinorhizal plants, occurred in 24 genera and 194 species among eight families of Angiosperms. These plants were more common in the temperate regions of the world where their distribution complemented that of tropically-centred legumes. Host plants were trees and shrubs, with only one herbaceous genus (*Datisca*) and nodules often grew big, up to tennis ball size in genera such as *Alnus* and *Coriaria*. The plants were often pioneers on poor soils and played a major ecological role in early regeneration of eroded areas and new soils. Actinorhizal plants had a limited economic role as timber species (*Alnus, Casuarina*), some had high value as fuelwood (*Casuarina*) but were generally most valued for their ecological role and for reclaiming eroded and waste ground (Silvester, 1995).

First use of the name *Frankia* was made by Brunchorst in 1888 to honour his mentor A.B. Franck. By the turn of the century, it was established that the organism was a filamentous bacterium and the nitrogen-fixing capacity of the nodules was confirmed by growth experiments. In 1959, Pommer had described an actinomycete, isolated from the nodule of *Alnus glutinosa*, that in fact had all the attributes of *Frankia*, but this isolate was lost. It remained until 1978 for Torrey's group to provide the first viable culture of *Frankia* which was infective and effective on *Alnus* plants. The family Frankiaceae included the genus *Frankia*, *Geodermatophilus* and *Blastococcus* (Silvester, 1995).

Frankia had variable structure both in symbiosis and in the free-living state. Strains were characterized by extensive hyphae and terminal or intercalary multilocular sporangia. A most important feature of the genus was the production of vesicles in culture. Vesicles were lipid encapsulated spheres 2-6 μm in diameter, borne on short vesicle stalks cut off by a cross wall. They developed in response to a low nitrogen environment and were the sites of nitrogenase activity. In symbiosis, the host plant played an important role in modifying the *Frankia* morphology as there was a wide variation in the presence or absence of sporangia and in the size, shape or presence of vesicles within nodules (Silvester, 1995).

In culture, *Frankia* showed a doubling time of at least 15 hours and this, along with the lack of homogeneity due to its filamentous forms, resulted in significant culturing difficulties. Growth media ranged from simple basal salts media containing a suitable carbon substrate to complex organic media and there was no evidence of any extra required growth factors. Some strains, notably those identified as genomic species 1, grew well on short chain fatty acids (acetate, propionate), variably on succinate, pyruvate, malate, and poorly or not at all on sugars. Other strains, particularly those which infected *Casuarina* and *Elaeagnus* grew well on sugars and organic acids. Propionate came close to being the universal carbon substrate for all *Frankia* strains (Silvester, 1995).

From the earliest isolations of *Frankia* it was reported that optimum nitrogenase activity was obtained at atmospheric pO_2, making *Frankia* and the cyanobacteria the only organisms expressing nitrogenase at those concentrations of oxygen. The onset of nitrogenase was correlated with the presence of vesicles in which the enzyme was located. The vesicle was a very specialized cell, often subdivided within and with a multilaminate lipid outer envelope that appeared to be the site of oxygen protection. When *Frankia* cultures were grown at very low pO_2, vesicles were not formed and nitrogenase was expressed in the filaments (Silvester, 1995).

Frankia cells had been shown to contain a high concentration of hopanoid lipids which were a class of pentacyclic triterpenoids with sterol-like properties. These bacterio-hopanes were common to many bacterial cells where they played a direct role in the stability and fluidity of membranes. However, in *Frankia*, the nature and position of the hopanoids emphasized the uniqueness of this organism: they were laid down in monolayers outside of the cell in a highly-structured envelope. There seemed little doubt that this envelope structure played a vital role in the control of gas diffusion into the vesicle and its thickness was essentially controlled by the ambient pO_2 of the cells (Silvester, 1995).

Actinorhizal nodules were well aerated and much of the oxygen control was at the host cell wall or in the vesicle. In those host plants that stimulated the formation of symbiotic vesicles, e.g. *Alnus*, it was likely that the vesicle wall was the major site of diffusion resistance. However, there were many genera that produced symbioses where there were no vesicles or where vesicles were simply enlarged filaments. In these cases, there was strong evidence that the cell wall or host cytoplasm played a major role in controlling gas exchange (Silvester, 1995).

Researchers believed that *Frankia* was a widespread soil saprophyte and that soil populations of *Frankia* were greatest in the presence of a host plant or even related host, e.g. *Betula* spp. were able to promote the growth of *Frankia* strains which could nodulate *Alnus*. There was reason to believe that some *Frankia* strains were ubiquitous and persisted in the absence of host plants; however, there was also evidence that in some cases the continued presence of a host plant was essential for the maintenance of inocula (Silvester, 1995).

Although a variety of attempts to assign species to the *Frankia* group had proved controversial, a considerable degree of host specificity occurred with the result that host-plant origin and nodulation within host-specificity groups were most relevant characteristics for strain identification. A wide range of studies using serology, isoenzyme analysis, whole cell protein, as well as DNA-homology indicated a great phenotypic and genotypic diversity within the genus *Frankia*. It might be possible that this diversity would span more than one genus within the nitrogen-fixing, nodulating actinomycetes (Silvester, 1995).

To sum up, *Frankia* biology came of age only in 1978 with the isolation of the first pure culture. The organism had a vast range of variability and physiological diversity: it had the unique capacity of being able to fix atmospheric nitrogen at almost any concentration of pO_2, a capacity shared only with cyanobacteria. In addition, it formed effective symbiosis with a wide range of Angiosperm hosts. Although little progress had been made on the nodulating genes associated with *Frankia*, it was likely that in the search for a manipulatable symbiotic diazotroph, *Frankia* would prove to be a more amenable subject than *Rhizobium* (Silvester, 1995).

The most efficient actinorhizal plants belonged to the genera *Alnus*, *Casuarina* and *Hippophae*. The latter were comparable to nitrogen-fixing tree legumes like *Leucaena leucocephala*. Actual nitrogen fixation was generally lower than the potential fixing power: for instance, in *Casuarina equisetifolia*, this potential was 45 g of nitrogen per tree per year, while actual fixation could be as low as 6 g of nitrogen per tree per annum (i.e. 12 kg nitrogen per year for a population of some 2,000 trees per hectare) in sites with severe constraints (e.g. aridity). In order to enhance the actual nitrogen-fixation capacity, three approaches could be followed: selection of host plants which were adapted to environmental stresses; identification of strains adapted to these stresses so as to be inoculated in nurseries, using alginate-embedded inoculants; and adoption of appropriate cultivation practices (e.g. inputs of minimum fertilizers, water management and association with a non-nitrogen-fixing plant species). While molecular biology tools would allow the construction of new *Frankia* strains and the genetic transformation of host plants, significant progress could be achieved through the screening of *Frankia* strains and clonal selection of their host plants.

At the BSFT Laboratory, studies were being carried out on the diversity of microsymbionts associated with plants belonging to the genera, *Casuarina*, *Allocasuarina* and *Gymnostoma*, of the Casuarinaceae originating from Asia and Oceania. The French researchers, in collaboration with Australia's Commonwealth Scientific and Industrial Research Organisation (Queensland), had succeeded in obtaining exponential growth of several strains on an inorganic medium containing a mixture of phosphatidyl cholines. It was also shown that synthetic 1,2-dipalmitoyl phosphatidyl choline, palmitic acid and certain fatty acids could replace the phosphatidyl cholines mixture. In addition, the study of esterases, dehydrogenases and aminopeptidases had demonstrated that the tested *Gymnostoma* strain had isoenzyme profiles very distinct from those of strains isolated from *Casuarina* and

Allocasuarina. These biochemical methods enabled the researchers to identify the strain.

Furthermore, molecular-biology methods were used for studying the diversity of *Frankia* strains associated with the genera *Allocasuarina*, *Casuarina* and *Gymnostoma*, while avoiding the isolation of the strains. Nodules had been collected in Australia, which is the natural distribution area of *Casuarina* and *Allocasuarina*. DNA had been extracted from nodules and two DNA regions had been amplified which corresponded to the endosymbiont present in the nodules. Five groups (PCR/RFLP) could be distinguished among the 'non-isolated' strains that nodulated *Casuarina equisetifolia*, *C. cunninghamiana*, *Allocasuarina torulosa* and *A. littoralis*. These strains were distributed in the five groups according to the host-plant species: strains associated with *Casuarina equisetifolia* in groups 1 and 2, strains associated with *C. cunninghamiana* in group 3, strains associated with *A. torulosa* in group 4 and strains associated with *A. littoralis* in group 5. The same method was used for nodules collected from different species of *Gymnostoma* in New Caledonia, and it was shown that there was no correlation between the groups and the host-plant species. It was also suggested that the strains associated with *Gymnostoma* were genetically close to those which nodulated Elaeagnaceae plants.

Surveys had shown that many actinorhizian plants could host, in addition to *Frankia*, arbuscular endomycorhizal fungi (AM) and ectomycorhizal fungi (EM), and sometimes both types of mycorhizae in the same plant species. Some observations suggested that there was compatibility between ectomycorhizae and their plant hosts: for instance, *Alpova diplophloeus* was one of the rare ectomycorhizal fungi capable of forming a complete Hartig network in the root cortex of *Alnus* spp. Similarly, ectomycorhizal fungi (*Pisolithus*) could form true mycorhizae with *Allocasuarina* and not with *Casuarina*. The presence of both *Frankia* and AM and/or EM fungi in the same plant gave rise to a multiple symbiosis, which was an obvious advantage for actinorhizian plants living in low-fertility soils.

Other actinorhizian plants belonging to the Casuarinaceae and Myricaceae showed an efficient adaptive response to the adverse environment where they lived: they could from specialized roots called proteoid roots or cluster roots in response to iron and phosphorus deficiencies in soils. Consequently, sylvicultural practices aiming at stimulating cluster-root formation (e.g. soil aeration and incorporation of plant residues) or selection of species or genotypes with high cluster-root-producing ability might improve growth performance of trees through increasing their adaptive potential to nutrient-impoverished soils. Selection of criteria were: total number and length of cluster roots; total number and length of rootlets in the clusters; presence or absence of root hairs on the rootlets; time needed for cluster-root formation; duration of cluster-root viability; estimation of the release by cluster roots of organic acids, reducing and chelating compounds. As cluster-root formation was a plant response to nutrient deficiencies, it might be considered an indicator of low soil fertility, e.g. phosphorus and iron deficiencies (Diem and Arahou, 1996).

It seemed that the presence of *Frankia*, even established in the prenodule, did not prevent the infection of the root by an ectomycorhizal fungus, thus leading to the formation of a fungal blanket around the root and of the Hartig network. The presence of *Frankia* did not change the recognition system of the fungus and its host plant, nor the mycorhizal infectious process. In contrast, in the *Rhizobium*-legume symbiosis, earlier mycorhization of a root inhibited the formation of the bacterial infectious thread and the induction of the nodular meristem, due to the probable disturbance by the mycorhizal fungus of the exchange of signals between the plant and its bacterial symbiont.

Since 1990, the BSFT had been carrying out gene transfer in *Casuarina* and *Acacia*. Researchers had performed the first gene transfer in a nitrogen-fixing tree, *Allocasuarina verticillata*; the roots of this actinorhizal plant were transformed by *Agrobacterium rhizogenes* strains A4 and 2659, followed by the regeneration of whole plantlets. The latter could be used for studying the regulation of certain genes, e.g. leghaemoglobin genes, but not for reforestation schemes, because they had an abnormal phenotype (characteristic of plants transformed by the Ri plasmid of *A. rhizogenes*): lack of apex dominance in the aerial part of the plant and hairy roots.

Other transformation techniques were used to obtain plants with a normal phenotype. Two wild strains of *Agrobacterium tumefaciens*, qualified as 'budding' strains (they could induce tumours with buds in the inoculated host plant), were used to produce tumours in 20% to 50% of the inoculated plants. No buds were observed on the tumours induced in *Casuarina glauca* and *Acacia mangium*, but buds developed on 40% of tumours induced in *Acacia albida*.

Transformation of *Casuarina glauca* was done by two disarmed strains of *A. tumefaciens*, GV 2260 and EHA 101, which included in the BIN19 vector the gene *nptII* for resistance to kanamycin and the reporter gene *gus* for beta-glucuronidase, the presence of which was demonstrated by the appearance of blue crystals when transformed tissues were incubated with the substrate X-glu. Several types of explants (cotyledons, epicotyles and hypocotyles excised from one- to two-month old plants) were co-cultivated with the two *A. tumefaciens* strains, then incubated on a nutrient medium containing growth regulators and kanamycin. After growing a culture for two months on a selective medium, 20% of explants showed an average of three calli expressing beta-glucuronidase activity. Research was being pursued to increase the transformation rate of *Casuarina glauca* by disarmed *Agrobacterium* strains. The regeneration of plants from transformed tissues had also been obtained.

BSFT researchers focused on: the study of regulation of expression of plant symbiotic genes in transgenic plants; and the transfer of useful traits like resistance to insect pests via genetic transformation.

The BSFT had established co-operation ties with the following institutions:

– Senegalese Institute for Agricultural Research/ORSTOM, Dakar, for genetic transformation of mahogany and transfer of genes coding for resistance to insect pests;

– Division of Plant Industry, Commonwealth Scientific and Industrial Research Organisation (CSIRO, Canberra), for the study of leghaemoglobin genes in *Casuarina*;

– Department of Biological Engineering, Technological University, Compiègne, France, for direct gene transfer (particle gun);

– Laboratory for Genetic Improvement of Fruit Trees, National Institute for Agricultural Research (INRA), Bordeaux, for transgenesis related to viral resistance;

– Laboratory of Genetics, University of Ghent, Belgium, for genetic transformation of forest trees;

– Division of Crop Protection, Rhône-Poulenc, Lyon, for direct gene transfer (Rhône-Poulenc was the first French private corporation to request the commercialization of a transgenic plant, a tobacco plant resistant to the herbicide bromoxynile; it was also experienced in direct gene transfer in maize; the bromoxynile resistance gene was used as a marker in genetic transformation of *Casuarina*).

The common name of fruit fly was given to several species of the Tephritidae family, three of which had an economic impact in The Réunion: *Ceratitis rosa*, called 'Natal', was present throughout the island up to an altitude of 1,500 metres; *C. capitata* was found in the low-lying zones of the northwest; *C. catoirii* in the south and east. The Natal fly caused the most extensive damage and tended to dominate the two other species; it attacked almost all fruits, except pineapple and banana; the fly oviposited a string of eggs in the fruit; the hatched larvae fed on the fruit for about 12 days until, at the end of the third larval stage, the larvae fell from the fruit, burrowed into the ground and pupated, to emerge as flies; the entire cycle lasted about three weeks. The cost of chemical treatment, added to that of lost sales from damaged fruit, was estimated at $1.2 million annually, more than enough to justify the decision, in 1990, to consider the fight against this pest a research priority (CIRAD, 1994). Sexual traps with a parapheromone (trimedlure), a substance which attracted males, had been developed; research into types of traps and recipes for trimedlure and associated insecticides was sufficiently advanced in 1991 for trapping to be standardized and made available to farmers; four traps per hectare were recommendded (CIRAD, 1994).

Also in The Réunion, the CIRAD was entrusted with the biological control of white grub, the larva of a cockchafer, the polyphagous *Haplochelus marginalis*, a sugar-cane pest. The insect was also found in Madagascar where it was endemic. The CIRAD was co-operating with the National Institute for Agricultural Research (INRA) and the University of The Réunion, as well as with the Mauritius Sugar Industry Research Institute and the National Centre for Applied Research to Rural Development in Madagascar. The biological study of the insect's life-cycle showed that the hatched larvae became dangerous at the L3 adult stage, which covered the period from April to the end of July, precisely the growth period for sugar-cane; the insect fed on the roots to the point of severing the cane from its water and nutrient supplies; the uprooted plant being no longer able to form tissue, it withered and toppled under pressure from the wind or its own weight. Each female laid an average of 40 eggs, the multiplication coefficient from one generation to the next being about 20. Field samples taken since 1981, during the first recorded attack by the insect, showed that only three to five grubs per stool caused enough damage to become an economic hazard. The rate at which the pest was spreading had also been determined: each year, the front line of attack was advancing by three to four kilometres (CIRAD, 1994).

In 1987, diseased larvae were found infected with an entomopathogenic fungus, *Beauveria brongniartii*, which was specific to the white grub as it could not develop in any other living organism. This discovery was followed by agronomic trials in the field from 1989 to 1993, which confirmed the fungus' high potency. In the laboratory, steamed rice was used as a culture medium for the fungus while, for industrial production, the INRA and the Calliope company came up with a substrate made of granulated clay; the recommended dose of 30 kg to 50 kg of pellets per hectare was economically acceptable. The treatment was incorporated when the sugar-cane was planted, along with a quarter of the usual dose of an insecticide to protect the plants while the pathogen developed. Immediately after the product was licensed by the Agriculture and Fisheries Ministry in 1993, its commercialization began (CIRAD, 1994).

The first advantage of this biological control was that the populations of white grub larvae were drastically reduced and that only a low, single dose of insecticide was necessary. The second advantage was economic: the biological treatment (including the insecticide) cost $240 per hectare and was only applied once; conventional chemical treatment cost $400 per hectare and could be repeated every three years (CIRAD, 1994).

Still in The Réunion, the distribution of healthy citrus planting material was associated with a biological control method for protecting the orchards by creating an equilibrium between the pests transmitting the greening disease and their parasites: the entomophagous *Tamarixia dryi* from Africa or *Tamarixia radiata* from Asia, which attacked the citrus psylla, the disease vector (CIRAD, 1994).

Over the first 70 years following its discovery at the beginning of this century, *Bacillus thuringiensis* (*Bt*) had captured the attention of relatively few microbiologists and entomologists. In 1995, 90 years later, it was being studied by scientists from a wide range of disciplines. Nowadays, *Bt* was not only the most succesful commercial microbial insecticide with world-wide applications for protection of crops, forests and human health, it was also replacing chemical insecticides (Klier, 1995).

Throughout the 1980s, the commercial applications of *Bacillus thuringiensis* as a biopesticide had increased to about 90% of the global biopesticide market. Estimated sales figures for 1990 showed that applications in agriculture accounted for 60% of world consumption, while forestry accounted for 20% and vector and nuisance control took up the balance of 20%. North America and the Far East were major markets, the European market being considerably smaller (Morris-Coole, 1995)[13 (see p. 693)].

Bacillus thuringiensis is a Gram positive, spore-forming bacterium, primarily recognized as an insect pathogen that is a ubiquitous soil micro-organism. The sole unequivocal difference between *B. thuringiensis* (*Bt*) and *B. cereus*, also a common soil inhabitant, is the absence of a parasporal crystal in *B. cereus*. *Bacillus cereus* has, in turn, a close evolutionary relationship with *B. sphaericus*, a producer of mosquitocidal proteinaceous inclusions (Morris-Coole, 1995).

Bt was a diverse group of bacteria. While in the early 1960s, *Bt* strains were considered to be toxic to Lepidoptera only, in the late 1970s and early 1980s, *Bt* strains had been isolated which were also toxic to Diptera such as mosquito and blackfly larvae, and to Coleoptera such as Colorado potato beetle and elm beetle larvae. More recently, the discovery of strains specifically toxic to protozoan pathogens, animal-parasitic liver flukes (Trematoda) or mites (Acari) had broadened the potential *Bt* product spectrum even further. With the increasing number of crystal protein genes identified in an ever increasing number of strains, however, it had become clear that the insecticidal activity and spectrum was almost exclusively determined by the crystal protein composition (Klier, 1995).

Crystal protein genes from strains belonging to a wide range of serotypes had been sequenced, constituting a total of about 20 distinct genes and corresponding crystal proteins. These proteins had a molecular weight either in the range of 130 kilodaltons and/or 70 kDa. Upon ingestion by the insects, the 130 kDa crystal proteins were proteolytically activated into a 60 kDa toxic fragment by removal of the C-terminal moiety of the molecule (Klier, 1995). The toxins react with the brush-border membrane of the mid-gut epithelial cells, with a consequent increase in membrane permeability through cation-selective channels. Swelling and lysis of the cells follow, with associated inhibition of feeding by the larvae. Leakage of ions from gut to haemolymph causes a sufficient ionic imbalance to cause paralysis and death. Death may also be caused by septicaemia induced by the vegetative propagation of *Bt* within the insect gut and haemocoel (Morris-Coole, 1995).

On the basis of their sequence homology and insecticidal activity spectrum, the crystal proteins had been grouped in five classes. The CryI proteins were toxic to Lepidopteran larvae and were the most comemonly found. Although some of these proteins were very closely related, each protein had its own characteristic insecticidal activity spectrum. The CryII proteins were typically accumulated in cuboid crystals. The CryIIA was active against both Lepidopteran and Dipteran larvae, while CryIIB was toxic only to Lepidopteran larvae. The CryIII proteins accumulated in rhomboidal crystals and they seemed to show a rather limited diversity in the activity spectrum against some Coleopteran larvae. The CryIV proteins were fairly heterogeneous in their molecular structure, but all CryIV proteins were toxic to mosquito and blackfly larvae. The CytA protein was not a true insecticidal protein, but rather a cytolytic protein; it was not related to the insecticidal crystal proteins and was found in association with Dipteran specific crystal proteins. *Bt* strains had been identified which were active against nematodes; the corresponding crystal genes belonged to group V (Klier, 1995).

Two major achievements consisted of determining the structure of a Cry *Bt* toxin by X-ray crystallography, and purifying a 120 kDa putative receptor to CryIA (c) and identifying it as a N-aminopeptidase. The full length receptor had been cloned and sequenced, and it was demonstrated that binding occurred via a sugar moiety. The importance of the binding to the midgut epithelial cells was further demonstrated in those few cases where insects had developed resistance to one or several crystal proteins. It was shown that in the *Bt* resistant populations the binding and/or number of receptors were significantly reduced. These studies demonstrated the presence in the midgut cells of different receptors for different crystal proteins, allowing a management of *Bt* resistance (Klier, 1995).

The commercial success of *Bt kurstaki* in forestry and the efficiency of *Bt israelensis* for blackfly control focused attention on this biopesticide. However, *Bt* sales were currently restricted to high-value or environmentally-sensitive market niches. This lack of widespread adoption was due partly to several inherent biological features of *Bt* which included: host range specificity; inability to target pests that fed internally or on roots; lack of residual activity on foliage due to degradation by sunlight or other environmental factors; lack of residual activity in water due to rapid settling of spores and crystals and adsorption to organic particles; lack of residual activity in soil due to degradation by soil micro-organisms. These features were frequently cited to stress the disadvantages of using *Bt*, i.e. the need for more frequent applications, improved application equipment and intensive scouting to improve timing of applications (in other words, increased time and financial investments). To overcome these limitations, the firms were trying to modify the formulations in order to protect the toxins and to keep the active product in the feeding zone of the larvae. Another possibility was genetic engineering of plants to introduce the genes for the toxins (Klier, 1995).

The plasmid location of the *Cry* genes enabled the construction of novel δ-endotoxin gene combinations using microbial genetic approaches such as plasmid using conjugal transfer. These strategies had been successfully employed and led to new *Bt* strains showing significantly improved insecticidal activities for specific target pests. Thus a strain active against both Lepidopteran and Coleopteran larvae had been constructed. In addition, the knowledge of the three-dimensional structure of the toxin and the identification of a receptor to the toxin allowed the construction of toxins with new or increased specific activity against a specific pest. Thus protein engineering was becoming a powerful tool to construct more potent toxins and this would avoid the emergence of resistance (Klier, 1995).

Mycogen Corp. had improved stability in the field by introducing a *Bt* crystal protein gene in *Pseudomonas fluorescens*, which was then killed and stabilized. An interesting side-effect of the CellCap^R technology was that the product consisted of a killed engineered organism and had received the first two approvals from the U.S. Environment Protection Agency for a genetically-engineered pesticide. Crop Genetics International had designed a system whereby the *Bt* crystal protein was targeted inside the plant. A crystal protein gene was engineered into a plant endophytic bacterium, *Clavibacter xyli* subsp. *cynodentis;* upon germination of seeds coated with this bacterium, the micro-organism replicated in the vascular system of the plant, thereby producing insecticidal amounts of the *Bt* crystal protein. To overcome the *Bt* limitations in the control of soil-dwelling insects, the *Bt* crystal genes had been successfully introduced into root-colonizing *Pseudomonas fluorescens* or nodulating *Bradyrhizobium*. However, the efficieny of this approach remained to be demonstrated in field conditions. Finally, to prolong the effectiveness of *Bt israelensis* toxins, various groups had investigated the expression of selected CryIV toxin genes in micro-organisms that lived in the same aquatic environments as targeted mosquitoes or blackflies. In this way, Dipteran active toxins would persist and possibly increase in number at the appropriate depth thus increasing delivery of *Bt* toxins to targeted aquatic insect species. However, whatever the system used, the expression level of the toxins remained too low to be efficient (Klier, 1995).

Agrobacterium-transformed tobacco with a δ-endotoxin gene generated the first transgenic plant made resistant to insect pests sensitive to this toxin. Since then, more than 25 plant species had been transformed and expressed Lepidopteran- and Coleopteran-specific crystal proteins. Laboratory, greenhouse and field experiments with engineered plants exhibited significant protection against the insect larvae. It was imperative that δ-endotoxin amounts in transgenic plants were sufficient to produce complete, or very near complete, insect control. This technology was being improved markedly and would allow a wider range of insect pests to be targeted thereby creating additional tools for an environmentally sound and efficient crop protection (Klier, 1995).

There were several on-going screening programmes still leading to the discovery of novel strains and genes with interesting activities against insects and even other pests. Beside the screening effect, a growing understanding of the mechanism of action was expected to lead to the engineering of proteins with a higher insecticidal activity and spectrum. As a delivery system, *Bt* was still a very useful vehicle for administering crystal proteins to pests. Engineering for broader activity spectra and formulations for prolonged field persistence, however, were expected to make *Bt* more successful. Other microbial hosts for crystal proteins could present interesting alternatives and, eventually, the plant itself might become the vehicle for administering biopesticides (Klier, 1995).

Resistance to *Bt* δ-endotoxins had been described for the first time in 1985 in the laboratory. It was currently known in ten species of Lepidoterans belonging to four families, two Coleopteran species (Chrysomelidae) and three Dipteran species (Culicidae and Muscidae). The first case of resistance in natural conditions was reported in 1990 in Hawaii; it concerned the Cruciferous pest, *Plutella xylostella*. Since then, other cases had been described in Florida, New York State, The Philippines, Malaysia and Thailand. Cases of crossed resistance, i.e. resistance to several endotoxins, had been described since 1992 (Sanchis *et al.*, 1995).

Little was known about the genetic determinism of resistance of insects to *Bt*, as well as its stability and biological cost. Resistance seemed to be accompanied by reduced fertility and fecundity. One possible resistance mechanism would be a pH modification or a change in the reducing capacity prevailing in the larvae gut, which would hinder the dissolution of crystal proteins; the latter would be therefore eliminated with the faeces. Another mechanism, demonstrated in a population of *Plutella interpunctella*, was the non-activation of the protoxins by the insect's proteases. It was also shown that resistance was due to a modification of the number and affinity of receptors for the endotoxin, existing on the surface of the gut epithelial cells. As the receptors were specific to different δ-endotoxins, an insect resistant to one endotoxin could still be sensitive to another one (Sanchis *et al.*, 1995).

However, although *Bt* had been used in agriculture for more than 30 years, the cases of populations of insects resistant to *Bt* in natural conditions were rare. This absence of natural selection of resistant insects might be due to: the fact that commercial preparations of *Bt* contained several genes encoding different δ-endotoxins, and that most of sensitive insects possessed several distinct receptors for these δ-endotoxins; selection pressure was still weak because massive and systematic utilization of *Bt* in agriculture was exceptional; δ-endotoxins were rapidly inactivated by ultra-violet radiation and consequently *Bt* formulations did not remain in the environment (Sanchis *et al.*, 1995).

But the development of resistance in a natural population of *Plutella xylostella* could be explained by the intense selection pressure (fields had been treated 50 to 100 times over five years) and in a relatively 'closed'environment where genetic exchange with other populations was limited, thus inducing the rapid development of a genetically homogenous resistant population; in addition, while the *Bt* strain used for spraying produced five different δ-endotoxins, only receptors to one of these toxins and to two others not produced by the *Bt* strain were found in *P. xylostella*. These observations pointed to ways and means for avoiding the emergence of resistance: firstly, it was recommended to use *Bt* strains containing several δ-endotoxins which were shown to recognize several distinct receptors in the target insect; secondly, the number of applications must be reduced, so as to reduce the selection pressure; thirdly, treatment with *Bt* should alternate with treatment by other pesticides.

In 1989, 15 companies heavily involved in *Bt* research (including Monsanto Co., Sandoz AG, Calgene Inc. and Abbott Laboratories) had created the *Bt* Management Working Group. With a $250,000 budget for four years, the Group had funded research on the molecular and cellular basis of *Bt* toxicity and resistance. The Group had also funded experimental tests of strategies for minimizing the threat of resistance, such as field experiments involving transgenic maize plants resistant to the European corn borer, and the use of computer modelling to determine if mixtures of genetically-modified and 'normal' maize could slow or avoid *Bt* resistance. The Group had concluded that the risk of resistance to *Bt* was minimal as part of integrated pest management programmes (*Seedling*, Quarterly Newsletter of Genetic Resources Action International-GRAIN, vol. 12, no. 4, December 1995, pp. 2–10).

However, according to Tabashnik and his colleagues of the University of Arizona, their work showed that a single gene in resistant moths conferred resistance to four different *Bt* toxins, and this gene appeared to be far more common than believed. These researchers found that 21% of moths in a population that had not been exposed to the toxin for at least 100 generations had the resistance gene. Geneticists had previously estimated that *Bt* resistance genes would be carried by as few as 1 in 10,000 insects. According to Hutchinson of the University of Minnesota, other laboratory studies showed the presence of resistant corn borers in field populations in Minnesota, Iowa and Kansas. One of the U.S. Environmental Protection Agency's (EPA) conditions for allowing the release of *Bt* cotton was that Monsanto Co. develop and implement effective resistance management plans. One component of these plans was that the *Bt* cotton had to produce a toxin dose sufficient to kill virtually all the bollworms. The USA-based Union of Concerned Scientists thought that component was not fulfilled and consequently demanded a hearing to the EPA on this subject (*Seedling,* the Quarterly Newsletter of Genetic Resources Action International-GRAIN, vol. 14, no. 1, March 1997, p. 30).

A number of environmental non-governmental organizations as well as organic farmers, who were the first to denounce the excessive use of pesticides, were reluctant to accept the trend that *Bt* (and other industrially-controlled biological control agents) must become *the* alternative to the dependency on pesticides in intensive agriculture. For them, the use of pesticides was merely one of the symptoms of unsustainable agricultural practices that relied on high-external energetic and chemical inputs, irrigation and monocropping to provide uniform harvests. For them, sustainable agriculture should be built upon the full realization of agro-ecosystem potentialities and synergies (including farmers' work and creativity) rather than on piecemeal action of external elements. For instance, a simple and proven alternative to Monsanto's *Bt*-engineered potato in controlling Colorado potato beetle was to rely on a number of cultural practices such as crop rotation, trap cropping, mulching and late planting, which limited pest proliferation. This kind of sustainable agriculture could also admit punctual input of external elements such as biopesticides, but without relying only on *Bt*. The position of industry was of course different, because none of the measures advocated by the environmentalist groups provided for an uniform and extensive market (*Seedling*, vol. 12, no. 4, December 1995, pp. 2–10).

Ciba-Geigy AG had estimated that 10% of all pesticides would be biologically-based by the year 2000, representing some $3 billion in world sales, compared to the $130–140 million market for biopesticides by the mid-1990s (*Seedling*, vol. 12, no. 4, December 1995, pp. 2–10).

In 1996, *Bt* continued to concentrate over one-third of all research on microbial control agents. If one takes the whole *Bacillus* family, this figure went up to 46%. If one takes the number of published research reports as a yardstick, the conclusion was that out of the thousands of possible approaches to biological control of crop pests, well over half (56%) of all biotechnology research on microbial control agents focused on two genera: *Bacillus* and *Pseudomonas*. Some sources indicated that currently 95% of all biotechnology research to develop microbial insecticides was directed at *Bt* (*Seedling*, vol. 12, no. 4, December 1995, pp. 2–10).

According to Ciba-Geigy AG, *Bt* genetically-engineered maize would have 75% of market share in the U.S. western corn belt within ten years, and 50% market share in other parts of the corn belt. It was thus not surprising that maize was at the heart of the industry's research efforts on *Bt*-engineered plants (particularly of those of major maize breeders such as Ciba-Geigy AG and Pioneer Hi-Bred International, Inc.). Many of the big *Bt* players were involved in maize *Bt* technology: Ecogen Inc. was working on bio-insecticides; Zeneca Seeds plc (former ICI Seeds) on the inoculation of bacteria genetically engineered to contain *Bt*; and Mycogen Corp., Plant Genetic Systems (PGS) N.V., Ciba-Geigy AG and Monsanto Co. were focusing their endeavours on building *Bt* genes into maize. Marketing agreements involved other big companies such as Sandoz AG (*Seedling*, vol. 12, no. 4, December 1995, pp. 2–10).

In addition, Monsanto Co.'s *Bt*-engineered potatoes and cotton had been granted commercial approval. The International Rice Research Institute (IRRI) was developing rice varieties resistant to yellow stem borer from genetically-engineered rice containing a synthetic *Bt* gene patented by Ciba-Geigy AG. Other crop species and plants like soybeans, wheat, tomato, brassica, white spruce and hybrid poplar, were also the subject of similar research (*Seedling*, vol. 12, no. 4, December 1995, pp. 2–10).

By March 1995, there were no less than 440 either granted or pending patents related to *Bt*. The public sector with some 12% of these patents was virtually excluded. The top ten *Bt* companies, including chemical giants lile Ciba-Geigy AG, ICI Ltd, Monsanto Co. and Sandoz AG controlled 44% of all patents and applications for patents. A single company, Mycogen Corp., accounted for 16% of all of them, while a number of other biotechnology companies, such as Plant Genetic Systems (PGS) N.V. and Ecogen Inc., were also actively present (*Seedling*, vol. 12, no. 4, December 1995, pp. 2–10).

While they fought each other on the patent front, the same companies formed alliances to get hold of missing pieces of technology, or to transfer the technology to the market. It was striking that most of the alliances were developed within the group that was already strong in *Bt* technology thus ensuring that no unwanted newcomers entered this field. For instance, Mycogen Corp. had cross licensing agreements with Ciba-Geigy AG and Pioneer Hi-Bred International, Inc. to work on *Bt*-engineered maize. In turn, Pioneer bought 13% of Mycogen's shares. Monsanto Co. had licensed *Bt* technology from Novo Nordisk (for their *Bt*-engineered potatoes), while it allowed Sandoz AG to commercialize Monsanto's *Bt*-engineered maize. Often the agreements were between big agrochemical corporations with direct access to the market and specialized biotechnology companies without infrastructure to get their products to the market, using their intellectual property rights portfolio to bargain joint ventures with seed companies or to earn royalties from licensing (*Seedling*, vol. 12, no. 4, December 1995, pp. 2–10).

The CIRAD BIOTROP Unit was focusing research on extending the range of action of *Bt* strains. The identification of *Bacillus thuringiensis* strains based on bioassays (effect of a particular toxin on an insect species) was impeded by a number of difficulties, some of them impossible to overcome. CIRAD researchers designed a rapid screening technique based on PCR (polymerase chain reaction), which relied on the use of the four specific starters of the genes encoding the four categories of *Bt* toxins, each active against a category of insects (CryI, CryII, CryIII, and CryIV). This first screening was followed by bioassays on the category of insects against which the toxin was effective, thus accelerating the identification of the useful *Bt* strains.

In collaboration with the University of Montreal and the Institut Pasteur, CIRAD researchers were trying to elucidate the mode of action of *Bt* toxins. The latter were made of two subunits, the 'receptor area' which recognized the binding sites on the membrane of epithelial cells of the insect gut, and the 'canal area' which induced the formation of a pore through the membrane, followed by its destruction. It was assumed that these two domains were independent and that toxin specificity was associated with the receptor area. Chimaeric toxins, comprising the receptor area of toxin CryIC, effective against *Plutella xylostella*, and the canal area of toxin CryIE, ineffective against this insect pest, and conversely, were constructed. Toxicity tests performed on the insect were negative, while the same toxins could induce the formation of pores in artificial lipid membranes and cell cultures. Therefore toxin specificity was not dependent on its receptor area only, but on the interaction between both areas.

Markets were often closed to meat exports from sub-Saharan African countries (Zimbabwe being an exception), because these countries were unable to guarantee the health of their livestock. The lack of trained personnel and veterinary equipment and the all-too-frequent disruptions in cold-transport services – where these existed – which altered the samples, made diagnosis difficult. However, progress in molecular biology made it possible to think in realistic terms of devising a diagnostic kit usable on-site. In 1991, the Office international des epizooties (OIE, International Office of Epizootics) appointed PATHOTROP (the CIRAD laboratory of tropical animal diseases), the first Centre of Applied Methodology for Diagnosing Animal Diseases (CAMDA). PATHOTROP was entrusted with the mission of devising field kits for rinderpest, goat plague, contagious bovine pleuropneumonia, caprine (goat) contagious pleuropneumonia and other mycoplasmoses, and was to train technicians how to use them. PATHOTROP was co-operating with the National Veterinary Institute in Ethiopia, the Farcha Laboratory in Chad, the Bingerville Laboratory in Côte d'Ivoire, Utrecht University and Uppsala University (CIRAD, 1994).

Rinderpest was the deadliest of the diseases affecting both cattle (oxen, zebus and domesticated buffalo) and wild artiodactyla. It was caused by a morbillivirus, an RNA virus related to the measles virus. The diseased animals developed ocular discharge, mouth lesions, severe diarrhoea and lost weight rapidly. The more virulent strains caused death in 90% of cases. Rinderpest was found in sub-Saharan Africa, Egypt, the Middle East, India and Sri Lanka, and it was making inroads into Turkey in 1991 (CIRAD, 1994). The symptoms of goat plague, which was also caused by a morbillivirus, were very similar to those of rinderpest. This disease was decimating goat and sheep flocks in Ethiopia and Senegal, the Middle East and the Arabian peninsula; it was suspected in India (CIRAD, 1994).

Diagnostic techniques were available for both diseases, but they were slow and required laboratory equipment. To isolate the virus in cell culture, for instance, took three to fifteen days in an absolutely sterile environment. However, characterization of the virus genomes of rinderpest and goat plague had led to the development of two specific radioactive probes formed from fragments of the gene coding for the nucleoprotein N and labelled with phosphorus 32. But these probes could not be used in the field; in addition, they had to be used quickly since phosphorus 32 has a very short half-life (i.e. losing half of its radioactivity every 14 days). Consequently, researchers devised two specific 'cold' probes, one for each disease, which consisted of oligonucleotides labelled with biotin or digoxigenin. These probes were not dangerous to use, but had a reduced specificity and sensitivity, plus the fact they had to be kept at a temperature of 4°C, which was difficult to achieve outside a laboratory (CIRAD, 1994).

To confirm that the rinderpest virus had disappeared, vaccinations on all livestock must be stopped and the animals monitored for signs of the disease. However, the vaccine also protected against goat plague. As the latter was still widespread, before stopping rinderpest vaccinations, a new specific vaccine against goat plague had to be developed. For the epidemiological monitoring of herds, CIRAD researchers had developed a diagnostic kit for direct identification of the two viruses by an ELISA immunocapture test using monoclonal antibodies specific to each virus. These were simple tools, well suited to the tropical environment, even though advanced biotechnologies were used to

674

produce the monoclonal antibodies contained in the test. The same techniques had been used by CIRAD researchers to develop another slightly different test for serological diagnosis of goat plague (*CIRAD News*, no. 12, December 1995, p. 7).

Gambia had already stopped rinderpest vaccinations. Guinea, Senegal and doubtless also Mali, which had been free of rinderpest for many years, could follow suit. Several States of India were also about to make the same decision (*CIRAD News*, no. 12, December 1995, p. 7).

Researchers were also working on a latex agglutination test. Genes coding for the N protein in the viruses that caused rinderpest and goat plague were inserted into the baculovirus genome. The baculovirus then produced large quantities of N protein, which was then fixed on latex microbeads. The latter agglutinated in the presence of anti-rinderpest or anti-goat plague antibodies. This test qualified as a field test since it could be performed quickly at the location of the diseased animal and the result was visible to the naked eye.

Similar research was conducted on the diagnosis of mycoplasma infections, e.g. contagious bovine and caprine pleuropneumonia, and contagious agalactia. The ELISA test for contagious bovine pleuropneumonia was being certified in member countries of the OIE and the International Atomic Energy Agency. It was therefore estimated that, given a network of minimally equipped laboratories and one or two technicians trained to use the various diagnosis tests, or mobile teams equipped with four-wheel drive vehicles, it would be possible to improve health supervision of livestock in sub-Saharan countries (CIRAD, 1994).

Since 1980, the CIRAD had been collaborating with the International Centre for the Development of Livestock Husbandry in Subhumid Zones (CIRDES) which was taken over by the Centre for Research on Animal Trypanosomiases (CTA), based in Bobo-Dioulasso, Burkina Faso. For the CIRDES, the control of the tse-tse fly was a key objective. By matching environmental factors affecting the presence of flies and the behaviour of herders, geographical information systems (GIS) could be used to identify high-risk zones and thus optimize expenditure on chemical control of the insects. Work on animal health, one of the Centre's four main research priorities, included studies of other diseases such as cowdriosis (heartwater) and dermatophilosis, two tick-borne diseases, and intestinal parasitoses. A second field of research focused on the causes of natural disease-resistance of certain cattle breeds, such as the Ndama and Baoulé races, and the improvement of productivity of certain breeds by cross-breeding or by selection of pure breeds. Work on nutrition was centred on the influence of undernutrition on trypanosome-resistance and the use of locally available by-products as animal feed.

The CIRDES concerned the five countries of the Conseil de l'Entente-Benin, Burkina Faso, Côte d'Ivoire, Niger and Togo, soon to be joined by Ghana and Mali. With a contribution of almost $1 million, the CIRAD was providing around one-third of the total CIRDES budget, which was also supported by the European Commission. CIRAD future commitments to the CIRDES would no longer concern overall financing but specific scientific projects, with their own budget and staff provided either from Africa or the CIRAD. Each operation must have a set of objectives, be subject to regular supervision and review on an annual basis if possible, and issue a final report once results had been obtained. All funding agencies were in fact proceeding in this way and financial support was provided on a contractual basis (*CIRAD News*, no. 13, July 1996, pp. 7–8).

A data-base on veterinary biotechnologies of the International Office of Epizootics was made freely accessible to CIRAD staff by the CIRAD Departments of Forestry and of Livestock and Veterinary Medicine (CIRAD-EMVT). Since 1991 this data-base had been storing all information on research on diagnosis, prevention and control of animal diseases. Data had been collected from 123 laboratories world-wide, including Pathotrop, the Laboratory of Tropical Pathology of the CIRAD-EMVT, (*CIRAD Information*, no. 63, 17 June 1996, p. 8).

United Kingdom

At the United Kingdom's Overseas Development Administration (ODA), biotechnologies were considered of increasing relevance to its strategy on Renewable Natural Resources. Particular areas of ODA focus on biotechnologies for developing countries were:

– taxonomy and genetic manipulation of staple crop species, domestic animals and fish;

– identification of plant, animal and fish diseases;

– tissue culture of economically important plants;

– food processing and storage;

– identification and mitigation of health hazards in water and from plant sources;

– soil microbiology (nitrogen fixation).

The ODA supported international agricultural biotechnology research through two programmes. The first and biggest was the Plant Sciences Research Programme, which was managed by the Centre for

Arid Zones Studies at the University of Wales. The programme was composed of several advanced plant breeding and crop physiology projects at various British public and private institutions, and International Agricultural Research Centers – IARCS. The ODA contributed approximately $1.6 million annually to this programme. The second programme, with funds totalling around $600.000 per year, was the Biotechnology Programme, managed directly by the ODA Natural Resources and Environmental Department. It acted as 'a pump-priming mechanism to encourage collaboration between commerce, research institutions and international centres'. Funds were distributed over some 12 research projects, mostly at British public institutions. Plant biotechnologies covered, for instance, the use of RFLPs in cassava breeding, biological nitrogen fixation in rice and bacterial wilt control in potato (Brenner and Komen, 1994).

One of the projects of the Plant Sciences Research Programme, to which $750,000 had been allocated over a three-year period, sought to introduce proprietary insect-resistance genes into both potato and sweet potato. The United Kingdom-based private company which held the gene patents, Agricultural Genetics Company (AGC), had been commissioned by the ODA to produce sweet-potato and potato transgenic germplasm expressing a number of its proprietary insect-resistance genes. The ODA was funding the research effort by AGC which, for its part, had granted the ODA a non-exclusive royalty-free license to the proprietary technology. This would enable the ODA to distribute any transgenic germplasm resulting from the research programme to plant breeders in developing countries (Brenner and Komen, 1994).

In the case of cassava, research projects benefiting from ODA support included the detoxification of cassava cultivars, and both disease and pest control (e.g. cassava mealy bug).

De Montfort University's Plant Development Biology group was identified as a centre of excellence under the terms of the PCFC's Special Research Funding Initiative. The University reinforced this award by allocating development research funds to the group so that it was possible, in August 1994, to set up the De Montfort University Norman Borlaug Institute for Plant Science Research (Leicester, Scraptoft), with a commitment to low input, low environmental impact, high-yielding and high-quality agriculture. Norman Borlaug had been awarded the Nobel Peace Prize in 1970 as a tribute to his accomplishment in breeding new sturdy high-yielding cereals; he was hailed as the 'father of the green revolution'. The international Institute comprised four Centres: the United Kingdom Centre in Leicester, the

Bulgarian Centre in Kostinbrod, the Czech Centre in Prague/Olomouc and the Chinese Centre in Beijing/Shanghai. The former head of the Department of Applied Biology and Biotechnology, M.C. Elliott, was the founding director of this Institute. About 45 plant scientists were working at the four centres by the end of 1996.

The Chinese centre was staffed by world-ranking scientists who were working in well-funded laboratories. Their publications tended to be placed in Chinese journals. A feature of the Institute's contracts with institutions and individuals was the expectation that all staff would publish in high-citation index journals in English.

The Institute's basic research on the regulation of plant cell division, enlargement and differentiation proved that the manipulation of these processes (in space and time) was the key to optimization of all aspects of crop development; this basic research underpinned strategic/applied research on the improvement of cereals, sugar- and oil-producing crops and fodder crops; genetic engineering was being used to increase pest-, disease- and stress-resistance and to improve nitrogen economy.

The work of De Montfort University scientists on the resolution of Unilever N.V./Unifield's problems concerning feminization of clonal oil-palms elucidated the causes of the problem. In addition, the Palm Oil Research Institute of Malaysia invited the British scientists to play a leading role in a $3 million programme aimed at optimizing clonal propagation of elite oil-palms.

Regarding rice, the United Kingdom Centre was working on the regulation of gene expression, vector construction, transformation (with the particle 'gene gun') and analysis of transformants; the Chinese Centre was developing hybrid rice and studying photosensitive male sterility, disease resistance and ways of improving quality; the Czech Centre was investigating the biochemistry and physiology of assimilate distribution, along with cytological and cytogenetic studies.

Khush and his colleagues at the International Rice Research Institute (IRRI, Los Baños, The Philippines) defined the Institute's strategy for producing new low-input, low-environmental impact, high-yielding and high-quality rice by genetic engineering as the 'very first priority' for support and action; IRRI scientists pressed the United Kingdom's Overseas Development Administration (ODA) to make a further important award to the De Montfort University Group. The objective of the latter was the development of routine procedures for transforming cereals in order to facilitate the modification of plant development by site-specific manipulation of phytohormone concentrations. Senior members of the Leicester Centre of the Norman Borlaug Institute for Plant Science Research were invited to visit IRRI during the spring of 1995 for discussing the ways in which the need for a high increase in rice yields during the next 25 years could be addressed by genetic engineering. The site-specific manipulation of phytohormone concentrations and profile was considered an appropriate way to reach this goal. In this regard, the work by Kaminek at the Czech Centre interdigitated with that of the Institute's visiting researcher Van Onckelen. Members of the Leicester Centre were invited to return to the IRRI in October 1995 to present a lecture on their work at the International Rice Genetics Symposium. From the 80,000 rice varieties stored at the IRRI, researchers selected the breeding stock to produce a radically different 'new plant type (NPT)' rice which promised to be 25% more productive.

The United Kingdom's Ministry of Agriculture, Fisheries and Food (MAFF) had shown particular interest in the Norman Borlaug Institute. The allocations of the £402,148 contract for developing wheat and barley transformation systems and a series of research studentships for sugar-beet investigations, were material demonstrations of appreciation. In addition, the Institute which had received £165,421 from the ODA for rice improvement through genetic engineering had in 1996 funding boosted to almost half a million Sterling pounds.

Some 2.858 million hectares of United Kingdom farmland were committed to wheat (1.777 million) and barley (1.081 million) annually. Crop yields were very high: 7.5 tonnes per hectare for wheat and 6 tonnes per hectare for barley. Such yields required very high inputs which imposed great financial pressures upon the farmer and rather negative environmental impact. Application of nitrogen fertilizers to wheat was of the order of 150 kg or even 200 kg per hectare. The rate of application to barley tended to be lower (40 kg to 100 kg per hectare), but it was conceivable that as much as 450,000 tonnes of nitrogen fertilizers were being applied to cereal fields in the United Kingdom each year. The Ministry of Agriculture, Fisheries and Food addressed the environmental impact of nitrogen fertilizer application by funding projects designed to improve our understanding of soil science and provide an informed basis for 'best practice recommandations'.

The Norman Borlaug Institute aimed to produce transgenic wheat and barley plants which maintained grain quality and yield when the nitrogen inputs were dramatically reduced.

Cytokinins are plant hormones which play key roles in the regulation of plant cell division, differentiation and development. Cytokinin applications prior to the tillering phase to wheat and barley grown under reduced nitrogen supply increased tiller number by 18% and 38% respectively; such treatment led to a grain yield increase up to 24% as a result of increased nitrogen uptake. When cytokinins were applied at the anthesis stage to cereal crop species grown under suboptimal nitrogen supply, the yield was restored, or even increased to that achieved with optimal nitrogen supply. This restoration or increase of yield was mainly due to the improvement of the uniformity of grain setting on both terminal and side tillers, which resulted fom better partitioning of assimilates before harvest. However, the following hurdles prevented the application of cytokinins to crops in routine agricultural practice: the price of cytokinins; the need for multiple applications arising from asynchronous tiller development; and the potential health risks. The research project at the Institute aimed to overcome these hurdles by targeted and controlled increases of endogenous concentrations of cytokinins in wheat and barley through genetic engineering.

The following major stages were envisaged:

– construction of chimaeric cytokinin biosynthesis genes, to be expressed at a specific developmental stage;

– stable transformation of wheat and barley (the transformation vectors would be introduced into wheat and barley immature embryo cultures using direct DNA delivery methods);

– assessment of the efficiency of nitrogen use by transgenic plants (selected transgenic and wild-type plants would be grown in pots with a range of nitrogen supply-minimum, intermediate and optimum; tiller number, grain setting, biomass formation and partitioning would be examined in these transgenic plants in relation to induced site-specific cytokinin biosynthesis and efficiency of nitrogen uptake and distribution).

For sugar-beet, the United Kingdom Centre was working along with the German sugar-producing company, Kleinwanzlebener Saatzucht AG, on the control of cell division, regulation of gene expression, transformation with *Agrobacterium* and analysis of transformants; the Czech Centre was carrying out research on transformation, cytology and cytogenetics, and the biochemistry and physiology of flowering; the Chinese and Bulgarian Centres were studying resistance to rhizomania and cell cycle control respectively.

Concerning alfalfa, the Bulgarian Centre was working on the regulation of direct somatic embryogenesis and nitrogen fixation, the Czech Centre on cytology and cytogenetics, and the United Kingdom Centre on the molecular mechanism of direct somatic embryogenesis.

One of the most far-reaching advances in plant science over the period 1955–1996 had been the recognition that somatic cells had the capacity to form embryo-like structures *in-vitro*. Somatic embryogenesis had been widely exploited for the propagation of commercial plant species and the regeneration of transgenic plants. A substantial research effort had, therefore, been focused on the optimization of somatic embryo production from a broad range of crop species. Somatic embryogenesis also provided a valuable model of early plant development which was more accessible to experimental manipulation than was zygotic embryogenesis. The two most widely-studied somatic embryogenesis systems (carrot cell suspension and alfalfa microcallus) were both indirect systems in which somatic embryogenesis was induced by manipulating growth regulator concentrations in the medium of cultured cells. It was proposed that during indirect somatic embryogenesis differentiated cells were redetermined through a process of dedifferentiation, cell proliferation and redifferentiation to become indirect embryogenic determined cells (IEDCs).

In contrast, direct somatic embryogenesis proceeded from cells within organized tissue which already had embryogenic potential. There were benefits from using a direct system of embryogenesis particularly for studying the characteristics and expression of embryogenic competence *in vivo*.

A system of direct embryogenesis in alfalfa was developed by the Bulgarian researchers at the Institute of Genetic Engineering affiliated to the Norman Borlaug Institute for Plant Science Research; the embryogenic response relied on the ability of cells in wounded (by chopping finely with a razor blade) leaf explants to form embryos directly in an induction medium containing 2,4-D. Subsequent development of the embryo did not require additional external signals. The cells in differentiated tissue, which had the potential to become embryogenic directly, had been described by some authors as pre-embryogenic determined cells (PEDCs). Unlike IEDCs, PEDCs required external stimuli only to induce the onset of cell division and the expression of embryogenesis. The capacity of cells to respond in this way to induction signals (wounding, plant growth regulators) was termed embryogenic competence. Various vegetative and floral tissues might contain a proportion of cells which were embryogenically competent. The developmental stage of the explant appeared to be critical and it was proposed that the stage of embryogenic competence overlapped with the early stages of cell differentiation and specialization. Thus, cells passed through a 'window of response' in which they had embryogenic competence as they matured and differentiated. Within the heterogenous population of cells in a more

681

mature tissue, the embryogenically competent cells would be those which differentiated more slowly.

Other factors influenced the proportion of competent cells within a tissue, notably genotype. For instance, there were 'embryogenic' and 'non-embryogenic' lines of alfalfa which varied considerably with respect to the proportion of competent cells within comparable explants. Studies of the alfalfa system led to the proposal that a distinct potentially embryogenic population of somatic cells existed in all explants regardless of genotype. However, the process was limited by the specific physiological state of the explant (degree of tissue differentiation, phytohormone balance, culture conditions, etc.). Thus differences in embryogenic competence between embryogenic and non-embryogenic alfalfa reflected differences in the physiological status of the two lines and the breadth of the 'window of response'. For instance, the analysis of phytohormone profiles in embryogenic and non-embryogenic alfalfa indicated that fast embryogenic induction was correlated with high indolyl-acetic acid (auxin) and low abscissic acid concentrations in the initial explants.

The primary trigger for direct embryogenesis in alfalfa appeared to be physical wounding, although there was also a requirement for 2,4-D. Wounding was known to initiate a variety of stress responses, including the induction of cell proliferation. Thus, in embryogenic lines, a proportion of those cells which were stimulated to divide by wounding proceeded to form somatic embryos. The early stages of embryogenic response were characterized by a unique polar cell division which was the key determinative stage in the process. The key role of the first division in this process prompted the construciton of a simple working hypothesis. In its most extreme form, this proposed that embryogenically competent cells had two distinct properties. One of these was cell division competence – the ability to respond to a mitogenic stimulus; the other was the predisposition to asymmetric division, which was a facet of embryogenic determination. This simple hypothesis might be tested experimentally since cell division competence could be characterized using molecular probes. This proposal also aimed to identify some of the determinants of asymmetric division. It would then be possible to correlate the expression of both of these properties with those of embryogenic competence.

The characterization of cell division competence stemmed from recent advances in understanding the regulation of plant cell division. Progression through the eukaryotic cell division cycle was regulated by the activity of cyclin-dependent protein kinases (Cdks) in association with regulatory cyclin subunits. Genes homologous to Cdks, and to several families of cyclins had been isolated from a number of plant species. The prototype Cdk gene, *cdc2*, in association with mitotic cyclins, was involved in regulating progression from the G2 phase into mitosis. Hovewer, comparison of the expression patterns of *cdc2* with those of mitotic cyclin genes in various plant tissues revealed some important differences. Whereas expression of the cyclins was restricted to dividing cells, low levels of *cdc2* expression could be detected in non-dividing cells which were known to be competent to divide given the appropriate induction signal. Thus, comparison of *cdc2* and cyclin gene expression permitted the detection of cells which had the potential to divide, but not currently progressing through the cell division cycle.

Differences in embryogenic competence between alfalfa lines could be due to differences in cell division competence and this was open to experimental testing. Many of the mechanisms of the first stage of embryogenesis which led from wounding to the first division would be the same as those in other cells stimulated to proliferate, i.e. the same signal transduction pathways would switch on essentially the same cell division-related cells and/or activate the same proteins. Indeed, somatic embryogenesis could be considered a particular type of stress response. On the other hand, some components of this general response might be specific for embryogenic cell division. Embryogenic programming might be primarily concerned with predetermination of asymmetric division. It was becoming clear that the determination of the location and plane of cell division involved elements of the cytoskeleton in association with cell-division cycle gene products. This was accessible to immunohistochemical investigation. Rho proteins appeared to be good candidates to mediate subcellular reorganization during proliferation and asymmetric division.

A £400,000 grant was awarded to the Norman Borlaug Institute for Plant Science Research by the European Commission INCO-Copernicus programme to research carried out on alfalfa somatic embryogenesis. The three-year project aimed to:

– determine the cellular origin of somatic embryos within alfalfa leaf explants;

– characterize embryogenic competence and investigate the role of genetic and physiological factors in the acquisition of embryogenic competence;

– determine the relationship between embryogenic competence and competence for cell division;

– investigate aspects of signal transduction pathways and early changes in gene expression following induction by wounding;

– monitor changes in expression of cell-division cycle genes during embryogenesis;

– analyze the role of the cytoskeleton and cell-division proteins in determining the asymmetric nature of the initial cell division following induction;

– investigate the involvement of Rho proteins in mediating cytoskeletal rearrangement and subcellular reorganization during asymmetric cell division;

– determine the role of phytohormones in establishing polarity during the early cell-division events;

– examine the commercial applications of direct somatic embryogenesis procedures to alfalfa and other leguminous crop species and the potential for manipulating the process.

Somatic embryogenesis was an important tool for applying plant biotechnologies to plant breeding by Agritech Ltd. It was used for somaclonal-variation studies in pea, as well as in pea transformation experiments. Agritech Ltd established somatic embryogenesis protocols for horsebean, pea and soybeans. But these systems were not as effective as that for alfalfa. Somatic embryogenesis could be induced from shoot apices (pea) or from immature zygotic embryos (horsebean, soybeans). Although these systems were considered examples of direct somatic embryogenesis, the regeneration products were accompanied by abundant callus formation. It was therefore very important to verify the alfalfa direct somatic embryogenesis protocol in other legume species (mainly in pea).

Lastly, with respect to sunflower, the Bulgarian Centre was working on transformation with *Agrobacterium*, disease resistance and the molecular basis of cytoplasmic male sterility in conjunction with the French National Centre for Scientific Research in Strasbourg (protoplast fusion and somatic embryogenesis), the Institute of Wheat and Sunflower General Toshevo in Bulgaria (breeding and tissue culture), while the United Kingdom Centre concentrated on the transformation and analysis of transformants.

The Bulgarian Institute of Genetic Engineering was set up in 1985 as part of the Academy of Agriculture as a National Centre for Co-ordination of Plant Biotechnology Activities (see p. 27). In Bulgaria, crop improvement had got off the ground in 1920 with the establishment of breeding and experimental stations for a wide range of crops spanning the country's various climatic zones. The ensuing breeding programmes had contributed significantly to the development of Bulgarian agriculture, which played a key role in the country's economy. Since 1980, 95% of arable land in Bulgaria had been planted with cultivars developed at local breeding institutes. The latter had also produced varieties which proved most successful in Croatia, France,

Greece, Romania, Slovenia, former Yugoslavia and the former Central Asian Republics. Although its territory was limited (111,000 km² of which no more than 40% was arable land), Bulgaria was renowned for a climatic diversity that allowed the cultivation of more than 75 crop species (Atanassov, in *Abstracts of the First Balkan Countries Workshop on Plant Biotechnology*, Varna, 3–5 July 1995, p. 7).

Since the 1970s, crop breeding had suffered major setbacks due to the reduced number of breeding lines, lack of expertise in modern methods for the evaluation of breeding material and the exclusive focus on breeding solely to increase productivity, thus minimizing the importance of breeding for resistance to biotic and abiotic stresses. To right the imbalance, a national crop breeding programme including plant biotechnologies was launched in 1983. The Institute of Genetic Engineering at Kostinbrod, near Sofia, played a key role in this undertaking.

More than 50 agreements for scientific co-operation had since been signed with leading research centres world-wide. The Institute was using molecular biology techniques in addition to routine tissue-culture methods (micropropagation, somaclonal variation, embryo rescue, haploidization), with a view to incorporating them into conventional breeding programmes. Consequently, many valuable breeding lines had been developed for wheat, barley, rice, sugar-beet, sunflower, tobacco, alfalfa, etc. The tobacco variety, Biopreslavna, *Datura innoxia*-INKA, Mariana rice and Zdravko wheat had been created through anther culture. Genetic engineering was expected to lead to the creation of the first tobacco cultivars resistant to economically important diseases, e.g. tomato spotted wilt virus, wild fire, etc. (Atanassov, in *Abstracts of the First Balkan Countries Workshop on Plant Biotechnology*, Varna, 3–5 July 1995, p. 7).

In 1993, the Institute of Genetic Engineering initiated a restructuration programme to overcome a financial handicap through the intensification of international co-operation and diversification of funding sources. This was made possible by the Institute's subsequent involvement in international programmes like the International Centre for Genetic Engineering and Biotechnology, the European Commission's Copernicus programme, the joint FAO/IAEA Division, etc., not to mention bilateral co-operation ventures and research contracts with multinational corporations. In 1994, the Institute was invited to join The Norman Borlaug Institute for Plant Science Research (Atanassov, in *Abstracts of the First Balkan Countries Workshop on Plant Biotechnology*, Varna, 3–5 July 1995, p. 7).

The institutional contract between the Norman Borlaug Institute and the Bulgarian Academy of Agriculture was signed in September

1994. In 1996, the collapse of the Bulgarian economy prevented the government from funding research, and several very good scientists left the Centre to take positions in 'Western' laboratories. The publication profiles of the staff remaining in Bulgaria were damaged by these problems.

European Consortium for Agricultural Research in the Tropics

On 15 May 1992, the National Resources Institute (NRI, United Kingdom), the Koninklijk Instituut voor de Tropen (KIT, Netherlands), the Instituto de Investigação Científica Tropical (IICT, Institute for Scientific Tropical Research, Portugal) and the CIRAD (Centre for International Co-operation in Agricultural Research for Development, France) decided to create the European Consortium for Agricultural Research in the Tropics (ECART), to assist developing countries. The joint capacities of the four institutions comprised more than 2,000 scientists working both in field projects and in the laboratory. ECART objectives were to:

– accede to requests by developing countries concerning the strengthening of their agricultural research systems (technological development and long-term structuration);

– contribute to setting policies for rural development and management of natural resources;

– ensure that tropical agricultural research was well understood by policy-makers in both developed and developing countries, and that it received adequate support;

– link the capacities of European organizations to those of national research systems and development agencies, and collaborate with other bodies of the international scientific community.

Management of environment and natural resources, as well as advisory services in the organization and management of research were priority topics of the ECART. This consortium was open to co-operation with partners in the North and South.

The secretaries-general of the ECART member institutions met in Paris on 20 and 21 December 1993. In addition to reviewing the activities carried out by the different working groups, the secretaries established a list of activities for implementation in 1994. These were oriented essentially toward the management of natural resources and the environment, development of small and medium-sized enterprises, research management and publications. The secretaries met again in

Lisbon, Portugal, on 9 February 1994, this rendez-vous being superseded by a plenary meeting in November of the directors-general of these institutions (*CIRAD Echos*, no. 8, April 1994, p. 5).

The German partner in the ECART, officially designated at the plenary meeting on 11 November 1994 in Amsterdam, represented both the German institutions involved in research for the development of Third World countries: the GTZ (Gesellschaft für Technische Zusammenarbeit) and ATSAF (Arbeitsgemeinschaft für Tropische und Subtropische Agrarforschung). The ECART represented about 2,500 researchers.

At the Amsterdam meeting, after two years of activity, there were more numerous exchanges among researchers and joint projects were formulated. Brochures describing the competence of ECART had been published prior to the meeting, a joint participation had been assured at international book fairs and a seminar organized with the Women in Agricultural Development Unit of Ghana's Ministry of Agriculture in December 1994 (*CIRAD Information*, no. 47, 15 December 1994, p. 5).

The six secretaries-general of the ECART member institutions met in Brussels on 6 April 1995. They decided to issue a newsletter to be disseminated with the internal bulletin of every institution, so as to keep members better informed of ECART activities. Furthermore, leaflets on the areas covered by the ECART were to be prepared. Published monthly by member organizations of the ECART, *Agriculture and environment for developing regions* was the changed title of the former TROPAG journal *Abstracts on tropical agriculture*. The Journal contained abstracts from literature on agricultural development, environmental management and production and processing technology in developing rural areas of Africa, Asia, the Pacific and the Americas.

The secretaries-general also reviewed different European initiatives, such as the meeting of the Consultative Group on International Agricultural Research in Lucerne, the meetings of donors with the European Commission, meetings of the councils of ministers, the colloquium on research in Europe and the Mediterranean. They also discussed the possible role the ECART could play in these meetings (*CIRAD Information*, no. 52, 16 May 1995, p. 5).

The secretaries-general and directors-general of the ECART member institutions met on 28 and 29 September 1995 respectively in the United Kingdom, in Chatham. They acknowledged the progress made in the development of the TROPAG data-base (an agreement was to be signed in this respect between the CIRAD and the Netherlands' Royal Tropical Institute, KIT). In addition, as a follow-up to the successful workshop on the role of women in the units of foodstuff processing, held in Ghana, the directors-general agreed to request the *ad-hoc* working group to develop a strategy for publishing the results, setting up networks and identifying projects. On the other hand, the ECART proposed to the Special Programme for African Agricultural Research (SPAAR) the extension to East and Southern Africa of the study undertaken by the CIRAD in West Africa on agrosystems, the main product chains and scientific partnerships. Two pamphlets on ECART competence in the field of natural resources management and peri-urban agriculture were being published.

In order to give a strong impetus to the Consortium's activities and to make it a European reference in research, a reflection body and a tool for advancing proposals within the European Union, a working group was created. The objective assigned to this working group was to suggest ways and means aimed at enhancing the position of ECART toward the European Commission and the Consultative Group on International Agricultural Research (*CIRAD Information*, no. 56, 23 October 1995, pp. 5–6).

Notes

1 Plants are not stable and unvariable organisms. They are the result of constant selection by man, so that most cultivated varieties did not exist thirty or forty years ago. For instance, soft wheat had been modified in a stepwise manner: resistance to disease, stiffness of the stem, flour quality, etc. Today, molecular biology tools are enabling the breeders to make a more precise and quick selection. The approach consists of identifying and isolating a gene in another organism, which governs an interesting trait, and then of transferring it to a crop species. The transformed plant keeps all its former characteristics and acquires a new trait. Currently, this transfer concerns only traits controlled by single genes, e.g. resistance to some pests, but not more complex traits like fruit quality, which depends on gene clusters (multigenic traits).

2 The Annual Crops Department resulted from the merging of the Institutes for Cotton (IRCT), annual food crops (IRAT) and the division of annual oil-seed crops of the IRHO (Institute for Research on Oils and Oil-seed Crops).

3 The Perennial Crops Department resulted from the merging of the IRHO (oil-palm and coconut), IRCA (rubber institute) and IRCC (coffee and cocoa institute).

4 This department included fruit crops, vegetable and flower species.

5 Rice, the cereal species most consumed world-wide, was produced mainly in Asia (about 90%) in both flooded or irrigated conditions. About 70% of the rice cultivated in Africa and Latin America was tropical rainfed rice, while irrigated rice in the Mediterranean region was grown on some 2 million hectares in 1995.

6 A dozen universities or research institutes in Japan, the Netherlands, Switzerland, the United Kingdom and the USA (with funding from the Rockefeller Foundation), as well as private laboratories in Belgium, Japan and the USA, had succeeded in regenerating transgenic rice plants derived from transformed protoplasts, or using electroporation and particle bombardment of tissues. The genes transferred were genes coding for resistance to insect pests (coding for endotoxins and inhibitors of digestive enzymes), viruses (tungro and rice yellow mottle virus via the introduction of the gene coding for the capsid protein of the virus), herbicides (transgenic rice plants with the *bar* gene were obtained in Japan, Switzerland and the USA), bacteria (phytoalexins, anti-microbial substances and detoxifying enzymes), fungi (glucanases and chitinases), drought (modification of the root architecture) and for grain quality (protein digestibility, vitamin content and amino-acid composition).

7 World consumption of oils and fats totalled 80 million tonnes in the early 1990s and was estimated to rise to 118 million tonnes between 2003 and 2007. Productivity per hectare of perennial oil crops was higher than that of annual oil crops, coconut and oil-palm providing more than 20% of world requirements for oil and fats by the mid-1990s. Palm oil ranked second after soybean oil among the edible oils produced and consumed throughout the world. It was in fact increasing its market share steadily. At the beginning of the 19th century, large plantations for the production of coprah had been established around the Pacific rim, The Philippines, Sri Lanka, and parts of Africa and the Caribbean. On a world scale, these plantations accounted for approximately 10 million hectares.

8 The coconut tree was grown throughout the humid tropical zones, located mainly in Asia and the Pacific. This crop species was a multipurpose tree: a food crop (coconut water, sap and flesh); an oil crop (coprah, meal); an energy-supplying crop (husk,

charcoal and fuel oil); an industrial crop (oil, milk, cream, grated coco, fibre); a source of handicrafts (sugar, vinegar, alcohol, wood, palms). In addition, it played an important environmental role as a cultivation system and in the turnover of biomass.

9 Cocoa was produced throughout the humid tropical regions (about 2.4 million tonnes over 5.3 million hectares); it was a cash crop essentially destined for export. Production systems varied from one country to the other: small plantations in Africa (less than five hectares), large plantations in Brazil and Ecuador, identical importance of the two types of exploitations in Asia. Productivity, quality and tolerance to climate vagaries required the fast obtention of plant material adapted to local conditions.

10 In 1743, as the French explorer Charles Marie de la Condamine sailed down the Amazon river, he described the following traits of the rubber tree for the French Academy of Sciences: 'in the Province of Esmeraldas, a tree called hévé was growing; one single wound led to the production of a liquid as white as milk, which gradually hardened and blackened on contact with the air; the Indians called the gum they extracted from the liquid 'cahutchu', which meant the 'weeping tree'. The French scientist brought hevea seeds back to France, but at Louis XVth's court and throughout France, rubber only triggered curiosity' (Dhombres, 1995).

Hevea brasiliensis, the rubber tree, was an important tree crop in the humid tropics, not only because it was the only exploitable source of natural rubber (latex), but also because its cultivation protected soils and plantations provided timber and firewood at the end of their production cycle. Rubber trees were cultivated on approximately 9 million hectares, mainly in South-East Asia, and represented an alternative crop for tropical Africa and Latin America.

11 Genomes differed in the number of genes and amount of DNA they contained. The DNA amount differed much more than the gene number. For instance, the human genome had 230 times more DNA than the yeast but only 13 times more genes. The corresponding yeast and human genes encoded proteins of similar sizes yet the human genes appeared to be larger. The explanation was that the human genome included many non-coding nucleotides between genes and additional non-coding nucleotides within genes (Bussey, 1996).

There were a number of aims implicit in the Human Genome Project, but all led to obtaining a complete description of all human genes and to a determination of the function of each. This was expected to drastically improve our knowledge of human biology and our ability to intervene at a molecular level to diagnose, and even to treat, human diseases. Major sequencing efforts had been initiated and the human sequence was expected to be largely complete by the year 2000. This sequence (3 billion nucleotides or 3,000 megabases-Mb) would lead to the identification of 80,000 genes and ultimately to an understanding of their functions (Bussey, 1996).

Cell structure allows the distinction between prokaryotes and eukaryotes. The latter included all animals, plants, algae, fungi and protozoans, while prokaryotes included the bacteria, i.e. the Eubacteria (e.g. *Escherichia coli*) and the Archaebacteria which lived in extreme environments such as ocean floor geothermal vents. Analysis of the genome sequences of micro-organisms like *Escherichia coli*, particularly the 'model' eukaryotes such as the yeast and the 'worm', *Caenorhabditis elegans*, had revealed a remarkable degree of conservation of gene structure and function among living beings. In many cases, it would be possible to move from studies on the model systems to identify related genes in humans, and often to predict successfully that specific genes would be there and the roles they would likely play (Bussey, 1996).

Genome sequencing had been carried out in a number of Eubacteria such as *E. coli*, *Bacillus subtilis* (completed), *Haemophilus influenzae* (completed), *Mycoplasma genitalium* (completed), and in Archaebacteria such as *Sulphobolus sulfotaricus*, the subject of a Canadian project headed by Ford Doolittle at Dalhousie University in Halifax. These organisms had genomes ranging from 0.6 to 5.0 Mb in size (Bussey, 1996).

Among model eukaryotes, more elaborate projects were in various stages of organization, from chromosome mapping to complete sequencing. These projects dealt with the yeast, *Saccharomyces cerevisiae* (13.5 Mb); the nematode, *Caenorhabditis elegans* (100 Mb); the dicotyledonous plant, *Arabidopsis thaliana* (120 Mb); the fruitfly, *Drosophila melanogaster* (170 Mb); and the mouse, *Mus musculus* (3,000 Mb). Genome analysis in these organisms would shed light on the genetic basis for most levels of organizational complexity seen in humans, such as the cellular, developmental and neural. In addition, the mouse would continue to offer an experimental model for mammals such as humans (Bussey, 1996).

Yeast had sophisticated yet tractable genetics and it was easy to grow and to manipulate. A critical mass of researchers were studying yeast, close to one worker for each of the 6,000 genes encoded in its genome, offering the possibility of rapid progress. A yeast genome project had been under way in earnest since initial efforts began in the European Union in 1988, spearheaded by Goffeau of the Pasteur Institute, Paris, who built on the pioneering efforts of Oliver on chromosome III. An international collaboration involving groups in the European Union and the Sanger Centre in the United Kingdom, the USA, Japan and Canada (a group led by Bussey at McGill University in Montreal), had sequenced all 16 chromosomes that made up the 13.5 Mb genome. Much of the information thus collected (75%) was stored in GenBank and at the *Saccharomyces* Genome Data-base, SGD, at Stanford, California. Papers describing the sequences of six of the chromosomes had been published and the entire annotated sequence of the yeast genome was made publicly available by mid-1996 (Bussey, 1996).

The 6,000 yeast genes provided both a basic eukaryotic gene set, defining what it took to be a eukaryote, and a reference set of genes against which the genomes of all other eukaryotes could be compared. Defining all the genes was only the first step in moving to function; and 40%, i.e. 2,400 genes, were new to biology and had no known function. Yeast genomics was already moving toward co-ordinated internationally-based programmes in attempts to systematically define gene function on a genome-wide scale. For instance, there was a three-year programme to genetically disrupt each of the 6,000 yeast genes in turn. This programme would provide each yeast laboratory (close to 1,000 world-wide) a complete set of individual yeast strains that were defective for each individual gene function (Bussey, 1996).

Humans and yeasts had evolved from a common ancestor that existed about one billion years ago. Some genes had remained highly conserved in structure over that period and this conservation was reflected in the obvious similarity of the amino-acid sequences of the proteins they encoded. Other genes had been less highly conserved during evolution and the degree of conserved amino-acid sequence similarity could be relatively low. Yet other genes had diverged sufficiently such that the proteins that they encoded had acquired distinct structures and functions. To pursue the yeast-human connection in a systematic way had been a project of Heiter and colleagues at Johns Hopkins University, Baltimore, in collaboration with Boguski at NCBI, Bethesda (Bussey, 1996).

While the yeast genome was being sequenced, a sneak preview of human genes was obtained by taking a short cut that avoided much of the work of genome sequencing. Human messenger RNAs were enzymatically copied back to DNA using reverse transcriptase, and cloned. Small sections or tags of these cloned DNA molecules were sequenced, giving snapshots or ESTs (expressed sequence tags) of much of the human genome. These tags, numbering more than 150,000 and growing, were stored in a data-base at GenBank called db EST. Of the human genes that had been cloned and that were implicated in genetic diseases, 71% had an EST tag in db EST, which already achieved a reasonably good coverage of the human genome (Bussey, 1996).

Heiter and colleagues had systematically compared yeast genes to these human EST collections. They found that about 39% of the 3,000 yeast genes examined appeared to be similar enough in sequence to a human EST that it merited further attention to determine if it was a counterpart to the human gene. Some human proteins were functionally interchangeable in yeast, an example being the yeast IRA2 gene and the human NFI gene. Fifteen per cent of yeast proteins had a human counterpart at least as conserved as this pair, and conversely 20% of human genes that had been cloned and implicated in human diseases had a yeast match at this level of sequence similarity (Bussey, 1996).

An immediate application of this finding to human disease genes was the following. Using the human ESTs, one could determine the chromosomal map positions of human genes with strong matches to known yeast genes. If done in a systematic way, some of these were likely to map to the same location as genes known to be associated with human diseases. This allowed the disease locus to be identified, currently a formidable task both in time and cost and a problem that was not unknown in positional cloning in plants. In addition, the approach provided a yeast gene whose function was likely known, or knowable, and conserved. Yeast biologists could thus experiment with the gene to try to find or refine cellular function in the more experimentally manipulable yeast cell. Heiter and colleagues were carrying out such a mapping project on a large scale (Bussey, 1996).

Despite fungi being classified in the phylum Plantae, recent phylogeny studies suggested that they were a separate phylum, the Mycotae. Perhaps more surprisingly, it appeared that the fungi had diverged from the animal lineage later than did plants, so that fungi were considered the closest relatives of animals. Thus one could argue that of course the yeast genes and cell biology resembled those of humans, they were closely related. The yeast genome was also worth a systematic approach by plant biologists despite a widespread scepticism about its value that it might remain in the plant community, and a deep rooted feeling that plants were different. Prospects for further insights into plants included the conventional, such as all aspects of cell biology, signaling, protein secretion, organelle assembly (fungi and especially plants had prominent vacuoles). But there were other organelles that plants and fungi shared that were less pronounced or even absent from animals, an example being the massive extracellular matrices and the cell walls (Bussey, 1996).

12 Transposons are mobile DNA sequences present in the genome. A transposon present in one location could be copied to a new location with or without removal of the original copy. Transposons could carry genes that were unrelated to mobility; however, to be mobile a transposon must include DNA sequence information that could act as a recognition sequence for its transposase, a protein that catalyzed the transposition event. The transposase could be encoded by the transposon or it could be encoded elsewhere in the genome. A transposon that did not encode its transposase could be introduced into the genome of an organism. The initial site of introduction tended to be random in plants. The introduced DNA segment might or might not produce a new phenotype by inactivating the gene that it jumped into. In any case, the introduced DNA segment represented a useful 'tag' for identifying that region of the genome and the 'tag' could be assigned a physical and genetic map location.

The gene encoding the transposase protein could be introduced by crossing the plant that carried the transposon to a plant carrying that transposase gene. In the progeny with both transposon and transposase, the transposon would become activated. In plants, the transposons would tend to transpose more frequently to chromosomal sites close to the original location. Thus a subpopulation of plants could be produced that contained a population of transposon 'tags' concentrated in a region of the genome.

13 In 1992, the world market of foliar insecticides was estimated at $2.5 billion. Part of this market (about $880 million) was accessible to *Bt* because it concerned pests sensitive to this bacterial species. However, *Bt* sales represented only $86 million, i.e. 10% of the sector concerned (Sanchis *et al.*, 1995).

In 1994, 1,200 tonnes of *Bt* were produced in China, where more than 1 million hectares were treated every year with *Bt*. In the former Soviet Union, some 3 million hectares were treated annually with bacterial insecticides, *Bt* being the major component. In Central Europe, 20,000 to 100,000 hectares of forests were protected every year with *Bt*-based products and, in many Canadian provinces, *Bt* was the only authorized insecticide. In 1990, 60% of the areas treated in Canada (i.e. some 700,000 hectares) had received *Bt* formulations. In Malaysia and Thailand, *Bt* was the only effective product for controlling *Plutella xylostella*, which became resistant to all other insecticides currently commercialized. Finally, *Bt* had been successfully used for many years to control onchocerciasis in West Africa (11 countries): every week, 18,000 km of rivers were being treated with insecticides and of a total 923,000 litres used, 750,000 lites corresponded to *Bt* formulations (Sanchis *et al.*, 1995).

In North America, from 1985 to 1988, about 2,9 million hectares of forests had been treated with various *Bt* formulations against spruce caterpillar, *Choristoneura pinus pinus* (1,856,248 hectares), grey pine caterpillar, *Choristoneura fumiferana* (836,171 hectares), *Lymantria dispar* (157,297 hectares) and *Lambdina fiscellaria* (35,756 hectares). Good results were obtained when the aerial application of the insecticide was done at the right period of the parasite's life-span and when weather conditions after spraying were favourable (Sanchis *et al.*, 1995).

Treatments against *Heliothis armigera* had been carried out in Israel on cotton plants during an important infestation by this lepidopteran species in 1985 (32 larvae per two-metre row). *Bt* was effective in reducing the pest population down to four to eight larvae per two-metre row, with the added advantage of preserving the natural parasites of the pest (Sanchis *et al.*, 1995).

In Mexico, a comparison in terms of efficiency, cost and benefits between chemical control and *Bt* use had been made on tomato cultures during 1992 and 1993. Damage caused by three main pests (*Keiferia lycopersicella*, Lepidoteran, *Helicoverpa zea*, Lepidopteran, *Macrosiphum euphorbiae*, Hymenopteran) had been reduced in the plots treated with *Bt*, but the overall benefits had been slightly lower than those corresponding to the plots treated with methomyl and permethrin. However, the number of *Bt* treatments was lesser than the number of chemical applications (four compared to nine in 1992 and three compared to seven in 1993). Consequently, the cost of treatment was less with *Bt*, especially with respect to manpower and water consumption. Other benefits were expected with the utilization of *Bt*, such as the reduction of soil trampling by less frequent passage of spraying machines, significant decrease in environmental pollution, advantages for the commercialization of the fruits produced and utilization of products less toxic for mammals (Sanchis *et al.*, 1995).

Between 1981 and 1988, under the aegis of the World Health Organization, more than 2 million litres of *Bt israelensis* formulations had been used in West Africa to control eight species of blackfly, called '*Simulium damnosum* complex', vectors of *Onchocerca volvulus*. In some regions, these species had become resistant to organophosphorus insecticides and pyrethroids. The mortality induced by *Bt* in blackflies had been equivalent to that obtained in regions treated with other active chemicals (Sanchis *et al.*, 1995).

In China, 10,000 tonnes of liquid formulations of *Bti* had been sprayed over 12,000 hectares. These applications and spraying of *Bacillus sphaericus* had reduced the number of mosquitoes per person and per hour from 8-9 in 1986 to 3.7 in 1987, 2 in 1988 and 1.3 in 1989; the number of persons infected with malaria had fallen from 5.6 per 10.000 in 1986 to 2.1 in 1987, 1.6 in 1988 and 0.8 in 1989 (Sanchis *et al.*, 1995).

Finally, between 1981 and 1991, inthe Upper Rhine Valley in Germany, about 50,000 hectares had been treated with 23 tonnes of wetable powder and 19,000 lites of concentrated solutions containing *Bt* for controlling mosquitoes. The insect population had been reduced by 90% (Sanchis *et al.*, 1995).

U.S. Agency for International Development

The U.S. Agency for International Development (U.S.AID) was the world's second-biggest governmental donor in 1995. However, the annual budget of almost $10 billion amounted to only 0.15% of the U.S. gross national product. In recent years, the U.S.AID budget had been drastically cut in the wake of economic recession, government deficits and a growing isolationist policy pushed by some lobbies. Since the new director's appointment in 1993, U.S.AID goals had been reduced from 33 to four: building democracy, stimulating environmental protection, encouraging sustainable economic development, and advancing population control (Manicad, 1995).

In 1990, the U.S.AID had requested a Panel of the Board on Science and Technology for International Development (BOSTID) of the National Research Council to produce an ordered list of priorities for biotechnology research-and-development in developing countries (National Research Council, NRC, 1990).

Given the objective of persuading the donor community of the importance of supporting plant biotechnology research, it was critical for scientists to focus on projects likely to pay dividends within three to five years. Research was also supported by the U.S. Department of Agriculture and National Science Foundation, which could complement U.S.AID in the basic sciences. U.S.AID support would also be essential in strengthening human resource development in recipient countries. It was pointed out that the Co-operative Research Support Programs (CRSPs) provided good examples of combining research, training and support for national systems. Their co-operation with the International Agricultural Research Centers (IARCs), also supported by U.S.AID, was exemplary (NRC, 1990).

The BOSTID Panel emphasized an emerging goal of international agricultural research to integrate biotechnologies with conventional crop improvement programmes; new initiatives were called for that would enhance the contribution of biotechnologies to sustainable agriculture; plant biotechnologies could be used to overcome disease, pests and environmental obstacles to production, or to improve the quality of food and fibre crops; plant biotechnology research was likely to be most productive when used in conjunction with conventional breeding programmes (NRC, 1990).

The BOSTID Panel recommended U.S.AID initiatives in three areas:

– biosafety: U.S.AID should assist developing countries to design and implement appropriate biosafety regulations, in particular with respect to the development of procedures for field-testing of transgenic plants and micro-organisms, and the movement of these plants and organisms from country to country;

– intellectual property rights: U.S.AID should promote international co-operation in intellectual property rights among U.S. research organizations (public and private), donor agencies, the IARCs and Least Developed Country governments to make proprietary techniques, gene clones and germplasm available to developing countries;

– training and networking: U.S.AID should enhance biotechnology capabilities in the LDCs through doctoral and post-doctoral fellowships, and non-degree training for LDC plant biotechnologists, but should also continue research training in complementary agricultural sciences. Support should be given to networks of scientists in developing countries linked to their counterparts in the IARCs and industrial countries through periodic workshops and, where feasible, electronic networks (NRC, 1990).

Regarding priorities in technical areas, the BOSTID Panel recognized that, although capabilities with tissue culture had developed rapidly since 1975, many developing countries still lacked effective techniques. Therefore, U.S.AID should continue to support capacity-building in developing countries in basic plant tissue culture technologies, which were necessary for genetic engineering and could augment conventional plant improvement programmes, including micropropagation, cell selection, embryo rescue, haploid techniques, protoplast fusion and protoplast regeneration. These techniques might directly produce plants with increased tolerance to plant diseases, insect pests and soil stresses, and, perhaps more important, they provided the foundation for more advanced biotechnology applications. An effective programme in this area would require, for each species addressed, a total of between $200,000 and $500,000 per year (calculated in 1990), and would likely require three to five years to produce routine methods of tissue culture; a functioning laboratory required around $75,000 worth of capital equipment (NRC, 1990).

U.S.AID should assist developing countries to acquire the capacity to use micropropagation to produce virus-free planting material of forest, plantation, fruit, vegetable and tuber crops. Regional networking of researchers in these areas might enhance effectiveness. Up to $1 million per year would produce an effective, focused programme at an estimated average cost of $50,000 per year per crop over a period of three to five years (NRC, 1990).

U.S.AID should support the development of transformation and regeneration techniques for tropical crops for which these techniques were not available, such as cassava, taro, millet, sorghum and groundnuts. Rice, potato, tomato, soybeans, *Phaseolus* beans and a number of other crop species had been transformed using these techniques but greater efficiency was required to make it routine. After initial broad screening, the programme ought to concentrate at most on the two or three crop species where transformation had proven feasible, while modest efforts could continue on a broader range of crops. It would probably require annual funding of from $500,000 to $1 million to support transformation/regeneration of one crop in five years. Rice, for instance, had been the subject of transformation research costing about $1 million a year between 1985 and 1990. Transformation of rice had been demonstrated by half-a-dozen laboratories up to 1990. Wheat, millet, maize, sorghum, cassava and legumes were also transformed after this date, the most striking accomplishments being the improved regeneration of cassava and the successful transformation of maize with production of fertile seed (NRC, 1990).

As novel *Bacillus thuringiensis* (*Bt*) toxin genes were isolated, cloned and utilized to produce new germplasm in the more industrialized countries, the corresponding exercise of intellectual property rights might diminish Third World access to this beneficial technology. Unless developing countries consolidated their capabilities in biotechnology research, the *Bt* strains most effective for their environmental conditions might not be identified. Co-operation for mutual benefit should be the objective. There was potential for joint ventures and technology transfer between the private sector in industrialized countries and those LDCs having developed some expertise in *Bt* research. Training in strain identification, gene isolation, recombinant strain production, bioassay procedures and new fermentation techniques would make the LDCs viable prospective partners for research and commercialization of *Bt* products (NRC, 1990).

On the subject of *Bt* strain identification, the BOSTID Panel recommended that U.S.AID assist developing countries to identify and clone *Bt* strains effective against major insect pests in tropical regions, in co-operation with advanced laboratories and private companies in the USA. The identification of *Bt* strains could probably be accomplished in two or three years at a cost of around $50,000 per strain. The production of bio-insecticides based on effective strains was a longer and more expensive process: an operating programme in this area would likely require between $70,000 and $300,000 for each *Bt* strain and would probably require eight years or more to produce significant results with cloning, testing and scale-up. *Bt* could be directly produced by cultures on suitable media and processed in appropriate formulations for spraying, or inserted into crop species via genetic engineering. U.S.AID should also encourage developing countries to develop integrated pest management techniques and programmes, within which *Bt* should be an important, though by no means the sole, approach. Examples of priority pests identified by developing country panelists for which effective *Bt* strains could contribute to their biological control were *Plutella xylostella* (diamondback moth), *Spodoptera exigua* (beet armyworm), *Chilo pastellus* (stalk borer) and *Maruca testulalis* (bean pod borer) [NRC, 1990].

As far as anti-viral strategies were concerned, U.S.AID should support the control of plant viruses attacking *Phaseolus* beans, cassava, sweet potatoes, groundnuts, and tropical fruits and vegetables. An effective programme in this area would likely require between $150,000 and $500,000 for each virus addressed and would only produce significant results after two to five years, depending on the target crop species and virus. Examples of priority viral diseases were: cassava viruses and geminivirus on cowpeas and groundnut in Africa; cassava viruses and geminivirus in *Phaseolus* beans in Latin America; soft rot in potato and other viral diseases of nutritionally important fruits and vegetables, and geminivirus in legumes in Asia (NRC, 1990).

With respect to pathogen diagnostics, U.S.AID should support research to develop DNA probes, as well as antisera and monoclonal antibody probes for plant bacteria, fungi and viruses that attacked economically important crop species. This vast area of research and development required sensitive and reliable tests to assure that seed was certifiably disease-free from key pathogens before it could be moved. Field-usable kits were available for some pathogens or mycotoxins in the USA and, if developed, they could be used in Third World countries instead of present methods, which required workers to culture and identify pathogens. An effective programme in this area would likely cost between $80,000 and $150,000 per pathogen and would probably require four to five years to produce reliable field-tested results. U.S. biotechnology companies were receiving numerous requests from developing countries for assays for viruses (especially from seed companies, and for cucumber mosaic virus and tomato spotted wilt), fungi (especially phytophthora and other root invaders) and mycotoxins, particularly aflatoxin. The cost of the assay or kit could limit general application to high-value commodities, such as cocoa, citrus, vanilla and black pepper (NRC, 1990).

On the last topic of genetic mapping with RFLPs, the BOSTID Panel called upon U.S.AID to assist the Consultative Group on International Agricultural Research (CGIAR) and developing country crop breeders to acquire the capacity to use RFLP maps in breeding of rice, maize, sorghum, cowpeas and other crop species. Even though a number of these maps were available, few developing country crop breeders had the equipment or training to use them. About $200,000 was needed to remedy this. A further $200,000 was needed to set up an RFLP laboratory with a capacity for several crop species; it might require yet another $200,000 per year for three years to develop an RFLP map for a crop on which no start had yet been made (e.g. groundnut). This work would have to be done at an advanced laboratory in the USA linked to a laboratory in a developing country able to grow the crop under field conditions and make agronomic observations. Material from a number of countries could be tested in this way without duplicating the sophisticated facilities required for this long-term work (NRC, 1990). See also Cohen (1989*a,b*); Cohen *et al.* (1988*b*); Edwards *et al.* (1990); Hauptli *et al.* (1990).

The total biotechnology research budget of U.S.AID was about $31 million in 1994. Major biotechnology expenditures were devoted to health ($18 million) and agriculture ($12.7 million), while support for environmental biotechnologies amounted to a paltry $0.20 million. Whereas overall U.S.AID budget cuts had reduced total funding for agricultural projects from $529 million in 1993 to $406 million in 1994, the budget of agricultural biotechnology remained $12.7 billion. Of this amount, about 60% was allocated to public institutions, the remainder being allocated to private companies. The majority of U.S.AID agricultural biotechnology programmes were implemented through its global bureau in Washington, D.C., and their regional missions (Manicad, 1995).

The Agricultural Biotechnology for Sustainable Productivity (ABSP) was one of the bureau main programmes. The ABSP began in 1991 as a six-year programme with the mission of enhancing the capacity in the USA and developing countries to use and manage agricultural biotechnology research. Technology was transferred through joint research and the training of counterparts, as well as the development of intellectual property rights and biosafety policies (U.S.AID, 1994).

While the ABSP lead institution – Michigan State University (which worked in collaboration with Cornell, Texas A&M and Stanford Universities) – was public, the programme included subcontracts to commercial companies. Financial contribution of firms to the ABSP amounted to about 18% of total funding. The public research efforts in which private companies were involved were as follows: Zeneca Seeds plc, former ICI Seeds Ltd (stem-borer resistance in maize), DNA Plant Technology Corporation and Agribiotecnología de Costa Rica (cloning of banana, pineapple, coffee and ornamental palm), DNA Plant Technology Corporation and Fitotek Unggul-Indonesia (micropropagation of pineapple) [Brenner and Komen, 1994].

The relative importance of crop species within the ABSP was: maize 20%, potato 15%, cucurbits 14%, pineapple 12%, banana 12%, coffee 12%, tomato 7% and palm 4%.

The developing countries involved in the programme included: Kenya (potato, maize, sweet potato for insect resistance), Egypt (melons, squash, cucumbers, maize, potato, tomato), Indonesia (pineapple cloning, genetic engineering of maize for insect resistance, potato, sweet potato), Costa Rica (banana, coffee and pineapple cloning, potato, sweet potato, maize).

The U.S.AID contributed some $6.7 million to this programme, while smaller sums were committed to less ambitious, more sharply-focused biotechnology programmes, which included the Bean/Cowpea Collaborative Research Support Programme based at several universities in the USA and two programmes which involved proprietary technology: Feathery Mottle Virus-Resistant Sweet Potato for African Farmers through Biotechnology Project and the International Service for the Acquisition of Agri-Biotechnological Applications (ISAAA).

The ABSP included, *inter alia*, the following projects:

– maize (collaborative research between the USA – U.S.AID, Zeneca Seeds plc and Michigan State University -, Indonesia – Central Research Institute for Food Crops – and Egypt – Agricultural Genetic Engineering Research Institute; the target insect pest was the stem borer, which caused a yield reduction of 40% world-wide, commercial maize lines being transformed with two protein genes from *Bacillus thuringiensis* coding for entomocide toxins; in Egypt, the development of resistance to *B. thuringiensis* toxins forced researchers to come up with novel strategies to defeat it;

– tomato (joint project between the Egyptian Agricultural Genetic Engineering Research Institute, the International Laboratory for Tropical Agricultural Biotechnology at the Scripps Research Institute, La Jolla, California, and U.S.AID, aimed at developing transgenic tomatoes resistant to the tomato yellow leaf curl virus (TYLCV-E), along with a method for diagnosing the disease; two Egyptian isolates of TYLCV-E were cloned and the genome of one of these was sequenced; in 1995, 327 transgenic tomato lines were produced; some of these lines produced seeds and were transferred to Egypt for further testing);

– banana, pineapple and coffee (DNA Plant Technology Corporation – DNAP, USA, and Agribiotecnología de Costa Rica carried out research on the micropropagation of banana, pineapple and coffee); DNAP had a similar project for pineapple with Fitotek in Indonesia, which used the germplasm provided by Costa Rica and Indonesia to produce superior seedlings available all year round and in big quantities, at a faster rate than the conventional tissue culture process, so as to reduce production and labour costs;

– cucurbit (Michigan State University, Cornell University, the Egyptian Horticulture Research Institute and Agricultural Genetic Engineering Research Institute collaborated to produce virus-resistant cucurbit crops through a combination of molecular and conventional breeding); Michigan State University cloned the Zucchini Yellow Mosaic Virus (ZYMV) capsid protein gene and introduced it into commercial Egyptian melon varieties. Conventionnally-bred melon varieties were tested in Egypt to determine potentially valuable resistance combinations, e.g. to ZYMV, cucumber mosaic virus and watermelon mosaic virus. Meanwhile, similar laboratory experiments were conducted on squash and cucumber (U.S.AID, 1994; Manicad, 1995).

The main strength of the ABSP was the collaboration between molecular biologists and plant breeders, and between scientists and policy-makers in both public and private sectors. This was in keeping with U.S.AID policy and goals. It was anticipated that the technologies developed under the ABSP programme would benefit both the USA and partner countries, for instance in terms of germplasm exchange, or public and private technology transfer agreements (Manicad, 1995).

The Feathery Mottle Virus Resistant Sweet Potato for African Farmers through Biotechnology Project, proposed by Monsanto Co., was the first where the U.S.AID had provided research grant funding to a commercial company. It concerned the development of virus-resistant sweet potato by means of coat protein recombinant technology, using proprietary expression vectors. The project was initiated at the end of 1991, following recruitment of a Kenyan scientist for training at Monsanto Co. in St Louis. The project involved three years of post-doctoral training in the techniques of genetic transformation of sweet potato for virus-resistance and 15 months training for a technician. In addition, the scientist participated in on-going Monsanto Co. biosafety field trials and procedures with a number of transgenic crop species, as well as took part in biosafety and intellectual property rights seminars and workshops. Monsanto Co. provided a royalty-free non-exclusive license as well as funding to the Kenyan Agricultural Research Institute (KARI) to develop the technology in sweet potato grown and sold in Africa. The U.S.AID financial contribution to the project amounted to $238,000 over a three-year period (Brenner and Komen, 1994).

The U.S.AID supported cassava research mainly through its contribution to the International Center for Tropical Agriculture and the International Institute of Tropical Agriculture. Funding was allocated to: the improvement of cassava regeneration from tissue culture; detoxification of cassava; genome characterization using RFLP markers; training of African scientists in tissue culture of cassava, sweet potato and potato (in collaboration with the company Monsanto Co.).

The official U.S. government policies on intellectual property rights (IPR) and biosafety were promoted through U.S.AID training and internship programmes. For instance, the ABSP had held a series of workshops and consultations on regulation in Africa, Asia and Latin America, with an eye to helping partner countries to design biosafety policies and IPR legislation. The IPR, international trade law issues and risk assessment in handling genetically-modified organisms received most assistance from the U.S.AID. Before the exchange of transgenic material could take place within ABSP projects, the collaborating countries were required to conduct a biosafety review before any testing (Manicad, 1995).

The Rodale Institute Research Center played an advocacy role for amaranth cultivation and development during the 1980s. Numerous experimental varieties were developed and tested. Its extension germplasm collection was maintained by the U.S. Department of Agriculture's Regional Plant Introduction Station. The National Research Council's Board on Science and Technology for International Development (BOSTID) acted as a catalyst agency for the promotion of amaranth cultivation in developing countries.

Amaranth acreage in 1990 was reported to be over 100,000 hectares in the then Soviet Union, where it was grown mainly as a forage crop. In the USA there were only about 1,500 hectares. The primary producers were China, Mexico, Guatemala, Peru, India and Kenya. The grain's qualities included:

– high protein content (13%-19%), amaranth being one of the world's most protein-rich grains;

– high lysine content (usually lacking in maize and rice);

– high caloric content, as amaranth seeds contained 1.5 to 3 times more oil than other grains;

– tolerance to adverse environmental conditions (drought, high temperatures and saline soils); amaranth was identified in places where average annual rainfall was as low as 200 mm; amaranth is a C-4 photosynthetic species, like sorghum, maize and sugar-cane, and uses a carbon fixation process particularly effective under adverse environmental conditions;

– multipurpose grain (food, forage, silage, green manure and animal feed) and multipurpose industrial uses (Komen, 1992a).

Through a grant programme, the BOSTID had initiated research in Thailand, Kenya, Guatemala, Mexico and Peru. The Chinese Institute of Crop Breeding and Cultivation of the Chinese Academy of Agricultural Sciences (CAAS) was the first institute in a developing country to explore the potential of grain amaranths on a large scale: more than 20 varieties were introduced from the Rodale Institute Research Centre and planted in different regions of China; in 1990, the acreage totalled 26,000 hectares; many institutions were carrying out research on grain amaranths and a National Co-ordination Committee for Grain Amaranth Research had been set up (Komen, 1992a).

Limiting factors of grain amaranth production included:

– lack of phosphorus in the soil, particularly in arid soils, as well as sparse soil moisture;

– low average production yields, compared to conventional grain crop species (0.8 tonnnes per hectare in Mexico, but in Nigeria certain varieties could yield about 2.0 tonnes per hectare);

– small seed size and a tendency toward lodging, which impeded large-scale commercial production; hence the little attention paid to researching amaranth in industrialized countries (Komen, 1992a).

The U.S.AID Tickborne Diseases Vaccine Development Program (TDV), based at the University of Florida, initiated in 1985, had been conducting research on improved vaccines and diagnostic tests for tick-borne diseases in livestock: heartwater, anaplasmosis and babesiosis, in collaboration with research institutes in Africa (Egypt, Kenya, Mali and

Zimbabwe), Thailand, Mexico and Costa Rica. Up to 1995, the U.S.AID contributed around $17 million of the total $21.5 million committed to this programme (Brenner and Komen, 1994).

Another biotechnology programme to which the U.S.AID contributed was the Small Ruminant Collaborative Research Support Program (SR-CRSP) which, in its Animal Health Component, had a biotechnology research programme on vaccines to protect sheep and goats against prevalent diseases. The U.S.AID also contributed to the International Laboratory of Molecular Biology for Tropical Disease Agents (ILMB) based at the University of California, Davis, which was developing recombinant virus vaccines for both animal and human diseases. The U.S.AID contributions to the two latter programmes were, however, modest compared to those for the TDV Programme (Brenner and Komen, 1994).

The rinderpest vaccine project had been launched in 1985 with a $870,000 grant from the U.S.AID. Contained testing had been implemented in Kenya by the Kenya Agricultural Research Institute (Yilma, 1993; Manicad, 1995).

As one of eleven specialized agricultural information centres at the U.S. National Agricultural Library (NAL), Beltsville, the Biotechnology Information Center (BIC) in Beltsville, provided a wide range of information services and publications in genetic engineering and agricultural biotechnologies. Specific areas included the theoretical and technical aspects of genetic engineering and molecular biology, RFLP genome mapping, monoclonal antibody production, food-processing and health issues, biomass applications, product development in forestry, plant protection, patent issues, risk assessment and bioethics. In addition, the BIC could perform brief complimentary searches of the Library's AGRICOLA data-base on specific biotechnology topics or conduct exhaustive searches of most major data-bases on a cost recovery basis. The BIC also maintained an extensive vertical file on current biotechnology research and programmes, and could provide information on public and private research organizations, regulatory agencies, scientists and other experts in agricultural biotechnologies.

The BIC produced reference materials via two publications available free of charge. Both series, *Quick Bibliographies* (QBs) and *Special Reference Briefs* (SRBs) were compilations of bibliographic citations on specific topics. The *Biotechnology User's Forum* provided information on upcoming conferences, suggestions for new bibliographic products, requests or questions for the Center's staff, or discussions of current issues in biotechnologies.

The Biotechnology Information Center and the Alternative Farming Systems Information Center had produced a bibliography on biotechnology and sustainable agriculture. The bibliography contained 127 books, articles and reports, and aimed at introducing people to the debate on the subject. The scope of the literature included material on the impact of biotechnologies on technical deployment of alternative control methods, on socio-economic and cultural issues, and on the role of biotechnologies in sustainable development in developing countries.

Other international institutions

International Laboratory for Tropical Agricultural Biotechnology

The International Laboratory for Tropical Agricultural Biotechnology (ILTAB) was set up in 1991 as a collaborative effort of The Scripps Research Institute (TSRI) and the French Scientific Research Institute for Development in Cooperation (ORSTOM), on the initiative of its founding directors, Roger N. Beachy (Division of Plant Biology, TSRI) and Claude Fauquet (tropical plant biologist at ORSTOM). Widely accessible to researchers from developing countries seeking to apply biotechnologies to tropical plants and transfer them to their institutions, the ILTAB was a good example of North-North and North-South co-operation.

The ILTAB facilities were located on the campus of The Scripps Research Institute, La Jolla, California, which provided the means for molecular biology and tissue-culture work. A new facility was built to provide additional laboratory space, as well as greenhouses, growth chambers and tissue-culture rooms. In 1992, the ILTAB's 26 researchers and technicians included representatives from France, Germany, the USA, China, Peru, Colombia, Egypt, India, Cameroon, Côte d'Ivoire, Togo and other developing countries.

The ILTAB mission was to link basic and applied research: ILTAB scientists developed prototype projects to allow the transfer of modern biotechnologies to developing countries. Projects were chosen with due consideration for major economic issues and agricultural needs in these countries. That is why the most damaging virus groups affecting

707

tropical crop species were selected as a subject for research and the development of virus-resistant plants. Once produced, the latter were expected to be quickly transferred to a variety of research institutes, universities and laboratories. The ILTAB also provided advanced training to scientists from developing nations and supplied products and techniques to any interested researcher.

In addition to rice and cassava, the initial subjects of research chosen at the request of the relevant International Agricultural Research Centers, two new projects were initiated in 1992 on tomato and sugar-cane, Egypt being the main partner in both cases. Two small projects (from the funding viewpoint) on sweet potato and yam were being implemented in collaboration with laboratories from the North. Current methods of controlling the viruses attacking cassava, rice and tomato were both inefficient and costly. The ILBTAB founders and scientists had to rely on engineering virus resistance via genetic transformation, gene expression and transgenic plant regeneration. The prevalent technology used was referred to as the coat protein-mediated resistance (CPMR), whereby the coding sequence of the coat protein of the pathogenic virus was incorporated into the genome of the susceptible plant; the coat protein gene expressed constitutively in the transgenic plant generated resistance to the specific virus and, for several virus groups, to related strains or viruses (Powell *et al.*, 1986; Fitchen and Beachy, 1993).

The first project to be developed concerned two viruses infecting cassava. In Africa alone, 20% to 80% decrease in cassava yields were due to the African cassava mosaic virus (ACMV), a geminivirus. The second virus, the cassava common mosaic virus (CCMV), was a potexvirus widespread in South America. Cassava was very difficult to transform and regenerate but, fortunately, the tobacco *Nicotiana benthamiana* was host for both viruses and was used to studying the efficacy of the CPMR with these viruses. After transferring the ACMV into the tobacco species, the coat protein was detectable in a few transgenic tobacco lines, at a low concentration (0.01% maximum). Therefore, the protection for ACMV was limited. In the case of the CCMV, the amount of coat protein was considerable (more than 2% of total protein in some cases), as was protection from the virus. The same coat protein gene constructs were used for stable transformation of cassava calli by *Agrobacterium tumefaciens*; the expression of CCMV coat protein was similar to that for tobacco, but the expression of ACMV coat protein was about 10 times higher and was detected in 20% of the transgenic cassava calli.

Transgenic cassava plants were obtained -a world first- through a three-stage protocol:

– DNA was first introduced into cassava embryogenic tissues using a particle gun;

– transformed tissues were then isolated and non-transformed ones discarded, thanks to the presence in the former of two marker genes, *nptII* (coding for resistance to antibiotics) and *gus* (coding for the enzyme beta-glucuronidase); thus the transformed tissues containing *nptII* could grow on a culture medium containing paromomycin, while the presence of *gus* was detected by a blue colour in histological tests;

– transformed tissues regenerated whole plants (more than 5-cm long) which were potted and grown in greenhouses.

ILTAB researchers were applying this transformation technique of embryogenic tissues, followed by their regeneration, to various cassava cultivars, using this time not marker genes but agronomically useful genes. The targeted genes were indeed numerous, because they were involved in resistance to viruses, bacteria and insect pests, improvement of starch quality and decrease of cyanoglycoside concentration in the roots.

The second project concerned three different rice viruses:

– the rice yellow mottle virus (RYMV), a small spherical virus having a single capsid protein, the genome of which consists of one single-stranded RNA with 4,450 nucleotides; this virus is a sobemovirus;

– the rice tungro bacilliform virus (RTBV), responsible for the rice tungro disease, is a badnavirus, with a single capsid protein, the genome of which consists of a circular double-stranded DNA with 8,000 nucleotide pairs (Qu *et al.*, 1991);

– the rice tungro sphaerical virus (RTSV), also responsible for the rice tungro disease and without which the RTBV cannot be transmitted from a plant to another by the natural vector, is a spherical virus with at least three capsid proteins; it is a machlovirus, the genome of which consists of one single-stranded RNA with 12,000 nucleotides.

Each virus genone sequence coding for the capsid proteins had been isolated and incorporated into expression vectors with various promoters. In the case of the RTSV, which has several capsid proteins, one, two or three genes were incorporated into one single vector (Kochko, 1993; see also Hayakawa *et al.*, 1992).

Several techniques for rice transformation were being applied in many laboratories world-wide with a varying degree of success. The most widely used were:

– protoplast transformation;

– electroporation of differentiated tissues (embryos);

– bombardment of all kinds of rice tissues.

ILTAB researchers had developed an efficient technique for transforming rice, using particle bombardment of immature embryos. This technique was chosen for the following reasons: the rice cultivated species, *Oryza sativa,* had a very high genetic variability; its two subspecies, *indica* and *japonica*, had distinct behaviour in tissue culture conditions, the *japonica* tissues showing a relatively easy regeneration, while the *indica* tissues were more difficult or impossible to regenerate; consequently, immature embryos were the optimum stages for the regeneration of both subspecies and for obtaining fertile plants. Protoplast transformation was easy, but the regeneration of transformed plants from protoplasts was difficult or even impossible and it often led to sterile plants, particularly for *indica* rice. Immature embryos were isolated, sterilized and placed in a Petri dish containing a nutrient medium. Alien DNA was adsorbed on gold particles with a diameter of 1 μm; they were used to bombard the immature embryos with a particle gun the propulsion of which was assured by high-pressure helium. Particles penetrated into the cells of the embryo outer layers making it possible for the alien DNA to recombine with the plant DNA. Embryos were thereafter placed on a culture medium that enabled the development of calli. With the DNA coding for the capsid protein of a virus, an antibiotic-resistance gene was also introduced into the plant; consequently, if the culture medium contained that antibiotic, only the transformed plants with the genes for antibiotic resistance and the virus capsid protein would develop normally. After several subcultures, the resistant calli were placed on a regeneration culture medium so as to give transformed plants containing the two introduced genes. This method had led to the production of several hundred transgenic plants belonging to the rice *indica* and *japonica* subspecies (Li *et al.*, 1993).

Selected transformed plants were tested for the presence and expression of the virus capsid gene, using several techniques (ELISA, polymerase chain reaction-PCR, Southern blotting, Western blotting, etc.). Plants containing one copy of the viral gene and showing a high expression of that gene were then subjected to segregation studies and challenged with the virus. In the case of the RTBV, several hundred transformed and fertile plants belonging to both subspecies were analyzed. Seeds from a dozen transformed independent lines were sent to the International Rice Research Institute for resistance tests. Other batches of seeds were sent to China and Malaysia, with which the ILTAB had good relations, to undertake multiple local tests (Kochko, 1993).

It should be emphasized that the ILTAB approach was used by Japanese and Chinese teams to obtain rice plants resistant to the rice stripe virus (Hayakawa *et al.*, 1992). Similarly, this approach was envisaged to control the rice hoja blanca virus, which affected rice in Central and South America, as well as the rice ragged stunt virus which caused heavy yield losses in Thailand and other Asian countries (Kochko, 1993).

Taking into account these results, the Rockefeller Foundation requested the ILTAB to organize a workshop on rice transformation in September 1993. This workshop was followed in 1994 by an international course open to participants from all the main rice-producing countries.

In collaboration with the University of California, Davis, ILTAB researchers were able to transfer, for the first time, a gene from a wild plant species to a crop species, i.e. gene Xa21 from *Oryza longistaminata* to *O. sativa*. Gene Xa21 was coding for resistance to one of the major bacterial diseases of rice in Africa and Asia caused by *Xanthomonas oryzae* and considered by the Rockefeller Foundation as one of the 25 biotic and physical constraints of rice cultivation world-wide. Conventional crossings with rice varieties containing this gene had led to low-productivity rice varieties, without knowing if this result was due to the gene itself or to other genes transferred along with it. The gene isolated by ILTAB researchers was introduced in embryogenic calli of a high-yielding rice variety using a particle gun. The researchers demonstrated that 50 transgenic plants challenged by *Xanthomonas oryzae* were resistant to the pathogen. Later on, three rice varieties, cultivated on some 22 million hectares world-wide, were made resistant and field trials followed in 1997 after greenhouse tests in 1996. It was also scheduled to transfer this gene to rice varieties widely cultivated in West Africa, in collaboration with the West Africa Rice Development Association.

The ILTAB was also working on the control of infectivity and losses caused by geminiviruses attacking tomatoes in Egypt and other African countries. The tomato yellow leaf curl virus could cause crop losses of 60% to 100%. Several strategies aimed at engineering resistance to the viruses, such as the CPMR, were being attempted. Transformation and regeneration of tomatoes was under control and could be adapted to particular varieties used in different countries.

The sugar-cane project was addressing another question: was it possible to control several potyviruses and a number of strains of the same potyvirus, using only one strategy and preferably one coat protein gene? Sugar-cane regeneration was easy to realize and transformation already proved, which could be helpful in the development of transgenic virus-resistant lines. Collaboration established with the

711

Sugarcane Institute of Alexandria, Egypt, was to be extended to other countries.

Scientists at the ILTAB were studying the sweet potato feathery mottle virus, the most widespread virus in the world. This research project was being carried out in collaboration with scientists at the Tuskegee Institute, Alabama, in order to produce transgenic sweet potato plants, and with the International Potato Center (CIP, Lima) to test virus resistance in these transgenic lines.

Like cassava and sweet potato, yams were a staple crop throughout the tropics, particularly in Africa. Some of the viruses infecting yams were the subject of investigation at the ILTAB, which was collaborating with five laboratories in Europe, Africa and the Caribbean. Each laboratory provided expertise in virology, molecular biology, yam transformation and gene expression, so as to develop transgenic virus-resistant yam lines.

The ILTAB was considered the first link in an international chain between countries from the North and South around tropical plant biotechnologies. Its aim was to open laboratories of world-renown to researchers from the South, in order to promote the transfer of knowledge, results and technologies obtained on temperate climate plants to tropical species. A network for tropical plant biotechnologies aimed at linking major laboratories in industrialized countries to those in developing nations planned to involve European, Australian and American laboratories from both the public and private sectors. This network would link up with existing biotechnological networks in South America, Africa and Asia.

International Service for the Acquisition of Agri-Biotechnological Applications

The International Service for the Acquisition of Agri-Biotechnological Applications (ISAAA) was a non-profit making initiative set up in 1991 with the aim of 'facilitating the acquisition and transfer of agricultural biotechnology applications from the industrial countries, particularly proprietary technology from the private sector, for the benefit of the developing world.' The ISAAA was a small international network with a planned professional staff of ten. Three centernodes were located at centres of excellence in North America (AmeriCenter of Cornell University, Ithaca), in Europe (EuroCenter at the Norwich Research Park, United Kingdom) and in the Asian Pacific Rim (AsiaCenter in Japan) [Knudsen, 1993b].

The ISAAA leading sponsor was the McKnight Foundation, which had awarded a $1 million grant. Other donors included large foundations, such as the Hitachi Foundation, MacArthur Foundation and the Rockefeller Foundation. In addition, a number of large companies, such as Monsanto Co., Pioneer Hi-Bred International, Inc., Sandoz Seeds, Imperial Chemical Industries Ltd, The Upjohn Co. and KWS (Kleinwanzlebener Saatzucht AG) contributed to the ISAAA (Knudsen, 1993*b*). Financial contributions amounted to some $6 million up to 1995 with commercial enterprises contributing around 10%, but the ISAAA President and Executive Director stated that it would need almost three times that amount to be fully operational.

The ISAAA had initiated a five-year pilot programme originally focusing on ten developing countries: Indonesia, Malaysia, The Philippines and Thailand in Asia; Egypt, Kenya and Zimbabwe in Africa; Brazil, Costa Rica and Mexico in Central and Latin America. These countries were chosen 'because they were among the group of developing nations that possessed a measure of capability and the political will to pursue various biotechnology activities'. The strategy designed to assist these countries was to:
– focus on short-term applications which had already been tested in industrial countries and had a high probability of success;
– emphasize applications to increase the productivity of food crop species and contribute to a safer environment, while assigning high priority to horticulture (vegetables and fruits) and to forestry;
– concentrate on tissue culture, diagnostics and transgenic plants;
– assign priority to the assessment of benefits and constraints including biosafety (Knudsen, 1993*b*).

Initially, the ISAAA was focusing on plant biotechnology applications in tissue culture, diagnostics and transgenic plants. Projects helping poor farmers to grow non-commercial crop species, in particular vegetatively propagated and open-pollinated fruit and vegetable species, were more favoured. Other projects focusing on forestry and the use of micropropagation techniques to propagate tropical tree species difficult to multiply through seed would contribute to maintaining biological diversity. The ISAAA was also working closely with the Stockholm Environmental Institute to provide developing countries with impartial advice on biosafety regulations.

More than 30 preliminary proposals had been identified by the client countries as projects with high priority for implementation in the short term. The ISAAA wanted to provide an honest broker service that matched needs and appropriate proprietary technologies, and to facilitate the formulation of proposals meeting the needs of both the technology recipient and the donor of the proprietary applications or know-how. It also provided advice on biosafety procedures, commercialization and trouble-shooting.

The ISAAA had brokered and secured funding for several projects, including:

– coat protein genes had been donated by Monsanto Co.[1] (see p. 718) to Mexico for conferring resistance to potato viruses PVX and PVY in the Alpha variety of potato; the project was funded by the Rockefeller Foundation; Monsanto Co. had later agreed to extending the donation for use with other cultivars; a companion project aimed to develop the infrastructure and regulatory biosafety procedures for testing and introducing recombinant products in Mexico; the donation was restricted in that Mexico could not export transgenic potatoes; the Monsanto/Mexico project was the most advanced of ISAAA projects; the Centre for Research and Advanced Studies (CINVESTAV) Unit at Irapuato conducted the research and field-testing which began in March 1993; the multiplication, production and marketing of the transgenic potato variety was carried out by a commercial potato producer group and by the National Institute of Forestry, Agriculture and Livestock Research (INIFAP), through its extension services;

– development of a non-radioactive DNA diagnostic probe for determining the presence of *Xanthomonas campestris* pv. *campestris*, an important crucifer disease, by Washington State University Research and Extension Center, so as to make it available to the Asian Vegetable Research and Development Center (AVRDC, Taiwan) and to its client countries around the world; the project was funded by the U.S.AID Program for Science and Technology Cooperation (PSTC);

– donation by the Asgrow Seed Company (Kalamazoo, Michigan) to the University of Costa Rica of a technology for the development of non-conventional virus resistance to the cucumber mosaic virus of 'criollo' melon; after testing in Costa Rica, the Asgrow Seed Company allowed the material to be shared with Mexico, where there was a greater acreage cultivated with the 'criollo' melon; this project was funded in part through the U.S.AID ABSP Programme;

– development of non-conventional virus resistance in tomato at the Agricultural Genetic Engineering Research Institute, Cairo, with the assistance of the John Innes Institute, Norwich (Knudsen, 1993*b*);

– use of ELISA to detect maize viruses in Brazil, through collaboration between Pioneer Hi-Bred International Inc. and Brazil's National Centre for Maize and Sorghum Research (CNPMS).

The ISAAA was involved in two projects in Zimbabwe: the first and most advanced project was developing *Bacillus thuringiensis*-induced transgenic resistance to lepidopteran and other cotton pests; the second entailed the micropropagation of introduced fruit trees, with funding from the German Co-operation Agency.

The Cotton Research Institute was a government-owned organization responsible for all research on cotton. The ISAAA project involved proprietary technology developed by Monsanto Co. Under an arrangement with the Cotton Research Institute, the latter would initially test imported *Bacillus thuringiensis* (*Bt*) protein on local pests under controlled conditions; thereafter, the tests would be repeated using imported transgenic plants and, if successful, would be followed by rapid backcrossing of the transgenic resistance into local cultivars. The results of initial *Bt* protein tests were encouraging. However, according to the Cotton Research Institute, the control of red bollworm (*Diparopsis castanea*) was problematic and required further investigation (Woodend, 1995)[2] (see p. 720).

One category of beneficiaries of the ISAAA strategy was the biotechnology companies for which the ISAAA aimed to facilitate the evaluation of proprietary biotechnology products and create institutional contacts in developing countries. Two other categories were farmers and consumers in developing countries. The ISAAA wished to direct its attention toward poor farmers and non-commercial crop species (fruits, vegetables and trees): vegetatively propagated and open-pollinated crop species, rather than hybrids (Knudsen, 1993*b*).

International Institute of Biological Control

The International Institute of Biological Control (IIBC), Ascot, Berks (United Kingdom), was an institute of Commonwealth Agricultural Bureaux International (CABI), an intergovernmental organization comprising 36 member countries, which provided services to agriculture, forestry, human health and management of natural resources, through the provision of information and associated technical services[3] (see p. 720). Since its creation in 1928, the IIBC, a non-profit making organization, had supported the development of biological control and integrated pest management.

A purpose-built facility completed in 1988 included constant temperature rooms and a quarantine unit equipped for work on insects and pathogens. Together with the quarantine greenhouse opened in 1986, this facility greatly expanded the Institute capacity to undertake intermediate quarantine of biological control agents being moved from one tropical region to another. The new building housed the IIBC

Training and Information Unit and the CABI Library Services Centre.

The IIBC main activity was research and development on contract for governments, international and bilateral development agencies, research foundations and commercial interests in agriculture. To do this, the Institute operated through seven bases around the world, most of them linked to leading national research institutes. IIBC staff recruited over 13 countries advised on over 80 projects a year. IIBC experts provided advisory services on: pest ecology, biology of pests' natural enemies, and the production, handling, shipment and release of natural enemies for conventional biological control. The IIBC investigated the conservation of natural enemies of insect and other arthropod pests and weeds.

Current programmes (1995) included:

– characterization screening and the supply of insects and pathogens for controlling major pasture weeds in environmentally sensitive areas;

– research on the natural enemies of pests in temperate and tropical forests;

– integrated pest management programmes relating to vegetables, cotton, coffee and rice;

– development of a fungal pesticide for controlling locusts and grasshoppers in Africa;

– investigations on the control of pests attacking cassava, sweet potato and Irish potato for the Eastern and Southern Africa Root Crops Research Network.

Technology transfer was an important part of the IIBC activities; short-term courses given on biological control and pest management were conducted at the Institute's own field stations or at collaborating institutions in developing countries. Customized, illustrated manuals were prepared for training courses, as were special self-training packages. The IIBC had also begun working with national programmes and the FAO on the development of training materials for farmers, to help them discover and appreciate the role of natural enemies for their crops. The IIBC co-operated with universities in Europe, Africa, Asia and Latin America to support degree-level training in biological control and to organize bench training in specialized techniques for scientists and technicians sponsored either by their own institutions or through training grants.

In 1993, the IIBC set up its Training Information and Policy Support Group (TIPS) to meet the demand for training and information on biological control. The TIPS added a new dimension to the IIBC, providing information materials and training for non-specialists, in the form of handbooks, posters and concise summaries.

The IIBC made available information on all aspects of biological control with the backing of the CAB ABSTRACTS data-base. Its Information Unit also had the resources of an unrivalled plant protection library and access to specialist knowledge from staff at the other CAB International Institutes and collaborating institutes. The IIBC compiled its own abstract journal, *Biocontrol News and Information*, which surveyed biological control research on a quarterly basis and provided critical reviews and a regular news section. The IIBC also maintained a global data-base of biological control introductions against insect pests, which practitioners consulted.

Where identification of natural enemies was required, the IIBC depended on CAB biosystematic institutes: the International Institute of Entomology, International Institute of Parasitology and International Mycological Institute. Besides identification, these Institutes produced guides and computerized keys to pests and natural enemies, monitored the global movements of exotic pests and undertook biochemical research into the taxonomy of difficult groups.

Center for the Application of Molecular Biology to International Agriculture

The Center for the Application of Molecular Biology to International Agriculture (CAMBIA) planned to become an independent, non-governmental, non-profit making research institute. The CAMBIA's main objective was to develop molecular biology-based methods to be applied to agriculture. Local researchers and farmers were expected to be actively involved in the application of the designed biotechnologies.

The CAMBIA was developing the Molecular Genetic Resource Service (MGRS) as an internationally mandated gene bank and service to acquire those genes, vectors and sequences in the public domain, support their use and distribute them to all participants. The MGRS was expected to develop novel approaches for assessment and utilization of biological diversity, for the automated distribution of DNA libraries for numerous crop species and organisms of importance to tropical and subtropical agriculture, the automated molecular genetic mapping of these organisms (Jefferson, 1993).

The CAMBIA wanted to focus its research programme on controlled apomyxis (see p. 369) and also wanted to explore the setting up of divisions for education and information.

Notes

1 Monsanto Co. long tradition as a chemical company went back to 1902. It consisted of four business groups:

– the Agricultural Group, which developed, produced and marketed crop protection products and lawn-and-garden products, its main product being the Round-up herbicide; another well-known product was the bovine somatotropin (BST);

– the Chemical Group, which produced and sold plastics, nylon and acrylic fibres, rubber chemicals, etc.;

– Searle, which developed, produced and marketed prescription pharmaceuticals;

– the NutraSweet Company, which produced sweeteners and other food ingredients.

Monsanto Co. involvement in plant biotechnology research and development dated back to the early 1980s. It had been at the forefront of research to develop *Agrobacterium*-mediated transformation techniques and, in 1983, was one of the first to introduce and express foreign genes in plants. *Petunia* was one of the first plants to be transformed, followed by canola, sugar-beet, maize, cotton, soybeans, tomato and potato, while the transformation of wheat was the subject of co-operation with the Plant Biotechnology Institute of the National Research Council of Canada (Saskatoon). Behind Monsanto Co.'s strategy lay a desire to improve not only the agronomic quality of plants but also the consumer quality of their products. The improvement of crop productivity included the control of weeds, diseases and insects (Kishore, 1994).

Crop improvement using biotechnologies could be divided into four different areas:

– production or system enhancements through improved control of weeds and diseases, including fungal, bacterial and viral diseases (viral diseases could not be controlled by conventional breeding because few genes coding for resistance were found even in wild relatives; biotechnologies could circumvent the problem);

– improvement in component or whole food traits (e.g. one could increase the quantity of starch, sugar or lipids being accumulated to arrive at an oilseed rape with 55% oil instead of the usual 45%; instead of accumulating just any oil, plants could accumulate specific oils- oleic acid for instance, which was nutritionally desirable);

– change of whole food traits (e.g. introduction of genes that extend the shelf-life of fruits, make them taste sweeter or increase their nutritional value);

– production of novel materials (e.g. bioplastics, plant-based materials, produced cheaply and massively, could compete with petroleum products) [Kishore, 1994].

Once a gene had been introduced into a plant, its expression was of primary importance. Plant biotechnologists could use promoters, which caused high-level expression of the gene in a number of different tissues. There were target specific promoters: genes could thus be expressed in root tissue, leaf tissue or seed tissue. Some promoters could even target the expression of genes within leaf epidermal cells or guard cells. Some promoters could come on at different stages of development, e.g. at specific developmental stages during which oil production was at a maximum in the seed (Kishore, 1994).

Gene sequencing was a major breakthrough. But sequencing 100 genes might mean that the function of only 30 could be determined. The major breakthrough in the future would be to know the exact function of a high number of genes, so as to be able to use the genetic transformation process effectively (Kishore, 1994).

Monsanto Co. was focusing mainly on two applications: herbicide-resistant and insect-resistant crop species. Monsanto Co. had obtained full approval in the USA for soybeans resistant or tolerant to the herbicide Roundup (glyphosate); the resistant variety was sold under the brand name Roundup Ready and was available in the USA in 1996. The Company also developed Roundup Ready varieties of canola (to be marketed in Canada), cotton, maize, sugar-beet (to be marketed in Europe) and oilseed rape (to be marketed in Europe).

Insect-resistance was obtained by inserting the *Bacillus thuringiensis* gene into various crop species. The first insect-resistant crop species to receive full approval in the USA was Monsanto Co.'s NewLeaf insect-resistant potato. The company was also developing insect-resistant varieties of cotton and maize (Monsanto 1994 Annual Report). In 1996, with Ecogen Inc. (Langhorne, Pennsylvania), Monsanto Co. concluded a collaborative agreement to develop crop species and varieties protected against insects, using Ecogen's extensive *Bacillus thuringiensis* (*Bt*) library and intellectual property rights.

Monsanto Co. claimed that planting its BollGard cotton would benefit from 'season-long in-plant control (. . .) without the use of in-season sprays' against cotton bollworm, tobacco budworm and pint bollworm. BollGard was Monsanto Co.'s genetically-engineered and patented cotton with a *Bt* gene producing a protein that made cotton poisonous for these pests. This transgenic cotton was commercialized by the world's biggest cotton seed dealer, Delta and Pine Land. However, the Union of Concerned Scientists (UCS) had called on the U.S. Environmental Protection Agency (EPA) to suspend the registration and sales of BollGard cotton 'pending development of new management plans that will prevent pest resistance' (*Seedling*, vol. 13, no. 3, October 1996, p. 32).

The NewLeaf potato variety was commercialized by Monsanto Co. itself through its potato breeding company Nature Mark. There were, however, no plans for vertical integration, potato production and marketing being a small-scale and regionally divided business. The tomato business was different: Monsanto Co.'s subsidiary in the tomato industry, Gargiulo, was a vertically integrated company, with its own breeding programme, production and marketing of tomatoes.

For soybeans, maize and cotton, the herbicide-, and insect-resistant varieties were expected to be commercialized in collaboration with existing seed companies. For instance, Monsanto Co. purchased Stoneville Pedigree Seeds Corporation, Asgrow and DeKalb (40%); in addition, on 6 January 1996, it announced the purchase of Holden's Foundation Seeds Incorporated, Corn States Hybrid Services Inc. and Corn States International for $1.02 billion. Holden was a producer of hybrid seeds, while the two other corporations commercialized Holden's seeds in the USA, Europe and South America. In 1996, Monsanto Co. purchased stocks and signed a long-term research-and-development agreement in agricultural biotechnologies, particularly maize and soybeans seeds, with DeKalb Genetics Corporation (DeKalb, Illinois).

On 28 June 1995, Monsanto Co. announced the signing of a letter of intent for the acquisition of 54.5% of equity stakes in Calgene Inc., a leading agricultural biotechnology firm well known for its FLAVR/SAVR transgenic tomato. In 1995, Calgene Inc. purchased a licensing option from DNA Plant Technology Corp. (Oakland, California) for its Transwitch technology, which delayed ripening by altering ethylene production in fruits. The company had also genetically engineered cotton and canola (oilseed rape). For cotton production, Calgene Inc. had developed a variety resistant to the herbicide bromoxynil (marketed as Buctril by the French agrochemical company Rhône-Poulenc). For both transgenic cotton and canola, Calgene Inc. had obtained the go-ahead in the USA to commercialize its varieties. Besides producing the FLAVR/SAVR tomato, which was contracted out to farmers, Calgene Inc. itself ensured each step in the marketing chain (vertical integration). For canola production and processing, Calgene Inc. had its own subsidiaries: Ameri-Can Seed for canola seed production and Calgene Chemical for processing oilseeds.

In accordance with the terms of the letter of intent, Monsanto Co. would provide Calgene Inc. with $30 million, certain research on fresh produce and oil seeds and its current equity interests and options in Gargiulo. Monsanto Co. would also provide long-term credit facilities for the general business needs of Calgene Inc. and

Gargiulo. The transaction would lead to full integration of Calgene Inc. into Monsanto Co., thus enabling the company to have access to Calgene's expertise in developing and commercializing genetically-engineered tomato, cotton and canola varieties, and on the other hand allowing Calgene Inc. to meet an urgent need for injected capital (Monsanto 1994 Annual Report). Monsanto Co. also acquired the U.S. biotechnology company Decogen.

The emphasis placed on biotechnologies led Monsanto Co. to sell its chemical branches (e.g. nylon, acrylic fibres and plastics used in the automobile industry) and to split into two new companies. The first one which will keep the name Monsanto, was devoted to agriculture, food and health (whose annual turnover amounted to $5 billion in 1995). The second company was regrouping all the chemical activities ($3.7 billion turnover in 1995). The funds needed for the split were estimated at $400-600 million, and 1,500 to 2,000 jobs were expected to be abolished, i.e. a 5% to 9% reduction in the group's total staff (in *Biofutur*, no. 164, February 1997, p. 39).

2 According to Kathen (1996), field releases of transgenic plants in developing countries amounted to 129 for maize, soybeans, cotton, tomato and potato, and 30 for other species, the overall total being 159. Of the 129 field releases, 70 concerned herbicide-resistant plants, 34 insect-resistant plants, 9 virus-resistant plants and 20 plants with modified product quality.

The 159 field releases occurred in Argentina (43), Puerto Rico (21), Mexico (20), Chile (17), the Republic of South Africa (17), Cuba (13), Costa Rica (8), Bolivia (5), Belize (4), Guatemala, India (3 each), Peru (2), Dominican Republic (1), Egypt (1) and Thailand (1). The predominance of Latin America was obvious. Kathen (1996) mentioned that no field releases of transgenic plants were documented in Brazil, China, Colombia, Indonesia, Kenya, Malaysia, Nigeria, Pakistan, The Philippines, Venezuela and Zimbabwe up to 1996.

3 The main tasks of the Information Services, located at the CAB International Centre (CABIC) at Wallingford, was the creation of a bibliographic data-base (CAB ABSTRACTS) of research on agriculture, forestry, the environment, applied social sciences and aspects of human medicine. Relevant scientific and technical literature was acquired world-wide for abstracting and indexing by almost 100 scientists/linguists in five divisions:
  − animal health and medical parasitology;
  − animal production and human nutrition;
  − crop protection and genetics;
  − crop production;
  − natural resources, forestry and economics.

The Information Services also published journals and books, and offered training for information professionals, especially from developing countries.

CABI's Scientific Services consisted of four institutes and Library Services:

  − International Institute of Entomology, located in London, in the Natural History Museum;

  − International Mycological Institute, located in Egham, Surrey;

  − International Institute of Parasitology, located in St Albans, Herts;

  − International Institute of Biological Control, with headquarters at Silwood Park, Ascot, and stations in Trinidad and Tobago, Switzerland, Pakistan, Kenya and Malaysia.

These institutes provided an authoritative identification service for agricultural pests and other organisms, a biological control service, and were conducting research, implementing projects and providing training in their fields of expertise.

An important aspect was the establishment of effective partnerships with relevant development assistance agencies aimed at increasing the delivery of CABI services to developing countries.

International Programme on Rice Biotechnology

Although world rice production doubled during the 1965–1990 period to 520 million tonnes, it was estimated that the demand for rice would exceed production by the end of the century. New rice varieties with higher yield potential were therefore essential for augmenting rice production (Khush and Toenniessen, 1991). In 1984, the International Rice Research Institute organized a conference on biotechnology and international agricultural research. As a follow-up to this conference, and also because rice, whose output was largely utilized for consumption by those producing it, was unlikely to attract attention from commercial biotechnology companies, the Rockefeller Foundation funded an International Programme on Rice Biotechnology. Biotechnologies were expected to complement the time-tested methods of crop improvement.

Plant breeding comprises two phases:
– the evolutionary phase, during which variable populations are produced; the time-tested methods used to create variability are hybridization and, to a lesser extent, mutation induction;
– the evaluation phase, where desirable genotypes are selected from the variable populations; various methods, such as bulk population breeding, pedigree selection, recurrent selection and single-seed descent, are used to identify desired genotypes; the yield performance of selected genotypes are then evaluated in replicated trials.

Advanced rice research was initiated under the International Programme on Rice Biotechnology set up by the Rockefeller Foundation in 1985. Progress achieved in rice biotechnologies was impressive and a large part could be attributed to the Programme, although Japan was said to be running the largest and best-funded rice genome project in the world, partially funded by the private sector. Rice molecular genetic markers and maps were being applied in rice breeding and genetic transformation of rice had been achieved by several laboratories (see pp. 389–391); various genes conferring resistance to pests and diseases, and controlling the nutritional value of rice were being cloned and studied.

Wide-cross hybridization allowed the transfer of useful genes from wild *Oryza* species to elite cultivars; many more potentially-useful genes remained available in wild relatives and biotechnological tools would speed up their utilization; RFLP maps and species-specific DNA probes would enable rice breeders to more effectively follow the introgression of alien genes from wild species into elite species. As protoplast regeneration protocols were becoming more efficient and available for a broader range of rice cultivars, protoplast fusion followed by regeneration was expected to become another technique for wide crossing.

Anther culture allowed the production of homozygous lines in two generations and could thereby reduce the time required to produce new rice varieties (the development of homozygous lines using conventional sexual crossing required five to seven generations) [Khush and Toenniessen, 1991]. This technique deserved to be more broadly utilized, particularly in locations where only one generation per year was feasible for conventional breeding. Further research aimed at improving the anther culture response of *indica* rice would contribute to the application of this valuable breeding tool.

Rice is particularly well-suited for DNA-based genetic mapping. It is a true diploid with a small genome showing an ample polymorphism and highly recombinogenic. There were major RFLP mapping programmes underway at public institutions; the International Rice Research Institute (IRRI) was facilitating collaboration, co-ordination, synthesis of results and integration of the RFLP map with the classical map. Both the IRRI and the International Centre for Genetic Engineering and Biotechnology's component in New Delhi were developing non-radioactive probes enabling routine use of the RFLP markers in developing country rice-breeding programmes. The RFLP map was sufficiently dense to allow chromosome mapping and cloning of rice genes. It would, therefore, be possible to clone rice genes with a known phenotype but unknown function.

The maize activator (AC) element was transferred to the genome of rice and shown to transpose. Assuming that transposition occurs in progeny plants, transposon tagging would also enable cloning of rice genes of unknown function, such as those controlling pest resistance (Khush and Toenniessen, 1991). The combination of RFLP mapping and transposon tagging in maize was also leading to the identification and cloning of many genes. These genes, or modified constructs, could be transferred to rice and confer useful traits and, in most cases, be used as heterologous probes for isolating the analogous genes from rice. At the end of the 1990s, many genes worthy of testing in rice would become available.

Protoplast transformation, through electroporation or chemical treatment of protoplasts, was the method from which stable, transformed rice plants were confirmed (Khush and Toenniessen, 1991). It would also be possible to transform rice with large DNA fragments (200–500 kilobases), shown by RFLP mapping to contain useful genes.

An international consultation had been held at Cholburi, Thailand, from 1 to 3 September 1992, to consider biosafety issues associated with the field-testing and commercialization of transgenic rice. The meeting was attended by 41 participants from 15 countries. They included a broad range of Asian, North American and European scientists working on rice biology, along with representatives of governmental agencies in charge of biosafety regulations, non-governmental agencies and private sector organizations. The consultation had been organized by Stanford University Law School and Thailand's National Center for Genetic Engineering and Biotechnology (BIOTEC) with the support of the U.S. Department of Agriculture (USDA), the Rockefeller Foundation and the World Bank.

As of September 1992, the USDA Animal and Plant Health Inspection Service (APHIS) had approved four applications for field tests of transgenic rice. The genes being introduced into rice included RNase constructs for cytoplasmic male sterility, *Bacillus thuringiensis* (*Bt*) toxin genes for insect resistance (particularly the yellow stem borer), herbicide tolerance genes, chitinase genes (insect resistance), viral coat protein genes, various seed storage protein constructs (nutritional quality) and the *Ac/Ds* transposable element system of maize. Most of these products could be expected to move to field testing in the near future.

The International Programme on Rice Biotechnology was supporting research leading to transgenic materials that needed to be tested under field conditions if they were to be brought to the developing world's farmers. Likewise, the World Bank was interested in bringing the benefits of agricultural biotechnologies to the developing world with respect to a variety of crops and in seeing that the appropriate regulatory structures were in place and effective. The APHIS was receiving applications for large-scale testing of transgenic plants and had organized a series of seminars to elucidate the scientific basis that underlay regulation.

The conclusions of the meeting held in Thailand were the following:

– the likelihood of gene transfer from cultivated rice to wild and weedy relatives was of sufficient magnitude to lead to the conclusion that, over the long term, some gene transfer probably would occur among AA genome species; nevertheless, several factors could limit that gene transfer – rice was a predominantly self-fertilizing crop species, cultivated rice had a short period of pollen viability, about five minutes, cultivated rice was rarely sympatric with wild and weedy rice species (with the exception of red rice in the USA), and the spread of an introduced gene required positive selection in the new hybrid background; consequently, attention needed to be focused on gene constructs that could be positively selected for in wild and weedy rice relatives;

– because of the breeding features mentioned above, isolation requirements were not specially stringent; a 10-metre isolation appeared adequate for normal breeding, but in most cases a more conservative isolation distance of 20 m to 40 m should be established that accounted for wind, size of plant populations and other factors;

– most of the significant potential biosafety implications of gene transfer in rice were associated with the possible creation of novel and/or agressive weeds; knowledge of the biology and distribution of various AA genome relatives of rice was incomplete; further research would be necessary in some regions to fully evaluate all possible biosafety issues; each gene construct must be considered on a case-by-case basis, because categorical biosafety predictions were not possible in light of the limited experience with field tests; special attention should be paid to stress-tolerance genes that could expand the ecological range of some wild or weedy varieties at the expense of others, as well as to genes conferring herbicide resistance because of their possible implications for patterns of herbicide use;

– the likelihood of gene transfer into associated bacteria and fungi was remote and should not delay development; genetic modification of endophytes associated with rice should be approached with caution.

The meeting recommended that, in order to minimize the risk of gene transfer from cultivated rice to wild and weedy relatives during breeding, a relatively conservative isolation distance of 20 metres that took into account such factors as wind, population size of both source and potential target, the duration of female receptivity in the target population and the potential risks associated with the introduced gene, was suitable. Until sufficient experience was accumulated to permit generalizations, each gene construct must be assessed on a case-by-case basis, since it was not yet possible to make categorical biosafety predictions. While further study of the ecology and distribution of wild and weedy rice was recommended, this should not delay field tests in areas where the ecology was well known. It would be useful to carry out some before-and-after field test surveys, to consider introduction of plants carrying neutral marker genes in order to examine the dynamics of gene flow, and to investigate the fitness of the resulting plants when engineered genes were introduced into hybrids between a crop plant and its wild relatives.

The goal of the Rockefeller Foundation International Programme on Rice Biotechnology was to apply biotechnologies to rice production in developing countries, through a series of co-operative projects and technology transfers, with a view to improving seeds and other materials used by farmers. The IRRI and CIAT (International Center for Tropical Agriculture) were facilitating the free exchange and distribution of rice breeding lines. Improved varieties ultimately reached the developing-country farmer either through the public sector or through commercial varieties distributed in the Third World.

The Rockefeller Foundation rice biotechnology grantees were expected to share materials and technology resulting from the Foundation-supported research, with co-operating researchers at zero royalty for use in developing countries. This policy covered intermediate steps such as research results, transformation procedures and rights under material transfer agreements, as well as final products and rights under patents and other forms of intellectual property. At the same time, it was recognized that grantees might wish to claim intellectual property rights on their discoveries and their improved materials, in order to obtain economic returns in industrialized countries for the support of further research and to maintain a strong negotiating position in the event of any intellectual property disputes.

Collaboration and the free exchange of research materials were hallmarks of the Programme and its network and contributed to much of its success. In many cases, materials were shared and technologies transferred prior to publication. The *Rice Biotechnology Quarterly* was being published to disseminate the results of the Programme.

Co-operation for small-scale agriculture

Assistance to small-scale agriculture and farmers was the main focus of the International Fund for Agricultural Development, Rome (IFAD). By the end of 1991, the IFAD reported that 12 new projects of agricultural production had been launched for a total investment of approximately $225 million. The IFAD's participation amounted to $110.5 million, a record figure, the rest being contributed by other international organizations and the recipient developing countries. More than 200,000 small landholders were expected to benefit from the projects, whose contribution ranged from technical assistance to agricultural training and soft loans. With the addition of these 12 projects, the IFAD was implementing 314 projects in 95 countries for a total of $3.3 billion.

The ratio of per capita income in countries like China and India to that in European countries had been 1:2 toward the end of the 19th century. It was nearer 1:70 by the 1990s. Socio-economic indicators forecast that the trend might continue unless concerted efforts were made to impart a pro-poor bias in technology, training and trade. The 'green revolution' had been unjustly accused of indifference to the fate of small farmers and it would be necessary to undertake pro-active social research from the earliest phases to avoid the same charges being levelled again. Bringing biotechnologies to bear on 'orphan commodities' was one way for benefits to be reaped by the most needy. A comprehensive treatment of methods for imparting a pro-poor bias in the development and dissemination of biotechnological innovations could be found in the book, *Biotechnology: reaching the unreached*, edited by M.S. Swaminathan and published in 1991. He considered rice a good illustration of how to benefit from the pro-poor potential of biotechnologies.

Dutch Government's initiatives

Since 1987, the subject of biotechnology and development co-operation had been given special attention by the Directorate-General for International Cooperation of the Dutch Ministry of Foreign Affairs. Its Research and Technology Section had executed and/or co-ordinated various activities which were the basis for a policy document entitled Biotechnology and Development Cooperation: a coordinated approach for responsible, problem-oriented use of biotechnology for and with the Third World (April 1989). On 16 May 1989, it was presented to both houses of Parliament.

Technical co-operation was directed toward: agriculture (plant production, animal production, storage and processing of agricultural commodities), human health care and environmental management. A survey of the current state of knowledge in biogas production was commissioned. As part of technical co-operation, the following activities were undertaken, where possible in an integrated fashion:

– biotechnological research projects by and for developing countries;

– creation of a biotechnological research capability in developing countries;

– technology assessment, socio-economic studies and risk analyses;

– support for biotechnology policy in developing countries;

– laws and regulations;

– provision of information;

– free exchange and conservation of genetic resources.

The following were regarded as priority subjects:

– agriculture (virus screening techniques for plant material, tissue culture, crop protection, biological manure and improvement of soil fertility, drought tolerance, special attention to so-called orphan crops-cassava, sweet potato, cowpea and beans; livestock feeding and fodder plants, control of animal diseases; post-harvest techniques, scaling-up and standardizing of local fermentation processes);

– human health care (local vaccine production, particularly against *Streptococcus pneumoniae, Neisseria meningitidis* A, measles virus, diagnosis and drug development);

– environmental management (purification processes to remove nitrogen, phosphate, sulphur and heavy metals, aerobic and anaerobic treatment of waste-waters, processing of waste products).

The Directorate-General for International Cooperation had participated in a World Bank/ISNAR (International Service for National Agricultural Research)/AIDAB (Australian International

Development Assistance Bureau) survey of local priorities in Zimbabwe, Kenya, Indonesia and Colombia, which provided guidelines for building up local capacity in biotechnologies. Five Dutch universities had expressed interest in co-operating with projects to build biotechnological research capability in these developing countries.

The Minister for Development Co-operation of the Netherlands also requested the Information Centre for Low External Input and Sustainable Agriculture (ILEIA) to organize a contest for case descriptions of rural people's biotechnologies, with a view to collecting documentation on indigenous knowledge and gaining a better insight into rural people's present practices and experiences in biotechnologies. This would help the ministry to foster the use of biotechnologies by small-scale and resource-poor farmers.

The Special Programme Biotechnology and Development Cooperation was approved by the Dutch Council of Ministers and officially started on 1 January 1992. For an initial period of five years and with a total budget of $6 million, the Programme was implemented through a 'biotechnology project' within the Directorate-General for International Cooperation (DGIS). Outside experts were brought in to implement tasks in the identified priority areas. An *ad-hoc* advisory group was set up to consider the allocation of resources to different priority areas; it met at least twice a year and its members were appointed in their personal capacity. The annual distribution of funds was the following: 50% for agriculture, 20% for human health care, 20% for environment and 10% freely disposable.

Under the Special Programme Biotechnology and Development Cooperation, Clancy and Hulscher (1994) of the Technology and Development Group of the University of Twente conducted a study on possibilities for biogas production in developing countries, with specific reference to the potential contribution of biotechnology. Biogas is a combustible mixture of gases (approximately 60% methane) formed during the anaerobic decomposition of organic material, known as anaerobic digestion. The latter not only had the advantage of producing a source of energy, but also offered environmental benefits and means of producing fertilizer. In industrialized countries, interest in anaerobic digestion focused on waste-water treatment while, in developing countries, emphasis continued to be laid primarily on energy production for households or communities.

Developing countries had made significant contributions to the development of anaerobic digestion. The largest number of digesters had been installed in Asia (more than 5 million were estimated to be in use in 1994); Latin America was currently the world leader in anaerobic digestion for sewage treatment; and, although the total number of digesters installed there was small, it was Africa that had seen some of the most recent significant developments in household digesters. Two broad areas for further application of anaerobic digestion in developing countries had been identified: in urban areas, for industrial and domestic waste pollution control, and in rural areas, as part of integrated rural development, through mitigating environmental degradation, increasing farm income (through electricity generation) and improvements in human and animal health (by treating excreta).

The obstacles to further dissemination of anaerobic digestion in developing countries were identified as political (e.g. low cost of alternative fuels), technical (e.g. ambient temperatures too low to give good gas production), managerial and socio-economic (e.g. high cost of digester).

Most of the work to develop anaerobic digestion related to the engineering aspects of reactor design; the microbial aspects received far less attention. As yet, the full range of biotechnologies had not been applied to the anaerobic digestion process itself. Urban and industrial waste treatment in developing countries would benefit from any improvements in high-technology, high-rate digestors. There were two areas in which biotechnologies could make a contribution: pre-treatment of leafy biomass to increase the range of feedstocks, and development of specialized inocula for adverse environments, such as low temperatures and high salt concentrations. These could both reduce digester cost and increase the number of people with access to the technology by extending the resource base. What hampered accessibility to the technology was not the lack of avenues available to users, but the socio-economic barrier of low-income levels. This meant that improvements in the technology were only likely to have a significant impact if they were coupled with a major reduction in digester cost. No evidence had been found that, in the short- to medium-term, biotechnologies could contribute to bringing about this reduction.

In their recommendations, Clancy and Hulscher (1994) emphasized the support institutes in developing countries and in the Netherlands were providing to joint programmes, with focus on skills development at all levels; research was designed to be of both a technical and socio-economic managerial nature, and based on a rolling project over five years to achieve meaningful results on both sides. Priority was to be given to biotechnological research aimed at increasing the range of feedstocks, through pre-treatment of biomass and the development of inocula adapted to adverse environments. In addition to the training of technicians in the construction of digesters and support for household and community biogas projects, the benefits of biogas production to women in developing countries merited assessment and it would be essential to design mechanisms to increase their participation in biogas projects. South-South co-operation also needed fostering to disseminate existing local knowledge and skills in developing countries, particularly from China, India and Brazil where anaerobic digestion was being actively studied and applied.

The *Biotechnology and Development Monitor* journal, a joint project of the Department of International Relations of the University of Amsterdam and the Special Programme Biotechnology and Development Co-operation, had been a source of information on biotechnologies and international development since 1989. The journal took a broad look at biotechnologies, including policy aspects, socio-economic issues, intellectual property protection, biosafety, etc. It focused both on issues of modern biotechnologies and on appropriate biotechnologies in developing countries. The Monitor was widely read, especially in these countries. The Special Programme Biotechnology and Development Co-operation had been funding the *Biotechnology and Development Monitor* since 1989.

The journal was evaluated during the summer of 1994. This evaluation, conducted by a team of researchers, headed by Boem Van Raavenswaaij (Socrates International Consultancies, Netherlands), Juan Izquierdo (FAO Technical Co-operation Network on Plant Biotechnology) and Nagesh Kumar (United Nations University, Netherlands), had been commissioned by the Directorate-General for International Cooperation (DGIS) of the Netherlands' Ministry of Foreign Affairs. The evaluation team consulted representatives of various main interest groups: readers, editors, outside experts, as well as the funding agency. The evaluation relied on three main components: a readers' survey; a questionnaire sent to the three partner institutes (Inter-American Institute for Cooperation on Agriculture, IICA, Costa Rica; African Centre for Technology Studies, ACTS, Kenya; and the Research and Information System for the non-aligned and other developing countries, RIS, India); and in-depth interviews with experts from several international organizations (Van Raavenswaaij and Van Roozendaal, 1995).

At the time of the evaluation, the 4,250 subscribers who received the journal represented about a hundred different countries, 63% of the subscribers being from developing countries. Before the closing date, the readers' survey resulted in a response rate of 14%. The survey showed that the readers could be broadly divided into two groups: one group was aware of the potential of biotechnologies as well as of the social and economic impact of their various applications, but lacked the time to scan the rapidly increasing amount of material published on different aspects of biotechnologies and development. In this group, the *Monitor* was mainly used to read about developments outside their own specialization. The other group, mainly outside the OECD countries, had only a limited access to material on biotechnologies due to the cost of publications. Therefore, the *Monitor* was an appreciated, inexpensive source of information; 75% of the respondents used the *Monitor* at some time for teaching or writing purposes. This was a main objective of the Journal (Van Raavenswaaij and Van Roozendaal, 1995).

On the whole, the respondents were satisfied with the information provided by the *Monitor*. The relevance of the subjects covered and the reliability of the information was praised. Nevertheless, criticism was voiced on the varying analytical content and on the topicality of the articles. About 25% of the respondents indicated that they would like more articles than present on 'technology in the South', while 40% of the respondents (50% of the non-OECD respondents) asked for more articles on 'technology in the North'. Since the respondents from non-OECD countries were the main focus of the *Monitor*, the editors decided to initiate a series of publications on Japan, the USA and Europe (Van Raavenswaaij and Van Roozendaal, 1995).

The in-depth interviews at several (international) organizations revealed that the *Monitor* was highly valued, but some regretted the emphasis on agriculture. On the other hand, it was admitted that this bias was justified in view of the needs of developing countries. Furthermore, more case studies of the nature of 'success and failure stories' were requested. The closed-club network of contributors was criticized, and more involvement of scientists from a wider range of developing countries was preferred (Van Raavenswaaij and Van Roozendaal, 1995).

In order to facilitate the internationalization, the following measures were to be taken:

– establishment of an international editorial advisory board, including about ten experts from governmental and non-governmental organizations on 'personal title'; the editorial staff in Amsterdam invited the current partner institutes to become members of this international board; the international editorial board would have an advisory function, while the final responsibility remained with the editorial staff of the *Monitor*; the board members would be able to suggest topics for articles, contacts and reviewers to the editors; the advisory board would also play the role of a forum for ideas and discussions on the future place and function of the *Monitor*;

– extension of a network of correspondents, located in different (developing) countries;

– award of about two fellowships a year, each with a duration of four months, to people invited to assist the *Monitor* editors in their work and to receive on-the-job training. The award of these fellowships aims to: train young professionals from developing countries in analyzing and reporting on socio-economic and policy issues concerning biotechnologies; establish long-term contacts with motivated correspondents in different developing countries; and include a wider diversity of opinions from the South on biotechnologies (Van Raavenswaaij and Van Roozendaal, 1995).

To increase the geographical coverage of the *Monitor*, the initiation of a Spanish edition and the resumption of the French edition were considered desirable. But financial assistance had to be sought for that purpose. The English version of the *Monitor* was fully subsidized by the Special Programme Biotechnology and Development Cooperation of the DGIS, which allowed free distribution. This arrangement was extended till 1998, but after this date the DGIS might change its policy, which would require the *Monitor* to find other donors, to commercialize (e.g. by introducing a system of differentiated subscription fees) or to interrupt the publication of the Journal (Van Raavenswaaij and Van Roozendaal, 1995).

To point out research fields and goals appropriate for improving small-scale food production and sustainable rural development, the Department of Biology and Society of the Free University of Amsterdam had been carrying out a 'programme study' on Biotechnology for small-scale farmers in developing countries, focusing on Bolivia, Pakistan and Zimbabwe. Comparisons were also made with other member countries of the Southern Africa Development Co-ordination Conference (SADCC, i.e. Angola, Botswana, Lesotho, Malawi, Mozambique, Swaziland, Tanzania, Zambia and Zimbabwe). Of these States, four figured among the least developed countries, while six were landlocked. Their economies were highly dependent on a slender range of export products. They were experiencing severe difficulties in terms of transport, declining trade, drought and depressed economic situation, and military conflict. For most countries, incomes (estimated growth of 1% to 2% per year) were projected to lag behind rapid population growth (3% per year, i.e. from 70 million to 100 million people by the year 2000). Food demand was growing by 3% to 5% annually. The agricultural sector engaged about 80% of the active population in the SADCC countries, while generating 35% of the gross national product and 25% of foreign exchange. According to the FAO estimates, food production per capita had decreased by about 20% over the two decades 1968–1988, with Zimbabwe the only country boasting an adequate food supply, mainly due to the 'maize revolution'. Malawi, Swaziland, Tanzania and Zambia acknowledged periodic food surpluses depending on weather conditions. Angola, Botswana, Lesotho and Mozambique suffered from serious structural shortages. Agriculture was carried out in small units (on communal or privately owned land) where subsistence farming dominated, and on large farms (owned by the government or foreign investors) where export crop species were cultivated. Food crop species included cassava, maize, sorghum and millet. In 1985, the Southern African Centre for Agricultural Research (SACCAR) was set up. Biotechnology was nascent or non-existent in the SADCC region. Zimbabwe was the main exception.

Within the 'programme study' of the Free University of Amsterdam, biotechnological and conventional solutions to the problems of small-scale farmers were compared and listed in order of priority according to three main criteria:

– inputs: were the necessary inputs for the use of (bio)technological innovations available? i.e. capital intensive inputs, norms and values concerning agricultural practices, etc.;

– output quality: would the innovation improve quality of life (direct and indirect consequences)?

– sustainability: would innovation be destructive to the agro-ecosystem? would it not harm the robustness of the farming system (resilience to changes in e.g. climate; international trade developments; local markets, etc.)?

The research team of the Department of Biology and Society of the Free University of Amsterdam published the findings of their study in 1990 (Bunders, 1990). They stressed the overriding complexity of small-farmer production systems and the difficulty in assessing the potential contribution of genetic engineering and other biotechnologies to resource-poor farming. However, guidelines for addressing future research and co-operation strategies were provided by the Dutch researchers, especially through case studies in Bolivia, Pakistan and Zimbabwe.

In April 1991, a public debate Biotechnology and farmers' rights; prospects and threats for small-scale farmers in developing countries, was organized by the same Department and NOVIB, the Netherlands Organization for International Development. This non-governmental organization financed many projects in developing countries for sustainable rural development. Since 1988, NOVIB had been working on a project concerning biotechnologies and plant improvement with respect to the world food issue. It had published a paper on *Biotechnology, plant improvement and the food issue*, in which NOVIB set out its position. Publication of *Biotechnology for small-scale farmers in developing countries; analysis and assessment procedures*, edited by Bunders (1990), from the Biology and Society Department, provoked positive reactions from developing countries and from international donor organizations such as the World Bank and various United Nations institutions.

The public debate concentrated on the following three themes:

– strategies for the organization of appropriate biotechnological research;

– protection of the legal position of small-scale farmers in developing countries;

– codes of conduct for multinational corporations.

Guidelines for appropriate biotechnological research could be split into three main categories:

– guidelines regarding the comparative advantage of a biotechnological innovation over other innovations;

– guidelines regarding the characteristics of the end-user's farming system;

– guidelines regarding the national context of the country in question.

Bunders (1990) summarized the criteria for assessing the appropriateness, feasibility and comparative advantage of biotechnological innovations for small-scale farmers:

---

1. National context
    a. Availability of scientific knowledge about the farming system of small-scale farmers.
    b. National and regional organizations for the adaptation and diffusion of (bio-)technological innovations.
    c. Decision-making structure in and between government bodies and organizations involved in research development for small-scale farmers.
    d. Commercial markets for agricultural products.
    e. Infrastructure for biotechnological research.

2. Farming system
    a. Severity of the problem addressed.
    b. Input requirements
        – external: access to capital-intensive inputs, credit facilities, education services;
        – internal: means of production (land, draught animals, capital, technological means, labour), the adjustability of the land-use pattern and distribution of labour, and the adaptability of the socio-cultural pattern.
    c. Output characteristics
        – income-generating effect;
        – quality of the output for marketing;
        – added nutritive value of food and fodder consumption;
        – possibilities of using the output for other productive or remunerative purposes within the farming system.
    d. Robustness
        – Output stability; persistence of the output against normal and mainly short-term fluctuations to which it was exposed, caused by pests, diseases, weeds, climate, internal and external inputs;
        – Sustainability of the farming system; resilience of basic farming resources in the face of structural disturbances such as biotic and abiotic factors (deterioration of gene pools of plant and animal species, or the exhaustion of soils and water, salinization and soil erosion); economic factors like loss of capital and labour (e.g. overburdening of the female agricultural workers); socio-cultural factors (like the disintegration of labour organization and the disappearance of such practices as co-operation and mutual help and of local knowledge of agricultural practices).
    e. Synergetic and/or antagonistic effects with other changes in the farming system and national context.

3. Comparative advantage of biotechnological innovations in terms of implementability (appropriateness and feasibility), problem-solving capacity and cost-effectiveness.

Researchers at the Biology and Society Department of the Free University of Amsterdam had identified the following research areas for biotechnological applications in Zimbabwe, Pakistan and Bolivia.

ZIMBABWE

Improvement of cheap inputs capable of increasing or maintaining soil fertility, e.g. nitrogen-fixing micro-organisms.
Improvement of those crops contributing to the nutrition of the farm household, such as vegetables, legumes, root and tuber species, and fruit species.
Changed composition of small grains.
Introduction and improvement of fodder crops.
Cheap methods of producing virus-free planting material.
Development of diagnostic tests and vaccines.
Disease resistance in cereals, cotton and sunflower.
Drought tolerance in cereals, cotton and sunflower.
The first two research areas were considered of highest priority. The special Programme Biotechnology and Development Cooperation had made an important contribution to biotechnology development in Zimbabwe since 1992.

PAKISTAN

Improvement of fodder crop production (e.g. new fodder crop varieties and nitrogen-fixing micro-organisms).
Silage making.
Biodegradation of agricultural residues.
Development of disease diagnostics.
Development of vaccines.
Milk, cheese and ghee processing methods.

BOLIVIA

Dutch researchers concluded that not enough information on the existing farming system was available to justify a priority assessment of possible biotechnological research fields. However, the following projects seemed relevant: courses on biotechnologies and their social aspects for students and scientists; establishment of a gene bank; farming system research.

Bunders (1994) attempted to offer a pragmatic methodology for ensuring that science-based innovations were beneficial to marginal groups in developing countries: the interactive bottom-up approach (IBU). The author was driven by the idea that negative effects of science-based innovations could be reduced and positive effects increased if the decision-making base were broadened to include scientists, policy-makers, farmers, consumers and environmental groups in the process and thereby empower marginal groups to influence the research-and-development agendas, research design and enhance the legitimacy of the projects. The IBU approach could be applied to multiply the aspects and groups included in the development of biotechnology innovations for small-scale farmers in developing countries. The author qualified her team's application of the IBU approach to biotechnology development in Bolivia, Pakistan and Zimbabwe as a positive experience. However, the approach would only be workable if scientists were willing to collaborate with different groups on a more or less equal footing (Bunders *et al.*, 1997).

Cassava Biotechnology Network

Many obstacles to cassava breeding and improvement difficult to resolve through conventional research were now amenable to biotechnologies within an international collaborative programme, in the form of a network involving both developing and developed country organizations.

A starchy root crop, cassava had been cultivated in tropical America for over 5,000 years. Prior to 1600, during the European exploration of America, Portuguese traders had introduced cassava into the Congo in Africa and later on into East Africa and Asia. By the end of the 19th century, it was growing throughout the tropical world. In 1995, this crop species supplied the staple food for about 500 million people and was grown in 92 countries in the tropics and subtropics.

Although each of the more than 5,000 known varieties of cassava has its own distinctive plant form, genetic structure and adaptability to different environments, the cassava plant (*Manihot esculenta*, a member of the Euphorbiaceae family) is a perennial, woody shrub that grows from about 1 m to 3 m tall. The woody stems are topped by hand-shaped (palmate), dark green, sometimes purplish, leaves. Flowering cassava varieties have small, unconspicuous flowers that lack petals. Male and female flowers grow on the same plant and are cross-pollinated by insects. Fruits are dehiscent and seed production low and erratic; seeds are oval-shaped, about 10 mm long, and mottled brown and gray.

The cone-shaped roots vary in number and size, according to variety and environmental conditions. Normally, they have a dark or light brown, papery bark, which often peels off, leaving a pink or cream cortex. This too can be peeled off to expose the white, starchy flesh. Through the centre of the root runs a usually thin and fibrous pith.

Cassava was usually grown from mature cuttings of the woody stems; the 7-to 30-cm long cuttings were planted horizontally, vertically or inclined, with or without tillage.

No wild direct ancestor of cassava was proven to exist. Of the 98 species of *Manihot* designated in the most recent monograph of the genus, 17 were native to North America. The main centre of species diversity was in Brazil, with a secondary centre located in Mexico. The North American species as a group were designated as high priority for collection and conservation of wild relatives of cassava. *Manihot aesculifolia*, a widespread species found from Panama to Mexico, was considered the wild species closest, morphologically, to the crop species. *Manihot pringhei*, native to northeastern Mexico, was the only wild relative of cassava thought to have low amounts of cyanogenic glucoside in the roots. *M. rhomboidea* and *M. walkerae* had a distinctive herbaceous growth habit. Other species were adapted to cold, drought and possibly to salt. The wide range of growth habit within the group of North American species, ranging from true herbs through vines to small trees, might reflect the varied climates and topography of Mexico and the subsequent broad array of adaptational pressures. All the species were thought to have large, tuberous roots (Bertram and Schaal, 1993).

The cassava circular chloroplast genome was mapped and found to be approximately 160 kbp in length; this placed it at the upper end of the range found among Angiosperms. It was colinear with that of *Petunia*, its increased length being found entirely within the inverted repeat region (Bertram and Schaal, 1993).

Concerning the biogeography of the North American *Manihot* species, they moved northwards parallel with the mountain ranges in eastern and western Mexico, evolving new and phenotypically different species. The phylogeny demonstrated that *M. aesculifolia* was the basal species in the North American group. Several genetic radiations had taken place in Mexico, the first being associated with Sierra Madre Oriental. Subsequently, a large group had evolved, which was found in western and central Mexico, extending north along the Sierra Madre Occidental and the Pacific Coast. It was suggested that Northwestern

South America and Southern Central America might be the location of plant populations related to important progenitors of cassava (Bertram and Schaal, 1993).

If the cultigen theory were correct and cassava was the product of introgression with a number of wild relatives, more information on wild relatives might be crucial to understanding its evolution. Bertram and Schaal (1993) intended to pursue this work, in collaboration with the CIAT (International Center for Tropical Agriculture), to gain a more complete picture of evolutionary relationships in the genus and in cultivated cassava in particular.

Under favourable experimental conditions, cassava as a single crop could yield as much as 90 tonnes of fresh roots per hectare (25 to 30 tonnes of dry matter per hectare), but cassava was usually grown under marginal soil conditions in a harsh climate, in association with crop species like maize, cowpeas and other root or tuber crops. Under these conditions, average yields recorded were an average world 9.8 tonnes of fresh roots per hectare, 7.7 tonnes in Africa, 12.4 tonnes in Latin America and 13.0 tonnes in Asia. In tonnes of grain per hectare, these yields were equivalent to 3.1, 2.5, 4.0 and 4.2 tonnes respectively. Cereal crops grown under similar conditions would produce 1 to 2 tonnes of grain per hectare. One tonne of fresh cassava yielded 280 kg of flour, 230 kg of starch, or 330 kg of dried chips. Researchers had also obtained 170 litres of fuel ethanol from one tonne.

Most cassava was produced by poor, small-scale farmers as a food, feed or cash crop. The total area harvested was about 16 million hectares, 57% of this being in Africa, 25% in Asia and 18% in Latin America. World cassava production amounted to 170.2 million tonnes of fresh roots in 1993 and about 167.2 million tonnes in 1994. According to the FAO 1994 *Food Outlook*, production increased by 4% in Nigeria as a result of expanding planting areas and the adoption of varieties developed by the International Institute of Tropical Agriculture (IITA). In Latin America, production also increased by an overall 5%. In Africa, it declined by more than 3% due to unfavourable climatic conditions, recurrent outbreaks of mealy bug and mosaic disease, and civil strife. In Asia, smaller international markets reduced 1994 production by almost 3%. The overall 1994 production figures were: 88.0 million tonnes for Africa, 49.1 million tonnes for Asia and 29.8 million tonnes for Latin America (*Cassava Newsletter*, vol. 19, no. 1, March 1995, pp. 9–10).

Annual consumption was greatest in Africa, averaging 96 kg per capita, with the greatest consumption in Zaire at 391 kg per capita (or 1,123 kcal per day). In Latin America and the Caribbean, cassava was also a major and growing source of animal feed. In Asia, consumption was high, with some countries even importing cassava starch and flour to meet domestic needs. Average world consumption was 18 kg per capita. About 85% of the world's cassava harvest was used domestically: food – 58%; animal feed – 28%; industrial uses – 3%; and wastage – 11%. The remaining 15% was exported to Europe and Japan as chips, pellets or starch, mainly by Thailand, Indonesia and China.

Cassava had been introduced to southern Thailand from Malaysia, probably in the 1850s, as a subsistence food crop. By the early 1920s, cassava processing was a cottage industry in Chonburi Province (bordering Cambodia). After the Second World War, Thailand's modern cassava industry was targeted at neighbouring export markets. In 1957, Thailand was exporting 420,000 tonnes of cassava products to the USA and Japan (mainly starch), and to Malaysia and Singapore (mostly other products). In 1983, due to the facilities offered by the European Economic Community's Common Agricultural Policy, cassava pellets for the European animal feed market alone accounted for 6.7 million tonnes of cassava exports, forming Thailand's major cassava export product (*Cassava Newsletter*, vol. 19, no. 1, March 1995, pp. 4–5).

The increased demand for pellets led to a rapid increase in the area planted with cassava: from 38,400 hectares in 1957 to 171,000 hectares in 1968, mostly in eastern Thailand. From 1968 to 1982, a parallel expansion occurred in northeastern Thailand, which eventually produced more than 50% of Thailand's cassava. In 1982, the EEC limited imports of Thai cassava products to 5 million tonnes a year, thus requiring Thai cassava producers to develop new products and search for other markets, such as modified starch for the American, European and Japanese markets (*Cassava Newsletter*, vol. 19, no. 1, March 1995, pp. 4–5).

Total cassava production increased from 19 million tonnes in 1983 to 20.4 million tonnes in 1992, but yields decreased from about 18 tonnes per hectare to 14 tonnes per hectare, as cassava production spread to northeast Thailand where fertilizers were not used. By 1992, about 14–15 million tonnes of roots had been converted into animal feed and about 6 million tonnes into 1.4 million tonnes of starch. Although the number of factories had decreased from 146 in 1978 to 45, most had been modernized to upgrade their output. International prices for cassava starch were comparable with domestic prices, making the latter attractive to cassava industrial entrepreneurs (*Cassava Newsletter*, vol. 19, no. 1, March 1995, pp. 4–5).

The Thailand Development Research Institute found that Thai industries consumed more than 511,000 tonnes of cassava starch in

1991 and estimated that consumption in 2001 would be 1.2 million tonnes a year. Future export markets would be Japan and Taiwan, which were already importing about 204,600 tonnes and 248,400 tonnes respectively, involving 69% of Thailand's cassava exports. But Thailand was obliged to compete with these markets' own domestic starch supplies and other imported starches, like potato starch from the European Union. Even so, the markets were expected to double: in Taiwan, from about 391,000 tonnes in 1994 to some 638,000 tonnes in 2001, and in Japan, from 278,000 tonnes in 1994 to 406,000 tonnes in 2001. In the year 2001, the total demand for cassava starch would probably hover around 2.6 million tonnes (i.e. 13 million tonnes of cassava roots), of which less than half would be destined for the domestic market. The cassava industry would therefore remain export-oriented (*Cassava Newsletter*, vol. 19, no. 1, March 1995, pp. 4–5).

The FAO expected world trade in dried cassava products to drop by more than 22% in 1994. The European Union had reformed its Common Agricultural Policy to favour grains and thus reduce international demand for cassava chips, pellets, flour and starch. Thailand, the European Union's largest supplier, was particularly affected. Non-European Union markets also reduced purchases – the Republic of Korea and Japan reduced theirs by about half. As a consequence, the share of non-European Union imports would drop from 29% to 19% during the year (*Cassava Newsletter*, vol. 19, no. 1, March 1995, pp. 9–10).

Cereals were likely to become cheaper, creating a substitution effect of about 6 to 7 million tonnes of cassava, especially for animal feed. Cassava prices would drop, thus encouraging cassava farmers and exporters to turn to other, more profitable crops. The Thai Government was already encouraging cassava producers to reduce their planting areas (*Cassava Newsletter*, vol. 19, no. 1, March 1995, pp. 4–5).

Cassava roots contain between 30% and 40% of dry matter, which is principally carbohydrate (124 kcal per 100g, the potato contains 76 kcal per 100 g). It is rich in vitamin C and calcium, has acceptable levels of B vitamins and provides other minerals; but it is low in protein (1% of fresh matter), although the leaves contain protein equivalent to 8% to 10% of fresh matter.

As human food, cassava was prepared in many ways: boiled, baked, fried, as meal, flour and even as beer. Starch extracted from the root was also used to make a wide range of sweet and savoury foods, such as crackers, tapioca peals, noodles or cheese breads. Fresh leaves were eaten as a vegetable, especially in West and Central Africa, Indonesia and parts of Brazil.

As animal feed, fresh roots were a good source of carbohydrate, whereas leaves could provide a protein supplement for beef and dairy cattle. Dried cassava was used to make concentrates for poultry, swine and cattle. The European Union member countries imported several tonnes of cassava pellets annually to incorporate into animal feed rations.

In industry, cassava starch was used directly in food-processing, paper-making, textiles, adhesives or as a lubricant in oil wells. It was also used in the manufacture of monosodium glutamate, citric acid, mannitol, sorbitol, glucose, high-fructose syrup and ethanol. Even in areas where cassava processing was carried out on an industrial scale, as in Thailand, Indonesia, China, The Philippines, India and Southern Brazil, most cassava was supplied by small-scale farmers.

Cassava was well known for its tolerance to drought and capacity for maintaining yields. Several factors were involved: leaf stomata were sensitive to humidity, closing whenever the air became dry; roots could extract water from deep soils, even as far as 2.5 metres; and the plant possessed a carbon dioxide fixation system that allowed cassava to continue effective photosynthesis under prolonged water stress. The crop also survived in soils with low phosphorus content by forming associations with mycorrhiza. It could also grow well in poor acid soils with high aluminium content.

The plant could be grown under rainfall regimes that ranged from less than 600 mm to more than 3,000 mm per year, but did not survive flooding. It was found at altitudes from sea level to 2,300 m. Although it could tolerate light frosts, it produced best in a warm climate, with temperatures ranging from 25°C to 35°C.

The plant could be harvested at any time from seven months to three years after planting. Being able to keep the roots in the ground was a particular advantage in countries opening up agricultural frontiers, or suffering natural disasters like drought and locust attacks, or social conflicts. Such flexibility was highly useful, considering that the roots, once harvested, perished within three or four days. They needed to be consumed at once, or processed into products, such as flour or starch that could be stored for longer periods.

The cassava plant contains substances, which release the poisonous cyanide or hydrocyanic acid, when plant tissues are damaged. 'Sweet' varieties produce as little as 20 mg of acid per kg of fresh roots, while 'bitter' varieties may produce more than 1,000 mg. No acyanogenic varieties were known. Traditional methods of food preparation were effective in reducing cyanogenic content to innocuous concentrations; but if the roots of bitter varieties were underprocessed and the diet lacked protein and iodine, cyanide poisoning could cause serious health problems.

Despite the disadvantages of the bitter varieties, some farmers actively selected them, probably because the cyanide helped protect the plant from potential pests and also because certain food products made from bitter varieties had a better texture than those made from sweet ones.

Although cassava was a hardy plant, yield losses occurred through disease and pests. Significant foliar and stem diseases were the widespread cassava bacterial blight and the African cassava mosaic virus. Root rot also caused considerable yield losses. Major pests were those which sucked or ate leaves: the green spider mite, mealybug, whitefly, lacebug and hornworm. Root-damaging pests were the burrowing bug and subterrannean mealybug.

For a long time, the crop had been unknown outside the tropics and been the subject of little research until the 1960s when the 'green revolution', based on new wheat and rice varieties, had stimulated the founding of several International Agricultural Research Centers working on tropical crop species. Two of these Centers had developed cassava research activities: the International Center for Tropical Agriculture (CIAT), based in Cali, Colombia, had a global mandate, while the International Institute of Tropical Agriculture (IITA), based in Nigeria, had a regional mandate for Africa. These two Centers also encouraged the development of national cassava research programmes, particularly as the advantages of cassava as a food crop and industrial material became obvious.

In September 1988, the Cassava Biotechnology Network (CBN) was formed in response to the need for a forum to discuss cassava biotechnology issues and to foster cassava biotechnology research on priority subjects. The CBN was supported by the Special Programme Biotechnology and Development Cooperation (Directorate-General for International Co-operation, DGIS, Netherlands)[1] (see p. 781). It was advised by a Steering Committee and a Scientific Advisory Committee; their members represented national programmes of cassava-growing regions, international centres, donors and biological and socio-economic sciences. The CBN Co-ordinator oversaw the formulation of cassava biotechnology research priorities; the exchange of information within the network; network publicity; working group facilitation and meetings. The Co-ordinator also represented the CBN to the research and donor communities. A small core budget provided seed money and training funds to get high-priority projects off the ground. The further funding of a project came from individual donors or institutions, the CBN not being a funding agency.

For five years, information about the CBN work and objectives had been spread informally. Co-ordination was provided by the CIAT and, as a voluntary service to the research community, by members of the CBN Steering Committee. The CIAT had obtained a grant from the Directorate-General for International Cooperation (DGIS) of the Netherlands to issue an informal, intra-network, biannual newsletter. An electronic mail network had been made accessible to all cassava biotechnology researchers.

The First International Scientific Meeting of the CBN (CBNI) was held in August 1992, at Cartagena de Indias, in the cassava-producing northern coast of Colombia. The 1993 Steering Committee meeting was held from 11 to 12 February at the Rockefeller Foundation headquarters in New York. It was suggested that the CBN call upon the Collaborative Study of Cassava in Africa (COSCA, of which the Rockefeller Foundation was a major supporter) for information on which to base research priorities for Africa. The Co-ordinator's biennial operational plan, approved by the Steering Committee at that meeting, included not only network co-ordination per se, but also integration of socio-economic perspectives into cassava biotechnology research priority setting. One of the Steering Committee's major tasks was to review and confirm, or revise, the recommendations made in Cartagena for priorities in cassava biotechnology research. A new CBN Scientific Advisory Committee (SAC) came into force at each successive scientific meeting.

The Second International Scientific Meeting of the CBN (CBN II), held in Bogor, Indonesia, from 22 to 26 August 1994, was co-organized by the Central Research Institute for Food Crops of Indonesia and the International Center for Tropical Agriculture. Seven Asian, four African and five South American countries were represented; two-thirds of the 150 participants were from developing countries, including 38 women. Financial support for the meeting was provided by the DGIS of the Netherlands, the Rockefeller Foundation, the U.S. Agency for International Development-Jakarta, the Thai Tapioca Development Foundation and the Technical Centre for Agricultural and Rural Cooperation-CTA (*CBN Newsletter*, vol. 2, no. 2, October 1994, pp. 1–2).

The meeting's sessions were devoted to:

– biotechnological tools for cassava research (cassava germplasm preservation and use, cassava genome research-genetic diversity, phylogeny and genetic mapping, regeneration and transformation of cassava);

– research for problem-solving (biotic stresses of cassava, abiotic stresses/physiology of cassava, cassava cyanogenesis-genetics and biochemistry, ecology and management);

– processing (cassava quality, new products, processing, biomass, waste management).

About 185 persons attended the Third International Scientific Meeting of the Cassava Biotechnology Network (CBN III) on the Contributions of biotechnology to cassava for Africa from 26 to 31 August 1996 in Kampala, Uganda. The meeting was organized by the CBN and the National Agricultural Research Organization of Uganda (NARO). The attendants came from 29 countries and represented five international and regional organizations. Two-thirds of the participants were from twenty cassava-growing countries in the developing world. About one-quarter of the participants were women of whom more than half were from cassava-growing countries (*CBN Newsletter*, vol. 4, no. 1, March 1996; vol. 4, no. 2, December 1996).

Farmers' organizations sending representatives to CBN III were UATAPPY, a cassava farmers' processing and marketing co-operative from Ecuador; and the Ugandan National Farmers' Association. Representatives of non-governmental organizations participated from the Tanzanian Home Economics Association and the Uganda Operations of World Vision and Action Aid, which were working closely with the NARO in cassava variety testing and distribution to local communities (*CBS Newsletter*, vol. 4, no. 2, December 1996).

CBN III was supported by the Special Programme Biotechnology and Development Cooperation (DGIS/BIOTECH) of the Netherlands; the Technical Centre for Agricultural and Rural Cooperation (CTA), the German Federal Ministry for Economic Cooperation and Development (BMZ), the United Kingdom's Overseas Development Administration (ODA) and the Rockefeller Foundation. For the first time, the CBN Scientific Meeting was preceded by a one-day course on Biotechnology for crop improvement (*CBN Newsletter*, vol. 4, no. 2, December 1996).

The overeaching theme of the CBN III Meeting was the epidemic of cassava mosaic disease in Uganda. It was found that there were two types of cassava mosaic viruses in Uganda – African cassava mosaic virus and East African cassava mosaic virus, and that the virus which caused the recent outbreak might be a third, novel form resulting from a recombination between the two types. Yet another type of cassava mosaic virus might be present in South Africa. Work on cassava mosaic virus typing with specific antisera, presented at the CBN III, illustrated the importance of pathogen surveys in disease control and prevention, and the necessity of being alert to new forms of viruses (*CBN Newsletter*, vol. 4, no. 2, December 1996).

This kind of programme had been undertaken by the French Scientific Research Institute for Development in Cooperation (ORSTOM), the International Center for Tropical Agriculture (CIAT) and the Instituto Agronomico de Campinas for the analysis of genetic variation in *Xanthomomas campestris* var. *manihoti*, the causative agent of bacterial blight in cassava. Up to the end of 1996, 80 genotypes of the bacterium had been identified and the important work of determining the relationship between genetic variation in the pathogen and resistance in the plant had begun. A putative avirulence gene, present on a plasmid, had been identified (*CBN Newsletter*, vol. 4, no. 2, December 1996).

The following CBN priorities for cassava biotechnology research over the period 1996–1998 were based on concerns expressed by cassava farmers and small-scale processors. They also reflected the results of consultation with crop scientists, post-harvest specialists and socio-economists, as well as biotechnologists (*CBN Newsletter*, vol. 4, no. 2, December 1996).

I. Priority cassava research objectives for which biotechnology tools offered significant advantages
   1. Faster availability of improved planting material of cassava
   2. Conservation and use of *Manihot* genetic diversity
   3. Crop adaptation in stress environments
      – Virus disease and pest resistance; integrated pest management; host-pathogen interactions; drought tolerance; photosynthesis; nutrient use efficiency; mycorrhiza
   4. Enhanced economic value of cassava
      – Starch quantity and quality for diversified uses; new product development; reduced perishability; improved traditional products; processing-waste management
   5. Cassava food safety vs. plant protection and quality (the cyanogen issue)
      – Ecological studies and farmer/processor evaluation of cassava with genetically-modified biochemistry; enhanced fermentation systems for cyanogen reduction
   6. Nutritional value of cassava

II. Biotechnology tools needed for priority cassava research objectives
   1. Micropropagation techniques and feasibility/cost/benefit studies developed for:
      – low-cost micropropagation of new varieties;
      – cryopreservation for long-term conservation of genetic diversity
   2. Efficient techniques for cassava plant regeneration and genetic transformation
   3. Useful genes and gene promoters, characterized and cloned
   4. Molecular genetic map used to tag useful genes for breeding programmes

5. Molecular/cytogenetic characterization of *Manihot* genomes
6. Disease diagnostic methods for clean germplasm transfer
7. Microbial biotechnologies
   – Consumer-oriented market research and product development for traditional and contemporary uses of cassava fermentation
8. True seed for cassava production
   – This would require biotechnology tools for regulation of reproductive biology, including flowering, pollen conservation, haploids, apomixis.

Recognizing that each of the three cassava-growing regions (Africa, Asia and South/Central America) was distinct with respect to the socio-economic role played by cassava and to the capacity to conduct and use biotechnology research, the CBN co-ordinator and regional representatives enhanced their interaction in 1996. The objective was to strengthen regional 'ownership' of the network while maintaining continuity, to move toward decentralization and to allow CBN activities in each region to be carried out at the appropriate pace in areas of greatest regional relevance, while the co-ordination office served the network as the focal point for identifying and executing responsibilities with world-wide implications (*CBN Newsletter*, vol. 4, no. 1, March 1996, p. 1).

Research priorities were expected to be dealt with regionally and small grants handled also at region level. Linkages between biotechnologies, applied research on cassava production, processing and marketing, non-governmental organizations and farmer/processor groups were also to be developed most meaningfully at the regional level. Regional representatives were entrusted with the task of developing links between various groups within the region so as to identify and foster cassava biotechnology research, relevant to the region, to be carried out within the region and/or with international collaboration (*CBN Newsletter*, vol. 4, no. 1, March 1996, p. 1).

In 1996–1997, out of a total of about 120 cassava biotechnology projects, some 60 were being carried out in 25 cassava-growing developing countries, with another 60 in 13 industrialized countries and two in international centres. In the developing countries, about half of cassava biotechnology projects focused on microbial biotechnologies for cassava processing. Another 30% involved tissue culture for germplasm conservation and exchange. The remaining 20% dealt with the development of biotechnology tools, genetic recombination for improving cassava quality and biotechnologies for integrated pest management, e.g. transformation for resistance to viral diseases. The analogous figures for the industrialized countries and international centres were 15% in microbial biotechnologies, 4% in tissue culture and over 80% in the development of biotechnology tools and genetic recombination (*CBN Newsletter*, vol. 2, no. 2, October 1994, p. 9).

Cassava tissue culture was used mostly in South and Central American countries, but also increasingly in Asia and in a few countries in Africa. In the latter, microbial biotechnologies played a prominent role due to the importance of microbial cassava processing for food security (*CBN Newsletter*, vol. 2, no. 2, October 1994, p. 9).

The Cassava Biotechnology Network Small Grants Program was supporting planning of specific proposals for international collaborative research into priority cassava biotechnology research needs. A few small grants might also be awarded in the form of grants-in-aid for developing country biotechnology research operational expenses; for emergency biotechnology research bridging funds; or for short-term training. It was expected that the majority of awards would be in plant biotechnologies, with some awards in microbial biotechnologies. Funding for CBN grants was provided by the Special Programme Biotechnology and Development Co-operation (DGIS), Netherlands.

It was compulsory for proposed development planning grants to bring together partners from at least one developing country and one developed country or international institution. Small grants-in-aid were intended to assist developing country laboratories carry out research consistent with national and CBN priorities. Bridging funds aimed to initiate, or prevent loss of momentum to, crucial projects in CBN's highest priority research topics in any country or institution. Short-term training grants might include technology transfer to national programmes (*CBN Newsletter*, vol. 2, no. 1, March 1994, p. 5).

Nineteen projects had been submitted for Set 1 in July 1994. Of these, four were in microbial biotechnologies, five in transformation/regeneration, one in cassava genome research, one in virus diagnostics, three in socio-economics, two in integrated pest management, two in cyanogenesis and one in non-microbial processing. Six projects were awarded small grants in the range of $5,000 to $10,000 (*CBN Newsletter*, vol. 2, no. 2, October 1994, p. 13).

The cassava genetic mapping project, or Manihot Genome Project, was funded by the Rockefeller Foundation and was carried out by Angel, Tohme and Bonierbale at the CIAT. Other researchers from the University of Georgia (Athens), Washington University (St Louis), and the IITA were participating in the project (*CBN Newsletter*, vol. 1, no. 1, March 1993, p. 14).

During the Second International Scientific Meeting of the CBN, the first molecular map of cassava was presented: 150 markers had been inserted, and by the end of 1995, there were enough markers to produce a map. The participants learnt that crosses were being made to produce populations segregating for important traits such as cyanogenesis, insect resistance (whitefly), photosynthetic rate and virus resistance (*CBN Newsletter*, vol. 2, no. 2, October 1994, p. 4).

At the Third International Scientific Meeting of the CBN, it was reported that the cassava molecular map was developing well and enough markers had been mapped to make it useful for plant breeding. Important cassava genes to tag included those for resistance to African cassava mosaic virus, for cyanogenic potential and for resistance to other diseases and pests. It would be important to determine whether the various sources of resistance to the African cassava mosaic virus (ACMV) were derived from a single locus or from multiple loci. If multiple loci were present and could be tagged, this would greatly facilitate the combination of several of these genes into one variety to produce a more durably resistant cultivar. Both the CIAT and IITA reported that they were developing populations segregating for agronomically valuable traits so that the map could be used to tag genes. In addition, a cassava genome base was being developed at the CIAT. It was generally thought that given sufficient resources it should be possible to build on the progress already made to enable cassava researchers to tag genes for use in plant breeding and eventually to clone useful genes by map-based methods (*CBN Newsletter*, vol. 4, no. 2, December 1996).

Concerning cyanogenesis, the Natural Resources Institute (NRI), United Kingdom, was investigating HPLC (high performance liquid chromatography) applications for the quantitative determination of fresh-root cyanogenic potential of clones from the germplasm collection held at the CIAT. Correlation with other methods and applicability for routine analysis were being assessed (*CBN Newsletter*, vol. 1, no. 1, March 1993, p. 13).

The CIAT Cassava Quality and Utilization Unit almost completed thorough evaluation of two semiquantitative rapid assay methods for cyanogens in cassava. One method was the modified picrate assay, and the other was the tetrabase assay; both methods, although not found excellent in their performance, should be useful in large-scale screening trials. The CIAT and NRI were testing a modified quantitative assay developed by Essers, Agricultural University, Wageningen. This method would replace the highly toxic solvent pyridine with isonicotinic acid; if it were successful, it would represent a major advance in cyanogen assay (*CBN Newsletter*, vol. 1, no. 1, March 1993, p. 13).

Since the Second International Scientific Meeting of the Cassava

Biotechnology Network (CBN II) in Bogor in 1994, a number of major advances in our knowledge of cyanogenesis in cassava had been made:

   – the genes encoding the degradative enzymes, linamarase (beta-glucosidase) and alpha-hydroxy-nitrile lyase, had been cloned; genomic sequence information had revealed complex multigene families encoding these enzymes; root-specific promoters of one beta-glucosidase and one hydroxy-nitrile lyase gene had been analyzed for *in-vivo* function;

   – both the cassava linamarase and alpha-hydroxy-nitrile lyase genes had been expressed in microbial expression vector systems; this was contributing to the studies of the relationship between enzyme structure and function which crystallographic analysis of protein structure had facilitated;

   – the biosynthetic pathway for the synthesis of linamarin and lotaustralin in cassava had been elucidated and demonstrated to be catalyzed by two multifunctional cytochrome P_{450} enzymes; a cDNA clone of a cyanogenic P_{450}, catalyzing the conversion of the amino-acid to the Z-oxime, had been isolated and functionally expressed in *Escherichia coli*.

The development of a transformation system based on direct organogenesis and *Agrobacterium* made it feasible to:

   – overexpress genes involved in the degradation of cyanogenic glucosides to improve endogenous detoxification mechanisms; and

   – use anti-sense techniques to either tissue-specifically or totally block synthesis of cyanogenic glucosides.

The second topic related to cyanogenesis which was given high priority at the CBN II, was manipulation of fermentation to improve detoxification. Preliminary studies suggested the use of new micro-organisms in developing starter cultures for producing fermented cassava products. However, new strains had not been tested for undesired properties, especially the production of mycotoxins.

At the CBN III, it was agreed that availability of an acyanogenic cassava cultivar would be valuable for the small-scale farmer as a substitute for the sweet cassava cultivars presently used, as well as in use of the crop in bigger industrial enterprises. The availability of such a cultivar would also make it possible to test whether it would show increased sensitivity to pests. It would also offer the possibility to reduce losses associated with prolonged processing (e.g. microbial contamination, yield losses and decrease in nutritional quality). The possibility to speed up cyanogenic degradation by overexpressing linamarase and alpha-hydroxy-nitrile lyase, now that the genes encoding both enzymes had been cloned and transformation using these genes was available, should be envisaged with the introduction of enzymes catalyzing cell wall degradation in order to facilitate the access of degradative enzymes to the cyanogens (*CBN Newsletter*, vol. 4, no. 2, December 1996).

The European Union's Science and Technology for Development (STD) Cassava Project was financing basic studies in the United Kingdom (Higher Department of Biochemistry and Genetics, the Medical School, University of Newcastle upon Tyne), Denmark (Moller, Copenhagen), Nigeria (Oke, Ogbomosa) and Thailand (Chulavatnatol, Bangkok). In Denmark, the cytochrome P_{450} and NADPH-cytochrome P_{450} oxidoreductase, which carried out the first N-hydroxylation step in cyanoglucoside biosynthesis in the model system sorghum, had been purified to produce sequence data. In the United Kingdom, sequence information had been produced for the cassava cyanogenic beta-glucosidase (linamarase) and alpha-hydroxynitrile lyase, involved in cyanoglucoside degradation. Cassava linamarase had been expressed in *Escherichia coli* and the relationship between structure and function was being studied. In addition, the function of several cassava UDP glucose-glucosyltransferase genes was under investigation.

The Cassava Safety Workshop was organized by the Working group on Cassava Biosafety at the International Institute of Tropical Agriculture in Ibadan in March 1994, as a sequel to international workshops on cassava cyanogenesis, sponsored by the International Development Research Centre (Ottawa), in 1973 and 1982. The Working Group on Cassava Biosafety was an international consortium of experts in medicine and toxicology, nutrition and food science, cassava biology and genetics, cassava production and social issues.

The major recommendations of the Workshop underlined that: most of the 400 million persons who daily consumed cassava were not at risk; the main public health concern was that the underlying conditions for cassava toxicity – social unrest, agro-ecological crisis and food insecurity – were becoming more common in parts of sub-Saharan Africa; the paralytic diseases of konzo and tropical ataxic neuropathy occurred only in populations suffering from severe deprivation, an unvaried diet and food insecurity; no epidemiological data supported association between dietary cyanide and malnutrition-related diabetes, tropical pancreatitis, or protein-energy malnutrition; dietary cyanide exposure might aggravate iodine deficiency disorders.

Regarding the solid-state fermentation of cassava roots, traditional processing in parts of sub-Saharan Africa included a heap fermentation step. After some drying, peeled roots were heaped and underwent for three days a predominantly fungal fermentation. Subsequent sun-drying, pounding and cooking resulted in a flour for preparation of ugali, a thick paste eaten with soup. One purpose of the process was to reduce bitterness and possible toxicity. The method could reduce cyanogen amounts from high to innocuous and was more effective than sun-drying alone. However, especially in times of haste or adverse weather, the process might be cut short, and high residual cyanogen amounts had been found in resulting flours.

The Food Science Departments of Makerere University, Uganda, and Agricultural University, Wageningen, were studying the effectiveness and mechanisms of reducing cyanogen amounts by this process. Dominant fungi were *Neurospora sitophila*, *Geotrichus candidum* and *Rhizopus oryzae*. Inoculated root chunks showed more efficient reduction in cyanogenic glucoside concentrations than sterilized ones, apparently because of enhanced endogenous enzyme-substrate contact effectuated by fungal cell-wall degrading enzymes. In 30 traditionnally fermented flours studied, no mutagenicity or cytotoxicity was detected. The feasibility and advantages of starter cultures were being studied by African and Dutch researchers (*CBN Newsletter*, vol. 1, no. 1, March 1993, p. 14).

Research on starch remained a high priority with regard to the role this major component of the root played in influencing cooking qualities and acceptability on the one hand, and commercialization options (linked with dry matter content) on the other hand. Significant progress had been made in our understanding of the molecular control of starch parameters, and genes were now available (*CBN Newsletter*, vol. 4, no. 2, December 1996).

Fresh cassava suffers from rapid post-harvest deterioration, rendering the roots inedible after two or three days, and often unsuitable for processing. Market price differentials studied in Ghana and Colombia suggested that cassava roots and products with longer storage life would provide producers, processors and marketers with greater flexibility, better quality and reduced costs. A 1991 meeting, supported by the Rockefeller Foundation and organized by the FAO, explored the possibility of applying advanced genetic techniques to improve the storage life of cassava. The project envisaged called for three five-year phases. Phase two would culminate in region-specific field tests of transgenic cultivars; and Phase three in the diffusion of transformed, locally preferred cultivars with longer storage life in the target environments (*CBN Newsletter*, vol. 1, no. 1, March 1993, p. 15).

Some progress had been made in understanding post-harvest deterioration (PHD) at the molecular level, particularly genes involved in wound response. A gene had been cloned for phenylalanine ammonia lyase induced during post-harvest physiological deterioration. However, we are still far from a comprehensive understanding of the mechanisms involved and an ability to control PHD through molecular approaches.

Cassava leaves were good sources of proteins and other nutrients, as would be other protein sources available in the farming systems (e.g. legumes). Nitrogen balance of the plant could be modified to have a redistribution to the roots whilst not affecting the plants' total nitrogen requirements from the environment. The possible dual role of raising beta-glucosidase content of roots, thereby increasing protein content, was suggested. These proteins would necessarily require to be stabilized to prevent their loss during processing (*CBN Newsletter*, vol. 4, no. 2, December 1996).

Micropropagation of cassava cultivars had been developed on a large scale in association with virus cleansing technologies. Pilot projects involving *in-vitro* multiplication schemes for cassava were being designed at a number of locations in Africa. Micropropagation systems were required for: rapid propagation to meet surges in demand for planting material; the sustainable supply of pathogen-tested planting material replacing at appropriate intervals the farmer-saved 'seed' when its performance fell below economic levels; the multiplication of pathogen-tested planting material in association with breeding programmes and epidemiological studies; storage of vegetative germplasm. It was essential to combine the *in-vitro* facility with suitable facilities for pathogen testing. These were not necessarily high-cost facilities, although improved virus-testing kits were likely to be made available throughout Africa from the IITA (*CBN Newsletter*, vol. 4, no. 2, December 1996).

The route of regeneration of cassava plantlets from tissue culture used by almost all groups was somatic embryogenesis from cassava leaf lobes. The cassava cultivars most often used were MCol 1505 and MCol 22, Colombian genotypes made available by the CIAT, but many others from South America, Africa and Indonesia had been used for the production of somatic embryos. The International Laboratory for Tropical Agricultural Biotechnology (ILTAB) had achieved a breakthrough in improving the efficiency of somatic embryogenesis and plant recovery in cassava (Mathews *et al.*, 1993).

With the use of a charcoal culture medium, after induction of secondary embryogenesis and dessication of matured embryos, germination of MCol 22 increased to 85%. Using cycles of induction and maturation, huge numbers ($>10^6$ in 12 months) of perfect cassava seeddlings would be produced in a very short period. The technique was being repeated with other African and South American cultivars to evaluate it with recalcitrant cassava cultivars. This method was considered an efficient and rapid micropropagation system in which a single leaflet could produce millions of cassava seedlings (Fauquet, 1993).

Cassava embryogenic suspension cultures were established in three laboratories for nine cultivars, demonstrating that this system could be applicable across a range of genotypes. To establish these culture systems still required considerable technical ability and at least three months. Nevertheless, the single cell origin of the somatic embryos and their liquid environment facilitated the efficient selection of transgenic material and minimized the possible regeneration of chimaeras. Embryogenic suspensions provided the starting material for the isolation of totipotent protoplasts and their regeneration through somatic embryos. This was the first confirmed report of regeneration from protoplasts in cassava (*CBN Newsletter*, vol. 4, no. 2, December 1996).

Regeneration of cassava plants from somatic embryo-derived cotyledons was achievable with efficiencies from 80% to 90% in cultivar MCol 22 and at reasonable frequencies in at least five other cultivars. This regeneration system was technically less demanding and more rapid in its production of regenerants compared to embryogenic suspensions (*CBN Newsletter*, vol. 4, no. 2, December 1996).

In 1997, several groups were involved in cassava transformation in Canada, USA, the Netherlands, United Kingdom, Colombia and Brazil. They were using all transformation techniques available in conjunction with the improved regeneration protocols (*CBN Newsletter*, vol. 2, no. 2, October 1994, p. 5).

Two laboratories reported optimized procedures for producing great numbers of independent, genetically-transformed embryogenic callus lines. This was achieved in both cases by microparticle bombardment of embryogenic suspension-derived tissue from the African cultivar TMS 60444. Numerous transgenic cassava plants were recovered from these tissues. One group of researchers used the *npt II* gene (in conjunction with *gus*) to select with the antibiotic paromomycin, while the other used visual selection for the expression of the luciferase gene in combination with resistance to the herbicide phosphinotricin (*bar* gene). Production of transgenic callus was considered straightforward and routine. However, difficulties were reported by both groups in the maturation and germination of embryos from these tissues. Research was continuing on genotype-independent transformation offered by microbombardment of cassava meristems. This could have important implications, especially for cultivars recalcitrant to somatic embryogenesis (*CBN Newsletter*, vol. 4, no. 2, December 1996).

Cotyledon tissue from somatic embryos of cultivar MCol 22 were used as the target tissue for *Agrobacterium*-mediated transformation with either the *hpt* or *npt II* genes, in addition to *gus*. Transgenic shoots were regenerated after selection on media containing the antibiotics geneticin or hygromycin. Evidence available indicated that chimaeras were rare, so that they were not considered a major problem. *Agrobacterium*-mediated transformation of embryogenic suspension cultures was also described. At this time, many lines of transgenic embryogenic callus were recovered, demonstrating the potential of this procedure. Efforts to regenerate plants from these tissues were ongoing. Finally, protoplasts derived from embryogenic suspension cultures were genetically transformed by electroporation, and regeneration to transformed embryogenic callus from these protoplasts was demonstrated; the recovery of plants from these tissues will follow (*CBN Newsletter*, vol. 4, no. 2, December 1996).

Protocols for cassava transformation might be available to plant breeders as early as 1998. As for transgenic cassava plants with altered starch quality, food technologists and plant breeders could expect to see these by 1999. A molecular map of cassava would be available as a tool for plant breeders in 1997 and molecular markers to tag specific genes would be ready for use by plant breeders and physiologists by 1999.

Three major biotic stresses had been identified: cassava geminiviruses, cassava bacterial blight and cassava root rot. There were serological and molecular diagnostic tests for several viruses. It was recommended that these tests be developed for technology transfer to national programmes on a large scale. Work had started on mapping genes for resistance to African cassava mosaic virus (ACMV) and cassava bacterial blight, and it was recommended that this kind of work be extended to include genes for resistance to other major pathogens and pests. Coat protein-mediated resistance to cassava common mosaic virus worked in tobacco, and there was evidence of stronger transgenic resistance to ACMV as conferred by a dysfunctional ACMV replicase gene (*CBN Newsletter*, vol. 2, no. 2, October 1994, p. 6).

After identifying genotypes which were contrasting in terms of drought tolerance and studying the inheritance of this tolerance, the mapping of the relevant genes might be considered, and drought tolerance might be enhanced through gene transfer (*CBN Newsletter*, vol. 2, no. 2, October 1994, p. 6).

An integrated project on cassava in Africa was planned by mid-1994 as follow-up to a recommendation made at a meeting in Cali, Colombia, in January 1994, on Flours and starches of cassava. The project involved a partnership between the CIAT, IITA, CIRAD, ORSTOM and NRI, as well as with local institutions conducting research on cassava (*CIRAD Information*, no. 40, 13 April 1994, p. 6).

The Cassava Biotechnology Network (CBN) considered it crucial for the users' perspective to influence the setting of research priorities. For this reason, case studies and other sources of farmer perspective were all valuable inputs to the CBN. In addition, when a problem (or opportunity) identified by cassava farmers and processors could be 'translated' into a technological challenge, it was then analyzed to see whether biotechnologies, or any other approach, could offer a solution. For instance, losses from rapid deterioration of harvested cassava roots could be prevented in several different ways, depending on the desired storage life: through genetic transformation to produce a cassava root with a storage life of several months, through plant breeding to produce a root with one or two weeks storage life, or through immediate post-harvest processing methods to produce a storable processed product (Thro *et al.*, 1994).

The evaluation of potential effects of a technology required estimates of expected changes at household, farming system, agro-ecosystem and market levels, as well as estimates of trade-offs between farmers, processors and consumers. This calculation could not be made without involving cassava users, nor could it be handled by participatory research alone. Many areas of concern to the CBN, such as cyanogenesis, delayed post-harvest deterioration and starch quality, required data-intensive evaluation within complex higher-system levels, especially processing and market systems (Thro *et al.*, 1994).

Two case studies had been carried out under the aegis of the CBN to gather information on practices, farmer perspectives and opinions related to cassava production, processing, use and marketing in Tanzania and China. In the Lake Victoria Zone of North Tanzania, cassava was a subject of considerable interest to villagers. Their major concerns were mealybug attacks, drought and the devastation when these co-incided. In a village close to the Serengeti National Park, farmers explained that they did not possess enough land to open new fields, resulting in declining cassava yields (because of declining soil fertility with continuous cropping). Lake Zone farmers grew many varieties to meet a range of needs: early maturity for food in a hurry; long-term in-ground storability for food security; suitability for processing into storable form vs. quick preparation; leaf production (cassava was an important green vegetable) and cooking fuel. Some varieties were grown for extreme 'bitterness' to prevent damage by wild pigs and rats; most villages grew two or three 'bitter' varieties on most of their cassava area and two to five or more 'sweet' varieties (Thro *et al.*, 1994).

Both women and men frequently asked how the speed, safety and nutritional value of their village's cassava processing methods could be improved. In the Lake Zone, cassava processing mainly included dry-fermentation, sun-drying into the storage form 'udaga', which was later pounded into flour to make 'ugali' (a stiff porridge). Some was used in brewing beer. 'Sweet' varieties were eaten boiled or raw. Some women had experimented (unsuccessfully) with mixtures of cassava and wheat flour, in an attempt to sustain their production of baked goods for sale in the local market during a shortage of imported wheat flour.

Men were responsible for most decisions in cassava production and processing, including the decision to resort to large-scale sales to meet substantial cash needs such as school fees, a food shortage, or some other hardship. Excluding beer brewing, cassava processing was exclusively a woman's activity in the Lake Zone, as were small-scale harvests to meet daily food needs and small sales of cassava to purchase household necessities (Thro *et al.*, 1994).

By the early 1980s, cassava in China was consumed on-farm by both family and pigs. Farmers now sold most of their cassava fresh or dried to starch factories. Farmers, especially women, complained about the amount of labour needed for chipping and drying cassava. Mostly hand-made with rudimentary tools, cassava chips were of varying quality, which was reflected in the price range. Soil fertility problems resulting in declining yields were often mentioned as a major impediment. However, in most regions, cassava was grown on the 'waste-lands', where few other crops could thrive. In stark contrast to cassava diversity in Tanzania, there were at most two or three varieties in South China, a potentially dangerous situation which highlighted the fact that biological diversity was a crucial issue. Another potential problem was the waste disposal from cassava-starch processing; although solid waste was turned into animal feed, the liquid and most toxic waste was often dumped in streams (Thro *et al.*, 1994).

The CBN was preparing a Geographic Information System (GIS) referenced data-base for cassava production, distribution, agro-ecosystem zones, and cassava marketing and uses. This data-base, the first of its kind, would be used for overlaying micro-data from participatory surveys of cassava farmers and small-scale processors (Thro *et al.*, 1994).

The role of biotechnologies in solving problems facing cassava users could be addressed for the short, medium and long terms. In the short term, micropropagation followed by clonal propagation could speed up cassava variety multiplication. Also in the short term, microbial biotechnologies could develop faster, safer, more nutritious cassava fermentation products. Superior microbial strains for starter cultures could be selected and tested in the villages themselves. Molecular markers and micropropagation were being used to optimize management of cassava germplasm collections that could be sources of cassava biodiversity for regions like South China, where genetic uniformity posed potential risks. Molecular markers could be used to assess existing variability and heritability of user-preferred traits, such as early maturity, in-field storability, drought tolerance and cyanogen content; this information could prove useful for identifying those traits most amenable to improvement (Thro *et al.*, 1994).

In the medium term, gene cloning and genetic transformation would be used to alter and study traits for which there was little or no genetic variation available in cassava. Examples were cyanogen metabolism and its relationship to cassava productivity, plant defence and processing quality; post-harvest deterioration; starch metabolism and its implications for processing and new products; or root nutritional value. Improvements in somatic embryogenesis permitted far higher levels of cassava plant regeneration, which were a prerequisite for transformation. A highly regenerable embryogenic suspension system had been used to produce the first fully transgenic embryoids. Experimental cassava genotypes created through genetic transformation were expected to be ready for initial field testing in 1996 or 1998, depending on the level of funding (Thro *et al.*, 1994).

In the longer term (six to ten years), experience with transgenic cassava would help identify which novel genotypes would be useful for breeding with locally-adapted varieties.

Yam projects in the Caribbean

A biotechnology yam project with an impact on small-scale agriculture in the Caribbean deserves mentioning.

Yam ranked second in the world among the tropical food root and tuber crop species, after cassava (Coursey, 1967). By the early 1990s, yam production world-wide amounted to 25 million tonnes. The most widely cultivated species were *Dioscorea cayenensis, D. rotundata* and *D. alata*. There was a great potential for expanding production and consumption once its quality, yield and shelf-life could be improved.

West Africa accounted for about 90% of world yam production and the average contribution of yam to the human diet in this region was about 300 kcal per day per person.

The West Indies was second to West Africa in sown acreage and Jamaica was the leading yam producer in the Carribbean. Yam was not only a major food source in Jamaica, but also a major foreign exchange earner for the country. Yams were grown as a subsistence crop, forming a significant part of the population's carbohydrate diet (in the Barbados, up to about 50% of total caloric intake). They were usually grown on small holdings of 0.5 ha or less, mainly for home consumption, although, in Barbados and Jamaica, they were grown on a larger scale of up to 10 ha for commercial purposes. Fresh yam tubers were chipped, dried and packaged ('instant yam' flakes) to provide a year-round source of carbohydrate for both local markets and exports (CARDI, 1984).

The potential for bigger exports could only be realized by rapidly expanding the area under cultivation, but this was hampered by a lack of planting material. Tissue culture had been used as a rapid method for the massive production of disease-free planting material in yams. Optimizing *in-vitro* growth, successful hardening and optimum development after transfer to the field were very important.

In the mid-1960s, shipments of *Dioscorea alata* yams from Barbados and other exporting countries had been badly affected by the internal brown spot (IBS) disease, characterized by the presence of small, brown necrotic spots in the flesh of the tubers. The outbreak was so serious that, in 1965, 50% of shipments from Barbados were lost. Viral diseases had become the limiting factor to commercial production of *Dioscorea trifida* yams in Guyana, while dry rot infestations imposed a severe constraint on yam production in Jamaica. Research carried out during the 1970s had shown that viral diseases affected all yams grown in the Caribbean. The IBS was widespread in *Dioscorea alata*, the most popular species, with the highest level of infection (71%) found in Barbados and the lowest (32%) in Dominica. Another constraint was the wide phenotypic variation and irregular shape of tubers of cultivated stocks, detrimental to export trade and industrial processing (CARDI, 1984).

A yam virus research project had been launched in 1973 at the Regional Research Centre (RRC) in Trinidad, funded for three years by the United Kingdom's Overseas Development Administration. Mantell and his co-workers of the Unit of Advanced Propagation Systems at Wye College, Ashford, Kent, established the first successful system for eradication of yam pathogens by tissue culture: meristem tip culture and micropropagation (the small disease-free plantlets produced by meristem cultures were used to give small stem pieces, subducted into further microcuttings to produce more shoot material; in this way, 65,000 plants could be obtained from a single parent over a six-month period; this propagation could be undertaken at any time, even during the natural dormant season for yam). Once the young plants had developed root and shoot tissues, they had to be hardened off; this involved growing them in a sterilized potting mixture (composed of soil, sand and an organic supplement such as peat moss or finely ground bagasse) in an insect-proof greenhouse. Once the plants had matured sufficiently, they were transferred from their pots to soil, at an isolated field site, where reinfection was prevented. The tubers produced at this site were known as 'elite stock'. The planting material produced during this phase of the project was classified into three grades, A, B and C, according to their degree of freedom from pathogens, 'A' having the highest degree of freedom from pathogens (CARDI, 1984).

Seventy-three accessions of B and C grade material were planted in isolated plots of the Caribbean Agricultural Research and Development Institute (CARDI), in Barbados in 1979. The average yield was about 24 tonnes per hectare, with a maximum of 31 tonnes per hectare, as against 15 tonnes per hectare for the Caribbean conventional yam stocks. It was therefore concluded that the production of disease-free yam tubers by tissue culture was technically viable and that the potential benefits to farmers were substantial in terms of production, quality and consistency of production. This led to a proposal by the CARDI for further multiplication and field trials, and for the setting up of a micropropagation unit in Barbados. Funding of the project between 1980 and 1984 was taken up by the European Development Fund through the Caribbean Development Bank. The overall co-ordination of the project was the direct responsibility of the CARDI and a scheme had been devised whereby selected 'approved growers' in Barbados would purchase planting material from the tissue culture unit and resell their output of yams to commercial and subsistence growers as certified disease-free tubers (CARDI, 1984).

The acreage of virus-tested material grown in Barbados increased from five hectares in 1981–1982 to 20 hectares in 1982–1983 and 70 hectares in 1983–1984. By 1983, a number of growers had either completely mechanized their cropping system or were at least harvesting yam mechanically. The export market for Barbados yams improved almost as soon as the first disease-free tubers were in the ground. In 1982, techniques similar to those successfully employed for the *Dioscorea alata* yam, were also applied to *Dioscorea trifida*. In addition, a number of cassava cultures, received from the International Center for Tropical Agriculture, were propagated with some success. After multiplication by the CARDI, certified yam tubers were distributed to selected farmers to be grown alongside their own varieties according to conventional practices (CARDI, 1984).

This case study showed that a project relying on plant biotechnologies could be implemented with moderate financial support and have an important impact on agricultural production. The yam project contributed significantly to research capacity building in the Caribbean. Donors provided long-term support, ten years in total, allowing for transition from the research to the implementation phase. The project focused on yam, a crop species neglected by research at the time. However, the project was not designed for small-scale farmers as a specific target group and the latter were not involved directly during any stage of the project cycle. The project major drawback was that, although initially yam production had increased, a decrease in production occurred in the longer term and innovation had been largely abandoned by farmers. Innovation needed to be more robust if it were to withstand the early days. The lessons drawn from this project could be helpful for the design of projects aimed at applying biotechnologies in small-scale agriculture.

Anthracnose, a fungal disease attacking yam, had virtually wiped out the White Lisbon variety, the most popular yam variety in the Caribbean, especially in Barbados. As this variety was particularly susceptible to anthracnose, farmers were failing to grow it successfully because of the ravages of the disease. A team of researchers at the Cave Hill campus of the University of the West Indies, led by O'Garro and Delauney of the Department of Biology, were trying to introduce resistance to the disease into the White Lisbon variety. The project had been initiated when the UWI researchers from the three UWI campuses and the CARDI attended a Caribbean Biotechnology Conference in Barbados. The researchers noted that previous attempts to control anthracnose in yams had been unsuccessful for a number of reasons: as yam flowers very rarely or hardly flowers at all, it was difficult to carry out crosses between susceptible and resistant varieties; in the few cases when crosses had been achieved, the progeny showed very low productivity. It was therefore concluded that this problem could be tackled using various biotechnological processes and the Cave Hill researchers developed a proposal for submission to funding sources. It received $85,000 from the United Nations Development Programme (UNDP) and UNESCO, and $15,000 from the Barclays Bank Development Fund. The allocated resources were used to purchase equipment, greenhouse facilities for growing specimens and to support post-graduate students. A collaborative arrangement was set up with Mantell (Wye College) to use in particular genetic engineering to transform yams.

A post-graduate student of the UWI had collected a number of different strains of the fungus from various parts of Barbados and was isolating the toxin causing the disease. The toxin was purified for use in screening for resistance to the fungus. The toxin would normally kill the White Lisbon variety, but modified plants were expected to be able to resist the toxin's effects and, consequently, anthracnose.

Rose *et al.* (1995) of the Biotechnology Centre and the Department of Botany at the University of West Indies, Mona, Kingston, Jamaica, had shown that the addition of an auxin to the basal medium used to grow *Dioscorea cayenensis* cv. Round Leaf Yellow Yam enhanced neither root initiation nor elongation, the endogenous amounts of auxin appearing to be adequate for rooting. Nodes from the base of the plant gave the best rooting with greater numbers and lengths of roots. It appeared that the low concentration of endogenous auxin found at the basal node stimulated rooting, whereas the higher auxin concentrations in the upper nodes inhibited rooting. In addition, the plants showed differential responses to colonization by the vesicular-arbuscular mycorrhizal (VAM) fungi; plant colonized by *Glomus pallidum* and *G. aggregatum* had much greater vine lengths, node numbers, stem and root dry biomass, and root lengths greater than control plants at 105 days after inoculation. The Jamaican researchers concluded that *in-vitro* rooting of basal nodes on culture media with no 6-benzylaminopurine supplement and subsequent inoculation of the yam plantlets with VAM fungi would result in better plant establishment and growth in the field.

Although yam was playing a major role in the food supply to millions of people, this crop species had not been studied thoroughly by scientists. In-depth knowledge of yam was highly needed when the demand for this tuber crop was steadily increasing and urbanization was changing consumption habits. For instance, yam genetic resources were unsufficiently known; but the range of cultivars was rather wide and farmers were still carrying out domestication of wild species. Consequently, the collection of the existing yam varieties, their characterization and identification were the first steps leading to the breeding and genetic improvement of cultivars. These activities were part of a project involving eight West African countries, the CIRAD, ORSTOM and the University of Frankfurt.

In addition, an international seminar on 'Yam, a secular plant and a crop for the future' (L'igname, plante séculaire et culture d'avenir) was held in Montpellier, south of France, from 3 to 6 June 1997. With more than 120 participants coming from Africa, Europe, the Caribbean, Latin America and the Pacific, and representatives of the African, European and international research-and-development institutions, as well as of the economic operators, the broad objective of the seminar was to set up and carry out an international research-and-development strategy for promoting yam cultivation. The seminar organizers, i.e. the Conference of Agronomic Research Executives of West Africa-CORAF, and the French CIRAD, ORSTOM and National Institute for Agricultural Research-INRA, involved in the Project for the promotion of tropical starchy crops-Proamyl, aimed to:

– overcome the difficulties associated with the cultivation of yam on low-fertility soils after deforestation or elimination of natural vegetation;

– improve the conservation of fresh tubers (e.g. peeling, precooking and sun-drying of tubers) as well as processing of dried tubers into flour to be consumed in urban settlements, and widely disseminate this technique among the countries concerned (*CIRAD Information*, no. 75, 11 July 1997, p. 5).

Asia Network for Small Scale Agricultural Biotechnology

The Appropriate Technology International (ATI)[2] (see p. 781), in co-operation with the NifTAL Project (Nitrogen Fixation by Tropical Agricultural Legumes, College of Tropical Agriculture, University of Hawaii, USA), SATE (Small Enterprise Development and Appropriate Technology Europe) and the Department of Biology and Society, Free University, Amsterdam, was developing a biotechnology network as part of a scheme referred to as the Lab to Land Program. The network focused on small-scale agricultural biotechnologies, according the resource-poor farmer the double role of beneficiary and participant.

The Lab to Land Program intended to redirect attention to a set of agricultural biotechnologies that could benefit poor farmers in Bangladesh, India, Indonesia, Nepal, The Philippines, Sri Lanka, Thailand and Viet Nam. The technologies selected included plant tissue culture for micropropagation; plant and soil inoculants such as *Rhizobium*, mycorrhiza, blue-green algae; biopesticides; and mushroom spawn production. These were relatively mature biotechnologies that required minimal investment in sophisticated equipment and were amenable to labour intensive and small-scale production.

An ATI identification mission to South and South-East Asia in 1990 explored with over 80 key individuals the concept, need and support for the Program and the question of participation. The Lab to Land Program had four main components. The network, called the Asia Network for Small Scale Agricultural Biotechnology (ANSAB) was the Program's core. The other three components were: demonstration projects and commercialization; monitoring and evaluation; and policy analysis (Ferchak and Ribeiro, 1992).

An independent, not-for-profit international non-governmental organization, the network initially linked Bangladesh, China, India, Indonesia, Nepal, Sri Lanka, Thailand, The Philippines and Viet Nam. It was established during the first ANSAB workshop (30 March-1 April 1992), held in Kathmandu, the site of its future headquarters, and attended by 70 participants from the afore-mentioned Asian countries[3] (see p. 781).

The ANSAB had a multifaceted membership including farmers, non-governmental organizations, researchers/biotechnologists from both the public and private sectors, private sector businesses, financial institutions and policy-makers. The unifying factor of this diverse membership was concern for the welfare of resource-poor farmers. The ANSAB was expected to facilitate the commercialization of relevant biotechnologies, provide low-cost biological inputs into agriculture; and increase productivity and income among resource-poor farmers. The Kathmandu workshop appointed the first ANSAB co-ordinator, G.L. Shrestha, a renowned Nepalese rice breeder who had succeeded in transferring the Masuli rice variety from the laboratory to farmers, with a view to bringing a 'green revolution' in Nepalese rice farming during the 1980s.

The ANSAB workshop identified the following mature agricultural biotechnologies in the nine participating countries:

country	mature agricultural biotechnologies (in order of priority)		
	1	2	3
Bangladesh	Biofertilizer	Mushroom cultivation	Bamboo propagation
China	Mushroom cultivation	Biofertilizer	Plant tissue culture
India	Biofertilizer	Mushroom cultivation	Seedling raising (trees and vegetables)
Indonesia	Biofertilizer (blue-green algae)	Biofertilizers (*Rhizobium* and mycorrhiza)	Biopesticide

765

Nepal	Plant tissue culture	Mushroom cultivation	Biofertilizer (*Rhizobium*)
Philippines	Biofertilizer	Biopesticide (*Trichoderma*)	Biofertilizers (*Rhizobium, Azospirillum,* mycorrhiza)
Sri Lanka	Biofertilizer (soybean *Rhizobium*)	Biofertilizer (Azolla)	Plant tissue culture (coconut, fruit trees)
Thailand	Plant tissue culture (asparagus and strawberry)	Plant tissue culture (for reforestation)	Biofertilizers (*Rhizobium,* algae, mycorrhiza)
Viet Nam	Biofertilizer	Biopesticide	Plant tissue culture.

The Lab to Land Program intended introducing demonstration projects in each of the participating countries. Experiences from the demonstration projects would be incorporated into developing, testing and refining a Lab to Land model that could be used in the preparation of business plans for small-scale commercialization of successful technologies.

The biotechnologies initially selected for the Program were in various stages of commercialization in different countries. Barriers to commercialization efforts often existed, such as a lack of research-and-development support or agricultural extension, poor technology transfer mechanisms, lack of entrepreneurial and technical skills, lack of venture capital, high product cost or poor product quality and subsidies for alternative products (such as chemical fertilizer). By providing a regional context for considering these issues, it was expected that the sharing of experience, technology implementation and regional transfer would be significantly improved.

The ANSAB Co-ordinator attended the workshop on the identification and formulation of inter-country projects in biotechnologies, held in Taejon, Republic of Korea, in September 1992, and organized jointly by the United Nations Economic and Social Commission for Asia and the Pacific (U.N. ESCAP) and the Genetic Engineering Research Institute (GERI) of the Republic of Korea. Representatives from Malaysia, The Philippines, Republic of Korea, Thailand and Viet Nam, and from Appropriate Technology

International attended the workshop. The latter identified approximately 17 projects in environmental, industrial, agricultural, medical and pharmaceutical biotechnologies which could benefit from bilateral and multilateral co-operation *(ANSAB Newsletter*, vol. 1, no. 2, 1992–1993, p. 4).

The ANSAB had participated in an international meeting on International biotechnology programs: providing opportunities for national participation, held at the ISNAR (International Service for National Agricultural Research) headquarters in The Hague, from 9 to 11 November 1993. The main objective of the meeting was to develop a data-base of agricultural biotechnology research-and-development activities within national systems in different developing countries and international agricultural biotechnology research-and-development centres. The data-base was expected to foster scientific communication among related organizations and allow for the application of mature agricultural biotechnologies, so that they could be moved from lab to land and help resource-poor farmers. About 48 participants from 28 countries attended the meeting.

Viet Nam was a pioneer in developing low-cost, simple methods for the rapid micropropagation of disease-free potato varieties. The Vietnamese example illustrated the practicality of small-scale operations in tissue culture with direct benefit for resource-poor farmers. It also pointed to the need for close co-operation between research centres, farmers and sources of capital. Such co-operation would be especially necessary for micropropagation schemes involving reforestation. The ATI was working with the National Herbarium and Plant Laboratories in Godawari, Nepal, to demonstrate and commercialize low-cost methods of micropropagation.

Biofertilizers could complement or substitute for inorganic fertilizer, whose use in any case was minimal on small farms in much of Asia due to lack of availability and cost. The most well-known and commercialized inoculant was *Rhizobium*. Soils from South and South-East Asia frequently tested low for *Rhizobium* and legume seed would benefit from inoculation (although phospate fertilizer application might also be needed, and low soil pH had to be corrected, for good response). If inoculant could be made available, the NifTAL recommended using inoculant at all times, unless there was clearly no response (which could occur for a variety of reasons). Legume yield increases of 10%–90% following inoculation were reported in South Asia. In The Philippines, inoculation trials gave an average yield increase of 124% for soybeans, 29% for mungbeans, and 37% for groundnuts; in spite of this potential, use of inoculant was very low.

The ATI was seeking to develop the commercial small-scale and decentralized production of *Rhizobium* inoculants to increase soybean yields. Launched in 1987, the project was designed to benefit about 10,000 small holders in the northern provinces of Thailand, which produced about 70% of the total soybean harvest. The expected benefits were: an increase in income of 17%-42%, due to higher yields, together with a reduction in the use of chemical nitrogen fertilizers; a decrease in soybean and nitrogen fertilizer imports; improved soil fertility through the nitrogen compounds remaining in the soil after harvest. The farmers involved in this scheme consisted of a first group (about 20%) participating in a government-sponsored seed exchange programme whereby native seeds were exchanged for those of high-yielding varieties and a second group (the largest one) whose members enjoyed limited access to the government seed stations (Pistorius and Smits, 1990).

The International Development Research Centre (IDRC, Ottawa) had awarded a $194,000 grant to the ANSAB for the creation of a Biofertilizer Production Network in India, Sri Lanka and The Philippines to assist in the commercial application of *Rhizobium* at farm level. The IDRC-supported initiative was expected to last from 1994 to 1996. The Production Network was handled: in Sri Lanka, by Plenty Canada/Lanka, the Institute of Fundamental Studies and the University of Peradeniya; in India, by the Hindustan Biofertilizer, National Dairy Development Board, Oil Seeds Co-operatives, BAIF Development Research Foundation and the Biotech Consortium of India Ltd; in The Philippines, by Appropriate Technology Philippines, the Philippine Council for Agriculture, Forestry and National Resources Research and Development, the Department of Agriculture, the National Institutes of Biotechnology and Applied Microbiology (BIOTECH) of the University of The Philippines at Los Baños, the Farmers' Co-operatives assisted by the Department of Agriculture, Co-operative Bank Cagayan Inc. and/or The Philippines Business of Social Progress (*ANSAB Newsletter*, vol. 2, no. 2, 1994, p. 2).

This project involved a minimum of 1,400 farmers participating directly in field application. It was expected to lead to the setting up of at least one facility in each country that would allow for a continuous, reliable supply of *Rhizobium* inoculants. The NifTAL Project was made responsible for training and technical supervision tasks in the three participating countries (*ANSAB Newsletter*, vol. 2, no. 2, 1994, p. 2).

The Bangladesh company, Biolink, in collaboration with the Department of Soil Science of the Bangladesh Agricultural University, had been producing inoculants since 1991. Biolink was using a number of highly effective *Rhizobium* strains as active ingredient. Yeast-mannitol liquid was used as the culture medium and processed peat soil was the inoculant carrier. The company was producing about 7 tonnes of different kinds of inoculants annually, the annual capacity being 10 tonnes. Agricultural extension programmes might further enlarge the market. In various field tests, the soybean inoculants were found to be four times more effective than chemical fertilization by urea; other inoculants were two to three times more effective. The company had plans to produce *Azotobacter* inoculants, blue-green algae and *Azolla* for rice and wheat, as well as plant-based biopesticides, such as the azadirachtin compound from neem (*Azadirachta indica*) [Haque, 1993].

Rice production had been sustained for centuries in Asia, due to the natural presence of blue-green algae fixing about 30 kg of atmospheric nitrogen per hectare. Blue-green algae are either free-living, or exist in symbiotic association with the water fern *Azolla*. In collaboration with the Thailand Institute for Scientific and Technological Research and the Thailand Rural Reconstruction Movement, the ATI was sponsoring trials to demonstrate the use and commercial viability of small-scale, decentralized production of a new blue-green alga inoculant. Yield increases in initial field trials during 1988–1989 for both off-season and in-season rice farming ranged from 16% to 39%.

In Nepal, under the direction of New ERA and in collaboration with the National Herbarium and Plant Laboratories, the National Potato Development Programme and Botanical Enterprises, Inc., the ANSAB assisted with field trials of the high-yielding, late blight-resistant potato variety MS 42.3. This variety had been received in 1986 by Nepal from the International Potato Center, Lima, in the form of a test-tube plantlet. Funded by the ATI, field trials were carried out in three districts during the 1991–1992 winter season. MS 42.3 yielded an average 32.4 tonnes per hectare, i.e. a 22% higher yield over the average yield of Kufri Jyoti and Cardinal, the two most popular commercial improved varieties. Furthermore, MS 42.3 being resistant to late blight disease, it did not require spraying. As for Kufri Jyoti and Cardinal, the cost to Nepalese farmers for spraying with Diathane M 45 was $90–$105 per hectare (*ANSAB Newsletter*, vol. 1, no. 2, 1992–1993, p. 2).

These trials represented a further step toward better potato 'seed' production and supply in Nepal, where potatoes – the fourth staple crop species after rice, maize and wheat – were cultivated on an estimated 86,000 hectares. However, the average yield of 8.5 tonnes per hectare was one of the lowest in the world. The MS 42.3 variety was obtained from tissue culture and the multiplication process, called sand rooting, bypassed rooting of microshoots in sterile media; instead, microshoots were directly rooted in clean but non-sterile sand, with more than a 90% survival rate. Trained farmers could be supplied with bottles of microshoots and the sand rooting carried out in the villages. After rooting and transfer to the fields, minitubers were produced. The ANSAB assisted in developing training programmes for farmers from different districts of Nepal. After training, the farmers were provided with a set of tools and equipments including material for temporary vinyl greenhouse, so that they would produce virus-free high-quality minitubers. Minituber production from sand-rooted potato plantlets resulted in significantly lower costs: cultivation costs for minituber production averaged $20 per hectare, compared to normal potato tuber production (1.5 tonnes) cost of $96 per hectare. Storage costs of minitubers were also much lower (*ANSAB Newsletter*, vol. 1, no. 2, 1992–1993, pp. 3–4).

The ANSAB was also investigating other potato varieties in co-operation with the Nepal Agricultural Research Council's Potato Research Program for demonstration in farmers' fields to maintain genetic diversity at farm level. The programme also sought to improve potato storage in villages.

The ANSAB had trained 104 farmers from different districts of Nepal at Botanical Enterprises Ltd., Godawari, Kathmandu. These farmers were participating in the Farmers to Farmers training programme to pass on the benefits of tissue culture techniques to larger groups of farmers in Nepal (*ANSAB Newsletter*, vol. 2, no. 2, 1994, pp. 1–2).

Quality mushroom cultivation could be done by small farmers in association with a spawn production centre, which could be co-operatively owned or part of a university laboratory. Being labour-intensive, production was suitable for small-scale enterprises and utilized agricultural wastes.

In June 1992, the ATI financed a study of the mushroom market in Nepal, Bangladesh and India by S.T. Chang, professor in the Department of Biology at the Chinese University of Hong Kong and president of the International Mushroom Society for the Tropics. It was found that Nepal had developed fairly good technology for the production of white button mushrooms (*Agaricus bisporus*) and oyster or abalone mushrooms (*Pleurotus* sp.). However, the current yield of 200 kg per tonne of substrate for *Agaricus* and 400 kg per tonne for *Pleurotus* could be raised to 250 kg and 500 kg per tonne respectively, through the improvement of sterility and cropping techniques. The spawn production system, primarily a governmental activity currently, was expected to be developed privately. The present domestic market in

Nepal for button mushrooms was estimated at 260–500 tonnes per year, and growth potential was good due to increasing tourism. The estimated production of fresh button mushrooms in 1991 was 80–100 tonnes, so that Nepal imported the balance as canned mushrooms from both China and India. The low cost of skilled labour, favourable climate, abundance of substrate and presence of direct air service to potential importing countries provided a good basis for a mushroom export industry (*ANSAB Newsletter*, vol. 1, no. 2, 1992–1993, p. 4).

Another market study carried out by a researcher from the International Agricultural College, Larenstein, the Netherlands, showed that the seasonal variations in mushroom production and the quantity of produce affected the price of fresh mushroom ranging from Rs.30 to Rs.120 per kg of fresh mushrooms. The difference between the farm-gate price and the retail price was about Rs.10–15 per kg fresh weight, and the mushroom marketing was still to be organized properly in Nepal (*ANSAB Newsletter*, vol. 1, no. 2, 1992–1993, pp. 3–4).

In Bangladesh, mushroom cultivation technology was only introduced in 1987. Consumption was limited to international hotels. The Department of Agriculture Extension had developed cultivation methods for oyster mushrooms, straw mushrooms (*Volvariella volvacea*) and *Auricularia* sp., as well as the procedures for spawn production of these species at a commercial scale. A 1991 economic study of straw mushroom production concluded that rural landless women were attracted by mushroom cultivation as a part-time activity. A domestic market was developing and one company was planning to set up a modern facility for export of button mushrooms (*ANSAB Newsletter*, vol. 1, no. 2, 1992–1993, p. 3).

In India, modern mushroom cultivation was initiated in the 1960s at Solan in Himachal Pradesh. In 1991, the total production of all types of mushrooms in India approached 7,000 tonnes: high production was recorded in Himachal Pradesh (2,000 tonnes) followed by Sonepat near Delhi (1,000 tonnes) and Uttar Pradesh (1,000 tonnes). Button mushrooms accounted for 80%-85% of total production, followed by oyster mushrooms (9%) and straw mushrooms. Production was also moving to the plains due to the availability of cheap substrate materials and ready access to markets. Average yields ranged from 60 kg to 80 kg per tonne of substrate in six to eight weeks cropping periods, in most of the seasonal growing areas. In modern medium-to-large cultivation operations using environmentally controlled conditions, the average yield was 150 kg to 160 kg per tonne of compost (*ANSAB Newsletter*, vol. 1, no. 2, 1992–1993, p. 3).

The Rockefeller Foundation awarded a $98,600 (1993–1995) grant to the ANSAB for a feasibility study on the Commercial micropropagation of the kapok tree, *Ceiba pentandra*, for land reclamation and small farmer benefit in Java. The kapok tree produces a fiber in its pod that is an export product, primarily from Indonesia and Thailand; the fiber is water-repellent and exceedingly buoyant and is used as a filler in life preservers and mattresses. The seeds produce an edible oil, also sold as an export product. The tree is used for lumber and furniture manufacture, and the shells of the pods are used for charcoal production. Finally, the nectar from flowers produces an excellent quality honey (*ANSAB Newsletter*, vol. 1, no. 2, 1992–1993, p. 1).

Small farmers in Central Java grew kapok trees and harvested them in the agricultural off-season as a source of supplementary income. The tree also grew well on marginal lands with acid or alkaline soils; it could therefore be used for reclamation on large tracts of hilly, degraded land in Java. Kapok trees were not propagated well from cuttings due to inadequate formation of roots; seed propagation resulted in too much variability in yield; the main propagation method was bud grafting, which was slow and suffered from a shortage of scion stock. Micropropagation via tissue culture would therefore offer important advantages such as true-to-type cloning, rejuvenation of the planting stock and fast multiplication (*ANSAB Newsletter*, vol. 1, no. 2, 1992–1993, pp. 1 and 4).

Selected trees supplied through Eurasia and United Corporations, Jakarta, were used by the laboratories of SEAMEO (South-East Asian Ministers of Education Organization)-BIOTROP (South-East Regional Centre for Tropical Ecology) in Bogor for the micropropagation studies. Bina Swadaya, a large non-governmental organization in Indonesia and a founding member of the ANSAB, was carrying out rural assessments and work with the small farmers (*ANSAB Newsletter*, vol. 1, no. 2, 1992–1993, p. 4).

The field of biological pest control was receiving particular attention in the agricultural community world-wide and had great potential for complementing and substituting for chemical pesticides at reduced costs. A fungal bionematocide was being developed for commercialization in The Philippines for the control of soil nematodes harmful to banana and other crop species. Other work at the University of The Philippines at Los Baños (UPLB) focused on the biological control of corn borers, trips and golden snails.

The biological diversity programme of the ANSAB was established in January 1994 with the following goals: co-ordinate research and technical assistance for non-timber forest products (NTFPs) and biological diversity in Nepal through networking; study the relation between extraction, processing and trade of these products, and examine how economic benefits from these activities could be re-invested in the areas of product origin in a fair way; promote the sustainable use and management of NTFPs; provide reliable information on issues relating to biological diversity and natural resource utilization. The main focus of the programme was currently on research, technical assistance and networking activities (*Nepal NTFP Network Newsletter*, vol. 1, no. 1, May 1996, pp. 1–6).

Nepal's biological diversity could be summarized by the following data: about 7,000 species of higher plants; over 250 species of endemic higher plants; more than 600 species of Ayurvedic medicinal plants; over 1,000 species of locally useful plants and more than 100 species used in industry and trade; and about 1,000 species of the Himalayan plants originally discovered and described from the Nepalese flora. The ANSAB biological diversity programme had been supported by a grant from the International Development Research Centre (IDRC), New Delhi, and had provided assistance to 19 researchers and institutions to conduct research on various non-timber forest species, their uses, sustainable utilization, indigenous knowledge and ethnobotany in a wide range of ecosystems and habitats. Preliminary findings confirmed that NTFPs could contribute significantly to the rural economy and that a strong link should be established between resource utilization and conservation (*Nepal NTFP Network Newsletter*, vol. 1, no. 1, May 1996, pp. 1–6).

The programme provided technical assistance to community groups and non-governmental organizations for biological diversity mapping, market assessment, technology assessment and selection, strengthening indigenous management capacity, enterprise development, and training. A grant had been received from the Ford Foundation, New Delhi, which enabled the provision of technical assistance to a Center for Community   Development and Research, Ayurvedic medicine companies, Neem Society (Nepalganj) to study the availability, use and economic significance of *Azadirachta indica* and *Madhuca latifolia*, Karnali Herbs Processing Co. Pvt. Ltd. (Jumla) for setting up a distillation unit of essential oils, etc. Business opportunities were found particularly promising for the exploitation of the fatty oil of *Madhuca latifolia*, as well as of essential oil and defatted cakes of neem (*A. indica*).

The Nepal Eco-Essential Medicinal Plants Society (NEEM Society) was a recently established local non-governmental organization with its headquarters in Nepalganj; the objectives of the

Society were to conserve indigenous trees producing non-timber products, create local employment, generate income through the collection, processing and marketing of NTFPs, promote agroforestry and protect the environment. Technical assistance to the Society included: resource survey and market feasibility concerning neem and mahuwa (*A. indica* and *M. latifolia*) products in the Banke district; nursery development with community participation for plantation in communal forests and private lands; processing and marketing of neem and mahuwa products to benefit local communities. The study showed that there were about 2,500 sizeable neem trees and over 5,000 mahuwa trees with a total annual production of over 66 tonnes of neem seeds, 272 tonnes of mahuwa seeds and 252 tonnes of mahuwa flowers. Despite indigenous knowledge on the use of these plants and their products, none had been traded yet, while there was a good international market, especially in India. That is why an expert had been working with the NEEM Society to explore the market and develop a business plan and marketing strategies (*Nepal NTFP Network Newsletter*, vol. 1, no. 1, May 1996, pp. 1–6).

The Nepal Non-Timber Forest Products Network was set up to link researchers, producer associations, local businesses involved in the collection, use, processing and marketing of non-timber forest products in Nepal. In 1996, the Network had over 50 institutional members and 240 individual members. A Co-ordination Committee and a Research Committee were in charge of general policy and programmes, and identification of research priorities respectively.

Biovillage project

In India, where nearly 50% of the land area was already under the plough, productivity and production of all commodities needed to be increased under conditions of shrinking land resources and reduction in both the soil potential and biological wealth of the country. According to M. S. Swaminathan (1991 *a,b*), Chairman of the Centre for Research on Sustainable Agricultural and Rural Development, Madras, any agricultural research strategy would therefore need to take into consideration the following requirements:

– enhancement of biological productivity per unit of land, water and time on an ecologically sustainable basis;

– greater reliance on non-traditional feeds, enriched cellulosic wastes, high-yielding fodder legumes and grasses, and locally available biomass;

– protection of long-term productivity of land, water, flora and fauna and atmosphere;

– promotion of livelihood, security of landless families and those without assets, particularly women;

– development of competitiveness in an unfavourable trade environment;

– careful identification of priorities in research-and-development investment based on comparative advantages;

– setting up of technology alert systems to analyze the social and trade implications of new technologies (e.g. substitution of export natural products or raw materials).

Over 70% of the population lived in villages in India, compared to nearly 80% in China. Unplanned migration of educated rural youth to towns and cities, besides causing new social problems in urban areas, hampered the upgrading of rural enterprises. Consequently, a majority of rural families depended on the primary sector (crop and animal husbandry, fisheries and forestry) for their livelihood. How therefore would it be possible to generate new opportunities for skilled or value-added jobs in rural areas both in farm and non-farm sectors?

According to Swaminathan (1992, personal communication), the new paradigm of rural development aimed to integrate the principles of environmental sustainability, economic viability and social equity. Rural ecotechnology was defined as a blend of technologies which could help link the livelihood security of rural families with the environmental security of rural areas. It might involve appropriate combinations of the following three approaches:

– preservation and popularization of local technologies, such as handicrafts, handlooms, sericiculture and agricultural practices with ecological, social and economic advantages;

– introduction of frontier technologies, such as remote sensing and computer sciences, which would help in collecting and spreading relevant information and data;

– development and dissemination of new technology blends involving the integration of local wisdom and technologies with frontier technologies, particularly in biotechnologies, informatics and micro-electronics; such blends were expected to satisfy the triple tests of environment, economics and equity.

The following goals had to be kept in mind:

– to conserve and enrich the ecological foundations essential for the sustainable productivity of terrestrial and aquatic farming systems;

– to ensure and strengthen nutrition security, i.e. physical and economic access to balanced diets and safe drinking water, at the household level;

– to pay concurrent attention to the technological, training, trade and public policy requirements needed for the programme to achieve a self-propelling momentum (Swaminathan, 1992, personal communication).

The biovillage project was born during an interdisciplinary dialogue on New technologies reaching the unreached 1. Biotechnology, organized by the M.S. Swaminathan Research Foundation in Madras in January 1991. In February 1993, the Foundation submitted a feasibility report for pilot biovillage projects in India and China to the Asian Development Bank, Manila, which had funded the study. The latter welcomed this approach to poverty alleviation. In 1992–1993, activities under the biovillage programme included: completion of the farming systems survey; pre-testing and adaptation of technologies; training and field visits; facilitating the implementation of government programmes relevant to the villages' assessed needs; formulation of a project for testing technologies with support from the International Fund for Agricultural Development (IFAD); and the formulation of an India-China Biovillage Project to be supported by the Asian Development Bank (M.S. Swaminathan Research Foundation, 1992–1993).

A year later, the Biovillage Pilot Project was being implemented in the Union Territory of Pondichery chosen for its diverse agroclimatic and socio-economic conditions. The three villages selected were: Pillayarkuppam, Kizhur and Sivaranthakam (Kizhur was the revenue village and Sivaranthakam its hamlet). The farming system survey was carried out on individual land holdings. They were classified as: landless (with no land except the homestead), marginal farmers (less than 0.5 hectare), small farmers (0.5-1 hectare) and medium farmers (1–2 hectares). The data collected included demographic data, cropping patterns, inputs and outputs both in quantity and value, disposal of farm products, cash expenditure, costs and returns, and farm income. The major constraints were identified as follows:

– scarcity of arable land (per capita cultivable land was only 800 m²; arable land surface area was decreasing rapidly due to the high rate of urbanization in the region);

– lack of income-generating opportunities for families;

– technologies unsuited to the socio-economic conditions of the rural poor;

– inadequate access to resources to translate technologies into production opportunities;

– disparate distribution of land ownership and prevalence of landlessness;

– conversion of highly productive lands from seasonal and annual to perennial crops, thereby reducing employment opportunities for resource-poor labouring families;

– depletion of the ground water regime resulting from an excessive number of water-demanding crops, like three paddy crops (increasing energy costs and intrusion of saline water);

– heavy dependence on energy resources of external origin for agricultural production (fertilizers and electricity);

– increasing dependence on chemical fertilizers to maintain a diminishing soil fertility;

– extremely poor sanitary conditions.

Conversely, the potential included:

– proximity to an urban centre, which provided a market for bulky and perishable, but high income-generating products like vegetables, mushrooms, flowers and milk;

– small farms and a surplus labour situation, which permitted the undertaking of labour-intensive farm enterprises, such as vegetable cultivation, flower growing, etc.;

– availability of local raw materials and inputs (cassava, groundnut, fish meal, etc.) for livestock feed for animal husbandry enterprises;

– possibility of high-level biomass production, at least on farms with access to water.

For the landless and women from poor households, the identified interventions included value-adding activities based on the biomass sources available within the village/community (mushroom production based on paddy straw), development of community resources (pisciculture in community ponds), linking land-owning farm families with the landless (fodder banks and mulberry banks), and the advantages of scale by decentralized production and centralized services (mushroom production and sericiculture).

For marginal and small farmers, rural women, the interventions were labour-intensive production enterprises (vegetable and flower production, fodder-dairy-biomass units, integrated aquaculture).

For the resource endowed, activities would enhance production efficiency on a sustainable basis (pisciculture in brick kiln lands, increased water use efficiency and conversion of a degraded resource to productive use) and foster activities supporting the endeavours of the resource poor (fodder and mulberry banks).

The technologies and systems introduced and being tested on an adaptive research trial basis were:

– mushroom production, an income-generating activity for landless women;

– group sericiculture integrated with mulberry banks to ensure the

supply of mulberry leaves for landless women;
– goat rearing based on stall feeding or fodder on community lands for landless women;
– setting up of fodder banks as a means of ensuring a fodder supply to landless dairy farmers;
– composite fish culture and management of community ponds for the landless;
– recycling of wastes and value addition through fodder-dairying-biogas integrated units for small and marginal farmers;
– evaluation of the suitability of *Azolla* as a biofertilizer in rice cropping systems;
– environmental sanitation and biogas production for landless households;
– nutrition gardens for schools and households;
– hybrid rice production;
– early evaluation trials in rice;
– community vegetable production with marketing facilities;
– aquaculture, vermiculture;
– flower production.

A trial integrating a fish farming system and the production of flowers and fruits was conducted in Pillayarkuppam village (M.S. Swaminathan Research Foundation, 1992–1993).

More than half of the vegetables required by the population of Pondichery came from areas as far away as 50–300 km. The vegetable production in Pondichery was only 43,000 tonnes in 1993, compared to a required 87,600 tonnes per year. The visits of farm men and women from the biovillages to Indo-American Hybrid Seeds (IAHS) company, Bangalore, culminated in most of the farmers taking up hybrid vegetable cultivation, especially hybrid tomato. Two tomato hybrids, namely Naveen and Rupali, were cultivated on an adaptive trial basis. Both hybrids showed good acclimatization in these villages. This successful endeavour motivated farmers to take up the cultivation of other hybrid vegetables like hybrid *Abelmoschatus esculentus* (okra) and hybrid *Solanum melongena* (egg-plant). This development was leading to the substitution of one rice crop with vegetable crops, thereby reducing pressure on dwindling ground water resources (M.S. Swaminathan Research Foundation, 1992–1993).

Based on the demand for different vegetables, production was to be planned for the whole year round. Pricing was based on the floor price fixed by the government. The transport system for vegetables from the farmer's field was assured by the Pondichery Agro Food Products and Civil Supplies Corporation (PAPSCo), while the Pondichery Agro

Service and Industries Corporation (PASIC) supplied good quality vegetable seeds to growers (M.S. Swaminathan Research Foundation, 1992–1993).

An organic fertilizer made of organic waste from sugar-cane factories (press mud) and composted during an aerobic process called 'bioearth' in combination with Micro 110, a special microbial starter developed by IBF Co. Inc., USA, contained most of the major and minor nutrients for improving soil fertility. The bioearth material was obtained from the Bio-systems group of Alfa-Laval, Dapodi, Pune, India. A trial conducted in Sivaranthakam village during the samba season (August-December) across an area of 1,000 m^2 showed that the application of 5 tonnes per hectare, plus the recommended dose of fertilizer, increased yield by 18% over the control (M.S. Swaminathan Research Foundation, 1992–1993).

A series of meetings for women in the three biovillages were held to create an awareness among landless women of the income-generating potential of mushroom production. Trials with oyster mushrooms (*Pleurotus ostreatus*) were conducted in three landless households in each of the three villages: the spawn material was procured from the Tamil Nadu Agricultural University, Coimbatore; the performance and adaptability of the mushroom proved satisfactory; each cyclindical bag containing 2 kg of wet weight of paddy straw and 150 g of spawn gave 500 g of fresh mushroom. It was therefore decided to initiate mushroom production, firstly at Sivaranthakam village. Through participatory meetings, initially twelve landless women were selected to take up mushroom production as a supplementary income-generating activity, the major constraint being the non-availability of spawn. A spawn-producing centre was set up with a capacity for 20 bottles per day (M.S. Swaminathan Research Foundation, 1992–1993).

A biovillage consortium of institutions consisting of departments and agencies of the Government of Pondichery involved in agriculture and rural development, universities, industry, financial institutions and non-governmental organizations was set up in 1991. It held its third meeting in June 1993, the main objective being to appraise partners in the on-going activities and seek their guidance on policy issues and support.

A Memorandum of Understanding had been signed between the M.S. Swaminathan Research Foundation and the Chinese Academy of Sciences (CAS) for an India-China Biovillage Project. For the Chinese biovillages, the generation of income and employment was sought through the management of community resources on sound ecological principles while, for the Indian biovillages, the same was to be achieved through off-land production activities especially focused on the resource poor. A detailed plan of action had been prepared for the Chinese biovillages, with emphasis on horticulture, animal husbandry and agricultural products processing (M.S. Swaminathan Research Foundation, 1992–1993).

Notes

1. A workshop on Cassava and Biotechnology had been held from 21 to 23 March 1990 in Amsterdam, under the aegis of the Directorate-General for International Cooperation (DGIS) of the Dutch Ministry of Foreign Affairs, in anticipation of the Special Programme Biotechnology and Development Cooperation, officially initiated by the DGIS on 1 January 1992. The objectives of the workshop were to: exchange information on cassava projects and programmes (e.g. the state of the art in cassava research and the potential role of biotechnologies, policies of donor agencies, of the International Institute of Tropical Agriculture and the International Center for Tropical Agriculture, which had a regional and global mandate respectively for research and development on cassava); discuss criteria for setting research priorities (based on the presented position paper, Cassava and biotechnology: production constraints and potential solutions). It was not a technical workshop, but one in which donor perspective, user orientation and problem orientation were central themes.

    The following low-technology research approaches were considered as deserving high priority:
    – *in-vitro* conservation of cassava germplasm;
    – induction of flowering through meristem culture;
    – micropropagation;
    – screening methods for diseases and pathogens;
    – selection and identification of vesicular-arbuscular mycorrhizae and nitrogen-fixing bacteria;
    – improved processing methods to reduce cyanide content, increase protein content and improve cassava starch processing into ethanol and fructose syrups.

    From a user viewpoint, biotechnological research would need to be directed toward yield stability, i.e. the development of disease-resistant and stress-tolerant cultivars, better root quality and improved processing techniques. From a research viewpoint, focus was on the development of an efficient regeneration protocol and on greater understanding of the cassava genome, using molecular biology tools (RFLP maps). A balance would need to be found between the two approaches for priority setting. It was also recommended that more attention be paid to the dissemination of available research findings to the National Agricultural Research Systems. Cassava status as an orphan crop was an advantage in this respect: all information was made public since, contrary to other commercially interesting crop species, there were hardly any privately-owned findings in existence.

2. Appropriate Technology International (ATI) was a private, non-profit making development assistance organization headquartered in Washington, D.C., with projects in Asia, Africa, Latin America and the Caribbean.

    For appropriate technologies, see also Edquist and Edquist (1979); Reddy (1988); Clark (1990); Madu (1990); and Willoughby (1990).

3. On 13 November 1992, the Nepalese Government approved the ANSAB statutes of incorporation and granted official status to the Asia Network for Small Scale Agricultural Biotechnology as a non-profit making international non-governmental organization, headquartered in Kathmandu. The Nepalese Government and the ATI were the Network's two sponsors (*ANSAB Newsletter*, 1992-1993, vol.1, no.2, p.1).

References

AHMED, I. (ed.). 1992*a*. *Biotechnology: A hope or a threat?* A study prepared for the International Labour Office within the framework of the World Employment Programme. The Macmillan Series of ILO Studies. London, Macmillan, 275 pp.

AHMED, I. 1992*b*. Biotechnology: key issues for the Third World. *Biotechnology and Development Monitor* (Joint Publication of the Directorate General International Co-operation of the Ministry of Foreign Affairs, The Hague, and the University of Amsterdam), 10, p. 19.

ALBERGANTI, M. 1995. Les insecticides se mettent à l'heure de l'écologie. *Le Monde* (Paris), 14 April 1995, p. 23.

ALENCAR, G. S. DE; VAN DER REE, M. C. 1996. 1996: an important year for Brazilian biopolitics? *Biotechnology and Development Monitor* (Amsterdam), 27, pp. 21–22.

ALLAVENA, A. 1984. Beans (*Phaseolus*). In: Sharp, W. K.; Evans, D. A.; Ammirato, P. V.; Yamada, Y. (eds.), *Handbook of plant cell culture*, vol. 2, pp. 137–68. New York, Macmillan.

AÑÉ, L. 1993. Looking for a biotech fix. *Cuba Business*, vol. 7, no. 1, January–February 1993.

AUGEREAU, J.-F. 1995. Après dix ans de recherches menées avec l'INRA, Lafarge-Coppée met sur le marché un nouvel hybride de blé. *Le Monde* (Paris), 4 January 1995, p. 30.

AUGEREAU, J.-F. 1996. Les aliments de demain se conservent mieux, en gardant leur saveur. *Le Monde* (Paris), 14 February 1996, p. 22.

BAJAJ, Y. P. S. (ed.). 1990. *Wheat*. Biotechnology in Agriculture and Forestry, vol. 13. Berlin, Springer-Verlag, 710 pp.

BARBER, C. V.; LA VIÑA, A. 1995. *Regulating access to genetic resources. The Philippine experience*. Paper presented at the Global Diversity Forum (Jakarta, 4–5 November 1995).

BARFOOT, P. D. 1993. Plant molecular biology for developing countries: a project to develop insect-resistant potatoes and sweet potatoes. *AgBiotech News and Information*, 5(11), pp. 397N–402N.

BAUMER, M. 1992. Le Centre international pour la recherche en agroforesterie (ICRAF), son intérêt pour les pastoralistes. *Parcours Demain*, 2/3, November 1992, pp. 6–11.

BELL, J. 1996. Investing in destruction. *Seedling* (The Quarterly Newsletter of Genetic Resources Action International-GRAIN), vol. 13, no. 4, December 1996, pp. 5–15.

BERTRAM, R. B.; SCHAAL, B. A. 1993. Phylogeny of *Manihot* and the evolution of cassava. *CBN* (*Cassava Biotechnology Network*) *Newsletter*, vol. 1, no. 1, March 1993, pp. 4–6. Published by the CIAT (International Center for Tropical Agriculture), Cali, Colombia.

BIJMAN, J. 1990. European biotechnology programmes and developing countries. *Biotechnology and Development Monitor* (Joint Publication of the Directorate General International Co-operation of the Ministry of Foreign Affairs, The Hague, and the University of Amsterdam), 2, pp. 18–9.

——. 1992a. Can biotechnology help to increase livestock productivity? *Biotechnology and Development Monitor* (Joint Publication of the Directorate General International Co-operation of the Ministry of Foreign Affairs, The Hague, and the University of Amsterdam), 11, pp. 3–5.

——. 1992b. Potatoes: improving disease resistance and quality. *Biotechnology and Development Monitor* (Joint Publication of the Directorate General International Co-operation of the Ministry of Foreign Affairs, The Hague, and the University of Amsterdam), 12, pp. 3–5.

——. 1994a. Plant Genetic Systems. *Biotechnology and Development Monitor* (A joint publication of the Department of International Relations and Public International Law of the University of Amsterdam, the African Centre for Technology Studies, ACTS, Nairobi, Kenya, the Research and Information System for the Non-aligned and Other Developing Countries, RIS, India, and the Instituto Interamericano de Cooperación para la Agricultura, IICA, Costa Rica, and the Directorate General for International Cooperation, DGIS, Ministry of Foreign Affairs, The Hague, Netherlands), 19, pp. 19–20.

——. 1994b. Agracetus: patenting all transgenic cotton. *Biotechnology and Development Monitor* (A joint publication of the Department of International Relations and Public International Law of the University of Amsterdam, and the Special Programme Biotechnology and Development Cooperation of the Directorate General for International Cooperation-DGIS-, the Netherlands' Ministry of Foreign Affairs, in co-operation with the African Centre for Technology Studies – ACTS -, Nairobi, Kenya, the Research and Information System for the Non-aligned and Other Developing Countries – RIS -, India, and the Inter-American Institute for Cooperation on Agriculture, IICA, Costa Rica), 21, pp. 8–9.

——. 1996. Recombinant bovine somatotropin in Europe and the USA. *Biotechnology and Development Monitor* (Amsterdam), 27, pp. 3–5.

BIJMAN, J.; MARTIN, M.; NYGÅRD, B. 1996. *The future of bovine somatotropin in the European Union: a study on public attitude, dairy policies and competitiveness of the EU dairy sector.* The Hague, Agricultural Economics Research Institute.

BILLARD, R. 1995. Les systèmes de production aquacole et leurs relations avec l'environnement. *Cahiers Agricultures* (Paris), vol. 4., no. 1, pp. 9–28.

BIO (Biotechnology Industry Organization). 1995. *The U.S. biotechnology industry: facts and figures* (1994/1995 edition). Washington, D.C., Biotechnology Industry Organization.

BRENNER, C.; KOMEN, J. 1994. *International initiatives in biotechnology for developing country agriculture: promises and problems.* Paris, OECD (Organisation for Economic Co-operation and Development) Development Centre, Technical Papers no. 100, 60 pp.

BUDDENHAGEN, I. W. 1993. Whence and whither banana research and development? In: INIBAP. *Biotechnology applications for banana and plantain improvement* (Proceedings of the Workshop held in San José, Costa Rica, 27–31 January 1992), pp. 27–31. Montpellier, France, INIBAP.

BUHRER, J.-C. 1996. Euphorie boursière après la fusion Sandoz- Ciba-Geigy. *Le Monde* (Paris), 9 March 1996, p. 15.

——. 1997. L'Union européenne est désavouée par l'OMC dans le conflit de la banane. *Le Monde* (Paris), 3 May 1997, p. 32.

BULLOCK, W. O.; DIBNER, M. D. 1994. The changing dynamics of strategic alliances between U.S. biotechnology firms and Japanese corporations and universities. *Trends in Biotechnology*, vol. 12, October 1994, pp. 397–400.

BUNDERS, J. (ed.). 1990. *Biotechnology for small-scale farmers in developing countries. Analysis and assessment procedures.* Amsterdam, VU University Press, 232 pp.

BUNDERS, J. F. G. 1994. *Participative strategies for science-based innovations: the case of biotechnology for small-scale farmers in developing countries.* Amsterdam, VU University Press, 236 pp.

BUNDERS, J.; HAVERKORT, B.; HIEMSTRA, W. 1997. *Biotechnology. Building on farmers' knowledge.* Macmillan Education, 256 pp.

BUSSEY, H. 1996. Genomic analysis reveals a deep conservation of gene function among eucaryotes. *PBI* (Plant Biotechnology Institute) *Bulletin* (National Research Council Canada, Saskatoon), February 1996, pp. 1–4.

CANTLEY, M. F. 1989. Managing an invisible elephant. *Biofutur* (Paris), 84, pp. 8–16.

CANS, R. 1995. L'excès de pêche épuise les ressources mondiales de poisson. *Le Monde* (Paris), 16 May 1995, p. 4.

CARDI (Caribbean Agricultural Research and Development Institute). 1984. *Virus-tested yam tuber multiplication project. Final report;* funded by the

European Development Fund through the Caribbean Development Bank (1980–1984).

CEC (Commission of the European Communities). 1991. *Life sciences and technologies for developing countries (STD 3)*. Brussels, CEE, Directorate-General XII for Science, Research and Development, 20 pp.

CHANG, S. T. 1993. *Mushroom biology: the impact on mushroom production and mushroom products*. Keynote lecture, First International Conference on Mushroom Biology and Mushroom Products (Hong Kong, 23–26 August 1993). Department of Biology, The Chinese University of Hong Kong, 37 pp.

CHANG, S. T.; SHAMSUDDIN, Z. H.; DASILVA, E. J. 1992. UNESCO Regional Network for Microbiology and allied activities in Southeast Asia: a model training and research network in microbiology for development. *World Journal of Microbiology and Biotechnology* (The Official Journal of the International Union of Microbiological Societies and of the MIRCEN Network, Oxford, U.K.), vol. 8, no. 3, pp. 236–41.

CHATURVEDI, S. 1994. India tries for drought tolerance. *Biotechnology and Development Monitor* (University of Amsterdam), p. 8.

CHIBBAR, R.; BÁGA, M.; HUCL, P. 1995. Wheat improvement in Canada. Starch – a target to improve wheat by genetic engineering. *PBI* (Plant Biotechnology Institute) *Bulletin* (National Research Council Canada, Saskatoon), May 1995, pp. 8–9.

CHRISTOU, P. *et al.* 1990. Soybean genetic engineering: commercial production of transgenic plants. *Trends in Biotechnology*, June 1990, pp. 145–51.

CIAT (International Center for Tropical Agriculture). 1989. *CIAT in the 1990s: a strategic plan*. Cali, Colombia, CIAT.

CIAT. 1990. *CIAT Report 1990*. Cali, Colombia, CIAT.

CIP (International Potato Center). 1991. *Meeting the challenge: the International Potato Center's strategy for the 1990s and beyond*. Lima, CIP.

CIRAD (Centre de coopération internationale en recherche agronomique pour le développement – Centre for International Co-operation in Agricultural Research for Development). 1993. *Le CIRAD en 1992. CIRAD 1992*. Paris, CIRAD, 128 pp.

CIRAD. 1994. *Images of Research*. Paris, CIRAD, 120 pp.

CLANCY, J. S.; HULSCHER, W. S. 1994. *Report of a desk study on the possibilities for biogas production in developing countries with specific reference to the potential contribution of biotechnology*. The Hague, the Netherlands, Directorate-General for International Cooperation, Ministry of Foreign Affairs, Special Programme Biotechnology and Development Cooperation.

CLARK, N. 1990. Development policy, technology assessment and the new technologies. *Futures*, vol. 22, no. 9, pp. 913–31.

CLARK, N.; JUMA, C. 1991. *Biotechnology for sustainable development. Policy options for developing countries*. Nairobi, Kenya, African Centre for Technology Studies (ACTS) Press, 117 pp.

COHEN, J. I. 1988. Models for integrating biotech into crop improvement programs. *Biotechnology*, 6, April 1988, pp. 387–92.

——. 1989*a*. Biotechnology research for the developing world. *Trends in Biotechnology* (TIBTECH, Elsevier Science Publishers, Cambridge, United Kingdom), vol. 7, pp. 295–303.

——. (ed.). 1989*b*. *Strengthening collaboration in biotechnology: international agricultural research and the private sector*. Washington, D.C., U.S. Agency for International Development (AID), Document #PN-ABC-819, 480 pp.

COHEN, J. I.; PLUCKNETT, D. L.; SMITH, N. J. H.; JONES, K. A. 1987. *Integration of biotechnology into international crop improvement*. Mimeographed document, 28 pp.

COHEN, J. I.; JONES, K. A.; PLUCKNETT, D. L.; SMITH, N. J. H. 1988*a*. Regulatory concerns affecting developing nations. *Bio/Technology*, 6, June 1988, p. 744.

——. 1988*b*. Models for integrating biotech into crop improvement programmes. *Bio/Technology*, 6(4), pp. 387–92.

COLLINSON, M. P.; WRIGHT PLATAIS, K. 1991. *Biotechnology and the International Agricultural Research Centers of the CGIAR*. Paper presented at the 21st Conference of the International Association of Agricultural Economists (Tokyo, Japan, 22–28 August 1991).

COMETTA, S. 1989. Strategic considerations for biotechnology business to the year 2000. *Drug research 39* (II), no. 8.

COMMANDEUR, P. 1994*a*. The politics of banana and plantain research. *Biotechnology and Development Monitor* (University of Amsterdam), 18, pp. 11–13.

——. 1994*b*. REDBIO and FAO's Global programme on Plant Biotechnology. *Biotechnology and Development Monitor* (A joint publication of the Department of International Relations and Public International Law of the University of Amsterdam, and the Special Programme Biotechnology and Development Cooperation of the Directorate General for International Cooperation-DGIS-, the Netherlands' Ministry of Foreign Affairs, in co-operation with the African Centre for Technology Studies – ACTS -, Nairobi, Kenya, the Research and Information System for the Non-aligned and Other Developing Countries – RIS -, India, and the Inter-American Institute for Cooperation on Agriculture, IICA, Costa Rica), 21, pp. 20 and 22.

CORREA, C. M. 1991*a*. Developing private biopharmaceutical capacity in developing countries. *Biotechnology and Development Monitor* (Joint Publication of the Directorate General Affairs, The Hague, and the University of Amsterdam), 9, pp. 7–8.

——. 1991*b*. The pharmaceutical industry and biotechnology – opportunities and constraints for developing countries. *World Competition* (Geneva), vol. 15, no. 2, pp. 43–63.

COURSEY, D.G. 1967. *Yams*. London, Longmans.

CROSBY, B.; HEMMINGSEN, S. 1996. Impact of plant genomics research on biotechnology. *PBI* (Plant Biotechnology Institute) *Bulletin* (National Research Council Canada, Saskatoon), February 1996, pp. 5–7.

DASILVA, E. 1997. The MIRCEN Network: a global resource for international co-operation. *World Journal of Microbiology and Biotechnology*, vol. 13, no. 1, pp. 1–6.

DASILVA, E. J.; TAGUCHI, H. 1987. An international network exercice: the MIRCEN programme. In: DaSilva, E. J.; Dommergues, Y. R.; Nyns, E. J.; Ratledge, C. (eds.), *Microbial technology in the developing world*, pp. 313–34. Oxford, United Kingdom, Oxford University Press, 444 pp.

DATLA, R.; SELVARAJ, G. 1995. Promoters in biotechnology. *PBI* (Plant Biotechnology Institute) *Bulletin* (National Research Council Canada, Saskatoon), August 1995, pp. 1–5.

DEBOVE, A. 1996. Le suédois Astra s'affirme comme la nouvelle étoile de la pharmacie. *Le Monde* (Paris), 25 April 1996, p. 14.

DE GROOT, C. 1990. ICGEB: UNIDO's Centre for biotechnology. *Biotechnology and Development Monitor* (Joint Publication of the Directorate General International Cooperation of the Ministry of Foreign Affairs, The Hague, and the University of Amsterdam), 3, pp. 18–9.

——. 1991. WHO: fighting tropical diseases at low cost. *Biotechnology and Development Monitor* (Joint Publication of the Directorate General International Co-operation of the Ministry of Foreign Affairs, The Hague, and the University of Amsterdam), 9, pp. 9–10.

——. 1992. OECD: an intergovernmental thinktank. *Biotechnology and Development Monitor* (Joint Publication of the Directorate General International Co-operation of the Ministry of Foreign Affairs, The Hague, and the University of Amsterdam), 11, pp. 18--9.

DEPAUW, R. M. 1995. Wheat improvement in Canada. Historical sketch. *PBI* (Plant Biotechnology Institute) *Bulletin* (National Research Council Canada, Saskatoon), May 1995, pp. 1–2.

DHOMBRES, D. 1995. Manaus, la ville qui tourne le dos à la forêt. *Le Monde* (Paris), 10 August 1995, p. 14.

DIEM, H.G.; ARAHOU, M. 1996. *Cluster root formation: a primary strategy of Casuarinaceae to overcome soil nutrient deficiency.* Paper presented to the 3rd International Casuarina Workshop (Danang, Viet Nam, 4–9 March 1996).

DÖBEREINER, J.; BALDANI, V. L. D. 1995. Endophytic diazotrophs other than Rhizobia. In Press.

DODDS, J. H.; HORTON, D. 1990. Impact of biotechnology on potato production in developing countries. *AgBiotech News and Information*, vol. 2, no. 3, pp. 397–400.

DODDS, J. H.; TEJADA, M. 1990. Potato. In: Persley, G. (ed.). *Agricultural biotechnology: opportunities for international development*, pp. 273–86. Biotechnology in Agriculture Series, no. 2. Wallingford, Oxon, United Kingdom, CAB International, 495 pp.

DOELLE, H. W. 1991. Biotechnology and sustainable development. The Pacific perspective. In: *International Symposium on Biotechnologies and Environment for Sustainable Development* (Montreal, Canada, 23–26 September 1991), section K.

DUFOUR, J.-P. 1994. L'INRA va commercialiser un colza hybride. *Le Monde* (Paris), 10 August 1994, p. 9.

DUVICK, D. N. 1996. Utilization of biotechnology in US plant breeding. *Biotechnology and Development Monitor* (Amsterdam), 27, pp. 15–7.

EDQVIST AND EDQVIST. 1979. *Social carriers of techniques for development.* Stockholm, SAREC.

EDWARDS, C. A.; HART, R.; DIXON, J. A.; DICKINSON, J. C. 1990. *A strategy for implementing sustainable agricultural strategies in developing countries.* Washington, D.C., U.S. Agency for International Development.

EICHER, C. K. 1993. *Revitalizing the CGIAR system and NARSs in the Third World. Pour un nouveau dynamisme des systèmes de recherche nationaux et internationaux.* Paris, CIRAD (Centre de coopération internationale en recherche agronomique pour le développement), Collection Notes et Documents, 14, 67 pp.

ELDERHORST, M. 1994. Will Cuba's biotechnology capacity survive the socio-economic crisis? *Biotechnology and Development Monitor* (A joint publication of the Department of International Relations and Public International Law of the University of Amsterdam, the African Centre for Technology Studies, ACTS, Nairobi, Kenya, the Research and Information System for the Non-aligned and Other Developing Countries, RIS, India, and the Instituto Interamericano de Cooperación para la Agricultura, IICA, Costa Rica, and the Directorate General for International Cooperation, DGIS, Ministry of Foreign Affairs, The Hague, Netherlands), 20, pp. 11–3 and 22.

ELMERICH, C. 1995. Associative symbiosis with cereals and other grasses: the case of *Azospirillum.* In: Aubert, J.-P.; Martin, P. M. W. (eds.), *Microbes, environment, biotechnology* ('The Year of Louis Pasteur International Symposia', Institut Louis Malardé, Papeete, Tahiti, French Polynesia, 8–12 May 1995), pp. 68–70. Paris, Institut Pasteur, 193 pp.

EYZAGUIRRE, P.; IWANAGA, M. (eds.), 1995. *Participatory plant breeding.* Proceedings of a workshop on participatory plant breeding (Wageningen, Netherlands, 26–29 July 1995). Rome, International Genetic Resources Institute (IPGRI), 164 pp.

FAUQUET, C. M. 1993. Status of cassava regeneration and transformation. *CBN (Cassava Biotechnology Network) Newsletter,* vol. 1, no. 1, March 1993, pp. 7–9. Published by the CIAT (International Center for Tropical Agriculture), Cali, Colombia.

FERCHAK, J.; RIBEIRO, S. (eds.) 1992. *Lab to land: biotechnology for sustainable agriculture in Asia* (Proceedings of the first ANSAB Workshop, Kathmandu, Nepal, 29 March-1 April 1992). Washington, D.C.,

Appropriate Technology International (ATI), and Kathmandu, Nepal, New Era, 187 pp.

FERNANDEZ HERMANA, L. A. 1994. The 'trials' of a malaria vaccine. *Seedling* (The Quarterly Newsletter of Genetic Resources Action International), vol. 12, no. 1, pp. 16–8.

FITCHEN, J. H.; BEACHY, R. N. 1993. Genetically engineered protection against viruses transgenic plants. *Annual Review of Microbiology* (Palo Alto, California), 47 pp.

FOLLÉA, L. 1995. Un rapport sur les 'médicaments orphelins'. L'INSERM propose d'encourager la fabrication des spécialités pharmaceutiques non rentables. *Le Monde* (Paris), 4 January 1995, p. 8.

GAIA FOUNDATION. 1996. *Intellectual property rights (IPRs), collective rights, biodiversity.* London, GAIA Foundation.

GALHARDI, R. M. A. A. 1993. *Employment and income effects of biotechnology in Latin America: a speculative assessment.* Geneva, International Labour Office, 64 pp.

GALINIER, P. 1996. La grande distribution ne veut pas du soja génétiquement modifié. *Le Monde* (Paris), 14 November 1996, p. 12.

GALINIER, P.; GALLOIS, D. 1996. Jean-François-Dehecq, président du groupe Sanofi: 'nous participerons aux restructurations dans l'industrie pharmaceutique'. *Le Monde* (Paris), 26 November 1996, p. 20.

GALLOIS, D. 1995*a*. Les regroupements se multiplient dans le secteur de la pharmacie. *Le Monde* (Paris), 28 January 1995, p. 19.

——. 1995*b*. La reprise de la chimie permet à Rhône-Poulenc de doubler son bénéfice. *Le Monde* (Paris), 9 February 1995, p. 21.

——. 1995*c*. Après l'achat de Wellcome, Glaxo devient le premier groupe pharmaceutique mondial. *Le Monde* (Paris), 9 March 1995, p. 18.

——. 1995*d*. Roussel-Uclaf organise sa recherche pour préserver son identité dans Hoechst. *Le Monde* (Paris), 22 March 1995, p. 16.

——. 1995*e*. En rachetant Marion Merrell Dow, Hoechst devrait redevenir numéro deux mondial de la pharmacie. *Le Monde* (Paris), 30 March 1995, p. 23.

——. 1995*f*. BASF achète les médicaments du groupe Boots. *Le Monde* (Paris), 2–3 April 1995, p. 14.

——. 1995*g*. La chimie européenne sort de la crise en multipliant les partenariats. *Le Monde* (Paris), 8 April 1995, p. 21.

——. 1995*h*. BASF accélère son redéploiement. *Le Monde* (Paris), 7–8 May 1995, p. 10.

——. 1995*i*. Le groupe pharmaceutique américain Eli Lilly s'intéresse à tous les métiers de la santé. *Le Monde* (Paris), 28 June 1995, p. 15.

——. 1995*j*. L'appétit des laboratoires. *Le Monde* (Paris), 11 July 1995, p. 13.

——. 1995*k*. Le rachat de Fisons illustre le recentrage stratégique de Rhône-Poulenc. *Le Monde* (Paris), 21 October 1995, p. 14.

——. 1995*l*. Le riz de la croissance au Vietnam. *Le Monde* (Paris), 21 October 1995, p. 14.

——. 1995*m*. Hoechst ménage ses filiales Roussel-Uclaf et Marion Merrell. *Le Monde* (Paris), 8 November 1995, p. 16.

——. 1995*n*. Le marché-phare de l'industrie pharmaceutique. *Le Monde* (Paris), 21 November 1995, p. 10.

——. 1996*a*. Fisons pèse sur les résultats de Rhône-Poulenc Rorer. *Le Monde* (Paris), 30 January 1996, p. 15.

——. 1996*b*. Rhône-Poulenc accélère ses désengagements après ses médiocres performances dans la chimie. *Le Monde* (Paris), 1 February 1996, p. 17.

——. 1996*c*. Synthélabo se renforce dans le domaine des biotechnologies. *Le Monde* (Paris), 22 May 1996, p. 16.

——. 1996*d*. L'Américain Baxter devient leader mondial des dérivés sanguins. *Le Monde* (Paris), 31 August 1996, p. 11.

——. 1996*e*. Rhône-Poulenc: pas de dénationalisation miracle. *Le Monde* (Paris), 19 November 1996, p. II.

——. 1996*f*. L'OPA de Hoechst sur Roussel Uclaf confirme son offensive dans la santé. *Le Monde* (Paris), 12 December 1996, p. 15.

——. 1996*g*. Rhône-Poulenc veut être un pharmacien sans perdre la chimie. *Le Monde* (Paris), 21 December 1996, p. 20.

——. 1997*a*. BASF veut développer en Asie son concept européen de plate-forme industrielle intégrée. *Le Monde* (Paris), 2 May 1997, p. 17.

——. 1997*b*. Roche devient le leader mondial du diagnostic en rachetant l'allemand Boehringer Mannheim. *Le Monde* (Paris), 28 May 1997, p. 25.

——. 1997*c*. Une vague de concentrations redessine le paysage de l'industrie chimique. *Le Monde* (Paris), 30 May 1997, p. 18.

GALLOIS, D.; GAY, P.-A. 1995. Sanofi joue son avenir sur trois molécules médicamenteuses. *Le Monde* (Paris), 7 June 1995, p. 16.

GALUS, C. 1995. L'arôme de la vanille produit à partir d'un champignon. *Le Monde* (Paris), 11 March 1995, p. 25.

——. 1997. La production de riz devra augmenter de 70% pour satisfaire la demande mondiale en 2020. *Le Monde* (Paris), 1 March 1997, p. 27.

GAUVIN, M.-L.; LAVIGNE, C.; GOUYON, P.-H. 1994. Colza transgénique et environnement. Les recherches en biosécurité: l'étude des flux de gènes. *Oléagineux Corps gras Lipides* (Paris), vol. 1, no. 1, pp. 45–9.

GRAIN. 1994*a*. Animal alarm. *Seedling* (The Quarterly Newsletter of Genetic Resources Action International), vol. 12, no. 1, pp. 3–10.

——. 1994*b*. Towards a world gene bank ? *Seedling* (The Quarterly Newsletter of Genetic Resources Action International), vol. 12, no. 2, pp. 3–10.

——. 1994*c*. A system in crisis. *Seedling* (The Quarterly Newsletter of Genetic Resources Action International), vol. 12, no. 2, pp. 11–9.

GRALL, J. 1996. La stratégie du grain de maïs. *Le Monde* (Paris), 14 February 1996, p. 22.

GROSRICHARD, F. 1995. La banane, pomme de discorde entre Anvers et Le Havre. *Le Monde* (Paris), 26–27 March 1995, p. 24.

HANSON, J.; RUREDZO, T. J. 1992. *In vitro* culture techniques for forage genetic resources. In: Moss, J. P. (ed.), *Biotechnology and crop improvement in*

Asia, pp. 149–51. Patancheru, Andhra Pradesh, India, International Crops Research Institute for the Semi-Arid Tropics.

HAQ, T. A.; MASON, H. S.; CLEMENTS, J. D.; ARNTZEN, C. J. 1995. Oral immunization with a recombinant bacterial antigen produced in transgenic plants. *Science* (Washington, D.C.), 268, pp. 714–16.

HAQUE, M. Z. 1993. Commercial bio-fertilizer production in Bangladesh. *Biotechnology and Development Monitor* (Amsterdam), p. 11.

HAUPTLI, H.; KATZ, D.; THOMAS, B. R.; GOODMAN, R. M. 1990. *Biotechnology and crop breeding for sustainable agriculture*. In: Edwards, C. A.; Lal, R.; Madden, P.; Miller, R. H.; House, G. (eds.), *Sustainable agricultural systems*, pp. 141–56. Ankeny, Iowa, Soil and Water Conservation Society.

HAYAKAWA, T.; ZHU, Y.; ITOH, K.; KIMURA, Y.; IZAWA, T.; SHIMAMOTO, K.; TORIYAMA, S. 1992. Genetically engineered rice resistant to rice stripe virus, an insect-transmitted virus. *Proceedings of the National Academy of Sciences of the USA*, 89, pp. 9865–9.

HEBLE, M. R. 1993. High value chemicals by tissue culture. *Chemical Industry Digest*, 3rd Quarter 1993 (September), pp. 113–8.

HEISSLER, M. 1994. Rhône-Poulenc. *Biotechnology and Development Monitor* (University of Amsterdam), 18, pp. 20–2.

——. 1996a. R&D cooperation between the EU and developing countries. *Biotechnology and Development Monitor* (Amsterdam), 26, pp. 12–4.

——. 1996b. Plant biotechnology in German ODA. *Biotechnology and Development Monitor* (Amsterdam), 27, pp. 18–20.

HEISSLER, M.; COMMANDEUR, P. 1995. The Japanese biotechnology industry. *Biotechnology and Development Monitor* (Amsterdam), 22, pp. 5–6.

HILL, W. A.; BONSI, C. K.; LORETAN, P. A. (eds.). 1992. *Sweet potato technology for the 21st century*. Tuskegee University, USA.

HOLZMAN, D. 1994. USDA files to re-examine the recombinant cotton patent. *Genetic Engineering News*, July 1994, pp. 1 and 13.

HUGHES, G. 1995. Wheat improvement in Canada. Breeding for disease resistance. *PBI* (Plant Biotechnology Institute) *Bulletin* (National Research Council Canada, Saskatoon), May 1995, p. 3.

ICLARM (INTERNATIONAL CENTER FOR LIVING AQUATIC RESOURCES MANAGEMENT). 1988. *ICLARM Five-Year Plan (1988–1992). Part I. Directions and opportunities*. Manila, Philippines, ICLARM.

ICRISAT (INTERNATIONAL CROPS RESEARCH INSTITUTE FOR THE SEMI-ARID TROPICS). 1988. *Biotechnology in tropical crop improvement*. Patancheru, Andhra Pradesh, India, ICRISAT, 160 pp.

——. 1991. *Pathways to progress in the semi-arid tropics: ICRISAT's strategic plan for the nineties*. Patancheru, Andhra Pradesh, India, ICRISAT.

——. 1993. *Annual Report 1992*. Patancheru, Andhra Pradesh, India, ICRISAT.

IITA (INTERNATIONAL INSTITUTE OF TROPICAL AGRICULTURE). 1990. *IITA Annual Report 1988–1989. Toward sustainable agriculture for Africa*. Ibadan, IITA.

ILRAD (INTERNATIONAL LABORATORY FOR RESEARCH ON ANIMAL DISEASES). 1991. *Annual Report 1990.* Nairobi, ILRAD.

INIBAP (INTERNATIONAL NETWORK FOR THE IMPROVEMENT OF BANANA AND PLANTAIN). 1993. *Annual Report 1992.* Montpellier, France, INIBAP.

IPGRI (INTERNATIONAL PLANT GENETIC RESOURCES INSTITUTE). 1993. *Diversity for development: the strategy of the International Plant Genetic Resources Institute.* Rome, IPGRI, 62 pp.

———. 1994. *Annual Report.* Rome, IPGRI, 128 pp.

IRRI (International Rice Research Institute). 1985. *Biotechnology and international agricultural research.* Los Baños, Philippines, IRRI Press, 435 pp.

———. 1993. *IRRI Rice Almanac.* IRRI (P.O. Box 933, 1099 Manila, Philippines), 142 pp.

JAFFÉ, W. R.; ROJAS, M. 1994*a*. Abiotic stress and biotechnology in Latin America. *Biotechnology and Development Monitor* (University of Amsterdam), 18, pp. 6–7. Transgenic potato tolerant to freezing. *Ibidem*, p. 10.

———. 1994*b*. Attempt to implement the Biodiversity Convention in the Andean region. *Biotechnology and Development Monitor* (Amsterdam), 21, p. 5.

JANSSON, R. K.; RAMAN, K. V. (eds.). 1991. *Sweet potato pest management: a global perspective.* Boulder, Colorado, Westview Press.

JEFFERSON, R. 1993. Agricultural biotechnology: by whom and for whom? *Biotechnology and Development Monitor* (Amsterdam), 14, p. 24.

JUMA, C.; MUGABE, J. M. 1994. *Technological development and the Convention on Biodiversity: emerging policy issues.* Nairobi, African Centre for Technology Studies (ACTS), discussion paper prepared for the Group of 77 and China.

JUMA, C.; MUGABE, J. M.; OJWANG, J. R. 1994. *Access to genetic resources: policy and institutional issues.* Outline prepared for the Stockholm Environmental Institute.

KATHEN, A. DE. 1996. *Gentechnik in Entwicklungsländern: Ein Überblick: Landwirtschaft.* Berlin, Umweltbundesant.

KHALIL, H. K.; REID, W. V.; JUMA, C. 1992. *Property rights, biotechnology and genetic resources.* ACTS Biopolicy International Series no. 7. Nairobi, African Centre for Technology Studies (ACTS) Press.

KHUSH, G. S.; TOENNIESSEN, G. H. (eds.). 1991. *Rice biotechnology.* Wallingford, Oxon, U.K., CAB International, Biotechnology in Agriculture Series no. 6, and IRRI (International Rice Research Institute, Manila, Philippines), 320 pp.

KISHORE, G. 1994. Monsanto emphasizes focus on agricultural applications of biotechnology. *PBI* (Plant Biotechnology Institute, National Research Council of Canada, Saskatoon), *Bulletin*, May 1994, pp. 5–9.

KLIER, A. 1995. *Bacillus thuringiensis* as a biopesticide: opportunities and challenges for the management of insect pests. In: Aubert, J.-P.; Martin, P. M. W. (eds.), *Microbes, environment, biotechnology* ('The year of Louis Pasteur International Symposia', Institut Louis Malardé, Papeete,

Tahiti, French Polynesia, 8–12 May 1995), pp. 81–3. Paris, Institut Pasteur, 193 pp.

KLOPPENBURG, J. R., Jr.; RODRIGUEZ, S. 1992. Conservationists or corsairs? *Seedling* (a bi-monthly publication of Genetic Resources Action International, GRAIN, Barcelona, Spain), vol. 9, nos. 2 and 3, pp. 12–7.

KNUDSEN, H. 1991*a*. World Bank bio-policy in the making. *Biotechnology and Development Monitor* (Joint Publication of the Directorate General International Co-operation of the Ministry of Foreign Affairs, The Hague, and the University of Amsterdam), 7, pp. 20–1.

——. 1991*b*. ICRISAT: biotechnology-induced institutional change? *Biotechnology and Development Monitor* (Amsterdam), 9, pp. 18–9.

——. 1993. ISAAA: proprietary biotechnology for small farmers? *Biotechnology and Developmment Monitor* (Amsterdam), pp. 12–3.

KOCHKO, A. DE.; FAUQUET, C. 1993. Du riz transgénique pour le tiers monde. *ORSTOM Actualités* (Paris), 41, pp. 19–23.

KOMEN, J. 1990*a*. CIMMYT: biotechnology for wheat and maize breeding. *Biotechnology and Development Monitor* (Joint publication of the Directorate General International Cooperation of the Ministry of Foreign Affairs, The Hague, and the University of Amsterdam), 2, pp. 20–1.

——. 1990*b*. The new research strategy of IRRI. *Biotechnology and Development Monitor* (Amsterdam), 3, pp. 20–1.

——. 1990*c*. IITA: biotechnology for the African smallholder. *Biotechnology and Development Monitor* (Amsterdam), 5, pp. 18–9.

——. 1991*a*. CIAT's advanced biotechnology networks. *Biotechnology and Development Monitor* (Amsterdam), 6, pp. 19–20.

——. 1991*b*. The potential of seaweeds in food production. *Biotechnology and Development Monitor* (Amsterdam), 7, pp. 10–11.

——. 1991*c*. ICLARM: the world's leading aquaculture centre. *Biotechnology and Development Monitor.* (Amsterdam), 7, pp. 12–3.

——. 1991*d*. ICARDA. *Biotechnology and Development Monitor* (Amsterdam), 8, pp. 12–3.

——. 1991*e*. Screening plants for new drugs. *Biotechnology and Development Monitor* (Amsterdam), 9, pp. 4–6.

——. 1991*f*. Biotechnology policy and the CGIAR: seminar on biosafety and intellectual property rights. *Biotechnology and Development Monitor* (Amsterdam), 9, p. 21.

——. 1992*a*. Grains for the tropical regions. *Biotechnology and Development Monitor* (Amsterdam), 10, pp. 3–5.

——. 1992*b*. WARDA: rice research in West Africa. *Biotechnology and Development Monitor* (Amsterdam), 10, pp. 10–11.

——. 1992*c*. ILRAD's research to control tropical livestock diseases. *Biotechnology and Development Monitor* (Amsterdam), 11, pp. 6–7.

——. 1992*d*. GGIAR statement on genetic resources and intellectual property. *Biotechnology and Development Monitor* (Amsterdam), 11, pp. 20–1.

———. 1992*e*. Genetic engineering and tissue culture at CIP. *Biotechnology and Development Monitor* (Amsterdam), 12, pp. 6–7.

———. 1993. ICGEB coming of age. *Biotechnology and Development Monitor* (Amsterdam), 14, p. 21.

———. 1995. IBS holds its first regional seminar on biotechnology policy in Southeast Asia. *Biotechnology and Development Monitor* (Amsterdam), 22, pp. 18–20.

KOMEN, J.; PERSLEY, G. 1993. *Agricultural biotechnology in developing countries. A cross-country review.* ISNAR Research Report no. 2. The Hague, ISNAR (International Service for National Agricultural Research), Intermediary Biotechnology Service, 45 pp.

KOMEN, J.; COHEN, J. I.; SING-KONG LEE (eds.). 1995. *Turning priorities into feasible programs.* Proceedings of a Regional Seminar on Planning, Priorities and Policies for Agricultural Biotechnology in Southeast Asia (Singapore, 25–29 September 1994). The Hague/Singapore, Intermediary Biotechnology Service/Nanyang Technological University, 133 pp.

KOMEN, J.; COHEN, J. I.; OFIR, Z. (eds.). 1996. *Turning priorities into feasible programs.* Proceedings of a Seminar on Planning, Priorities and Policies for Agricultural Biotechnology for East and Southern Africa (South Africa, 23–28 April 1995). The Hague/Pretoria, Intermediary Biotechnology Service/Foundation for Research Development, 179 pp.

KRUGER, J. E.; PRESTON, K. 1995. Wheat improvement in Canada. Evolving markets for Western Canadian wheat. *PBI* (Plant Biotechnology Institute) *Bulletin* (National Research Council Canada, Saskatoon), May 1995, pp. 5–6.

KUO, C. G. 1992. Biotechnology for crop stress tolerance. *Biotechnology and Development Monitor* (Joint Publication of the Directorate General International Co-operation of the Ministry of Foreign Affairs, The Hague, and the University of Amsterdam), 12, p. 16.

LANDRY, B. 1994. Identifying genes for disease resistance. Canola. *PBI* (Plant Biotechnology Institute) *Bulletin* (National Research Council Canada, Saskatoon), November 1994, pp. 3–4.

LEE, C. H. 1992. Industrialization of lactic acid fermentation technology of cereals and its dissemination to developing countries. In: *Applications of biotechnology to food processing in Africa* (Ibadan, Nigeria, 16–20 December 1991), pp. 76–83. Vienna, UNIDO, IPCT 164, 244 pp.

LEON, R. DE. 1991. Contribution of the Guatemala MIRCEN to international cooperation in Central America. In: *International Symposium on Biotechnologies and Environment for Sustainable Development* (Montreal, Canada, 23–26 September 1991), section J.

LEPARMENTIER, A. 1995. Les biotechnologies ont besoin des grands groupes pharmaceutiques. *Le Monde* (Paris), 11 July 1995, p. 13.

LEPARMENTIER, A.; ORANGE, M. 1996. Sandoz et Ciba-Geigy créent le deuxième groupe pharmaceutique mondial. *Le Monde* (Paris), 8 March 1996, p. 17.

LESER, E. 1996. Toujours plus grand. *Le Monde* (Paris), 8 March 1996, p. 17.

LI, L.; QU, R.; KOCHKO, A. DE; FAUQUET, C.; BEACHY, R.N. 1993. An improved rice transformation system using the biolistic method. *Plant Cell Reports*, 12, pp. 250–5.

LIMONTA, M. 1992. Biotechnology and the Third World: development strategies in Cuba. In: Bloom, B. R.; Cerami, A. (eds.), *Biomedical science and the Third World: under the volcano*, pp. 325–33. Annals of the New York Academy of Sciences, vol. 569 (The Second L.W. Frohlich Award Conference in the series Science and the Human Prospect).

LIMONTA, M. 1993a. Centre for Genetic Engineering and Biotechnology (CIGB), Havana, Cuba. The answer to a challenge. *Pharmaceutical Manufacturing International* (The International Review of Pharmaceutical Technology Research and Development).

——. 1993b. Development and biotechnology in Cuba: marketing policies and present opportunities. In: *Issues in the commercialization of biotechnology* (Proceedings of the Expert Group Meeting on the Commercialization of Biotechnology, Vienna, Austria, 28 October-1 November 1991), pp. 114–23. Vienna, UNIDO, General Studies Series.

——. 1995. Some considerations about the development of biotechnology in the Caribbean area. In: Joseph K. (ed.), *Proceedings of the Fourth Caribbean Biotechnology Conference* (Port of Spain, Trinidad and Tobago, 12–13 September 1994), pp. 75–8. Port of Spain, UNESCO, Caribbean Biotechnology Network, 137 pp.

LIPTON, M.; PAARLBERG, R. 1990. *The role of the World Bank in agricultural development in the 1990s.* Washington, D.C., International Food Policy Institute.

MACLEAN, J. L.; DIZON, L. B. (eds.). 1990. *ICLARM Report 1989.* Manila, Philippines, ICLARM.

MADU, C. 1990. Prescriptive framework for the transfer of appropriate technology. *Futures,* vol. 22, no. 9, pp. 932–50.

MAHON, J. 1995. The development of transgenic legumes. *PBI* (Plant Biotechnology Institute) *Bulletin* (National Research Council Canada, Saskatoon), November 1995, pp. 5–6.

MAKKOUK, K.; BECK, D.; LASHERMES, P.; WEIGAND, F. 1991. *Biotechnology research trends at ICARDA.* Aleppo, Syria, International Center for Agricultural Research in Dry Areas.

MANICAD, G. 1995. Agricultural biotechnology projects within USAID. *Biotechnology and Development Monitor* (joint publication of the Department of Political Science of the University of Amsterdam and the Special Programme Biotechnology and Development Cooperation of the Directorate-General for International Cooperation -DGIS- of the Netherlands' Ministry of Foreign Affairs), 24, pp. 8–10.

——. 1996. Biodiversity conservation and development. The collaboration of formal and non-formal institutions. *Biotechnology and Development Monitor* (Amsterdam), 26, pp. 15–7.

MARTIN, P.; THOMAS, S. M. 1997. Des essais cliniques à foison. *Biofutur* (Paris), 163, pp. 12–8.

MASON, H. S.; ARNTZEN, C. J. 1995. Transgenic plants as vaccine production systems. *Trends in Biotech*, 13, pp. 388–92.

MATHEWS, H.; SCHÖPKE, C.; CARCAMO, R.; CHAVARRIAGA, P.; FAUQUET, C.; BEACHY, R. N. 1993. Improvement of somatic embryogenesis and plant recovery in cassava. *Plant Cell Reports*, 12, pp. 334–8.

MAURICE, J. 1995. Paludisme: l''affaire Patarroyo'. *La Recherche* (Paris), 277, vol. 26, pp. 674–7.

McGARVEY, P. B. *et al.* 1995. Expression of the rabies virus glyco-protein in transgenic tomatoes. *Bio/Technology*, vol. 13, no. 13, pp. 1484–7.

MEEK, S. 1996. The Biodiversity Convention. Summary of progress in negotiations. *Australasian Biotechnology* (Australian Biotechnology Association, Gardenvale, Victoria, Australia), vol. 6, no. 2, pp. 107–10.

MESSÉAN, A. 1994*a*. La réglementation. État des lieux. *Oléagineux Corps gras Lipides* (Paris), vol. 1, no. 1, pp. 40–3.

———. 1994*b*. L'impact économique et social. Agriculteurs: premiers éléments de réflexion. *Oléagineux Corps gras Lipides* (Paris), vol. 1, no. 1, pp. 49–51.

MESTEL, R. 1994. Rich pickings for cotton's pioneers. *New Scientist* (London), 19 February 1994, pp. 13–4.

MILLER, S. A.; WILLIAMS, R. J. 1990. Agricultural diagnostics. In: Persley, G. J. (ed.), *Agricultural biotechnology. Opportunities for international development*, pp. 87–107. Biotechnology in Agriculture Series no. 2. Wallingford, Oxon, United Kingdom, CAB International, 495 pp.

MOFFAT, A. S. 1995. Exploring transgenic plants as a new vaccine source. *Science* (Washington, D.C.), 268, pp. 658–60.

MOLONEY, M. 1995. The future of molecular farming. *PBI* (Plant Biotechnology Institute) *Bulletin* (National Research Council Canada, Saskatoon), August 1995, pp. 6–9.

MONTECINOS, C. 1994. Bringing the farmer and non-farmer breeders together. *Seedling* (The Quarterly Newsletter of Genetic Resources Action International-GRAIN), vol. 11, no. 4, December 1994, pp. 13–5.

MORRIS-COOLE, C. 1995. *Bacillus thuringiensis*: ecology, the significance of natural genetic modification, and regulation. *World Journal of Microbiology and Biotechnology*, vol. 11, no. 5, pp. 471–7.

M.S. SWAMINATHAN RESEARCH FOUNDATION. 1992–1993. *Programme Area 300 – Biovillages*. Extracted from Third Annual Report, pp. 92–103. Madras, M.S. Swaminathan Research Foundation, Centre for Research on Sustainable Agricultural and Rural Development (Third Cross Road, Institutional Area, Tharumani, Madras 600 113, India).

MUGABE, J. 1994. Research on biofertilizers: Kenya, Zimbabwe and Tanzania. *Biotechnology and Development Monitor* (University of Amsterdam), 18, pp. 9–10.

MUGABE, J.; OUKO, E. 1994. Control over genetic resources. *Biotechnology and Development Monitor* (Amsterdam), 21, pp. 6–7.

MUÑOZ, L. C.; LAIGNELET, A.; HOYOS, R.; ROCA, W. M. 1987. Differentiation of embryo-like structures from immature sexual embryos and *in-vitro* micropropagation of *Phaseolus vulgaris* and *Phaseolus lunatus.* In: Angarita, A. (ed.), *Abstracts of International Congress on Plant Tissue culture of Tropical Species*, pp. 58–9. Bogota.

NATIONAL RESEARCH COUNCIL. 1989. *Triticale: a promising addition to the world's cereal grains.* Washington, D.C., National Academy Press.

——. 1990. *Plant biotechnology research for developing countries.* Report of a panel of the Board on Science and Technology for International Development. Washington, D.C., National Academy Press, 44 pp.

NAU, J.-Y. 1994. Selon l'OMS, un remède traditionnel chinois permet de lutter efficacement contre les formes graves de paludisme. *Le Monde* (Paris), 19 April 1994, p. 22.

——. 1995. L'efficacité du premier vaccin contre le paludisme est remise en cause. *Le Monde* (Paris), 16–17 April 1995, p. 10.

——. 1996*a.* En Ecosse, le lait de brebis vaut de l'or. *Le Monde* (Paris), 4 May 1996, p. 32.

——. 1996*b.* Un nouveau médicament devrait améliorer la prévention des affections cardio-vasculaires. *Le Monde* (Paris), 15 November 1996, p. 32.

NELSON, L.; HYNES, R. 1995. Traditional and novel legume inoculants. *PBI* (Plant Biotechnology Institute) *Bulletin* (National Research Council Canada, Saskatoon), November 1995, pp. 7–8.

NG, S. Y. C. 1992. Root and tuber crops tissue culture research activity at IITA. In: *Applications of biotechnology to food processing in Africa* (Ibadan, Nigeria, 16–20 December 1991), pp.159–63. Vienna, UNIDO, IPCT 164, 244 pp.

NG, S. Y. C.; HAHN, S. K.; THOTTAPPILLY, G. 1990. *Biotechnology research and application at the International Institute of Tropical Agriculture.* Ibadan, IITA, unpublished.

NICOLAOU, K. C.; GUY, R. K.; POTIER, P. 1996. Taxoids: new weapons against cancer. *Scientific American* (New York), vol. 274, no. 6, pp. 84–8.

NILSSON, A. 1992. International efforts to prevent bio-hazards. *Biotechnology and Development Monitor* (Joint Publication of the Directorate General International Co-operation of the Ministry of Foreign Affairs, The Hague, and the University of Amsterdam), 10, pp. 16–8.

NOIROT, M.; LASHERMES, P.; DUSSERT, S.; CHARRIER, A.; HAMON, S.; LE PIERRES, D.; LOUARN, J.; ANTHONY, F. 1994. Vingt-cinq ans de recherche sur les caféiers. *ORSTOM Actualités* (Paris), 43, pp. 37–46.

OECD (ORGANISATION FOR ECONOMIC CO-OPERATION AND DEVELOPMENT). 1992. *Biotechnology, agriculture and food.* Paris, OECD, 219 pp.

——. 1994. *Biotechnology for a clean environment: prevention, detection, remediation.* Paris, Organisation for Economic Co-operation and Development, 201 pp.

OELCK, M. 1996. AgrEvo. Liberty Link canola: a Canadian success story. Industry-government collaborations. *PBI* (Plant Biotechnology

Institute) *Bulletin* (National Research Council Canada, Saskatoon), September 1996, pp. 3–6.

PAILLARD, M.; LASHERMES, P.; PETIARD, V. 1996. Construction of a molecular linkage map in coffee. *Theoretical and Applied Genetics*, no. 93.

PANDEY, B.; CHATURVEDI, S. 1994. Prospects for aquaculture in India. *Biotechnology and Development Monitor* (Amsterdam), 21, pp. 16–7.

PARLEVIET, J. E.; HAAN, A. A. DE; SCHELLEKENS, J. J. A. M. 1991. *Drought tolerance research: possibilities and constraints.* The Hague, Directorate for International Cooperation, Ministry of Foreign Affairs, March 1991.

PATARROYO, M. E. 1995. Development and field-testing of the SPf66 synthetic malaria vaccine. In: *Vaccines, one hundred years after Louis Pasteur* ('The Year of Louis Pasteur International Symposia', Institut Pasteur, Paris, 24–28 September 1995), pp. 99–100. Paris, Institut Pasteur, 228 pp.

PEACOCK, W. J. 1989. In: Brown, A. H. D.; Frankel, O. H.; Marshall, D. R.; Williams, J. T. (eds.), *The use of plant genetic resources*, pp. 363–76. Cambridge, Cambridge University Press.

PEARCE, H. 1990. Chinese super-rice in the balance. *Panoscope* (The Panos Institute, London), 16, pp. 4–6.

PENNER, G.; LAROCHE, A. 1994. Do we need a map of the wheat genome? *PBI* (Plant Biotechnology Institute) *Bulletin* (National Research Council Canada, Saskatoon), November 1994, pp. 2–3.

PERSLEY, G. J. 1989. The application of biotechnology to agriculture in developing countries. *AgBiotech News and Information*, vol. 1, no. 1, pp. 23–6.

——. (ed.). 1990a. *Beyond Mendel's garden: biotechnology in the service of world agriculture.* Biotechnology in Agriculture Series no. 1. Wallingford, Oxon, United Kingdom, CAB International, 176 pp.

——. (ed.). 1990b. *Agricultural biotechnology: opportunities for international development.* Biotechnology in Agriculture Series no. 2. Wallingford, Oxon, United Kingdom, CAB International, 495 pp.

PISTORIUS, R. 1992a. Biotechnology in Nigeria, Cameroon, Gabon and Ghana. *Biotechnology and Development Monitor* (Amsterdam), 10, pp. 6–9.

——. 1992b. The Global Environment Facility: a key fund for biodiversity preservation? *Biotechnology and Development Monitor* (Amsterdam), 11, p. 21–2.

——. 1995. Biodiversity policies within FAO or GOP? *Biotechnology and Development Monitor* (Amsterdam), 25, pp. 21–3.

——. 1996. The Leipzig Conference and its backgrounds. *Biotechnology and Development Monitor* (Amsterdam), 28, p. 4.

PISTORIUS, R.; SMITS, P. 1990. Biotechnology in South-East Asia. *Biotechnology and Development Monitor* (Joint Publication of the Directorate General International Cooperation of the Ministry of Foreign Affairs, The Hague, and the University of Amsterdam), 3, pp. 13–7.

PLUCKNETT, D. L. 1989. *An overview of biotechnology research in the CGIAR.* Washington, D.C., World Bank, CGIAR Study Paper (CGIAR/Japanese forum on biotechnology, Tokyo).

PLUCKNETT, D. L.; COHEN, J. I. 1989. *Future role of the IARCs in the application of biotechnology in developing countries.* Commissioned Paper no. 20 for the World Bank-ISNAR-AIDAB-ACIAR Study, Mimeo. 25 pp. + 2 appendices.

PLUCKNETT, D. L.; COHEN, J. I.; HORNE, M. 1990. *Future role of the IARCs in the application of biotechnology in developing countries.* CAB Press.

PONTIS, H.G. 1989. Fructans and cold stress. *J. Plant Physiol.*, 134, pp. 148–50.

POSEY, D.A.: DUTFIELD, G. 1995. *Beyond intellectual property: Towards traditional resources rights for indigenous peoples and local communities.* Ottawa, International Development Research Centre (IDRC), 305 pp.

POWELL, A. P.; NELSON, R. S.; DE, B.; HOFFMAN, N.; ROGERS, S. G.; FRALEY, R.; BEACHY, R. N. 1986. Delay of disease development in transgenic plants that express the tobacco mosaic virus coat protein gene. *Science* (Washington, D.C.), 232, pp. 738–43.

PRAKASH, C.S. 1994. Sweet potato biotechnology: progress and potential. *Biotechnology and Development Monitor* (Amsterdam), 18, pp. 18–9 and 22.

——. 1996. Edible vaccines and antibody producing plants. *Biotechnology and Development Monitor* (Amsterdam), 27, pp. 11–3.

PRAKASH, C. S.; VARADARAJAN, V. 1992. Genetic transformation of sweet potato by particle bombardment. *Plant Cell Reports*, 11, pp. 53–7.

PRAMER, D. 1992. The MIRCEN network. An international network spreads biotechnological and microbiological benefits to less-developed countries. *ASM (American Society of Microbiology) News*, vol. 58, no. 5, pp. 271–3.

QU, R.; BHATTACHARYA, M.; LACO, G.; KOCHKO, A. DE; SUBBA RAO, B. L.; KANIEWSKA, M.; ELMER, J. S.; ROCHESTER, D. E.; SMITH, C. E.; BEACHY, R. N. 1991. Characterization of the genome of rice tungro bacilliform virus: comparison with Commelina Yellow Mottle virus and caulimo-viruses. *Virology*, 185, pp. 354–64.

RAFI (RURAL ADVANCEMENT FOUNDATION INTERNATIONAL). 1994. *Conserving indigenous knowledge: integrating two systems of innovation.* New York, UNDP, Bureau for Policy and Programme Support, 63 pp.

REDDY, A. K. 1988. Appropriate technology: a reassessment. In: *The revenge of Athena: science exploitation & the Third World.* London, Mansell Publishing.

REED, D. (ed.). 1993. *The Global Environment Facility: sharing responsibility for the biosphere, vol. II.* Washington, D.C., WWF International Institutions Policy Programme.

RENARD, M.; LOUTER, J. H.; DUKE, L. H. 1994. Oilseed rape. In: *Traditional crop breeding practices: an historical review to serve as a baseline for assessing the role of modern biotechnology.* Paris, Organisation for Economic Co-operation and Development.

RENARD, M.; PELLETIER, G.; GUERCHE, P. 1994. Colza et génie génétique. Les applications industrielles. *Oléagineux Corps gras Lipides* (Paris), vol. 1, no. 1, pp. 31–3.

REYES, V. 1996. The value of sangre de drago. *Seedling* (The Quarterly Newsletter of Genetic Resources Action International, GRAIN, Barcelona, Spain), vol. 13, no. 1, pp. 16–21.

RHONE-POULENC. 1993. *Annual Report 1992.*

RISSLER, J.; MELLON, M. 1993. *Perils amidst the promise: ecological risks of transgenic crops in a global market.* Cambridge, Massachusetts, Union of Concerned Scientists (26 Church Street, Cambridge, MA02238, USA), 92 pp.

RIVES, M. 1987. Les centres internationaux de recherche agronomique. *Biofutur* (Paris), no. 59, pp. 58–65.

ROCA, W. M. 1991. *Biotechnology research at CIAT.* Cali, Colombia, CIAT, unpublished article.

ROCHE, M. 1995. Glaxo lance son OPA sur Wellcome. *Le Monde* (Paris), 9 February 1995, p. 21.

ROGERS, P. L. 1992. UNESCO Regional Network for Microbiology in S.E. Asia: its educational role. *Australasian Biotechnology* (Australian Biotechnology Association, Gardenvale, Victoria), vol. 2, no. 2, pp. 89–90.

ROSE, A. M.; RAJU, P. S.; AHMAD, M. H. 1995. *In vitro* rooting and subsequent inoculation with VAM fungi for enhanced growth of yam plantlets. In: Joseph, K. (ed.), *Proceedings of the Fourth Caribbean Biotechnology Conference* (Port of Spain, Trinidad and Tobago, 12–3 September 1994), pp. 37–43. Port of Spain, UNESCO, Caribbean Biotechnology Network, 137 pp.

RUIVENKAMP, G.; RICHARDS, P. 1994. Drought tolerance research as a social process. *Biotechnology and Development Monitor* (University of Amsterdam), 18, pp. 3–4 and 22.

SADASIVAIAH, R. S. 1995. Wheat improvement in Canada. Soft white spring wheat for ethanol production. *PBI* (Plant Biotechnology Institute) *Bulletin* (National Research Council Canada, Saskatoon), May 1995, pp. 9–10.

SANCHEZ, V.; JUMA, C. (eds.). 1994. *Biodiplomacy: genetic resources and international relations.* Nairobi, African Centre for Technology Studies, 370 pp.

SANCHIS, V.; CHAUFAUX, J.; LERECLUS, D. 1995. Utilisation de *Bacillus thuringiensis* en protection des cultures et résistance des insectes. *Cahiers Agricultures* (Paris), vol. 4, no. 6, pp. 405–16.

SASSON, A. 1990. *Feeding tomorrow's world.* Paris, UNESCO/CTA (Technical Centre for Agricultural and Rural Co-operation, Ede-Wageningen, Netherlands), 805 pp.

——. 1992*a.* Production of useful biochemicals by higher- plant cell cultures: biotechnological and economic aspects. In: DaSilva, E. J.; Ratledge, C.; Sasson, A. (eds.), *Biotechnology: economic and social aspects; issues for developing countries,* pp. 81–109. Cambridge, United Kingdom, Cambridge University Press/UNESCO, 388 pp.

——. 1992*b.* *Biotechnology and natural products. Prospects for commercial production.* Nairobi, Kenya, African Centre for Technology Studies (ACTS), 97 pp.

SAUNDERS, D. A. (ed.). 1991. *Wheat for the non-traditional, warm areas.* Mexico, D.F., CIMMYT.

SAVIDAN, Y. 1995. Les promesses de l'apomixie. *ORSTOM Actualités* (Paris), no. 47, pp. 2–7.

SCHOUBOE, A.; PLOUGMANN, O. 1997. The new EU draft biotech directive ('Mark II'). *Australasian Biotechnology* (Australian Biotechnology Association, Gardenvale, Victoria, Australia), vol. 7, no. 1, pp. 25–6.

SCOTTO, M. 1996. L'Europe renonce à renforcer le contrôle sur les aliments génétiquement modifiés. *Le Monde* (Paris), 14 March 1996, p. 10.

——. 1997. Aliments génétiquement transformés: compromis au Parlement européen. *Le Monde* (Paris), 18 January 1997, p. 34.

SEGUIN, M.; BESSE, P.; LESPINASSE, D.; LEBRUN, P.; RODIER-GOUD, M.; NICOLAS, D. 1996. Hevea molecular genetics. *Plantations, recherche, développement* (CIRAD, Montpellier, France), vol. 3, no. 2, pp. 85–8.

SHIVA, V. 1991. *The violence of the green revolution.* London, Zed Books; Penang, Malaysia, Third World Network.

SILVESTER, W. B. 1995. *Frankia,* a most versatile microbe. In: Aubert, J.-P.; Martin, P. M. W. (eds.), *Microbes, environment, biotechnology* ('The Year of Louis Pasteur International Symposia', Institut Louis Malardé, Papeete, Tahiti, French Polynesia, 8–12 May 1995), pp. 65–74. Paris, Institut Pasteur, 193 pp.

SIMMONDS, D. 1995. Canadian soybean production: past, present and future. *PBI* (Plant Biotechnology Institute) *Bulletin* (National Research Council Canada, Saskatoon), November 1995, pp. 6–7.

SMITS, P. 1991. UNESCO MIRCENs: global network for microbes. *Biotechnology and Development Monitor* (Joint publication of the Directorate General International Cooperation of the Ministry of Foreign Affairs, The Hague, and the University of Amsterdam), 6, pp. 6–8.

——. 1992. Modern agricultural diagnostics: relevance and applicability for developing countries. *Biotechnology and Development Monitor* (Joint Publication of the Directorate General International Co-operation of the Ministry of Foreign Affairs, The Hague, and the University of Amsterdam), 10, pp.20–1.

SOMASEGARAN, P.; BEN BOHLOOL, B. 1991. The NifTAL Project/MIRCEN and its contribution to international cooperation. In: *International Symposium on Biotechnologies and Environment for Sustainable Development* (Montreal, Canada, 23–26 September 1991), section P.

SOMASEGARAN, P.; HOBEN, H. J. 1994. *Handbook for rhizobia. Methods in legume-Rhizobium technology.* Berlin, Springer-Verlag, 450 pp.

SONG, DA-KANG. 1991. The China MIRCEN and its contribution to international cooperation. In: *International Symposium on Biotechnologies and Environment for Sustainable Development* (Montreal, Canada, 23–26 September 1991), section Q.

STABA, E. J.; ZITO, S. W. 1985. The production of pyrethrins by *Chrysanthemum cinerariaefolium.* In: Neuman; Barz; Reinhard (eds.), *Primary and secondary metabolism of plant cell cultures.* Berlin, Springer-Verlag.

SWAMINATHAN, M. S. (ed.). 1991*a*. *Biotechnology in agriculture, a dialogue.* Madras, MacMillan India Ltd, 370 pp.

———. 1991*b*. Biotechnology and our agricultural future. *Biotechnology and Development Review* (New Delhi), 1, pp. 1–2 and 6.

TARDIEU, V. 1995. Les biologistes s'inquiètent des abus de la pêche industrielle. *Le Monde* (Paris), 9 February 1995, p. 25.

———. 1996. Le colza transgénique laisse échapper ses gènes. *Le Monde* (Paris), 26 June 1996, p. 22.

TAYLHARDAT, A. R. 1989. The ICGEB: a center of excellence. *Biofutur* (Paris), 79, pp. 53–9.

TAYLHARDAT, A. R.; ZILINSKAS, R. A. 1992. Agenda 21: biotechnology at the United Nations Conference on Environment and Development. *Biotechnology*, 10, pp. 402–4.

TEN KATE, K. 1995. The role of providers, collectors and users: biodiversity prospecting partnerships. *Biotechnology and Development Monitor* (A joint publication of the Department of International Relations and Public International Law of the University of Amsterdam, and the Special Programme Biotechnology and Development Cooperation of the Directorate General for International Cooperation-DGIS-, the Netherlands' Ministry of Foreign Affairs, in co-operation with the African Centre for Technology Studies – ACTS -, Nairobi, Kenya, the Research and Information System for the Non-aligned and Other Developing Countries – RIS -, India, and the Inter-American Institute for Cooperation on Agriculture, IICA, Costa Rica), 25, pp. 16–21.

THANAVALA, Y.; YANG, Y.-F.; LYONS, P.; MASON, H. S.; ARNTZEN, C. J. 1995. Immunogenicity of transgenic plant-derived hepatitis B surface antigen. *Proc. Natl. Acad. Sci. USA*, 92, pp. 3358–61.

THOTTAPPILLY, G.; VYLSTEKE, D.; NG, S. Y. C.; HAHN, S. K.; MYERS, G.; ASIEDU, R.; NG, N. Q.; BOKANGA, M.; WINSLOW, M. D.; BAI, K. V.; TERAUCHI, R. 1992*a*. An overview of IITA's biotechnology activities for crop improvement. In: *Applications of biotechnology to food processing in Africa* (Ibadan, Nigeria, 16–20 December 1991), pp. 164–79. Vienna, UNIDO, IPCT 164, 244 pp.

THOTTAPPILLY, G.; MONTI, L. M.; MOHAN RAJ, D. R.; MOORE, A. W. (eds.). 1992*b*. *Biotechnology: enhancing research on tropical crops in Africa.* Technical Centre for Agricultural and Rural Cooperation (CTA) and International Institute of Tropical Agriculture (IITA) co-publication. Ibadan, Nigeria, IITA, 376 pp.

THRO, A. M.; HENRY, G.; LYNAM, J. K. 1994. Biotechnology and small- scale cassava farmers. *Biotechnology and Development Monitor* (Amsterdam), 21, pp. 18–9.

TIWARI, P. N. *et al.* 1993. Assessment of relative tolerance of wheat (*Triticum aestivum*) varieties by nuclear magnetic resonance. *Indian Journal of Agricultural Sciences*, 63 (7).

TUQUOI, J.-P. 1995. La mort lente de l'huile de coprah. *Le Monde* (Paris), 12–13 March 1995, p. 18.

U.S.AID. 1994. *Agricultural biotechnology for sustainable productivity project.* Mid-point report to the Technical Advisory Group. Michigan State University.

VAN RAAVENSWAAIJ, B.; VAN ROOZENDAAL, G. 1995. Biotechnology and Development Monitor evaluated. *Biotechnology and Development Monitor* (Amsterdam), 22, pp. 21–2.

VAN ROOZENDAAL, G. 1996. Enhancing the nutritional qualities of crops: a second green revolution? *Biotechnology and Development Monitor* (Amsterdam), 29, pp. 12–5.

VAN ROOZENDAAL, G.; VAN WIJK, J. 1992. Pioneer Hi-Bred International. *Biotechnology and Development Monitor* (Amsterdam), 12, pp. 14–5.

VAN WIJK, J. 1992. GATT and the legal protection of plants in the Third World. *Biotechnology and Development Monitor* (Amsterdam), 10, pp. 14–5.

VAN WIJK, J.; KOMEN, J. 1991. Editorial: biotechnology and human health. *Biotechnology and Development Monitor* (Amsterdam), 9, pp. 2–3.

VAN WIJK, J.; COHEN, J. J.; KOMEN, J. 1993. *Intellectual property rights for agricultural biotechnology: options and implications for developing countries.* ISNAR Research Report no. 3. The Hague, International Service for National Agricultural Research, Intermediary Biotechnology Service, 40 pp.

VARNEY, M. DE. 1993. La banane après la tempête. *Le Monde* (Paris), 22–23 August 1993, p. 15.

——. 1994. Les visées de l'Amérique latine bananière. *Le Monde* (Paris), 10–11 April 1994, p. 19.

VASIL, V.; SRIVASTAVA, V.; CASTILLO, A. M.; FROMM, M. E.; VASIL, I. K. 1993. Rapid production of transgenic wheat plants by direct bombardment of cultured immature embryos. *Bio/Technology*, 11, pp. 1553–5.

VAYDA, M. E.; PARK, W. D. (eds.). 1990. *The molecular and cellular biology of the potato.* Biotechnology in Agriculture Series no. 3. Wallingford, Oxon, United Kingdom, CAB International, 260 pp.

VICUÑA, R. 1993. Biotechnological research in Chile. In: *Biotechnology in Chile today. An entrepreneurial perspective* (Proceedings of the workshop held in Santiago, 22–23 November 1993, organized by the European Community-Chile Business Foundation, EUROCHILE), pp. 11–5.

VILLAREAL, R. L.; GRIGGS, T. D. (eds.). 1982. *Sweet potato.* Proceedings of the First International Symposium on sweet potato. Taiwan, Asian Vegetable Research and Development Center.

VINCENT, C. 1996a. A la recherche des bovins parfaits. *Le Monde* (Paris), 14 February 1996, p. 22.

——. 1996b. Faut-il avoir peur des plantes transgéniques? *Le Monde* (Paris), 29 March 1996, p. 21.

——. 1996c. Les généticiens deviennent les nouveaux maîtres des fleurs. *Le Monde* (Paris), 29 March 1996, p. 21.

——. 1996*d.* Au fond des océans, les archéobactéries sont la troisième forme de vie. De précieuses alliées industrielles. *Le Monde* (Paris), 25–26 August 1996, p. 12.

——. 1996*e.* Risques et promesses des plantes modifiées par la génétique. *Le Monde* (Paris), 24 October 1996, p. 21.

——. 1997. Alain Juppé interdit la culture du maïs transgénique. *Le Monde* (Paris), 14 February 1997, p. 30. M. Kahn, président de la Commission du génie biomoléculaire, démisionne. *Le Monde* (Paris), 15 February 1997, p. 32.

VISEUR, J. 1993. Technical and economic cooperation mechanisms between Europe and Latin America. In: *Biotechnology in Chile today. An entrepreneurial perspective* (Proceedings of the workshop held in Santiago, 22–23 November 1993, organized by the European Community-Chile Business Foundation, EUROCHILE), pp. 49–52.

VISSER, B. 1994*a.* Technical aspects of drought tolerance. *Biotechnology and Development Monitor* (A joint publication of the Department of International Relations and Public International Law of the University of Amsterdam, the African Centre for Technology Studies, ACTS, Nairobi, Kenya, the Research and Information System for the Non-aligned and Other Developing Countries, RIS, India, and the Instituto Interamericano de Cooperación para la Agricultura, IICA, Costa Rica, and the Directorate General for International Cooperation, DGIS, Ministry of Foreign Affairs, The Hague, Netherlands), 18, p. 5.

——. 1994*b.* The prospects for technical guidelines for safety in biotechnology. *Biotechnology and Development Monitor* (Amsterdam), 20, pp. 21–2.

VON LOESCH, H. 1996. The green revolution protects the environment. *Biotechnology and Development Monitor* (Amsterdam), 29, p. 24.

WALGATE, R. 1990. *Miracle or menace? Biotechnology and the Third World.* London, The Panos Institute, Dossier 3, 200 pp.

WARD, M. 1993. Rhône-Poulenc: from bioscience to markets. *Biotechnology,* July 1993.

WARDA (WEST AFRICAN RICE DEVELOPMENT ASSOCIATION). 1989. *WARDA's Medium-Term Implementation Plan 1990–1994.* Bouaké, Côte d'Ivoire, WARDA.

——. 1991. *WARDA's Program of Work and Budget 1992.* Bouaké, Côte d'Ivoire, WARDA.

WEBSTER, F. H. 1994. Molecular mapping – the bottom line. *PBI* (Plant Biotechnology Institute) *Bulletin* (National Research Council Canada, Saskatoon), November 1994, pp. 5–6.

WEIGAND, F.; LASHERMES, P. 1991. *ICARDA's strategy for biotechnology: objectives, concepts of technology transfer, structure and research.* Paper presented at the International Seminar on Place and Role of Biotechnologies in the Agricultural Research Systems of the Mediterranean Countries (Valencia, Spain, 18–20 June 1990).

WIEGELE, T. C. 1991. *Biotechnology and international relations: the political dimension.* Gainsville, Florida, University of Florida Press, 212 pp.

WILLOUGHBY, K. 1990. *Technology choice: a critique of the appropriate technology movement.* London, Intermediate Technology Publications.

WITCOMBE, J. R. 1996. Participatory approaches to plant breeding and selection. *Biotechnology and Development Monitor* (Amsterdam), 29, pp. 2–6.

WOODEND, J. J. 1995. *Biotechnology and sustainable crop production in Zimbabwe.* Technical Papers no. 109. Paris, OECD (Organisation for Economic Co-operation and Development) Development Centre, 79 pp.

WORLD BANK. 1991. *Agricultural biotechnology: the next 'green revolution'?.* Washington, D.C., World Bank Technical Paper no. 133 (Agriculture and Rural Development Department), Australian Centre for International Agricultural Research, Australian International Development Assistance Bureau, International Service for National Agricultural Research, 51 pp.

——. 1993. *Marine biotechnology and developing countries.* Washington, D.C., World Bank Discussion Paper, no. 210.

YILMA, T. 1993. Transfer of technologies in molecular biology to developing countries. In: Tzotzos, G. (ed.), *Biotechnology R&D trends. Science policy for development.* New York, The New York Academy of Science.

YUAN, R. T.; DIBNER, M. D. 1990. *Japanese biotechnology: a comprehensive study of government policy, R&D and industry.* New York, Stockton Press.

ZECKHAUSER, R. J.; VISCUSI, W. K. 1990. Risk within reason. *Science* (Washington, D.C.), 248, pp. 559–64.